CALCULUS

WITH ANALYTIC GEOMETRY

ALLYN AND BACON, INC.   BOSTON

CALCULUS

WITH ANALYTIC GEOMETRY

FOURTH EDITION

R. E. JOHNSON
UNIVERSITY OF NEW HAMPSHIRE

F. L. KIOKEMEISTER
MOUNT HOLYOKE COLLEGE

EXERCISES BY M. S. KLAMKIN
FORD SCIENTIFIC LABORATORY, DEARBORN, MICHIGAN

LIBRARY OF CONGRESS CATALOG CARD NUMBER: 75-78925

PRINTED IN THE UNITED STATES OF AMERICA

PREFACE

This fourth edition of CALCULUS WITH ANALYTIC GEOMETRY preserves the basic features of the previous editions, most important of which is the interplay between intuition and rigor in the presentation of each topic. It is our strong feeling that both intuition and rigor are essential to a full understanding of the calculus. By its very nature, mathematics must be done rigorously. Nevertheless, almost everything in the calculus arose intuitively from the consideration of a geometrical or physical problem.

The first three chapters cover the essentials of algebra and analytic geometry needed in the calculus. Limits, derivatives, and applications are given in the next three chapters. The first major changes in the new edition are to be found in Chapters 7, 8, and 9 on the integral. The measure-theoretic approach of the third edition has been replaced by the upper and lower integral (step-function) approach of the second edition. Proofs of the integration theorems, which were in Chapter 13 of the last edition, are now in Chapter 8. In Chapters 10 and 11 on transcendental functions, the logarithm function is now defined before the exponential function. Such diverse topics as formal integration, centroids, conic sections, improper integrals, indeterminate forms, and infinite series occur in Chapters 12–15. After a brief introduction to two-dimensional curves and vectors in Chapter 16, most of the rest of the book is concerned with multidimensional calculus. This material has been compressed into three chapters (Chapters 17, 18, and 19), and the notation has been somewhat simplified. Chapter 20 on linear algebra is new. It covers matrices, determinants, linear transformations, and characteristic values, as well as geometric applications.

It is not anticipated that an instructor will discuss every section of the book in class; some sections may be left for the student to read and others may be omitted altogether. For example, for some classes it might be appropriate to linger only briefly on the proofs of the limit theorems (Chapter 4, Section 6), the integrability of a continuous function (Chapter 8, Section 4), the inverse of a function (Chapter 11, Section 6), proof of the arc-length formula (Chapter 16,

Section 11), and so on. The chapter on infinite series may be postponed to the end of the course without affecting the continuity of the rest of the book. On the other hand, the chapter on linear algebra may be covered earlier in the course if the teacher desires.

The exercises have been carefully revised and augmented in the fourth edition. Group I and Group II exercises appear at the end of most sections. For the most part, the Group I exercises are routine ones covering the material of the section. The more challenging Group II exercises are of three types: (1) Non-routine problems covering the material of the section; (2) problems anticipating later sections of the text; and (3) problems introducing new topics. An illustration of exercises of the third type are those in Chapter 12 on convexity and orthogonal projections. There is a review section at the end of each chapter, consisting of oral exercises and Group I and II exercises. Answers to most of the odd-numbered exercises appear at the end of the book. These answers include sketches of solutions of the more difficult exercises. Answers to most of the even-numbered exercises appear in a separate booklet which is available to the teacher upon request from the publisher. Any questions concerning the exercises or their suggested solutions should be addressed to Mr. M. S. Klamkin, Ford Scientific Laboratory, Dearborn, Michigan 48121.

We acknowledge with gratitude the help of Professor Elliot S. Wolk in this revision. His detailed criticism has improved many sections of the book. Many users of previous editions of this book have also suggested changes, for which we are most grateful. We shall continue to welcome such suggestions in the future. To all the people who have helped so greatly in the formation of this book, we express our deep appreciation.

R. E. Johnson

F. L. Kiokemeister

CONTENTS

1 TOPICS FROM ALGEBRA 1

NUMBERS • SETS AND INTERVALS • ABSOLUTE VALUES • COORDINATE LINES

2 INTRODUCTION TO ANALYTIC GEOMETRY 21

RECTANGULAR COORDINATE SYSTEMS • PLANE GRAPHS • DISTANCE FORMULA • CIRCLES • SLOPE OF A LINE • PARALLEL AND PERPENDICULAR LINES • EQUATIONS OF LINES • PARABOLAS

3 FUNCTIONS 58

DEFINITIONS • TYPES OF FUNCTIONS • GRAPHS OF FUNCTIONS • COMBINATIONS OF FUNCTIONS

4 LIMITS 73

INTRODUCTION TO LIMITS • DEFINITION OF LIMIT CONTINUITY • ONE-SIDED LIMITS • INFINITE LIMITS • THE LIMIT THEOREMS

5 DERIVATIVES 106

DEFINITIONS • TANGENT LINES • CONTINUITY OF A DIFFERENTIABLE FUNCTION • DIFFERENTIATION FORMULAS • PRODUCT AND QUOTIENT DIFFERENTIATION FORMULAS • THE CHAIN RULE • ALGEBRAIC FUNCTIONS • IMPLICIT DIFFERENTIATION • HIGHER DERIVATIVES • A WORD ON NOTATION

6 APPLICATIONS OF THE DERIVATIVE 136

EXTREMA OF A FUNCTION • MONOTONIC FUNCTIONS • RELATIVE EXTREMA OF A FUNCTION • CONCAVITY • ENDPOINT EXTREMA • APPLICATIONS OF THE THEORY OF EXTREMA • VELOCITY AND ACCELERATION • ANTIDERIVATIVES

7 INTEGRALS 185

COMPLETENESS OF THE REAL NUMBER SYSTEM • AREA • THE SIGMA NOTATION • UPPER AND LOWER INTEGRALS • INTEGRALS • THE FUNDAMENTAL THEOREM OF THE CALCULUS

• INTEGRATION FORMULAS • CHANGE OF VARIABLE • INTERMEDIATE VALUE THEOREM FOR INTEGRALS

8 THEORY OF THE INTEGRAL 225

BOUNDEDNESS OF A CONTINUOUS FUNCTION • SEQUENCES • RIEMANN SUMS • INTEGRABILITY OF CONTINUOUS FUNCTIONS

9 APPLICATIONS OF THE INTEGRAL 246

AREAS • VOLUME • WORK • ARC LENGTH • APPROXIMATIONS BY THE TRAPEZOIDAL RULE • APPROXIMATIONS BY SIMPSON'S RULE •

10 EXPONENTIAL AND LOGARITHMIC FUNCTIONS 280

INTUITIVE APPROACH • THE NATURAL LOGARITHM • THE NATURAL EXPONENTIAL FUNCTION • DERIVATIVES AND INTEGRALS • HYPERBOLIC FUNCTIONS • CHANGE OF BASE • EXPONENTIAL LAWS OF GROWTH AND DECAY

11 TRIGONOMETRIC AND INVERSE TRIGONOMETRIC FUNCTIONS 310

RADIAN MEASURE • THE SINE AND COSINE FUNCTIONS • THE OTHER TRIGONOMETRIC FUNCTIONS • INVERSE TRIGONOMETRIC FUNCTIONS • DERIVATIVES OF INVERSE TRIGONOMETRIC FUNCTIONS • THE INVERSE OF A FUNCTION

12 FORMAL INTEGRATION 342

ELEMENTARY INTEGRATION FORMULAS • INTEGRATION BY PARTS • TRIGONOMETRIC SUBSTITUTIONS • INTEGRATION OF RATIONAL FUNCTIONS • SEPARABLE DIFFERENTIAL EQUATIONS

13 FURTHER APPLICATIONS OF THE CALCULUS 374

THE CENTRAL CONICS; THE ELLIPSE • THE HYPERBOLA • TRANSLATION OF AXES • MOMENTS AND CENTERS OF MASS • CENTROID OF A PLANE REGION • CENTROIDS OF SOLIDS OF REVOLUTION • FORCE ON A DAM

14 INDETERMINATE FORMS, IMPROPER INTEGRALS, AND TAYLOR'S FORMULA 415

CAUCHY'S FORMULA • INDETERMINATE FORMS • FURTHER INDETERMINATE FORMS • IMPROPER INTEGRALS • TAYLOR'S FORMULA • APPROXIMATIONS BY TAYLOR'S POLYNOMIALS

15 INFINITE SERIES 448

CONVERGENCE AND DIVERGENCE • POSITIVE TERM SERIES • COMPARISON TEST • ALTERNATING SERIES • ABSOLUTE CONVERGENCE • POWER SERIES • DERIVATIVE AND INTEGRAL OF A POWER SERIES • BINOMIAL SERIES • TAYLOR'S SERIES

16 PLANE CURVES, VECTORS, AND POLAR COORDINATES 500

PLANE CURVES • CONTINUITY OF A CURVE • TWO-DIMENSIONAL VECTOR ALGEBRA • TANGENT VECTORS • PLANE MOTION • POLAR COORDINATE SYSTEMS • THE CONIC SECTIONS • TANGENT LINES IN POLAR COORDINATES • AREAS IN POLAR COORDINATES • ARC LENGTH OF A CURVE • PROOF OF THE ARC-LENGTH FORMULA • AREA OF A SURFACE OF REVOLUTION

17 THREE-DIMENSIONAL ANALYTIC GEOMETRY 563

THREE-DIMENSIONAL SPACE OF POINTS • THREE-DIMENSIONAL VECTOR SPACE • LINES IN SPACE • PLANES IN SPACE • THE CROSS PRODUCT IN V_3 • CYLINDERS AND SURFACES OF REVOLUTION • QUADRIC SURFACES • SPACE CURVES • CURVATURE • CYLINDRICAL AND SPHERICAL COORDINATE SYSTEMS

18 DIFFERENTIAL CALCULUS OF FUNCTIONS OF SEVERAL VARIABLES 617

CONTINUITY • DIRECTIONAL DERIVATIVES • PARTIAL DERIVATIVES • DIFFERENTIALS • TANGENT PLANES • THE CHAIN RULE AND OTHER TOPICS • IMPLICIT DIFFERENTIATION • EXTREMA OF A FUNCTION OF TWO VARIABLES • LINE INTEGRALS

19 MULTIPLE INTEGRATION 663

REPEATED INTEGRALS • DOUBLE INTEGRALS • VOLUME • INTEGRALS OVER NONRECTANGULAR REGIONS • POLAR COORDINATES • CENTER OF MASS OF A LAMINA • MOMENTS OF INERTIA • TRIPLE INTEGRALS • PHYSICAL APPLICATIONS OF TRIPLE INTEGRALS • CYLINDRICAL AND SPHERICAL COORDINATES

20 LINEAR ALGEBRA 712

VECTOR SPACES • MATRICES • SYSTEMS OF LINEAR EQUATIONS • DETERMINANTS • ALGEBRA OF MATRICES • LINEAR TRANSFORMATIONS • EUCLIDEAN SPACES • CHARACTERISTIC VALUES • SYMMETRIC MATRICES • QUADRATIC EQUATIONS

21 DIFFERENTIAL EQUATIONS 759

INTRODUCTION • FAMILIES OF CURVES • BOUNDARY CONDITIONS • EXACT DIFFERENTIAL EQUATIONS • THE DIFFERENTIAL NOTATION • HOMOGENEOUS EQUATIONS • FIRST-ORDER LINEAR DIFFERENTIAL EQUATIONS • APPLICATIONS • SECOND-ORDER LINEAR DIFFERENTIAL EQUATIONS • NONHOMOGENEOUS LINEAR EQUATIONS • SOLUTIONS IN SERIES

APPENDIX 808

FACTS AND FORMULAS FROM TRIGONOMETRY • • TABLE OF INTEGRALS • NUMERICAL TABLES

ANSWERS TO ODD-NUMBERED EXERCISES 825

INDEX 951

1

TOPICS FROM ALGEBRA

CALCULUS, like algebra, is a study of numbers and functions. However, unlike algebra, it is primarily concerned with limiting processes rather than with factoring and solving equations. Some of the basic algebraic concepts of use in the calculus will be presented in this first chapter.

1 NUMBERS

The number system of elementary calculus is called the system of real numbers. In advanced mathematics the complex number system plays a vital role. Since we are concerned with elementary calculus in this book, we shall restrict our attention almost exclusively to real numbers.

Included among the real numbers are the *integers*

$$\cdots, -5, -4, -3, -2, -1, 0, 1, 2, 3, 4, 5, \cdots$$

and the ratios of integers, called *rational numbers*. Thus each rational number has the form p/q, where p and q are integers with $q \neq 0$. Every integer p is also a rational number, since it can be expressed in the form $p/1$.

There are real numbers that are not rational numbers; such numbers are called *irrational numbers*. For example, $1 + \sqrt{3}$, $\sqrt[3]{2}$, and π are irrational numbers.

Complex numbers are numbers of the form $a + bi$, where a and b are real numbers and i is a (nonreal) number having the property that $i^2 = -1$. If

$b \neq 0$, the complex number $a + bi$ is also called an *imaginary number*. For example, the quadratic equation

$$x^2 - 2x + 5 = 0$$

has as its solutions the imaginary numbers $1 + 2i$ and $1 - 2i$.

Whenever we use the word *number* by itself, it is tacitly understood we mean *real number*.

In modern terminology the system of real numbers is called a *field* because it has operations of addition and multiplication with the following properties, which define the concept of a field.

P1. *Associative laws.* $a + (b + c) = (a + b) + c$ and $a(bc) = (ab)c$ for all numbers a, b, and c.

P2. *Commutative laws.* $a + b = b + a$ and $ab = ba$ for all numbers a and b.

P3. *Distributive law.* $a(b + c) = ab + ac$ for all numbers a, b, and c.

P4. *Identity elements.* There exist numbers 0 and 1 such that $a + 0 = a$ and $a \cdot 1 = a$ for every number a.

P5. *Inverse elements.* Each number a has a negative $-a$ such that $a + (-a) = 0$; and each nonzero number a has a reciprocal $1/a$ such that $a \cdot (1/a) = 1$.

As is commonly known, other operations of subtraction and division may be defined in terms of addition and multiplication.

Just as the system of real numbers is a field, so too is the system of rational numbers and the system of complex numbers. However, the system of integers is not a field because the reciprocal of an integer need not be an integer.

A property of any field of numbers is that if a and b are numbers such that $ab = 0$, then either $a = 0$ or $b = 0$. Conversely, if either $a = 0$ or $b = 0$, then $ab = 0$. These two statements may be combined into one:

$$ab = 0 \text{ if and only if } a = 0 \text{ or } b = 0.$$

An important property of the real number field is that it is *ordered;* i.e., the set of nonzero real numbers can be separated into two parts, one made up of the positive numbers and the other of the negative numbers. Thus every real number is either a positive number, zero, or a negative number.

Both the sum and the product of two positive numbers are positive numbers. Two nonzero numbers a and b either *agree in sign* (i.e., both are positive or both are negative) or *differ in sign* (i.e., one is positive and one is negative). If a and b agree in sign, ab and a/b are positive numbers, whereas if a and b differ in sign, ab and a/b are negative numbers. The nonzero numbers a and $1/a$ always agree in sign; a and $-a$ always differ in sign.

If $a \neq b$, then either a or b is greater than the other number. We write $a > b$ if a is greater than b, and $a < b$ if a is less than b (that is, b is greater than a). The relations "is greater than" and "is less than" ($>$ and $<$) may be formally defined as follows:

1.1 DEFINITION. If a and b are real numbers, then

(i) $a > b$ if $a - b$ is a positive number,

(ii) $a < b$ if $a - b$ is a negative number.

A meaningful algebraic expression involving relations such as "$>$" and "$<$" is called an *inequality*.

According to **1.1**, if a is a positive number, $a - 0$ is positive and $a > 0$. Conversely, if $a > 0$, then $a = a - 0$ is a positive number.
Therefore

the number a is positive if and only if $a > 0$,

and, similarly,

the number a is negative if and only if $a < 0$.

The following laws of inequalities will be useful for our study.

1.2 If $a > b$ and $b > c$, then $a > c$ (transitive law).

1.3 For any number c, $a > b$ if and only if $a + c > b + c$.

1.4 For any $c > 0$, $a > b$ if and only if $ac > bc$.

1.5 For any $c < 0$, $a > b$ if and only if $ac < bc$.

The distinction between **1.4** and **1.5** should be noted. Thus multiplication by a positive number maintains the direction of the inequality, whereas multiplication by a negative number reverses the direction of the inequality.

These laws may be proved by using the properties of positive and negative numbers stated above. We illustrate this fact by proving one of the laws.

Proof of **1.4**: If $a > b$ and $c > 0$, then both $a - b$ and c are positive numbers. Hence $(a - b)c$, which is equal to $ac - bc$, is a positive number, and $ac > bc$ according to **1.1**. Conversely, if $ac > bc$ and $c > 0$, then both $ac - bc$ and $1/c$ are positive numbers. Hence $(ac - bc)\cdot(1/c)$, or $a - b$, is a positive number and $a > b$.

Each of **1.2–1.5** may be read in a somewhat different manner by replacing $a > b$ by $b < a$, and so on. Thus **1.4** could be read as follows: for any $c > 0$, $b < a$ if and only if $bc < ac$.

We may write

$$a < x < b \qquad \text{or} \qquad b > x > a$$

if $a < x$ and $x < b$. In this case x is a number between a and b. In a continued inequality such as this, the inequality signs always have the same direction. Thus we never write $a < x > b$ or $a > x < b$.

Other useful relations are "greater than or equal to" and "less than or equal to" ($\geq$ and $\leq$), which are defined in an obvious way:

$$a \geq b \text{ if } a > b \text{ or } a = b,$$
$$a \leq b \text{ if } a < b \text{ or } a = b.$$

A continued inequality such as

$$a \leq x < b$$

indicates either that x is between a and b or that $x = a$.

2 SETS AND INTERVALS

We have already had occasion to use the word *set* in discussing sets of numbers. In mathematics a collection of objects is called a *set*. Thus we speak of the set of all integers, the set of all real numbers, the set of all circles in a plane, and the set of all solutions of a given equation. The objects in a set are called *elements*.

It is common practice to designate sets by letters such as A, C, or S. For example, the set of all integers is designated by Z (perhaps for the German word *Zahl*) in many present-day algebra books. We frequently designate the elements of a set by lowercase letters such as a, c, or x. If A and B are sets such that every element of A is also an element of B, then we call A a *subset* of B and say that A is *contained in* B. Two sets A and B are equal if and only if each is a subset of the other, in which case we write $A = B$.

If the elements of a set can be enumerated, then we indicate the set by listing the elements and enclosing them with braces, $\{\quad\}$. For example,

$$\{1, 3, 5, 7, 9\}$$

indicates the set consisting of the five integers 1, 3, 5, 7, and 9. Clearly $\{1, 5, 9\}$ is a subset of this set.

We often describe a set by listing a typical element and stating its properties. For example,

$$\{2n + 1 \mid n \text{ an integer}\}$$

is the set of all odd integers. In this example $2n + 1$ is a typical element of the set; the statement after the vertical bar tells the allowable choices for the variable n. As another example,

$$\{x \mid x \text{ a real number and } x > 3\}$$

is the set of all real numbers greater than 3.

Given two sets A and B, we can form two other sets, namely their *union* $A \cup B$ and their *intersection* $A \cap B$. By definition,

$$A \cup B = \{x \mid x \text{ in } A \text{ or } x \text{ in } B\}$$
$$A \cap B = \{x \mid x \text{ in } A \text{ and } x \text{ in } B\}.$$

In words, $A \cup B$ is the set made up of every element x in either set A or set B (or both); $A \cap B$ is the set made up of every element x in both set A and set B.

It is convenient to have a set with no elements; this is called the *empty set*. We shall use the symbol $\varnothing$ to designate the empty set. The empty set is considered to be a subset of every other set. If sets A and B have no elements in common, then clearly $A \cap B = \varnothing$.

Intervals are sets of particular importance in the calculus. If a and b are real numbers such that $a < b$, then the *open interval* determined by a and b is designated by (a,b) and is defined as follows:

$$(a,b) = \{x \mid a < x < b\}.$$

In words, the open interval (a,b) is made up of every real number x between a and b. We have omitted the phrase "x a real number" from the description of this set because all sets are assumed to be sets of real numbers unless otherwise stated. The *closed interval* determined by a and b, designated $[a,b]$, is defined by

$$[a,b] = \{x \mid a \leq x \leq b\}.$$

There are two half-open or, half-closed intervals, designated $[a,b)$ and $(a,b]$ and defined as follows:

$$[a,b) = \{x \mid a \leq x < b\}$$
$$(a,b] = \{x \mid a < x \leq b\}.$$

The symbol ∞, called *infinity*, is useful in many situations. However, in using this symbol, we must realize that it is not a number in the ordinary sense of the word. For example, we cannot add 3 to ∞ or divide 1 by ∞.

We shall use the notation (a,∞) to designate the set of all numbers greater than a:

$$(a,\infty) = \{x \mid x > a\}.$$

Other infinite intervals which we shall find useful are defined below.

$$(-\infty,a) = \{x \mid x < a\},$$
$$[a,\infty) = \{x \mid x \geq a\},$$
$$(-\infty,a] = \{x \mid x \leq a\}.$$

We shall on occasion use the notation $(-\infty,\infty)$ for the set of all real numbers.

For each real number c, any open interval containing c is called a *neighborhood* of c. Thus each neighborhood of c has the form (a,b) where $a < c < b$. For example, $(1,7)$ and $(3,4.1)$ are neighborhoods of 4. We note that $(3,4)$ is not a neighborhood of 4.

If (a,b) is a neighborhood of c, then the set (a,b) with c removed is called a *deleted neighborhood* of c. That is, $(a,c) \cup (c,b)$ is a deleted neighborhood of c whenever $a < c < b$. For example, $(1,4) \cup (4,7)$ is a deleted neighborhood of 4.

For any real number c and any positive number r, the neighborhood $(c - r, c + r)$ is called a *symmetric neighborhood* of c of *radius* r. It is clear that every neighborhood of c contains a symmetric neighborhood. For example, $(1,4\frac{1}{2})$ is a neighborhood of 4 which contains the symmetric neighborhood $(3\frac{1}{2},4\frac{1}{2})$ of 4 of radius $\frac{1}{2}$.

Given an equation or inequality in one variable, its *solution set* is defined to be the set of all numbers which yield a true statement when substituted for the variable in the equation or inequality. We solve an equation or inequality by replacing it with equivalent equations or inequalities (that is, ones having the same solution set) until we obtain one whose solution set is obvious. This technique is illustrated in the following examples.

EXAMPLE 1. Solve the inequality $7x - 5 > 3x + 4$.

Solution: By adding $5 - 3x$ to each side of this inequality, we obtain an equivalent inequality (by **1.3**)

$$(7x - 5) + (5 - 3x) > (3x + 4) + (5 - 3x).$$

This simplifies to

$$4x > 9.$$

Now multiplying each side by $\frac{1}{4}$, a positive number, we obtain an equivalent inequality (by **1.4**)

$$x > \tfrac{9}{4}.$$

The solution set of this final inequality is the infinite interval

$$(\tfrac{9}{4}, \infty).$$

Since the final inequality is equivalent to the given one, this is also the solution set of the given inequality.

EXAMPLE 2. Solve the inequality $-3 < 1 - 2x < 4$.

Solution: Adding -1 to each member of the inequality, we get an equivalent inequality (by **1.3**)

$$-4 < -2x < 3.$$

Multiplying each member of the new inequality by $-\frac{1}{2}$, a negative number, we obtain an equivalent inequality

$$2 > x > -\tfrac{3}{2}.$$

Since the solution set of the final inequality is the open interval

$$(-\tfrac{3}{2},2),$$

this must also be the solution set of the given inequality.

EXAMPLE 3. Prove that if a, b, c, and d are numbers such that $a > b$ and $c > d$, then

$$a + c > b + d.$$

Solution: If $a > b$ and $c > d$, then by adding c to each side of the first inequality and b to each side of the second, we obtain

$$a + c > b + c \quad \text{and} \quad b + c > b + d.$$

Hence, by the transitive law (1.2), $a + c > b + d$.

If $a \geq 0$, then it is false that $a < 0$. In other words, if $a \geq 0$, then a is *nonnegative*. The set of nonnegative numbers is made up of all the positive numbers and the number zero. If a is a nonzero number, then $a^2 > 0$ since the two factors in the product $a \cdot a = a^2$ agree in sign. Also, $0^2 = 0$, and we may make the following statement:

1.6 $a^2 \geq 0$ for every real number a.

Every real number a has a square root b; that is, $b^2 = a$ for some (not necessarily real) number b. Since $b^2 \geq 0$ if b is real, evidently only nonnegative real numbers have real square roots. Negative numbers have imaginary square roots. For example, $2i$ is a square root of -4. Each positive real number has two real square roots. Thus 2 and -2 are square roots of 4. The radical sign ($\sqrt{\ }$) is used to indicate the nonnegative square root of a nonnegative number. That is, for each number $a \geq 0$, $\sqrt{a}$ designates the nonnegative square root of a.

EXAMPLE 4. For what set of real numbers is $\sqrt{1 - 2x}$ a real number?

Solution: The number $\sqrt{1 - 2x}$ is real if and only if $1 - 2x \geq 0$, or if and only if $x \leq \frac{1}{2}$. Hence $\sqrt{1 - 2x}$ is real for every number x in the infinite interval $(-\infty, \frac{1}{2}]$.

EXAMPLE 5. If $a \geq 0$ and $b \geq 0$, prove that $a > b$ if and only if $a^2 > b^2$.

Solution: If $a > b$ and $b \geq 0$, then $a > 0$ and we may multiply each side of the inequality $a > b$ first by a and then by b to obtain $a^2 > ab$ and $ab \geq b^2$. Therefore $a^2 > b^2$ by the transitive law (1.2).

Conversely, if a and b are nonnegative numbers such that $a^2 > b^2$, then $a^2 - b^2 > 0$ and $(a - b)(a + b) > 0$. Hence both $a + b$ and $a - b$ are nonzero. Since $a \geq 0$ and

$b \geq 0$, clearly $a + b > 0$. On multiplying each side of the inequality $(a - b)(a + b) > 0$ by $1/(a + b)$, we obtain $a - b > 0$, or $a > b$.

An important property of the real number system is that between any two unequal real numbers there is at least one rational number. Stated in another way, every open interval (a,b) contains at least one rational number. It is this property that allows us to approximate any real number by a rational number to any desired degree of accuracy. For example, it may be shown that

$$\sqrt{7} < 2.646 < \sqrt{7} + .001.$$

Therefore 2.646 is a rational approximation of the irrational number $\sqrt{7}$, accurate to within .001 (that is, $2.645 < \sqrt{7} < 2.646$). In turn,

$$\sqrt{7} < 2.6458 < \sqrt{7} + .0001.$$

That is, 2.6458 is a rational approximation of $\sqrt{7}$, accurate to within .0001. And so on, as accurately as we desire.

EXERCISES

I

In each of Exercises 1–10, solve the given inequality.

1. $3x + 1 < x + 5$.
2. $1 - 2x < 5x - 2$.
3. $3 - 2x > 0$.
4. $\frac{3x}{4} - \frac{1}{2} < 0$.
5. $\frac{3x - 5}{2} \leq 0$.
6. $.01x - 2.32 \geq 0$.
7. $-.1 < x - 5 < .1$.
8. $-.01 < x + 3 < .01$.
9. $-.03 \leq \frac{2x + 3}{5} \leq .03$.
10. $-.001 \leq \frac{5 - 2x}{4} \leq .001$.

In each of Exercises 11–14, determine the set of all numbers x for which the given square root is a real number.

11. $\sqrt{2x - 8}$.
12. $\sqrt{3 + 4x}$.
13. $\sqrt{b^2 - 4ax}$.
14. $\sqrt{16 - 7x}$.

In each of Exercises 15–20, find the set of all numbers x satisfying the given conditions.

15. $x + 1 > 0$ and $x - 3 < 0$.
16. $x - 1 < 0$ and $x + 2 > 0$.
17. $\frac{1}{x + 3} < 0$.
18. $\frac{1}{2x - 5} > 0$.

19. $3x - 2 \geq 0$ and $5x - 1 \leq 0$.

20. $2x + 1 > 0$ and $x - 1 > 0$.

21. If $A = [3,5]$ and $B = [0,3)$, describe $A \cup B$, $A \cap (B \cup A)$, $A' \cap B$, $(A \cap B)'$, $A \cup B'$. (For any interval I, the complement of I is denoted by I' and is defined by $I' = \{x \mid x \text{ a real number not in } I\}$.)

22. Same as Exercise 21, except that $A = (7,10)$ and $B = [8,\infty)$.

23. Same as Exercise 21, except that $A = (-\infty,7]$ and $B = [7,15]$.

For each of the following exercises, describe $A \cup B \cup C$, $A' \cup B \cup C$, $A \cap (B \cup C)'$, and $A' \cap B' \cap C$.

24. $A = (-\infty,3]$, $B = (-\infty,4)$, $C = (3,4]$.

25. $A = [1,2]$, $B = (1,2)$, $C = (1,2]$.

26. $A = (1,100]$, $B = [-1,100)$, $C = [100,\infty)$.

If in the following exercises, (a,b) and (c,d) are neighborhoods of m and n, respectively, show that:

27. $(a + c, b + d)$ is a neighborhood of $m + n$.

28. $(a - d, b - c)$ is a neighborhood of $m - n$.

29. (ra,rb) is a neighborhood of rm, if $r > 0$.

30. (ac,bd) is a neighborhood of mn, if $c > 0$.

31. $(a/d,b/c)$ is a neighborhood of m/n, if $c > 0$.

II

1. If $a \neq b$, prove that $(a + b)/2$ is strictly between a and b.

2. If $a > 0$ and $b > 0$, and if $a \neq b$, prove that $\sqrt{ab}$ (called the *geometric average* or *mean* of a and b) is strictly between a and b.

3. If $a \geq 0$ and $b \geq 0$, prove that $a^n \geq b^n$ if and only if $a \geq b$ (n a positive integer).

4. If $a \geq 0$ and $b \geq 0$, prove that $(a + b)/2 \geq \sqrt{ab}$ with equality if and only if $a = b$.

5. Show that, of all rectangles having the same perimeter, the square has the largest area.

6. Prove the dual of Exercise 5, i.e., of all rectangles having the same area, the square has the minimum perimeter.

7. Find the greatest value of $(5 + x)(4 - x)$ in the closed interval $[-5,4]$.

8. If $b_r > 0$ ($r = 1, 2, 3$), then prove that

$$\min_r \left(\frac{a_r}{b_r}\right) = \min\left(\frac{a_1}{b_1}, \frac{a_2}{b_2}, \frac{a_3}{b_3}\right) \leq \frac{a_1 + a_2 + a_3}{b_1 + b_2 + b_3} \leq \max\left(\frac{a_1}{b_1}, \frac{a_2}{b_2}, \frac{a_3}{b_3}\right) = \max_r \left(\frac{a_r}{b_r}\right).$$

3 ABSOLUTE VALUES

Each real number a is either a negative number or a nonnegative number. If a is negative, then $-a$ is positive. In other words, corresponding to each real number a is a nonnegative number which is either a or $-a$. This fact is the basis of the following definition.

1.7 **DEFINITION.** If a is a real number, then the *absolute value* of a is designated by $|a|$ and defined by

$$|a| = a \text{ if } a \geq 0, \qquad |a| = -a \text{ if } a < 0.$$

For example,

$$|2| = 2, |-2| = -(-2) = 2;$$
$$|\sqrt{2} - 1| = \sqrt{2} - 1, |1 - \sqrt{2}| = -(1 - \sqrt{2}) = \sqrt{2} - 1.$$

As these examples indicate,

1.8 $$|a| = |-a| \text{ for every real number } a.$$

For if $a = 0$, then $|0| = |-0| = 0$; if $a > 0$, then $-a < 0$ and $|a| = a = |-a| = -(-a)$; if $a < 0$, then $-a > 0$ and $|a| = -a = |-a|$.

Since $|a|^2 = a^2$ or $|a|^2 = (-a)^2 = a^2$ and $a^2 \geq 0$, clearly $|a|^2 = |a^2| = a^2$ for every real number a.

From the definition of absolute value, it is clear that $a = |a|$ or $a = -|a|$ for every real number a. That is, $-|a| \leq a \leq |a|$ for every real number a, with equality holding in one position. A useful result of a similar nature is as follows.

1.9 If $c > 0$, then $|x| < c$ if and only if $-c < x < c$.

Proof: Let us first show that if $|x| < c$ then $-c < x < c$. Since $x \leq |x|$ and $|x| < c$, clearly $x < c$. On the other hand, $-c < -|x|$ and $-|x| \leq x$, so that $-c < x$. Hence $-c < x < c$.

Conversely, let us show that if $-c < x < c$ then $|x| < c$. If $x \geq 0$, then $|x| = x$ and $x < c$ so that $|x| < c$. If $x < 0$, then $|x| = -x$, and since $-c < x$, $-x < c$ so that $|x| < c$. Thus $|x| < c$ in either case.

In place of **1.9**, we could equally well have proved the following:

1.10 If $c \geq 0$, then $|x| \leq c$ if and only if $-c \leq x \leq c$.

We should recognize that **1.10** simply states that the solution set of the inequality $|x| \leq c$ is the closed interval $[-c,c]$.

We can apply **1.10** as follows. For all real numbers a and b,

$$-|a| \leq a \leq |a| \qquad \text{and} \qquad -|b| \leq b \leq |b|.$$

Adding corresponding members of these two inequalities, we obtain

$$-(|a| + |b|) \leq a + b \leq (|a| + |b|).$$

This inequality has the form $-c \leq x \leq c$. Therefore, by **1.10**, the following inequality also is true.

1.11 $$|a + b| \leq |a| + |b| \text{ for all real numbers } a \text{ and } b.$$

If $a \geq 0$ and $b \geq 0$, then $ab \geq 0$ and $|ab| = ab = |a| \cdot |b|$. If $a < 0$ and $b < 0$, then $ab > 0$ and $|ab| = ab = (-a)(-b) = |a| \cdot |b|$. Finally, if $a \geq 0$ and $b < 0$, then $ab \leq 0$ and $|ab| = -(ab) = a \cdot (-b) = |a| \cdot |b|$. A similar result holds if $a < 0$ and $b \geq 0$. These remarks prove the following result.

1.12 $$|a \cdot b| = |a| \cdot |b| \text{ for all real numbers } a \text{ and } b.$$

It may be shown similarly that $|a/b| = |a|/|b|$ for all real numbers a and b, with $b \neq 0$.

We recall that if $a \geq 0$ then $\sqrt{a}$ is the nonnegative square root of a. Therefore, since $|a|^2 = a^2$, evidently $|a|$ is the nonnegative square root of a^2. Thus

1.13 $$\sqrt{a^2} = |a| \text{ for every real number } a.$$

Note that $\sqrt{a^2}$ is not necessarily equal to a. For example, $\sqrt{(-2)^2} = \sqrt{4} = 2$, and not -2. Of course, if $a \geq 0$, then $\sqrt{a^2} = a$.

EXAMPLE 1. Solve the inequality $|3 - 2x| < 1$.

Solution: By **1.9**,

$$-1 < 3 - 2x < 1$$

is an equivalent inequality. We solve this inequality by replacing it by each of the following equivalent inequalities:

$$-4 < -2x < -2,$$
$$2 > x > 1.$$

Hence the solution set is the open interval (1,2).

EXAMPLE 2. Solve the inequality $|3x + 5| > 2$.

Solution: A number x is a solution of the given inequality if and only if it is not a solution of the inequality

$$(1) \qquad |3x + 5| \leq 2.$$

We solve this as follows, first using **1.10**.

$$-2 \leq 3x + 5 \leq 2;$$
$$-7 \leq 3x \leq -3;$$
$$-\tfrac{7}{3} \leq x \leq -1.$$

Thus the solution set of (1) is the closed interval $[-\frac{7}{3},-1]$. The solution set of the given inequality is the set of all other real numbers, that is,

$$(-\infty,-\tfrac{7}{3}) \cup (-1,\infty).$$

EXAMPLE 3. Solve the inequality $|(1/x) - .01| < .01$.

Solution: By **1.9**, the given inequality is equivalent to

$$-.01 < \frac{1}{x} - .01 < .01$$

or, on adding .01 to each member,

$$0 < \frac{1}{x} < .02.$$

Since $0 < 1/x$, we must have $x > 0$. Hence we can multiply each member of the above inequality by x to obtain an equivalent inequality

$$1 < .02x,$$

or

$$50 < x.$$

The solution set of the given inequality is therefore the infinite set $(50,\infty)$.

EXERCISES

I

In each of Exercises 1–8, solve the given inequality.

1. $|x - 1| < 3$.
2. $|x + 2| < 5$.
3. $|2x - 1| < .1$.
4. $|3x - 5| \leq .05$.
5. $|4 - 3x| < 5$.
6. $|1 - 2x| \leq 1$.
7. $|1 + 2x| \leq 1$.
8. $|x + \pi| < 2$.
9. Show that $|1/x - 5| < 1$ if and only if $\frac{1}{6} < x < \frac{1}{4}$.
10. Prove that if $b > 0$ then $|x - a| < b$ if and only if $a - b < x < a + b$.
11. Prove that if $d > 0$ then $|c| > d$ if and only if either $c < -d$ or $c > d$.

In each of Exercises 12–15, solve the given inequality.

12. $|x| > 2$.
13. $|3x| > 6$.
14. $|x - 1| > 3$.
15. $|x + 2| \geq 5$.

II

1. Prove that $|a - b| \leq |a| + |b|$.

2. Prove that $|a| - |b| \leq |a - b|$.

3. Prove that $|a + b + c| \leq |a| + |b| + |c|$.

4. Generalize Exercise 3.

In each of Exercises 5–9, solve the given inequality.

5. $|x - 3| < 2|x + 5|$.

6. $|x - 1| + |x + 3| \geq 6$.

7. $|x - 1| - |x + 3| \leq 6$.

8. $|x - 1| + 2|x + 1| + |x - 2| \leq 8$.

9. $4|x^2 - 1| + |x^2 - 4| \geq 6$.

4 COORDINATE LINES

It is possible to use real numbers as coordinates for points on a line in such a way that there is associated with each point a real number and with each real number a point on the line. Such an association is a basic tool of analytic geometry, as will be described in Chapter 2. Let us briefly deal with coordinate lines in this section.

Each line of our discussion is assumed to be in a Euclidean plane, so that the methods and results of Euclidean geometry may be used at will. For example, each pair A,B of distinct points in a plane determines a line L and a segment, AB, of L. We may think of AB as the set of all points between and including A and B. Congruence of geometric objects is defined in a Euclidean plane, and is designated by the symbol "$\equiv$". Thus if two segments AB and CD are congruent, we indicate this fact by writing $AB \equiv CD$.

Let O and A be any two distinct points on a line L. We assign to O the number 0 and to A the number 1. We also assign a *direction* to L, the direction from O toward A, and indicate the direction by an arrowhead, as in Figure 1.1.

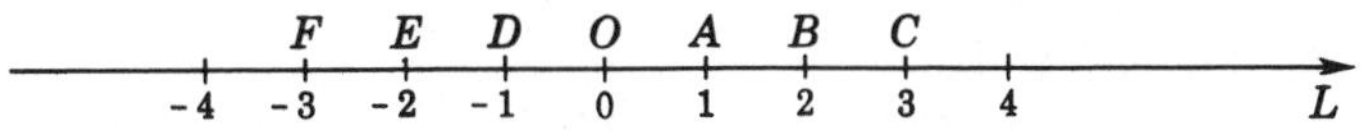

FIGURE 1.1

With the point B on the opposite side of A from O and such that $OA \equiv AB$, we assign to point B the number 2. With the point D on the opposite side of O from A and such that $DO \equiv OA$, we assign to point D the number -1. Continuing in this fashion, we may assign all the integers to equispaced points on L, as indicated in Figure 1.1.

On each of the unit segments OA, AB, BC, DO, ED, FE, and so on, n equispaced points may be selected for each positive integer n. For example, we can divide OA into three congruent parts, as shown in Figure 1.2. The points

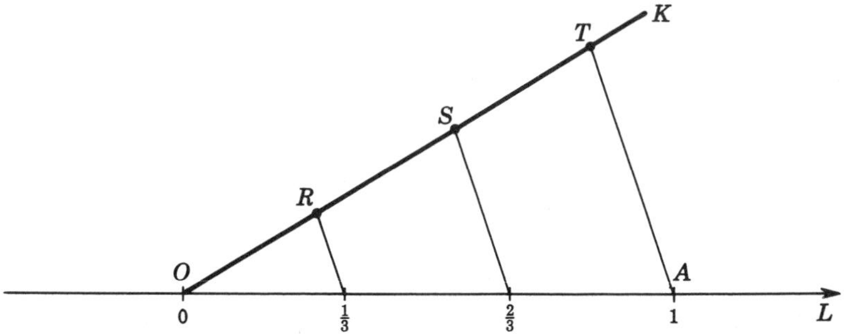

FIGURE 1.2

R, S, and T are marked off on any line K through O so that $OR \equiv RS \equiv ST$, and the line through T and A is drawn. Then lines are constructed through R and S parallel to line TA. These parallel lines divide segment OA into three congruent or equal parts.

Having constructed n equispaced points on each of the unit segments OA, AB, DO, and so on, we assign the rational number m/n to the mth point of OA, $1 + m/n$ to the mth point of AB, $2 + m/n$ to the mth point of BC, and so on, counting in the direction of L. We then assign the number $-m/n$ to the mth point of OD, $-1 - m/n$ to the mth point of DE, and so on, counting in the direction opposite to that of L. In this way all the rational numbers can be assigned to points of line L. These points are called the *rational points* of L.

There are many points on L that are not rational. To each of the non-rational points on L we may assign an irrational number. Considerations of rational approximations of an irrational number q and the positions of the corresponding rational points of L allow us to select the point Q to which the the number q is assigned.

The number x assigned to a point P on L is called the *coordinate* of P. The notation $P(x)$ is used to signify that point P has coordinate x. We assume that each point on L has a unique coordinate and that each real number is the coordinate of a unique point on L. A given assignment of coordinates on a line L is called a *coordinate system* on L, and L is then called a *coordinate line*. The point O with coordinate 0 is called the *origin* of L. Clearly the coordinate system depends solely on the choice of the origin O and the point $A(1)$.

Let a coordinate line L be thought of as a horizontal line directed toward the right, as in Figure 1.3. Then the correspondence that associates with each

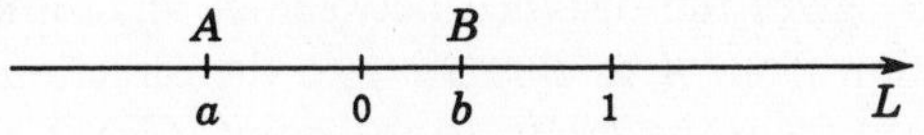

FIGURE 1.3

real number x the point $P(x)$ of L is such that

$$a < b \text{ if and only if } A(a) \text{ is to the left of } B(b).$$

1.14 **DEFINITION.** If $A(a)$ and $B(b)$ are points on a coordinate line, then the *length* of the segment AB is designated by $|AB|$ and is defined to be

$$|AB| = |b - a|.$$

The number $|AB|$ is also called the *distance* between A and B.

The length of a segment of a line evidently depends on the coordinate system. For example, a segment of length 24 units on a line marked off in inches has a length of 2 units if the line is marked off in feet.

Since $|b - a| = |a - b|$, it follows that

$$|AB| = |BA|;$$

that is, the length of a segment AB does not depend on the direction from A to B. We note that the distance from the origin O to any point $A(a)$ is simply

$$|OA| = |a|.$$

If A, B, C, and D are four points on L, then

$$AB \equiv CD \text{ if and only if } |AB| = |CD|.$$

It is useful at times to consider a distance on a coordinate line L that takes into account the direction of L. Such a distance is defined below.

1.15 **DEFINITION.** The *directed distance* from the point $A(a)$ to the point $B(b)$ on a coordinate line is designated by $\overline{AB}$ and is defined to be

$$\overline{AB} = b - a.$$

Since $\overline{AB} = b - a$ and $\overline{BA} = a - b$, it is immediate that

$$\overline{AB} = -\overline{BA}.$$

Also, we have

$$|\overline{AB}| = |AB|.$$

If coordinate line L is horizontal and directed to the right, then point B is to the right of point A if and only if $\overline{AB} > 0$; and point B is to the left of point A if and only if $\overline{AB} < 0$. Thus the directed distance $\overline{AB}$ between two points not only gives the distance between A and B, namely $|\overline{AB}|$, but it also tells the direction from A to B relative to the direction of L. In particular, the directed distance from the origin to the point $A(a)$ is a, the coordinate of A.

If $A(a)$ and $B(b)$ are two points on a coordinate line L, then the point $P(x)$ of L is the midpoint of segment AB if and only if $\overline{AP} = \overline{PB}$; that is,

$$x - a = b - x.$$

We easily solve this equation for x, obtaining $x = (a + b)/2$. Thus the coordinate of the midpoint of AB is the arithmetic average, $(a + b)/2$, of the coordinates of a and b. We have proved the following result.

1.16 **THEOREM.** If $A(a)$ and $B(b)$ are points on a coordinate line, then $M[(a + b)/2]$ is the midpoint of segment AB.

Segments of a coordinate line L are closely related to intervals. Thus, if $A(a)$ and $B(b)$ are points of L, with $a < b$, the closed interval $[a,b]$ is precisely the set of all coordinates of points on segment AB. If we define an *open segment* of L to be a segment excluding its two endpoints, then the set of all coordinates of points on an open segment is an open interval. Similarly, we can define half-open segments, which correspond to half-open intervals.

1.17 **DEFINITION.** If S is a set of real numbers and L is a coordinate line, then the set of all points $P(x)$ of L having coordinates x in S,

$$\{P(x) \mid x \text{ in } S\},$$

is called the *graph* of S on L.

For example, if $A(a)$ and $B(b)$ are points on L with $a < b$, then the (closed) segment AB is the graph of the interval $[a,b]$ and the open segment AB is the graph of the open interval (a,b).

The graph of the solution set of an equation or inequality in one variable is called the graph of the equation or inequality.

EXAMPLE 1. Find the graph of the inequality $|x - 7| \leq 4$.

Solution: By **1.10**, the given inequality is equivalent to

$$-4 \leq x - 7 \leq 4.$$

In turn, this is equivalent to

$$3 \leq x \leq 11.$$

Hence the closed interval [3,11] is the desired solution. Its graph on L is the segment AB shown in Figure 1.4. Note that the brackets at A and B indicate that A and B are included in the graph.

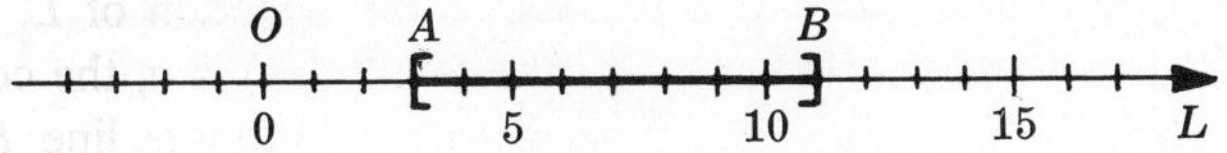

FIGURE 1.4

In the same way that we worked this example, we can show that the solution of the inequality (assuming $c > 0$)

$$|x - a| \leq c \text{ is the closed interval } [a - c, a + c];$$
$$|x - a| < c \text{ is the open interval } (a - c, a + c).$$

We observe that a is the midpoint of each of the intervals $[a - c, a + c]$ and $(a - c, a + c)$. Thus, the solution of the inequality $|x - a| < c$ is the symmetric neighborhood of a with radius c.

EXAMPLE 2. Graph the inequality $7 \leq 3 - 2x < 11$ on a coordinate line L.

Solution: We solve the inequality as follows:

$$7 - 3 \leq -2x < 11 - 3$$
$$4 \leq -2x < 8$$
$$-2 \geq x > -4.$$

Hence its solution set is the half-open interval $(-4,-2]$. The graph of $(-4,-2]$ is the half-open segment of L shown in Figure 1.5. The parenthesis at -4 indicates that the

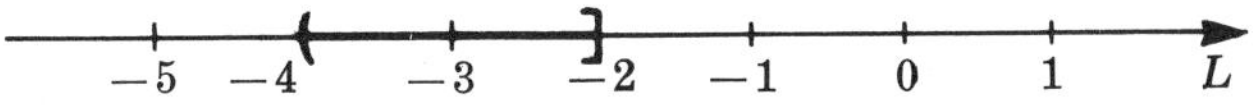

FIGURE 1.5

point with coordinate -4 is excluded from the segment; the bracket at -2 indicates that the endpoint at -2 is included.

EXAMPLE 3. Find the graph of the inequality $3x - 5 \leq 5x + 3$ on a coordinate line L.

Solution: Each of the following inequalities is equivalent to the given one.

$$(3x - 5) + (-5x + 5) \leq (5x + 3) + (-5x + 5)$$
$$-2x \leq 8$$
$$x \geq -4.$$

Therefore the infinite interval $[-4, \infty)$ is the desired solution set. The graph of $[-4, \infty)$ is indicated in Figure 1.6. It is a *half-line* including its endpoint at -4.

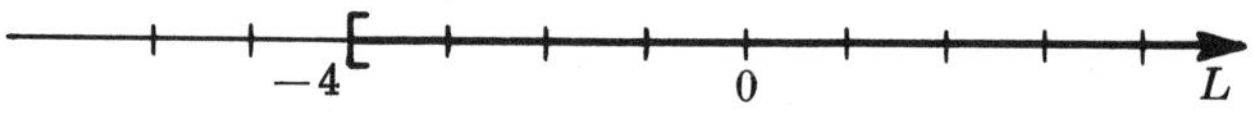

FIGURE 1.6

EXERCISES

In each of the following, give the interval solution of the inequality. Also sketch the corresponding segment of a coordinate line.

1. $-3 < x + 3 < 2$.
2. $1 < 2x - 1 < 3$.
3. $|x - 5| \leq 1$.
4. $|x + 2| \leq .1$.
5. $2 \leq 3 - 4x < 3$.
6. $5 < 5x + 1 \leq 7$.
7. $|2x + 3| < .01$.
8. $|3 - x| < .02$.
9. $-1 < 4 + 2x \leq 0$.
10. $-5 < 1 - 3x \leq 4$.
11. $|x - .01| \leq .001$.
12. $|.1x + 3| < .12$.
13. $-9 \leq 3x - 6 < 0$.
14. $x^2 < 4$.
15. $\dfrac{1}{x} > 10$.
16. $\dfrac{2}{x - 1} > -1$.
17. Show that if $|x| > b$ where $b > 0$, then x lies outside the interval $[-b,b]$.
18. Give a geometric solution of the inequality $|x - 1| > 5$.

Find the interval solution of each of the following inequalities (ϵ a positive number).

19. $|5x + 10| < \epsilon$.
20. $|(mx + b) - (ma + b)| < \epsilon, (m > 0)$.
21. $|x^2 - a^2| < \epsilon, (a > 0)$.
22. $\left|\dfrac{1}{x} - \dfrac{1}{a}\right| < \epsilon, (a > 0)$.
23. $|\sqrt{a} - \sqrt{x}| < \epsilon, (a > 0)$.

REVIEW

Oral Exercises

Explain or define each of the following.

1. Rational number.
2. Irrational number.
3. Complex number.
4. An ordered field.
5. The associative, commutative, and distributive laws of addition and multiplication.
6. The union and intersection of two sets.
7. Open interval.
8. Closed interval.
9. Half-closed interval.
10. Coordinate line.
11. Directed distance.
12. Neighborhood.
13. Deleted neighborhood.
14. Symmetric neighborhood.

I

In each of Exercises 1–6, solve the inequality.

1. $x + 5 > 0,\ 2 - x < 0.$
2. $|x^2 - 1| < 10.$
3. $4 \leq x^2 < 25.$
4. $|x^2 - 1| < 10,\ |x^2 + 1| > 11|.$
5. $|x| > -x,\ |2x + 1| \leq 1.$
6. $|x^2 - 4x + 4| > 4.$
7. Prove that there is a rational number between any two distinct rational numbers.
8. Show that

$$\max(x_1,x_2) = (x_1 + x_2 + |x_2 - x_1|)/2.$$

9. Show that

$$\min(x_1,x_2) = (x_1 + x_2 - |x_2 - x_1|)/2.$$

II

In each of Exercises 1–8, solve the inequality.

1. $|x - 4| \leq |x - 9|.$
2. $|x - 3| < 2|x - 4|.$
3. $|x - 1| + 2|x - 3| \geq 4.$
4. $|x - 1| - 2|x - 3| \geq 4.$
5. $|x^2 - 4| \geq |x^2 - 9|.$
6. $|x^2 + x + 1| < 3.$
7. $|x^2 - 2x - 1| + 2|x - 1|^2 \geq 2.$
8. $|x - 1| + |x - 2| + |x - 4| \leq 7.$

9. If a and b are observed values of two positive numbers A and B, subject to errors whose numerical values are not greater than α and β respectively, determine an upper limit to the error in taking
   a. $a + b$ to represent $A + B$.
   b. $a - b$ to represent $A - B$.
   c. ab to represent AB
   d. a/b to represent A/B $(bB \neq 0)$.

10. The length of a man's step is approximately 30 inches, correct to the nearest inch. What is the maximum error in the number of steps taken per mile if it is calculated on the basis that he steps exactly 30 inches?

11. Determine $\sqrt{1.0000020} - \sqrt{1.0000010}$ correct to six decimal places.

12. Find explicit expressions for max (x_1,x_2,x_3), min (x_1,x_2,x_3), and mid (x_1,x_2,x_3) where mid $(x_1,x_2,x_3) = x_2$ if $x_1 \leq x_2 \leq x_3$. (Use Exercises I, 8, 9.)

13. If r is a positive rational approximation to $\sqrt{2}$, show that $(r + 2)/(r + 1)$ is *always* a better rational approximation.

14. Generalize Exercise 8 for $\sqrt{N}$.

15. For what number x is $a_1|x - b_1| + a_2|x - b_2| + a_3|x - b_3|$ a minimum where $\{a_r,b_r|r = 1, 2, 3\}$ is a set of given numbers and $a_r > 0$, $(r = 1, 2, 3)$? Give a geometric interpretation and generalize.

2

INTRODUCTION TO ANALYTIC GEOMETRY

MANY APPLICATIONS of the calculus are found in the solution of geometric problems such as that of finding the area of a region, the length of a curve, the tangent line to a curve, or the volume of a solid. The basis of these applications lies in that branch of mathematics, known as analytic geometry, in which numbers are used to determine the position of points, and equations are used to describe geometric figures.

1 RECTANGULAR COORDINATE SYSTEMS

We saw in Chapter 1 how a coordinate system could be introduced on a line. Let us now show how a coordinate system may be introduced in a plane with the aid of two coordinate lines. These two coordinate lines are assumed to be perpendicular, to meet at their origins, and to have congruent unit segments (i.e., to have the same scale). As is customary, we designate these coordinate lines as the "x axis" and the "y axis" in the plane. The x axis is usually taken to be a horizontal line directed to the right and the y axis to be a vertical line directed upward.

The projection of a point P on a line L is the point Q of intersection of L and the line L' through P perpendicular to L. If P lies on L, P is its own projection on L.

For a point P in the plane, let $A(a)$ and $B(b)$ be the projections of P on the x axis and y axis, respectively (Figure 2.1). Then the numbers a and b are called

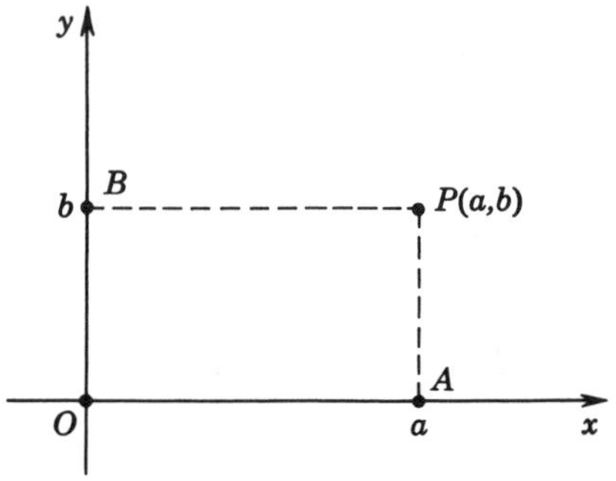

FIGURE 2.1

the *coordinates* of P and we write $P(a,b)$ to indicate that P has x *coordinate* (or *abscissa*) a and y *coordinate* (or *ordinate*) b.

In this way there is associated with each point P in the plane an ordered pair of numbers (a,b). We call (a,b) an *ordered pair* because the order in which the numbers are given is important. Thus $(2,-5)$ is a different ordered pair than $(-5,2)$. Conversely, with each ordered pair of numbers (a,b) there is associated a point $P(a,b)$ in the plane. This association of ordered pairs of numbers with points is called a *rectangular coordinate system* in the plane, and a plane together with a coordinate system is called a *coordinate plane*. Some examples of points and their coordinates are given in Figure 2.2.

The coordinate axes divide the plane into four *quadrants*, numbered as in Figure 2.3. For example, quadrant I consists of the set of points $\{P(x,y) \mid x > 0$

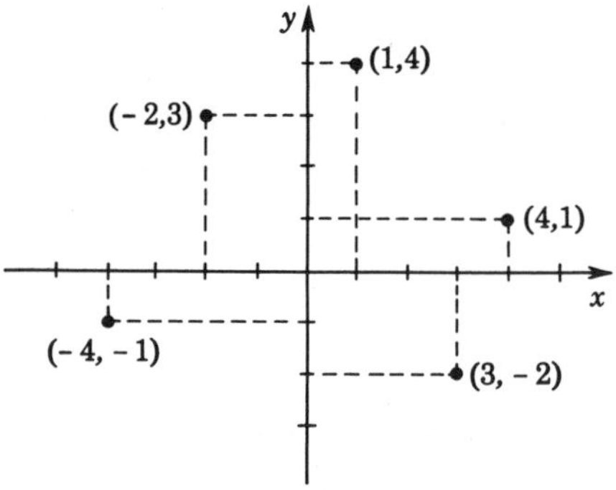

FIGURE 2.2

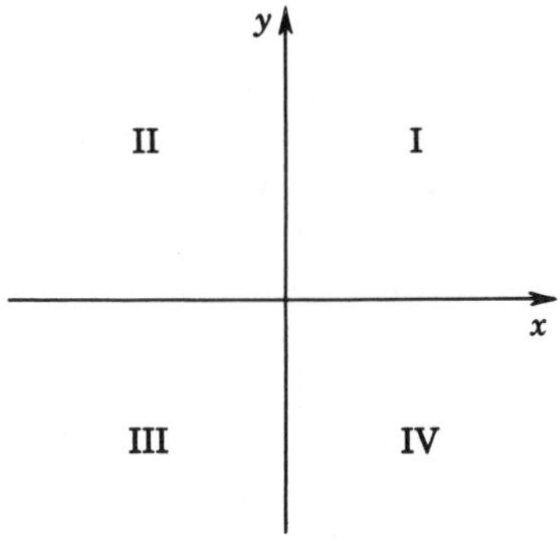

FIGURE 2.3

and $y > 0\}$; quadrant III of $\{P(x,y) \mid x < 0$ and $y < 0\}$. Every point in the plane is either in one of the quadrants or on a coordinate axis. The x axis consists of the set of points $\{P(x,0) \mid x$ any number$\}$; the y axis of $\{P(0,y) \mid y$ any number$\}$. The point $O(0,0)$ of intersection of the axes is again called the *origin.*

We recall that the notation (a,b) is also used for an open interval. No confusion should result from this double usage, since the context will always make clear which meaning of (a,b) is intended.

The analogue of the midpoint formula on a line (**1.16**) is as follows.

2.1 THEOREM. If $P(x_1,y_1)$ and $Q(x_2,y_2)$ are two points in a coordinate plane, then

$$M\left(\frac{x_1 + x_2}{2}, \frac{y_1 + y_2}{2}\right)$$

is the midpoint of segment PQ.

Proof: The projections of P and Q on the x axis are the points $A(x_1,0)$ and $B(x_2,0)$, respectively (Figure 2.4). By a result of Euclidean geometry, the projec-

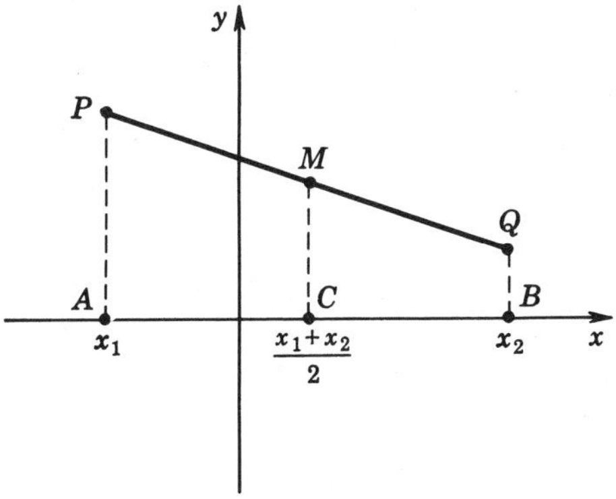

FIGURE 2.4

tion C of the midpoint M of PQ on the x axis is the midpoint of AB. Hence C has coordinates

$$\left(\frac{x_1 + x_2}{2}, 0\right),$$

according to **1.16**. Thus, by definition, $(x_1 + x_2)/2$ is the abscissa of M. A similar argument relative to the y axis shows that M has ordinate $(y_1 + y_2)/2$. This proves **2.1**.

2 PLANE GRAPHS

Any set of ordered pairs of numbers has associated with it a set of points in a coordinate plane; thus each ordered pair (x,y) has associated with it the point $P(x,y)$. Again, as in **1.17**, we call this set of points the *graph* (in the plane) of the given set of ordered pairs of numbers.

EXAMPLE 1. Find the graph of the set $\{(0,0), (1,1), (-1,1), (2,4), (-2,4)\}$.

Solution: The graph consists of the set $\{0, A, B, C, D\}$ of points shown in Figure 2.5.

EXAMPLE 2. Find the graph of the set $\{(x,y) \mid 1 \leq x \leq 3, 0 \leq y \leq 4\}$.

Solution: The graph is the rectangular region of the plane shaded in Figure 2.6.

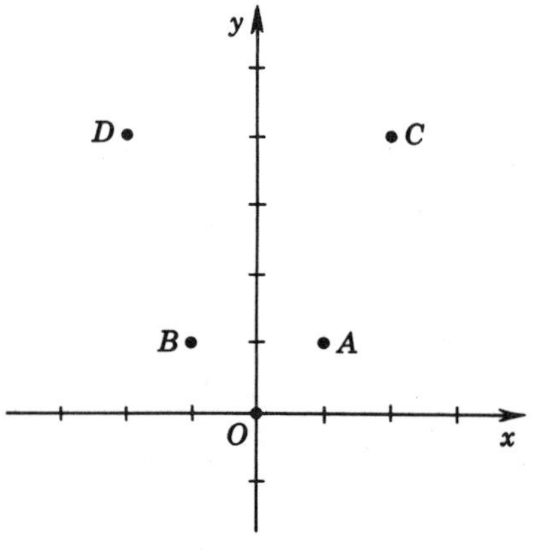

FIGURE 2.5

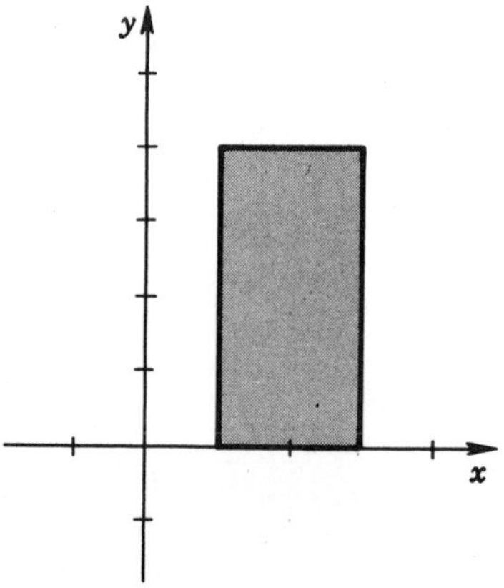

FIGURE 2.6

Given an equation or inequality in two variables, say x and y, a *solution* consists of an ordered pair of numbers (a,b) such that the equation or inequality is true when we let $x = a$ and $y = b$.

For example, (2,4) is a solution of the equation

$$y = x^2,$$

since $4 = 2^2$ is a true equation. Also, $(-\sqrt{7},7)$ is a solution since $7 = (-\sqrt{7})^2$. On the other hand, (3,5) is not a solution since the equation $5 = 3^2$ is false.

The set S of all solutions of an equation or inequality in two variables is called the *solution set* of the equation or inequality. In turn, the graph of S in a coordinate plane is called the *graph of the equation or inequality*.

EXAMPLE 3. Find the graphs of the equations $y = x$ and $y = -x$.

Solution: The solution set S of the equation $y = x$ is given by

$$S = \{(x,x) \mid x \text{ a real number}\}.$$

Its graph is the straight line L bisecting the first and third quadrants (Figu re 2.7) The solution set T of the equation $y = -x$ is given by

$$T = \{(x,-x) \mid x \text{ a real number}\}.$$

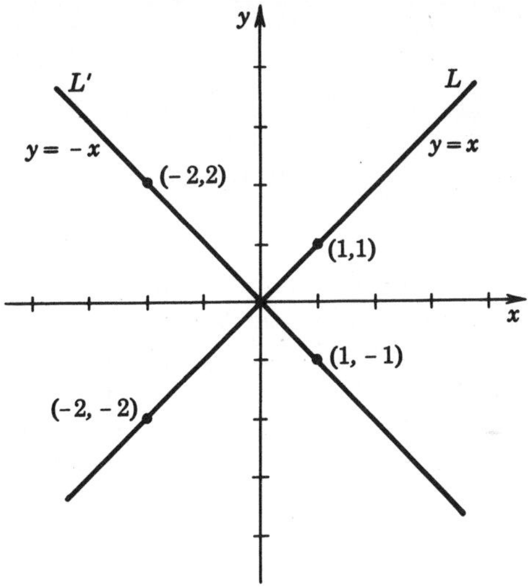

FIGURE 2.7

The graph of T is the straight line L' bisecting the second and fourth quadrants (Figure 2.7).

Since $|x| = x$ if $x \geq 0$ whereas $|x| = -x$ if $x < 0$, evidently the graph of the equation

$$y = |x|$$

is the same as that of $y = x$ if $x \geq 0$, and the same as $y = -x$ if $x < 0$. Therefore the graph of $y = |x|$ is as shown in Figure 2.8.

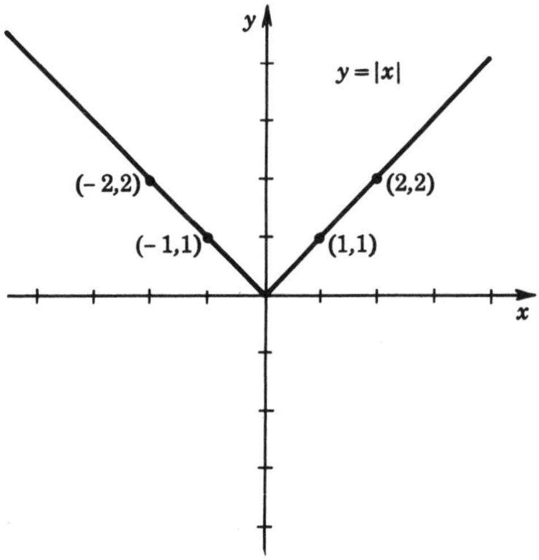

FIGURE 2.8

Given a set C of points on a coordinate plane, an equation or inequality whose graph is C (if one exists) is called an *equation or inequality of C.*

For example, let us find an equation of $L \cup L'$ in Figure 2.7. Thus we are seeking an equation whose graph consists of all the points in the plane on either L or L'. Since $y - x = 0$ is an equation of L and $y + x = 0$ is an equation of L', we claim that

$$(y - x)(y + x) = 0,$$

$$\text{or} \qquad y^2 - x^2 = 0$$

is an equation of $L \cup L'$. For $(b - a)(b + a) = 0$ if and only if either $b - a = 0$ or $b + a = 0$. That is, $P(a,b)$ is on the graph of $y^2 - x^2 = 0$ if and only if either $P(a,b)$ is on L, the graph of $y - x = 0$, or $P(a,b)$ is on L', the graph of $y + x = 0$.

EXAMPLE 4. Describe the graphs of the inequalities $y \geq x$ and $x < 2$.

Solution: A point $P(a,b)$ is on the graph of $y \geq x$ if and only if $b \geq a$. Hence the graph consists of all points (a,b) on (if $b = a$) or above (if $b > a$) the line $y = x$. It is the shaded half-plane of Figure 2.9.

A point $P(a,b)$ is on the graph of the inequality $x < 2$ if and only if $a < 2$. Such

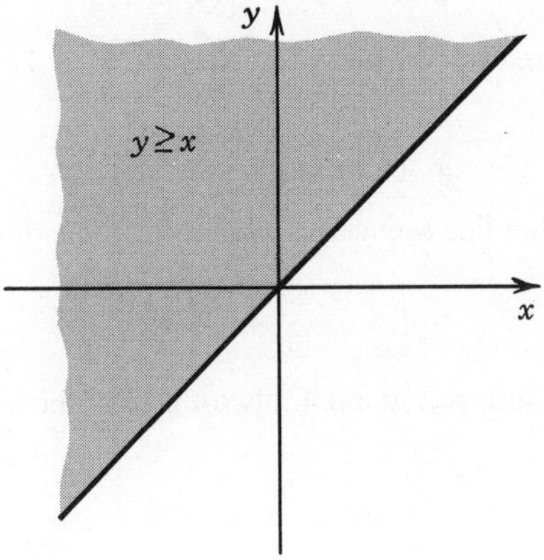

FIGURE 2.9

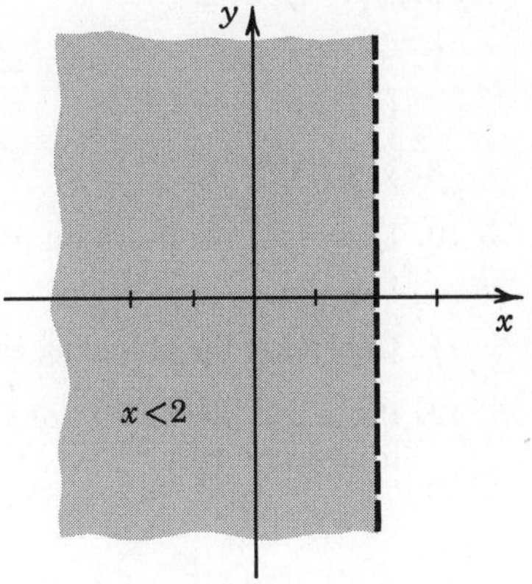

FIGURE 2.10

points lie to the left of the vertical line having all its abscissas equal to 2. The graph is sketched in Figure 2.10. The vertical line $x = 2$ is broken to indicate that it is not part of the graph.

EXERCISES

I

In each of Exercises 1–12, sketch the graph of the given equation or inequality.

1. $y = 2x$.
2. $y = 2x + 1$.
3. $y = -2x$.
4. $y = -2x - 3$.
5. $y + 3x \leq 1$.
6. $y - 3x > 1$.
7. $y^2 \geq 4$.
8. $x^2 < 1$.
9. $y < -|x|$.
10. $x = -|y|$.
11. $y = |x| + 1$.
12. $x = -|y| - 1$.

II

In each of Exercises 1–9, sketch the graph of the given equation or inequality.

1. $y \geq |x - 1|$.
2. $x = -2|y + 1|$.

3. $x^2 + y^2 = 2xy + 1$.

4. $|x| + |y| = 1$.

5. $|x| - |y| = 2$.

6. $x^2 + y^2 + 2|xy| < 1$.

7. $y = [x]$, where $[x]$ denotes the greatest integer $\leq x$, e.g., $[\sqrt{2}] = 1$, $[\pi] = 3$, $[-\sqrt{3}] = -2$.

8. $y = |[x]|$.

9. $[x] + [y] = 4$.

10. Determine the trisection points of the line segment between the points (x_1,y_1) and (x_2,y_2).

11. Generalize the preceding exercise.

12. Prove that the medians of a triangle intersect at a point two-thirds of the way down from any vertex.

3 DISTANCE FORMULA

The distance $|AB|$ between two points $A(x_1,0)$ and $B(x_2,0)$ on the x axis was defined (1.15) to be $|x_2 - x_1|$. The four points $A(x_1,0)$, $B(x_2,0)$, $C(x_1,y_1)$, and $D(x_2,y_1)$ are vertices of a rectangle, and hence the segments AB and CD are congruent, $AB \equiv CD$ (see Figure 2.11). Thus the segment CD may be assigned a length $|CD|$ given by $|CD| = |AB| = |x_2 - x_1|$.

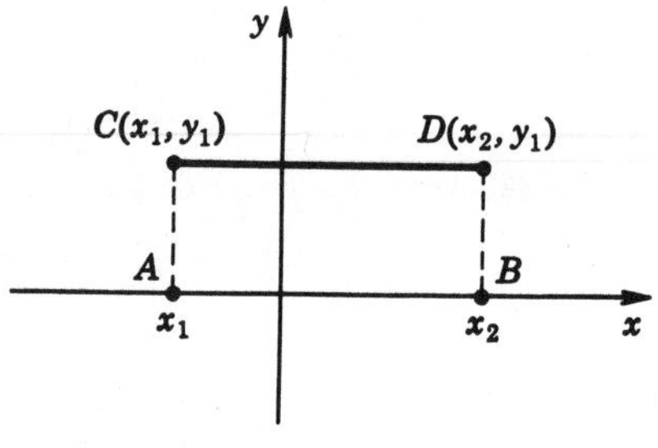

FIGURE 2.11

Similarly, a line segment parallel to the y axis, say with endpoints $E(x_1,y_1)$ and $F(x_1,y_2)$, has a length given by

$$|EF| = |y_2 - y_1|.$$

Each line segment PQ in a coordinate plane is congruent to some line segment AB of the x axis (or y axis). Therefore PQ has a length $|PQ| = |AB|$. The formula giving $|PQ|$ in terms of the coordinates of P and Q is as follows.

2.2 DISTANCE FORMULA. The distance $|PQ|$ between the points $P(x_1,y_1)$ and $Q(x_2,y_2)$ is given by

$$|PQ| = \sqrt{(x_2 - x_1)^2 + (y_2 - y_1)^2}.$$

Proof: The points $P(x_1,y_1)$, $Q(x_2,y_2)$, and $R(x_1,y_2)$ are vertices of a right triangle, as in Figure 2.12. Since the segment RQ is parallel to the x axis and the segment PR is parallel to the y axis, our arguments above yield

$$|RQ| = |x_2 - x_1|, \quad |PR| = |y_2 - y_1|.$$

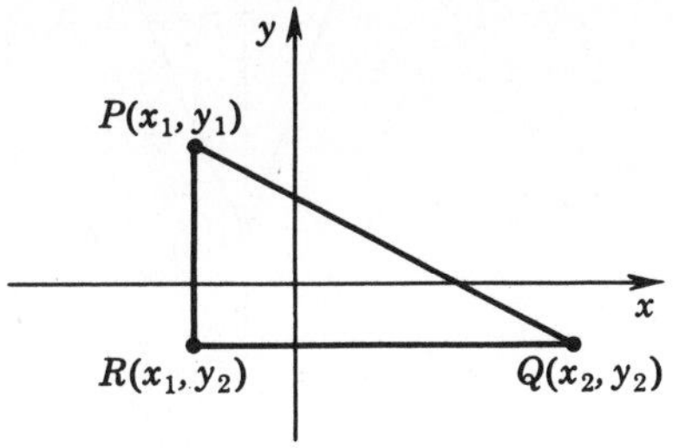

FIGURE 2.12

Hence, by the Pythagorean theorem,

$$|PQ|^2 = |x_2 - x_1|^2 + |y_2 - y_1|^2$$
$$= (x_2 - x_1)^2 + (y_2 - y_1)^2,$$

or

$$|PQ| = \sqrt{(x_2 - x_1)^2 + (y_2 - y_1)^2}.$$

This proves 2.2.

The distance formula, when applied to the points $C(x_1,y_1)$ and $D(x_2,y_1)$, gives

$$|CD| = \sqrt{(x_2 - x_1)^2 + (y_1 - y_1)^2} = \sqrt{(x_2 - x_1)^2} = |x_2 - x_1|,$$

which agrees with the results given at the beginning of this section.

We have used the Pythagorean theorem in establishing the distance formula. The converse of the Pythagorean theorem may be used to determine if a given triangle on a coordinate plane is a right triangle. Thus, if

$$|PQ|^2 = |PR|^2 + |RQ|^2,$$

the triangle with vertices P, Q, and R will be a right triangle with hypotenuse PQ and right angle at vertex R.

EXAMPLE. Show that the triangle with vertices $A(-3,1)$, $B(5,4)$, and $C(0,-7)$ is a right triangle, and find its area (see Figure 2.13).

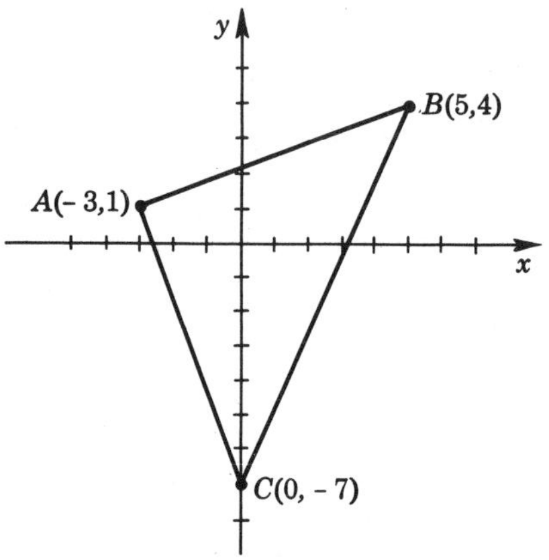

FIGURE 2.13

Solution: We have by the distance formula that

$$\begin{aligned}|AB| &= \sqrt{[5-(-3)]^2 + (4-1)^2} \\ &= \sqrt{73}, \\ |AC| &= \sqrt{[0-(-3)]^2 + (-7-1)^2} \\ &= \sqrt{73}, \\ |BC| &= \sqrt{(0-5)^2 + (-7-4)^2} \\ &= \sqrt{146}.\end{aligned}$$

Since

$$|AB|^2 + |AC|^2 = 73 + 73 = 146 = |BC|^2,$$

the triangle has a right angle at vertex A. It happens that this triangle also is isosceles, since $|AB| = |AC|$.

The area of the right triangle ABC is given by

$$\tfrac{1}{2}|AB|\cdot|AC| = \tfrac{1}{2}\sqrt{73}\cdot\sqrt{73} = \tfrac{73}{2}.$$

4 CIRCLES

A circle may be defined as the set of all points in a plane at a given distance from a fixed point. The distance formula of Section 3 can be used to give the following analytic description of a circle.

2.3 THEOREM. The circle with center $C(h,k)$ and radius r has the equation

$$(x - h)^2 + (y - k)^2 = r^2.$$

Proof: The point $P(x,y)$ is on the given circle if and only if

$$|PC| = r;$$

that is, if and only if

$$\sqrt{(x - h)^2 + (y - k)^2} = r,$$

or

$$(x - h)^2 + (y - k)^2 = r^2.$$

This is therefore an equation of the circle.

In the light of the definition of the graph of an equation, we have also proved that the *graph of the equation*

$$(x - h)^2 + (y - k)^2 = r^2$$

is the circle with center $C(h,k)$ and radius r.

As a particular case,

$$x^2 + y^2 = r^2$$

is an equation of the circle with radius r and center at the origin.

EXAMPLE 1. Find an equation of the circle with center $C(4,-3)$ and radius 6.

Solution: In this example $h = 4$, $k = -3$, $r = 6$. By 2.3,

$$(x - 4)^2 + [y - (-3)]^2 = 6^2,$$
$$(x - 4)^2 + (y + 3)^2 = 36$$

is an equation of the circle. After noting that $(x - 4)^2 = x^2 - 8x + 16$ and $(y + 3)^2 = y^2 + 6y + 9$, we may also write the following equation of the circle:

$$x^2 + y^2 - 8x + 6y - 11 = 0.$$

The circle is shown in Figure 2.14.

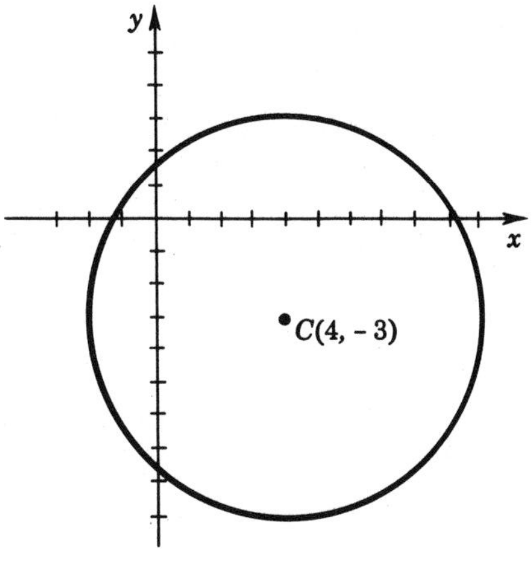

FIGURE 2.14

EXAMPLE 2. Show that the graph of the equation

$$x^2 + y^2 + 4x - 2y - 1 = 0$$

is a circle, and find its center and radius.

Solution: The given equation is equivalent to the equation

$$x^2 + y^2 + 4x - 2y = 1.$$

Adding the numbers 4 and 1 to each side of this equation to complete the squares, we have

$$x^2 + 4x + 4 + y^2 - 2y + 1 = 1 + 4 + 1,$$

$$\text{or} \quad (x + 2)^2 + (y - 1)^2 = (\sqrt{6})^2.$$

We recognize this as an equation of the circle with center $C(-2,1)$ and radius $r = \sqrt{6}$ (Figure 2.15).

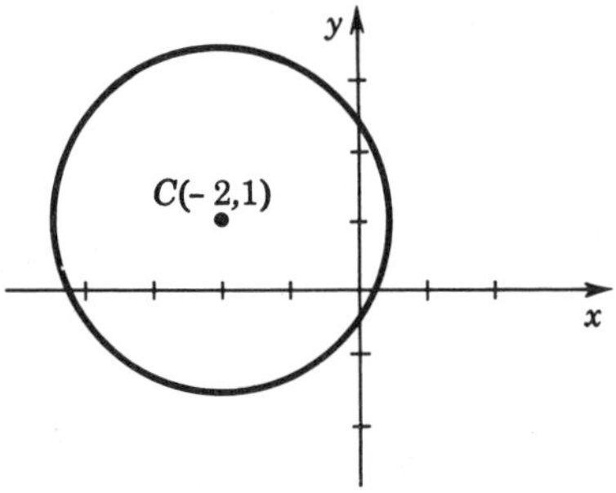

FIGURE 2.15

EXAMPLE 3. Find an equation of the set S of all points P in a coordinate plane such that the distance between P and $A(5,1)$ is three times the distance between P and $B(-3,1)$.

Solution: If $P(x,y)$ is a point in the plane, then P is in set S if and only if

$$|PA| = 3|PB|,$$

(Figure 2.16), or, by the distance formula,

$$\sqrt{(x - 5)^2 + (y - 1)^2} = 3\sqrt{(x + 3)^2 + (y - 1)^2}.$$

Therefore this is an equation of set S.

If we observe that the quantities under the radical signs in the above equation are nonnegative for every choice of x and y, then it is clear that this equation is equivalent to the equation

$$(x - 5)^2 + (y - 1)^2 = 9[(x + 3)^2 + (y - 1)^2].$$

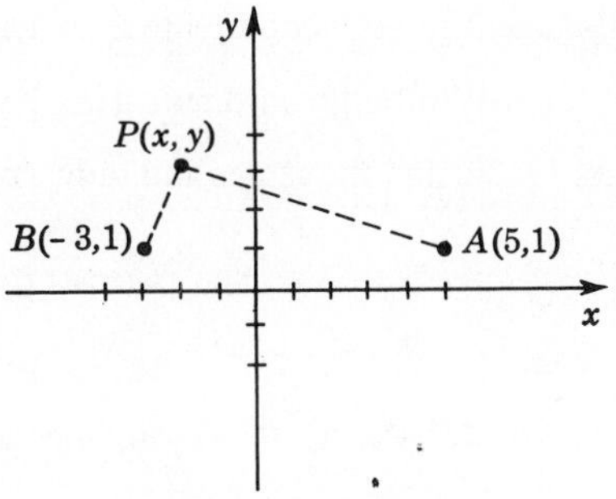

FIGURE 2.16

Hence this too is an equation of set S. In turn, this equation can be changed into an equivalent form

$$8x^2 + 8y^2 + 64x - 16y + 64 = 0,$$
$$\text{or} \quad x^2 + y^2 + 8x - 2y + 8 = 0.$$

Completing squares, we get

$$(x + 4)^2 + (y - 1)^2 = 9.$$

From this final form of an equation of set S, we deduce that S is a circle with center $C(-4,1)$ and radius $r = 3$.

EXERCISES

I

In each of Exercises 1–6, show that ABC is a right triangle. Find the equation of each circumscribed circle, using the fact that the center of the circle circumscribed about ABC is the midpoint of the hypotenuse. Sketch.

1. $A(1,0)$, $B(5,3)$, $C(4,-4)$.
2. $A(1,0)$, $B(4,2)$, $C(-3,6)$.
3. $A(4,4)$, $B(1,5)$, $C(-2,-4)$.
4. $A(3,-2)$, $B(4,3)$, $C(-6,5)$.
5. $A(0,1)$, $B(2,3)$, $C(0,5)$.
6. $A(1,-2)$, $B(0,0)$, $C(-2,-1)$.

In each of Exercises 7–12, find an equation of the circle and sketch it.

7. Center $(-1,-3)$, radius $r = 3$.
8. Center $(3,0)$, radius $r = 5$.
9. Center $(2,4)$, passing through the origin.
10. Center $(0,0,)$ passing through the point $(3,7)$.

11. Radius $r = 4$, tangent to both coordinate axes, lying in the second quadrant.

12. Radius $r = 1$, tangent to both coordinate axes, lying in the fourth quadrant.

In each of Exercises 13–20, find the center and radius of the circle with given equation. Sketch.

13. $x^2 + y^2 - 16 = 0.$

14. $x^2 + y^2 - 2x - 4y + 1 = 0.$

15. $x^2 + y^2 + 6x - 10y + 25 = 0.$

16. $4x^2 + 4y^2 + 16x + 15 = 0.$

17. $2x^2 + 2y^2 + 4y + 1 = 0.$

18. $x^2 + y^2 + 6x + 8y = 0.$

19. $9x^2 + 9y^2 - 6x + 12y + 4 = 0.$

20. $4x^2 + 4y^2 + 4x - 12y + 7 = 0.$

21. Find an equation of the graph of all points $P(x,y)$ in a coordinate plane twice as far from the point $A(1,0)$ as from the point $B(-2,0)$.

22. Find an equation of the graph of all points $P(x,y)$ in a coordinate plane equidistant from the points $A(2,1)$ and $B(4,-1)$.

23. Show that the point $P(x,y)$ is equidistant from the point $(0,4)$ and the x axis if and only if $x^2 - 8y + 16 = 0$.

24. Find the center and radius of the circle with equation

$$x^2 + y^2 + ax + by + c = 0.$$

Under what conditions on a, b, and c will the equation have no graph? Is the graph ever just a point?

II

1. Find the points of intersection of the two circles

$$x^2 + y^2 + 8y = 64,$$
$$x^2 + y^2 - 6x = 16.$$ Also, sketch the figure.

2. Determine an equation of a circle tangent to both coordinate axes and passing through the given point (h,k).

3. Prove that an angle inscribed in a semicircle is a right angle.

4. Show how to determine the radius and center of the circle passing through the three given points (x_r,y_r), $r = 1, 2, 3$, by:
   a. Considering the three simultaneous equations

$$(x_r - h)^2 + (y_r - k)^2 = a^2,\ r = 1, 2, 3;$$

   b. Considering the determinant

$$\begin{vmatrix} x^2 + y^2 & x & y & 1 \\ x_1^2 + y_1^2 & x_1 & y_1 & 1 \\ x_2^2 + y_2^2 & x_2 & y_2 & 1 \\ x_3^2 + y_3^2 & x_3 & y_3 & 1 \end{vmatrix}.$$

5. Determine an equation of the circle which passes through the two points of intersection of the two circles

$$x^2 + y^2 + a_r x + b_r y + c_r = 0, \; r = 1, 2,$$

and the point (m,n).

5 SLOPE OF A LINE

It is convenient to think of an angle between two lines in a plane as being formed by rotating one of the lines about the fixed vertex of the angle until it coincides with the other line. The angle has positive measure if the rotation is counterclockwise and negative measure if it is clockwise.

Given two lines L_1 and L_2 intersecting at V, the angle from L_1 to L_2 is defined to be the angle of least positive measure formed by rotating L_1 about V to L_2. The congruent angles θ and ϕ of Figure 2.17 are the angles from L_1 to L_2. It is

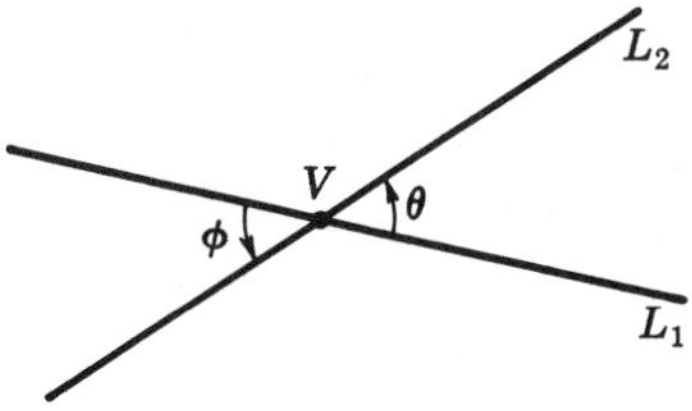

FIGURE 2.17

clear that the angle from L_1 to L_2 has measure between 0° and 180° (or between 0 and π radians). We shall follow the conventional practice of considering parallel lines as intersecting in an angle of measure 0°.

Useful concepts in the determination of an equation of a straight line in a coordinate plane are inclination and slope; these are defined below.

2.4 **DEFINITION.** The *inclination* of a line is the angle α from the x axis to the line. The *slope* m of the line is given by

$$m = \tan \alpha.$$

The inclination α of a line L satisfies the inequality

$$0° \leq \alpha < 180°,$$

where $\alpha = 0°$ if and only if L is parallel to the x axis. A line parallel to the y axis has an inclination of 90°.

For each number r there exists a unique angle α, $0° \leq \alpha < 180°$, such that $\tan \alpha = r$. Thus the slope of a line can be any real number. *The slope of a line parallel to the x axis is zero.* Since tan 90° does not exist, *a line parallel to the y axis does not have slope.* Conversely, a line that does not have slope is parallel to the y axis.

Since $\tan \alpha > 0$ if $0° < \alpha < 90°$, the lines that are rising (as we move from left to right along the line) have positive slope; and since $\tan \alpha < 0$ if $90° < \alpha < 180°$, the lines that are falling have negative slope.

In the pages to follow, we shall frequently identify a point by its coordinates. Thus we shall often speak of "the point (a,b)" rather than "the point with coordinates (a,b)," or "the vertex (h,k)" rather than "the vertex with coordinates (h,k)," and so on.

EXAMPLE 1. Construct the line on the point (3,1) that has slope 2; construct the line that has slope −2.

Solution: Start from the point (3,1) and construct a right triangle with altitude twice its base, as shown in Figure 2.18. Then draw the line L on the vertices (3,1) and (4,3) of this triangle. The inclination α of L is an angle of the right triangle, and we see that $\tan \alpha = 2$. The line L of slope 2 is rising.

In order to construct a line of slope −2, start from the point (3,1) and construct a right triangle with altitude twice its base, as shown in Figure 2.19. Then draw the

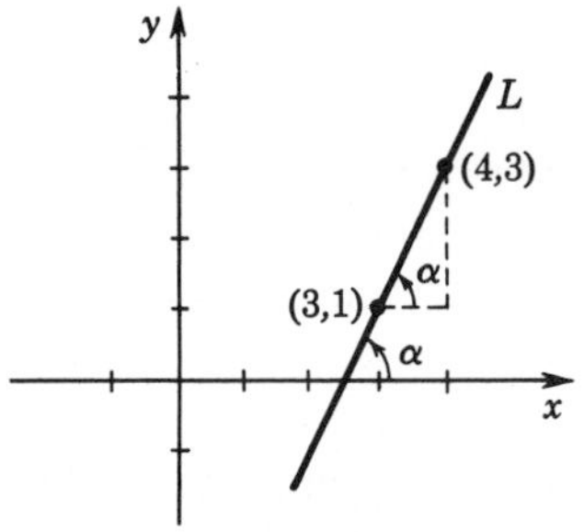

FIGURE 2.18

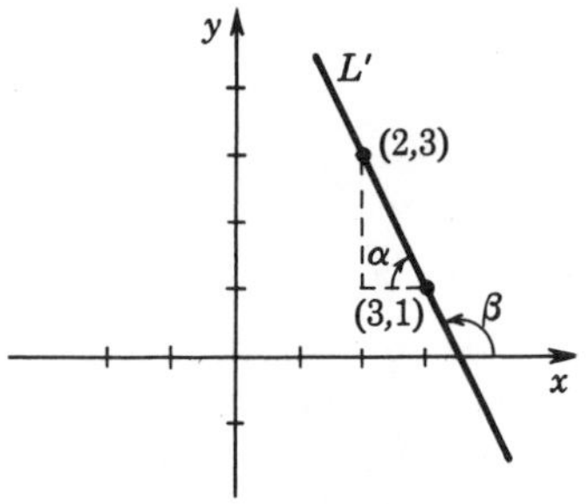

FIGURE 2.19

line L' on the vertices (3,1) and (2,3) of this right triangle. The inclination β is the supplement of the angle α of the right triangle, and therefore

$$\tan \beta = -\tan \alpha = -2.$$

The line L' of slope −2 is falling.

Given two distinct points on a line not parallel to the y axis, the slope of the line may be found by the following theorem.

2.5 **THEOREM.** The slope m of the line L on the points $P(x_1,y_1)$ and $Q(x_2,y_2)$ is given by

$$m = \frac{y_2 - y_1}{x_2 - x_1}, \qquad (x_2 \neq x_1).$$

Proof: Let us assume that $y_1 < y_2$, so that Q is above P. Construct a line x' through P and parallel to the x axis (Figure 2.20). Then the inclination α

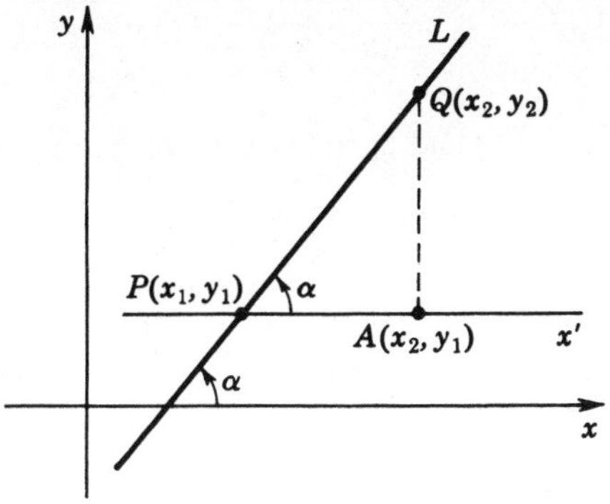

FIGURE 2.20

of L is the same relative to both the x axis and the x' axis. By definition (notation of Figure 2.20),

$$\tan \alpha = \frac{\overline{AQ}}{\overline{PA}};$$

and since $\overline{AQ} = y_2 - y_1$ and $\overline{PA} = x_2 - x_1$,

$$m = \tan \alpha = \frac{y_2 - y_1}{x_2 - x_1}.$$

If $y_2 < y_1$, we construct the line x' through Q and obtain, by the same reasoning as above,

$$m = \frac{y_1 - y_2}{x_1 - x_2}.$$

Since

$$\frac{y_2 - y_1}{x_2 - x_1} = \frac{y_1 - y_2}{x_1 - x_2},$$

this agrees with the previous result.

If $y_1 = y_2$, the line L is parallel to the x axis and $m = 0$. Since

$$\frac{y_2 - y_1}{x_2 - x_1} = 0$$

in this case, the formula again gives the correct result.

EXAMPLE 2. Find the slope m of the line on the points (3,4) and (5, −1).

Solution: We identify one of these points, say (3,4), with $P(x_1,y_1)$ and the other, (5, −1), with $Q(x_2,y_2)$ in **2.5**. Hence

$$m = \frac{-1 - 4}{5 - 3} = -\frac{5}{2}.$$

If we let P be (5, −1) and Q be (3,4), we again obtain

$$m = \frac{4 - (-1)}{3 - 5} = -\frac{5}{2}.$$

6 PARALLEL AND PERPENDICULAR LINES

If the lines L_1 and L_2 are parallel, then their inclinations are equal and their slopes are equal. Conversely, if the slopes of lines L_1 and L_2 are equal, then so are their inclinations, and lines L_1 and L_2 are parallel (or equal). We state these observations in the following compact form.

2.6 THEOREM. The lines L_1 and L_2 with slopes m_1 and m_2, respectively, are parallel if and only if $m_1 = m_2$.

A test for the perpendicularity of two lines is given by the next theorem.

2.7 THEOREM. The lines L_1 and L_2 with slopes m_1 and m_2, respectively, are perpendicular if and only if $m_1 = -(1/m_2)$.

Proof: Construct lines L_1' and L_2' through the origin O parallel to L_1 and L_2, respectively, so that the angle between L_1 and L_2 is congruent to the angle θ between L_1' and L_2' (Figure 2.21). Next, select points A and B on L_1' and L_2', respectively, so that each has abscissa 1. If point A has ordinate b, then $(b - 0)/(1 - 0)$, or b, is the slope of L_1 by **2.5**; i.e., A has coordinates $(1,m_1)$ and, similarly, B has coordinates $(1,m_2)$.

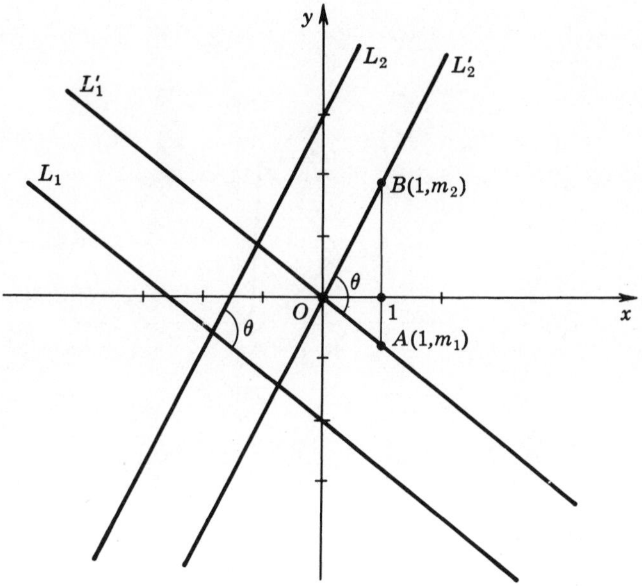

FIGURE 2.21

Triangle OAB is a right triangle, with right angle θ, if and only if $|OA|^2 + |OB|^2 = |AB|^2$; i.e., if and only if

$$(1^2 + m_1^2) + (1^2 + m_2^2) = (m_2 - m_1)^2,$$

or

$$2 + m_1^2 + m_2^2 = m_2^2 - 2m_1m_2 + m_1^2,$$

or

$$-1 = m_1m_2.$$

This proves 2.7.

According to this theorem, two lines (neither of which is parallel to an axis) are perpendicular if and only if their slopes are *negative reciprocals* of each other.

EXAMPLE 1. Show that the triangle with vertices $A(-1,-1)$, $B(-9,6)$, and $C(-2,14)$ is a right triangle.

Solution: The slopes of the sides of triangle ABC (Figure 2.22) are as follows:

$$\text{slope of } AB = \frac{6-(-1)}{-9-(-1)} = -\frac{7}{8},$$

$$\text{slope of } AC = \frac{14-(-1)}{-2-(-1)} = -15,$$

$$\text{slope of } BC = \frac{14-6}{-2-(-9)} = \frac{8}{7}.$$

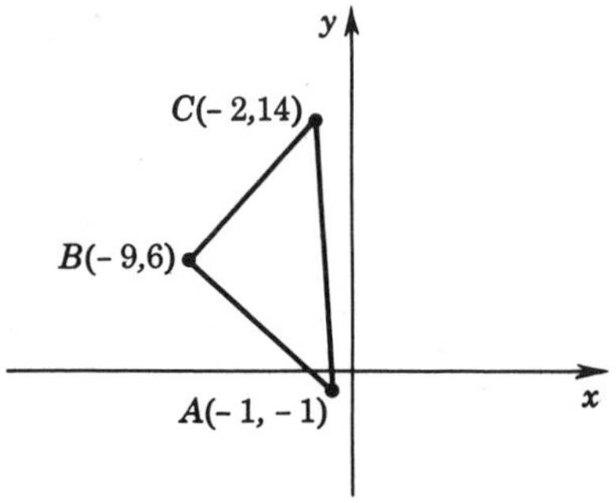

FIGURE 2.22

Since $-\frac{7}{8}$ and $\frac{8}{7}$ are negative reciprocals, sides AB and BC are perpendicular. Hence, ABC is a right triangle with right angle at B.

EXAMPLE 2. Show that the points $A(-1,4)$, $B(0,2)$, $C(2,-2)$ are collinear.

Solution: If m_1 is the slope of AB, then

$$m_1 = \frac{4-2}{-1-0} = -2.$$

If m_2 is the slope of BC, then

$$m_2 = \frac{2-(-2)}{0-2} = -2,$$

and $m_1 = m_2$. The lines AB and BC have the point B in common, and since there is one and only one line L on B with given slope, it follows that A, B, C lie on L.

EXAMPLE 3. Determine y so that the point $P(1,y)$ lies on the perpendicular bisector of the line segment whose endpoints are $A(-1,2)$ and $B(-3,0)$.

Solution: The midpoint of the line segment AB is the point $M(-2,1)$. The slope of AB is $m = 1$. Hence the point $P(1,y)$ will lie on the perpendicular bisector of AB if and only if the slope of PM is $-1/m = -1$; i.e., if and only if

$$\frac{y-1}{1-(-2)} = -1, \text{ or } y = -2.$$

EXERCISES

I

1. Show that $(0,3)$, $(-2,12)$, $(-4,11)$, and $(2,4)$ are vertices of a rectangle.

2. Determine x so that the line on the points $(2,-3)$ and $(x,3)$ has slope 2.

In each of Exercises 3–6, show by means of slopes that the three points are collinear.

3. $(1,-1)$, $(-2,5)$, $(3,-5)$.

4. $(2,0)$, $(4,1)$, $(-6,-4)$.

5. $(-1,1)$, $(2,3)$, $(-4,-1)$.

6. $(-6,3)$, $(4,-1)$, $(3,-\frac{3}{5})$.

7. How could one do Exercises 3–6 without using slopes?

8. Show that the point $(6,3)$ is on the perpendicular bisector of the line segment with endpoints $(3,2)$ and $(7,6)$.

9. Prove that the line segment joining the midpoints of two sides of a triangle is parallel to the third side and has length half that of the third side.

10. If $ABCD$ is a trapezoid with AB and CD the parallel sides, prove that the line segment joining the midpoints of AD and BC is parallel to AB and CD and has as its length the arithmetic average of the lengths of AB and CD. How is this problem related to Exercise 9?

II

1. Show that the angle of intersection of two lines of slope m_1 and m_2, respectively, is given by

$$\tan\theta = \frac{m_2 - m_1}{1 + m_2 m_1}.$$

2. Find the tangents of the angles of a triangle whose vertices are

$$(0,0),\ (4,10),\ (-8,8).$$

3. If (x_1,y_1) and (x_2,y_2) are two adjacent vertices of a square, what are the coordinates of the other vertices?

4. If (x_1,y_1) and (x_2,y_2) are two vertices of an equilateral triangle, what are the coordinates of the third vertex?

5. Let O be the center of a circle and PQ any chord. Prove that the line through O and the midpoint of PQ is perpendicular to PQ.

7 EQUATIONS OF LINES

The line on the point (a,b) and parallel to the y axis has equation

$$x = a,$$

since a point $P(x,y)$ is on this line if and only if $x = a$ (Figure 2.23). Similarly, the line on the point (a,b) and parallel to the x axis has equation

$$y = b,$$

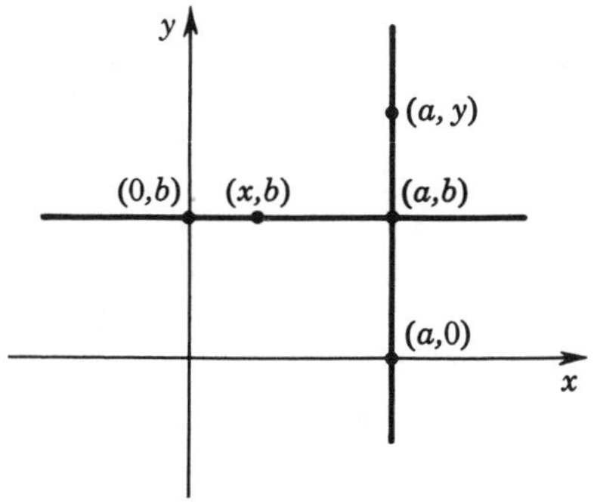

FIGURE 2.23

since a point is on this line if and only if it has coordinates of the form (x,b) (Figure 2.23).

An equation of a line not parallel to a coordinate axis may be obtained in the following way. Let L be a line with given slope m that passes through a given point $Q(x_1,y_1)$, as in Figure 2.24. Then a point $P(x,y)$, different from Q, is on L if and only if the line on P and Q has slope m; i.e., if and only if

$$m = \frac{y - y_1}{x - x_1}, \qquad (x \neq x_1).$$

When this equation is written in the form

2.8 $$y - y_1 = m(x - x_1),$$

it is called the *point-slope form* of the equation of the line passing through the point (x_1,y_1) and with slope m. Note that (x_1,y_1) also is a solution of **2.8,** since obviously

$$y_1 - y_1 = m(x_1 - x_1).$$

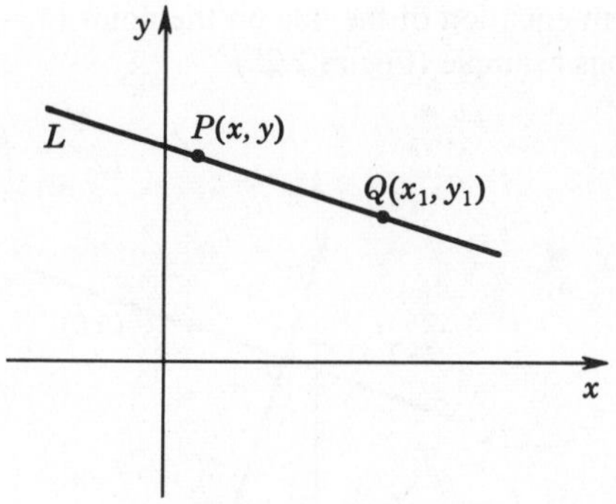

FIGURE 2.24

EXAMPLE 1. Find an equation of the line on the points $(-1,4)$ and $(5,6)$ (Figure 2.25).

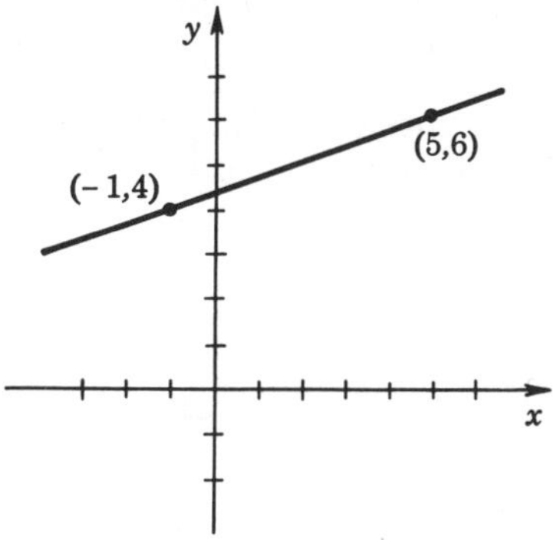

FIGURE 2.25

Solution: The slope of the line is given by

$$m = \frac{6-4}{5+1} = \frac{1}{3}.$$

Taking $(-1,4)$ as the given point (x_1,y_1) and $m = \frac{1}{3}$, we have, by **2.8**, that an equation of the line is

$$y - 4 = \tfrac{1}{3}(x + 1).$$

This may be simplified to the form

$$(1) \qquad x - 3y + 13 = 0.$$

Had we chosen $(5,6)$ for the point (x_1,y_1) in **2.8**, we would have obtained

$$y - 6 = \tfrac{1}{3}(x - 5)$$

as an equation of the line. However, it may be verified that this reduces to equation (1) above.

EXAMPLE 2. Find an equation of the line on the point $(3,-2)$ and perpendicular to the line of the previous example (Figure 2.26).

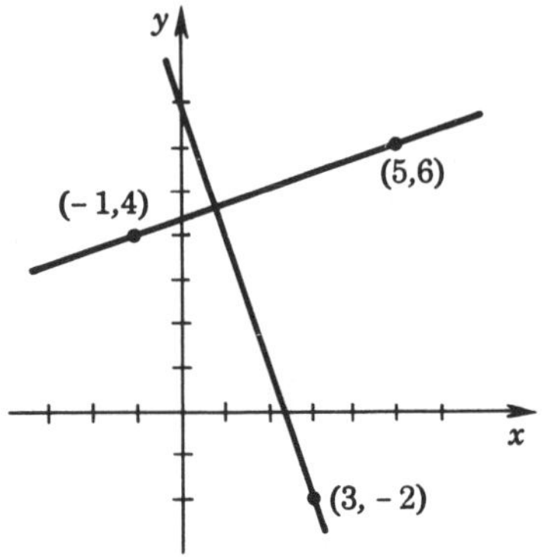

FIGURE 2.26

Solution: Since the slope of the line of Example 1 is $\frac{1}{3}$, the slope of the line in question here is the negative reciprocal of $\frac{1}{3}$, i.e., -3. Hence its equation is

$$y + 2 = -3(x - 3)$$
$$\text{or} \qquad 3x + y - 7 = 0.$$

If a line L crosses the x axis at the point $(a,0)$, then the number a is called the x *intercept* of L. Similarly, if L crosses the y axis at $(0,b)$, the number b is called the y *intercept* of L.

An equation of the line with slope m and passing through the point $(0,b)$ is, by **2.8**, $y - b = m(x - 0)$, or

2.9 $$y = mx + b.$$

This is called the *slope-intercept form* of the equation of L, since it involves only the slope m and the y intercept b of L.

For example,

$$y = -3x + 7$$

is an equation of the line with slope -3 and y intercept 7. This is the line of Figure 2.26.

An equation of the form

2.10 $$Ax + By + C = 0,$$

where A, B, and C are given numbers with not both A and B equal to zero, is called an *equation of the first degree* in x and y. It is clear from our previous results that every straight line has an equation of the first degree. We shall now show that, conversely, the graph of every first-degree equation is a straight line.

If $B = 0$, then $A \neq 0$ and **2.10** has the form

$$Ax + C = 0,$$

or, equivalently,

$$x = -\frac{C}{A},$$

which is an equation of a straight line parallel to the y axis. Multiplication of both sides of an equation by a nonzero number or transposition of terms in an equation does not change the graph of the equation. Hence, if $B = 0$, the graph of **2.10** is a straight line parallel to the y axis.

If $B \neq 0$, **2.10** may be put in the form

$$y = -\frac{A}{B}x - \frac{C}{B},$$

which is the slope-intercept form of an equation of a line with slope $-A/B$ and y intercept $-C/B$. Hence, if $B \neq 0$, the graph of **2.10** is a straight line.

This proves what we started out to show, namely that the graph of every equation of the first degree in x and y is a straight line. Since the graph of every first-degree equation is a straight line, such an equation is frequently called a *linear equation*.

An easy way to graph a linear equation is to put the equation in the slope-intercept form, as illustrated in the following example.

EXAMPLE 3. Sketch the graph of the linear equation

$$3x + 4y - 6 = 0.$$

Solution: The given equation may be solved for y as follows:

$$4y = -3x + 6,$$
$$y = -\tfrac{3}{4}x + \tfrac{3}{2}.$$

We recognize this equation as the equation of the line with slope $-\frac{3}{4}$ and y intercept $\frac{3}{2}$. Its graph is sketched in Figure 2.27. The x intercept of the line is 2, as may be seen by letting $y = 0$ in the equation and solving the resulting equation for x.

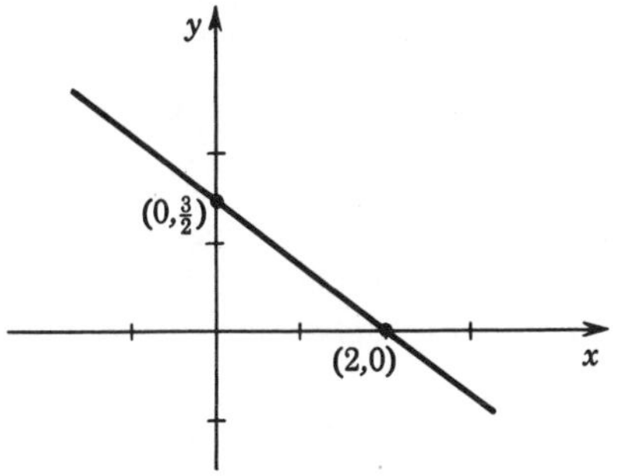

FIGURE 2.27

Two nonparallel lines have a point of intersection. This point can be found by solving simultaneously the equations of the lines, since a point lies on two graphs if and only if its coordinates satisfy the equations of both graphs.

EXAMPLE 4. Find the point of intersection of the lines with equations

$$6x - 3y - 10 = 0 \quad \text{and} \quad 2x + 6y - 1 = 0.$$

Solution: The coordinates of the point of intersection of these two lines must satisfy both equations; that is, they must be the simultaneous solution of these equations. The given equations have slope-intercept form

$$y = 2x - \tfrac{10}{3} \quad \text{and} \quad y = -\tfrac{1}{3}x + \tfrac{1}{6}.$$

Their simultaneous solution may be found by eliminating y as follows:

$$\begin{aligned} 2x - \tfrac{10}{3} &= -\tfrac{1}{3}x + \tfrac{1}{6}, \\ 12x - 20 &= -2x + 1, \\ 14x &= 21, \\ x &= \tfrac{3}{2}. \end{aligned}$$

Then

$$y = 2\cdot\tfrac{3}{2} - \tfrac{10}{3} = -\tfrac{1}{3},$$

so that $(\frac{3}{2}, -\frac{1}{3})$ is the required point of intersection (see Figure 2.28).

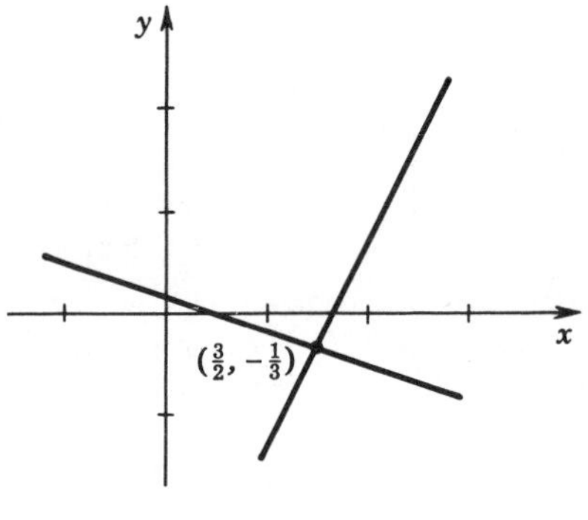

FIGURE 2.28

The points of intersection of any two graphs can be found similarly by solving simultaneously the equations of the graphs. We illustrate this procedure by finding the points of intersection of a circle and a straight line.

EXAMPLE 5. Find the points of intersection of the circle with equation

$$x^2 - 8x + y^2 + 11 = 0$$

and the line with equation

$$x + y - 5 = 0.$$

Solution: The slope-intercept form of the equation of the line is

$$y = -x + 5.$$

Substituting this value of y in the equation of the circle, we obtain

$$x^2 - 8x + (-x + 5)^2 + 11 = 0,$$

which reduces to

$$x^2 - 9x + 18 = 0.$$

This quadratic equation may be factored to yield

$$(x - 3)(x - 6) = 0.$$

Thus $x = 3$ and $x = 6$ are the abscissas of the points of intersection of the line and the circle. The ordinate of each point may be found by substituting each x value in the second of the given equations and solving for y. Thus, if $x = 3$, $y = -3 + 5 = 2$; if $x = 6$, $y = -6 + 5 = -1$. The points of intersection are (3,2) and (6,−1), as shown in Figure 2.29.

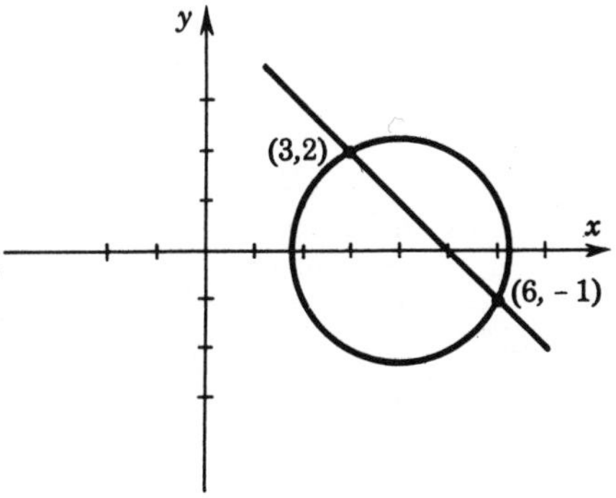

FIGURE 2.29

EXERCISES

I

In each of Exercises 1–12, find an equation of the line satisfying the given conditions.

1. On (5,1) and (−1, −1).
2. On (3,3) and (7,6).

3. With slope 3 and y intercept -3.

4. With slope $-\frac{1}{2}$ and passing through the point $(-3,-5)$.

5. With slope 4 and passing through the point $(1,6)$.

6. With x intercept 3 and y intercept 2.

7. With x intercept $-\frac{1}{3}$ and slope 6.

8. On $(-1,2)$ and $(-1,-3)$.

9. On $(-4,1)$ and $(3,1)$.

10. With x intercept a and y intercept b.

11. With x intercept a and slope m.

12. With inclination 135° and y intercept -2.

In each of Exercises 13–20, find the slope and intercepts, and sketch the line with given equation.

13. $2x - y + 3 = 0$.

14. $3x - 2y + 2 = 0$.

15. $x + 2y + 6 = 0$.

16. $5x + y - 2 = 0$.

17. $3x + 5 = 0$.

18. $4y - 1 = 0$.

19. $5x + y + 15 = 0$.

20. $2x + 4y - 1 = 0$.

In each of Exercises 21–26, find the equations of the lines on the given point that are, respectively, parallel and perpendicular to the given line. Sketch.

21. $(3,3)$, $2x + y - 1 = 0$.

22. $(-1,4)$, $3x - y + 5 = 0$.

23. $(2,-1)$, $3x - 2y - 8 = 0$.

24. $(5,1)$, $2x - 4y - 5 = 0$.

25. $(0,0)$, $4x + 7y - 1 = 0$.

26. $(-1,-1)$, $3x + 7 = 0$.

In each of Exercises 27–30, find the point of intersection of the lines with given equations.

27. $3x - y + 4 = 0$
$x - 2y + 18 = 0$.

28. $2x + y - 3 = 0$
$x - 3y - 12 = 0$.

29. $3x + 2y - 7 = 0$
$2x + 3y + 2 = 0$.

30. $5x + y - 2 = 0$
$3x - 2y + 7 = 0$.

In each of Exercises 31–34, find the points of intersection of the line and circle with given equations.

31. $4x - 3y - 10 = 0$
$x^2 + y^2 - 2x + 4y - 20 = 0$.

32. $x - y + 1 = 0$
$x^2 + y^2 + 6x - 10y + 9 = 0$.

33. $3x - 4y + 10 = 0$
$x^2 + y^2 - 10x = 0.$

34. $x - y - 5 = 0$
$x^2 + y^2 - 4y - 1 = 0.$

35. Show that $Ax + By = Ax_1 + By_1$ is an equation of the line on the point (x_1,y_1) and parallel to the line $Ax + By + C = 0$.

36. Show that $Bx - Ay = Bx_1 - Ay_1$ is an equation of the line on the point (x_1,y_1) and perpendicular to the line $Ax + By + C = 0$.

II

1. Determine an equation of the line of slope m passing through the intersection of the two lines $a_rx + b_ry + c_r = 0$, $(r = 1, 2)$, without finding their point of intersection.

2. Determine an equation of the line passing through the intersection of the two lines $a_rx + b_ry + c_r = 0$, $(r = 1, 2)$, and the point (h,k) without finding their point of intersection.

In each of Exercises 3–8, sketch the graph of the inequality or system of inequalities.

3. $\begin{cases} 2x + y > 2, \\ x - y \leq 3. \end{cases}$

4. $\begin{cases} x + 2y < 4, \\ x - 2y > 4, \\ 2x + y < 9. \end{cases}$

5. $\begin{cases} |3x - 2y| \leq 1, \\ x + 2 > y. \end{cases}$

6. $|y - 2| < |x|.$

7. $\begin{cases} x^2 + y^2 - 2x + 4y - 20 > 0, \\ x^2 + y^2 - 2y + 4x - 20 > 0. \end{cases}$

8. $\begin{cases} x^2 + y^2 - 2x - 2y \leq 4, \\ x^2 + y^2 \geq 25. \end{cases}$

9. Show that the common chord of two intersecting circles is perpendicular to the line joining their centers.

10. Determine r such that $x^2 + y^2 = r^2$ is perpendicular to $(x + 1)^2 + (y + 3)^2 = 4$.

8 PARABOLAS

If a right circular cone is cut by a plane, the curve of intersection is called a *conic section.* There are essentially three types of curves obtainable in this way: parabolas, ellipses, and hyperbolas. We shall study parabolas in this section, postponing until a later chapter the study of ellipses and hyperbolas.

If we think of the cone as lying on a table (like an ice cream cone lying on its side), then a parabola is obtained when we cut the cone with a plane parallel to the table top.

2.11 **DEFINITION.** A *parabola* is the set of all points in a plane equidistant from a fixed point (the *focus*) and a fixed line (the *directrix*) in the plane.

We may find an equation of a parabola by introducing a coordinate system in its plane. Although it might seem natural to choose the directrix as one axis, a better choice is a line parallel to the directrix and halfway between the focus and the directrix. Then the other axis is chosen through the focus, as in Figure 2.30.

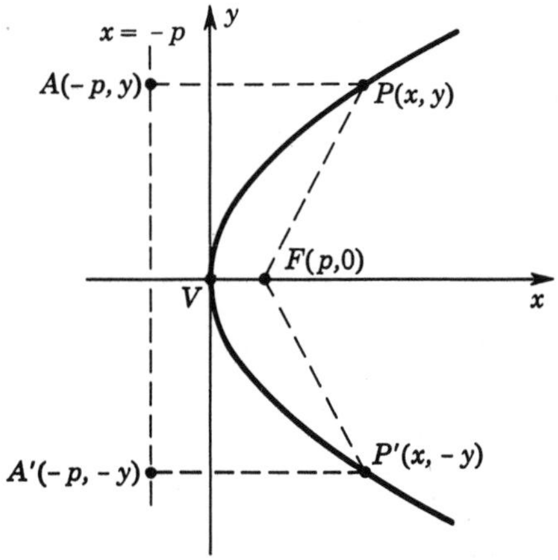

FIGURE 2.30

A point $P(x,y)$ is on the given parabola if and only if

$$|PF| = |PA|;$$

that is, if and only if

$$\sqrt{(x-p)^2+y^2} = \sqrt{(x+p)^2+(y-y)^2},$$

or, equivalently,

$$(x-p)^2+y^2 = (x+p)^2.$$

This equation reduces to

2.12 $$y^2 = 4px.$$

Thus 2.12 is an equation of the parabola having focus $F(p,0)$ and directrix $x = -p$.

The point V midway between the focus and the directrix (Figure 2.30) lies on the parabola and is called the *vertex*. The line passing through the vertex V

and the focus F of a parabola is called the *axis* of the parabola. For example, the axis of the parabola in Figure 2.30 is the x axis. For each point $P(x,y)$ on the parabola, the point $P'(x, -y)$ is also on the parabola, since

$$|FP| = |FP'| = \sqrt{(x-p)^2 + y^2} \qquad \text{and} \qquad |PA| = |P'A'| = \sqrt{(x+p)^2}.$$

We say that the parabola is *symmetric to its axis*; i.e., for every point $P(x,y)$ on the parabola, the reflection of this point in the x axis, namely $P'(x, -y)$, is also on the parabola. Thus, if we imagine folding the plane along the x axis until the upper half-plane coincides with the lower half-plane, the graph of the parabola above the x axis will coincide with the part below the x axis.

It is easy to test the symmetry of the graph of an equation to the x axis. All we need do is replace each y by $-y$ in the equation, and then observe whether the resulting equation is equivalent to the given one. The graph is symmetric to the x axis if and only if the new equation is equivalent to the given one. A similar test, with x and y interchanged, holds for symmetry to the y axis.

For example, if we replace y by $-y$ in **2.12**, we obtain the equation $(-y)^2 = 4px$, or $y^2 = 4px$. Since the resulting equation is the same as **2.12**, we conclude that the parabola is symmetric to the x axis.

If the number p in **2.12** is greater than 0 (as it is in Figure 2.30), then evidently the parabola (except for its vertex) lies to the right of the y axis and extends indefinitely far. If $p < 0$ in **2.12**, the focus $F(p,0)$ is to the left of the y axis and the parabola (except for its vertex) lies to the left of the y axis. In either case the parabola opens up around its focus.

If we start with the point $F(0,p)$ as the focus and $y = -p$ as the directrix (Figure 2.31),

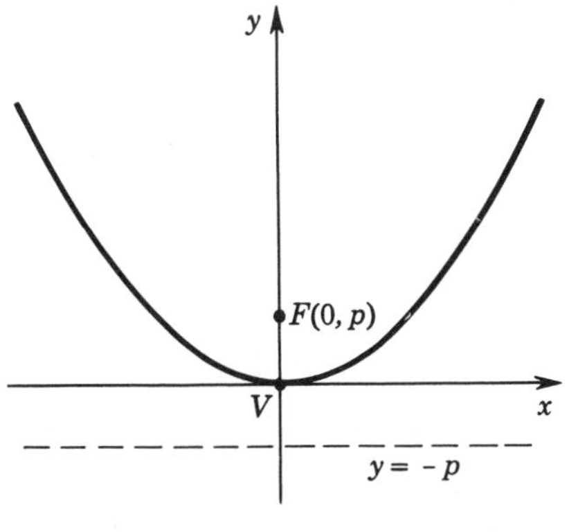

FIGURE 2.31

2.13 $$x^2 = 4py$$

is an equation of the parabola. This is evident since we have just interchanged the roles of x and y in the two cases. We recognize that the parabola is now symmetric to the y axis. The axis of this parabola is the y axis. If $p > 0$, the parabola opens as in Figure 2.31, whereas if $p < 0$ the parabola opens downward.

EXAMPLE 1. Find an equation of the parabola with focus at $(-2,0)$ and directrix $x = 2$.

Solution: This is simply **2.12** with $p = -2$. The equation is therefore

$$y^2 = -8x.$$

In sketching this parabola (Figure 2.32), it is convenient to draw in the chord that is on the focus and perpendicular to the axis. This chord is called the *latus rectum* of the parabola. In Figure 2.32 AB is the latus rectum. Note that $|AB| = 8$.

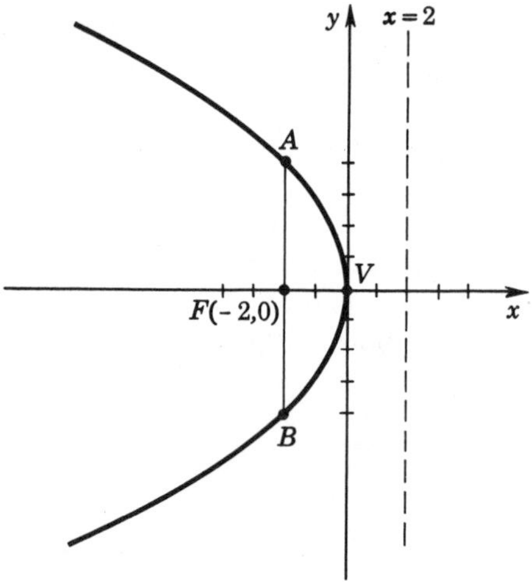

FIGURE 2.32

EXAMPLE 2. Discuss and sketch the graph of the equation

$$x^2 = 6y.$$

Solution: This equation has the form **2.13** with $4p = 6$, or

$$p = \tfrac{3}{2}.$$

Therefore the graph is a parabola with the y axis as its axis, focus $(0,\tfrac{3}{2})$, and directrix $y = -\tfrac{3}{2}$. The parabola is sketched in Figure 2.33. The segment AB, of length 6, is its latus rectum.

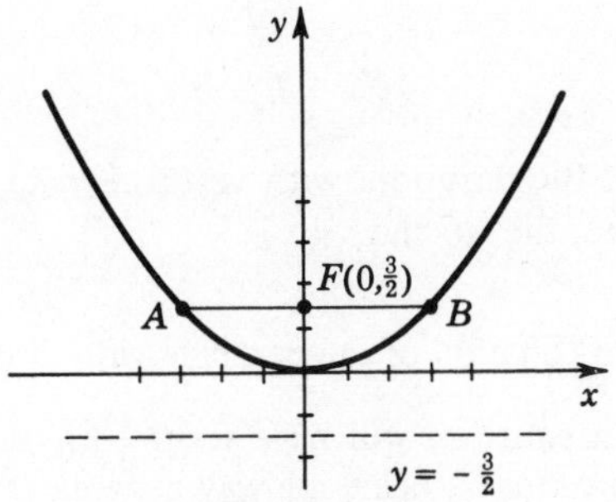

FIGURE 2.33

It is easy to derive an equation for a parabola even though the coordinate axes are not placed as in Figure 2.30 or Figure 2.31, as long as the directrix is parallel to a coordinate axis. For example, let the directrix D be parallel to the y axis, as in Figure 2.34. If we designate the coordinates of the vertex V by (h,k),

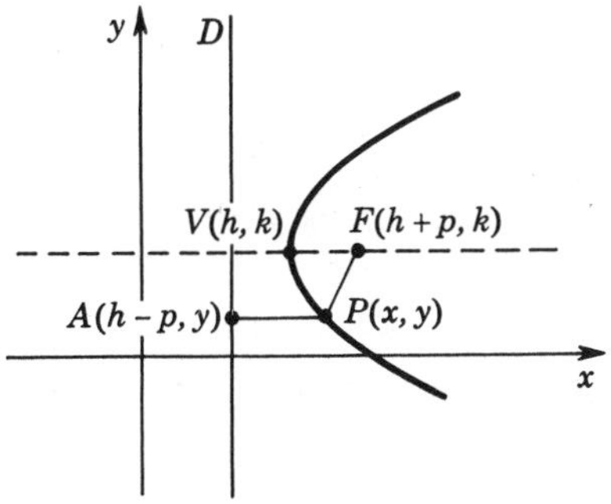

FIGURE 2.34

then the focus is $F(h + p,k)$ and the directrix has equation $x = h - p$, where the number p has the same meaning as before. Again, a point $P(x,y)$ is on the parabola if and only if $|FP| = |PA|$; i.e.,

$$\sqrt{(x - h - p)^2 + (y - k)^2} = \sqrt{(x - h + p)^2}.$$

We easily reduce this equation to the form

2.14 $$(y - k)^2 = 4p(x - h).$$

Thus **2.14** is an equation of the parabola with vertex $V(h,k)$, focus $F(h + p,k)$, and directrix $x = h - p$ parallel to the y axis.

By analogy,

2.15 $$(x - h)^2 = 4p(y - k)$$

is an equation of the parabola with vertex $V(h,k)$, focus $F(h,k + p)$, and directrix $y = k - p$ parallel to the x axis.

EXAMPLE 3. Find an equation of the parabola with directrix $y = 1$ and focus $F(3,-5)$.

Solution: An equation will have form **2.15**, since the directrix, D, is parallel to the x axis. The vertex V, being midway between D and F, has coordinates $(3,-2)$. Thus $-5 = -2 + p$ and $p = -3$. Hence

$$(x - 3)^2 = -12(y + 2)$$

is an equation of the parabola. An equivalent equation, obtained by squaring $x - 3$ and simplifying, is

$$x^2 - 6x + 12y + 33 = 0.$$

EXAMPLE 4. Describe the graph of the equation $y^2 + 4y - 6x + 22 = 0$.

Solution: By completing the square on the y terms, the given equation may be shown to be equivalent to one of form **2.14**:

$$\begin{aligned} y^2 + 4y &= 6x - 22 \\ y^2 + 4y + 4 &= 6x - 18 \\ (y + 2)^2 &= 6(x - 3). \end{aligned}$$

This is like **2.14** if we let $k = -2$, $h = 3$, and $4p = 6$, or $p = \frac{3}{2}$. Thus the graph of the given equation is a parabola with vertex $V(3,-2)$, focus $F(\frac{9}{2},-2)$, and directrix $x = \frac{3}{2}$.

EXERCISES

I

Discuss and sketch the graph of each of the following equations.

1. $y^2 = 12x$.
2. $x^2 = -4y$.
3. $x^2 = y$.
4. $4y^2 - x = 0$.
5. $y^2 - 6y - 2x - 11 = 0$.
6. $x^2 + 2x + 3y - 8 = 0$.
7. $x^2 - 4y + 7 = 0$.
8. $y^2 - 14y + 8x + 49 = 0$.

In each of Exercises 9–14, find an equation of the parabola having:

9. Focus (4,0), directrix $x = -4$.

10. Focus (0,2), vertex (0,0).

11. Focus $(-3,-3)$, directrix $y = 3$.

12. Focus (0,0), directrix $x = 2$.

13. Directrix $x = 0$, vertex (2,2).

14. Directrix $y = -4$, vertex $(2,-6)$.

II

1. Sketch the graph of $|x - y^2| = 1$.
2. In the parabola $y^2 = 4ax$, an equilateral triangle is inscribed with one vertex at the origin. Find the length of a side.
3. Determine a such that the circle $x^2 + y^2 = 2ay$ intersects the parabola $x^2 = 2py$ in exactly one point.
4. Describe the graph of the midpoints of all the chords of the parabola $x^2 = 4ay$ that pass through the vertex.
5. A circle and the parabola $y^2 = 4ax$ are such that they intersect at four points. Show that the sum of the ordinates at these four points is zero.
6. Show that the graph of $\sqrt{x} + \sqrt{y} = 1$ is part of a parabola whose axis is inclined 45° to the coordinate axes.

REVIEW

Oral Exercises

Explain or define the terms in Exercises 1–4.

1. A rectangular coordinate system (in a plane).
2. Slope of a line.
3. A parabola.
4. Latus rectum.
5. What is a general equation for a straight line?
6. What is a general equation for a circle?
7. What is the distance formula?
8. If two lines have slopes m_1, and m_2, what is the condition that the lines be parallel? Perpendicular?

I

1. A line segment joining two points is bisected at the origin. If the coordinates of one end are $(-a,b)$, what are the coordinates of the other end?

2. A line segment joining two points is bisected by
   a. the x axis,
   b. the y axis,
   c. the line $x = y$.

If the coordinates of one end are (a,b), what are the coordinates of the other end in each case?

3. A triangle has vertices (0,0), (10,0), and (8,4). Find the center and radius of the circumscribed circle.

4. Find an equation of the circle having points (12,6) and $(-4,-2)$ as ends of the same diameter.

5. Determine equations of parabolas satisfying the following:
   a. directrix $y = 5$, focus $(0,-5)$,
   b. vertex (0,0), focus $(0,-6)$,
   c. directrix $x = 4$, vertex (0,1).

6. Prove that the sum of the squares of the lengths of the medians of a triangle equals three-fourths the sum of the squares of the lengths of the sides.

7. A square with side of length s has its center at the origin. What will be the coordinates of its vertices if the diagonals are along the axes? If the sides are parallel to the axes?

8. Determine the longest side of a triangle whose vertices are (1,1), $(-1,-1)$, $(\sqrt{3},-\sqrt{3})$.

9. Find the area of a triangle whose vertices are (6,0), (12,8), $(-2,6)$.

10. Show that (11,2), $(-1,7)$, $(-6,-5)$, $(6,-10)$ are the vertices of a square.

11. Show by means of slopes that the diagonals of the square in Exercise 6 are perpendicular.

12. Find an equation of a circle which is tangent to both coordinate axes and which passes through the point (1,2).

13. A point moves in such a way that the ratio of its distances from two fixed points is constant. Determine the graph of the moving point.

14. Find the distance from the point (h,k) to the line $ax + by + c = 0$ by first finding the foot of the perpendicular from the point to the line.

II

1. A graph is said to be centrosymmetric (with respect to a point, say O) if for any point P of the graph there is a corresponding point P' such that the segment PP' is bisected by O. Which of the following equations have graphs which are centrosymmetric? Determine their centers when they have one.

a. $x^2 + y^2 = 2$.
b. $x^2 = y$.
c. $ax + by = c$.
d. $x^2 + y^2 + 2x - 4y = 20$.
e. $y = x^3$
f. $y + 1 = x^3 + x$.

2. Prove that a triangle with two equal medians is isosceles.

3. Find the distance from the point (h,k) to the line $ax + by + c = 0$ by considering a special circle centered at (h,k). (See also Exercise I, 14.)

4. Prove that the midpoints of all chords parallel to a given chord of a parabola lie on a line parallel to its axis.

5. Show how to construct the vertex of a given parabola with a straightedge and compass.

6. Find the least distance from the point (h,k) to the circle $x^2 + y^2 + ax + by + c = 0$.

7. Find the length of the tangent from the given point in Exercise 6.

8. If (x_1,y_1) is a point on the circle $x^2 + y^2 + 2ax + 2by + c = 0$, show that the tangent line at that point is given by $xx_1 + yy_1 + a(x + x_1) + b(y + y_1) + c = 0$.

9. Determine the lengths of the tangents common to two disjoint circles $(x - h_i)^2 + (y - k_i)^2 = r_i^2$, $(i = 1, 2)$.

10. Given the four points (x_r,y_r), $(r = 1, 2, 3, 4)$, no three of which are collinear, determine the length of a side of a square such that each side of the square passes through one of the given points.

3

FUNCTIONS

A GENERAL theory of the calculus is not possible without the use of functions. Indeed, it is significant that the word *function* was introduced into mathematical language by Leibnitz, one of the discoverers of the calculus. Therefore, before entering the calculus proper, it is fitting that we first discuss functions.

1 DEFINITIONS

In its general mathematical usage, a function is a mapping of one set into another set. Instead of attempting to define the word *mapping*, we shall illustrate its meaning with several examples.

If set A consists of all cards in the index file of a library and set B consists of all books in the same library, then there is a natural mapping of set A into set B that associates with each card in A the book in B described on that card.

Each person has a unique surname. Hence, if P is the set of all persons in a country and N is the set of all surnames in that country, there is defined a mapping of set P into set N. Associated with each person in P is a surname in N.

If the two sets are imagined to be regions of a plane, as in Figure 3.1, then a mapping of set A into set B can be indicated by arrows showing the point of B mapped into by each point of A. Thus in Figure 3.1 a_1 is mapped into b_1, a_2 is mapped into b_2, and so on.

Having illustrated the concept of a mapping, we repeat that a *function is a mapping of some set A into some set B*. The set A is called the *domain* of the function. For each a in A, the unique element b of B into which a is mapped is

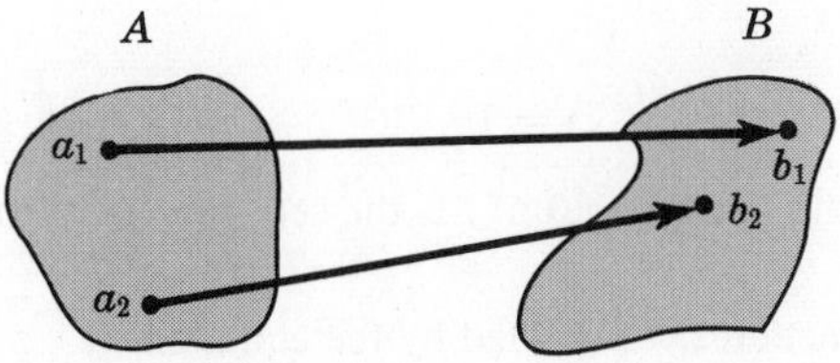

FIGURE 3.1

called the *image* of *a*. The set of all images of the elements of *A* is a subset of *B*, called the *range* of the function.

We are primarily interested in the calculus with functions whose domains and ranges are sets of real numbers. Such functions are often called *real functions*.

Just as we use letters such as *x*, *y*, *a*, and *b* to designate numbers, so shall we use letters to designate functions. The letters, *f*, *F*, *g*, and *G* are commonly used for this purpose. If *f* is a given function with domain *A* and range *B*, then the image in *B* of each *x* in *A* is designated by

$$f(x),$$

read "*f* of *x*" or "*f* at *x*." * Thus, if *f* is a function with domain *A* and range *B*, then corresponding to each real number *x* in *A* there is one and only one real number $f(x)$ in *B*. We shall now give some examples of real functions and the use of the functional notation.

EXAMPLE 1. The usual formula

$$S = 6x^2$$

for the area *S* of the surface of a cube in terms of the length *x* of each edge defines an area function. If we designate this function by *F*, then

$$F(x) = 6x^2$$

for each positive number *x*. For example,

$$F(1) = 6, \quad F(2) = 6 \cdot 2^2 = 24, \quad F(10) = 6 \cdot 10^2 = 600.$$

The domain (and the range) of *F* is the set $(0, \infty)$ of all positive real numbers.

EXAMPLE 2. The equation

$$s = 16t^2$$

gives the number of feet, *s*, an object falls in *t* seconds from a point of rest if the only force acting on the object is the earth's gravity. This equation defines a function *f*, the function that maps each number *t* into the number of feet the object falls in *t* seconds,

$$f(t) = 16t^2.$$

* This functional notation is credited to the Swiss mathematician Leonhard Euler (1707–1783), probably the most prolific mathematician of all time. The form of many of our present-day mathematics textbooks is due to Euler.

Thus

$$f(1) = 16, \quad f(2) = 16 \cdot 2^2 = 64, \quad f(\tfrac{9}{2}) = 16 \cdot (\tfrac{9}{2})^2 = 324.$$

The natural domain (and range) of f is the set $[0, \infty)$ of all nonnegative real numbers.

EXAMPLE 3. Let function G be defined by the equation

$$G(u) = \sqrt{u - 3}.$$

When a function is defined by an equation and no mention is made of the domain, it is understood to be the set of all real numbers for which the equation makes sense. In this example we must have $u - 3 \geq 0$ and therefore $u \geq 3$. Thus the domain of G is the infinite interval $[3, \infty)$. We note that

$$G(3) = 0, \quad G(4) = \sqrt{4 - 3} = 1, \quad G(8) = \sqrt{8 - 3} = \sqrt{5}.$$

Although the letter u was used in the definition of G, we could just as well have defined G by the equation

$$G(x) = \sqrt{x - 3},$$

or by the equation

$$G(z) = \sqrt{z - 3}.$$

A function need not be defined by an explicit equation, as were those in the above examples. One of the celebrated functions of mathematics is the counting function p: for each positive integer n,

$$p(n) = \text{the number of positive prime integers} \leq n.$$

Thus $p(1) = 0$, $p(2) = 1$, $p(3) = 2$, and $p(18) = 7$, the prime integers ≤ 18 being 2, 3, 5, 7, 11, 13, and 17. There is no known formula giving $p(n)$ for any positive integer n.

EXAMPLE 4. To send a parcel by first-class mail costs 6 cents per ounce or fraction thereof. Any parcel not exceeding 20 pounds may be sent by first-class mail. If we let $F(w)$ be the cost in cents of sending a parcel of weight w ounces, then

$$\begin{aligned} F(w) &= 6 \text{ if } 0 < w \leq 1, \\ F(w) &= 12 \text{ if } 1 < w \leq 2, \\ &\cdots\cdots\cdots \\ &\cdots\cdots\cdots \\ F(w) &= 6n \text{ if } n - 1 < w \leq n, \quad n \text{ an integer} \\ &\cdots\cdots\cdots \end{aligned}$$

The postage function F has the interval $(0,320]$ as its domain and $\{6n \mid n \text{ an integer}, 1 \leq n \leq 320\}$ as its range.

2 TYPES OF FUNCTIONS

If the range of a function contains only one number, say c, then f is called a *constant function*. Thus $f(x) = c$ for every x in the domain of f. We shall often represent this function by its value c, and speak of the constant function c.

If $a_0, a_1 \cdots, a_n$ are given numbers and n is a given nonnegative integer, then an expression of the form

$$a_0x^n + a_1x^{n-1} + \cdots + a_{n-1}x + a_n$$

is called a *polynomial in x*. A function f defined by a polynomial,

$$f(x) = a_0x^n + a_1x^{n-1} + \cdots + a_{n-1}x + a_n,$$

is called a *polynomial function*. The domain of f is taken to be the set of all real numbers.

Special polynomial functions are the *linear function f* defined by

$$f(x) = a_0x + a_1,$$

the *quadratic function g* defined by

$$g(x) = a_0x^2 + a_1x + a_2, \qquad (a_0 \neq 0),$$

and the *cubic function h* defined by

$$h(x) = a_0x^3 + a_1x^2 + a_2x + a_3, \qquad (a_0 \neq 0).$$

A function defined by a quotient of two polynomials in x is called a *rational function*. For example, the function f defined by

$$f(x) = \frac{x^2 - 3x + 1}{x + 2}$$

is a rational function having as its domain the set of all real numbers except -2.

A function defined in terms of polynomials and roots of polynomials is called an *algebraic function*. For example, the function f defined by

$$f(x) = \frac{x - 1}{x\sqrt{x^2 + 1}}$$

is an algebraic function. Its domain is the set of all nonzero real numbers.

Examples of nonalgebraic functions are the six trigonometric functions sine, cosine, tangent, cotangent, secant, and cosecant; the logarithmic function f defined by

$$f(x) = \log_a x;$$

the exponential function g defined by

$$g(x) = a^x;$$

and combinations of algebraic functions and the functions above, such as

$$h(x) = x \sin x + x^2 - 2^x.$$

These are examples of *transcendental functions.* They are discussed in detail in Chapter 9.

EXERCISES

I

In Exercises 1–3, if $f(x) = x^2 - 3x + 1$, find:

1. $f(0); f(-1); f(-\sqrt{3})$.
2. $f(-2 + h); f(x + h)$.
3. $\dfrac{f(x) - f(a)}{x - a}$, $(x \neq a)$, $\dfrac{f(x + h) - f(x)}{h}$, $(h \neq 0)$.

In Exercises 4 and 5, if $g(x) = (x - 1)/(x + 1)$, $(x \neq -1)$, find:

4. $g(1)$; $g(-\sqrt{2})$; $g(a^3)$.
5. $g(-1 + 2h)$; $g(x + y)$.
6. If $f(x) = 2x^2 - 5x$, find an equation of the line passing through the following pairs of points:
   a. $(2,f(2))$ and $(\frac{5}{2},f(\frac{5}{2}))$.
   b. $(a,f(a))$ and $(a + h,f(a + h))$.
7. If $f(x) = x^2 - 3x + 1$, for what numbers x is $f(x) = f(2x)$? Is $f(x) = f(ax?)$ Is $2f(x) = f(2x)$?
8. If $F(x) = \sqrt{x}$, $(x > 0)$, show that
$$\frac{F(x + h) - F(x)}{h} = \frac{1}{\sqrt{x + h} + \sqrt{x}}, \qquad (h \neq 0).$$

Write an equation which defines each of the functions in Exercises 9–12.

9. The function f such that $f(r)$ is the area of a circle of radius r.
10. The function F such that $F(r)$ is the surface area of a sphere of radius r.
11. The function G such that $G(A)$ is the surface area of a sphere with great circles of area A.
12. The function g such that $g(h)$ is the volume of a right circular cone having a vertex angle of 90° and height h.

II

1. If $F(x) = x^4 + 4x^3 + 6x^2 + 4x$, find:

   a. $F(3x - 1)$.

   b. $\dfrac{F(x) - F(-1)}{x + 1}$, $(x \neq -1)$.

2. If $a_{n+1} = (1 - a_n)/(1 + a_n)$, $(n = 0, 1, 2, \cdots$, and $a_0 = x)$, express a_1, a_2, a_{10}, a_{11} as functions of x.

3. Same as Exercise 2, except $a_0 = x - 1$.

4. For what polynomials $P(x)$ does $P(nx) = nP(x)$ for all x and a fixed integer n?

5. If $F(x) = \sqrt[3]{x}$, show that

$$\frac{F(x + h) - F(x)}{h} = (\sqrt[3]{(x + h)^2} + \sqrt[3]{x^2 + xh} + \sqrt[3]{x^2})^{-1}, \qquad (h \neq 0).$$

In each of Exercises 6–8, write an equation which defines the function given.

6. The function V such that $V(R)$ is the volume of an inscribed right circular cylinder of radius R in a sphere of radius $2R$.

7. The function M such that $M(P)$ is the maximum area of a rectangle of perimeter $2P$.

8. The function G such that $G(n)$, (n a positive integer), is the number of different divisors (positive and integral) of

   a. 2^n, b. 4^n, c. 6^n, d. 60^n.

3 GRAPHS OF FUNCTIONS

The *graph of a function f* in a coordinate plane is the graph of the set

$$\{(x,f(x)) \mid x \text{ in domain of } f\}.$$

Or, equivalently, it is the graph of the equation

$$y = f(x).$$

That is, the point $P(a,b)$ is in the graph of f if and only if $b = f(a)$.

Some examples of graphs of functions are given below.

EXAMPLE 1. Determine the graph of the constant function f defined by $f(x) = 3$ for every real number x; of the linear function g defined by $g(x) = 3x - 2$ for every real number x.

Solution: The graph of f is the graph of the equation $y = 3$; the graph of g is the graph of the equation $y = 3x - 2$. Both are sketched in Figure 3.2.

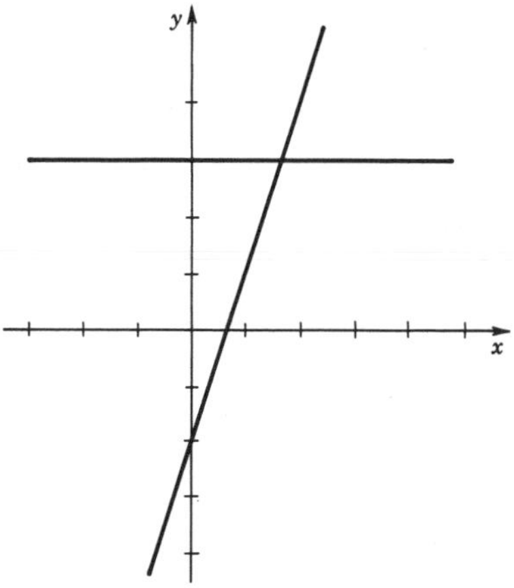

FIGURE 3.2

EXAMPLE 2. Discuss the graphs of the functions f and g defined by

$$f(x) = \sqrt{4 - x^2}, \qquad g(x) = -\sqrt{4 - x^2},$$

each function having the closed interval $[-2,2]$ as its domain.

Solution: The graph of the equation $y = \sqrt{4 - x^2}$ lies on or above the x axis since $\sqrt{4 - x^2} \geq 0$, while the graph of the equation $y = -\sqrt{4 - x^2}$ lies on or below the x axis since $-\sqrt{4 - x^2} \leq 0$. Thus the graph of f is the upper half of the circle with equation

$$y^2 = 4 - x^2 \qquad \text{or} \qquad x^2 + y^2 = 4;$$

the graph of g is the lower half of the same circle. These graphs are shown in Figure 3.3.

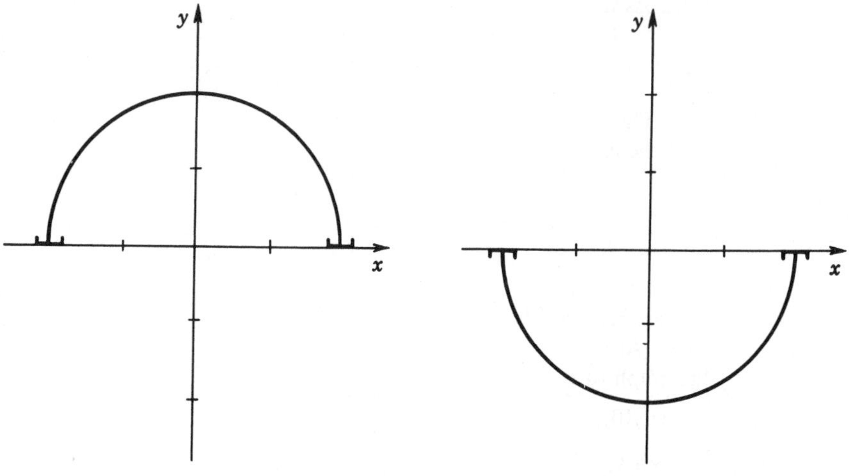

FIGURE 3.3

EXAMPLE 3. Determine the graph of the postage function given in Section 1, Example 4, page 60.

Solution: For this function F we know that

$$F(x) = 6n \text{ if } n - 1 < x \leq n,$$

with (0,320] the domain of F. Thus F has a constant value $6n$ over each half-open interval $(n - 1, n]$. The graph is made up of "steps," as shown in Figure 3.4. For this reason a function such as F is frequently called a *step function.*

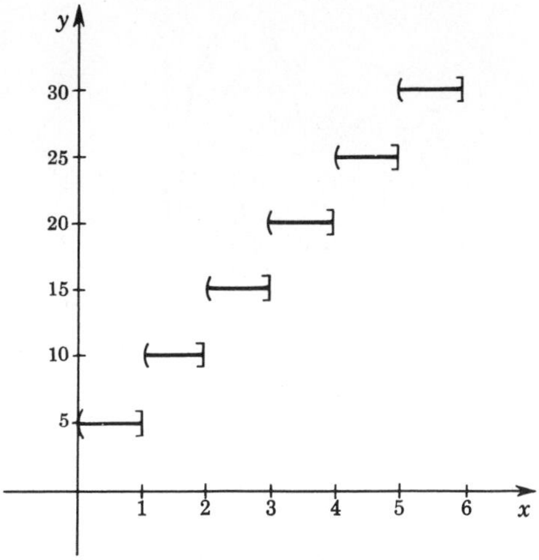

FIGURE 3.4

EXAMPLE 4. Discuss the graph of the function G defined by

$$G(x) = \frac{1}{x}.$$

Solution: The domain of G is the set of all nonzero numbers, and the graph of G is the graph of the equation

$$y = \frac{1}{x},$$

or

$$xy = 1.$$

Since x and y are reciprocals of each other, y is small when x is large and y is large when x is small. Also, x and y are either both positive or both negative. Some specific points on the graph of G are:

$$(.1,10), \quad (.2,5), \quad (.5,2), \quad (1,1), \quad (2,.5), \quad (5,.2), \quad (10,.1).$$

Then $(-.1,-10)$, $(-.2,-5)$, and so on are also on the graph. From this information the graph is sketched in Figure 3.5.

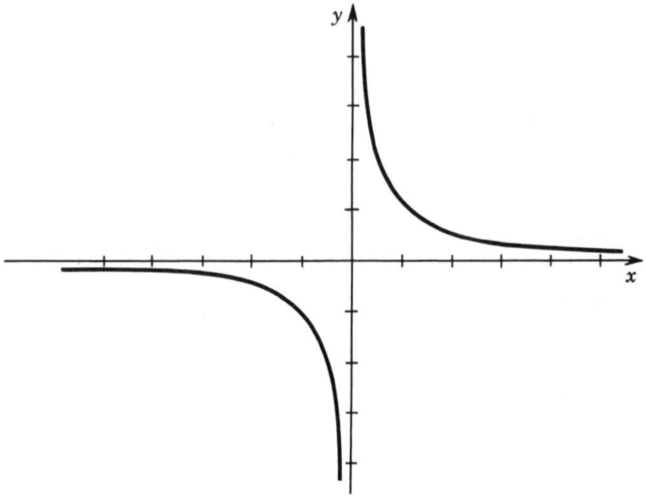

FIGURE 3.5

EXERCISES

I

In each of Exercises 1–6, sketch the graph of the function defined.

1. $G(x) = 3 - 5x$.
2. $F(x) = x^2/2$.
3. $f(r) = 2/r$, $(r \neq 0)$.
4. $g(t) = |t + 1|$.
5. $G(x) = -\sqrt{1 - x}$, $(x \leq 1)$.
6. $F(x) = -n$ if $n \leq x < n + 1$ (n an integer).

II

In each of Exercises 1–12, sketch the graph of the function.

1. $F(t) = |t - 1|^{-1}$, $(t \neq 1)$.
2. $f(y) = 1/y^2$, $(y \neq 0)$.
3. $G(x) = \dfrac{3x + 1}{x}$, $(x \neq 0)$.
4. $B(r) = r + \dfrac{1}{r}$ $(r \neq 0)$.
5. $B(r) = r - \dfrac{1}{r}$, $(r \neq 0)$.
6. $H(x) = \dfrac{(x - 1)^2}{x^2}$, $(x \neq 0)$.
7. $E(m) = 2^m$.
8. $P(\lambda) = 3^{-\lambda}$.
9. $C(x) = a^x + a^{-x}$, $(a > 1)$.
10. $C(x) = a^x + a^{-x}$, $(0 < a < 1)$.
11. $f(y) = \begin{cases} 0 & (y \text{ rational}). \\ 1 & (y \text{ irrational}). \end{cases}$
12. $f(y) = \begin{cases} 0 & (y \text{ irrational}). \\ 1 & (y \text{ rational}). \end{cases}$

4 COMBINATIONS OF FUNCTIONS

Just as we can combine numbers with operations of addition, subtraction, multiplication, and division, so can we combine functions with these operations. Each of these operations with functions depends on the corresponding operation with numbers.

If f and g are functions with respective domains A and B, then the functions $f+g$ and $f-g$, each having domain $A \cap B$, are defined as follows:

$$(f+g)(x) = f(x) + g(x) \text{ for each number } x \text{ in } A \cap B,$$
$$(f-g)(x) = f(x) - g(x) \text{ for each number } x \text{ in } A \cap B.$$

For example, if f and g are functions defined by

$$f(x) = x^2 + 1, \qquad g(x) = \sqrt{x},$$

then

$$(f+g)(x) = x^2 + 1 + \sqrt{x}, \qquad (f-g)(x) = x^2 + 1 - \sqrt{x}.$$

The domain of f is the set of all real numbers; the domain of g is the infinite interval $[0, \infty)$. Therefore the domain of each of $f+g$ and $f-g$ is the interval $[0, \infty)$.

If f and g are functions with respective domains A and B, then the functions fg and f/g are defined in the obvious way:

$$(fg)(x) = f(x)g(x),$$
$$\left(\frac{f}{g}\right)(x) = \frac{f(x)}{g(x)}.$$

The domain of fg is again $A \cap B$; the domain of f/g is $C = \{x \mid x \text{ in } A \cap B, g(x) \neq 0\}$.

For example, let functions f and g be defined by the equations

$$f(x) = \sqrt{4 - x^2}, \qquad g(x) = x^2 - 1.$$

Thus $[-2,2]$ is the domain of f and the set of all real numbers is the domain of g. The functions fg and f/g are given by

$$(fg)(x) = (\sqrt{4 - x^2})(x^2 - 1), \text{ domain } fg = [-2,2],$$

$$\frac{f}{g}(x) = \frac{\sqrt{4 - x^2}}{x^2 - 1}, \text{ domain } \frac{f}{g} = \{x \mid x \text{ in } [-2,2], x \neq 1, x \neq -1\}.$$

We could express the domain of f/g as $[-2,-1) \cup (-1,1) \cup (1,2]$.

It is customary to write f^2 for $f \cdot f$, f^3 for $f \cdot f \cdot f$, and so on. For example, if $f(x) = x - 1$, then

$$f^3(x) = (x - 1)^3.$$

Another useful combination of two functions f and g is their *composite* designated by $f \circ g$ and defined as follows:

$$(f \circ g)(x) = f(g(x)), \text{ domain } f \circ g = \{x \mid x \text{ in domain } g, g(x) \text{ in domain } f\}.$$

For example, if $f(x) = \sqrt{x}$ and $g(x) = x^2 + 1$, then

$$(f \circ g)(x) = f(g(x)) = f(x^2 + 1) = \sqrt{x^2 + 1}.$$

Since $g(x) > 0$ for every number x, $g(x)$ is in the domain of f for every number x, and the domain of $f \circ g$ is the set of all real numbers. We might note that $g \circ f$ is a function different from $f \circ g$. Thus

$$(g \circ f)(x) = g(f(x)) = g(\sqrt{x}) = (\sqrt{x})^2 + 1 = x + 1,$$

and the domain of $g \circ f$ is the infinite interval $[0, \infty)$. Incidentally, the domain of $g \circ f$ is always a subset of the domain of f. We see that $f \circ f$ and $g \circ g$ are defined as follows:

$$(f \circ f)(x) = f(f(x)) = f(\sqrt{x}) = \sqrt{\sqrt{x}} = \sqrt[4]{x}, \text{ Domain } f \circ f = [0, \infty)$$
$$(g \circ g)(x) = g(g(x)) = g(x^2 + 1) = (x^2 + 1)^2 + 1 = x^4 + 2x^2 + 2.$$

The domain of $g \circ g$ evidently is the set of all real numbers.

EXERCISES

I

1. If $f(x) = x^2 - 1$ and $g(x) = 3x + 1$, describe the following functions.
   a. $f + g$.
   b. $f - g$.
   c. fg.
   d. f/g.
   e. $f \circ g$.
   f. $g \circ f$.
2. Describe the functions in Exercise 1 for $f(x) = \sqrt{x - 1}$, $(x \geq 1)$, $g(x) = x^2 + 1$.
3. Describe the functions in Exercise 1 for $f(x) = 1/(x + 1)$, $(x \neq -1)$, $g(x) = x/(x - 1)$, $(x \neq 1)$.
4. Describe the functions in Exercise 1 for $f(x) = 1/x^2$, $g(x) = \sqrt{x}$, $(x \geq 0)$.
5. If $f(x) = x^2$, find a function g such that $f(g(x)) = x$. Is $g(f(x)) = x$ also?
6. If $f(x) = \sqrt[3]{x}$, find a function g such that $f(g(x)) = x$. Is $g(f(x)) = x$ also?
7. If $f(x) = |x|$, find $f(f(x))$.
8. If $f(x) = ax^2 + bx + c$, and $f(x + h) = f(x) + f(h)$ for all real numbers x and h, what can be said about the numbers a, b, and c?

II

In each of Exercises 1–6, find $F \circ F$ and $F \circ (F \circ F)$ for the function F defined.

1. $F(x) = x^{-1}$.
2. $F(x) = x^n$.
3. $F(x) = a + bx$.
4. $F(x) = 2/(1 + x)$.
5. $F(x) = \sqrt{1 + x}$.
6. $F(x) = x + 1/x$.
7. If $a_0 = x$ and $a_{n+1} = F(a_n)$, $(n = 0, 1, 2, 3, \cdots,)$, find a_3 and a_4 when
   a. $F(x) = a + bx$,
   b. $F(x) = \sqrt{1 + x}$.
8. How are Exercises 3 and 5 related to Exercise 7?
9. For what polynomial functions P does

$$P(x + h) = P(x) + P(h)$$

   a. for all x and h in $(-\infty, \infty)$?
   b. for every x in $(-\infty, \infty)$ and a fixed value of h?
   c. for every x in $[0,1]$ and $h = 2$.

REVIEW

Oral Exercises

1. What is a function?
2. What is a rational function? Give an example.
3. What is an algebraic function? Give an example.
4. What is a transcendental function? Give an example.
5. What is the composite of two functions? Of three functions?

A function F is said to be even if $F(x) = F(-x)$ for every x in the domain of F and said to be odd if $F(-x) = -F(x)$.

6. Give examples of an even function; of an odd function.
7. Which function is both even and odd?
8. For each of the functions defined below, state whether it is even, odd, or neither.
   a. $f(x) = |x|$.
   b. $g(x) = \sin x$.
   c. $h(x) = \sin x^2$.
   d. $F(x) = 10^{2x} - 10^{-2x}$.
   e. $G(x) = x - x^3$.
   f. $H(x) = x + x^2$.
   g. $g(x) = \sin x + \cos x$.
   h. $f(x) = |x| + 1 + 2^x + 2^{-x}$.

I

1. Often when a function is given by means of a formula or equation, its domain is not explicitly stated. We then understand the domain to be the largest set of numbers for which the formula or equation is meaningful. For example, if f is defined by the equation $f(x) = 1/x$, we understand the domain of f to be the set of all nonzero numbers. For each of the functions defined below, state the implied domain.

   a. $f(x) = (x^2 - 1)^{-1}$.
   b. $g(x) = \sqrt{x - 2}\sqrt{x^2 - 1}$.
   c. $h(x) = \sqrt{x - 2}/\sqrt{x^2 - 1}$.
   d. $F(x) = (2x - x^3)^{-1/4}$.
   e. $G(x) = (x + x^5)^{-1}$.

2. For each of the following pairs of functions, find $F + G$, $F \cdot G$, F/G, $F \circ G$, and $G \circ F$.

   a. $F(x) = x + 2, \quad G(x) = -x + 5$.
   b. $F(x) = x^2, \quad G(x) = 2x - 3$.
   c. $F(x) = (x^2 + 1)^{-1}, \quad G(x) = (x^2 - 1)^{-1}, x^2 \neq 1$.
   d. $F(x) = x^3 - 1, \quad G(x) = x^3 - 1, x \neq 1$.

3. For each of the following pairs of functions, graph the equations $y = f(x)$, $y = g(x)$, $y = f(x) + g(x)$, $y = f(x) - g(x)$. Describe the method (addition and subtraction of ordinates) that is illustrated by this exercise.

   a. $f(x) = x, \quad g(x) = 2x$.
   b. $f(x) = x^2, \quad g(x) = x$.
   c. $f(x) = x, \quad g(x) = \sqrt{4 - x^2}$, ($x$ in $[-2,2]$).
   d. $f(x) = 1/x, \quad g(x) = 2x + 4$, ($x$ in $[-3,-1]$).

4. Describe the graphs of even and odd functions (see the definition in the oral exercises, page 69).

5. What kind of a function is each of the following? Give examples.
   a. The product of an odd function by an odd function.
   b. The product of an odd function by an even function.
   c. The product of an even function by an even function.

6. Let F and G be functions with a common domain.
   a. Show that the graph of the equation

   $$[y - F(x)][y - G(x)] = 0$$

   is the union of the graphs of F and G.
   b. Show that the graph of the equation

   $$[y - F(x)]^2 + [y - G(x)]^2 = 0$$

   is the intersection of the graphs of F and G.

7. Use Exercise 6 to find the graphs of the following equations.
   a. $y^2 - x^2 = 0$.
   b. $y^2 - x^4 = 0$.
   c. $x^6 = y^6$.
   d. $(y - x)^2 + (y - |x|)^2 = 0$.

II

In each of Exercises 1–4, sketch the graph of the functions defined.

1. $H(t) = \begin{cases} 1 & (t > 0), \\ 0 & (t < 0), \end{cases}$ (Heaviside unit function).

2. $F(t) = H(t) - H(t - 1)$.

3. $f(x) = H(x^2 - 4)$.

4. $m(t) = t^2[H(t) + H(t + 1)]$.

5. Let F and G be functions with a common domain. Show that the graph of the equation $y - F(x) + k(y - G(x)) = 0$ contains the intersection of the graphs of F and G.

6. Using Exercise 5, determine an equation of the straight line containing the common chord of the two circles

$$x^2 + y^2 = 5^2, \qquad (x - 3)^2 + (y - 4)^2 = 3^2.$$

7. Using Exercise 5, show how to find an equation of the circle which passes through a given point and through the two points of intersection of two given circles.

In each of Exercises 8–11, write an equation which defines the function given.

8. The function P such that $P(r)$ is the perimeter of an equilateral triangle inscribed in a circle of radius r.

9. The function V such that $V(v)$ is the volume of the sphere which circumscribes a regular tetrahedron of volume v.

10. The function S such that $S(a)$ is the surface area of the sphere inscribed in a regular tetrahedron of surface area a.

11. The function Z such that $Z(n)$ is the number of zeros that $n!$ ends in when expanded out [e.g., $Z(4) = 0$, $Z(5) = 1$, $Z(10) = 2$].

12. If $a_0 = x$, $a_{n+1} = F(a_n)$, $(n = 0, 1, 2, \cdots)$, find a_m when:
   a. $F(x) = x^2$.
   b. $F(x) = \sqrt{|x|}$.
   c. $F(x) = a + bx$.
   d. $F(x) = (1 - x)^{-1}$.
   e. $F(x) = \sqrt{1 - x^2}$.

13. For what rational functions R does $R(x) = R(2x)$ for every x in $(-\infty, \infty)$?

14. What kind of a function is the composite of the following functions? Give examples.
   a. An odd function by an odd function.
   b. An odd function by an even function.
   c. An even function by an even function.
   d. An even function by an odd function.

15. Show that every function can be expressed as the sum of an even function and an odd function. Give examples.

16. Using Exercise 15, solve the functional equation

$$F(x)F(-x) = 1.$$

17. If $F(x) = (ax^3 + b)^5$, find a function G such that $F(G(x)) = G(F(x))$.

18. If $F(x) = \sqrt{x^2 + 1}$, show that
a. $F(x) + F(y) > F(x + y)$.
b. $F(x)F(y) \geq F(xy)$.

19. Give examples of functions satisfying the following (functional) equations for all real numbers x and y.

a. $F(2x) = 2F(x)$.

b. $F(2x) = \dfrac{2F(x)}{1 - F^2(x)}$.

c. $F(x) + F(y) = F(x + y)$.

d. $G(x) \cdot G(y) = G(x + y)$.

4

LIMITS

IN THIS CHAPTER we lay a foundation for the calculus. This foundation will consist of definitions and basic theorems. The new concepts of limit and continuity play a fundamental role throughout the calculus.

Early in our mathematical training we were faced with problems whose solutions involved the use of limits, although we were probably unaware of it at the time. To select just one example: according to a formula of geometry, the area of a circle of radius r is πr^2 where π is a number approximately equal to 3.1416. How is such a formula derived? The usual way is to inscribe regular polygons in the circle, find the areas of these polygons, and then determine the "limiting value" of these areas as the numbers of sides of the polygons increase without bound. Thus even such a seemingly simple formula as that for the area of a circle depends on the concept of limit for its derivation.

1 INTRODUCTION TO LIMITS

We shall postpone the formal definition of limit until the next section. Let us first discuss informally the meaning of this concept.

If x is a number close to 2, then the number $3x + 5$ is close to 11. An inspection of the accompanying table of values bears out this contention. Although $3x + 5$ equals 11 when x equals 2, this is not of primary concern to us

x	1.8	1.9	1.95	1.999	2.0001	2.1	2.2
$3x + 5$	10.4	10.7	10.85	10.997	11.0003	11.3	11.6

at the moment. Since $3x + 5$ is close to 11 provided x is close to (but unequal to) 2, we shall say that the limit of $3x + 5$ as x approaches 2 is 11, and we shall write symbolically

$$\operatorname*{limit}_{x \to 2} (3x + 5) = 11.$$

Similarly,

$$\operatorname*{limit}_{x \to -1} \frac{2x}{x + 2} = -2,$$

since $2x/(x + 2)$ is close to -2 provided x is close to -1.

Consider now the more complicated problem of evaluating

$$\operatorname*{limit}_{x \to 0} \left(\frac{1}{2}\right)^{1/x^2}.$$

We cannot predict the answer, as we could in the previous examples, by giving x the value 0, since $(\frac{1}{2})^{1/0}$ is meaningless. However, an inspection of the accompanying table leads us to believe that $(\frac{1}{2})^{1/x^2}$ is close to 0 provided x is close to 0; i.e.,

x	± 1	$\pm \frac{1}{2}$	$\pm \frac{1}{3}$	$\pm \frac{1}{4}$	$\pm \frac{1}{n}$
$(\frac{1}{2})^{1/x^2}$	$\frac{1}{2}$	$\frac{1}{16}$	$\frac{1}{512}$	$1/2^{16}$	$1/2^{n^2}$

$$\operatorname*{limit}_{x \to 0} \left(\frac{1}{2}\right)^{1/x^2} = 0.$$

These examples are simply instances of the limit of a function f. We shall say that the limit of f as x approaches a is b, written symbolically as

$$\operatorname*{limit}_{x \to a} f(x) = b,$$

if the *number* $f(x)$ is close to b whenever x is close to (but unequal to) a.

Let us look at some other examples of limits.

EXAMPLE 1. Find $\displaystyle\operatorname*{limit}_{y \to 3} \frac{1/y - \frac{1}{3}}{y - 3}$.

Solution: If we define the function g by

$$g(y) = \frac{1/y - \frac{1}{3}}{y - 3}, \qquad (y \neq 3),$$

then we are asked to find

$$\operatorname*{limit}_{y \to 3} g(y).$$

It is clear that the answer is not to be found by letting $y = 3$ in $g(y)$, since $g(3)$ is undefined. However, if $y \neq 3$,

$$g(y) = \frac{1/y - \frac{1}{3}}{y - 3} = \frac{(3 - y)/3y}{y - 3} = -\frac{y - 3}{3y(y - 3)} = -\frac{1}{3y},$$

since the *nonzero* factor $y - 3$ can be canceled out of the numerator and denominator. Evidently, $-1/3y$ is close to $-\frac{1}{9}$ if y is close to 3, and therefore the number $g(y)$ is close to $-\frac{1}{9}$ if y is close (but unequal) to 3. Hence

$$\operatorname*{limit}_{y \to 3} \frac{1/y - \frac{1}{3}}{y - 3} = -\frac{1}{9}.$$

EXAMPLE 2. Find $\operatorname*{limit}_{x \to 1} \dfrac{\sqrt{x} - 1}{x - 1}$.

Solution: If the function f is defined by

$$f(x) = \frac{\sqrt{x} - 1}{x - 1}, \qquad (x \geq 0,\ x \neq 1),$$

then we are asked to find

$$\operatorname*{limit}_{x \to 1} f(x).$$

As in the previous example, we cannot guess the answer by letting $x = 1$, since $f(1)$ is undefined. However, since $x \geq 0$,

$$x - 1 = (\sqrt{x} - 1)(\sqrt{x} + 1),$$

and therefore

$$f(x) = \frac{\sqrt{x} - 1}{x - 1} = \frac{1}{\sqrt{x} + 1}, \qquad (x \neq 1).$$

Now it is clear that $f(x)$ is close to $\frac{1}{2}$ if x is close (but unequal) to 1. Hence

$$\operatorname*{limit}_{x \to 1} \frac{\sqrt{x} - 1}{x - 1} = \frac{1}{2}.$$

EXAMPLE 3. Find $\operatorname*{limit}_{h \to 0} \dfrac{(2 + h)^2 - 4}{h}$.

Solution: If the function G is defined by

$$G(h) = \frac{(2 + h)^2 - 4}{h}, \qquad (h \neq 0),$$

then we wish to find

$$\operatorname*{limit}_{h \to 0} G(h).$$

Again, we cannot find this limit by letting $h = 0$, since $G(0)$ is undefined. Thus we proceed as before by simplifying $G(h)$:

$$G(h) = \frac{(4 + 4h + h^2) - 4}{h} = \frac{4h + h^2}{h} = 4 + h,$$

since $h \neq 0$. Then it is clear that $G(h)$ is close to 4 if h is close (but unequal) to 0; i.e.,

$$\underset{h \to 0}{\text{limit}} \frac{(2+h)^2 - 4}{h} = 4.$$

The next example illustrates the use of limits in a geometrical problem.

EXAMPLE 4. Let $P(3,4)$ and $Q(x, \sqrt{25 - x^2})$ be two distinct points on the semicircle (Figure 4.1) with equation

$$y = \sqrt{25 - x^2},$$

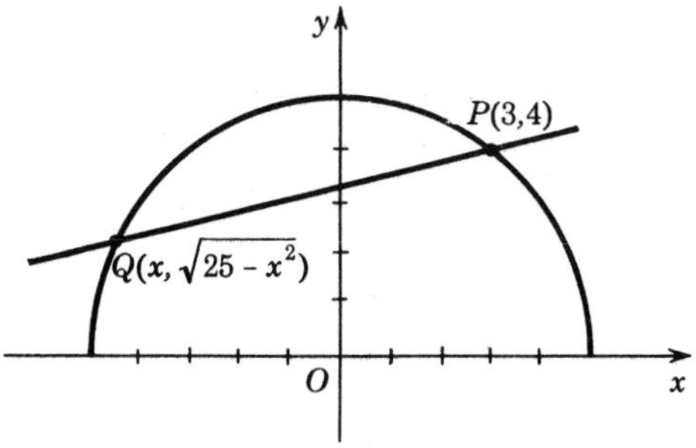

FIGURE 4.1

and let $M(x)$ designate the slope of the secant line through P and Q. Find

$$\underset{x \to 3}{\text{limit}}\, M(x).$$

Solution: We cannot let $x = 3$ in $M(x)$, because the points P and Q coincide if $x = 3$ and the secant line is not well defined. Clearly,

$$M(x) = \frac{\sqrt{25 - x^2} - 4}{x - 3}, \qquad (x \neq 3).$$

We can rationalize the numerator of $M(x)$ as follows:

$$M(x) = \frac{(\sqrt{25 - x^2} - 4)(\sqrt{25 - x^2} + 4)}{(x - 3)(\sqrt{25 - x^2} + 4)}$$

$$= \frac{(25 - x^2) - 16}{(x - 3)(\sqrt{25 - x^2} + 4)} = \frac{9 - x^2}{(x - 3)(\sqrt{25 - x^2} + 4)}$$

$$= -\frac{x + 3}{\sqrt{25 - x^2} + 4}, \qquad (x \neq 3).$$

If x is close to 3, $\sqrt{25 - x^2}$ is close to 4 and $M(x)$ is close to $-\frac{6}{8}$; i.e.,

$$\underset{x \to 3}{\text{limit}}\, M(x) = -\tfrac{3}{4}.$$

The slope of the radius OP is $\frac{4}{3}$, and therefore the slope of the tangent line to the circle at P is $-\frac{3}{4}$, which is the same as the limit of $M(x)$ as x approaches 3. Thus the secant line of the circle approaches the position of the tangent line as Q approaches P.

Example 4 suggests the possibility of defining the tangent line to a curve other than a circle as the limiting position of the secant line. Tangent lines are considered from this standpoint in Chapter 5.

The meaning of the word *close*, which is used so frequently above, is left to the interpretation of the reader. Actually, it is the uncertainty of the meaning of this word that impels us to give a more mathematical definition of limit in the next section.

EXERCISES

I

In each of Exercises 1–14, find the limit.

1. $\lim_{x\to 3} (x^3 - 5x^2 + 2x - 1)$.

2. $\lim_{x\to 2} \dfrac{x^2 - 4}{x - 2}$.

3. $\lim_{x\to -3} \dfrac{x^2 - 9}{x + 3}$.

4. $\lim_{x\to 3} \dfrac{\frac{1}{x} - \frac{1}{3}}{x - 3}$.

5. $\lim_{x\to -2} \dfrac{\frac{1}{x+1} + 1}{x + 2}$.

6. $\lim_{x\to 3} \dfrac{\frac{1}{x+2} - \frac{1}{5}}{x - 3}$.

7. $\lim_{z\to 1} \dfrac{z - 1}{z^2 - 1}$.

8. $\lim_{h\to 0} \dfrac{(a + h)^2 - a^2}{h}$.

9. If $f(x) = x^2 - 2x + 3$, find

   a. $\lim_{x\to 1} \dfrac{f(x) - f(1)}{x - 1}$.

   b. $\lim_{h\to 0} \dfrac{f(1 + h) - f(1)}{h}$.

10. If $g(x) = \sqrt{25 - x^2}$, find

$$\lim_{x\to 4} \frac{g(x) - g(4)}{x - 4},$$

and give a geometrical interpretation of this limit.

11. If $G(x) = -\sqrt{16 - x^2}$, find

$$\lim_{x\to 1} \frac{G(x) - G(1)}{x - 1},$$

and give a geometrical interpretation of this limit.

12. For the parabola $y = x^2$, find the limit as x approaches 1 of the slope of a secant line passing through the two points (1,1) and (x,x^2).

For Exercises 13–16, follow Example 2, p. 75.

13. $\lim\limits_{x\to 4} \dfrac{\sqrt{x} - 2}{x - 4}$.

14. $\lim\limits_{x\to 1} \dfrac{\sqrt{x+3} - 2}{x - 1}$.

15. $\lim\limits_{h\to 0} \dfrac{\sqrt{2+h} - \sqrt{2}}{h}$.

16. $\lim\limits_{h\to 0} \dfrac{\sqrt{a+h} - \sqrt{a}}{h}$, $a > 0$.

II

In each of Exercises 1–8, find the limit if it exists.

1. $\lim\limits_{x\to 1} \dfrac{\sqrt{x} - 2}{x - 1}$.

2. $\lim\limits_{y\to 2} \dfrac{\frac{1}{4} - \frac{1}{\sqrt{y}}}{y - 2}$.

3. $\lim\limits_{m\to 0} \dfrac{\sqrt{4 + m + m^2} - 2}{m}$.

4. $\lim\limits_{r\to 1} \dfrac{1 - r^3}{2 - \sqrt{r^2 + 3}}$.

5. $\lim\limits_{t\to 1} \dfrac{t^3 - 1}{t - 1}$.

6. $\lim\limits_{t\to 2} \dfrac{t^4 - 16}{t - 2}$.

7. $\lim\limits_{x\to 0} \left\{\lim\limits_{y\to 0} \dfrac{ax^2 + bxy + cy^2}{dx^2 + exy + fy^2}\right\} - \lim\limits_{y\to 0} \left\{\lim\limits_{x\to 0} \dfrac{ax^2 + bxy + cy^2}{dx^2 + exy + fy^2}\right\}$,

$ad \neq 0, \quad cf \neq 0.$

8. $\lim\limits_{y\to 8} \dfrac{8 - y}{\sqrt[3]{y} - 2}$.

2 DEFINITION OF LIMIT

We shall now give a precise definition of the limit concept discussed in Section 1. This definition will allow us to determine whether any given limit does or does not exist.

4.1 DEFINITION The *limit* of a function f at a is b, and we write

$$\lim_{x\to a} f(x) = b$$

if for every neighborhood N of b there exists a deleted neighborhood D of a contained in the domain of f such that $f(x)$ is in N for every x in D.

Although a need not be in the domain of f in order for the limit of f at a to equal b, it is clear from the definition above that some deleted neighborhood of a must be contained in the domain of f.

If there exists a number b such that

$$\lim_{x \to a} f(x) = b,$$

then we shall say that $\lim_{x \to a} f(x)$ *exists;* whereas if no such b exists, we shall say that $\lim_{x \to a} f(x)$ *does not exist.* A limit, if it exists, may be proved to be unique.

The definition of limit states that

$$\lim_{x \to a} f(x) = b$$

if for each neighborhood $N = (b_1,b_2)$ of b, *no matter how small,* there exists some deleted neighborhood $D = (a_1,a) \cup (a,a_2)$ of a such that

$$b_1 < f(x) < b_2 \qquad \text{whenever} \qquad a_1 < x < a_2,\ x \neq a.$$

Geometrically, this means that for any lines $y = b_1$ and $y = b_2$ below and above $y = b$, there exist lines $x = a_1$ and $x = a_2$ to the left and right of $x = a$ such that the graph of f between $x = a_1$ and $x = a_2$ (excluding the graph of f at $x = a$) lies between the lines $y = b_1$ and $y = b_2$ (Figure 4.2). There is no unique choice for the deleted neighborhood D, for clearly once we have found one such neighborhood any *smaller* one would serve equally well. In particular, we can always choose D symmetric: i.e., $D = (a - \delta, a) \cup (a, a + \delta)$ for some $\delta > 0$.

When a neighborhood N of b is given to us, we can always find a symmetric neighborhood N_1 of b which is contained in N. Then, to verify that $\lim_{x \to a} f(x) = b$,

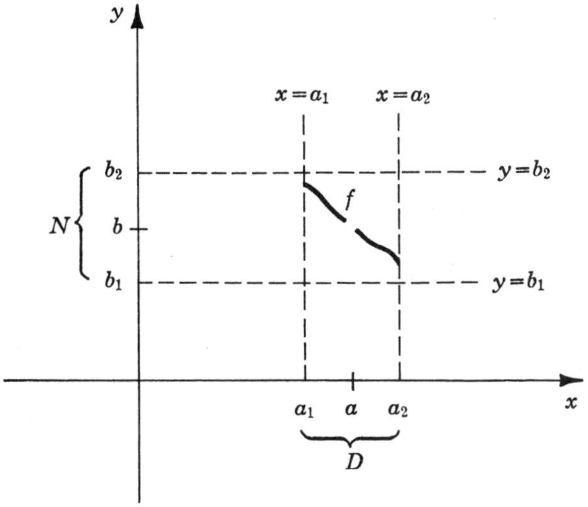

FIGURE 4.2

we need only show that for every symmetric neighborhood N_1 of b there exists a symmetric deleted neighborhood D of a such that $f(x)$ is in N_1 for every x in D.

For example, to *prove* that

$$\lim_{x\to 2} (3x + 5) = 11 \tag{1}$$

we need only show that for each symmetric neighborhood $(11 - \epsilon, 11 + \epsilon)$ of 11 there exists a symmetric deleted neighborhood $(2 - \delta, 2) \cup (2, 2 + \delta)$ of 2 such that

$$11 - \epsilon < 3x + 5 < 11 + \epsilon \qquad \text{whenever} \qquad 2 - \delta < x < 2 + \delta,\ x \neq 2. \tag{2}$$

Since the inequality $11 - \epsilon < 3x + 5 < 11 + \epsilon$ is equivalent to

$$6 - \epsilon < 3x < 6 + \epsilon$$

and also to

$$2 - \frac{\epsilon}{3} < x < 2 + \frac{\epsilon}{3},$$

statement (2) is true if we let $\delta = \epsilon/3$. Therefore, (1) is proved.

In other examples, it might be much more difficult to select the interval $(a - \delta, a + \delta)$ corresponding to each interval $(b - \epsilon, b + \epsilon)$. However, the following limit theorem can be proved in the same way we proved the example above.

4.2 THEOREM. $\lim_{x\to a} (mx + b) = ma + b.$

Proof: If $m > 0$, then we can show as above that $ma + b - \epsilon < mx + b < ma + b + \epsilon$ whenever $a - \epsilon/m < x < a + \epsilon/m$. If $m < 0$, then the inequality $ma + b - \epsilon < mx + b < ma + b + \epsilon$ is equivalent to

$$ma - \epsilon < mx < ma + \epsilon$$

and also to

$$a - \frac{\epsilon}{m} > x > a + \frac{\epsilon}{m}$$

Therefore, we can select $\delta = -\epsilon/m$ (remember, $m < 0$ so that $-\epsilon/m > 0$). Finally, if $m = 0$, $b - \epsilon < b < b + \epsilon$ whenever $a - \delta < x < a + \delta$ for every choice of the positive number δ.

As special cases of **4.2**, we have

4.3 THEOREM. $\lim_{x\to a} b = b;$

4.4 THEOREM. $\lim_{x\to a} x = a.$

We obtain **4.3** by letting $m = 0$ in **4.2**. This theorem states that the limit of a constant function b at any number a in its domain is b. We obtain **4.4** from **4.2** by letting $m = 1$ and $b = 0$.

In finding $\lim_{x \to a} f(x)$, we need only look at values of f in some deleted neighborhood of a. To be more precise, the following result holds.

4.5 THEOREM. If f and g are functions and a is a number such that $f(x) = g(x)$ at every number x in some deleted neighborhood K of a, and if $\lim_{x \to a} f(x)$ exists, then so does $\lim_{x \to a} g(x)$ and

$$\lim_{x \to a} f(x) = \lim_{x \to a} g(x).$$

Proof: If $\lim_{x \to a} f(x) = b$, then for every neighborhood N of b there exists a deleted neighborhood D of a such that $f(x)$ is in N for every x in D. Hence $D \cap K$ is also a deleted neighborhood of a such that $f(x)$ is in N for every x in $D \cap K$. Since $f(x) = g(x)$ for every x in $D \cap K$, $g(x)$ is in N for every x in $D \cap K$. Therefore $\lim_{x \to a} g(x) = b$ also.

EXAMPLE 1. Prove that $\lim_{x \to a} x^2 = a^2$ for every positive number a.

Solution: Since the graph of $y = x^2$ rises as we move to the right from the origin it is clear from Figure 4.3 that for every neighborhood $N = (b_1, b_2)$ of a^2, the neighborhood $D = (\sqrt{b_1}, \sqrt{b_2})$ of a accomplishes the desired result. That is, for every x in D, x^2 is in N.

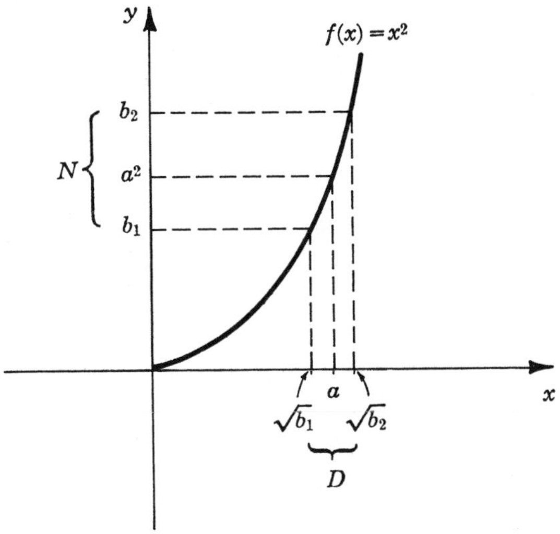

FIGURE 4.3

EXAMPLE 2. Prove that $\lim_{x \to a} \sqrt{x} = \sqrt{a}$ for every positive number a.

Solution: The inequality

$$0 < \sqrt{a} - \epsilon < \sqrt{x} < \sqrt{a} + \epsilon$$

is equivalent to

$$(\sqrt{a} - \epsilon)^2 < x < (\sqrt{a} + \epsilon)^2$$

or

$$a - (2\sqrt{a}\epsilon - \epsilon^2) < x < a + (2\sqrt{a}\epsilon + \epsilon^2)$$

Therefore, for every neighborhood $N = (\sqrt{a} - \epsilon, \sqrt{a} + \epsilon)$ of $\sqrt{a}$ we have found a neighborhood $D = (a - (2\sqrt{a}\epsilon - \epsilon^2), a + (2\sqrt{a}\epsilon + \epsilon^2))$ of a such that $\sqrt{x}$ is in N whenever x is in D, $x \neq a$. This proves the given limit.

EXAMPLE 3. Prove that $\lim_{x \to a} 1/x = 1/a$ for every positive number a.

Solution: The inequality

$$0 < \frac{1}{a} - \epsilon < \frac{1}{x} < \frac{1}{a} + \epsilon$$

is equivalent to

$$\frac{a}{1 + \epsilon a} < x < \frac{a}{1 - \epsilon a}.$$

Also, a is in the interval $(a/[1 + \epsilon a], a/[1 - \epsilon a])$. You should now be able to prove the given limit.

With a similar proof, Examples 1 and 3 can also be shown to be true if $a < 0$.

A useful result on limits is as follows.

4.6 THEOREM. If $\lim_{x \to a} f(x) = b$ and $b > 0$, then there exists a deleted neighborhood D of a such that $f(x) > 0$ for every x in D. Similarly, if $b < 0$ there exists a D such that $f(x) < 0$ for every x in D.

Proof: The symmetric neighborhood $N = (b/2, 3b/2)$ of b contains only positive numbers if $b > 0$. Since $\lim_{x \to a} f(x) = b$, there exists a deleted neighborhood D of a such that $f(x)$ is in N whenever x is in D. Therefore, $f(x) > 0$ for every x in D.

An example in which the limit does not exist is given below.

EXAMPLE 4. Let the function f be defined as follows:

$$f\left(\frac{1}{n}\right) = 1 \text{ for every nonzero integer } n,$$

$$f(x) = x \text{ for every other real number } x.$$

Prove that $\lim_{x \to 0} f(x)$ does not exist.

Solution: The graph of f is the line $y = x$, with the exception that when $x = 1/n$, n a nonzero integer, $y = 1$. It is sketched in Figure 4.4. Since $f(0) = 0$ and $f(x)$ is close to 0 when x is close to 0, $x \neq 1/n$, we might suspect that

$$\lim_{x \to 0} f(x) = 0.$$

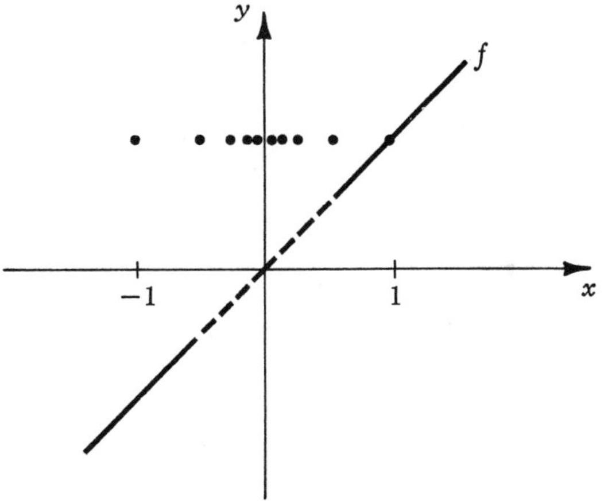

FIGURE 4.4

However, this is not correct. For if we take the neighborhood $N = (-1/2, 1/2)$ of 0, there is no deleted neighborhood $D = (-\delta,0) \cup (0,\delta)$ of 0 such that $f(x)$ is in N for every x in D. Thus, we can always find a positive integer n such that $1/n < \delta$; and for this number $f(1/n)$ is not in N since $f(1/n) = 1$. In a similar way, we can show that $\lim_{x \to 0} f(x)$ is not equal to any other number b. Therefore, this limit does not exist.

EXERCISES

I

Using only the definition of a limit, prove that each of the following statements is correct.

1. $\lim_{x \to 2} (2x + 1) = 5.$
2. $\lim_{x \to -1} (3x - 4) = -7.$
3. $\lim_{x \to 0} (7x + 3) = 3.$
4. $\lim_{x \to -1} (4x - 1) = -5.$
5. $\lim_{x \to 2} (x^2 + 1) = 5.$
6. $\lim_{x \to 0} x^2 = 0.$
7. $\lim_{x \to 3} \sqrt{x + 1} = 2.$
8. $\lim_{x \to -1} \frac{1}{x} = -1.$
9. $\lim_{x \to 3} \frac{3}{x} = 1.$
10. $\lim_{x \to -3} x^2 + x = 6.$

In Exercises 11–14, prove that the limits do not exist.

11. $\lim_{x \to -1} \frac{x + 2}{x + 1}.$
12. $\lim_{x \to -2} \frac{|x + 2|}{x + 2}.$
13. $\lim_{y \to 0} \frac{|y| - y}{y}.$
14. $\lim_{y \to 1} \frac{|y - 1| - y + 1}{|y - 1| + y - 1}.$

II

In each of Exercises 1–8, prove that the limit exists.

1. $\lim_{x \to 0} \frac{x^2 + 4}{x - 2}.$
2. $\lim_{x \to 2} \frac{x^3 + 1}{x - 1}.$
3. $\lim_{x \to a} \sqrt[3]{x}.$
4. $\lim_{x \to a} x^3.$
5. $\lim_{x \to 1} \frac{1}{x^2}.$
6. $\lim_{x \to 9} \frac{1}{\sqrt{x}}.$
7. $\lim_{x \to -1} \frac{(x + 1)^2}{x^3 + 1}.$
8. $\lim_{x \to 0} \frac{|x|^3 + x^3}{x}.$

In Exercises 9–10, prove that the limits do not exist.

9. $\lim_{x \to 5} x - [x]$ ($[x]$ denotes the greatest integer $\leq x$).
10. $\lim_{x \to 0} \frac{|x| - x}{|x|^3 - x^3}.$
11. Prove that if $\lim_{x \to a} f(x)$ exists then it is unique.
12. Prove that if $\lim_{x \to a} f(x) = b$ then $\lim_{x \to a} cf(x) = cb$ for every positive constant c.

3 CONTINUITY

We saw in 4.2 and Examples 1–3 of Section 2 that not only did $\lim_{x\to a} f(x)$ exist in each case but also $\lim_{x\to a} f(x) = f(a)$. This situation arises often enough to be given a special name, as stated below.

4.7 DEFINITION. The function f is *continuous* at the number a if (1) a is in the domain of f, (2) $\lim_{x\to a} f(x)$ exists, and (3)

$$\lim_{x\to a} f(x) = f(a).$$

Going back to the definition of limit, we find that f is continuous at a if a is in the domain of f and if for every neighborhood N of $f(a)$ there exists a neighborhood D of a such that $f(x)$ is in N for every x in D. Note that we need no longer delete a from D.

The function f might be continuous at every number in some set A, in which case we say f is *continuous in A*. For example, the function f defined by

$$f(x) = \frac{1}{x}$$

is continuous in the set of all nonzero numbers. The function f is not continuous at 0, since $f(0)$ is undefined.

An example of a function g for which $\lim_{x\to a} g(x)$ exists and $g(a)$ exists but g is not continuous at a is given in Figure 4.5. Thus $\lim_{x\to 1} g(x) = 1$ while $g(1) = 3$. Hence g is not continuous at 1.

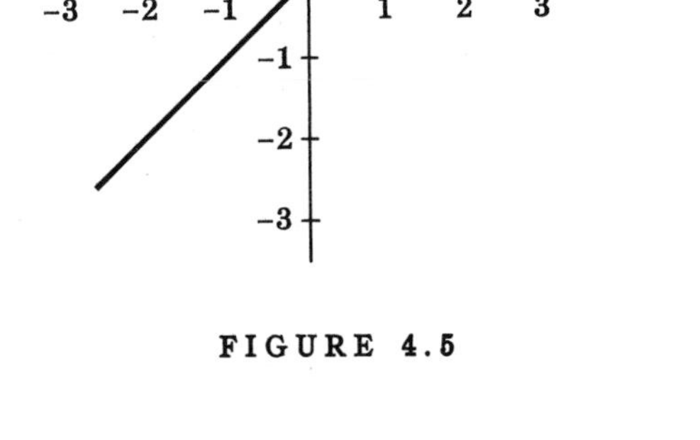

FIGURE 4.5

Roughly speaking, if a function f is continuous in an interval $[a,b]$, then the graph of f between $x = a$ and $x = b$ has no breaks in it.

If functions f and g have limits at some number a, then so do the various combinations of f and g, and their limits are the obvious ones listed below. Thus if

$$\operatorname*{limit}_{x\to a} f(x) = b \quad \text{and} \quad \operatorname*{limit}_{x\to a} g(x) = c,$$

then

4.8 $$\operatorname*{limit}_{x\to a} (f+g)(x) = b + c, \qquad \operatorname*{limit}_{x\to a} (f-g)(x) = b - c,$$

4.9 $$\operatorname*{limit}_{x\to a} (fg)(x) = bc,$$

4.10 $$\operatorname*{limit}_{x\to a} \left(\frac{f}{g}\right)(x) = \frac{b}{c}, \text{ provided } c \neq 0.$$

We shall postpone the proofs of **4.8–4.10** until Section 7, but shall use them in the meantime whenever the occasion arises.

An immediate application of **4.8–4.10** is to polynomial functions and rational functions. In the first place, if $f(x) = x$, then $\operatorname*{limit}_{x\to a} f(x) = a$ by **4.4.** Hence, by **4.9,**

$$\operatorname*{limit}_{x\to a} x^2 = \operatorname*{limit}_{x\to a} f^2(x) = a^2.$$

Knowing that

$$\operatorname*{limit}_{x\to a} x^k = a^k$$

for some positive integer k, we have, by **4.9,**

$$\operatorname*{limit}_{x\to a} x^{k+1} = \operatorname*{limit}_{x\to a} x^k \cdot x = a^k \cdot a = a^{k+1}.$$

Hence, by mathematical induction,

4.11 $$\operatorname*{limit}_{x\to a} x^n = a^n \text{ for every positive integer } n.$$

If f is any polynomial function so that

$$f(x) = c_0x^n + c_1x^{n-1} + \cdots + c_{n-1}x + c_n,$$

then repeated applications of **4.8** give

$$\operatorname*{limit}_{x\to a} f(x) = \operatorname*{limit}_{x\to a} c_0x^n + \operatorname*{limit}_{x\to a} c_1x^{n-1} + \cdots + \operatorname*{limit}_{x\to a} c_{n-1}x + \operatorname*{limit}_{x\to a} c_n.$$

Since $\lim_{x \to a} c_0 = c_0$ by **4.3**, evidently $\lim_{x \to a} c_0 x^n = c_0 a^n$ by **4.9** and **4.11**. A similar argument for each term in the expression above yields

$$\lim_{x \to a} f(x) = c_0 a^n + c_1 a^{n-1} + \cdots + c_{n-1} a + c_n.$$

Since the right side of the equation above is simply $f(a)$, this proves that a *polynomial function is continuous at every number.*

A rational function is a quotient of two polynomial functions. If f and g are rational functions and a is a number such that $g(a) \neq 0$, then, by **4.10**,

$$\lim_{x \to a} \frac{f}{g}(x) = \frac{f(a)}{g(a)}.$$

Since $g(a) \neq 0$ for every a in the domain of f/g, we have proved the following theorem.

4.12 THEOREM. A rational function is continuous in its domain.

Since every polynomial function is also a rational function, this theorem also contains the statement above that a polynomial function is continuous.

EXAMPLE. Find $\lim_{x \to 2} \dfrac{x^3 - 8}{x - 2}$.

Solution: We cannot apply **4.12** directly to the rational function F defined by

$$F(x) = \frac{x^3 - 8}{x - 2},$$

since 2 is not in the domain of F. Note, however, that

$$\frac{x^3 - 8}{x - 2} = x^2 + 2x + 4, \qquad (\text{if } x \neq 2).$$

Therefore, if f is the polynomial function

$$f(x) = x^2 + 2x + 4,$$

we have

$$F(x) = f(x), \qquad (\text{for every } x \neq 2).$$

Hence, by **4.5** and **4.12**,

$$\lim_{x \to 2} \frac{x^3 - 8}{x - 2} = \lim_{x \to 2} (x^2 + 2x + 4) = 2^2 + 2 \cdot 2 + 4 = 12.$$

EXERCISES

I

In each of Exercises 1–6, prove that the limit exists by citing appropriate limit theorems and find the limit.

1. $\displaystyle\lim_{x\to a} (x^3 - 3x + 4)$.

2. $\displaystyle\lim_{x\to a} (x^5 + 4x^2 - 2\sqrt{x})(a \geq 0)$.

3. $\displaystyle\lim_{z\to 4} \frac{\sqrt{z}(\sqrt{z} - 2)}{z - 4}$.

4. $\displaystyle\lim_{x\to 2} \frac{x^2 - 4}{x^3 - 8}$.

5. $\displaystyle\lim_{x\to b} \left(\frac{1}{\sqrt{x}} + \frac{x - b}{x^3 - b^3}\right)$.

6. $\displaystyle\lim_{x\to -y} \frac{x^3 + y^3}{x^5 + y^5}$.

7. Prove that $\lim_{x\to a} F(x) = b$ if and only if

$$\lim_{x\to a} |F(x) - b| = 0.$$

In each of Exercises 8–12, discuss the continuity of the function and sketch its graph.

8. $F(x) = \dfrac{|x|}{x}$.

9. $G(x) = \dfrac{x + a}{x - a}$.

10. $T(x) = \dfrac{|x^2 - 1|}{x + 1}$.

11. $M(x) = \dfrac{|x|}{x}(x^2 - 1)$.

12. $\phi(x) = \begin{cases} x^2/a, \text{ if } 0 < x < a, \\ a, \text{ if } x = a, \\ 2a - a^3/x^2, \text{ if } x > a. \end{cases}$

II

1. Prove $\lim_{x\to a} \sqrt[n]{x} = \sqrt[n]{a}$, ($a > 0$, n a positive integer).

2. Show that if $f(x) = \sqrt[n]{x^m}$, (m and n positive integers), then f is continuous in the interval $(0, \infty)$.

3. If $F(x) \leq G(x) \leq H(x)$ for every x in some deleted neighborhood of a, and if $\lim_{x\to a} F(x) = \lim_{x\to a} H(x) = L$, prove that $\lim_{x\to a} G(x) = L$. (This result is often called the *squeeze theorem*.)

4 ONE-SIDED LIMITS

The function f defined by

$$f(x) = \sqrt[n]{x}$$

has as its domain $[0, \infty)$ if the positive integer n is even, and the set $(-\infty, \infty)$ if n is odd. Therefore

$$\operatorname*{limit}_{x \to 0} f(x)$$

does not exist if n is even, because no deleted neighborhood of 0 is contained in the domain of f (see **4.1**). However, for every positive number ϵ,

$$f(x) \text{ is in } (0,\epsilon) \text{ for every } x \text{ in } (0,\epsilon^n),$$

since $0 < \sqrt[n]{x} < \epsilon$ if and only if $0 < x < \epsilon^n$. Thus $f(x)$ is "close" to 0 when x is "close" to 0. This example illustrates part of the following definition.

4.13 DEFINITION. The *right-hand limit* of a function f at a equals b, and we write

$$\operatorname*{limit}_{x \to a^+} f(x) = b$$

if for every neighborhood N of b there exists an open interval $(a, a + \delta)$ contained in the domain of f such that $f(x)$ is in N for every x in $(a, a + \delta)$.

The definition of the *left-hand limit*

$$\operatorname*{limit}_{x \to a^-} f(x) = b$$

is the same, except that the open interval $(a, a + \delta)$ is replaced by $(a - \delta, a)$.

By our remarks above,

$$\operatorname*{limit}_{x \to 0^+} \sqrt{x} = 0,$$

since for every neighborhood $(-\epsilon_1, \epsilon_2)$ of 0 there exists an open interval of the form $(0,\delta)$, namely $(0,\epsilon_2^2)$, such that $\sqrt{x}$ is in N for every x in $(0,\epsilon_2^2)$.

The limit theorems of Section 2 hold for one-sided limits as well as for ordinary limits, with the obvious changes when necessary. For example, **4.5** becomes: If $f(x) = g(x)$ at every x in some open interval (a,c) and if $\operatorname*{limit}_{x \to a^+} f(x)$ exists, then so does $\operatorname*{limit}_{x \to a^+} g(x)$ and

$$\operatorname*{limit}_{x \to a^+} f(x) = \operatorname*{limit}_{x \to a^+} g(x).$$

An illustration of the use of one-sided limits is afforded by the *greatest-integer function*. The greatest integer in a number x, designated by $[x]$, is defined to be the greatest integer $\leq x$; i.e.,

$$[x] = n \text{ if } n \leq x < n + 1, \qquad (n \text{ an integer}).$$

The graph of the function [ ] is similar to that of the postage function (page 65) it is given in Figure 4.6.

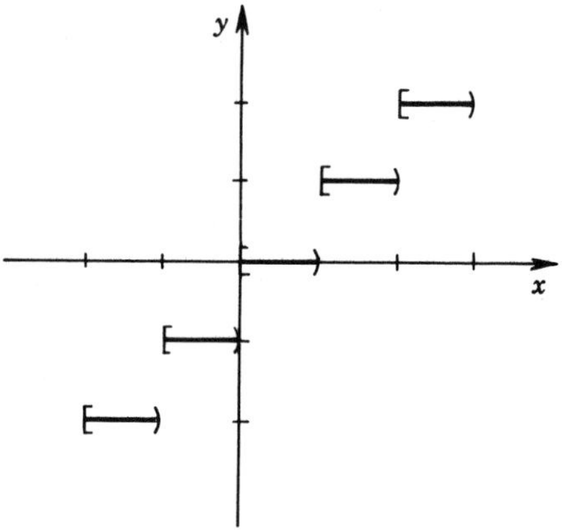

FIGURE 4.6

If g is the constant function defined by

$$g(x) = n \text{ for every real number } x,$$

then

$$[x] = g(x) \text{ for every } x \text{ in the open interval } (n, n + 1).$$

Hence, by **4.5**,

$$\operatorname*{limit}_{x\to n^+} [x] = \operatorname*{limit}_{x\to n^+} g(x) = n$$

and

$$\operatorname*{limit}_{x\to(n+1)^-} [x] = \operatorname*{limit}_{x\to(n+1)^-} g(x) = n.$$

That is, the limit at the left-hand end and the right-hand end of each step (in Figure 4.6) is simply the height of the step above (or below) the x axis. Hence $\operatorname*{limit}_{x\to n^+} [x] = [n]$, whereas $\operatorname*{limit}_{x\to n^-} [x] = n - 1 \neq [n]$.

One-sided limits are related to ordinary limits in the manner stated below.

4.14 THEOREM. For a given function f, $\lim_{x \to a} f(x) = b$ if and only if

$$\lim_{x \to a^+} f(x) = \lim_{x \to a^-} f(x) = b.$$

Proof: If $\lim_{x \to a} f(x) = b$, then for every neighborhood N of b there exists a deleted neighborhood $D = (a - \delta, a) \cup (a, a + \delta)$ of a such that $f(x)$ is in N for each x in D. Hence $f(x)$ is in N for every x in $(a, a + \delta)$ and also for every x in $(a - \delta, a)$. This proves that $\lim_{x \to a^+} f(x) = b$ and also $\lim_{x \to a^-} f(x) = b$.

Conversely, if $\lim_{x \to a^+} f(x) = b$ and $\lim_{x \to a^-} f(x) = b$, then for every neighborhood N of b there exists an open interval $(a, a + \delta)$ such that $f(x)$ is in N for every x in $(a, a + \delta)$, and also an open interval $(a - \delta, a)$ such that $f(x)$ is in N for every x in $(a - \delta, a)$. Therefore for every neighborhood N of b there exists a deleted neighborhood $D = (a - \delta, a) \cup (a, a + \delta)$ of a such that $f(x)$ is in N for every x in D. This proves that $\lim_{x \to a} f(x) = b$. Hence **4.14** is proved.

As an application of this theorem, we see that $\lim_{x \to n} [x]$ does not exist if n is an integer, since $\lim_{x \to n^-} [x] = n - 1$ whereas $\lim_{x \to n^+} [x] = n$. Thus the greatest-integer function is discontinuous (i.e., not continuous) at each integer n. It is continuous at every other number.

We shall follow the usual practice of saying that a function f is continuous in a closed interval $[a,b]$ if it is continuous in the open interval (a,b) and $\lim_{x \to a^+} f(x) = f(a)$, $\lim_{x \to b^-} f(x) = f(b)$. Thus, for example, the function g defined by $g(x) = \sqrt{1 - x^2}$ is continuous in the interval $[-1,1]$. Similarly, the function h defined by $h(x) = \sqrt{x}$ is continuous in the infinite interval $[0, \infty)$.

EXERCISES

I

Find each of the following limits (if it exists):

1. $\lim_{x \to 0^+} \dfrac{x}{|x|}$.

2. $\lim_{x \to -2^-} \dfrac{|x + 2|}{x + 2}$.

3. $\lim_{x \to 5^-} [x] - x$.

4. $\lim_{x \to 1^+} \dfrac{2x|x - 1|}{x - 1}$.

5. $\lim_{x \to 3^-} \dfrac{x^3 - 27}{|x - 3|(x - 3)}$.

6. $\lim_{x \to -7^+} \dfrac{|x + 7| + x + 7}{|x + 7| - x - 7}$.

II

Find each of the following limits (if it exists):

1. $\lim_{x \to 2^+} \frac{x - [x]}{x - 2}$.

2. $\lim_{x \to 2^-} \frac{x - [x]}{x - 2}$.

3. $\lim_{x \to 4^+} [[x]]$.

4. $\lim_{x \to 1^+} \frac{[x^2] - [x]^2}{x^2 - 1}$.

5. $\lim_{x \to 0^+} \frac{\sqrt{x}}{\sqrt{1 + \sqrt{x}} - 1}$.

6. $\lim_{x \to 10^-} \frac{[x^3] - x^3}{[x] - x}$.

5 INFINITE LIMITS

It is convenient to say that the limit of a function f at some number a is infinite if $f(x)$ is "large" when x is "close" to a. A more precise definition is given below.

4.15 **DEFINITION.** The right-hand limit of the function f at a is infinite, and we write

$$\lim_{x \to a^+} f(x) = \infty$$

if for every positive number k, no matter how large, there exists an open interval $(a, a + \delta)$ such that $f(x)$ is in (k, ∞) for every x in $(a, a + \delta)$. If for every positive number k there exists an open interval $(a - \delta, a)$ such that $f(x)$ is in (k, ∞) for every x in $(a - \delta, a)$, then we write

$$\lim_{x \to a^-} f(x) = \infty .$$

For example,

$$\lim_{x \to 0^+} \frac{1}{x} = \infty,$$

since for every positive number k

$$\frac{1}{x} \text{ is in } (k, \infty) \text{ for every } x \text{ in the interval } \left(0, \frac{1}{k}\right).$$

The definition of negative infinite limits is similar to **4.15**. Thus, for example, we write

$$\lim_{x \to a^+} f(x) = -\infty$$

if for every negative number k there exists an open interval $(a, a + \delta)$ such that $f(x)$ is in $(-\infty, k)$ for every x in $(a, a + \delta)$. The definition of $\lim_{x \to a^-} f(x) = -\infty$ is left to the reader.

For example,

$$\lim_{x \to 0^-} \frac{1}{x} = -\infty,$$

since for every negative number k

$$\frac{1}{x} \text{ is in } (-\infty, k) \text{ for every } x \text{ in the interval } \left(\frac{1}{k}, 0\right).$$

Most of the infinite limits that we shall encounter are of the following type.

4.16 $$\lim_{x \to a^+} \frac{1}{(x - a)^p} = \infty \qquad (\text{if } p > 0).$$

Proof: We must show that for every positive integer k, no matter how large, there exists an open interval $(a, a + \delta)$ such that

$$\frac{1}{(x - a)^p} \text{ is in } (k, \infty) \text{ for every } x \text{ in } (a, a + \delta).$$

If $x - a > 0$, then the inequality $1/(x - a)^p > k$ is equivalent to

$$0 < (x - a)^p < \frac{1}{k},$$

which in turn is equivalent to

$$0 < x - a < \left(\frac{1}{k}\right)^{1/p}.$$

The solution set of this last inequality is evidently $(a, a + \delta)$, where $\delta = (1/k)^{1/p}$. Hence $1/(x - a)^p$ is in (k, ∞) if x is in the open interval $(a, a + \delta)$. This proves **4.16.**

Limit **4.16** above still holds for x approaching a from the left if $p = m/n > 0$, where m is an even integer and n is odd.

If p is either an odd positive integer or the ratio of two odd positive integers, then $(x - a)^p < 0$ if $x < a$ and

$$\lim_{x \to a^-} \frac{1}{(x - a)^p} = -\infty,$$

by a proof similar to that of **4.16.**

The graph of the function f defined by

$$f(x) = \frac{1}{(x - a)^p}, \qquad (p > 0)$$

is, according to **4.16**, unbounded to the right of the line $x = a$. That is, for any line $y = k$ (no matter how large k is), there is some point on the graph of f above this line. The graph near $x = a$ is roughly as indicated in Figure 4.7.

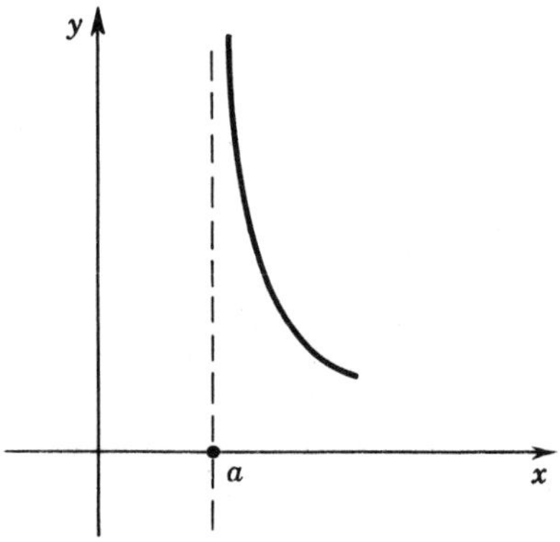

FIGURE 4.7

Evidently, the graph is "approaching" the line $x = a$ as it gets farther and farther from the x axis. A line such as $x = a$ is called an *asymptote* of the graph of f.

More generally, the line $x = a$ is called a *vertical asymptote* of the graph of a function f if one of

$$\lim_{x \to a^+} f(x), \qquad \lim_{x \to a^-} f(x)$$

is either ∞ or $-\infty$. Clearly, f is discontinuous at a if $x = a$ is an asymptote.

Modified limit theorems hold for infinite limits. We state without proof two such theorems that will be useful to us in the sequel.

If $\lim_{x \to a^+} f(x) = \infty$ or $-\infty$, and $\lim_{x \to a^+} g(x) = b$, then

4.17 $$\lim_{x \to a^+} (f + g)(x) = \lim_{x \to a^+} f(x)$$

and

4.18 $$\lim_{x \to a^+} (fg)(x) = \begin{cases} \lim_{x \to a^+} f(x) \text{ if } b > 0. \\ -\lim_{x \to a^+} f(x) \text{ if } b < 0. \end{cases}$$

Similar theorems hold for left-hand limits.

EXAMPLE 1. Find $\lim_{x\to 1^+} \dfrac{1}{x^2 - x}$ and $\lim_{x\to 1^-} \dfrac{1}{x^2 - x}$.

Solution: We first express

$$\frac{1}{x^2 - x} = \frac{1}{x} \cdot \frac{1}{x - 1}.$$

Then, by **4.16** and **4.18**, with $f(x) = 1/(x - 1)$ and $g(x) = 1/x$,

$$\lim_{x\to 1^+} \frac{1}{x^2 - x} = \lim_{x\to 1^+} \frac{1}{x - 1} = \infty,$$

$$\lim_{x\to 1^-} \frac{1}{x^2 - x} = \lim_{x\to 1^-} \frac{1}{x - 1} = -\infty.$$

For the function f defined by

$$f(x) = 3 - \frac{1}{x},$$

it is clear that $f(x)$ is "close" to 3 when x is "large." This type of a limiting value of a function is defined as follows.

4.19 DEFINITION. If for every neighborhood N of b there exists a positive number k such that $f(x)$ is in N for every x in (k, ∞), then we say

$$\lim_{x\to\infty} f(x) = b.$$

Similarly, we say for the function f that

$$\lim_{x\to -\infty} f(x) = b$$

if for every neighborhood N of b there exists a negative integer k such that $f(x)$ is in N for every x in $(-\infty, k)$.

A useful instance of an infinite limit of type **4.19** is:

4.20 $$\lim_{x\to\infty} \frac{1}{x^p} = 0, \qquad (\text{if } p > 0).$$

Proof: Since we are interested only in the behavior of $1/x^p$ when x is large, we might as well let $x > 0$. Then for each neighborhood $(-\epsilon, \epsilon)$ of 0, we have $-\epsilon < 1/x^p < \epsilon$ if and only if

$$0 < \frac{1}{x^p} < \epsilon.$$

This inequality is equivalent to

$$x^p > \frac{1}{\epsilon},$$

$$\text{or} \qquad x > \left(\frac{1}{\epsilon}\right)^{1/p}$$

Hence $1/x^p$ is in $(-\epsilon,\epsilon)$ for every $x > (1/\epsilon)^{1/p}$. This proves **4.20**.

The ordinary limit theorems hold for limits as x approaches ∞ or $-\infty$. Their proofs are but slight modifications of those for finite limits.

It is convenient to write

$$\operatorname*{limit}_{x\to\infty} f(x) = \infty$$

if $f(x)$ is large when x is large, or more precisely, if for every number k (no matter how large) there exists a number n such that $f(x) > k$ for every $x > n$. The many variations of this limit involving $-\infty$ are defined analogously. Clearly,

$$\operatorname*{limit}_{x\to\infty} x^p = \infty, \qquad (\text{if } p > 0).$$

EXAMPLE 2. Find

$$\operatorname*{limit}_{x\to\infty} \frac{2 - x + 3x^2}{1 + x^2}.$$

Solution: In order to use **4.20**, we divide numerator and denominator of the given expression by x^2, and then proceed as indicated below:

$$\operatorname*{limit}_{x\to\infty} \frac{2 - x + 3x^2}{1 + x^2} = \operatorname*{limit}_{x\to\infty} \frac{2/x^2 - 1/x + 3}{1/x^2 + 1}$$

$$= \frac{2 \operatorname*{limit}_{x\to\infty} 1/x^2 - \operatorname*{limit}_{x\to\infty} 1/x + \operatorname*{limit}_{x\to\infty} 3}{\operatorname*{limit}_{x\to\infty} 1/x^2 + \operatorname*{limit}_{x\to\infty} 1}$$

$$= \frac{3}{1} = 3.$$

The existence of a limit involving ∞ for a function f tells us something about the graph of f far away from the origin. If

$$\operatorname*{limit}_{x\to\infty} f(x) = b,$$

then $f(x)$ is close to b when x is large, and the graph of f gets close to the line $y = b$ as x gets large. Such a line $y = b$ is an asymptote of the graph. Thus, if either

$$\operatorname*{limit}_{x\to\infty} f(x) = b \quad \text{or} \quad \operatorname*{limit}_{x\to-\infty} f(x) = b,$$

the line $y = b$ is called a *horizontal asymptote* of the graph of f.

EXAMPLE 3. Discuss and sketch the graph of the equation

$$y = \frac{4x^2}{x^2 + 1}.$$

Solution: The graph is symmetric to the y axis, since x occurs to even powers only.

Since

$$0 \leq \frac{x^2}{x^2+1} < 1,$$

$0 \leq y < 4$ for every number x. Thus the graph lies between the lines $y = 0$ and $y = 4$. Since

$$\operatorname*{limit}_{x\to\pm\infty} \frac{4x^2}{x^2+1} = \operatorname*{limit}_{x\to\pm\infty} \frac{4}{1+1/x^2} = 4,$$

the line $y = 4$ is an asymptote of the graph of the given equation [i.e., of the graph of the function f defined by $f(x) = 4x^2/(x^2+1)$]. When a few points are plotted, the graph may be drawn as in Figure 4.8.

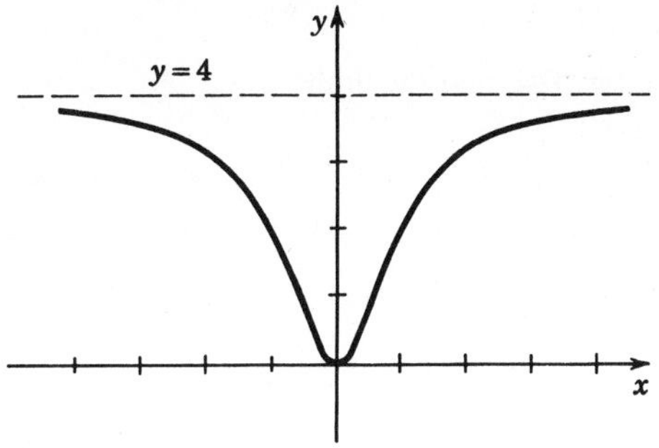

FIGURE 4.8

EXERCISES

I

In each of Exercises 1–6, find the limit.

1. $\operatorname*{limit}_{x\to\infty} \dfrac{x^2}{1-x}$.

2. $\operatorname*{limit}_{x\to 0^+} \dfrac{(x+1)^2}{(x-1)^2-1}$.

3. $\operatorname*{limit}_{t\to\infty} \dfrac{at^2+bt+c}{dt^2+et+f}$. (Consider the possibilities of various coefficients being zero.)

4. $\operatorname*{limit}_{x\to\infty} \dfrac{[x]-1}{x}$.

5. $\operatorname*{limit}_{x\to 1^-} \dfrac{[x^2]-1}{x^2-1}$.

6. $\operatorname*{limit}_{x\to-\infty} \dfrac{1}{x} - \dfrac{1}{x+2}$.

In each of Exercises 7–14, determine the vertical and horizontal asymptotes of the graph of the given function F and sketch the graph.

7. $F(x) = \dfrac{1}{x-2}$.

8. $F(x) = \dfrac{2x}{x+2}$.

9. $F(x) = \dfrac{1}{(x-2)^2}$.

10. $F(x) = \dfrac{2x}{(x+2)^2}$.

11. $F(x) = \dfrac{2x^2}{(x+2)^2}$.

12. $F(x) = \dfrac{2}{x^2-9}$.

13. $F(x) = \dfrac{2x^2}{x^2+9}$.

14. $F(x) = x + \dfrac{1}{x}$.

II

In each of Exercises 1–4, find the limit.

1. $\operatorname*{limit}_{t \to -1^+} \dfrac{\sqrt{1+t}}{1+t^5}$.

2. $\operatorname*{limit}_{x \to 0^+} 1 - x + [x] - [1 - x]$.

3. $\operatorname*{limit}_{x \to 1^-} 1 - x + [x] - [1 - x]$.

4. $\operatorname*{limit}_{s \to \infty} \dfrac{\sqrt[5]{s + 10^9}}{\sqrt{1 + \sqrt[3]{s}}}$.

Sketch the graph of each of the following functions, indicating the vertical and horizontal asymptotes.

5. $F(x) = \dfrac{x^2-1}{x^2-4}$.

6. $F(x) = \dfrac{x^2-1}{x^2+4}$.

7. $F(x) = \dfrac{x^2+1}{x^2-4}$.

8. $F(x) = \dfrac{x^2+1}{x^2+4}$.

6 THE LIMIT THEOREMS

This section will be devoted to proofs of the fundamental limit theorems of the calculus.

First, let us prove **4.8**, which we now restate.

4.8 THEOREM. If $\operatorname*{limit}_{x \to a} f(x) = b$ and $\operatorname*{limit}_{x \to a} g(x) = c$,

then

$$\operatorname*{limit}_{x \to a} (f + g)(x) = b + c, \qquad \operatorname*{limit}_{x \to a} (f - g)(x) = b - c.$$

Proof: Let us prove that $\operatorname*{limit}_{x \to a} (f + g)(x) = b + c$, leaving the analogous proof for the function $f - g$ to the reader. We must show that for every neighborhood $(b + c - \epsilon, b + c + \epsilon)$ of $b + c$ there exists a deleted neighborhood D of a such that $f(x) + g(x)$ is in $(b + c - \epsilon, b + c + \epsilon)$ for every x in D. Since $\lim_{x \to a} f(x) = b$, there is corresponding to the neighborhood $(b - \epsilon/2, b + \epsilon/2)$ of b some deleted neighborhood D_1 of a such that $f(x)$ is in $(b - \epsilon/2, b + \epsilon/2)$ for every x in D_1, and since $\lim_{x \to a} g(x) = c$, $g(x)$ is in $(c - \epsilon/2, c + \epsilon/2)$ for every x in some deleted neighborhood D_2 of a. Then $D = D_1 \cap D_2$ is a deleted neighborhood of a such that

$$b - \frac{\epsilon}{2} < f(x) < b + \frac{\epsilon}{2} \quad \text{and} \quad c - \frac{\epsilon}{2} < g(x) < c + \frac{\epsilon}{2}$$

for every x in D. Adding like members of these inequalities, we have

$$b + c - \epsilon < f(x) + g(x) < b + c + \epsilon$$

for every x in D. Thus we have shown that $f(x) + g(x)$ is in $(b + c - \epsilon, b + c + \epsilon)$ for every x in D. This proves **4.8**.

By mathematical induction, **4.8** can be extended to a sum of any finite number of functions. We state such a result as follows:

4.21 THEOREM. If $\lim_{x \to a} f_1(x) = b_1$, $\lim_{x \to a} f_2(x) = b_2 \cdots$, $\lim_{x \to a} f_n(x) = b_n$, then

$$\lim_{x \to a} (f_1 + f_2 + \cdots + f_n)(x) = b_1 + b_2 + \cdots + b_n.$$

Before proving the corresponding product limit theorem (**4.9**), we state and prove the special case when one function is a constant.

4.22 THEOREM. If $\lim_{x \to a} f(x) = b$, then $\lim_{x \to a} kf(x) = kb$.

Proof: If $k = 0$, then the theorem follows from **4.3**. So let us assume $k > 0$. The proof for $k < 0$ is similar and hence omitted. We must show that for every neighborhood $(kb - \epsilon, kb + \epsilon)$ of kb there exists a deleted neighborhood D of a such that $kf(x)$ is in $(kb - \epsilon, kb + \epsilon)$ for every x in D. Since $\lim_{x \to a} f(x) = b$, there is corresponding to the neighborhood $(b - \epsilon/k, b + \epsilon/k)$ of b some deleted neighborhood D of a such that $f(x)$ is in $(b - \epsilon/k, b + \epsilon/k)$ for every x in D. Thus

$$b - \epsilon/k < f(x) < b + \epsilon/k \quad \text{for every } x \text{ in } D,$$

and on multiplying each member of the above inequality by k, we have

$$kb - \epsilon < kf(x) < kb + \epsilon \quad \text{for every } x \text{ in } D.$$

Hence $kf(x)$ is in $(kb - \epsilon, kb + \epsilon)$ for every x in D. This proves **4.22**.

Another special case of the product limit theorem is as follows:

4.23 **THEOREM.** If $\lim_{x\to a} f(x) = 0$ and $\lim_{x\to a} g(x) = 0$, then $\lim_{x\to a} (fg)(x) = 0$.

Proof: We must show that for every neighborhood $(-\epsilon,\epsilon)$ of 0 there exists a deleted neighborhood D of a such that $f(x)g(x)$ is in $(-\epsilon,\epsilon)$ for every x in D. Since $\lim_{x\to a} f(x) = \lim_{x\to a} g(x) = 0$, there are corresponding to the neighborhood $(-\sqrt{\epsilon}, \sqrt{\epsilon})$ of 0 deleted neighborhoods D_1 and D_2 of a such that $f(x)$ is in $(-\sqrt{\epsilon}, \sqrt{\epsilon})$ for every x in D_1 and $g(x)$ is in $(-\sqrt{\epsilon}, \sqrt{\epsilon})$ for every x in D_2. Therefore, if we let $D = D_1 \cap D_2$,

$$-\sqrt{\epsilon} < f(x) < \sqrt{\epsilon} \quad \text{and} \quad -\sqrt{\epsilon} < g(x) < \sqrt{\epsilon} \quad \text{for every } x \text{ in } D.$$

Hence $|f(x)| < \sqrt{\epsilon}$, $|g(x)| < \sqrt{\epsilon}$, and $|f(x)\cdot g(x)| < \epsilon$, or

$$-\epsilon < f(x)\cdot g(x) < \epsilon \quad \text{for every } x \text{ in } D.$$

This proves **4.23.**

We can now prove **4.9** algebraically.

4.9 **THEOREM.** If $\lim_{x\to a} f(x) = b$ and $\lim_{x\to a} g(x) = c$, then $\lim_{x\to a} (fg)(x) = bc$.

Proof: Since $\lim_{x\to a} [f(x) - b] = 0$ and $\lim_{x\to a} [g(x) - c] = 0$ by **4.8,** we have, by **4.23,**

$$\lim_{x\to a} [f(x) - b][g(x) - c] = 0.$$

Hence by **4.21,**

$$\lim_{x\to a} [f(x)g(x) - bg(x) - cf(x) + bc] = 0$$

and

$$\lim_{x\to a} f(x)g(x) - \lim_{x\to a} bg(x) - \lim_{x\to a} cf(x) + \lim_{x\to a} bc = 0.$$

Thus by **4.22,**

$$\lim_{x\to a} f(x)g(x) - bc - cb + bc = 0,$$

and **4.9** follows easily.

The product limit theorem can be extended to any finite number of functions by mathematical induction.

4.24 THEOREM. If $\lim_{x \to a} f_1(x) = b_1$, $\lim_{x \to a} f_2(x) = b_2$, $\cdots$, $\lim_{x \to a} f_n(x) = b_n$, then

$$\lim_{x \to a} (f_1 \cdot f_2 \cdot \cdots \cdot f_n)(x) = b_1 \cdot b_2 \cdot \cdots \cdot b_n.$$

A special case of **4.24** is that in which $f_1 = f_2 = \cdots = f_n = f$.

4.25 THEOREM. If $\lim_{x \to a} f(x) = b$, then $\lim_{x \to a} f^n(x) = b^n$ for every positive integer n.

The composite $f \circ g$ of functions f and g has the following limit property.

4.26 THEOREM. If $\lim_{x \to a} g(x) = b$ and f is continuous at b, then $\lim_{x \to a} (f \circ g)(x) = f(b)$.

Proof: Since f is continuous at b, for every neighborhood N of $f(b)$ there exists a neighborhood C of b such that $f(y)$ is in N for every y in C. In turn, since $\lim_{x \to a} g(x) = b$, there exists a deleted neighborhood D of a such that $g(x)$ is in C for every x in D. Combining these remarks, we see that for every neighborhood N of $f(b)$ there exists a deleted neighborhood D of a such that $g(x)$ is in C, and therefore $f(g(x))$ is in N, for every x in D. This proves **4.26.**

A function such as F, where

$$F(x) = \frac{1}{x^2 + 3},$$

is a composite of the polynomial function

$$g(x) = x^2 + 3$$

and the reciprocal function

$$f(x) = \frac{1}{x};$$

i.e.,

$$f(g(x)) = \frac{1}{g(x)} = \frac{1}{x^2 + 3}.$$

Thus $F = f \circ g$. Therefore, since $\lim_{x \to a} g(x) = g(a)$ and f is continuous at $g(a)$ (by Example 3, page 82),

$$\lim_{x \to a} F(x) = \frac{1}{a^2 + 3},$$

by **4.26.**

In the same way, we can prove that if $\lim_{x\to a} g(x) = c \neq 0$ then

$$\lim_{x\to a} \frac{1}{g(x)} = \frac{1}{c}.$$

If, also,

$$\lim_{x\to a} f(x) = b,$$

then

$$\begin{aligned}\lim_{x\to a} \frac{f(x)}{g(x)} &= \lim_{x\to a} f(x) \cdot \frac{1}{g(x)} \\ &= \lim_{x\to a} f(x) \cdot \lim_{x\to a} \frac{1}{g(x)} \qquad \text{(by 4.9)} \\ &= b \cdot \frac{1}{c}, \quad \text{or} \quad \frac{b}{c}.\end{aligned}$$

This proves **4.10**, which we now restate.

4.10 THEOREM. If $\lim_{x\to a} f(x) = b$ and $\lim_{x\to a} g(x) = c$, then

$$\lim_{x\to a} \frac{f(x)}{g(x)} = \frac{b}{c}, \text{ provided } c \neq 0.$$

Such limits as

$$\lim_{x\to 2} \sqrt{x^2 + x + 1}$$

occur quite often. We easily compute them by using **4.26**. Thus if $f(x) = \sqrt{x}$ and $g(x) = x^2 + x + 1$,

$$(f \circ g)(x) = \sqrt{x^2 + x + 1}.$$

Hence by **4.26** and Example 2, page 82,

$$\lim_{x\to 2} \sqrt{x^2 + x + 1} = \sqrt{2^2 + 2 + 1} = \sqrt{7}.$$

By the same argument, we may prove the following result.

4.27 THEOREM. If $\lim_{x\to a} f(x) = b$, then $\lim_{x\to a} \sqrt[n]{f(x)} = \sqrt[n]{b}$,

provided, of course, $\sqrt[n]{b}$ exists.

EXERCISES

I

By referring to the appropriate limit theorems, prove that each of the following limits exists.

1. $\lim_{x\to a} (x^5 + 3x^2 + 2x + 1)$.

2. $\lim_{x\to 2} \dfrac{x+2}{\sqrt{x^3 - 4x + 1}}$.

3. $\lim_{x\to 1^+} \sqrt{\dfrac{x^2 - 1}{x^2 + 1}}$.

4. $\lim_{t\to 1} \dfrac{\sqrt{t}}{t+1} - \dfrac{t^2 - t}{t^4 - 1}$.

5. $\lim_{x\to 1} \dfrac{\sqrt{x}(x+2)}{x+1}$.

6. $\lim_{y\to -3} \sqrt[3]{(y+2)^5}$.

7. $\lim_{k\to 0} \dfrac{k^{15} - 1}{k^{15} + 1}$.

8. $\lim_{s\to 2} \sqrt{s+1} \cdot \sqrt[3]{s-1}$.

9. $\lim_{h\to 0} \dfrac{\sqrt{h^3 + 1} - 1}{h^2}$.

10. $\lim_{x\to 0} \dfrac{\sqrt{4+x} - 2}{x}$.

11. $\lim_{z\to -1} \dfrac{z^{-2} - 1}{z+1}$.

12. $\lim_{y\to b^2} \dfrac{\dfrac{y}{b^2} - \dfrac{b^4}{y^2}}{y - b^2}$.

II

In each of Exercises 1–6, prove that the limit exists and find it.

1. $\lim_{r\to 1} \dfrac{1 - r^3}{2 - \sqrt{r^2 + 3}}$.

2. $\lim_{t\to 2} \dfrac{\sqrt{1 + \sqrt{2+t}} - \sqrt{3}}{t - 2}$.

3. $\lim_{m\to 0} \dfrac{\sqrt{4 + m + m^2} - 2}{\sqrt{4 + m - m^2} - 2}$.

4. $\lim_{x\to 0} \dfrac{x}{\sqrt{9 - x + x^3} - 3}$.

5. $\lim_{p\to \infty} (\sqrt{1+p} - \sqrt{p})$.

6. $\lim_{n\to -\infty} \sqrt[3]{n^3 + n} - \sqrt[3]{n^3 + 1}$.

7. Show that if $\lim_{x\to a} g(x) = b$, with $g(x) \neq b$ for every x in some deleted neighborhood of a, and if $\lim_{x\to b} f(x) = c$, then $\lim_{x\to a} f(g(x)) = c$. (This theorem is sometimes useful if f is discontinuous at b. Compare this theorem with **4.26**.)

REVIEW

Oral Exercises

What is meant by each of Exercises 1–6?

1. $\lim_{x \to a} F(x) = b$.
2. $\lim_{x \to a^-} F(x) = c$.
3. $\lim_{x \to a} F(x) = -\infty$.
4. $\lim_{x \to -\infty} F(x) = d$.
5. A continuous function: (a) at a point, (b) in an interval.
6. A vertical asymptote; a horizontal asymptote.
7. If a limit of a function exists at some point, why must it be unique?
8. If $\lim_{x \to a} F(x) = b$, does $\lim_{x \to a} |F(x)| = |b|$? Give an example.
9. If $\lim_{x \to a} |F(x)| = b$, is $\lim_{x \to a} F(x)$ equal to either b or $-b$? Give an example.
10. If the function g is continuous at a and the function f is continuous at $g(a)$, is $f \circ g$ continuous at a?

I

In each of Exercises 1–4, prove that the limit exists by referring to the appropriate limit theorems and find it.

1. $\lim_{x \to -2} (1 + (x + 2)^2 + x)^3$.
2. $\lim_{x \to 2} \sqrt{2 + \sqrt{2 + x}}$.
3. $\lim_{y \to 3} \dfrac{y^2 - 2y - 3}{y^2 + y - 12}$.
4. $\lim_{r \to 25} \dfrac{5 - \sqrt{r}}{r - 25}$.

In each of Exercises 5–10, discuss the continuity of the function and sketch its graph.

5. $G(x) = \sqrt{x - a}$.
6. $G(x) = \dfrac{1}{\sqrt{x - a}}$.

(For Exercises 7–10, assume $b > a$.)

7. $H(x) = \sqrt{(x - a)(b - x)}$.
8. $H(x) = \sqrt{\dfrac{x - a}{b - x}}$.
9. $h(x) = \sqrt[3]{(x - a)(b - x)}$.
10. $h(x) = \sqrt[3]{\dfrac{x - a}{b - x}}$.
11. If $\lim_{x \to a} G(x) = b$ and $G(a)$ is undefined, how might $G(a)$ be defined so that G is continuous at a?

12. Prove that if F and G are continuous at a so is their sum, difference, and product. Is their quotient also continuous at a?

II

In each of Exercises 1–5, determine the limit.

1. $\displaystyle \operatorname*{limit}_{h\to 0} \frac{\sqrt[3]{(t+h)^2} - \sqrt[3]{t^2}}{h}.$

2. $\displaystyle \operatorname*{limit}_{x\to 27} \frac{\sqrt{1+\sqrt[3]{x}} - 2}{x - 27}.$

3. $\displaystyle \operatorname*{limit}_{m\to 0} \frac{\sqrt[3]{8+m^2+m^3} - \sqrt[3]{8+m}}{\sqrt[3]{8+m} - \sqrt[3]{8+m^2-m^3}}.$

4. $\displaystyle \operatorname*{limit}_{x\to 0} \frac{\sqrt[5]{1+x^5} - \sqrt[5]{1+x^2}}{\sqrt[5]{1-x^2} - \sqrt[5]{1-x}}.$

5. $\displaystyle \operatorname*{limit}_{t\to 0} \frac{\sqrt[5]{1+t^5} - \sqrt[3]{1+t^3}}{t^3}.$

6. Find

$$\operatorname*{limit}_{x\to\infty}\left[\operatorname*{limit}_{y\to\infty} \frac{ax^2+bxy+cy^2}{dx^2+exy+fy^2}\right] - \operatorname*{limit}_{y\to\infty}\left[\operatorname*{limit}_{x\to\infty} \frac{ax^2+bxy+cy^2}{dx^2+exy+fy^2}\right], \qquad (acdf \neq 0).$$

7. If $\lambda_{n+1} = \sqrt{2+\lambda_n}$, $(\lambda_0 = \sqrt{x})$, find

$$\operatorname*{limit}_{x\to 4} \frac{\lambda_r - 2}{x - 4}, \qquad (r = 1, 3).$$

8. If $a_{n+1} = (a_n + x)^{-1}$, $(a_0 = 0)$, $b_{n+1} = (b_n + y)^{-1}$, $(b_0 = 0)$, find

$$\operatorname*{limit}_{x\to y} \frac{a_n - b_n}{x^2 - y^2} \text{ for } n = 2, 3.$$

In each of Exercises 9–14, discuss the continuity of the function and sketch its graph.

9. $F(x) = x^3 - x.$

10. $F(x) = \dfrac{1}{x^3 - x}.$

11. $H(x) = \operatorname*{limit}_{n\to\infty} x^n.$

12. $H(x) = x - [x].$

13. $G(x) = [x] + \sqrt{x - [x]}.$

14. $G(x) = \sqrt{[x] - x}.$

5

DERIVATIVES

OUR FIRST APPLICATION of the limit concept will be to the problem of determining the instantaneous rate of change of a function. Geometrically, this problem is equivalent to that of finding a tangent line to the graph of the function. Both of these problems are solved by finding the derivative of the given function, as will be described in this chapter.

1 DEFINITIONS

Assume that a chemical reaction is taking place and that $f(t)$ designates the amount of a substance present t units of time after the reaction starts. Then the change in the amount of the substance from time t_1 to time t_2 is $f(t_2) - f(t_1)$, and the average rate of change of the amount per unit of time during the time interval $[t_1,t_2]$ is

$$\frac{f(t_2) - f(t_1)}{t_2 - t_1}.$$

It is natural to call

$$\lim_{t_1 \to t_2} \frac{f(t_2) - f(t_1)}{t_2 - t_1}$$

the instantaneous rate of change of the amount of the substance at time t_2. This number is the derivative of the function f at t_2, according to the following definition.

5.1 **DEFINITION.** The *derivative* of a function f is the function f' defined by

$$f'(a) = \lim_{x\to a}\frac{f(x) - f(a)}{x - a}.$$

The domain of f' is the set consisting of every number a at which the above limit exists.

Df is another common notation for the derivative of a function f;

$$Df(a) = \lim_{x\to a}\frac{f(x) - f(a)}{x - a}.$$

If $Df(a)$ exists, we say that the function f is *differentiable* at a.

If in the definition of the derivative we let $x - a = h$, so that $x = a + h$, then h is close to 0 when x is close to a. Hence it seems reasonable that also

5.1′
$$f'(a) = \lim_{h\to 0}\frac{f(a + h) - f(a)}{h}$$

at each number a in the domain of f'.

To prove **5.1′**, we have by the definition of $f'(a)$ that for every neighborhood N of $f'(a)$ there exists a deleted neighborhood $(a - \delta, a + \delta)$ of a such that

$$\frac{f(x) - f(a)}{x - a} \text{ is in } N \text{ for each } x \text{ in } (a - \delta, a + \delta), \qquad (x \neq a).$$

Letting $h = x - a$, we see that $\dfrac{f(a + h) - f(a)}{h}$ is in N for each h in $(-\delta,\delta)$, $(h \neq 0)$. This proves **5.1′**.

If for a function f and a number a we define the function g by

$$g(x) = \frac{f(x) - f(a)}{x - a},$$

then

$$f'(a) = \lim_{x\to a} g(x).$$

The function g gives the average rate of change of f from a to any other number x in the domain of f. We note that g is not continuous at a, since $g(a)$ is undefined. Hence we cannot evaluate $\lim_{x\to a} g(x)$ by replacing x by a in $g(x)$. The following examples show how to find the derivatives of some particular functions.

EXAMPLE 1. If $f(x) = x^2$, find the derivative f' of f.

Solution: By **5.1**,

$$f'(a) = \lim_{x\to a}\frac{x^2 - a^2}{x - a}.$$

Hence

$$f'(a) = \operatorname*{limit}_{x \to a} (x + a) = 2a.$$

Since the above limit exists at every number a, the domain of f' is the set of all real numbers.

EXAMPLE 2. If $g(x) = 1/x$, find the derivative g' of g.

Solution: By 5.1′,

$$g'(a) = \operatorname*{limit}_{h \to 0} \frac{\dfrac{1}{a+h} - \dfrac{1}{a}}{h}.$$

Hence

$$g'(a) = \operatorname*{limit}_{h \to 0} \frac{a - (a+h)}{ha(a+h)}$$

$$= \operatorname*{limit}_{h \to 0} \frac{-1}{a(a+h)}$$

$$= -\frac{1}{a^2}.$$

Evidently, the domain of g' is the set of all nonzero numbers, just as is the domain of g.

EXAMPLE 3. If $F(z) = \sqrt{z}$, find the derivative DF of F.

Solution: By 5.1,

$$DF(x) = \operatorname*{limit}_{z \to x} \frac{\sqrt{z} - \sqrt{x}}{z - x}.$$

Since $z - x = (\sqrt{z} - \sqrt{x})(\sqrt{z} + \sqrt{x})$, we see that

$$DF(x) = \operatorname*{limit}_{z \to x} \frac{1}{\sqrt{z} + \sqrt{x}} = \frac{1}{2\sqrt{x}}.$$

Clearly, the domain of DF is $(0, \infty)$, whereas the domain of F is $[0, \infty)$.

2 TANGENT LINES

One of the many applications of the derivative is to the problem of finding the tangent line to the graph of a function at some point on the graph.

It is possible to define the tangent line to a circle at a point P on the circle either as the line perpendicular to the radius at P or as the line intersecting the circle in only one point P. Neither of these definitions of a tangent line carries

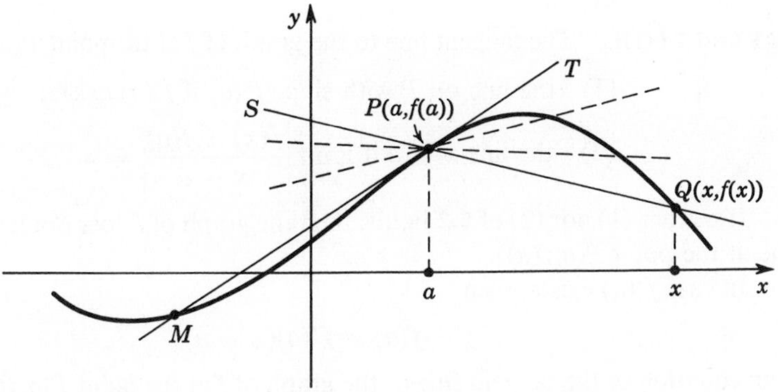

FIGURE 5.1

over to a general curve. In Figure 5.1, for example, the tangent line T at P intersects the curve in another point M.

The tangent line T at P to a curve such as that shown in Figure 5.1 should be the line on P that is nearest to the curve in the neighborhood of P. We interpret this to mean that each secant line S on P and some other point Q of the curve should be close to T when Q is close to P. The limiting position of the secant line S as Q approaches P should be the tangent line T.

These rather vague statements as to the nature of the tangent line to the graph of f at a point $P(a,f(a))$ can be made precise by the use of slopes. If $Q(x,f(x))$ is another point on the graph of f (Figure 5.1), then the slope $m(x)$ of the secant line S on P and Q is given by

$$m(x) = \frac{f(x) - f(a)}{x - a}.$$

The slope of the tangent line to the graph of f at the point $P(a,f(a))$ is now defined to be $\lim_{x \to a} m(x)$, if this limit exists. Since

$$\lim_{x \to a} m(x) = \lim_{x \to a} \frac{f(x) - f(a)}{x - a},$$

evidently the slope of the tangent line is $f'(a)$, the derivative of f evaluated at a.

If $\lim_{x \to a} m(x)$ does not exist in the ordinary sense, but

$$\lim_{x \to a} |m(x)| = \infty,$$

then the secant line S is getting steeper and steeper as x approaches a. In this case the tangent line to the graph of f at the point $P(a,f(a))$ appears to be the vertical line $x = a$.

These remarks lead us to the following definition.

5.2 DEFINITION. The tangent line to the graph of f at the point $P(a,f(a))$ is

(1) the line on P with slope $f'(a)$ if $f'(a)$ exists;

(2) the line $x = a$ if $\lim_{x \to a} \left| \frac{f(x) - f(a)}{x - a} \right| = \infty$.

If neither (1) nor (2) of **5.2** holds, then the graph of f does not have a tangent line at the point $P(a,f(a))$.

In case $f'(a)$ exists, then

5.3 $$y - f(a) = f'(a)(x - a)$$

is an equation of the tangent line to the graph of f at the point $P(a,f(a))$.

The *normal line* N to the graph of a function f at the point $P(a,f(a))$ is defined to be the line through P perpendicular to the tangent line. It follows that if $f'(a) \neq 0$ the slope of N is $-1/f'(a)$ and

5.4 $$y - f(a) = -\frac{1}{f'(a)}(x - a)$$

is an equation of N. If $f'(a) = 0$, then N is the vertical line $x = a$; and if the tangent line is vertical, then N is the horizontal line $y = f(a)$.

EXAMPLE 1. Find equations of the tangent line T and the normal line N to the graph of the function f defined by $f(x) = x^2$ at the point $P(2,4)$.

Solution: By Example 1, page 107, $f'(a) = 2a$. Therefore $f'(2) = 4$ and, by **5.3**,

$$y - 4 = 4(x - 2) \quad \text{or} \quad y = 4x - 4$$

is an equation of T. By **5.4**,

$$y - 4 = -\tfrac{1}{4}(x - 2) \quad \text{or} \quad x + 4y - 18 = 0$$

is an equation of N. The graph of f, T, and N are sketched in Figure 5.2.

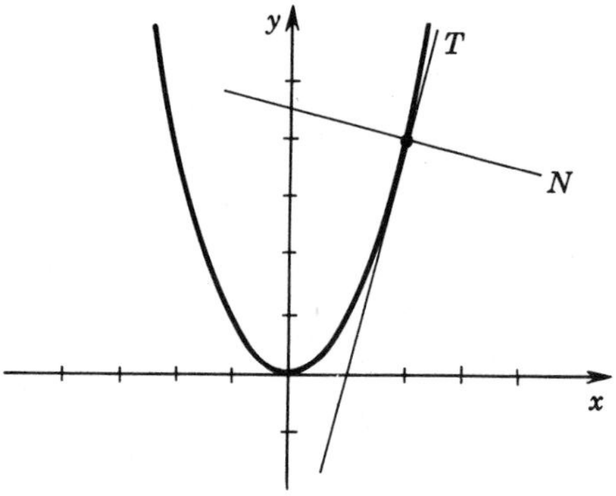

FIGURE 5.2

EXAMPLE 2. Find equations of the tangent line T and the normal line N to the graph of the function g defined by $g(x) = \sqrt{1+x}$ at the point $P(0,1)$.

Solution: By **5.1**,

$$g'(0) = \lim_{x\to 0} \frac{\sqrt{1+x} - \sqrt{1+0}}{x - 0} = \lim_{x\to 0} \frac{\sqrt{1+x} - 1}{x}.$$

Since $(\sqrt{1+x} - 1)(\sqrt{1+x} + 1) = x$, we have

$$g'(0) = \lim_{x\to 0} \frac{1}{\sqrt{1+x} + 1} = \frac{1}{2}.$$

Therefore, by **5.3**,

$$y - 1 = \tfrac{1}{2}(x - 0) \quad \text{or} \quad x - 2y + 2 = 0$$

is an equation of T, and

$$y - 1 = -2(x - 0) \quad \text{or} \quad 2x + y - 1 = 0$$

is an equation of N.

EXAMPLE 3. Find equations of the tangent line T and the normal line N to the graph of the function F defined by $F(x) = \sqrt[3]{x}$ at the origin.

Solution: We have, by **4.16**,

$$\lim_{x\to 0} \frac{F(x) - F(0)}{x - 0} = \lim_{x\to 0} \frac{\sqrt[3]{x}}{x} = \lim_{x\to 0} \frac{1}{x^{2/3}} = \infty.$$

Therefore T is the vertical line $x = 0$ and N is the horizontal line $y = 0$. In other words, T is the y axis and N is the x axis. The graph of F is shown in Figure 5.3.

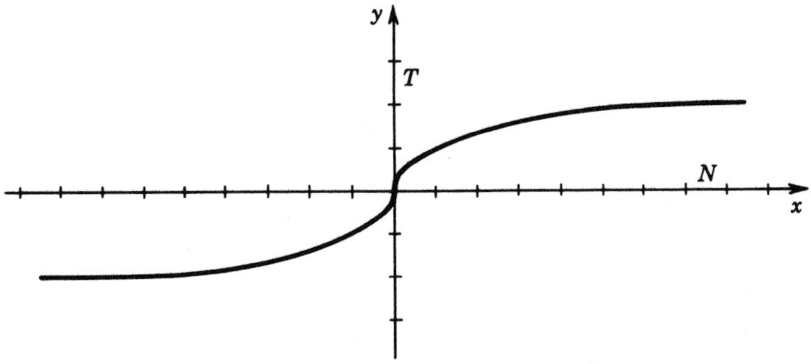

FIGURE 5.3

EXERCISES

I

In each of Exercises 1–6, find the derivative DF of the given function F.

1. $F(x) = 2x^2 - 3$.
2. $F(x) = x^3$.
3. $F(x) = (3x + 1)^3$.
4. $F(x) = x^{-2}$.
5. $F(x) = \sqrt{5x - 6}$.
6. $F(x) = 1/\sqrt{x}$.
7. If $F(x) = x^3 - 3x^2 + 3x$, find the slope of the tangent line to the graph of F at each of its points corresponding to $x = -1, 0, 1, 2, 3$. Sketch the graph of F and the tangent lines at each of the above points.

In each of Exercises 8–11, find equations for the tangent line and the normal line to the graph at the indicated point and sketch the graph and the two lines.

8. $f(x) = x^2 - 3x + 2$, $(-2,f(-2))$.
9. $G(x) = x^3 - 1$, $(1,G(1))$.
10. $g(x) = \sqrt{1 - 4x}$, $(-2,g(-2))$.
11. $F(x) = 1 - (x + 1)^{1/3}$, $(-1,F(-1))$.
12. Find the area of the triangle formed by the coordinate axes and the tangent line to the graph of $f(x) = x^2 - 9$ at the point $(2,-5)$.

II

1. If $DF(x) = G(x)$ and $H(x) = F(ax + b)$, show that $DH(x) = aG(ax + b)$.
2. Show that the graphs of the equations
$$y = 3x^2, \qquad y = 2x^3 + 1$$
are tangent at the point $(1,3)$, i.e., that they have a common tangent line at this point. Sketch the graphs.
3. Show that there are exactly two tangent lines to the graph of $y = (x + 1)^3$ which pass through the origin, and find their equations.
4. Show that $y_1y = 2p(x + x_1)$ is an equation of the tangent line to the parabola $y^2 = 4px$ at the point (x_1,y_1) on the parabola.
5. Show that the tangent lines at the ends of the latus rectum of a parabola are perpendicular and intersect on the directrix.
6. Show that the area of a triangle determined by three points on a given parabola is twice the area of the triangle determined by the tangents at these three points.

3 CONTINUITY OF A DIFFERENTIABLE FUNCTION

The condition that a function have a derivative is stronger than that of being continuous, as we shall now prove.

5.5 **THEOREM.** If the function f is differentiable at a, then f is continuous at a.

Proof: By assumption and by **5.1**, a is in the domain of f and

$$\lim_{x \to a} \frac{f(x) - f(a)}{x - a} = f'(a).$$

It is possible to write $f(x) - f(a)$ as a product in the following way:

$$f(x) - f(a) = \frac{f(x) - f(a)}{x - a} \cdot (x - a), \qquad (x \neq a).$$

Hence, by the product limit theorem,

$$\lim_{x \to a} [f(x) - f(a)] = \lim_{x \to a} \frac{f(x) - f(a)}{x - a} \cdot \lim_{x \to a} (x - a)$$

$$= f'(a) \cdot 0 = 0.$$

Thus

$$\lim_{x \to a} f(x) = f(a)$$

and the theorem is proved.

The converse of this theorem is not true. That is, there are functions continuous but not differentiable at some number. The example below illustrates this fact.

EXAMPLE. If f is the absolute-value function,

$$f(x) = |x|,$$

show that f is continuous but not differentiable at the number 0.

Solution: The graph of f, consisting of two half-lines meeting at the origin, is shown in Figure 5.4. By definition,

$$f(x) = x \text{ if } x \geq 0;$$

$$f(x) = -x \text{ if } x \leq 0.$$

Hence

$$\lim_{x \to 0^+} f(x) = \lim_{x \to 0^+} x = 0,$$

$$\lim_{x \to 0^-} f(x) = \lim_{x \to 0^-} (-x) = 0,$$

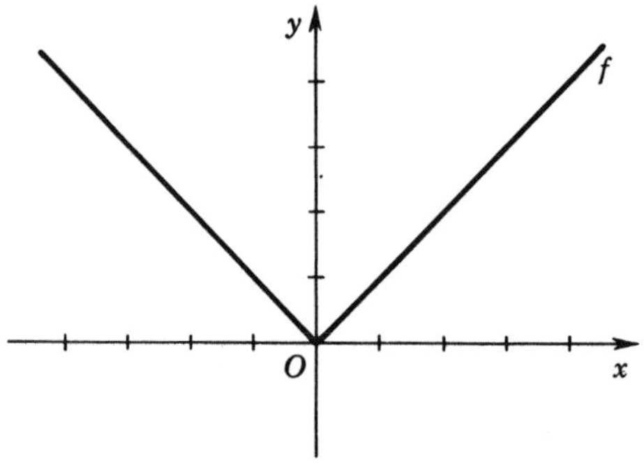

FIGURE 5.4

and therefore, by **4.14**,

$$\lim_{x\to 0} f(x) = 0.$$

Since $f(0) = 0$, this proves that f is continuous at 0.

In order to prove that f is not differentiable at 0, we must show that

$$\lim_{x\to 0} \frac{f(x) - f(0)}{x - 0} = \lim_{x\to 0} \frac{|x|}{x}$$

does not exist. We will do this by showing that the one-sided limits at 0 are different. Thus

$$\lim_{x\to 0^+} \frac{|x|}{x} = \lim_{x\to 0^+} \frac{x}{x} = \lim_{x\to 0^+} 1 = 1,$$

whereas

$$\lim_{x\to 0^-} \frac{|x|}{x} = \lim_{x\to 0^-} \frac{-x}{x} = \lim_{x\to 0^-} (-1) = -1.$$

Hence the derivative of f at 0 does not exist.

It is geometrically clear that the graph of f (Figure 5.4) has no tangent line at the origin O. For each secant line on O and a point P to the right of O has slope 1, whereas each secant line on O and a point P to the left of O has slope -1. Obviously, these slopes are not approaching some fixed number as P approaches O.

4 DIFFERENTIATION FORMULAS

If f is a constant function, say

$$f(x) = k$$

for every x in some interval A, then the derivative of f at a, $Df(a)$, is given by

$$Df(a) = \lim_{x\to a} \frac{k - k}{x - a} = \lim_{x\to a} 0 = 0.$$

Thus Df is the zero function with domain A, indicated as follows:

5.6 $$Dk = 0 \quad \text{for every constant function } k.$$

The linear function g defined by

$$g(x) = x$$

has derivative Dg given by

$$Dg(a) = \lim_{x \to a} \frac{x - a}{x - a} = \lim_{x \to a} 1 = 1.$$

We will often indicate this fact by writing

$$Dx = 1.$$

Let us call a function f defined by

$$f(x) = x^n \qquad (n \text{ a given real number}),$$

a *power function*. When $n = 1$, f is the linear function g discussed above. Other examples of power functions are the functions f, G, and F defined below.

$$f(x) = x^3, \quad G(x) = x^{-2} = \frac{1}{x^2}, \quad F(x) = x^{3/2} = \sqrt{x^3}.$$

The domain of f is the set of all real numbers; that of G the set of all non-zero numbers; that of F the interval $[0, \infty)$.

Before attempting to differentiate a power function, we mention the identity

5.7 $$u^n - v^n = (u - v)(u^{n-1} + u^{n-2}v + \cdots + uv^{n-2} + v^{n-1}),$$

which holds for every integer $n > 1$. Identity **5.7** may be verified by multiplying out the right side of the equation and observing that all terms in the identity cancel with the exception of the two on the left side. We note that the second factor on the right side of **5.7** is a sum of n terms.

The special cases of **5.7** for $n = 2$, 3, and 4 are listed below.

$$\begin{aligned} u^2 - v^2 &= (u - v)(u + v) \\ u^3 - v^3 &= (u - v)(u^2 + uv + v^2) \\ u^4 - v^4 &= (u - v)(u^3 + u^2v + uv^2 + v^3). \end{aligned}$$

If $f(x) = x^n$, (n an integer > 1), then

$$\begin{aligned} f'(a) &= \lim_{x \to a} \frac{x^n - a^n}{x - a} && \text{(by 5.1)} \\ &= \lim_{x \to a} (x^{n-1} + x^{n-2}a + \cdots + xa^{n-2} + a^{n-1}), && \text{(by 5.7).} \end{aligned}$$

By the continuity of the polynomial function, we have

$$f'(a) = a^{n-1} + a^{n-2}\cdot a + \cdots + a\cdot a^{n-2} + a^{n-1} = na^{n-1}.$$

We indicate this result as follows:

5.8 $$Dx^n = nx^{n-1}, \qquad (n \text{ a positive integer}).$$

Note that **5.8** is true if $n = 1$ by a previous result.

For example, we have immediately from **5.8** that

$$Dx^2 = 2x, \qquad Dx^7 = 7x^6, \qquad Dx^{29} = 29x^{28}.$$

That is, if f is the power function defined by $f(x) = x^{29}$, then the derivative of f is the function f' defined by $f'(x) = 29x^{28}$, and so on.

The derivative of a constant function k times a function f is easily computed as follows:

$$\begin{aligned} Dkf(a) &= \lim_{x\to a} \frac{kf(x) - kf(a)}{x - a} && \text{(by 5.1)} \\ &= \lim_{x\to a} k\left[\frac{f(x) - f(a)}{x - a}\right] \\ &= k \lim_{x\to a} \frac{f(x) - f(a)}{x - a} && \text{(by 4.22)} \\ &= kDf(a). \end{aligned}$$

That is,

5.9 $$D(kf) = k(Df) \quad \text{for any constant function } k.$$

For example, using **5.8** and **5.9**, we have

$$D7x^6 = 7\cdot 6x^5 = 42x^5, \quad D(-8x^3) = (-8)\cdot 3x^2 = -24x^2.$$

We will be able to find the derivative of any polynomial function as soon as we have a formula for finding the derivative of a sum of functions. Let us find the derivative of the sum of two functions:

$$\begin{aligned} D(f+g)(a) &= \lim_{x\to a} \frac{[f(x) + g(x)] - [f(a) + g(a)]}{x - a} \\ &= \lim_{x\to a} \left[\frac{f(x) - f(a)}{x - a} + \frac{g(x) - g(a)}{x - a}\right] \\ &= \lim_{x\to a} \frac{f(x) - f(a)}{x - a} + \lim_{x\to a} \frac{g(x) - g(a)}{x - a} \\ &= Df(a) + Dg(a). \end{aligned}$$

Thus we have proved that

5.10 $$D(f+g) = Df + Dg.$$

Of course, the domain of $D(f+g)$ is the intersection of the domains of Df and Dg.

Formulas 5.9 and 5.10 may be extended by mathematical induction to the following form:

5.11 $$D(k_1f_1 + k_2f_2 + \cdots + k_nf_n) = k_1Df_1 + k_2Df_2 + \cdots + k_nDf_n$$

for any constant functions $k_1, k_2, \cdots, k_n$ and any functions $f_1, f_2, \cdots, f_n$. For example,

$$\begin{aligned} D(4x^2 - 8x + 3) &= 4Dx^2 - 8Dx + D3 \\ &= 4\cdot 2x - 8\cdot 1 = 8x - 8. \end{aligned}$$

As another example,

$$\begin{aligned} D(x^6 - x^4 + \sqrt{3}x^3 + x - 7) &= Dx^6 - Dx^4 + \sqrt{3}Dx^3 + Dx - D7 \\ &= 6x^5 - 4x^3 + 3\sqrt{3}x^2 + 1. \end{aligned}$$

We are now able to find with ease the derivative f' of any polynomial function f. Note that the degree of f' is exactly one less than the degree of f.

5 PRODUCT AND QUOTIENT DIFFERENTIATION FORMULAS

The derivative of the product of two functions is not the product of the derivatives of the two functions, as one might suspect from the sum formula (5.10). The correct formula is derived below.

If f and g are functions, then

$$D(fg)(a) = \operatorname*{limit}_{x\to a} \frac{f(x)g(x) - f(a)g(a)}{x - a}$$

at every number a at which the above limit exists. The evaluation of this limit is not evident. We would like to separate the functions f and g, if possible, as in the proof of 5.10. The following device of adding and subtracting a term allows us to make such a separation.

$$\begin{aligned} \frac{f(x)g(x) - f(a)g(a)}{x - a} &= \frac{f(x)g(x) - f(x)g(a) + f(x)g(a) - f(a)g(a)}{x - a} \\ &= f(x)\frac{g(x) - g(a)}{x - a} + \frac{f(x) - f(a)}{x - a}g(a). \end{aligned}$$

Hence, by the limit theorems,

$$D(fg)(a) = \lim_{x\to a} f(x) \lim_{x\to a} \frac{g(x) - g(a)}{x - a} + g(a) \lim_{x\to a} \frac{f(x) - f(a)}{x - a}.$$

If $f'(a)$ and $g'(a)$ exist, then, by **5.5**, f is continuous at a, and we have

$$D(fg)(a) = f(a)g'(a) + g(a)f'(a).$$

We have proved the following *product differentiation formula.*

5.12 $$D(fg) = fDg + gDf.$$

The domain of $D(fg)$ is the intersection of the domains of Df and Dg.

The derivation of a formula for the derivative of the quotient of two functions is similar:

$$D\frac{f}{g}(a) = \lim_{x\to a} \frac{\dfrac{f(x)}{g(x)} - \dfrac{f(a)}{g(a)}}{x - a}$$

$$= \lim_{x\to a} \frac{1}{g(x)g(a)} \cdot \frac{f(x)g(a) - f(a)g(x)}{x - a}$$

$$= \frac{1}{g^2(a)} \lim_{x\to a} \frac{f(x)g(a) - f(a)g(a) + f(a)g(a) - f(a)g(x)}{x - a}$$

$$= \frac{1}{g^2(a)}\left[\lim_{x\to a} g(a)\frac{f(x) - f(a)}{x - a} - \lim_{x\to a} f(a)\frac{g(x) - g(a)}{x - a}\right]$$

$$= \frac{g(a)f'(a) - f(a)g'(a)}{g^2(a)}$$

This proves the following *quotient differentiation formula:*

5.13 $$D\left(\frac{f}{g}\right) = \frac{gDf - fDg}{g^2}$$

The domain of $D(f/g)$ is the intersection of the domains of f/g, Df, and Dg.

The quotient formula allows us to find the derivative of any rational function, as illustrated below.

EXAMPLE. If function F is defined by $F(x) = x^2/(x^2 - 4)$, find DF

Solution: The function F is a quotient of two polynomial functions, $F = f/g$ where $f(x) = x^2$ and $g(x) = x^2 - 4$. Hence, by **5.13**,

$$DF(x) = \frac{g(x)f'(x) - f(x)g'(x)}{g^2(x)}$$

$$= \frac{(x^2 - 4)\cdot 2x - x^2 \cdot 2x}{(x^2 - 4)^2} = \frac{-8x}{(x^2 - 4)^2}.$$

The domain of DF is the same as that of F, namely the set of all real numbers except 2 and -2.

We may use **5.13** to develop a formula for Dx^{-n}, (n a positive integer), as shown below.

$$Dx^{-n} = D\frac{1}{x^n} = \frac{x^n D1 - 1Dx^n}{(x^n)^2}$$

$$= \frac{x^n \cdot 0 - nx^{n-1}}{x^{2n}} = -nx^{-n-1}.$$

If we let $r = -n$, then we have proved that $Dx^r = rx^{r-1}$. This, together with **5.8**, proves the following formula:

5.14 $$Dx^r = rx^{r-1} \quad \text{for every integer } r.$$

For example,

$$Dx^{-2} = -2x^{-3}, \quad Dx^{-12} = -12x^{-13}, \quad Dx^0 = 0x^{-1} = 0.$$

EXERCISES

I

In each of Exercises 1–12, differentiate the function.

1. $f(x) = (x^2 + 3x - 1)(x^2 - 3x + 1)$.
2. $G(t) = (3t^2 + 1)^2$.
3. $F(z) = z^3(3z^2 - 7z + 5)$.
4. $g(y) = \dfrac{y^2}{y + 1}$.
5. $M(x) = \dfrac{x - 1}{x + 1}$.
6. $F(t) = (t^2 + 1)(t^4 + 1)(t^8 + 1)$.
7. $f(x) = \left(1 + \dfrac{2}{x}\right)\left(2 + \dfrac{1}{x}\right)$.
8. $G(x) = \left(x^2 - \dfrac{1}{x^2}\right)^2$.
9. $N(x) = \dfrac{x - 1}{x^2 - 2x + 2}$.
10. $F(z) = \dfrac{z^4 - 16}{z^4 + 16}$.

11. $H(x) = (x^n + 1)(x^{2n} - x^n + 1)$, ($n$ an integer).

12. $f(t) = \dfrac{\sqrt{t}}{\sqrt{t} + 1}$.

II

Find the derivative of each of the following functions and state the domain of each derivative.

1. $f(x) = |x^2 - 4|$.
2. $G(x) = |x^3 - 1|$.
3. $g(t) = (|t| - |t - 1|)^2$.
4. $h(y) = y^3|y - 1|$.
5. $F(x) = [x]$.
6. $G(x) = \begin{cases} x^2, & (x \geq 0) \\ -x^2, & (x < 0). \end{cases}$

7. Prove that if the functions f, g, and h are differentiable at x, then so is the function fgh and

$$D(fgh)(x) = fgDh(x) + fhDg(x) + ghDf(x).$$

Generalize this result to a product of n functions.

8. Use Exercise 7 to find:
   a. $D(2x + 1)(3x - 1)(x - 2)$.
   b. $D(3x - 2)^2(2x + 3)$.
   c. $D(7x + 1)^2(2x - 5)^2$.
   d. $Dx(x + 1)(x + 2)(x + 3)$.

9. For a given differentiable function f, what are Df^2 and Df^3? Generalize your result to Df^n, (n any positive integer).

6 THE CHAIN RULE

If f and g are functions, then the composite function $f \circ g$ was defined in Chapter 3 by $(f \circ g)(x) = f(g(x))$. For example, if

$$f(x) = x^{20}, \qquad g(x) = x^2 + 1,$$

then

$$(f \circ g)(x) = (x^2 + 1)^{20}.$$

The problem we now pose is to find the derivative of $f \circ g$, knowing the derivatives of f and g. By definition,

$$D(f \circ g)(a) = \operatorname*{limit}_{x \to a} \frac{f(g(x)) - f(g(a))}{x - a}.$$

If $g(x) \neq g(a)$ for every x in some deleted neighborhood of a, we have

$$D(f \circ g)(a) = \operatorname*{limit}_{x \to a} \frac{f(g(x)) - f(g(a))}{g(x) - g(a)} \cdot \frac{g(x) - g(a)}{x - a}.$$

Since

$$\lim_{z\to g(a)} \frac{f(z) - f(g(a))}{z - g(a)} = f'(g(a)),$$

it is intuitively clear that as x approaches a, $z = g(x)$ approaches $g(a)$ and

$$D(f\circ g)(a) = \lim_{z\to g(a)} \frac{f(z) - f(g(a))}{z - g(a)} \lim_{x\to a} \frac{g(x) - g(a)}{x - a}$$

$$= f'(g(a))g'(a).$$

This suggests the following differentiation formula.

5.15 $$D(f\circ g)(a) = Df(g(a)) \cdot Dg(a).$$

Another way of expressing this formula is:

5.15′ $$D(f\circ g) = [(Df)\circ g] \cdot Dg.$$

Formula **5.15** (or **5.15′**) is called the *chain rule*.

A more rigorous proof of **5.15** is as follows. Define the function G by

$$G(z) = \frac{f(z) - f(b)}{z - b} \quad \text{if} \quad z \neq b,$$

$$G(b) = f'(b).$$

Since

$$\lim_{z\to b} G(z) = \lim_{z\to b} \frac{f(z) - f(b)}{z - b} = f'(b)$$

and

$$G(b) = f'(b),$$

G is continuous at b. We note that

$$f(z) - f(b) = G(z)(z - b)$$

for every z in domain f. Thus, if we let $F(x) = f(g(x))$, $z = g(x)$, and $b = g(a)$, we have

$$\lim_{x\to a} \frac{F(x) - F(a)}{x - a} = \lim_{x\to a} \frac{G(g(x))(g(x) - g(a))}{x - a}$$

$$= \lim_{x\to a} G(g(x)) \lim_{x\to a} \frac{g(x) - g(a)}{x - a}$$

$$= f'(g(a))g'(a) \qquad \text{(by 4.26)}$$

that is, $F'(a) = f'(g(a))g'(a)$. This proves **5.15**.

EXAMPLE 1. Find $D(x^2 + 1)^{20}$.

Solution: If $F(x) = (x^2 + 1)^{20}$, then $F = f \circ g$ where $f(x) = x^{20}$ and $g(x) = x^2 + 1$, as we saw above. Hence

$$Df(x) = 20x^{19}, \qquad Dg(x) = 2x,$$

and, by the chain rule,

$$\begin{aligned} D(f \circ g)(x) &= Df(g(x)) \cdot Dg(x) \\ &= 20(x^2 + 1)^{19} \cdot 2x. \end{aligned}$$

Therefore $D(x^2 + 1)^{20} = 40x(x^2 + 1)^{19}$.

For any function f and any integer n, the function F defined by

$$F(x) = f^n(x)$$

is the composite $h \circ f$ where $h(x) = x^n$. Hence $Dh(x) = nx^{n-1}$ and

$$DF(x) = Dh(f(x)) \cdot Df(x) = n(f(x))^{n-1}Df(x).$$

This proves the following *power differentiation formula.*

5.16 $$Df^n = nf^{n-1}Df \quad \text{for every integer } n.$$

EXAMPLE 2. Find $D[1/(x^3 - 4x^2 + 1)^2]$.

Solution: Using negative exponents, we have, by **5.16**,

$$\begin{aligned} D(x^3 - 4x^2 + 1)^{-2} &= -2(x^3 - 4x^2 + 1)^{-2-1}D(x^3 - 4x^2 + 1) \\ &= -2(x^3 - 4x^2 + 1)^{-3}(3x^2 - 8x) \\ &= \frac{-6x^2 + 16x}{(x^3 - 4x^2 + 1)^3}. \end{aligned}$$

7 ALGEBRAIC FUNCTIONS

The nth root function

$$f(x) = \sqrt[n]{x}, \qquad (n \text{ an integer} > 1),$$

may be differentiated in much the same way that the nth power function was. By definition,

$$Df(a) = \lim_{x \to a} \frac{\sqrt[n]{x} - \sqrt[n]{a}}{x - a}.$$

If in **5.7** we let $u = \sqrt[n]{x}$ and $v = \sqrt[n]{a}$, then $(u - v)/(u^n - v^n) = 1/(u^{n-1} + u^{n-2}v + \cdots + uv^{n-2} + v^{n-1})$ and

$$Df(a) = \lim_{x \to a} \frac{1}{(\sqrt[n]{x})^{n-1} + (\sqrt[n]{x})^{n-2}\sqrt[n]{a} + \cdots + \sqrt[n]{x}(\sqrt[n]{a})^{n-2} + (\sqrt[n]{a})^{n-1}}.$$

Since $\lim_{x \to a} \sqrt[n]{x} = \sqrt[n]{a}$, the above limit is evaluated by use of the limit theorems to be

$$Df(a) = \frac{1}{n(\sqrt[n]{a})^{n-1}} = \frac{1}{n} a^{(1/n)-1}.$$

Thus **5.14**,

$$Dx^r = rx^{r-1},$$

holds for r the reciprocal of a positive integer as well as for r an integer.

We now easily find the derivative of the power function

$$g(x) = x^{m/n}, \qquad (m \text{ and } n \text{ integers}, n > 0).$$

If $n = 1$, then **5.14** holds. If $n > 1$, then

$$g = f \circ h, \qquad \text{and also } g = h \circ f, \qquad \text{where } f(x) = \sqrt[n]{x} \text{ and } h(x) = x^m.$$

Hence $Dg = (Df \circ h)Dh$ by the chain rule. Thus

$$Dg(x) = \frac{1}{n}(x^m)^{(1/n)-1} \cdot mx^{m-1}$$

$$= \frac{m}{n} x^{(m/n)-m} \cdot x^{m-1} = \frac{m}{n} x^{(m/n)-1}.$$

Hence **5.14** holds for every rational number r:

5.17 $$Dx^r = rx^{r-1}, \qquad (r \text{ any rational number}).$$

If $g(x) = x^r = x^{m/n}$ as above, then the domains A of g and B of Dg depend on m and n. *Case 1:* n odd. A is the set of all real numbers if $m \geq 0$ and the set of all real numbers excluding 0 if $m < 0$. B is the set of all real numbers if $m \geq n$ (> 0) and the set of all real numbers excluding 0 if $m < n$. *Case 2:* n even. $A = [0, \infty)$ if $m > 0$ and $A = (0, \infty)$ if $m < 0$. $B = [0, \infty)$ if $m > n$ and $B = (0, \infty)$ if $m < n$. That $Dg(0)$ does not exist if $0 < r < 1$ is demonstrated below. By definition,

$$Dg(0) = \lim_{x \to 0} \frac{x^r - 0}{x - 0}$$

if this limit exists. However, this limit does not exist, since, by **4.16**,

$$\lim_{x \to 0^+} \frac{x^r}{x} = \lim_{x \to 0^+} \frac{1}{x^{1-r}} = \infty.$$

Another proof of the power differentiation formula, one which shows that it is actually valid for any real number power r, is given in Chapter 10. Using **5.17** and the chain rule, we obtain the following general form of **5.16**:

5.18 $$Df^r = rf^{r-1}Df, \qquad (r \text{ any rational number}).$$

EXAMPLE 1. Find $D[x\sqrt{x^2+4}]$.

Solution: We first use the product formula **5.12** and then the power formula **5.18**:

$$\begin{aligned}D[x(x^2+4)^{1/2}] &= xD(x^2+4)^{1/2} + (x^2+4)^{1/2}Dx\\ &= x\cdot\frac{1}{2}(x^2+4)^{1/2-1}D(x^2+4) + (x^2+4)^{1/2}\cdot 1\\ &= \frac{x}{2}(x^2+4)^{-1/2}(2x) + (x^2+4)^{1/2}\\ &= \frac{x^2}{\sqrt{x^2+4}} + \sqrt{x^2+4} = \frac{2x^2+4}{\sqrt{x^2+4}}.\end{aligned}$$

EXAMPLE 2. Find equations of the tangent line T and the normal line N to the graph of the function F defined by

$$F(x) = \frac{x}{\sqrt[3]{2x-1}}$$

at the point $P(1,1)$.

Solution: We first find Df as follows:

$$\begin{aligned}DF(x) &= \frac{\sqrt[3]{2x-1}\cdot Dx - x\cdot D(2x-1)^{1/3}}{(\sqrt[3]{2x-1})^2}\\ &= \frac{\sqrt[3]{2x-1}\cdot 1 - x\cdot\frac{1}{3}\cdot(2x-1)^{-2/3}\cdot 2}{\sqrt[3]{(2x-1)^2}}.\end{aligned}$$

Hence $Df(1) = (1-\frac{2}{3})/1 = \frac{1}{3}$. Therefore T has equation

$$y - 1 = \tfrac{1}{3}(x-1) \qquad \text{or} \qquad x - 3y + 2 = 0,$$

and N has equation

$$y - 1 = -3(x-1) \qquad \text{or} \qquad 3x + y - 4 = 0.$$

EXERCISES

I

In each of Exercises 1–10, differentiate the function.

1. $f(x) = x\sqrt{1-x^2}$.
2. $h(z) = \sqrt{\dfrac{1-z}{1+z}}$.
3. $F(t) = (2t+t^2)^{3/2}$.
4. $G(x) = \dfrac{\sqrt{x^2+1}}{x+1}$.

5. $S(t) = \sqrt[3]{3t + 1}$.

6. $F(y) = \left(y - \frac{1}{y}\right)^{3/2}$.

7. $g(x) = \sqrt{1 + (1/x^2)}$.

8. $f(x) = (1 + \sqrt{x})\sqrt[3]{x^2 + x + 1}$.

9. $G(z) = \sqrt{2z} + \sqrt{z/2}$.

10. $H(x) = \dfrac{(x^3 + 1)^2\sqrt{1 + x^2}}{1 + \sqrt{x}}$.

In each of Exercises 11–16, find equations of the tangent line and the normal line to the graph of the equation at the indicated point.

11. $y = \sqrt{x + 1}$, (3,2).

12. $y = \dfrac{x}{\sqrt{7 - 3x}}$, $(-3, -\frac{3}{4})$.

13. $y = x\sqrt{x^2 + 1}$, (0,0).

14. $y = \dfrac{x}{\sqrt{5x + 1}}$, $(5, \frac{5}{6})$.

15. $y = \sqrt{2 + \sqrt{x}}$, (4,2).

16. $y = \sqrt[n]{x^n + 1}$, (0,1).

II

In each of Exercises 1–4, find the derivative of the given function.

1. $f(x) = \sqrt{x + \sqrt{x + \sqrt{x}}}$.

2. $f(x) = \sqrt{x + (x^2 + 1)^3}$.

3. $f(x) = \sqrt[3]{x + |x|}$.

4. $f(x) = [(x^2 + (2x + 1)^7 + 1)^3 + 1]^{1/3}$.

8 IMPLICIT DIFFERENTIATION

Most of the functions we have discussed so far have been *explicitly* defined by an algebraic equation. For example, the equation

$$y = x^3 + 1$$

defines a function f where $f(x) = x^3 + 1$. The graph of the function f is simply the graph of the given equation.

Not all functions are defined in such an explicit way. For example, an equation in x and y such as

$$x^3 - x = y^3 - y^2 + 24$$

is not easily solved for y in terms of x (or, for that matter, x in terms of y). However, there might exist a function f such that the equation

$$x^3 - x = f^3(x) - f^2(x) + 24$$

is true for every x in the domain of f. Such a function is said to be defined *implicitly* by the given equation.

The derivative of a function defined implicitly by an equation in x and y can often be found without explicitly solving the equation for y in terms of x. The process of finding a derivative in this case is called *implicit differentiation.* We illustrate this process in the following examples.

EXAMPLE 1. On the assumption that there is a differentiable function f defined implicitly by the equation

$$x^3 - x = f^3(x) - f^2(x) + 24,$$

find its derivative.

Solution: If we let functions F and G be defined by

$$F(x) = x^3 - x, \qquad G(x) = f^3(x) - f^2(x) + 24,$$

with domain of F = domain of G = domain of f, then $F = G$ by what is given. Hence $DF = DG$; i.e.,

$$D(x^3 - x) = D[f^3(x) - f^2(x) + 24]$$

and

$$3x^2 - 1 = 3f^2(x)Df(x) - 2f(x)Df(x).$$

Solving this equation for $Df(x)$, we get

$$Df(x) = \frac{3x^2 - 1}{3f^2(x) - 2f(x)}.$$

If, for example, we are given that (3,1) is a point on the graph of f, then

$$Df(3) = \frac{3 \cdot 3^2 - 1}{3 \cdot 1^2 - 2 \cdot 1} = 26.$$

Hence

$$y - 1 = 26(x - 3) \qquad \text{or} \qquad y = 26x - 77$$

is an equation of the tangent line to the graph of f at (3,1). This gives us an indication of the nature of the graph of f near (3,1); it must be a steep curve in the neighborhood of this point.

EXAMPLE 2. Two differentiable functions are defined by the equation

$$x^2 + y^2 = 16$$

of a circle, namely those defined by the equations

$$y = \sqrt{16 - x^2} \qquad \text{and} \qquad y = -\sqrt{16 - x^2}.$$

Find the derivative of each function.

Solution: If f designates either of these two functions, then

$$x^2 + f^2(x) = 16$$

for every x in $[-4,4]$, the domain of f. By implicit differentiation,

$$D(x^2 + f^2(x)) = D16,$$
$$2x + 2f(x)Df(x) = 0$$
$$Df(x) = -\frac{x}{f(x)}.$$

Note that -4 and 4 must be excluded from the domain of Df, since $f(-4) = f(4) = 0$. By the above formula for Df, we have

$$D\sqrt{16 - x^2} = -\frac{x}{\sqrt{16 - x^2}} \quad \text{and} \quad D(-\sqrt{16 - x^2}) = \frac{x}{\sqrt{16 - x^2}}.$$

Example 2 illustrates the fact that implicit differentiation gives the derivative of every differentiable function defined by the given equation.

9 HIGHER DERIVATIVES

If f' is the derivative of the function f, then f' is called the *first derivative* of f. The derivative of the function f' is designated by f'' and is called the *second derivative* of f. Similarly, the derivative f''' of f'' is called the *third derivative* of f, and so on. In general, the nth derivative of f is designated by $f^{[n]}$ in order to distinguish it from the nth power f^n of f.

In terms of the D notation for the derivative, the first, second, third, and, in general, the nth derivatives of a function f are designated by Df, D^2f, D^3f, and, in general, D^nf, respectively.

If f is a polynomial function of degree $n > 0$, then D^nf is a constant function and $D^{n+1}f = 0$. In particular,

$$D^nx^n = n!$$

where $n!$ (read *n factorial*) is defined by

$$n! = n\cdot(n-1)\cdot(n-2)\cdot \cdots \cdot 2\cdot 1.$$

For example,

$$Dx^4 = 4x^3$$
$$D^2x^4 = D4x^3 = 4\cdot 3x^2$$
$$D^3x^4 = D(4\cdot 3x^2) = 4\cdot 3\cdot 2x$$
$$D^4x^4 = D(4\cdot 3\cdot 2x) = 4\cdot 3\cdot 2\cdot 1.$$

Thus $D^4x^4 = 4!$, or 24.

Conversely, we shall show in Chapter 6 that if f is a function such that $f^{[n]} = 0$ for some positive integer n then f is a polynomial function.

EXERCISES

I

In each of Exercises 1–4, use implicit differentiation to find the first and second derivative at the indicated point of each differentiable function f [letting $y = f(x)$] defined by the equation.

1. $\sqrt{x} + \sqrt{y} = 3$, (1,4).
2. $x^2 + y^2 = 25$, (4,3).
3. $x^3 + 3xy + y^2 = 5$, (1,1).
4. $\dfrac{y^2}{x + y} = 1 - x^2$, (1,0).

In each of Exercises 5–8, find f' and f'' for each differentiable function f [letting $y = f(x)$] defined by the equation:

5. $x = \dfrac{y^5 + y + 1}{y^2 + y + 1}$.
6. $y + \sqrt{xy} = x^2$.
7. $x = \dfrac{1 - \sqrt{y}}{1 + \sqrt{y}}$.
8. $x^2y^2 + xy = 2$.

Find an equation of the tangent line, at the indicated point, to the graph of each of the following equations:

9. $xy = 4$, $(-2,-2)$.
10. $x + x^2y^2 - y = 1$, (1,1).
11. $x^2 + xy + y^2 = 3$, (1,1).
12. $x^3 + y^3 = 6xy$, (3,3).
13. Give a geometric explanation for the results in Exercises 9, 11, 12.

II

Find f''' for each differentiable function f [letting $y = f(x)$] defined by the equation:

1. $x^3 - 3xy + y^3 = -1$.
2. $x^m + y^m = 2a^m$.

Find the nth derivatives of the following functions:

3. $f(t) = at^{2n}$ (n an integer).
4. $f(t) = at^m$ (m-rational).
5. $g(x) = (ax + b)^{-1}$.
6. $g(x) = (x^2 - a^2)^{-1}$.

10 A WORD ON NOTATION

Present-day symbolism in the calculus has evolved from the work of many mathematicians over the past three centuries. The notation f', f'', and f''' for derivatives of a function f, for example, is credited to the great eighteenth-century French mathematician Lagrange. However, the greatest inventor of symbolism for the calculus was Leibnitz, one of the founders of the subject. His contributions to this facet of the calculus date back as early as 1675. Let us devote some time to a description of his notation.

Given a function f and an equation of the form

$$y = f(x),$$

let

$$\Delta y = f(x) - f(a), \qquad \Delta x = x - a.$$

We think of Δy (delta y) as the *change in y* caused by a *change in x*, Δx. Clearly, Δy depends on the function f and on the number a also, but f and a are to stay the same throughout the present discussion. For this reason $\Delta y[= f(\Delta x + a) - f(a)]$ depends on Δx alone for its value. The derivative of f at a was denoted by dy/dx by Leibnitz; thus

$$\frac{dy}{dx} = \operatorname*{limit}_{\Delta x \to 0} \frac{\Delta y}{\Delta x}.$$

One can think of dy/dx as "the derivative of y with respect to x". It should be evident that

$$\operatorname*{limit}_{\Delta x \to 0} \frac{\Delta y}{\Delta x} = \operatorname*{limit}_{h \to 0} \frac{f(a + h) - f(a)}{h}.$$

In the notation of Leibnitz, if

$$y = x^3 - 5x^2 + 1, \quad \text{then } \frac{dy}{dx} = 3x^2 - 10x.$$

If the notation dy/dx is used for the first derivative of a function, then the second, third, and higher derivatives of the function are denoted as follows:

$$f'(x) = \frac{dy}{dx}, \quad f''(x) = \frac{d^2y}{dx^2}, \quad f'''(x) = \frac{d^3y}{dx^3}, \quad \ldots, \quad f^{[n]}(x) = \frac{d^ny}{dx^n}.$$

In the notation of Leibnitz, the sum and product formulas can be written as follows:

$$\frac{d}{dx}(u + v) = \frac{du}{dx} + \frac{dv}{dx}, \quad \frac{d}{dx}(uv) = u\frac{dv}{dx} + v\frac{du}{dx},$$

where $u = f(x)$ and $v = g(x)$ for some functions f and g. The chain rule has a particularly simple form in this notation: if

$$y = f(z) \quad \text{and} \quad z = g(x) \qquad [\text{so that } y = (f \circ g)(x)]$$

then

$$\frac{dy}{dx} = \frac{dy}{dz}\frac{dz}{dx} \qquad \left[\frac{dy}{dz} = f'(g(x)), \quad \frac{dz}{dx} = g'(x)\right].$$

For example, if

$$y = z^4 - 3z \qquad \text{and} \qquad z = x^5 + 1,$$

then

$$\frac{dy}{dx} = (4z^3 - 3)(5x^4).$$

We can express dy/dx in terms of x alone by replacing z by $x^5 + 1$.

The other founder of the calculus, Newton, used a completely different notation. His derivatives (which he called *fluxions*) were designated by $\dot{y}$ and $\ddot{y}$, in place of dy/dx and d^2y/dx^2. This notation is still used today, primarily to show derivatives with respect to time [i.e., if $y = f(t)$ where t designates time, then $\dot{y} = f'(t)$].

It is undoubtedly true that Leibnitz thought of dx and dy as "changes" in the variables x and y, and of the derivative as the ratio dy/dx when the changes dx and dy became infinitely small. The modern theory of limits was unknown to him.

The quantities dx and dy introduced by Leibnitz are called *differentials*. If f is a function and a is a number, and

$$y = f(x),$$

then dx is taken to be a variable and dy is defined by

$$dy = f'(a)\,dx.$$

Thus dy is a function of two variables, a and dx, for any given function f.

For example, if $y = x^2 + 1$, then $f'(x) = 2x$ and

$$dy = (2a)\,dx.$$

Also, if $a = 3$, then

$$dy = 6\,dx.$$

Returning to the delta notation, we recall that

$$f'(a) = \operatorname*{limit}_{\Delta x \to 0} \frac{\Delta y}{\Delta x},$$

where $\Delta y = f(x) - f(a)$ and $\Delta x = x - a$ [or Δx is a variable and $\Delta y = f(a + \Delta x) - f(a)$]. Therefore

$$\operatorname*{limit}_{\Delta x \to 0} \frac{\Delta y - f'(a)\,\Delta x}{\Delta x} = 0$$

and

$$\Delta y \doteq f'(a)\,\Delta x$$

($\doteq$ means "is approximately equal to"), with the error small in comparison to Δx when Δx is close to 0. If we let $\Delta x = dx$, then we see that

$$\Delta y \doteq dy \quad \text{when } dx \text{ is close to } 0.$$

The relationship between dy and Δy is indicated geometrically in Figure 5.5.

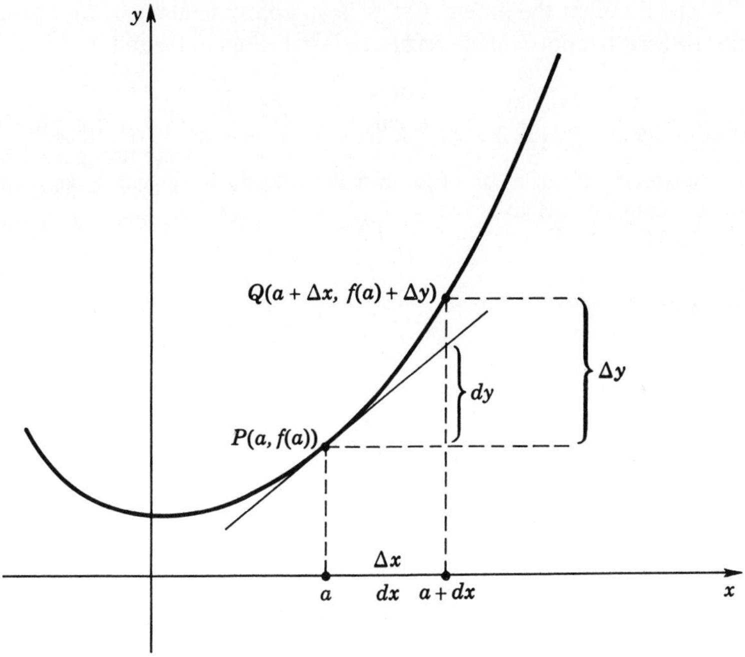

FIGURE 5.5

Thus Δy is the actual difference in ordinates between points P and Q, whereas dy is the rise (or fall) in the tangent line at P when x changes from a to $a + dx$.

For example, if

$$y = x^2 + 1 \qquad \text{and} \qquad a = 3$$

as in the notation above, then

$$\Delta y = (3 + \Delta x)^2 + 1 - (3^2 + 1) = 6\,\Delta x + (\Delta x)^2.$$

Letting $\Delta x = dx$, we have

$$\Delta y = 6\,dx + (dx)^2.$$

On the other hand,

$$dy = f'(3)\,dx = 6\,dx.$$

Note that $\Delta y \doteq dy$, with $\Delta y - dy = (dx)^2$, if dx is small. For example,

$$\begin{aligned}&\text{if } dx = .1, \;\; \Delta y = .61 \text{ and } dy = .6;\\ &\text{if } dx = .01, \Delta y = .0601 \text{ and } dy = .06.\end{aligned}$$

The fact that the differential dy is an approximation of Δy when dx is small may be used to approximate errors, as is indicated in the following example.

EXAMPLE. A box in the form of a cube has an edge of length $x = 4$ in. with a possible error of .05 in. What is the possible error in the volume, V, of the box?

Solution: If the length of the edge is changed from x to $x + dx$, then the change in the volume, ΔV, is given by

$$\Delta V = (x + dx)^3 - x^3.$$

By our results above, $\Delta V \doteq dV$, where $V = x^3$, $V' = 3x^2$, and

$$dV = 3x^2\, dx.$$

If we let $x = 4$ and $dx = \pm .05$, then

$$dV = 3 \cdot 16 \cdot (\pm .05) = \pm 2.4.$$

Hence the possible error in the volume is approximately ± 2.4 in.^{3}

The superiority of Lagrange's notation over that of Leibnitz is that it indicates the basic fact that the derivative of a function f is another function f'. The notation of Leibnitz for the derivative, dy/dx, focuses our attention on the definition of the derivative of a function at a particular value of x. It makes us tend to lose sight of the fact that the derivative is again a function.

REVIEW

Oral Exercises

1. What is a derivative?
2. How would you define the speed of a moving particle?
3. What are tangent and normal lines to a curve?
4. Why must a function which is differentiable at a number be continuous at that number?
5. If a function is everywhere continuous in an interval $[a,b]$, must it have a derivative at some point in the interval?

6. Why is differentiation a linear operator, i.e., why is $D[aF(x) + bG(x)] = aDF(x) + bDG(x)$?

7. What are the product and quotient rules for differentiation?

8. What is the chain rule?

9. What is an algebraic function?

10. What is implicit differentiation?

I

In each of exercises 1–4, find the derivative G' of the given function G.

1. $G(t) = t^{2/7} - 3t^{-7/2}$.

2. $G(t) = \sqrt{1 + |t|}$.

3. $G(t) = \sqrt{t^3}(t^{-2} - 2t^{-1} + 1)^3$.

4. $G(t) = \dfrac{\sqrt[3]{t}}{\sqrt[3]{t} + t}$.

5. At what points is the slope of the tangent line to the curve $y = x^3$ equal to 12?

6. Determine the slope of the tangent line to the circle $(x - 1)^2 + (y + 3)^2 = 17$ at the point (2,1).

7. At what points of the curve $y = x^3 + x - 2$ is the tangent line parallel to the line $y = 4x - 1$?

8. If $F(x) = kx^2$, show that the tangent line to the graph of F at the point $(c,F(c))$ is parallel to the secant line on the points $(a,F(a))$ and $(b,F(b))$ if and only if $c = (a + b)/2$.

9. Find f', f'', and f''' for each differentiable function f [letting $y = f(x)$] defined by $x = y^5 + y + 1$.

10. Discuss the continuity and differentiability of the function $f(x) = |x|^3$ at $x = 0$.

11. Show that the method of approximation of differentials is equivalent to writing

$$F(x + \Delta x) \doteq F(x) + F'(x)\,\Delta x.$$

The goodness of this approximation will depend on how small Δx is. Approximate $\sqrt[3]{1001}$ by letting $F(x) = \sqrt[3]{x}$, $(x = 1000, \Delta x = 1)$. How accurate is your answer?

12. Approximate:
    a. $\sqrt[3]{996}$
    b. $\sqrt{99}$.

13. If $y = F(x)$, $x = G(z)$, and $z = H(t)$, find an expression for dy/dt, assuming differentiability of all functions involved.

II

1. How many tangent lines can be drawn to a given parabola from a given point? Prove your answer.

2. Determine equations of the common tangent line and common normal line to:

$$x^2 + y^2 = 2ax \text{ and } y^2 = 2ax.$$

3. Prove the focusing property of parabolas, i.e., all rays which come in parallel to the axis and are reflected such that the angle of incidence equals the angle of reflection pass through the focus. It will be a subsequent problem to show this is the only smooth curve having this property. Give some applications of this property.

4. Let L be the tangent line at an arbitrary point A of a parabola. If F is the focus of the parabola and B is the point of intersection of L and the directrix, prove that the lines AF and BF are perpendicular.

5. Let L be the tangent line at a point A other than the vertex of a parabola, K the tangent line at the vertex, and F the focus of the parabola. If B is the point of intersection of K and L, prove that the lines AB and BF are perpendicular.

6. Establish Leibnitz's formula for the nth derivative of a product,

$$D^n f(x)g(x) = \sum_{i=0}^{n} \binom{n}{i} f^{(i)}(x)g^{(n-i)}(x),$$

[the $\binom{n}{i}$ are binomial coefficients], e.g.,

$$D^3 fg = fg''' + 3f'g'' + 3f''g' + f'''g.$$

7. Find the nth derivative of $(x^2 + a^2)^{-1}$.

8. Given that the functions S and C satisfy the following derivative equations (differential equations):

$$DS = C, \qquad DC = -S.$$

Prove that $D[C^2 + S^2] = 0$.

9. Given functions F, G, and H satisfying

$$F' = G, \qquad G' = H, \qquad \text{and} \qquad H' = F.$$

Prove that

a. $D(F + G + H) = F + G + H$.
b. $D(F^3 + G^3 + H^3 - 3FGH) = 0$.

10. Show that the derivative of an even function is an odd function and vice versa.

11. One application of tangent lines is Newton's method for approximating the real roots of an arbitrary equation $F(x) = 0$(F, however, must be differentiable). The method consists of first making an initial approximation x_0 (sufficiently close) to

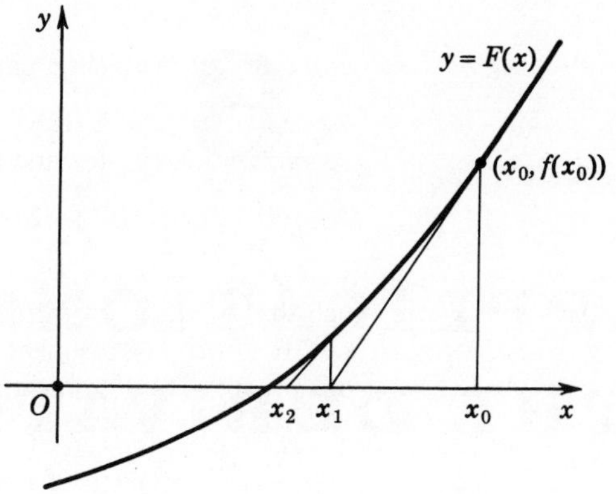

the root to be approximated. For a "better" approximation, a tangent line is drawn to the graph of $y = F(x)$ at the point $(x_0, F(x_0))$. The x intercept of this tangent line is the "better" approximation x_1. Starting at x_1, this process is repeated again and is continued until the desired degree of accuracy is obtained. If the initial approximation is too coarse (not sufficiently close), the successive approximations could progressively get worse each time. One should avoid starting at a point which is close to a local maximum or minimum value of the function.

Show that two successive approximations are related by (difference equation)

$$x_{n+1} = x_n - \frac{F(x_n)}{F'(x_n)}, \qquad (n = 0, 1, 2, 3, \cdots).$$

12. Use Exercise 11 to approximate to $\sqrt[3]{1001}$, correct to four decimal places. How is this method related to that in Exercise 11, Review I?

13. Show that if we use Newton's method on the function

$$F(x) = \begin{cases} \sqrt{x}, & (x \geq 0) \\ -\sqrt{-x}, & (x < 0) \end{cases}$$

then $x_0 = -x_1 = x_2 = -x_3 = \cdots$. This is a pathological case.

6

APPLICATIONS OF THE DERIVATIVE

WE HAVE ALREADY DISCUSSED one application of the derivative, namely, to the problem of finding tangent lines to the graph of a function.

One of the most useful and interesting applications of the derivative is to aid in the determination of the maximum and minimum values of a function. Many practical problems seeking the "best" way to do something can be formulated as problems to find maximum or minimum values of a function. Much of this chapter is devoted to the study of maxima and minima.

When a derivative is thought of as the instantaneous rate of change of a function, many physical applications of the derivative present themselves. The most obvious application of the derivative of this type is that of finding the velocity and acceleration of a moving object. This is discussed toward the end of the present chapter.

1 EXTREMA OF A FUNCTION

If f is a function and A is a set of numbers contained in the domain of f, then a number k in the range of f is called the *maximum value of f in A* if $f(x) \leq k$ for every x in A and, furthermore, if $f(c) = k$ for some c in A. The minimum value of a function in a set is defined similarly. When $f(c)$ is a maximum (or minimum) value of f in set A and when B is a subset of A containing c, then clearly $f(c)$ is also a maximum (or minimum) value of f in B.

For example, if

$$f(x) = x^2 + 1 \quad \text{and} \quad A = [-1,2],$$

then $f(2) = 5$ is the maximum value of f in A and $f(0) = 1$ is the minimum value of f in A.

A function need not have a maximum or minimum value in a set. For example, if $g(x) = 1/x$, then g does not have a maximum value in $(0,1]$. It does have a minimum value $g(1) = 1$ in $(0,1]$. Evidently, g has neither a maximum nor a minimum value in $(0, \infty)$.

The following basic theorem is given here without proof. Its proof is to be found in **8.3**, after a more detailed analysis of the real number system has been carried out.

6.1 THEOREM. If a function f is continuous in a closed interval I, then f has both a maximum value and a minimum value in I.

The example above, $f(x) = x^2 + 1$, illustrates this theorem. Thus f is continuous in the closed interval $[-1,2]$, and $f(2) = 5$ is the maximum value and $f(0) = 1$ is the minimum value of f in $[-1,2]$.

The word *extremum* is used for a maximum or minimum value of a function in a set. Thus to say that $f(c)$ is an extremum of a function f in a set A is to say that $f(c)$ is either a maximum value or a minimum value of f in A.

If a function f is continuous in a neighborhood of c and if $f(c)$ exists and is nonzero, then $f(c)$ is not an extremum of f. To prove this if $f'(c) > 0$, we note that, since

$$\lim_{x \to c} \frac{f(x) - f(c)}{x - c} > 0,$$

there exists a neighborhood N of c by 4.6 such that

$$\frac{f(x) - f(c)}{x - c} > 0 \qquad \text{for every } x \text{ in } N,\ x \neq c.$$

Hence $f(x) - f(c)$ and $x - c$ have the same sign in N; that is, for every x in N, $f(x) < f(c)$ if $x < c$ and $f(x) > f(c)$ if $x > c$. Thus, $f(c)$ is neither a maximum value nor a minimum value of f in N or in any other neighborhood of c. A similar proof holds if $f'(c) < 0$. These remarks may be stated as follows.

6.2 THEOREM. If $f(c)$ is an extremum of a function f in some neighborhood of c, then either $f'(c) = 0$ or $f'(c)$ does not exist.

It is convenient to call a number c in the domain of f a *critical number of f* if either $f'(c) = 0$ or $f'(c)$ does not exist. By **6.2**, if $f(c)$ is an extremum of a continuous function f in a closed interval $[a,b]$ and if $a < c < b$, then necessarily either $f'(c) = 0$ or $f'(c)$ does not exist.

It is not true, however, that if c is a critical number of f then $f(c)$ is an extremum of f in some neighborhood of c. For example, if $f(x) = x^3$, then $f'(x) = 3x^2$ and 0 is a critical number of f. If N is any neighborhood of 0, then $f(0) = 0$ and $f(x) < 0$ if $x < 0$, $f(x) > 0$ if $x > 0$ for every x in N. Thus $f(0)$ is not an extremum of f in N.

If the derivative of a continuous function has both positive and negative values in an interval, then necessarily the function has a critical number in the interval. Specifically, we have the following result.

6.3 THEOREM. If a function f is continuous in an interval I and if $f'(a) > 0$, $f'(b) < 0$ for some a, b in I, then f has a critical number in I.

To prove **6.3** assume that $a < b$ and then select c in $[a,b]$ so that $f(c)$ is the maximum value of f in $[a,b]$. Do you see why c cannot equal a or b? Then c is a critical number by **6.2**.

EXAMPLE. Show that the function f defined by

$$f(x) = x^4 - 2x^3 + 3x - 1$$

has a critical number in the interval $(-1,2)$.

Solution: We have

$$f'(x) = 4x^3 - 6x^2 + 3$$

and $f'(-1) = -7$, $f'(2) = 11$. Since f clearly is continuous in $[-1,2]$, f has, by **6.3**, a critical number c in $(-1,2)$. Evidently, $f'(c) = 0$. Thus c is a root of the equation $4x^3 - 6x^2 + 3 = 0$.

6.4 ROLLE'S THEOREM.* If f is a continuous function in the closed interval $[a,b]$ and if $f(a) = f(b)$, then f has at least one critical number in the open interval (a,b).

Proof: If $f(x) = f(a)$ for every x in $[a,b]$, then f is a constant function and $f'(x) = 0$. Hence every x in (a,b) is a critical number. If $f(x) \neq f(a)$ for some x in (a,b), then either the maximum value [if $f(x) > f(a)$] or the minimum value

* Michel Rolle (1652–1719) was a French mathematician principally known for his book, *Traite d'algebre*, published in 1690.

[if $f(x) < f(a)$] of f occurs at a number c in (a,b). The number c is, by **6.2**, a critical number of f.

To illustrate Rolle's theorem, consider

$$f(x) = 4 - x^2$$

(Figure 6.1). Since $f(-2) = 0$ and $f(2) = 0$, f has a critical number between -2 and 2. We know that 0 is such a critical number.

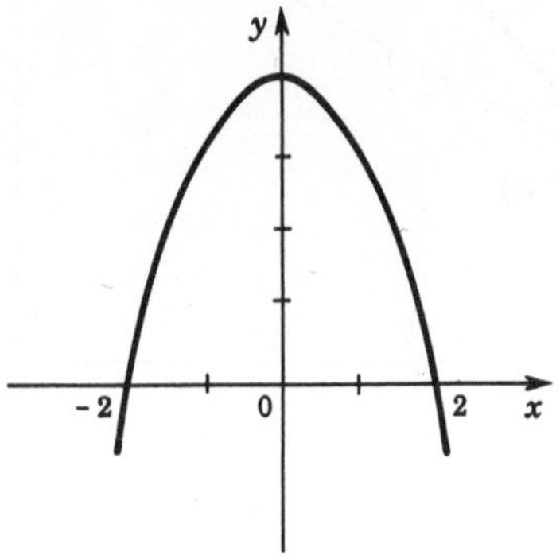

FIGURE 6.1

If

$$f(x) = |x|,$$

then $f(-1) = 1$ and $f(1) = 1$. Hence, by Rolle's theorem, f has a critical number between -1 and 1. Such a number is 0, since $f'(0)$ does not exist.

If f is a continuous function in the closed interval $[a,b]$, if $f(a) = f(b)$, and if f' exists in the open interval (a,b), then $f'(c) = 0$ for some c in (a,b) by Rolle's theorem. Therefore the tangent line to the graph of f at $(c,f(c))$ is horizontal; i.e., the tangent line is parallel to the line on the points $(a,f(a)$ and $(b,f(b))$.

We might expect a similar geometric result to hold even if $f(a) \neq f(b)$. That is, if f is continuous in $[a,b]$ and f' exists in (a,b), then perhaps there exists a number c in (a,b) such that the tangent line T to the graph of f at $(c,f(c))$ is parallel to the secant line S on the points $(a,f(a))$ and $(b,f(b))$ (Figure 6.2.). If this is so, then the slopes of these two lines must be equal; i.e.,

$$f'(c) = \frac{f(b) - f(a)}{b - a}.$$

That such is actually the case is the gist of the basic theorem that is given below.

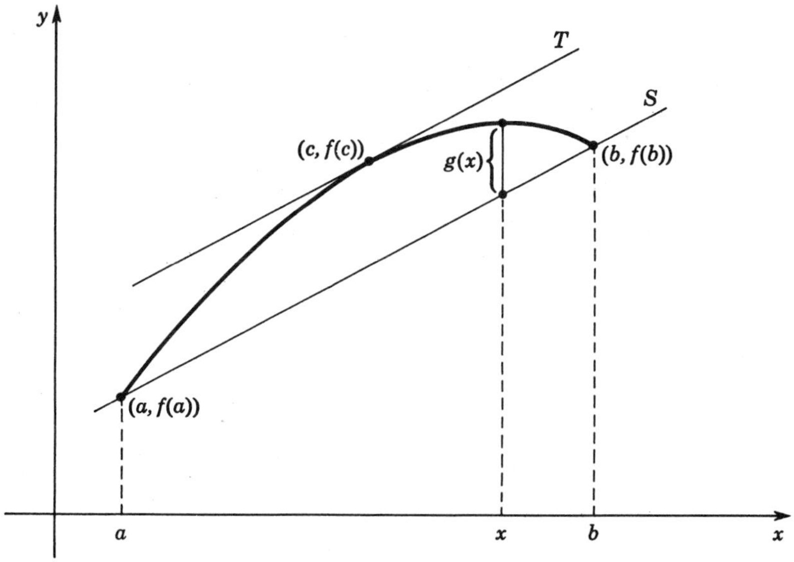

FIGURE 6.2

6.5 **MEAN VALUE THEOREM.** If f is a continuous function in a closed interval $[a,b]$ and if f' contains the open interval (a,b) in its domain, then there exists a number c in (a,b) such that

$$f(b) - f(a) = (b - a)f'(c).$$

Proof: Let S be the secant line of the graph of f passing through the points $(a,f(a))$ and $(b,f(b))$, as shown in Figure 6.2. Evidently,

$$y = m(x - a) + f(a), \qquad \text{where } m = \frac{f(b) - f(a)}{b - a},$$

is an equation of S. For each number x in $[a,b]$ let $g(x)$ be the directed distance from line S to the graph of f, measured parallel to the y axis (Figure 6.2). Clearly,

$$g(x) = f(x) - [m(x - a) + f(a)]$$

for every x in $[a,b]$, and $g(a) = g(b) = 0$. Since g is continuous in $[a,b]$ and g' exists in (a,b), we may apply Rolle's theorem to the function g to conclude that $g'(c) = 0$ for some c in (a,b). We have

$$g'(x) = f'(x) - m \qquad \text{for every } x \text{ in } (a,b),$$

and therefore

$$g'(c) = f'(c) - m = 0$$

for some c in (a,b). Thus

$$f'(c) = m = \frac{f(b) - f(a)}{b - a}$$

and

$$f(b) - f(a) = (b - a)f'(c).$$

This proves the theorem.

EXERCISES

I

In each of Exercises 1–12, find the extrema and sketch the graph of the given function in the given interval.

1. $f(x) = 4 - x$, $[-2,4]$.
2. $g(x) = x^{-1}$, $[-2,-1]$.
3. $F(x) = \sqrt{x - 2}$, $[2, \infty)$.
4. $G(x) = x^2 - 2x + 2$, $(-\infty, \infty)$.
5. $F(x) = 3 - 5x - x^2$, $[-3,0]$.
6. $G(z) = 2z^3 + 3z - 1$, $[-3,3]$.
7. $f(x) = x^3 + x^2 + x - 4$, $[-1,1]$.
8. $g(x) = x^4 - x^3$, $[0,1]$.
9. $F(t) = (t + 2)^2(t - 3)^3$, $[-3,4]$.
10. $G(y) = y^2(y^2 - 1)^2$, $[-2,2]$.
11. $f(r) = r^2 + \dfrac{4}{r^2}$, $[-2,2]$.
12. $g(x) = \dfrac{x - 1}{x^2 + 3}$, $[-4,2]$.

In each of Exercises 13–15, verify Rolle's theorem by finding the values of x for which $F(x)$ and $F'(x)$ vanish.

13. $F(x) = 3x - x^3$.
14. $F(x) = x^3 - ax^2$.
15. $F(x) = x^n(x - a)$, (n any positive integer).
16. If $(y + 4)^3 = x^2$, then $y = 0$ when $x = 8$ or $x = -8$. Does Rolle's theorem justify the conclusion that $dy/dx = 0$ for some number x in the interval $(-8,8)$? Check by sketching the graph of the given equation.

In each of Exercises 17–20, either verify that the mean value theorem holds for the given function or give a reason why it does not.

17. $g(x) = \dfrac{x - 1}{x}$; $a = 1$, $b = 3$.
18. $f(x) = |x|$; $a = -1$, $b = 2$.
19. $F(x) = [x]$; $a = -\frac{1}{2}$, $b = \frac{3}{2}$.
20. $G(x) = \begin{cases} 1 + x^2, & (x \geq 0) \\ 1 - x^2, & (x < 0) \end{cases}$; $a = -1$, $b = 1$.

II

1. Prove that if the equation

$$x^n + a_1x^{n-1} + a_2x^{n-2} + \cdots + a_{n-1}x = 0$$

has a positive root $x = r$, then the equation

$$nx^{n-1} + (n-1)a_1x^{n-2} + (n-2)a_2x^{n-3} + \cdots + a_{n-1} = 0$$

has a positive root less than r.

2. Prove that the polynomial $P(x) = x^n + ax + b$ of degree n cannot have more than two real roots if n is even or more than three real roots if n is odd.

2 MONOTONIC FUNCTIONS

A function f is said to be *increasing in an interval* I contained in the domain of f if

$$f(x_1) \leq f(x_2) \quad \text{whenever } x_1 \leq x_2$$

for all numbers x_1, x_2 in I. If

$$f(x_1) < f(x_2) \quad \text{whenever } x_1 < x_2$$

for all numbers x_1, x_2 in I, then f is said to be *strictly increasing in the interval* I. Decreasing and strictly decreasing functions are defined in a similar way. If f is strictly increasing in I, then the graph of f is rising as we traverse it from left to right; if f is strictly decreasing in I, the graph of f is falling in I. Some examples are shown in Figure 6.3.

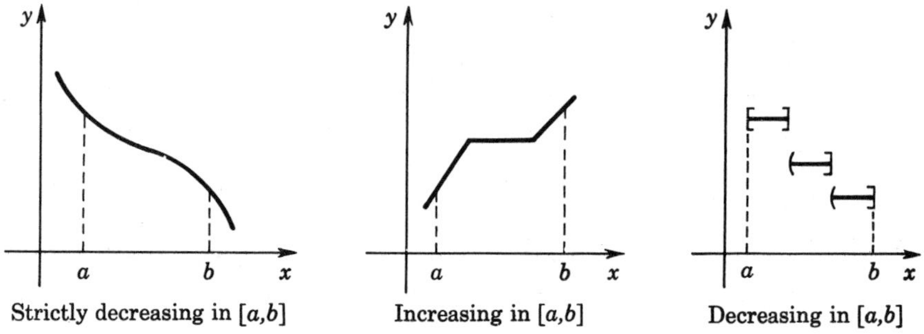

FIGURE 6.3

If a function f is either increasing in an interval I or decreasing in I, then f is said to be *monotonic in* I. Similarly, f is said to be *strictly monotonic in* I if f is either strictly increasing in I or strictly decreasing in I.

6.6 **THEOREM.** If a function f is continuous in an interval I, then:

(1) f is strictly increasing in I if $f'(x) > 0$ for every x in I, x not an endpoint of I.

(2) f is strictly decreasing in I if $f'(x) < 0$ for every x in I, x not an endpoint of I.

Proof: (1) If x_1, x_2 are in I and $x_1 < x_2$, then, by the mean value theorem,

$$f(x_2) - f(x_1) = (x_2 - x_1)f'(c)$$

for some c in (x_1,x_2). Since $x_2 - x_1 > 0$ and $f'(c) > 0$ by assumption, evidently $f(x_2) - f(x_1) > 0$ and $f(x_1) < f(x_2)$. Hence f is strictly increasing in I.

The proof of (2) is similar and hence is omitted.

If a function f is continuous in an interval I and has no critical numbers in I, except possibly at an endpoint of I, then by **6.3** either $f'(x) > 0$ for every x in I, or $f'(x) < 0$ for every x in I, x not an endpoint. This fact together with **6.6** proves the following useful theorem.

6.7 **THEOREM.** If a function f is continuous in an interval I and has no critical numbers in I, except possibly at an endpoint of I, then f is strictly monotonic in I.

Once we have enumerated the critical numbers of a function f, we can easily find the intervals in which f is monotonic. For example, if a and b are consecutive critical numbers of f and if f is continuous in $[a,b]$, then by **6.7**:

(1) f is strictly increasing in $[a,b]$ if $f(a) < f(b)$.

(2) f is strictly decreasing in $[a,b]$ if $f(a) > f(b)$.

We note that $f(a) \neq f(b)$ by Rolle's theorem. Theorem **6.7** also applies to infinite intervals, as illustrated below.

EXAMPLE 1. Find the intervals in which the function g defined by

$$g(x) = x^3 - 3x + 1$$

is strictly monotonic.

Solution: The function g has derivative $g'(x) = 3x^2 - 3$, or

$$g'(x) = 3(x - 1)(x + 1).$$

Therefore, -1 and 1 are the only critical numbers of g. From the following table of values, we see that

x	-2	-1	1	2
$g(x)$	-1	3	-1	3

$g(-2) < g(-1)$, $g(-1) > g(1)$, $g(1) < g(2)$. Since there is no critical number of g in the interval $(-\infty,-1)$ and since $g(-2) < g(-1)$, g is strictly increasing in $(-\infty,-1]$

by **6.7**. For similar reasons, g is strictly decreasing in $[-1,1]$ and strictly increasing in $[1,\infty)$. The graph of g is sketched in Figure 6.4.

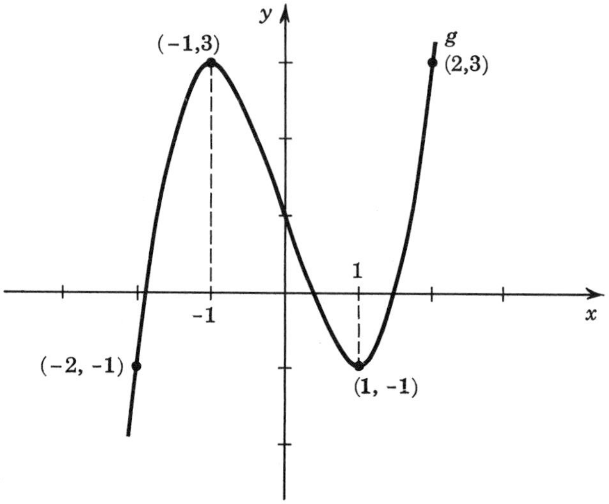

FIGURE 6.4

EXAMPLE 2. Find the intervals in which the function f defined by

$$f(x) = x + \frac{4}{x^2}$$

is strictly monotonic.

Solution: The function f is undefined at $x = 0$, but continuous elsewhere. Evidently

$$f'(x) = 1 - \frac{8}{x^3},$$

and $f'(x) = 0$ if, and only if, $x = 2$. Thus 2 is the only critical number. Therefore, by **6.7**, f is strictly monotonic in each of the intervals

$$(-\infty,0), \qquad (0,2], \qquad [2,\infty).$$

Since $f'(-1) > 0$, $f'(1) < 0$, $f'(3) > 0$, we have by **6.6** that f is strictly increasing in $(-\infty,0)$, strictly decreasing in $(0,2]$, and strictly increasing in $[2,\infty)$. Since $\underset{x\to 0}{\text{limit}}\, f(x) = \infty$, the line $y = 0$ is a vertical asymptote of the graph of f. When $|x|$ is large, $f(x)$ is close to x; i.e., $\underset{x\to -\infty}{\text{limit}}\,[f(x) - x] = \underset{x\to \infty}{\text{limit}}\,[f(x) - x] = 0$. This leads us to call the line $y = x$ an asymptote also. The graph of f is sketched in Figure 6.5.

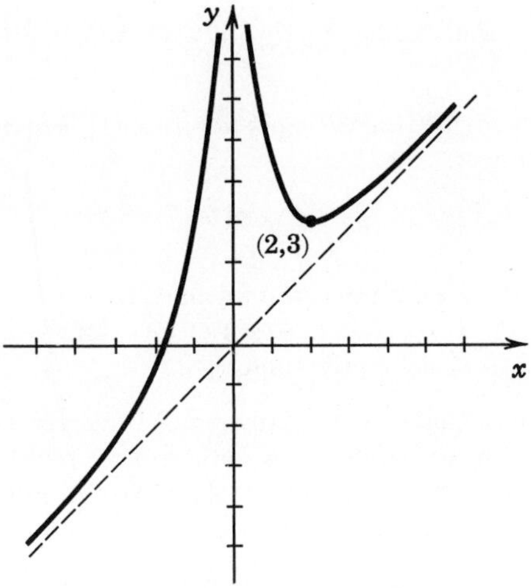

FIGURE 6.5

EXERCISES

I

In each of Exercises 1–8, find the intervals in which the given function is strictly increasing and those in which it is strictly decreasing. From this information sketch the graph of each function.

1. $f(x) = x^2 - 2x - 8.$
2. $G(x) = 4 - 4x - x^2.$
3. $g(x) = (x - a)^2 + (x - b)^2, (a \neq b).$
4. $F(x) = (x - 2)^3(x + 1)^2.$
5. $f(x) = \sqrt{x} + \sqrt{x + 1}.$
6. $F(x) = (x - 1)^{1/3} + \frac{1}{2}(x + 1)^{2/3}.$
7. $G(x) = x + \dfrac{1}{x}.$
8. $g(x) = x + \dfrac{5}{2x + 3}.$

In each of Exercises 9–14, find the extrema of the function and sketch its graph.

9. $F(x) = \dfrac{12}{x^2 + 2}.$
10. $f(x) = (x - 2)^4.$
11. $G(x) = -x^{1/5}.$
12. $g(x) = x^2 + \dfrac{4}{x^2}.$
13. $H(x) = \dfrac{x - 1}{x^2 + 3}.$
14. $h(x) = \dfrac{x^2 - 1}{x}.$

15. If a function f is increasing in $[a,b]$ and also in $[b,c]$, is it increasing in $[a,c]$? Prove your answer.

16. If functions f and g are increasing in $[a,b]$, are $f + g$ and fg also increasing in $[a,b]$? Prove your answer.

II

1. Describe the graph of the function f defined by
$$f(x) = (x - a_1)^2 + (x - a_2)^2 + \cdots + (x - a_n)^2,$$
where $a_1, a_2, \cdots, a_n$ are n given numbers.

2. It is a theorem of algebra that a polynomial of degree n has at most n roots. If f is a polynomial function of degree n, is there a relationship between the number of real roots of the polynomial f and its derivative f'? For example, can f have three distinct roots and f' have no roots? Can f have no roots and f' have roots?

3. Let f be a differentiable function in an interval I and let $c_1 < c_2 < c_3$ be all the critical numbers of f in I. Let a and b be selected from I so that $a < c_1$ and $c_3 < b$. Give a rough sketch of the graph of f for each of the following:
   a. $f(a) < f(c_1), f(c_1) > f(c_2), f(c_2) > f(c_3), f(c_3) < f(b)$.
   b. $f(a) > f(c_1), f(c_1) < f(c_2), f(c_2) > f(c_3), f(c_3) < f(b)$.
   e. $f(a) > f(c_1) > f(c_2) > f(c_3) > f(b)$.

4. If function F is constant in an open interval I, then $F'(x) = 0$ for every x in I. Prove, conversely, that if $F'(x) = 0$ for every x in I then F is constant in I.

3 RELATIVE EXTREMA OF A FUNCTION

The graph of a function may have many "relative" maximum and minimum points. In Figure 6.4, for example, $P(-1,3)$ is a "relative" maximum point and $Q(1,-1)$ is a "relative" minimum point of the graph of g. Note that P is not the highest point on the graph of g, but it is the highest point of the graph in a neighborhood of P. Similarly, Q is not the lowest point on the graph, but it is the lowest point in a neighborhood of Q. With this example in mind, let us make the following definition.

6.8 **DEFINITION.** The number $f(c)$ is called a *relative extremum* of a function f if there exists a neighborhood N of c contained in the domain of f such that $f(c)$ is an extremum of f in N and $f(x) \neq f(c)$ if $x \neq c$, x in N.

If $f(c)$ is a relative extremum of a function f, then by **6.2** either $f'(c) = 0$ or $f'(c)$ does not exist; i.e., c is a critical number of f. Whether or not $f(c)$ is a relative extremum of f in case c is a critical number may be decided by use of **6.6** and 6.7. Thus, a possible working procedure for finding the relative extrema of a function f is as follows.

(1) Find the critical numbers of f.

(2) If c is a critical number of f, find (if possible) a neighborhood (a,b) of c such that f is continuous in $[a,b]$ and c is the only critical number of f in $[a,b]$.

(3) Compute $f(a)$, $f(b)$, and $f(c)$.

- (i) If $f(a) < f(c)$ and $f(b) < f(c)$, then $f(c)$ is a relative maximum value of f.
- (ii) If $f(a) > f(c)$ and $f(b) > f(c)$, then $f(c)$ is a relative minimum value of f.
- (iii) If neither (i) nor (ii) holds, then $f(c)$ is not an extremum of f.

In place of step (3), we could use (3′) as follows.

(3′) Compute $f'(a)$ and $f'(b)$.

- (i) If $f'(a) > 0$ and $f'(b) < 0$, then $f(c)$ is a relative maximum value of f.
- (ii) If $f'(a) < 0$ and $f'(b) > 0$, then $f(c)$ is a relative minimum value of f.
- (iii) If neither (i) nor (ii) holds, then $f(c)$ is not an extremum of f.

For example, the function

$$f(x) = x^3$$

has derivative

$$f'(x) = 3x^2.$$

The only critical number of f is 0. Select the interval $(-1,1)$ containing 0. Clearly f is continuous in $[-1,1]$. Since $f(-1) < f(0) < f(1)$, we have that $f(0)$ is not an extremum by (3), (iii). Or, since $f'(-1) > 0$ and $f'(1) > 0$, we have that $f(0)$ is not an extremum by (3′), (iii).

We further illustrate the use of the above procedure in the following examples.

EXAMPLE 1. Find the relative extrema of the function f defined by

$$f(x) = x^3 + 3x^2 - 1.$$

Solution: The functions f and f' have $(-\infty, \infty)$ as their domain. Clearly,

$$f'(x) = 3x(x + 2)$$

and $\{-2,0\}$ is the set of critical numbers of f. Now

$$f(-3) = -1, f(-2) = 3, f(-1) = 1, f(0) = -1, f(1) = 3.$$

Since $f(-3) < f(-2)$ and $f(-1) < f(-2)$, $f(-2)$ is a relative maximum value of f; and since $f(-1) > f(0)$ and $f(1) > f(0)$, $f(0)$ is relative minimum value of f. Using this information, the graph of f is sketched in Figure 6.6.

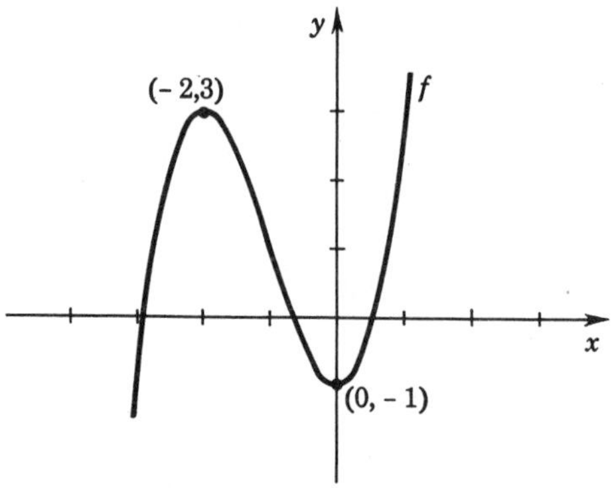

FIGURE 6.6

EXAMPLE 2. Find the relative extrema of the function g defined by

$$g(x) = x^3 + \frac{3}{x}.$$

Solution: We have

$$g'(x) = 3x^2 - \frac{3}{x^2} = \frac{3(x^4 - 1)}{x^2}.$$

Evidently, the domain of both g and g' is the set of nonzero real numbers. Thus the set of critical numbers of g is $\{x|g'(x) = 0\}$ or $\{x|x^4 - 1 = 0\}$. That is, $\{-1,1\}$ is the set of critical numbers of g. Since g is continuous in the interval $[-2,-\frac{1}{2}]$ and $g'(-2) > 0$, $g'(-\frac{1}{2}) < 0$, we know that $g(-1) = -4$ is a relative maximum value of g. Since g is continuous in the interval $[\frac{1}{2},2]$ and $g'(\frac{1}{2}) < 0$, $g'(2) > 0$, we know that $g(1) = 4$ is a relative minimum value of g. Note that the relative minimum value of g exceeds the relative maximum value of g. The graph of g in Figure 6.7 shows how this can happen.

EXAMPLE 3. Find the relative extrema of the function F defined by

$$F(x) = \sqrt[3]{x}(x - 7)^2.$$

Solution: The function F is continuous in the interval $(-\infty, \infty)$. Its derivative is given by

$$F'(x) = \frac{1}{3}x^{-2/3}(x - 7)^2 + 2x^{1/3}(x - 7) = \frac{7(x - 7)(x - 1)}{3x^{2/3}}.$$

Thus the domain of F' is the set of nonzero numbers. The critical numbers of F are 0, at which $F'(x)$ is undefined, and 1 and 7, at which $F'(x) = 0$. We compute

$$F(-1) < 0, F(0) = 0, F(\tfrac{1}{8}) > 0.$$

Therefore, $F(0)$ is not an extremum of F. Also,

$$F(\tfrac{1}{8}) < \tfrac{49}{2}, F(1) = 36, F(6) < 36.$$

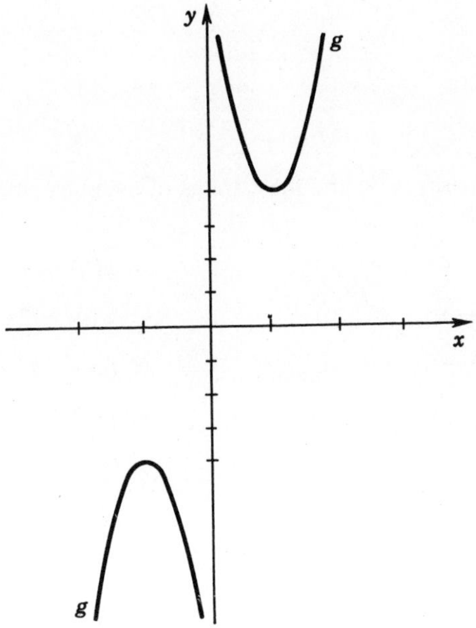

FIGURE 6.7

Therefore, $F(1)$ is a relative maximum value of F. Finally,

$$F(6) > 0, \; F(7) = 0, \; F(8) > 0.$$

Therefore $F(7)$ is a relative minimum value of F. The graph of F is sketched in Figure 6.8. Evidently, F has a vertical tangent line at the origin.

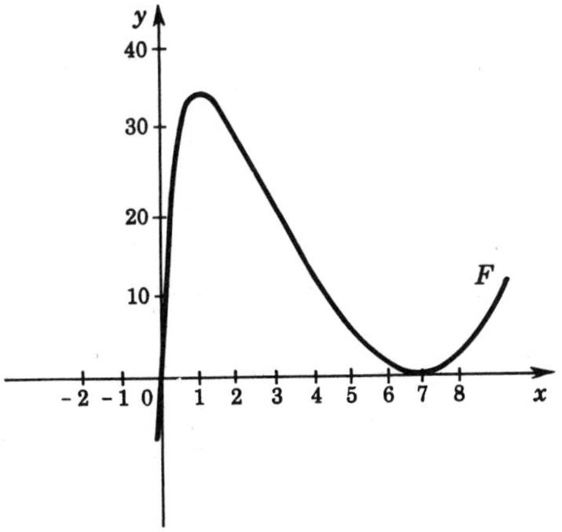

FIGURE 6.8

EXERCISES

I

In each of Exercises 1–18, find the extrema of the polynomial function and sketch the graph.

1. $f(x) = x^2 - 4x + 4$.
2. $g(x) = 4 - x^2$.
3. $F(x) = 3 - 5x - x^2$.
4. $G(x) = 3x^2 - 4x + 7$.
5. $g(x) = 2x^3 + 3x - 1$.
6. $f(x) = x^3 - 6x^2 + 9x - 2$.
7. $G(x) = x^3 + x^2 + x - 4$.
8. $F(x) = x^4 - x^3$.
9. $g(x) = (x + 2)^2(x - 3)^3$.
10. $h(x) = (x + 2)^2(x - 3)^2$.
11. $f(x) = (x^2 - 4)^2$.
12. $g(x) = x^2(x^2 - 1)^2$.
13. $F(x) = 3x^5 - 25x^3 + 60x$.
14. $G(x) = x^4 - 4x$.
15. $f(x) = x^3 + 3x^2 - 9x + 1$.
16. $g(x) = x^3 + 3x^2 + 3x - 2$.
17. $h(x) = x^3 + 3x$.
18. $F(x) = x^2 + 2$.

In each of Exercises 19–30, find the extrema of the function and sketch the graph.

19. $g(x) = x^4 - 2x^2$.
20. $G(x) = 2x^3 - 3x^2$.
21. $f(x) = x^2(x - 3)^3$.
22. $g(x) = (2x^2 - 3x - 2)^2$.
23. $g(x) = x^{2/3}(x - 5)$.
24. $h(x) = x^{1/3}(x - 8)$.
25. $F(x) = x\sqrt[3]{3x - 4}$.
26. $f(x) = \sqrt[3]{x - 1} + \sqrt{x + 1}$.
27. $f(x) = \sqrt[3]{x^3 - 9x}$.
28. $F(x) = \sqrt[3]{x^2 - 2x}$.
29. $G(x) = x^2 + \dfrac{1}{x^2}$.
30. $g(x) = \dfrac{x - 1}{x^2 + 3}$.

II

1. If p and q are integers and $f(x) = (x - 1)^p(x + 1)^q$, $(p \geq 2,\ q \geq 2)$, show that f has the three critical numbers, $-1, \dfrac{q - p}{q + p}, 1$. Find the extrema of f for the following cases:
   a. p and q are both even.
   b. p is even and q is odd.
   c. p is odd and q is even.
   d. p and q are both odd.
2. Show that the function G defined by $G(x) = (ax + b)/(cx + d)$ has no extrema regardless of the values of a, b, c, and d. Sketch the graph of G.

4 CONCAVITY

Just as the sign of the first derivative of a function f tells us about the rising and falling of the graph of f, so the sign of the second derivative of f tells us about the concavity of the graph of f. The concavity of a graph is defined below.

6.9 DEFINITION. The graph of a function f is said to be *concave upward* at the point $(c,f(c))$ if $f'(c)$ exists and if there exists a deleted neighborhood D of c such that the graph of f in D is above the tangent line at $(c,f(c))$. *Downward concavity* is defined analogously.

For example, the graph of f is concave upward at $(c,f(c))$ in Figure 6.9, and is concave downward at $(c,f(c))$ in Figure 6.10.

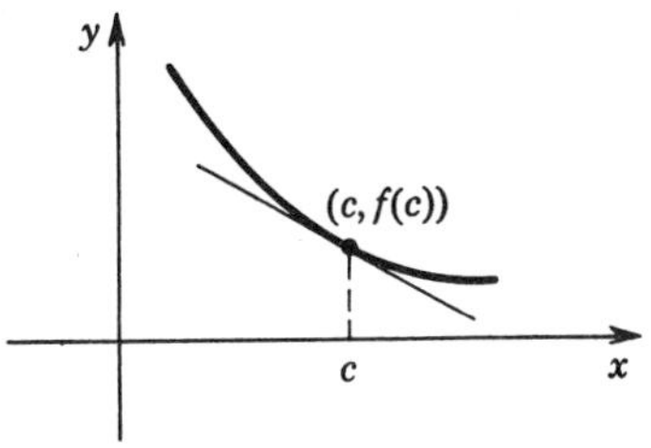

FIGURE 6.9

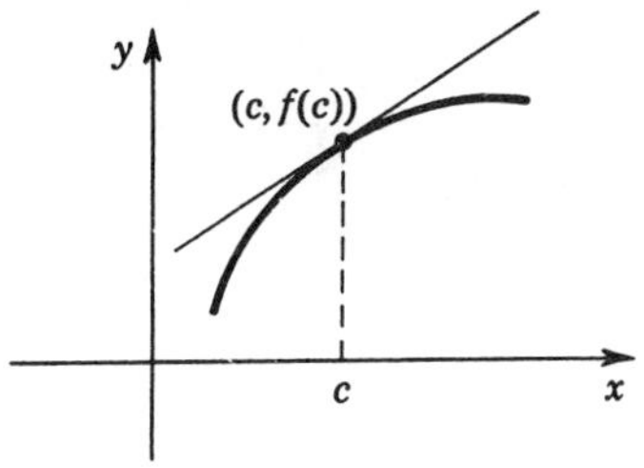

FIGURE 6.10

The equation of the tangent line T to the graph of f at point $(c,f(c))$, assuming $f'(c)$ exists, is given by

$$y = f(c) + f'(c)(x - c).$$

Hence the directed distance $g(x)$ from T to the graph of f at x, measured parallel to the y axis, is given by (Figure 6.11)

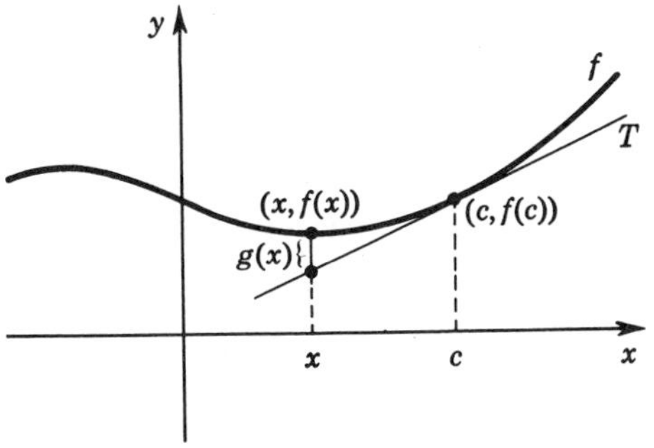

FIGURE 6.11

6.10 $$g(x) = f(x) - [f(c) + f'(c)(x - c)].$$

Since $g(x)$ is a directed distance, the point $(x,f(x))$ is above T if $g(x) > 0$ and below T if $g(x) < 0$. Clearly, $g(c) = 0$.

The concavity of a graph is easily stated in terms of the function g of **6.10**. Thus the graph of f at $(c,f(c))$ is concave upward if $g(x) > 0$ for every x in some deleted neighborhood of c, and concave downward if $g(x) < 0$ for every x in some deleted neighborhood of c.

6.11 TEST FOR CONCAVITY. If f is a function and c is a number such that the derivative f' is defined in some neighborhood of c, then:

(1) The graph of f is concave upward at $(c,f(c))$ if $f''(c) > 0$.
(2) The graph of f is concave downward at $(c,f(c))$ if $f''(c) < 0$.

Proof: If $f''(c) > 0$, then there exists a neighborhood N of c such that $f'(x) < f'(c)$ if $x < c$, $f'(x) > f'(c)$ if $x > c$, for every x in N. Using the mean value theorem in **6.10**, we have

$$\begin{aligned} g(x) &= [f(x) - f(c)] - f'(c)(x - c) \\ &= f'(d)(x - c) - f'(c)(x - c) \\ &= [f'(d) - f'(c)](x - c) \end{aligned}$$

for some number d between x and c. If x is in N and $x < c$, then $x < d < c$, $f'(d) < f'(c)$, and $g(x) > 0$. If x is in N and $x > c$, then $c < d < x, f'(c) < f'(d)$, and once again $g(x) > 0$. Hence $g(x) > 0$ for every x in N, $(x \neq c)$, and the graph of f is concave upward at $(c,f(c))$.

The proof of (2) is similar and is therefore omitted.

A useful corollary of **6.11** is given in the following theorem.

6.12 SECOND DERIVATIVE TEST FOR EXTREMA. If f is a function and c a critical number of f such that the derivative f' is defined in some neighborhood of c, then:

(1) $f(c)$ is a relative maximum value of f if $f''(c) < 0$.
(2) $f(c)$ is a relative minimum value of f if $f''(c) > 0$.

These results follow easily from **6.11**, since the tangent line is now horizontal and the graph of f is below the tangent line in (1) and above the tangent line in (2) for some neighborhood of c.

If c is a critical number of f for which either $f''(c) = 0$ or $f''(c)$ does not exist, then the second derivative test cannot be applied.

A special name is given below to those points on the graph of a function at which the tangent line cuts the graph in the sense indicated in Figure 6.12.

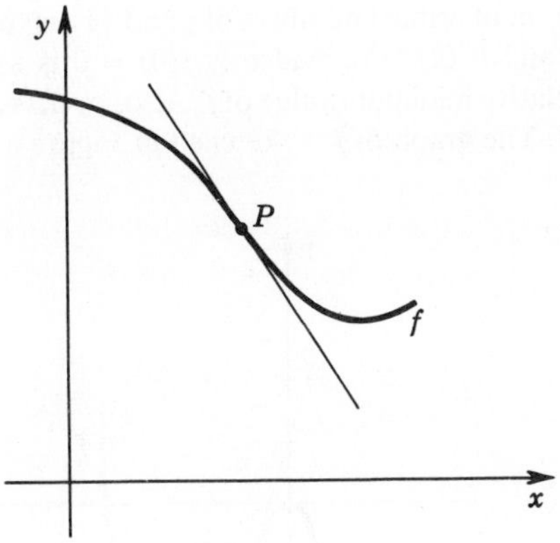

FIGURE 6.12

6.13 **DEFINITION.** The point $(c,f(c))$ is a *point of inflection* of the graph of f if there exists a neighborhood (a,b) of c such that $f''(x) > 0$ for every x in (a,c) and $f''(x) < 0$ for every x in (c,b), or vice versa.*

If $(c,f(c))$ is a point of inflection of the graph of f and if $f''(c)$ exists, then necessarily $f''(c) = 0$. For if (a,b) is a neighborhood of c having the property stated in 6.13 and if $g = f'$, then the function g has a critical number in (a,b) by 6.3. Clearly, this critical number must be c, and $g'(c) = f''(c) = 0$, since $g'(c)$ exists. In other words, the points of inflection occur at critical numbers of f'.

That not every critical number of f' gives a point of inflection of the graph of f is easily seen by example. Thus, if $f(x) = x^4$, then $f'(x) = 4x^3$ and $f''(x) = 12x^2$. Since $f'(0) = 0$ and $f''(x) > 0$ for every $x \neq 0$, 0 is a critical number of f', whereas $(0,0)$ is not a point of inflection of the graph of f.

The following theorem is a consequence of the theory in Section 2.

6.14 **THEOREM.** If f is a function and c is a number such that $f''(c) = 0$, then $(c,f(c))$ is a point of inflection of the graph of f provided there exists a neighborhood (a,b) of c such that (1) $f''(x)$ exists and is nonzero for every x in $[a,b]$, $x \neq c$, and (2) $f''(a)$ and $f''(b)$ differ in sign.

EXAMPLE 1. If $f(x) = x^3 - 3x^2$, find the relative extrema of f and the points of inflection of the graph of f.

Solution: We have

$$f'(x) = 3x^2 - 6x = 3x(x-2), \qquad f''(x) = 6x - 6 = 6(x-1).$$

---

* An interesting discussion of possible definitions of points of inflection may be found in an article by A. M. Bruckner, *The American Mathematical Monthly*, 69 (1962), 787.

Thus $\{0,2\}$ is the set of critical numbers of f and $\{1\}$ is the set of critical numbers of f'. Since $f''(0) < 0$ and $f''(2) > 0$, evidently $f(0) = 0$ is a relative maximum value and $f(2) = -4$ is a relative minimum value of f. Also, by **6.14**, $(1, -2)$ is a point of inflection of the graph of f. The graph of f is sketched in Figure 6.13.

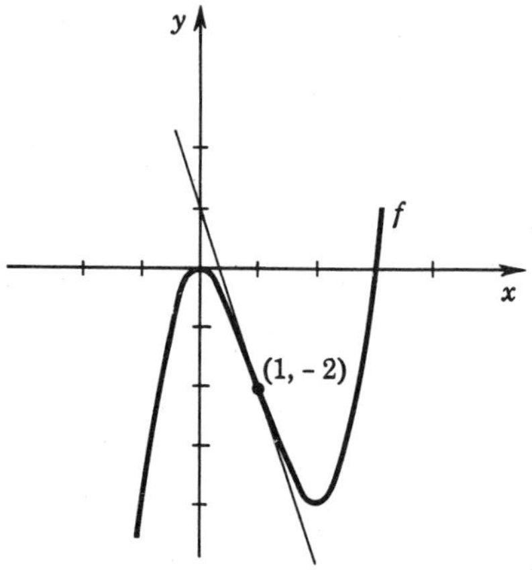

FIGURE 6.13

EXAMPLE 2. If $f(x) = x^4 - 4x^3 + 10$, find the relative extrema of the function f and the points of inflection of its graph.

Solution: Since

$$f'(x) = 4x^3 - 12x^2 = 4x^2(x - 3),$$

$\{0,3\}$ is the set of critical numbers of f. The second derivative of f is given by

$$f''(x) = 12x^2 - 24x = 12x(x - 2).$$

Thus the points of inflection can occur only at $x = 0$ and $x = 2$.

Since $f''(3) > 0$, the number $f(3) = -17$ is a relative minimum value of f. On the other hand, $f''(0) = 0$ and the second derivative test does not apply to the critical number 0. However,

$$f''(x) > 0, \quad (\text{if } x < 0), \qquad f''(x) < 0, \quad (\text{if } 0 < x < 2),$$

and therefore $(0,10)$ is an inflection point of the graph of f. Thus $f(0)$ is not an extremum of f. Also,

$$f''(x) < 0, \quad (\text{if } 0 < x < 2), \qquad f''(x) > 0, \quad (\text{if } x > 2),$$

and we conclude that $(2, -6)$ is a point of inflection of the graph. The graph of f is sketched in Figure 6.14.

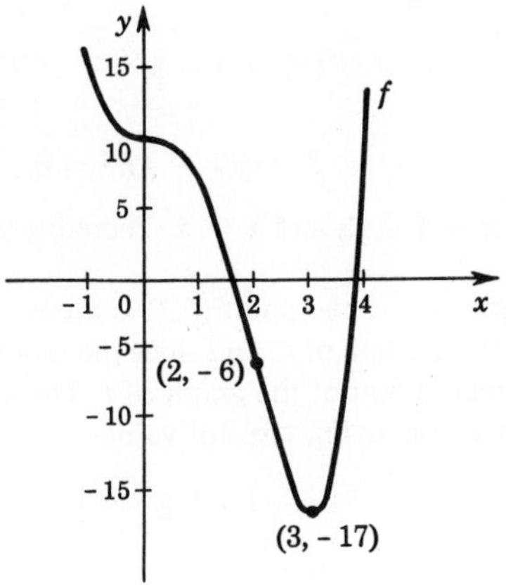

FIGURE 6.14

5 ENDPOINT EXTREMA

A point $(c,f(c))$ is called an *endpoint* of the graph of the function f if there exists an interval (a,b) containing c such that the domain of f contains every number of the interval (a,c) and no number of the interval (c,b), or vice versa.

If $(c,f(c))$ is an endpoint of the graph of f such that $f(c)$ is the maximum or minimum value of f in some interval containing c, then $f(c)$ is called an *endpoint extremum* of f. Note the difference between this definition and that of a relative extremum, in which it is assumed that some open interval containing c is contained in the domain of the function.

The graph of the function f where

$$f(x) = \sqrt{4 - x^2}$$

is a semicircle. Clearly, $f(-2) = 0$ and $f(2) = 0$ are endpoint extrema of f; they are minimum values of f. Also, $f(0) = 2$ is a (relative) maximum value of f.

If $f(c)$ is an endpoint extremum of f, the number c must be a critical number of f, since $f'(c)$ does not exist.

EXAMPLE. Find the extrema of the function f defined by

$$f(x) = 3x - (x - 1)^{3/2}.$$

Solution: Since $(x - 1)^{3/2}$ is a real number only if $x \geq 1$, the domain of f is the set $[1, \infty)$. Thus $(1,3)$ is an endpoint of the graph of f.

We have

$$f'(x) = 3 - \tfrac{3}{2}(x - 1)^{1/2}.$$

If

$$3 - \tfrac{3}{2}(x - 1)^{1/2} = 0,$$

then $\sqrt{x - 1} = 2$, $x - 1 = 4$, and $x = 5$. Therefore $\{1,5\}$ is the set of critical numbers of f.

Since f is continuous and the point (5,7) is above the point (1,3), then (1,3) is an endpoint minimum of the graph of f. And since the point (10,3) is below the point (5,7), then (5,7) is a maximum point of the graph of f. The graph is sketched in Figure 6.15 with the aid of the accompanying table of values.

x	1	2	5	10
$f(x)$	3	5	7	3

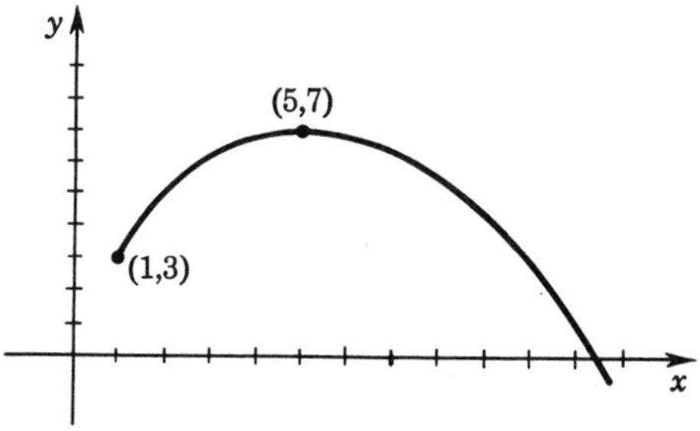

FIGURE 6.15

EXERCISES

I

In each of Exercises 1–8, find the extrema of the function, using the second derivative test.

1. $f(x) = 5x^2 - 2x + 1.$
2. $g(x) = 3 + x - x^2.$
3. $g(x) = x^3 + 3x^2 - 9x + 10.$
4. $F(x) = x^3 + 4x^2 - 3x - 9.$
5. $F(x) = \dfrac{x^2}{4} + \dfrac{4}{x}.$
6. $f(x) = x^3 + \dfrac{3}{x}.$
7. $f(x) = \dfrac{1}{\sqrt{x}} + \dfrac{\sqrt{x}}{9}.$
8. $g(x) = \dfrac{x^3}{x^2 + 1}.$

In each of Exercises 9–14, find the extrema of the function, using the second derivative test. Also find the points of inflection and sketch the graph.

9. $G(x) = 3 - 2x - x^2$.

10. $F(x) = x^2 - 4x + 5$.

11. $F(x) = x^3 - x^2 - x + 2$.

12. $F(x) = x^3 - 5x^2 - 8x + 20$.

13. $f(x) = 3x^4 - 4x^3 - 12x^2 + 3$.

14. $g(x) = x^5 - 5x + 2$.

In each of Exercises 15–24, find the extrema of the function, using whatever test is more convenient.

15. $g(x) = x^3 - 15x$.

16. $F(x) = x^{7/5}$.

17. $G(x) = x^{5/3}(x - 1)$.

18. $g(x) = \dfrac{ax}{x^2 + a^2}$, $(a \neq 0)$.

19. $F(x) = x\sqrt{x + 3}$.

20. $G(x) = 6\sqrt[3]{x} + x^2$.

21. $f(x) = x^{2/3}(x - 2)^2$.

22. $f(x) = 5x^{2/5} + 2x$.

23. $g(x) = \dfrac{x + a}{\sqrt{x^2 + 1}}$, $(a \neq 0)$.

24. $g(x) = \dfrac{x + 2}{x^2 + 2x + 4}$.

25. Find the points of inflection of the graph of

$$y = \frac{1}{x^2 + 3}.$$

Sketch this graph, showing the tangent lines at the points of inflection.

26. Find the points of inflection and extrema of the graph of

$$y = x^{1/3}(x - 4).$$

Sketch this graph, showing the tangent lines at the points of inflection.

27. Find the point of inflection of the graph of

$$y = x^2 - \frac{1}{6x^3}.$$

Find the equation of the tangent line to the graph at this point.

28. Let $f(x) = 2x^3 - 3(a + b)x^2 + 6abx$. Find the extrema of f if: (a) $a < b$; (b) $a = b$.

29. Determine a and b so that 1 is a critical number of the function f defined by

$$f(x) = x^3 + ax^2 + bx, \quad f(1) = -3.$$

Is $(1, -3)$ a maximum or minimum point on the graph of f?

II

1. Determine a and b so that 2 is a critical number of the function g defined by

$$g(x) = \frac{a}{x} + bx, \quad g(2) = 1.$$

Is (2,1) a maximum or minimum point on the graph of f?

2. Prove that the graph of the equation

$$y = x^3 + ax^2 + bx + c$$

has no extremum if and only if $a^2 \leq 3b$.

3. Let k be a rational number, $k > 1$, and let the function f be defined by the equation

$$f(x) = (1 + x)^k - (1 + kx), \qquad (x \geq -1).$$

Show that f has an absolute minimum value 0 and that this occurs at the unique number $x = 0$. This result will be used later in the following form: if k is an integer, $k > 1$, and if $x > -1$, $x \neq 0$, then $(1 + x)^k > 1 + kx$.

4. Show that the graph of the general cubic

$$y = ax^3 + 3bx^2 + 3cx + d$$

is centrosymmetric about its point of inflection. (A graph is said to be *centro-symmetric* about a point O if for every point P of the graph there is a corresponding point P' such that the line segment PP' is bisected by O.)

5. Find all the extrema of the function F defined by

$$F(x) = 12x^5 - 45x^4 + 40x^3 + 6.$$

6. Determine the relationship among the numbers a, b, and c in order that the function f defined by $f(x) = (x - a)(x - b)/(x - c)$ has $(-\infty, \infty)$ as its range.

6 APPLICATIONS OF THE THEORY OF EXTREMA

It is frequently possible to solve a problem which asks for the largest area or the least volume or the lowest cost by recognizing that the solution of the problem is a maximum or minimum value of some function. We illustrate the procedure with the following examples.

EXAMPLE 1. A rectangular field is to be adjacent to a river and is to have fencing on three sides, the side on the river requiring no fencing. If 100 rods of fencing is available, find the dimensions of the field with largest area.

Solution: Let the two sides of the field which are perpendicular to the river each have length x rods. Then the side parallel to the river has length $100 - 2x$ rods, since the sum of the lengths of the three sides is 100 rods (Figure 6.16). Clearly, $0 < x < 50$.

The area of the field is described by the function f where

$$f(x) = x(100 - 2x) = 100x - 2x^2, \qquad \text{domain } f = (0,50).$$

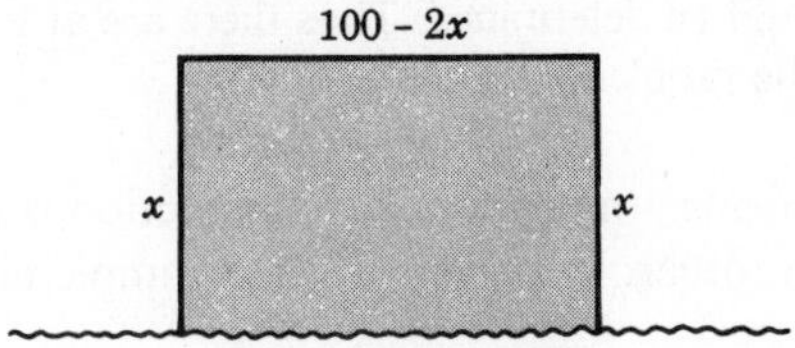

FIGURE 6.16

The field of Figure 6.16 will have the largest possible area if $f(x)$ is the maximum value of f.

Now

$$f'(x) = 100 - 4x,$$

and $f'(x) = 0$ only if $x = 25$. Thus 25 is the critical number of f. Since

$$f''(x) = -4,$$

$f''(25) = -4$ and $f(25)$ is a maximum value of f. The dimensions of this field of largest area are $x = 25$ rods and $100 - 2x = 50$ rods; its area is 1250 square rods.

The graph of the function f is sketched in Figure 6.17. The ordinate $f(x)$ of each point $(x,f(x))$ on the graph is the area of the field with given width x.

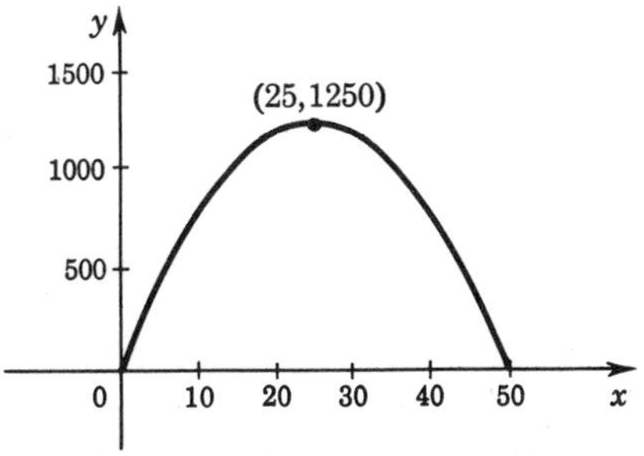

FIGURE 6.17

We might have started differently, letting z be the length of the side of the field parallel to the river. Then each of the other two sides would have length $(100 - z)/2 = 50 - z/2$, and the area of the field would be given by

$$g(z) = z\left(50 - \frac{z}{2}\right) = 50z - \frac{1}{2}z^2.$$

Since

$$g'(z) = 50 - z,$$

we would discover that $g(50)$ is a maximum value of g, and since

$$g(50) = 1250,$$

the same field would be determined. Thus there are at least two functions which give us a solution of the problem.

In some problems, it may be that one function is easier to recognize or easier to handle than another. However, in the example above, the choice would not be important.

EXAMPLE 2. Show that a tin can of specified volume K will be made of the least amount of metal if its height equals the diameter of its base.

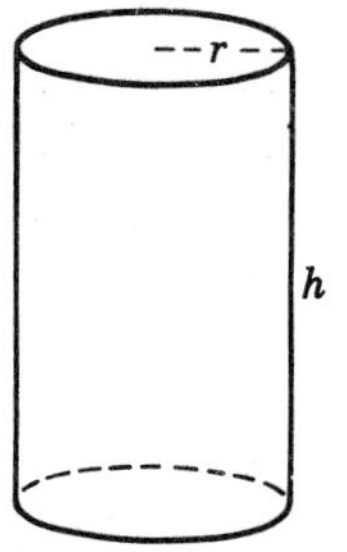

FIGURE 6.18

Solution: We are assuming, of course, that the tin can is in the form of a right circular cylinder and has both top and bottom. The least amount of metal will be used when the surface area of the cylinder is a minimum. Let r be the radius of the base and h the height of the cylinder (Figure 6.18). Then the area of the base is πr^2, as is the area of the top. The lateral area is $2\pi rh$, the product of the circumference and the height of the cylinder. Thus the total area A is given by

$$A = 2\pi rh + 2\pi r^2.$$

The volume of the cylinder has been specified as a (positive) number K, and hence

$$K = \pi r^2 h.$$

We can solve this equation for h,

$$h = \frac{K}{\pi r^2},$$

and then express A in terms of r (by replacing h by $K/\pi r^2$) as follows:

$$A = \frac{2K}{r} + 2\pi r^2.$$

We can now say that the area of the cylinder is described by the function f where

$$f(r) = \frac{2K}{r} + 2\pi r^2, \qquad \text{domain} f = (0, \infty).$$

We seek a minimum value of the function f. Since

$$f'(r) = -\frac{2K}{r^2} + 4\pi r$$

for every positive number r, the critical numbers of f are the positive solutions of the equation

$$-\frac{2K}{r^2} + 4\pi r = 0,$$

$$\text{or} \quad \frac{2}{r^2}(-K + 2\pi r^3) = 0.$$

Thus the only critical number of f is

$$r = \sqrt[3]{\frac{K}{2\pi}}.$$

Since

$$f''(r) = \frac{4K}{r^3} + 4\pi,$$

$f''(r) > 0$ for every positive number r. Hence

$$f\left(\sqrt[3]{\frac{K}{2\pi}}\right)$$

is a minimum value of f.

We have shown above that $h = K/\pi r^2$, and therefore

$$\frac{h}{r} = \frac{K}{\pi r^3}.$$

At $r = \sqrt[3]{K/2\pi}$,

$$\frac{h}{r} = \frac{K}{\pi \dfrac{K}{2\pi}} = 2,$$

$$\text{and} \quad h = 2r.$$

This proves that the height and diameter of the tin can of least area are equal.

We might have solved the equation $K = \pi r^2 h$ for r, getting

$$r = \sqrt{\frac{K}{\pi h}},$$

and then used the function g given by

$$g(h) = 2\sqrt{K\pi h} + \frac{2K}{h}$$

to describe the area of the cylinder. However, the function f is somewhat easier to handle than g.

EXAMPLE 3. Find a triangle of maximum area inscribed in a circle of radius r.

Solution: If triangle ABC is inscribed in a circle and if $AC \neq BC$, then there exists a triangle $AC'B$ inscribed in the circle with $AC' = BC'$ and with greater area than the given triangle, as can be seen from Figure 6.19. Thus it is clear geometrically that a triangle of maximum area inscribed in a circle is equilateral.

We have shown above that if there is a triangle of maximum area inscribed in a circle then it must be equilateral. A more difficult problem, which we will not discuss, is to show that an inscribed triangle of maximum area actually exists.

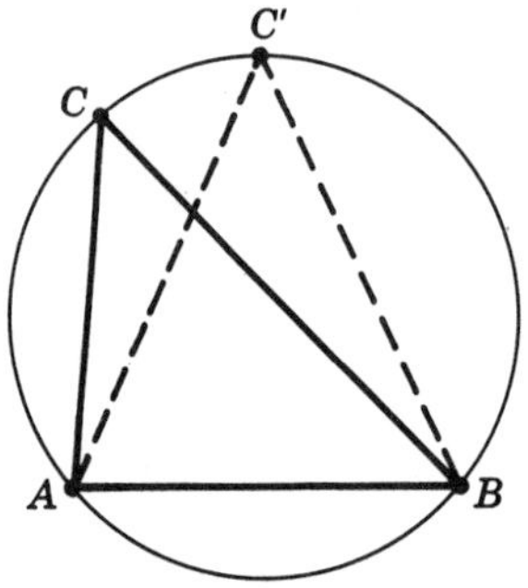

FIGURE 6.19

We see from Example 3 that not all problems in maxima and minima require calculus for their solution. As another example, it is obvious that if

$$f(x) = \frac{1}{1 + x^2}$$

then $f(0) = 1$ is the only maximum value of f.

EXAMPLE 4. Find the point of the graph of the equation

$$y = x^2$$

that is nearest the point $A(3,0)$.

Solution: For every real number x, the point $P(x,x^2)$ is on the graph of the given equation (Figure 6.20), and

$$\begin{aligned} |PA|^2 &= (x - 3)^2 + (x^2)^2 \\ &= x^4 + x^2 - 6x + 9. \end{aligned}$$

If we let

$$g(x) = \sqrt{x^4 + x^2 - 6x + 9},$$

then $g(x)$ is the distance between P and A, and we wish to find a minimum value of g. Now

$$g'(x) = \tfrac{1}{2}(4x^3 + 2x - 6)(x^4 + x^2 - 6x + 9)^{-1/2},$$

and $g'(x) = 0$ only if

$$4x^3 + 2x - 6 = 0.$$

It is clear by inspection that $x = 1$ is a solution of this equation. By dividing the polynomial $4x^3 + 2x - 6$ by $x - 1$, we see that

$$4x^3 + 2x - 6 = (x - 1)(4x^2 + 4x + 6),$$

and, since the equation

$$4x^2 + 4x + 6 = 0$$

has no real solution, that 1 is the only critical number of g.

Clearly, $g'(0) < 0$ and $g'(2) > 0$, and therefore $g(1) = \sqrt{5}$ is a minimum value of g. The point on the graph nearest A is (1,1).

Since $Dx^2 = 2x$, the slope of the tangent line T to the graph of $y = x^2$ at the point $P(1,1)$ is 2. The slope of the line AP is $-\frac{1}{2}$, and therefore A lies on the normal line N of the graph at $P(1,1)$ (Figure 6.20).

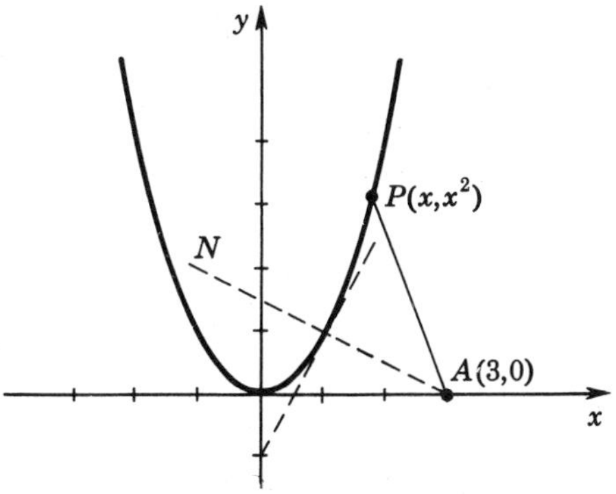

FIGURE 6.20

EXAMPLE 5. An apple orchard now has 30 trees per acre, and the average yield is 400 apples per tree. For each additional tree planted per acre, the average yield per tree is reduced by approximately 10 apples. How many trees per acre will give the largest crop of apples?

Solution: If x is the number of new trees planted per acre, then there are $30 + x$ trees per acre having an average yield of $400 - 10x$ apples per tree. Hence the total yield y of apples per acre is given by

$$\begin{aligned} y &= (30 + x)(400 - 10x) \\ &= 12{,}000 + 100x - 10x^2. \end{aligned}$$

Since

$$\frac{dy}{dx} = 100 - 20x,$$

$dy/dx = 0$ if $x = 5$. Hence an addition of 5 trees per acre will give the largest crop; then there will be 35 trees per acre, each yielding an average of 350 apples.

EXERCISES

I

1. A man has 600 yd of fencing which he is going to use to enclose a rectangular field and then subdivide the field into two plots with a fence parallel to a side. Of all the possible fields that can be so fenced, what are the dimensions of the one of maximum area?

2. Generalize Exercise 1 by dividing the field into n plots.

3. An open box is to be made by cutting out squares from the corners of a rectangular piece of cardboard and then turning up the sides. If the piece of cardboard is 12 in. by 24 in., what are the dimensions of the box of largest volume made in this way?

4. A rectangular box with square base and open top is to be made from 12 sq. ft of cardboard. What is the maximum possible volume of such a box?

5. A cylindrical cup (open top) is to hold a half-pint. How should it be made so as to use the least amount of material?

6. A wire 24 in. long is cut in two, and then one part is bent into the shape of a circle and the other into the shape of a square. How should it be cut if the sum of the areas of the circle and the square is to be a minimum? A maximum?

7. A rectangle of perimeter p is rotated about one of its sides so as to form a cylinder. Of all such possible rectangles, which generates a cylinder of maximum volume?

8. A rectangle has two of its vertices on the x axis and the other two above the x axis and on the graph of the parabola $y = 16 - x^2$. Of all such possible rectangles, what are the dimensions of the one of maximum area?

9. Show that (2,2) is the point on the graph of the equation $y = x^3 - 3x$ that is nearest the point (11,1).

10. Find the point on the graph of the equation $y^2 = 4x$ which is nearest to the point (2,1).

11. A ladder is to reach over a fence 8 ft high to a wall 1 ft behind the fence. What is the length of the shortest ladder that can be used?

12. Find the rectangle of maximum area that can be inscribed in a semicircle of radius r.

13. Show that the greatest area of any rectangle inscribed in a triangle is one-half that of the triangle.

14. A real estate office handles 80 apartment units. When the rent of each unit is \$60 per month, all units are occupied. However, for each \$2 increase in rent, one of the units becomes vacant. Each occupied unit requires an average of \$6 per month for service and repairs. What rent should be charged to realize the most profit?

15. A man in a motorboat 4 miles from the nearest point P on the shore wishes to go to a point Q 10 miles from P along the straight shoreline. The motorboat can travel 18 miles/hr and a car, which can pick up the man at any point between P and Q, can travel 30 miles/hr. At what point should the man land so as to reach Q in the least amount of time?

16. Three sides of a trapezoid have the same length a. Of all such possible trapezoids, show that the one of maximum area has its fourth side of length $2a$.

17. A Boston lodge has asked the railroad company to run a special train to New York for its members. The railroad company agrees to run the train if at least 200 people will go. The fare is to be \$8 per person if 200 go, and will decrease by 1¢ for everybody for each person over 200 that goes (thus, if 250 people go, the fare will be \$7.50). What number of passengers will give the railroad maximum revenues?

II

1. In an experiment repeated n times to determine a certain physical quantity x, the experimental values $x_1, x_2, \cdots, x_n$ were obtained. What value of x should we take if our criterion is to minimize the sum of the squares of the deviations, i.e., to minimize

$$(x - x_1)^2 + (x - x_2)^2 + \cdots + (x - x_n)^2?$$

2. Redo Exercise 1 if our criterion now is to minimize

$$|x - x_1| + |x - x_2| + \cdots + |x - x_n|.$$

3. Locate a point P within a triangle ABC such that $AP^2 + BP^2 + CP^2$ is a minimum.

4. Find the dimensions of the right circular cylinder of maximum volume inscribed in a sphere of radius r.

5. Find the dimensions of the right circular cone of maximum volume inscribed in a sphere of radius r.

6. Of all the right circular cylinders that can be inscribed in a given right circular cone, show that the one of greatest volume has altitude one-third that of the cone.

7. Find the greatest value of $x^m y^n$ where x and y are positive and $x + y = a$.

8. A line is drawn through the fixed point (h,k) to meet the axes OX and OY in points R and S. Find the minimum value of
   a. RS. b. $OR + OS$. c. $OR \cdot OS$.

The arithmetic-geometric mean inequality for two positive numbers a and b asserts that

$$\frac{a+b}{2} \geq \sqrt{ab}$$

with equality, if and only if, $a = b$. This follows immediately from $(\sqrt{a} - \sqrt{b})^2 \geq 0$. This inequality can be used to solve a large number of extrema problems. When it applies, it provides a more elegant approach than the calculus one of this section. This is to be expected, since the latter approach is much more general. As an example, let us find a rectangle of given perimeter P which has the maximum area. If a and b are the sides, then

$$a + b = \frac{P}{2} \text{ (specified)}$$

and

$$\text{Area} = ab.$$

By the above inequality ab is a maximum when $a = b$, or when the figure is a square. Dually, when the area is specified, the perimeter will be a minimum when the rectangle is a square.

In each of Exercises 9–12, solve the exercise from Part I by the arithmetic-geometric mean inequality.

9. Exercise 1.

10. Exercise 12.

11. Exercise 13.

12. Exercise 5; (use $\frac{a+b+c}{3} \geq \sqrt[3]{abc}$).

7 VELOCITY AND ACCELERATION

The derivative is closely related to the rate of change of a function as defined below. Before discussing rates of change in general, let us consider the special case of the motion of a point on a straight line.

We shall assume for the present that L is a horizontal coordinate line with unit point to the right of the origin, as in Figure 6.21. At the time t the expression $s(t)$ will designate the coordinate of the point P which is in motion on L. The

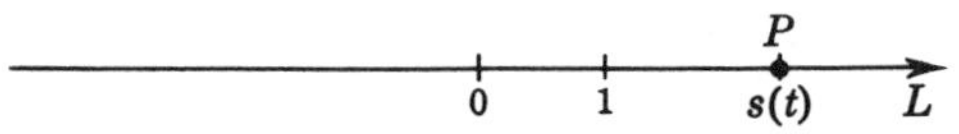

FIGURE 6.21

function s so determined by the position of P on L is called the *position function* of the moving point P.

For example, if

$$s(t) = t^2 - 2t,$$

then at the time $t = 0$ the position is $s(0) = 0$ and the point P is at the origin. At the time $t = 1$, $s(1) = -1$ and P is one unit to the left of the origin. Since $s(2) = 0$, then P returns to the origin after 2 units of time. When $t = 3$, $s(3) = 3$ and the point P has moved 3 units to the right. When $t = 4$, the position of P will be given by $s(4) = 8$.

In this example the point P moves from the position 0 to the position 8, a distance of 8 units, between time $t = 2$ and $t = 4$. Thus the point P moves 8 units of distance in 2 units of time. Average velocity is the ratio of distance traveled to time elapsed, so the average velocity of P from time $t = 2$ to $t = 4$ is $\frac{8}{2} = 4$ units of distance per unit of time. If, for example, distance is measured in feet and time in seconds, the average velocity of P from time $t = 2$ to time $t = 3$ is given by

$$\frac{s(3) - s(2)}{3 - 2} = 3 \text{ ft/sec.}$$

More generally, if s is the position function of a moving point P, the *average velocity* of P from time t to time $t + h$ is

$$\frac{s(t + h) - s(t)}{h}.$$

Knowledge of the average velocity of a moving point P gives us little if any information about the motion of the point at a particular instant. We cannot conclude, for example, that a jet airplane did not break the sound barrier if its average velocity on a certain flight was 500 miles per hour, nor can we conclude that it did break the sound barrier. The average velocity does not describe the "momentary" or "instantaneous" character of the motion.

This need for knowledge of the instantaneous character of the motion of a point leads us to the following definition.

6.15 DEFINITION. If s is the position function of a moving point P, the *velocity of P at the time t* is defined to be

$$\underset{h \to 0}{\text{limit}} \frac{s(t + h) - s(t)}{h},$$

and is designated by $v(t)$. Thus

$$v(t) = \underset{h \to 0}{\text{limit}} \frac{s(t + h) - s(t)}{h}.$$

We do not append to **6.15** the condition "if this limit exists," since we are working in the realm of physical motion and it is to be assumed that any point P in motion has a velocity at any time t.

What we have done above with the position function of a moving point can be done in general with any function. If a function f is defined in an interval $[a,b]$, then $f(b) - f(a)$ is the *change* in f between a and b, and

$$\frac{f(b) - f(a)}{b - a}$$

is the average change in f over each unit of the interval $[a,b]$; i.e., it is the *average rate of change of f* in $[a,b]$.

The *instantaneous rate of change* of f at a can then be defined as the limit of the average rate of change of f,

$$\operatorname*{limit}_{h\to 0} \frac{f(a + h) - f(a)}{h},$$

if this limit exists. Since this limit is just the derivative of f at a, it follows that $f'(a)$ may be considered the instantaneous rate of change of f at a.

To return to the position function s, we recognize the limit in **6.15** to be the derivative of s, so that

$$v(t) = s'(t).$$

Thus s is increasing at t if $v(t) > 0$ and decreasing at t if $v(t) < 0$. To say that s is increasing is to say that the point P is moving to the right on L; and to say that s is decreasing is to say that P is moving to the left on L. When $v(t) = 0$, the point P is said to be (momentarily) *at rest.*

Thus we have:

(1) If $v(t) > 0$, then P is moving to the right.
(2) If $v(t) < 0$, then P is moving to the left.
(3) If $v(t) = 0$, then P is at rest.

We are assuming that $v(t)$ exists for every time t, and hence $s'(t)$ always exists. Therefore the only critical numbers of s are those for which $s'(t) = 0$, and we may make the following observation: *A point in motion on a straight line cannot change its direction without coming to rest.*

If s is the position function of a jet plane which leaves at time t_1 and arrives at its destination at time t_2, and if its average velocity is 500 miles per hour, then

$$\frac{s(t_2) - s(t_1)}{t_2 - t_1} = 500$$

By the mean value theorem 6.5, the left side of the equation above is equal to $s'(t) = v(t)$ for some time t between t_1 and t_2. Thus the velocity of the plane is exactly 500 miles per hour at some instant t in its flight.

In the example above,

$$s(t) = t^2 - 2t,$$

and hence

$$v(t) = 2t - 2.$$

Since $v(0) = -2$, then P is moving to the left at time $t = 0$. When $t = 1$, $v(1) = 0$ and P is at rest. In fact, P is at rest at no other time, since the equation

$$v(t) = 2(t - 1) = 0$$

has the unique solution $t = 1$. Clearly, $v(t) > 0$ (and P is moving to the right) if $t > 1$. The motion of P for $t \geq 0$ is indicated in Figure 6.22.

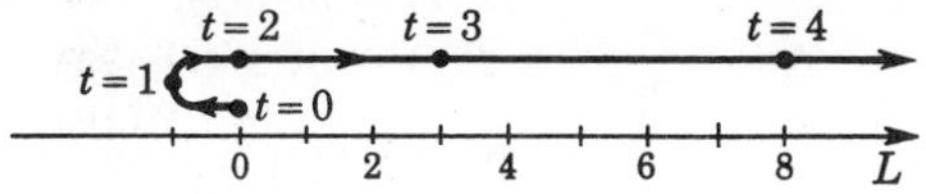

FIGURE 6.22

It is to be remembered that the point P always remains on the line L and that the figure is diagrammatic.

The *speed* of a moving point P at time t is defined to be

$$|v(t)|.$$

Thus the speed is the magnitude of the velocity, and it does not indicate the direction of motion.

Average acceleration is defined to be the average rate of change in velocity relative to time. Thus, if v is the velocity function of the moving point P, the *average acceleration* of P from time t to time $t + h$ is

$$\frac{v(t + h) - v(t)}{h}.$$

The acceleration of P at a given time is defined as follows.

6.16 **DEFINITION.** If v is the velocity function of a moving point P, the *acceleration of P at the time t* is defined to be

$$\lim_{h \to 0} \frac{v(t + h) - v(t)}{h},$$

and is designated by $a(t)$.

It follows that

$$a(t) = v'(t) = s''(t).$$

In the example above,

$$s(t) = t^2 - 2t, \quad v(t) = 2t - 2, \quad a(t) = 2.$$

If distance is measured in feet and time in seconds, the units of velocity are feet per second (ft/sec) and those of acceleration are feet per second per second (ft/sec^2). Thus in this example the acceleration is a constant of 2 ft/sec^2.

The *second law of Newtonian mechanics* states that the force acting on an object is the product of the mass of the object and its acceleration. If m is the mass of the object P moving along a straight line with position function s, then the force $F(t)$ acting on P at time t is given by the equation

$$F(t) = m \cdot a(t),$$

or

$$F(t) = m \cdot s''(t).$$

If at some time t, $a(t) = 0$, then also $F(t) = 0$ and no force is acting on P. In this event P can be said to be coasting.

If at time t_1 the point P is at rest $[v(t_1) = 0]$ and if $a(t_1) < 0$, then by the second derivative test [recalling that $a(t_1) = s''(t_1)$], $s(t_1)$ is a maximum value of s; i.e., $s(t) < s(t_1)$ for $t \neq t_1$ in some time interval (t_2,t_3) containing t_1. Then P must have approached the position $s(t_1)$ from the left, it must have come to rest at the position $s(t_1)$, and it must have reversed the direction of its motion.

A similar argument may be made if $v(t_1) = 0$ and $a(t_1) > 0$, in which case $s(t_1)$ is a minimum value of s. In either case we may make the following statement:

If $v(t_1) = 0$ and $a(t_1) \neq 0$, then P must reverse its direction of motion at the position $s(t_1)$.

EXAMPLE 1. Discuss the motion of the point P if its position at time t on a coordinate line L is given by

$$s(t) = t^3 - 6t^2 + 20, \qquad \text{domain } s = [-2,6]$$

Solution: Since $v(t) = s'(t)$ and $a(t) = v'(t)$,

$$v(t) = 3t^2 - 12t, \qquad a(t) = 6t - 12.$$

The point P will be at rest when

$$v(t) = 3t(t - 4) = 0,$$

i.e., when $t = 0$ or $t = 4$. Thus 0 and 4 are the critical times of s. Since $a(0) < 0$ and $a(4) > 0$, point P changes its direction of motion at each critical time; and $s(0) = 20$ is a maximum value of s and $s(4) = -12$ is a minimum value of s.

An indication of the motion of P can be obtained from the accompanying table of values and Figure 6.23.

t	$s(t)$	$v(t)$	$a(t)$
-2	-12	36	-24
-1	13	15	-18
0	20	0	-12
2	4	-12	0
4	-12	0	12
6	20	36	24

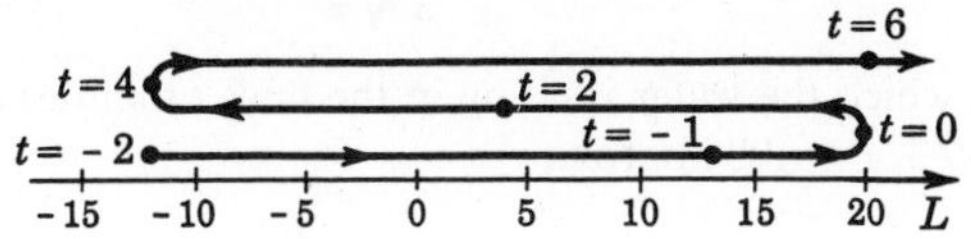

FIGURE 6.23

We give now a somewhat different type of problem involving rates of change of a function.

EXAMPLE 2. Water is running into the conical tank shown in Figure 6.24 at a constant rate of 2 cubic feet per minute (ft^3/min). How fast is the water rising in the tank at any instant?

Solution: At any time t min after the water starts running, let $h(t)$ be the depth of the water and $r(t)$ the radius of the surface of the water in the tank (Figure 6.24). Clearly, $r(t) = h(t)/2$, and the volume $V(t)$ of the water in the tank is $2t$, $V(t) = 2t$. By geometry,

$$V = \tfrac{1}{3}\pi r^2 h;$$

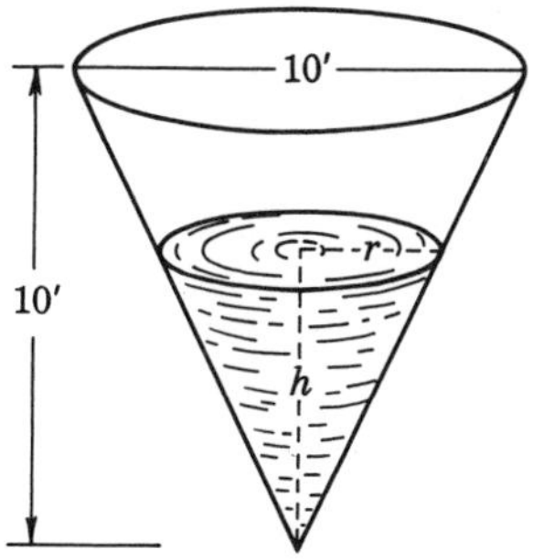

FIGURE 6.24

thus
$$2t = \frac{1}{3}\pi\left(\frac{h}{2}\right)^2 h,$$

and
$$24t = \pi h^3 \quad \text{or} \quad h^3 = \frac{24}{\pi}t.$$

Hence
$$h(t) = \left(2\sqrt[3]{\frac{3}{\pi}}\right)t^{1/3}.$$

The rate of rise of the water is the instantaneous rate of change of h, which is h', by our discussion above. Thus

$$h'(t) = \frac{2}{3}\sqrt[3]{\frac{3}{\pi}}\,t^{-2/3} \text{ ft/min}$$

is the rate at which the water is rising in the tank t minutes after the water starts running. Since $\sqrt[3]{3/\pi} = .98$ approx.,

$$h'(t) \doteq \frac{.65}{\sqrt[3]{t^2}}.$$

Thus, at $t = 8$, $\sqrt[3]{t^2} = 4$ and

$$h'(t) \doteq .16 \text{ ft/min}.$$

EXERCISES

I

In each of Exercises 1–10 the position function of a point moving on a straight line is given. Discuss the motion of the point.

1. $s(t) = -16t^2 + 80t$, $(0 \le t \le 5)$.
2. $s(t) = -16t^2 + 32t + 20$, $(0 \le t \le 4)$.
3. $s(t) = t^2 - 8t + 4$, $(-2 \le t \le 6)$.
4. $s(t) = 12 + 6t + t^2$, $(-6 \le t \le 0)$.
5. $s(t) = t^3 - 3t$.
6. $s(t) = t^3 - 3t^2 - 24t$.
7. $s(t) = 2 + t - t^2 - t^3$.
8. $s(t) = t^4 - 4t^3$.
9. $s(t) = t^2 + \frac{16}{t}$, $(t \ge 1)$.
10. $s(t) = 4t + \frac{9}{t}$, $(t \ge 1)$.
11. Gas is being pumped into a balloon so that its volume is constantly increasing at the rate of 4 in.^{3}/sec. Find the rate of increase of the radius of the balloon at any time t seconds after the inflation begins. Approximate this rate at $t = 8$.

12. A ladder 25 ft long is leaning against a wall, with the bottom of the ladder 7 ft from the base of the wall. If the lower end is pulled away from the wall at the rate of 1 ft/sec, find the rate of descent of the upper end along the wall. Approximate this rate of descent at the end of 8 sec.

13. Ship A is 60 miles due north of ship B at 10 A.M. Ship A is sailing due east at 20 miles/hr, while ship B is sailing due north at 16 miles/hr. Find the distance $d(t)$ between the ships t hours after 10 A.M. Also find the rate of change of the distance between them. At what time are the ships closest together?

14. A conical tank, full of water, is 12 ft high and 20 ft in diameter at the top. If the water is let out at the bottom at the rate of 4 ft³/min, find the rate of change of the depth of the water t minutes after the water starts running out. Approximate this rate at $t = 10$ min.

15. A trough 9 ft long has as its cross section an isosceles right triangle with hypotenuse of length 2 ft along the top of the trough. If water is pouring into the trough at the rate of 2 ft³/min, find the depth $h(t)$ of the water t minutes after the water is turned on. Also find the rate at which the depth is increasing when $t = 2$.

II

Each of the following figures is the graph of some function F. Using the same set of axes, make a rough sketch of the derivative function F'. The encircled points indicate relative extrema points or points of inflection.

1.

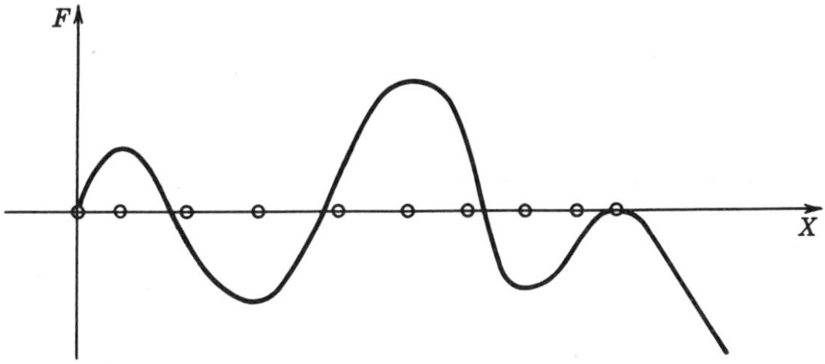

2.

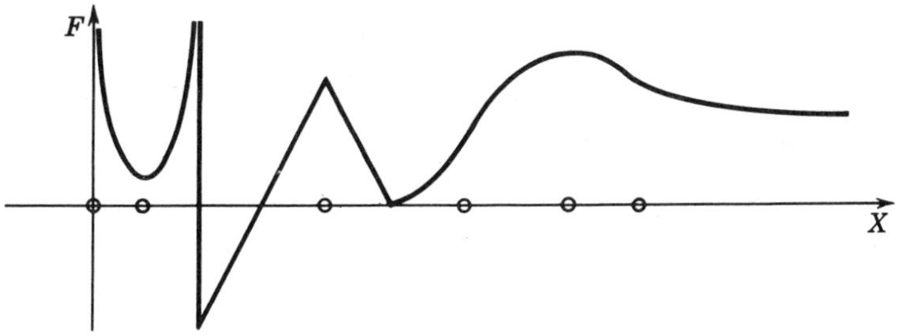

3.

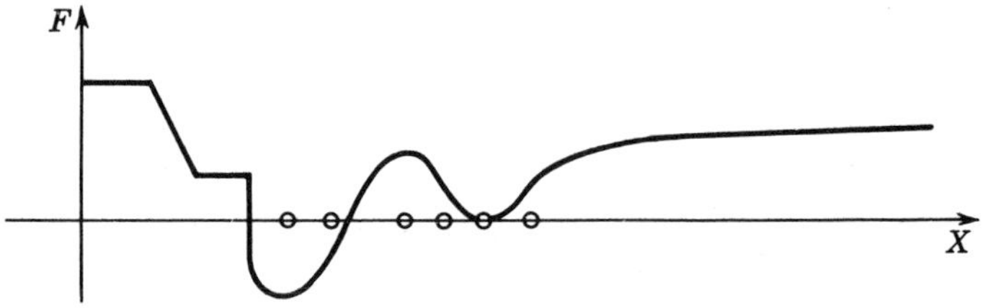

8 ANTIDERIVATIVES

Corresponding to each function f is its derived function f'. For example, if f is defined by

$$f(x) = x^3 - 6x + 12,$$

then f' is defined by

$$f'(x) = 3x^2 - 6.$$

We now ask the following question. Given a function g, does there exist a function f such that g is the derivative of f? If, for example, g is defined by

$$g(x) = 3x^2 - 6,$$

then g is the derivative of f defined by

$$f(x) = x^3 - 6x + 12.$$

The answer to this question is yes if g is a continuous function. The proof of this fact will come in Chapter 7 after the concept of the integral has been introduced. Here we shall be concerned only with formal properties of the antiderivative, defined as follows:

6.17 **DEFINITION.** The function f is called an *antiderivative* of the function g if $f' = g$.

For example, if

$$g(x) = 6x^2,$$

then the function f_1 defined by

$$f_1(x) = 2x^3$$

is an antiderivative of g since

$$f_1'(x) = g(x).$$

It is equally true that the function f_2 defined by

$$f_2(x) = 2x^3 + 7$$

is an antiderivative of g, since

$$f_2'(x) = g(x).$$

It is clear that if f_1 is an antiderivative of g, and if $f_2(x) = f_1(x) + c$, (c a real number), then

$$f_2'(x) = f_1'(x) = g(x)$$

and f_2 also is an antiderivative of g. The converse of this statement is also true, as we shall now prove.

6.18 **THEOREM.** If for the functions f_1 and f_2 there exists an interval $[a,b]$ such that

$$f_1'(x) = f_2'(x)$$

in $[a,b]$, then there exists a number c such that

$$f_1(x) = f_2(x) + c$$

in $[a,b]$.

Proof: Let the function F be the difference between f_1 and f_2,

$$F(x) = f_1(x) - f_2(x), \quad x \text{ in } [a,b].$$

By hypothesis,

$$F'(x) = 0, \quad x \text{ in } [a,b].$$

Hence, by the mean value theorem, for every x in $(a,b]$ there exists a number z in (a,x) such that

$$F(x) - F(a) = (x - a)F'(z) = 0.$$

Thus $F(x) = F(a)$ for every x in $[a,b]$, and

$$f_1(x) = f_2(x) + c, \quad x \text{ in } [a,b],$$

where $c = F(a)$. This proves **6.18.**

If

$$f'(x) = 6x^2,$$

as in the example above, then

$$f(x) = 2x^3 + c$$

for some number c, according to **6.18.**

According to a previous differentiation formula (5.17),

$$D\left[\frac{a}{m+1}x^{m+1}\right] = ax^m,$$

(m a rational number, $m \neq -1$, a any real number). Thus, if

$$g(x) = ax^m, \qquad (m \neq -1),$$

the function f defined by

$$f(x) = \frac{a}{m+1}x^{m+1}$$

is an antiderivative of g, since

$$Df(x) = g(x).$$

We state this as a formula: If $f'(x) = ax^m$, then

$$f(x) = \frac{a}{m+1}x^{m+1} + c, \qquad (m \neq -1).$$

If $g = g_1 + g_2$, and if f_1 and f_2 are antiderivatives of g_1 and g_2, respectively, then $f = f_1 + f_2$ is an antiderivative of g, since

$$Df(x) = Df_1(x) + Df_2(x) = g_1(x) + g_2(x) = g(x).$$

More generally, *an antiderivative of a sum of functions is the sum of antiderivatives of the functions.*

EXAMPLE 1. Find $f(x)$ if

$$f'(x) = 4x^3 - 2x^2 + 5x + 3.$$

Solution: Since

$$D(x^4 - \tfrac{2}{3}x^3 + \tfrac{5}{2}x^2 + 3x) = 4x^3 - 2x^2 + 5x + 3,$$
$$f(x) = x^4 - \tfrac{2}{3}x^3 + \tfrac{5}{2}x^2 + 3x + c$$

for some number c.

If

$$f'(x) = 4x - 3 \quad \text{and} \quad f(1) = 3,$$

then

$$f(x) = 2x^2 - 3x + c$$

for some number c. Since

$$f(1) = 2 - 3 + c = 3,$$

$c = 4$. Thus

$$f(x) = 2x^2 - 3x + 4,$$

and there is just one function f satisfying the given conditions.

The equation

$$f'(x) = 4x - 3$$

is an example of a *differential equation*, and the equation

$$f(1) = 3$$

is called a *boundary condition* of f. Given f' and a boundary condition on f, there is a unique antiderivative f of f' satisfying the given boundary condition. This function f is called the *solution* of the given differential equation.

EXAMPLE 2. Solve the differential equation

$$f'(x) = x^2 + 5$$

with boundary condition

$$f(0) = -1.$$

Solution: Clearly,

$$f(x) = \tfrac{1}{3}x^3 + 5x + c$$

for some number c. Since

$$f(0) = 0 + 0 + c = -1,$$

$c = -1$ and

$$f(x) = \tfrac{1}{3}x^3 + 5x - 1.$$

If s, v, and a are the respective position, velocity, and acceleration functions of some point P in motion on a coordinate line L, then s is an antiderivative of v and v is an antiderivative of a, since

$$s'(t) = v(t), \qquad v'(t) = a(t).$$

Hence, given the velocity or acceleration function and some boundary conditions, called *initial conditions* if given for $t = 0$, it is possible to determine the position function. This is illustrated in the following example.

EXAMPLE 3. Find $s(t)$ if it is known that

$$a(t) = 6t - 2,$$

and $\quad v(0) = 3, \qquad s(0) = -1.$

Solution: Since $a(t) = v'(t)$,

$$v'(t) = 6t - 2,$$

and $\quad v(t) = 3t^2 - 2t + c_1,$

for some number c_1. However,

$$v(0) = 0 - 0 + c_1 = 3,$$

and $c_1 = 3$. Thus

$$v(t) = 3t^2 - 2t + 3.$$

Again, $v(t) = s'(t) = 3t^2 - 2t + 3$, and

$$s(t) = t^3 - t^2 + 3t + c_2$$

for some number c_2. Since

$$s(0) = c_2 = -1,$$

$c_2 = -1$ and

$$s(t) = t^3 - t^2 + 3t - 1.$$

An object P is pulled toward the earth by a *force of gravity*. The *acceleration of gravity* due to this force is designated by g. The number g varies with the distance of P from the center of the earth, but is essentially a constant over a small range of distances. An approximate value of g is

$$g = 32 \text{ ft/sec}^2$$

if the object P is near sea level.

EXAMPLE 4. A ball is thrown directly upward from a point 24 ft above the ground with an initial velocity of 40 ft/sec. Assuming no air resistance, how high will the ball rise and when will it return to the ground?

Solution: In Figure 6.25 the vertical line L indicates the path of the ball and the horizontal line represents the ground. The units on L are feet. If s is the position function of the ball,

$$s(0) = 24,$$

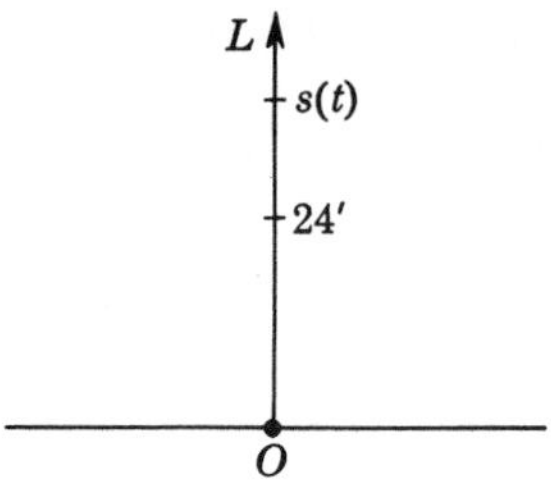

FIGURE 6.25

by the assumption that the ball starts 24 ft above the ground. Also,

$$v(0) = 40,$$

since the initial velocity is 40 ft/sec.

Since L is directed upward whereas the force of gravity pulls the ball toward the earth, the velocity will decrease, and therefore

$$a(t) = -32.$$

Since v is an antiderivative of a,

$$v(t) = -32t + c_1.$$

However, $v(0) = 40$, and therefore $c_1 = 40$ and

$$v(t) = -32t + 40.$$

Also, s is an antiderivative of v, so that

$$s(t) = -16t^2 + 40t + c_2.$$

Again, $s(0) = 24$ and $c_2 = 24$. Thus

$$s(t) = -16t^2 + 40t + 24.$$

The ball reaches its maximum height when $v(t) = 0$, i.e., when

$$-32t + 40 = 0$$

or

$$t = \tfrac{5}{4} \text{ sec.}$$

The actual maximum height is given by

$$s(\tfrac{5}{4}) = -16(\tfrac{5}{4})^2 + 40(\tfrac{5}{4}) + 24 = 49 \text{ ft.}$$

The ball reaches the ground when $s(t) = 0$, i.e., when

$$-16t^2 + 40t + 24 = 0.$$

Since

$$-16t^2 + 40t + 24 = -8(2t + 1)(t - 3),$$

the ball reaches the ground when $t = 3$, i.e., after 3 sec. The number $t = -\frac{1}{2}$ is not in the domain of s, since the ball was thrown at the time $t = 0$.

EXERCISES

I

In each of Exercises 1–6, find an antiderivative of the given function.

1. $f(x) = 1 - 4x + 9x^2$.
2. $g(x) = 5x^4 - 6x^2 + 3x$.

3. $F(x) = x\sqrt{x} + \sqrt{x} - 5.$

4. $G(z) = \sqrt[3]{z} + 2z^{3/2}.$

5. $H(x) = \sqrt[4]{x+1}.$

6. $h(x) = 3(x-2)^4.$

In each of Exercises 7–10, find the solution of the given differential equation that satisfies the given boundary conditions.

7. $F'(x) = 3(x+2)^3, \quad F(0) = 0.$

8. $G'(x) = \sqrt{2} - 2x + x^2, \quad G(\sqrt{2}) = 1.$

9. $s''(t) = 8, \quad s'(0) = 7, \quad s(-1) = -3.$

10. $f''(x) = \dfrac{1}{\sqrt{x}} - 10, \quad f'(1) = 3, \quad f(4) = 0.$

11. A ball is thrown directly upward from the ground with an initial velocity of 56 ft/sec. Assuming no air resistance, how high will the ball rise and when will it return to the ground?

12. An object slides down an inclined plane with an acceleration of 16 ft/sec^2. If the object is given an initial velocity of 4 ft/sec from the top of the inclined plane, find the position function of the object. If the plane is 60 ft long, when does the object reach the end of the plane?

13. A ball is thrown directly downward from a point 144 ft above the ground with enough initial velocity so that it reaches the ground in 2 sec. Ignoring air resistance, find the initial velocity.

14. A car is coasting along a level road at an initial speed of 30 ft/sec. If the car is retarded by friction at the rate of 2 ft/sec^2 (i.e., an acceleration of -2 ft/sec^2), in how many seconds will the car stop? How far will it have coasted?

15. A ball rolls down an inclined plane 200 ft long with an acceleration of 8 ft/sec^2. Find the position function of the ball if it is given no initial velocity. How long does it take the ball to reach the end of the plane? What initial velocity must it be given to reach the end of the plane in 4 sec?

16. Starting from rest, with what constant acceleration must a car proceed to go 200 ft in 4 sec?

II

1. A point moving with uniform acceleration describes distances s_1, s_2 feet in successive intervals of t_1, t_2 seconds respectively. Determine the acceleration.

2. A ball is projected vertically upward. Show that if t_1, t_2 are the times at which it passes a point at a height h above the point of projection in ascending and descending, respectively, then $gt_1t_2 = 2h$. (Neglect air resistance.)

REVIEW

Oral Exercises

Explain or define the following:

1. Extrema of a function in an interval.
2. An increasing function.
3. A critical number of a function.
4. Rolle's theorem.
5. Mean value theorem.
6. Monotonic function.
7. Strictly monotonic function.
8. A strictly decreasing function in an interval.
9. Relative extrema.
10. Concavity of a graph.
11. Point of inflection.
12. Endpoint extrema.
13. Velocity and acceleration of a point moving in a straight line.
14. Antiderivative.
15. Differential equation.
16. Boundary condition.
17. Initial condition.

REVIEW

I

In each of Exercises 1–6, sketch the graph of the polynomial function. Find extremal points and points of inflection.

1. $f(x) = x^2 - 4$.
2. $g(x) = (x^2 - 4)^2$.
3. $f(x) = x(x^2 - 1)$.
4. $g(x) = x^2(x^2 - 1)^2$.
5. $F(x) = 3x^5 - 40x^3 - 135x$.
6. $G(x) = x^4 - 4x$.
7. Let $g(x) = x^{1/2} + mx$. Find the extrema of g when $m > 0$, $m = 0$, $m < 0$.
8. Discuss the graph of g if:
   a. $g(x) = x^{2/3}\sqrt{9 - x^2}$.
   b. $g(x) = (x - 4)^{4/3} + 2(x + 4)^{2/3}$.
9. Let $f(x) = x^4 - 8x^2 + 4$. Sketch graphs of f, f', and f'' on the same coordinate axes and interpret the relationships among these graphs in terms of the theorems of this chapter.

10. Let $f(x) = (x - a)^n g(x)$, where $g'(a)$ exists, $g(a) \neq 0$, and n is a positive integer. Under what conditions on n will the graph of f cross the x axis at $(a,0)$? Under what conditions is the x axis the tangent line to the graph of f at $(a,0)$?

11. Find all the normal lines to the graph of the equation $y = x^2$ which pass through the point $(0,2)$.

12. Let $f(x) = x^2|x|$. Sketch the graph of f. Is $(0,0)$ a point of inflection of this graph? Show that $f'''(0)$ does not exist.

13. Analyze the graph of the function g defined by $g(x) = x|x - 1|$.

14. The total area of a page in a book is to be 96 sq in. The margins at the top and bottom of the page are each to have width $1\frac{1}{2}$ in. and those at the sides are to have width 1 in. For what dimensions of the page is the printed area the greatest, and what is this maximum area?

15. A truck has a minimum speed of 10 mph in high gear. When traveling x mph in high gear, the truck burns diesel oil at the rate of

$$\frac{1}{300}\left(\frac{900}{x} + x\right) \text{ gal/mile.}$$

The truck cannot be driven over 50 mph. If diesel oil costs 20¢ a gallon, find:
a. The steady speed that will minimize the cost of fuel for a 500-mile trip.
b. The steady speed that will minimize the total cost of the trip if the driver is paid \$1.50 an hour.

16. Determine the minimum area of a triangle formed by the x axis, the y axis, and a line through the point (h,k).

17. Two points A and B lie on the same side of the line l. If P be a point on l, determine its position such that $AP + PB$ is a minimum. Show that for this point AP and BP make equal angles with l.

In Exercises 18–21, find the maxima and minima of the given functions in the stated intervals.

18. $y = \sqrt{25 - x^2} \quad (-3 \leq x \leq 4)$.

19. $y = \dfrac{1 - x + x^2}{1 + x - x^2} \quad (0 \leq x \leq 1)$.

20. $y = \dfrac{x - 2}{x + 2} \quad (0 \leq x \leq 4)$.

21. $y = \dfrac{a^2}{x} + \dfrac{b^2}{1 - x} \quad (0 < x < 1)$.

II

1. Discuss the significance of the signs of the first and second derivatives of a function in regard to the graph of the function. Illustrate by sketches what the graph of the function F can look like near a point where:

a. $F' > 0, \quad F'' > 0.$
b. $F' > 0, \quad F'' < 0.$
c. $F' < 0, \quad F'' > 0.$
d. $F' < 0, \quad F'' < 0.$
e. $F' > 0, \quad F'' = 0.$
f. $F' < 0, \quad F'' = 0.$
g. $F' = 0, \quad F'' > 0.$
h. $F' = 0, \quad F'' < 0.$
i. $F' = 0, \quad F'' = 0.$

In each of Exercises 2 and 3, discuss the character of the graph of the function F at the points where its derivative is zero if its derivative is as given.

2. $F'(x) = (x - 1)(x - 2)^2(x - 3)^3(x - 4)^6.$

3. $F'(x) = (2x - 1)^2(x + 1)^3(x + 3)^5(5x + 4)^4/(x^2 + 1).$

4. Find the minimum value of $x^2 + y^2$ subject to the constraint $xy = a^2$. Give a geometric interpretation.

5. Show that for every real number x,

$$\frac{1}{5} \leq \frac{x^2 - 4x + 9}{x^2 + 4x + 9} \leq 5.$$

6. Show that the relative extrema of the function f defined by

$$f(x) = \frac{(x + a)(x + b)}{(x - a)(x - b)}$$

are c and $1/c$, where $c = -(\sqrt{a} + \sqrt{b})^2/(\sqrt{a} - \sqrt{b})^2$. Sketch the graph of f.

7. For which values of a does the function f defined by

$$f(x) = \frac{(x^2 + 2x + a)}{(x^2 + 4x + 3a)}$$

have $(-\infty, \infty)$ as its range?

8. Generalize Exercise 10, Section 6, I.

9. Generalize Exercise 3. Section 6, II.

10. If function G is such that G'' is continuous and positive-valued in an interval (a,b), then what is the maximum number of roots of each of the equations $G(x) = 0$ and $G'(x) = 0$ in (a,b)? Prove your answer and illustrate it with some examples.

11. The functions F, G, and their derivatives are continuous in a certain interval, and $FG' - F'G$ never vanishes in this interval. Show that between any two zeros of F [i.e., numbers at which $F(x) = 0$] there lies one of G, and conversely. (*Hint:* Consider F/G.)

12. If the velocity v of a point moving on the x axis is given by $v(x) = F(x)$, show that the acceleration a is given by $a(x) = F(x)F'(x)$.

13. If the acceleration a of a point moving on the x axis is given by $a(x) = F(x)$, show that the velocity v is given by

$$\frac{v^2(x)}{2} = \text{an antiderivative of } F(x).$$

14. If a particle of mass m is projected outwardly normal to the earth (assumed spherical), the equation of motion, ignoring air resistance and other bodies, is given by

$$ma = -\frac{kmM}{r^2},$$

where a = acceleration, k = universal gravitational constant, M = mass of the earth, r = distance of the particle from the center of the earth. Using Exercise 13, show that the minimum velocity of escape is V (escape) $= \sqrt{2gR} \doteq 6.9$ miles/sec, where R is the radius of the earth ($\doteq 4000$ miles) and $g \doteq 32.2$ ft/sec. (Note that at the earth's surface $mg = kmM/R^2$.)

15. If in Exercise 14 the initial velocity is p percent of $\sqrt{2gR}$, what is the maximum distance the particle travels away from the earth?

7

INTEGRALS

WE INTERRUPT our study of the derivative to describe the other basic concept of the calculus, namely the integral. Before defining the integral, we must state another property of the real number system that will enter into this definition.

1 COMPLETENESS OF THE REAL NUMBER SYSTEM

If the square root process is applied in finding $\sqrt{2}$, we get successively the rational numbers

$$1, 1.4, 1.41, 1.414, 1.4142, 1.41421, \cdots.$$

The set A of numbers so obtained has the property that $x < \sqrt{2}$ for every x in A. We call $\sqrt{2}$ an upper bound of set A.

For any set S, a number c is called an *upper bound* of S if $x \leq c$ for every x in S. Similarly, a number d is called a *lower bound* of S if $x \geq d$ for every x in S.

If, for example, A is the set $\{1, 1.4, 1.41, 1.414, 1.4142, 1.41421, \cdots\}$ described above, then $\sqrt{2}$ is an upper bound of A, since $\sqrt{2} \geq x$ for every x in A. Actually, $\sqrt{2} > x$ for every x in A, so that $\sqrt{2}$ is not an element of set A. Also, 1 is a lower bound of set A, since $1 \leq x$ for every x in A. The number $\sqrt{2}$ is not the only upper bound of set A. Thus 2, 7, $\frac{3}{2}$, and 10^6 are also upper bounds of A. Other lower bounds of A are -1, $\frac{1}{2}$, 0, and -100. A lower bound (or an upper bound), when it exists, is never unique.

As another example, the set $(0, \infty)$ has 0 as a lower bound. Other lower bounds of this infinite interval are $-\frac{1}{2}$, -2, and -99. It is clear that the set $(0, \infty)$ has no upper bound.

The open interval (a,b) has a and every number less than a as lower bounds; and b and every number greater than b as upper bounds. If $c > a$, then c is not a lower bound of set (a,b). For if $c > a$, then either $a < c < b$ or $c \geq b$. If $a < c < b$, then

$$a < \frac{a+c}{2} < c < b,$$

and c is not a lower bound of (a,b) since $(a + c)/2$ is an element of (a,b) such that $c > (a + c)/2$. If $c \geq b$, then $(a + b)/2$ is an element of (a,b) such that $c > (a + b)/2$. Thus, among all lower bounds of set (a,b), the greatest one is a. Similarly, among all upper bounds of set (a,b), the least one is b. This example illustrates the following definition.

7.1 **DEFINITION.** Let S be a set of real numbers. A lower bound c of S is called the *greatest lower bound* (abbreviated g.l.b.) of S if no lower bound of S is greater than c. Similarly, an upper bound d of S is called the *least upper bound* (abbreviated l.u.b.) of S if no upper bound of S is less than d.

For example by our remarks above, the open interval $(-1,3)$ has -1 as its g.l.b. and 3 as its l.u.b.

As another example, the infinite interval $[2, \infty)$ has 2 as its g.l.b. This interval has no upper bound, and hence no l.u.b.

The set $A = \{1, 1.4, 1.41, 1.414, 1.4142, 1.41421, \cdots\}$ consisting of rational approximations of $\sqrt{2}$ has 1 as its g.l.b. and $\sqrt{2}$ as its l.u.b.

We are now ready to state the final property of the real number system. This property, together with the algebraic and order properties discussed in Chapter 1, completely characterizes the system of real numbers.

7.2 **THE COMPLETENESS PROPERTY.** Every set S of real numbers that has a lower bound has a greatest lower bound, and every set S that has an upper bound has a least upper bound.

This is not a theorem to be proved. Rather, we take it to be one of the basic defining properties of the real number system.

Let us use the completeness property to prove a seemingly obvious fact, namely that the set Z of all integers has no upper bound. If, on the contrary, Z does have an upper bound, then Z has a l.u.b., say d. Thus $x \leq d$ for every integer x. Now if x is an integer, so is $x + 1$; therefore $x + 1 \leq d$ for every x in Z. But then $x \leq d - 1$ for every integer x, and $d - 1$ is an upper bound of set Z. However, this contradicts our choice of d as the l.u.b. of set Z. We conclude that Z has no upper bound. Similarly, it may be proved that Z has no lower bound.

If c is the g.l.b. of a set S and t is any number such that $t > c$, then necessarily $t > x \geq c$ for some x in S. For if no such number x in S existed, then t would be a lower bound of S greater than the g.l.b. of S. Similarly, if d is the l.u.b. of a set S and $t < d$, then $t < x \leq d$ for some number x in S.

As an illustration of the use of the completeness property, let us prove the following result.

7.3 INTERMEDIATE VALUE THEOREM FOR FUNCTIONS. If a function f is continuous in a closed interval $[a,b]$, then f assumes every value between $f(a)$ and $f(b)$.

Proof: We wish to show that for every number d between $f(a)$ and $f(b)$, there exists a number c in $[a,b]$ such that $f(c) = d$. For convenience, let us assume that $f(a) < d < f(b)$. Let S denote the set of all numbers x in $[a,b]$ for which $f(x) < d$. Clearly a is in S, b is not in S, and b is an upper bound of S. Hence, S has a l.u.b. c by the completeness property.

One of three possible situations holds: $f(c) < d$, $f(c) = d$, $f(c) > d$. If $f(c) - d < 0$, then $f(x) - d < 0$ in some neighborhood $(c - \delta, c + \delta)$ of c by **4.6**. However, then $f(x) < d$ for some $x > c$, contrary to the fact that $c =$ l.u.b. S. If $f(c) - d > 0$, then $f(x) - d > 0$ in some neighborhood $(c - \delta, c + \delta)$ of c by **4.6**, contrary to the fact that $f(x) < d$ for some x in *every* neighborhood of c. Therefore, we must have $f(c) = d$. This proves **7.3**.

EXERCISES

I

1. If S is a set of real numbers and b is a number such that (1) b is an upper bound of S, and (2) for every upper bound b' of S the relation $b \leq b'$ holds, then b is a least upper bound (l.u.b.) of S. Prove that b is unique. (*Hint:* Assume that b and c are least upper bounds of S. Show that $b \leq c$ and $c \leq b$ both hold.) State a similar theorem for greatest lower bound (g.l.b.).

2. It is shown in the text that a is the g.l.b. and b is the l.u.b. of the open interval (a,b). Prove that a is the g.l.b. and b is the l.u.b. of the closed interval $[a,b]$ also.

3. Give examples of sets which contain their l.u.b. and sets which do not. Similarly, give examples for g.l.b.

4. If a set S contains a greatest element b, prove that b is the l.u.b. of S. State and prove a similar result for g.l.b.

5. Prove that every set S consisting of a finite number $a_1, a_2, \cdots, a_n$ of real numbers contains its l.u.b. and g.l.b.

6. If $c > 0$ and S is the set of all multiples $c, 2c, 3c, \cdots, nc, \cdots$ of c, prove that S has no upper bound, and hence no l.u.b.

7. Use the preceding exercise to prove the *Archimedean Principle:* Let c and d be any numbers with $c > 0$. Then there exists some positive integer n such that $nc > d$. Illustrate this principle for the following cases:

   a. $c = 2, \quad d = 131.$ b. $c = 10^{-6}, d = 10^6.$

8. Let S be the set consisting of the rational numbers $\frac{1}{2}, \frac{2}{3}, \frac{3}{4}, \frac{4}{5}, \cdots, n/(n+1), \cdots$. Prove that 1 is the l.u.b. of S. [*Hint:* If $0 < c < 1$, use Exercise 7 to show that there exists a positive integer m such that $c < m/(m+1)$.]

9. Let the set S consist of the reciprocals of all positive integers: $1, \frac{1}{2}, \frac{1}{3}, \frac{1}{4}, \cdots, 1/n, \cdots$. Prove that 0 is the g.l.b. of S. [*Hint:* If $c > 0$, use Exercise 7 to prove that there exists a positive integer n such that $c > 1/n$.]

10. Prove that if a and b are any positive real numbers with $a < b$, then there exists some rational number r between a and b, $a < r < b$. [*Hint:* Select a positive integer n such that $na > 1$ and $n(b - a) > 1$. Then select a positive integer m such that $m > na$ and $m - 1 \leq na$. Show that $a < m/n < b$.]

11. Let S be the set of all rational numbers less than a given real number b. Use Exercise 10 to prove that b is the l.u.b. of S.

12. If the number $a > 1$, then show that the set of all powers of a, $\{a, a^2, a^3, \cdots, a^n, \cdots\}$ has no upper bound. Hence prove that if $b > 0$ then $a^{-n} < b$ for some integer $n > 0$.

II

1. Let S be the set of irrational numbers

$$S = \{\sqrt{2}, \sqrt{2\sqrt{2}}, \sqrt{2\sqrt{2\sqrt{2}}}, \cdots, a_n, \cdots\},$$

   where $a_1 = \sqrt{2}$ and $a_{n+1} = \sqrt{2a_n}$ for each $n > 1$.
   a. Show that 2 is an upper bound of S.
   b. Is 2 the l.u.b.?

2. Generalize Exercise 1 by using some positive number other than 2.

3. Let S be the set of irrational numbers

$$S = \{\sqrt{2}, \sqrt{2 + \sqrt{2}}, \sqrt{2 + \sqrt{2 + \sqrt{2}}}, \cdots, a_n, \cdots\},$$

   where $a_1 = \sqrt{2}$ and $a_{n+1} = \sqrt{2 + a_n}$ for each $n \geq 1$.
   a. Show that 2 is an upper bound of S.
   b. Is 2 the l.u.b.?

4. Generalize Exercise 3.

5. Prove that every real number $a > 1$ has a unique positive nth root for every integer $n > 1$. [*Hint:* The function $f(x) = x^n$ is continuous. If we select $b > a$, then $b^n > a$. Hence, $f(1) < a < f(b)$ and $a = c^n$ for some c in $[1,b]$ by **7.3**.]

6. Prove that every real number a, $0 < a < 1$, has a unique positive nth root for every integer $n > 1$. [*Hint:* Use Exercise 5 with $1/a$ in place of a.]

2 AREA

Associated with each rectangle A having length l and width w is the number lw called the *area* of A. Every triangle is "half" a rectangle (Figure 7.1), and

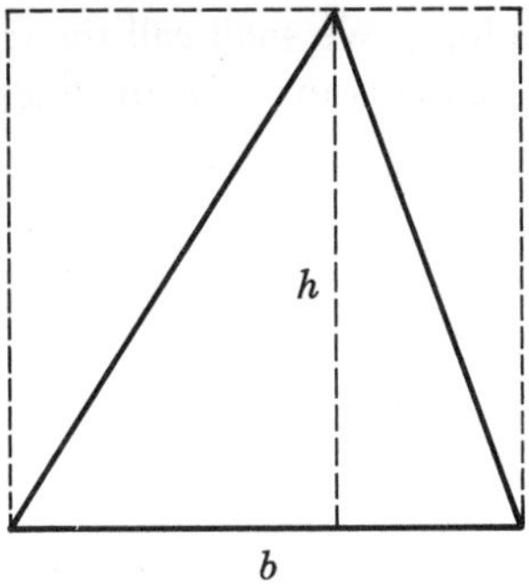

FIGURE 7.1

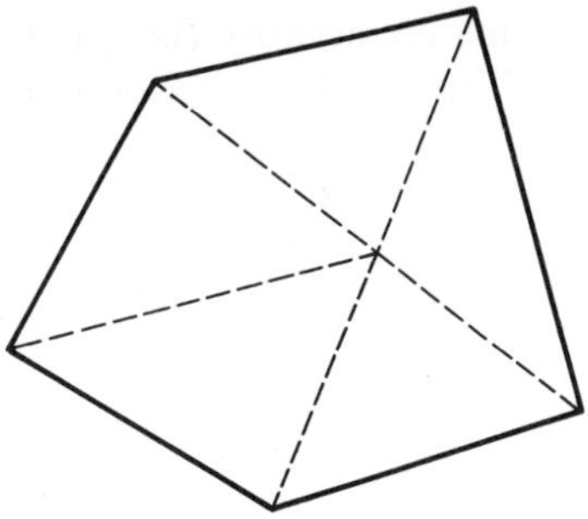

FIGURE 7.2

hence is defined to have area $bh/2$ where b is its base and h its altitude. Since any polygon can be subdivided into triangles (Figure 7.2), the area of a polygon can be defined to be the sum of the areas of the triangles into which it is subdivided. It can be proved that the area so obtained is the same no matter how the polygon is divided up into triangles.

If a region R of the plane has a curved boundary, then it is not clear if the region has area. However, if the region is placed on a piece of graph paper (Figure 7.3), then we can underapproximate the area A of R by counting the number of squares of the graph paper completely contained in R and overapproximate its area by counting the number of squares containing some part of R. The actual area of R should lie between these two numbers. By using finer and finer graph paper, we should be able to get a closer and closer approximation of the area of R.

To make the problem of finding the area of a region with a curved boundary mathematically tractable, we shall assume that the curved part of the boundary

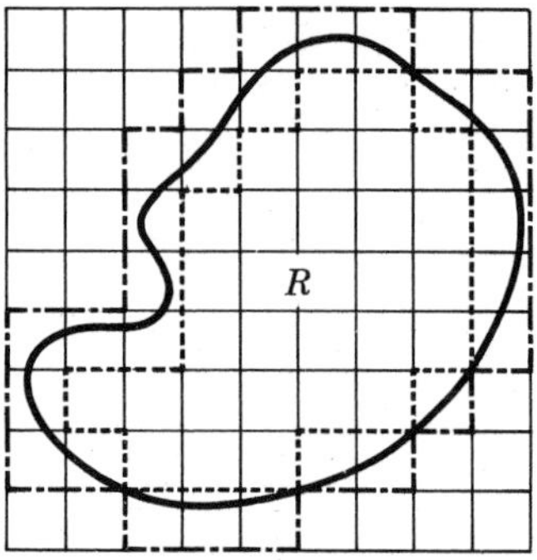

FIGURE 7.3

is the graph of a continuous function. Thus, let f be a function that is continuous and nonnegative (i.e., $f(x) \geq 0$) in an interval $[a,b]$. We shall call the region R (Figure 7.4) in the coordinate plane bounded by the graph of f, the lines $x = a$

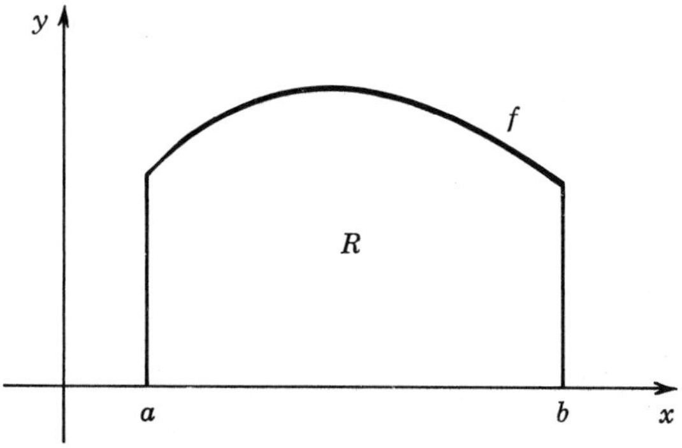

FIGURE 7.4

and $x = b$, and the x axis, *the region under the graph of f from a to b*. We wish to associate with R a number A to be called the *area* of R. The area A should be consistent with the area of a polygon. That is, A should be greater than or equal to the area of each polygon contained in R, and less than or equal to the area of each polygon containing R. We shall see in due course that there is one and only one number A having this property.

Before discussing the area in detail, we need to introduce the concept of a partition of an interval. A *partition* of a closed interval $[a,b]$ is a division of $[a,b]$ into subintervals. If $x_0, x_1, \cdots, x_{n-1}, x_n$ are numbers in $[a,b]$, with

$$a = x_0 < x_1 < \cdots < x_{n-1} < x_n = b,$$

then these $n + 1$ numbers partition $[a,b]$ into n subintervals

$$[x_0,x_1],\ [x_1,x_2],\ \cdots,\ [x_{n-1},x_n].$$

The notation

$$P = \{x_0,x_1,\ \cdots,\ x_n\}$$

is used to designate this set of n subintervals of $[a,b]$. For example,

$$P = \{1,\tfrac{3}{2},3,\sqrt{13},5,6\}$$

denotes the partition of the interval $[1,6]$ into the 5 subintervals

$$[1,\tfrac{3}{2}],\ [\tfrac{3}{2},3],\ [3,\sqrt{13}],\ [\sqrt{13},5],\ [5,6].$$

A partition P of $[a,b]$ is called *regular* if every subinterval has the same length. For example,

$$P = \{1,2,3,4,5,6\}$$

is the regular partition of $[1,6]$ into the 5 subintervals

$$[1,2],\ [2,3],\ [3,4],\ [4,5],\ [5,6].$$

each of length 1. In general, the partition

$$P = \{x_0,x_1,\ \cdots\ ,x_n\}$$

of $[a,b]$ is the regular partition of $[a,b]$ into n subintervals if and only if

$$x_1 - x_0 = x_2 - x_1 = \cdots = x_n - x_{n-1} = \frac{b-a}{n}.$$

Returning to the problem of finding the area of region R, let $P = \{x_0,\ x_1,\ \cdots,\ x_n\}$ be any partition of $[a,b]$. Since f is continuous in $[a,b]$, we can select numbers $u_1,\ u_2,\ \cdots,\ u_n$ in the n subintervals of P such that $f(u_1)$ is the minimum value of f in $[x_0,x_1]$, $f(u_2)$ is the minimum value of f in $[x_1,x_2]$, and so on **(6.1)**. Then we can construct n rectangles whose bases are the segments of the x axis defined by the subintervals of P and whose respective heights are $f(u_1)$, $f(u_2)$, $\cdots,f(u_n)$. These rectangles taken together form a polygon, called a *rectangular polygon*, inscribed in R. The first rectangle has area $f(u_1)(x_1 - x_0)$, the product of the length of its base and its height; the second has area $f(u_2)(x_2 - x_1)$; and so on. Therefore, the area $I(P)$ of the inscribed rectangular polygon associated with partition P is given by

$$I(P) = f(u_1)(x_1 - x_0) + f(u_2)(x_2 - x_1) + \cdots + f(u_n)(x_n - x_{n-1}).$$

The case in which P consists of 4 subintervals is illustrated in Figure 7.5.

Similarly, we can select numbers $v_1,\ v_2,\ \cdots,\ v_n$ in the n subintervals of partition P such that $f(v_1)$ is the maximum value of f in $[x_0,x_1]$, $f(v_2)$ is the maximum value of f in $[x_1,x_2]$, and so on **(6.1)**. Then we can construct n rectangles whose

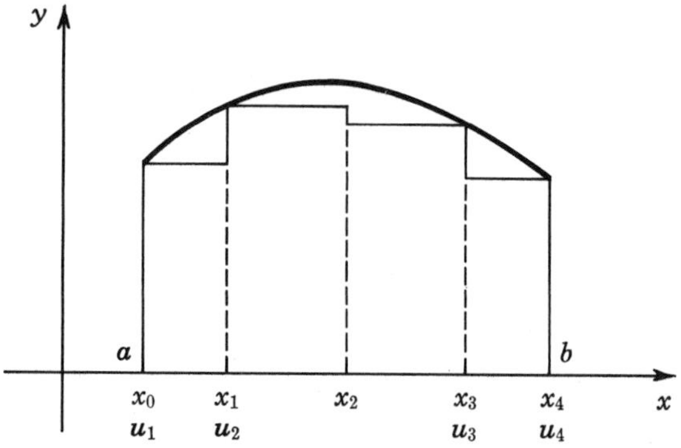

FIGURE 7.5

bases are the segments of the x axis defined by the subintervals of P and whose respective heights are $f(v_1), f(v_2), \cdots, f(v_n)$. These n rectangles form a rectangular polygon circumscribed about R. The area $C(P)$ of this circumscribed rectangular polygon is given by

$$C(P) = f(v_1)(x_1 - x_0) + f(v_2)(x_2 - x_1) + \cdots + f(v_n)(x_n - x_{n-1}).$$

The case in which P consists of 4 subintervals is illustrated in Figure 7.6.

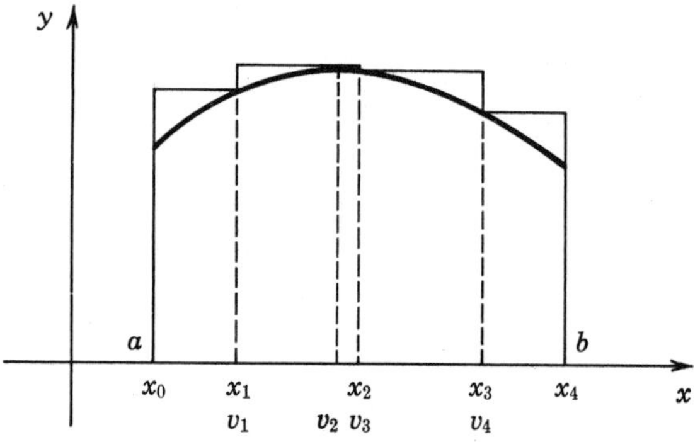

FIGURE 7.6

Since each rectangular polygon inscribed in the region under the graph of f from a to b is contained in each circumscribed polygon, we must have

$$I(P_1) \leq C(P_2)$$

for any partitions P_1 and P_2 of $[a,b]$. Thus if we let

$$L = \{I(P) \mid P \text{ a partition of } [a,b]\}$$

and

$$U = \{C(P) \mid P \text{ a partition of } [a,b]\},$$

every number in L is a lower bound of set U and every number in U is an upper bound of L. Hence, by the completeness property of the real numbers (7.2), set L has a l.u.b. and set U has a g.l.b. If we let

$$A_l = \text{l.u.b. } L, \qquad A_u = \text{g.l.b. } U$$

then

$$A_l \leq A_u$$

by our remarks above. If it should happen that $A_l = A_u$, then we would have an obvious choice for the area A of the region R under the graph of f from a to b (Figure 7.4), namely $A = A_l = A_u$. Actually, we shall prove in Chapter 8 that for every function f which is continuous in $[a,b]$, A_l does equal A_u. Therefore, every region such as R in Figure 7.4 does have an area A. How we go about computing A will be discussed later. In the meantime, let us compute some $I(P)$ and $C(P)$ as discussed above.

EXAMPLE. If $f(x) = 4 - x^2$, let R be the region under the graph of f from -2 to 2 (Figure 7.7). Find $I(P)$ and $C(P)$ in case:

(a) $P = \{-2, -\frac{1}{2}, 1, 2\}$.

(b) P is the regular partition of $[-2,2]$ into 8 subintervals.

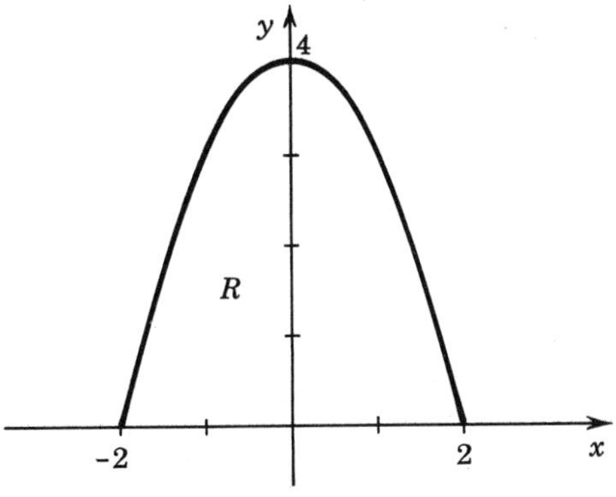

FIGURE 7.7

Solution: (a) The minimum value of f in $[-2,-1/2]$ is $f(-2) = 0$; in $[-1/2,1]$ is $f(1) = 3$; in $[1,2]$ is $f(2) = 0$. Hence

$$I(P) = 0\cdot(-\tfrac{1}{2} + 2) + 3\cdot(1 + \tfrac{1}{2}) + 0\cdot(2 - 1) = \tfrac{9}{2}.$$

The maximum value of f in $[-2,-1/2]$ is $f(-1/2) = 15/4$; in $[-1/2,1]$ is $f(0) = 4$; in $[1,2]$ is $f(1) = 3$. Hence

$$C(P) = \tfrac{15}{4}\cdot(-\tfrac{1}{2} + 2) + 4\cdot(1 + \tfrac{1}{2}) + 3(2 - 1) = \tfrac{117}{8}.$$

Evidently $I(P)$ and $C(P)$ differ considerably.

(b) In this case

$$P = \{-2,-\tfrac{3}{2},-1,-\tfrac{1}{2},0,\tfrac{1}{2},1,\tfrac{3}{2},2\},$$

and

$$\begin{aligned} I(P) &= \tfrac{1}{2}f(-2) + \tfrac{1}{2}f(-\tfrac{3}{2}) + \tfrac{1}{2}f(-1) + \tfrac{1}{2}f(-\tfrac{1}{2}) + \tfrac{1}{2}f(\tfrac{1}{2}) + \tfrac{1}{2}f(1) + \tfrac{1}{2}f(\tfrac{3}{2}) + \tfrac{1}{2}f(2) \\ &= \tfrac{17}{2}, \\ C(P) &= \tfrac{1}{2}f(-\tfrac{3}{2}) + \tfrac{1}{2}f(-1) + \tfrac{1}{2}f(-\tfrac{1}{2}) + \tfrac{1}{2}f(0) + \tfrac{1}{2}f(0) + \tfrac{1}{2}f(\tfrac{1}{2}) + \tfrac{1}{2}f(1) + \tfrac{1}{2}f(\tfrac{3}{2}) \\ &= \tfrac{25}{2}. \end{aligned}$$

Now $I(P)$ and $C(P)$ are closer together. If we would select a regular partition P of $[-2,2]$ with many more subintervals, we would obtain $I(P)$ and $C(P)$ which were still closer to each other.

EXERCISES

I

1. For $f(x) = x^2$, sketch the region under the graph of f from 2 to 4.
   a. Compute $I(P)$ and $C(P)$ associated with the partition $\{2,\tfrac{5}{2},3,\tfrac{7}{2},4\}$ of $[2,4]$.
   b. Compute $I(P)$ and $C(P)$ for the regular partition of $[2,4]$ into 8 subintervals.

2. For $f(x) = x^3$, sketch the region under the graph of f from 1 to 2.
   a. Compute $I(P)$ and $C(P)$ for the partition $\{1,2\}$ of $[1,2]$.
   b. Compute $I(P)$ and $C(P)$ for the partition $\{1,\tfrac{3}{2},2\}$ of $[1,2]$.
   c. Compute $I(P)$ and $C(P)$ for the regular partition of $[1,2]$ into 4 subintervals.

3. For $f(x) = 1 - x^3$, sketch the region bounded by the graph of f and the coordinate axes.
   a. Compute $I(P)$ and $C(P)$ for the partition $\{0,\tfrac{1}{2},1\}$ of $[0,1]$.
   b. Compute $I(P)$ and $C(P)$ for the regular partition of $[0,1]$ into 8 subintervals.

4. For $f(x) = 1/x$, sketch the region under the graph of f from $\tfrac{1}{2}$ to 2. (Use a large unit segment.)
   a. Compute $I(P)$ and $C(P)$ for the regular partition of $[\tfrac{1}{2},2]$ into 6 subintervals.
   b. Same as (a) except 12 subintervals.

5. For $f(x) = 1/x^2$, sketch the region under the graph of f from 1 to 4 (use a large unit segment).
   a. Compute $I(P)$ and $C(P)$ for the regular partition of $[1,4]$ into 3 subintervals.
   b. Same as (a) except 6 subintervals.

6. If R is the region under the graph of $f(x) = b$ from 0 to a, then R is a rectangle. Show that $I(P)$ and $C(P)$ equal the area of R for every partition P of $[0,a]$.

II

1. Let R be the trapezoidal region under the graph of $f(x) = x$ from a to b $(0 < a < b)$. Find $I(P)$ and $C(P)$ for the partition $\{x_0, x_1, \cdots, x_{n-1}, x_n\}$ of $[a,b]$ and show that

$$I(P) < \frac{b^2 - a^2}{2} < C(P).$$

(Note that $(b^2 - a^2)/2$ is the area of the trapezoid.)

2. Let R be the region under the graph of $f(x) = x^3$ from a to b $(0 \leq a < b)$. Show that for any partition P of of $[a,b]$

$$I(P) < \frac{b^4 - a^4}{4} < C(P).$$

3. Let R be the region under the graph of $f(x) = 1/x^2$ from a to b $(0 < a < b)$ and let $P = \{x_0,x_1,\cdots,x_{n-1},x_n\}$ be a partition of $[a,b]$.
   a. Write down the sums $I(P)$ and $C(P)$ associated with this partition.
   b. Show that for each integer i between 0 and $n - 1$,

$$\frac{1}{x_{i+1}^2} < \frac{1}{x_i x_{i+1}} < \frac{1}{x_i^2}.$$

   and hence that

$$\frac{x_{i+1} - x_i}{x_{i+1}^2} < \frac{1}{x_i} - \frac{1}{x_{i+1}} < \frac{x_{i+1} - x_i}{x_i^2}.$$

   Then show that

$$I(P) < \frac{1}{a} - \frac{1}{b} < C(P).$$

4. Let R be the region under the graph of $f(x) = 1/x^3$ from a to b $(0 < a < b)$ and let $P = \{x_0,x_1,\cdots,x_{n-1},x_n\}$ be a partition of $[a_1b]$.
   a. Write down the sums $I(P)$ and $C(P)$ associated with this partition.
   b. Show that

$$I(P) < \frac{1}{2}\left(\frac{1}{a^2} - \frac{1}{b^2}\right) < C(P).$$

3 THE SIGMA NOTATION

A sum of n terms such as $a_1 + a_2 + \cdots + a_n$ is designated by

$$\sum_{i=1}^{n} a_i$$

in the handy *sigma notation;* i.e.,

$$\sum_{i=1}^{n} a_i = a_1 + a_2 + \cdots + a_n.$$

Some examples of the use of the sigma notation are given below.

$$\sum_{i=1}^{n} i = 1 + 2 + \cdots + n.$$

$$\sum_{j=2}^{m} j^2 = 2^2 + 3^2 + \cdots + m^2.$$

$$\sum_{i=1}^{n} c = c + c + \cdots + c = nc.$$

$$\sum_{k=3}^{6} k(k-2) = 3\cdot 1 + 4\cdot 2 + 5\cdot 3 + 6\cdot 4 = 50.$$

$$\sum_{i=0}^{5} \frac{i-1}{i+1} = \frac{-1}{1} + \frac{0}{2} + \frac{1}{3} + \frac{2}{4} + \frac{3}{5} + \frac{4}{6} = 1.1.$$

Listed below are a few useful summation formulas for future reference. These may be proved by mathematical induction.

7.4 $$\sum_{i=1}^{n} i = \frac{n(n+1)}{2}.$$

7.5 $$\sum_{i=1}^{n} i^2 = \frac{n(n+1)(2n+1)}{6}.$$

7.6 $$\sum_{i=1}^{n} i^3 = \left[\frac{n(n+1)}{2}\right]^2.$$

It follows directly from the associative, commutative, and distributive laws that:

7.7 $$\sum_{i=1}^{n} (a_i + b_i) = \sum_{i=1}^{n} a_i + \sum_{i=1}^{n} b_i$$

7.8 . $$\sum_{i=1}^{n} ka_i = k \sum_{i=1}^{n} a_i.$$

We may use **7.4–7.8** to work problems of the following type.

EXAMPLE 1. Find $\sum_{i=1}^{20} i(2i-3)$.

Solution: We have

$$\sum_{i=1}^{20} i(2i-3) = \sum_{i=1}^{20} (2i^2 - 3i)$$

$$= \sum_{i=1}^{20} 2i^2 + \sum_{i=1}^{20} (-3)i \qquad \text{(by 7.7)}$$

$$= 2\sum_{i=1}^{20} i^2 - 3\sum_{i=1}^{20} i \qquad \text{(by 7.8)}$$

$$= 2\frac{(20)(21)(41)}{6} - 3\frac{(20)(21)}{2} \qquad \text{(by 7.4, 7.5)}$$

$$= 20\cdot 287 - 10\cdot 63 = 5{,}110.$$

EXAMPLE 2. Find $\sum_{i=1}^{n} (3-i)(2+i)$.

Solution: We have

$$\sum_{i=1}^{n} (3-i)(2+i) = \sum_{i=1}^{n} (6+i-i^2)$$

$$= \sum_{i=1}^{n} 6 + \sum_{i=1}^{n} i - \sum_{i=1}^{n} i^2$$

$$= 6n + \frac{n(n+1)}{2} - \frac{n(n+1)(2n+1)}{6}$$

$$= \tfrac{1}{3}n(19-n^2).$$

I

Using 7.4–7.8, evaluate the following sums:

1. $\sum_{i=1}^{n} (ai+b)^2$.
2. $\sum_{i=1}^{n} (4i^2 - 4i + 1)$.
3. $\sum_{i=1}^{n} i(i+1)$.
4. $\sum_{i=1}^{n} i(i+1)(i+2)$.
5. Show that $\sum_{i=1}^{n} [F(i) - F(i-1)] = F(n) - F(0)$.
6. Using Exercise 5 with $F(i) = i^5$ and 7.4–7.6, evaluate $\sum_{i=1}^{n} i^4$.

II

1. a. What does Exercise I–5 reduce to for the case

$$F(i) = i(i+1)(i+2)\cdots(i+r)?$$

b. Check the answers of Exercises I–3, 4 with this result.

2. In a manner similar to that of the previous exercise, determine

a. $\sum_{i=1}^{n} \frac{1}{i(i+1)}$. b. $\sum_{i=1}^{n} \frac{1}{i(i+1)(i+2)}$.

3. If we are given i^4 in the form

$$i^4 = i(i+1)(i+2)(i+3) + ai(i+1)(i+2) + bi(i+1) + ci,$$

find the sum $\sum_{i=1}^{n} i^4$ by using Exercise II–1.

4 UPPER AND LOWER INTEGRALS

What was done in Section 2 for a nonnegative continuous function can be done for any bounded function. We call a function f *bounded in an interval* I if the domain of f contains I and there exist numbers m and M such that $m \leq f(x) \leq M$ for every x in I. The number m is called a *lower bound* of f in I and M an *upper bound* of f in I. Whenever f is bounded in an interval I, f has a l.u.b. in I and also a g.l.b. in I by the completeness property. If f is continuous in a closed interval I, then the g.l.b. of f in I is simply its minimum value $f(u)$ and the l.u.b. its maximum value $f(v)$ for some u, v in I.

Let f be a bounded function in a closed interval $[a,b]$. For each partition $P = \{x_0,x_1,\cdots,x_n\}$ of $[a,b]$, we can form the sums

$$S(P) = m_1(x_1 - x_0) + m_2(x_2 - x_1) + \cdots + m_n(x_n - x_{n-1}),$$
$$T(P) = M_1(x_1 - x_0) + M_2(x_2 - x_1) + \cdots + M_n(x_n - x_{n-1}),$$

where m_1 is the g.l.b. and M_1 the l.u.b. of f in $[x_0,x_1]$, m_2 is the g.l.b. and M_2 the l.u.b. of f in $[x_1,x_2]$, and so on. We call $S(P)$ a *lower sum* and $T(P)$ an *upper sum* of f relative to the partition P of $[a,b]$. Since $m_i \leq f(x) \leq M_i$ for every x in $[x_{i-1},x_i]$, $i = 1, 2, \cdots, n$, clearly

$$S(P) \leq T(P).$$

It is convenient to use the *delta notation* in describing the lengths of the subintervals of a partition $P = \{x_0,x_1,\cdots,x_n\}$ of $[a,b]$ as follows:

$$\Delta x_1 = x_1 - x_0,\ \Delta x_2 = x_2 - x_1,\ \cdots,\quad \Delta x_n = x_n - x_{n-1}$$

The Greek letter delta Δ is used in mathematics to indicate a difference: thus Δx_i is the difference between x_i and x_{i-1} for each $i = 1, 2, \cdots, n$. Evidently

$$\sum_{i=1}^{n} \Delta x_i = b - a.$$

Using the sigma and delta notations, the lower sum $S(P)$ and the upper sum $T(P)$ above can be expressed compactly as follows.

$$S(P) = \sum_{i=1}^{n} m_i \Delta x_i, \quad T(P) = \sum_{i=1}^{n} M_i \Delta x_i.$$

If some of the subintervals of a partition P of $[a,b]$ are further subdivided, the resulting partition P' of $[a,b]$ is called a *refinement* of P. For example, if

$$P = \{1,3,4,6\} \qquad \text{and} \qquad P' = \{1,\tfrac{3}{2},2,\tfrac{7}{3},3,4,5,6\},$$

then P' is a refinement of P. Thinking of P and P' as simply the sets of points of subdivision of $[a,b]$, P' is a refinement of P if and only if P is a subset of P'.

Whenever we have a refinement P' of a partition P, then

$$S(P) \leq S(P') \qquad \text{and} \qquad T(P') \leq T(P).$$

To prove these relations, we need only consider a partition P' having one more subinterval than P. Every other refinement of P can be arrived at by a succession of such simple partitions. For simplicity, assume that the first subinterval $[x_0,x_1]$ of $P = \{x_0,x_1,x_2,\cdots,x_n\}$ is subdivided into two subintervals $[x_0,x]$ and $[x,x_1]$ in P'. Then $P' = \{x_0,x,x_1,x_2,\cdots,x_n\}$ and

$$S(P') = m(x - x_0) + m'(x_1 - x) + \sum_{i=2}^{n} m_i \Delta x_i,$$

where m is the g.l.b. of f in $[x_0,x]$ and m' in $[x,x_1]$. Since m_1 is the g.l.b. of f in $[x_0,x_1]$ and $[x_0,x]$, $[x,x_1]$ are subintervals of $[x_0,x_1]$, evidently $m_1 \leq m$ and $m_1 \leq m'$. Hence

$$m_1 \Delta x_1 = m_1[(x - x_0) + (x_1 - x)] \leq m(x - x_0) + m'(x_1 - x)$$

and

$$S(P) = \sum_{i=1}^{n} m_i \Delta x_i \leq S(P').$$

The proof that $T(P') \leq T(P)$ is similar, and hence is omitted.

Given two partitions P_1 and P_2 of $[a,b]$, then the set of all intersections of subintervals of P_1 with those in P_2 forms a common refinement of P_1 and P_2. For example, if

$$P_1 = \{1,2,3,5,6\} \qquad \text{and} \qquad P_2 = \{1,2,4,4.5,6\}$$

then the union P of sets P_1 and P_2,

$$P = \{1,2,3,4,4.5,5,6\}$$

is the common refinement of P_1 and P_2.

Let us now prove the following theorem.

7.9 **THEOREM.** If f is a bounded function in $[a,b]$ and P_1 and P_2 are any partitions of $[a,b]$,then

$$S(P_1) \leq T(P_2).$$

Proof: Let P be a common refinement of P_1 and P_2. Then $S(P_1) \leq S(P)$ and $T(P) \leq T(P_2)$ by our remarks above. Hence, $S(P_1) \leq S(P) \leq T(P) \leq T(P_2)$ and $S(P_1) \leq T(P_2)$.

If f is a bounded function in $[a,b]$, L is the set of all lower sums of f over $[a,b]$, and U is the set of all upper sums of f over $[a,b]$, then each number of L is a lower bound of U and each number of U is an upper bound of L by **7.9.** Therefore, we can apply the completeness property of the real numbers to L and U as follows.

7.10 **DEFINITION.** Let f be a bounded function in a closed interval $[a,b]$, L be the set of all lower sums of f over $[a,b]$, and U of upper sums of f over $[a,b]$. The *lower integral* of f from a to b is denoted by $\underline{\int_a^b} f$ and is defined by

$$\underline{\int_a^b} f = \text{l.u.b. } L.$$

The *upper integral* of f from a to b is denoted by $\overline{\int_a^b} f$ and is defined by

$$\overline{\int_a^b} f = \text{g.l.b. } U.$$

In view of the definition of l.u.b., for every number $\epsilon > 0$ there must exist some partition P_1 of $[a,b]$ such that

$$0 \leq \underline{\int_a^b} f - S(P_1) < \epsilon.$$

Similarly,

$$0 \leq T(P_2) - \overline{\int_a^b} f < \epsilon$$

for some partition P_2 of $[a,b]$. If P is the common refinement of P_1 and P_2, then we see that *for every* $\epsilon > 0$ *there exists a partition* P *of* $[a,b]$ *such that*

7.11 $$0 \leq \underline{\int_a^b} f - S(P) < \epsilon, \quad 0 \leq T(P) - \overline{\int_a^b} f < \epsilon.$$

Since every upper sum $T(P)$ is an upper bound of set L and $\underline{\int_a^b} f = \text{l.u.b. } L$, we have $\underline{\int_a^b} f \leq T(P)$ for every partition P of $[a,b]$. Therefore, $\underline{\int_a^b} f$ is a *lower bound* of set U. Since $\overline{\int_a^b} f = \text{g.l.b. } U$, we must have

7.12 $$S(P) \leq \underline{\int_a^b} f \leq \overline{\int_a^b} f \leq T(P)$$

for every partition P of $[a,b]$.

If a bounded function f is monotone in $[a,b]$, then we can easily make $S(P)$ and $T(P)$ close to each other by properly choosing the partition P of $[a,b]$. For each positive integer n, let $P_n = \{x_0,x_1,\cdots,x_n\}$ be the regular partition of $[a,b]$ into n subintervals. Thus

$$\Delta x_1 = \Delta x_2 = \cdots = \Delta x_n = \frac{b-a}{n}.$$

Let us assume that f is increasing in $[a,b]$. Then $f(x_{i-1})$ is the g.l.b. and $f(x_i)$ is the l.u.b. of f in $[x_{i-1},x_i]$, $i = 1, 2, \cdots, n$, and $S(P_n)$, $T(P_n)$ are given by

$$S(P_n) = \sum_{i=1}^{n} f(x_{i-1})\Delta x_i = \left(\sum_{i=1}^{n} f(x_{i-1})\right)\frac{b-a}{n}$$

$$T(P_n) = \sum_{i=1}^{n} f(x_i)\Delta x_i = \left(\sum_{i=1}^{n} f(x_i)\right)\frac{b-a}{n}$$

When we subtract $S(P_n)$ from $T(P_n)$, most of the terms cancel; in fact,

$$T(P_n) - S(P_n) = [f(x_n) - f(x_0)]\frac{b-a}{n}$$

$$= \frac{(b-a)[f(b) - f(a)]}{n}$$

For each positive number ϵ, we can find a positive integer n such that for the increasing function f

$$0 \leq \frac{(b-a)[f(b)-f(a)]}{n} < \epsilon.$$

Thus we need only select n so that

$$n > \frac{(b-a)[f(b)-f(a)]}{\epsilon}.$$

We conclude that *for each* $\epsilon > 0$ *there exists an integer* n *such that*

7.13 $$0 \leq T(P_n) - S(P_n) < \epsilon.$$

If f is decreasing instead of increasing, a similar argument also yields **7.13**. Thus, we have proved that *for a monotone function f we can choose a partition P so that $S(P)$ is as close as we wish to $T(P)$.*

From **7.12** we easily derive that for every bounded function f in an interval $[a,b]$ and every partition P of $[a,b]$,

$$0 \leq \overline{\int_a^b} f - \underline{\int_a^b} f \leq T(P) - S(P).$$

If, in addition, f is monotonic then for every $\epsilon > 0$ there exists a partition P of $[a,b]$ such that $T(P) - S(P) < \epsilon$. Hence

$$0 \leq \overline{\int_a^b} f - \underline{\int_a^b} f < \epsilon$$

for every $\epsilon > 0$. Since 0 is the g.l.b. of the set of all positive numbers ϵ, we must have $\overline{\int_a^b} f - \underline{\int_a^b} f = 0$. We state this result below.

7.14 THEOREM. For every bounded, monotonic function f in an interval $[a,b]$, we have

$$\underline{\int_a^b} f = \overline{\int_a^b} f.$$

Consider the following examples.

EXAMPLE 1. The function $f(x) = 4 - x$ is bounded (in fact, continuous) and decreasing in $[1,3]$. Find the lower (upper) integral of f from 1 to 3.

Solution: The regular partition P_n of $[1,3]$ into n subintervals has the form

$$P_n = \{1, 1 + \Delta x, 1 + 2\Delta x, \cdots, 1 + (n-1)\Delta x, 3\}, \qquad \text{where } \Delta x = \frac{2}{n}.$$

The g.l.b. of f in the ith subinterval $[1 + (i-1)\Delta x, 1 + i\Delta x]$ is $f(1 + i\Delta x) = 4 - (1 + i\Delta x) = 3 - i\Delta x$, $i = 1, 2, \cdots, n$. Hence

$$\begin{aligned} S(P_n) &= \sum_{i=1}^{n} (3 - i\Delta x)\Delta x \\ &= \sum_{i=1}^{n} 3\Delta x - \sum_{i=1}^{n} i(\Delta x)^2 \\ &= (3\Delta x)n - \frac{n(n+1)}{2}(\Delta x)^2 \end{aligned}$$

Using the fact that $\Delta x = 2/n$, this becomes

$$S(P_n) = 6 - \left(2 + \frac{2}{n}\right) = 4 - \frac{2}{n}.$$

By our work above (interchanging $f(b)$ and $f(a)$ because f is now decreasing), we find that

$$T(P_n) - S(P_n) = \frac{(b-a)[f(a)-f(b)]}{n} = \frac{2\cdot 2}{n}.$$

Hence,

$$T(P_n) = 4 + \frac{2}{n}.$$

Since the lower integral is between $S(P_n)$ and $T(P_n)$,

$$4 - \frac{2}{n} \le \underline{\int_1^3} f \le 4 + \frac{2}{n}$$

for every positive integer n. Therefore

$$\underline{\int_1^3} f = 4.$$

This is also the value of the upper integral by **7.13**.

Geometrically, we expect $\underline{\int_1^3} f$ to be the *area* of the region R of Figure 7.8.

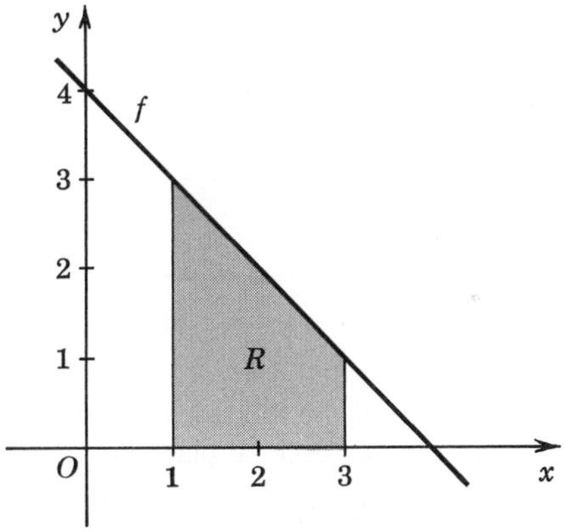

FIGURE 7.8

This region is a trapezoid whose area A is commonly given by the formula

$$A = \tfrac{1}{2}(b_1 + b_2)h,$$

where b_1 and b_2 are the lengths of the parallel sides and h is the distance between them. For region R,

$$A = \tfrac{1}{2}(3 + 1)\cdot 2 = 4,$$

which agrees with $\underline{\int_1^3} f$.

EXAMPLE 2. The greatest integer function $f(x) = [x]$ is bounded and increasing in [2,5]. Find the lower (upper) integral of f from 2 to 5.

Solution: If we take a regular partition of [2,5] having $3n$ subintervals, then the first n subintervals will be a partition of [2,3], the next n of [3,4], and the final n of [4,5]. Each subinterval has length $1/n$. The g.l.b. of f in each of the first n subintervals is 2, in each of the next n is 3, and in each of the last n is 4. Therefore

$$S(P_{3n}) = \sum_{i=1}^{n} 2 \cdot \frac{1}{n} + \sum_{i=n+1}^{2n} 3 \cdot \frac{1}{n} + \sum_{i=2n+1}^{3n} 4 \cdot \frac{1}{n} = 2 + 3 + 4 = 9.$$

Since

$$T(P_{3n}) - S(P_{3n}) = \frac{(5-2)[f(5) - f(2)]}{3n} = \frac{3}{n},$$

we have

$$T(P_{3n}) = 9 + \frac{3}{n}.$$

Hence

$$9 \le \underline{\int_2^5} f \le 9 + \frac{3}{n} \qquad \text{for every positive integer } n,$$

and we conclude that

$$\underline{\int_2^5} f = 9.$$

EXERCISES

I

Find $S(P)$ and $T(P)$ for each of the following functions and partitions P. (You may approximate your answers to two decimal places).

1. $f(x) = 1 - x^2, \quad P = \{0, \frac{1}{2}, 1, \frac{3}{2}, 2\}.$
2. $f(x) = 1 - x^2, \quad P = \{0, \frac{1}{4}, \frac{3}{4}, 1, \frac{7}{4}, 2\}.$
3. $f(x) = 2x^2, \quad P = \{-1, -\frac{1}{2}, 0, \frac{1}{2}, 1\}.$
4. $f(x) = 2x^2, \quad P = \{-1, -\frac{5}{8}, \frac{1}{8}, \frac{1}{2}, \frac{3}{4}, 1\}.$
5. $f(x) = x^3, \quad P = \{-2, -\frac{5}{3}, -\frac{4}{3}, -1, -\frac{2}{3}, -\frac{1}{3}, 0\}.$
6. $f(x) = x^3, \quad P = \{-2, -\frac{3}{2}, -\frac{5}{4}, -1, -\frac{1}{2}, -\frac{1}{4}, 0\}.$
7. $f(x) = 1/x, \quad P = \{-4, -3, -2, -1\}.$
8. $f(x) = 1/x, \quad P = \{-4, -\frac{7}{2}, -\frac{13}{4}, -3, -\frac{5}{2}, -\frac{3}{2}, -1\}.$

9. $f(x) = 1/x^2, \qquad P = \{1,\frac{3}{2},2,\frac{5}{2},3,\frac{7}{2},4\}.$

10. $f(x) = 1/x^2, \qquad P = \{1,\frac{5}{4},\frac{7}{4},\frac{9}{4},3,\frac{13}{4},4\}.$

II

1. If $f(x) = x$, then by Exercise 1, Section 2, Part II,

$$S(P) < \frac{b^2 - a^2}{2} < T(P)$$

for every partition P of $[a,b]$. Prove that

$$\underline{\int_a^b} f = \overline{\int_a^b} f = \frac{b^2 - a^2}{2}.$$

2. If $f(x) = x^3$, then by Exercise 2, Section 2, Part II,

$$S(P) < \frac{b^4 - a^4}{4} < T(P)$$

for every partition P of $[a,b]$. Prove that

$$\underline{\int_a^b} f = \overline{\int_a^b} f = \frac{b^4 - a^4}{4}.$$

3. If $f(x) = \frac{1}{x^2}$, then by Exercise 3, Section 2, Part II,

$$S(P) < \frac{1}{a} - \frac{1}{b} < T(P)$$

for every partition P of $[a,b]$ $(0 < a < b)$. Prove that

$$\underline{\int_a^b} f = \overline{\int_a^b} f = \frac{1}{a} - \frac{1}{b}.$$

4. If $f(x) = \frac{1}{x^3}$, then by Exercise 4, Section 2, Part II,

$$S(P) < \frac{1}{2}\left(\frac{1}{a^2} - \frac{1}{b^2}\right) < T(P)$$

for every partition P of $[a,b]$ $(0 < a < b)$. Prove that

$$\underline{\int_a^b} f = \overline{\int_a^b} f = \frac{1}{2}\left(\frac{1}{a^2} - \frac{1}{b^2}\right).$$

5. If the function f is defined by

$$f(x) = \begin{cases} 0 & \text{if } x \text{ is rational} \\ 1 & \text{if } x \text{ is irrational,} \end{cases}$$

find

$$\underline{\int_0^1} f \quad \text{and} \quad \overline{\int_0^1} f.$$

6. If

$$f(x) = \begin{cases} x & \text{if } x \text{ is rational} \\ 0 & \text{if } x \text{ is irrational,} \end{cases}$$

find

$$\underline{\int}_0^1 f \quad \text{and} \quad \overline{\int}_0^1 f.$$

7. If the functions f and g are continuous in $[a,b]$ and if $f(x) \leq g(x)$ for every x in $[a,b]$, prove that

$$\underline{\int}_a^b f \leq \underline{\int}_a^b g,$$

and similarly for the upper integral.

5 INTEGRALS

If a bounded function f is monotonic in a closed interval $[a,b]$, then the upper and lower integrals of f from a to b are equal by **7.14**. We shall presently show that the upper and lower integrals are equal for almost all the functions encountered in elementary mathematics. This fact prompts us to make the following definition.

7.15 DEFINITION. A bounded function f is said to be *integrable* in a closed interval $[a,b]$ if and only if

$$\underline{\int}_a^b f = \overline{\int}_a^b f.$$

If f is integrable in $[a,b]$, then the *integral* of f from a to b is denoted by

$$\int_a^b f(x)\,dx$$

and is defined to be

$$\int_a^b f(x)\,dx = \underline{\int}_a^b f = \overline{\int}_a^b f.$$

By **7.11**, for every $\epsilon > 0$ there exists a partition P of $[a,b]$ such that (replacing ϵ by $\epsilon/2$ in **7.11** and adding the two inequalities)

$$0 \leq [T(P) - S(P)] - \left[\overline{\int}_a^b f - \underline{\int}_a^b f\right] < \epsilon.$$

On the other hand, by **7.12**,

$$0 \leq \overline{\int}_a^b f - \underline{\int}_a^b f \leq T(P) - S(P)$$

for every partition P. Together, these inequalities yield the following useful criterion for integrability.

7.16 **THEOREM.** A function f is integrable in $[a,b]$ if and only if for every $\epsilon > 0$ there exists a partition P of $[a,b]$ such that

$$0 \leq T(P) - S(P) < \epsilon.$$

If a function f is integrable in $[a,b]$ and if $[c,d]$ is contained in $[a,b]$, then f is also integrable in $[c,d]$. For if $\epsilon > 0$ and P is a partition of $[a,b]$ such that $0 \leq T(P) - S(P) < \epsilon$, then we can form a refinement P' of P which contains the points c and d as endpoints of subintervals. Since $S(P') \geq S(P)$ and $T(P') \leq T(P)$, we have $0 \leq T(P') - S(P') \leq T(P) - S(P) < \epsilon$. Now if we consider the subset P_1 of P' which is a partition of $[c,d]$, then $0 \leq T(P_1) - S(P_1) \leq T(P') - S(P') < \epsilon$. This proves that f is integrable in $[c,d]$. We state this result below.

7.17 **THEOREM.** If a function is integrable in a closed interval I, then it is integrable in every closed subinterval of I.

The symbol $\int$ for the integral was introduced by Leibnitz in 1675. This elongated S stood for a "sum" in his notation. Thus $\int_a^b f(x)\,dx$ indicated a sum of elements of the form $f(x)\,dx$, just as the lower sum is a sum of elements of the form $m_i \Delta x_i$ and similarly for the upper sum. If $f(x) \geq 0$, then we can think of $f(x)\,dx$ as the product of the height $f(x)$ and width dx of one of the rectangles inscribed in the graph of f.

We realize now that only part of the notation $\int_a^b f(x)\,dx$ is needed to indicate the integral of f from a to b, namely $\int_a^b f$. However, because there are many useful features of the notation of Leibnitz, we shall use it throughout this book.

The letter x occurring in $\int_a^b f(x)\,dx$ is of no special significance. Thus

$$\int_a^b f(x)\,dx = \int_a^b f(t)\,dt = \int_a^b f(u)\,du, \text{ etc.}$$

So far, $\int_a^b f(x)\,dx$ has been defined only if $a < b$. For convenience, let us define

$$\int_a^b f(x)\,dx = 0 \qquad \text{if } a = b,$$

and

$$\int_a^b f(x)\,dx = -\int_b^a f(x)\,dx \qquad \text{if } a > b.$$

Areas are additive in the sense that if a polygon is made up of nonoverlapping smaller polygons, then the area of the larger polygon is the sum of the areas of the smaller polygons. The integral is also additive in the following sense.

7.18 **THEOREM.** If a function f is integrable in $[a,b]$ and in $[b,c]$, then f is integrable in $[a,c]$ and

$$\int_a^b f(x)\,dx + \int_b^c f(x)\,dx = \int_a^c f(x)\,dx$$

Proof: By **7.16**, for every $\epsilon > 0$ there exist partitions P_1 of $[a,b]$ and P_2 of $[b,c]$ such that

$$0 \le T(P_1) - S(P_1) < \frac{\epsilon}{2}, \qquad 0 \le T(P_2) - S(P_2) < \frac{\epsilon}{2}.$$

Hence

$$0 \le [T(P_1) + T(P_2)] - [S(P_1) + S(P_2)] < \epsilon. \tag{1}$$

Since $S(P_1) + S(P_2)$ is a lower sum and $T(P_1) + T(P_2)$ an upper sum of f over $[a,c]$, the function f is integrable in $[a,c]$ by **7.16**.

We also have by **7.12**,

$$S(P_1) \le \int_a^b f(x)\,dx \le T(P_1), \qquad S(P_2) \le \int_b^c f(x)\,dx \le T(P_2)$$

and hence

$$S(P_1) + S(P_2) \le \int_a^b f(x)\,dx + \int_b^c f(x)\,dx \le T(P_1) + T(P_2).$$

Since $\int_a^c f(x)\,dx$ is also between its lower sum $S(P_1) + S(P_2)$ and its upper sum $T(P_1) + T(P_2)$, we derive from (1) that for every $\epsilon > 0$,

$$\left|\int_a^c f(x)\,dx - \int_a^b f(x)\,dx - \int_b^c f(x)\,dx\right| < \epsilon.$$

We conclude that

$$\int_a^c f(x)\,dx = \int_a^b f(x)\,dx + \int_b^c f(x)\,dx.$$

This completes the proof of **7.18**.

We state without proof the fact that if $\int_a^b f(x)\,dx$ and $\int_b^c f(x)\,dx$ exist, then so does $\int_a^c f(x)\,dx$, and

$$\int_a^b f(x)\,dx + \int_b^c f(x)\,dx = \int_a^c f(x)\,dx,$$

even if $a > b$ or $b > c$.

A function is integrable if it is made up of a finite number of monotone pieces by **7.14** and **7.18**. For example, the function $f(x) = x^2$ is decreasing in $[-2,0]$ and increasing in $[0,3]$. Since f is bounded, the integrals $\int_{-2}^{0} f(x)\,dx$ and $\int_{0}^{3} f(x)\,dx$ exist by **7.14**. Therefore, $\int_{-2}^{3} f(x)\,dx$ exists by **7.18**.

Since any polynomial function has a finite number of extrema, it is made up of a finite number of monotone pieces in any closed interval and is integrable by **7.14** and **7.18**. Thus, for example, the following integrals are meaningful.

$$\int_{-2}^{5} (x^2 + 3x)\,dx, \qquad \int_{0}^{2} (-3x^3 + x - 4)\,dx.$$

We shall find out how to evaluate such integrals in the next section.

EXERCISES

I

1. Using the fact that Theorem **7.10** is valid for $a < b < c$, show that the theorem is also valid if:
   a. $b < c < a$.
   b. $b < a < c$.
   c. $c < a < b$.
   d. $c < b < a$.
   e. $a < b = c$.
   f. $a = c$.

2. If the function f is integrable in a closed interval containing a, b, c, and d, prove that

$$\int_a^b f(x)\,dx + \int_b^c f(x)\,dx + \int_c^d f(x)\,dx = \int_a^d f(x)\,dx.$$

3. Find the area of the region bounded by the graph of $f(x) = x^3$ and the lines $x = 1$, $x = 3$, $y = 0$. (Use Exercise 2, Section 3, Part II.)

4. Find the area of the region bounded by the graph of $f(x) = 9 + x^{-2}$ and the lines $x = 1$, $x = 3$, $y = 0$. (Use Exercise 3, Section 3, Part II.)

II

State whether or not each of the following functions is integrable in the given interval. Give reasons for each answer.

1. $f(x) = x^2 - 3x + 1$, $[-2,4]$.
2. $g(x) = \sqrt{x}$, $[1,4]$.
3. $f(x) = |x - 1|$, $[0,3]$.
4. $g(x) = 1/x$, $[-1,1]$.
5. $F(x) = \begin{cases} 1 & \text{if } x \text{ rational} \\ -1 & \text{if } x \text{ irrational}, \end{cases}$ $[0,1]$.

6 THE FUNDAMENTAL THEOREM OF THE CALCULUS

The concepts of the derivative and the integral were well known before the time of Newton and Leibnitz. However, the great English physicist and mathematician Isaac Newton (1642–1727) and the great German mathematician and philosopher Gottfried Wilhelm von Leibnitz (1646–1716) established the intimate relationship between these two concepts. Because of this insight, gained independently of each other, these men are usually credited with the discovery of the calculus.

Before stating the relationship between the derivative and the integral of a function, now known as the fundamental theorem of the calculus, let us study functions defined by integrals.

If a function f is integrable in a closed interval I and a is some number in I, then by **7.17**, the integral of f from a to x exists for every number x in I. This allows us to define an integral function F by

(1) $$F(x) = \int_a^x f(t)\,dt, \qquad \text{domain } F = I.$$

We observe that

$$F(a) = \int_a^a f(t)\,dt = 0.$$

Also, if c and x are numbers in I, then by **7.18**

$$\int_a^x f(t)\,dt = \int_a^c f(t)\,dt + \int_c^x f(t)\,dt.$$

Hence

(2) $$F(x) - F(c) = \int_c^x f(t)\,dt.$$

If the integrable function f is continuous* in I and $c < x$ in (2) above, then we can select u and v in $[c,x]$ such that $f(u)$ is the minimum value (i.e., g.l.b.) of f and $f(v)$ is the maximum value (i.e., l.u.b.) of f in $[c,x]$. If we consider $[c,x]$ as being partitioned into one subinterval, then $f(u)(x - c)$ is a lower sum and $f(v)(x - c)$ is an upper sum of f from c to x, and hence

(3) $$f(u)(x - c) \le \int_c^x f(t)\,dt \le f(v)(x - c).$$

From (2) and (3) we get

(4) $$f(u) \le \frac{F(x) - F(c)}{x - c} \le f(v).$$

---

* We shall prove in Chapter 8 that every continuous function is integrable. In the meantime, we shall use this fact without proof.

When x is close to c, both $f(u)$ and $f(v)$ are close to $f(c)$ by the continuity of f in I. Therefore it seems reasonable that

(5) $$\lim_{x \to c^+} \frac{F(x) - F(c)}{x - c} = f(c).$$

A similar argument with $x < c$ convinces us that

(6) $$\lim_{x \to c^-} \frac{F(x) - F(c)}{x - c} = f(c).$$

Putting (5) and (6) together and recalling the definition of the derivative, we are led to believe that

(7) $$F'(c) = f(c) \quad \text{for every } c \text{ in } I.$$

That is, F is an antiderivative of f in I.

To prove (5) we must show that for every neighborhood N of $f(c)$ there exists an interval (c,d) such that

$$\frac{F(x) - F(c)}{x - c} \quad \text{is in } N \text{ for every } x \text{ in } (c,d).$$

Now f is continuous at c, so that for every neighborhood N of $f(c)$ there exists a neighborhood D of c such that $f(x)$ is in N for every x in D. Let d be any number in D, $(d > c)$, and x be any number in (c,d). If u and v are chosen in $[c,x]$ so that $f(u)$ is the minimum value and $f(v)$ is the maximum value of f in $[c,x]$, then $f(u)$ and $f(v)$ are in N and therefore, by (4), $[F(x) - F(c)]/(x - c)$ is in N. Hence

$$\frac{F(x) - F(c)}{x - c} \quad \text{is in } N \text{ for every } x \text{ in } (c,d),$$

and (5) is proved.

The proof of (6) is similar and hence is omitted. Thus (7) is proved and we have proved part of the following theorem.

7.19 FUNDAMENTAL THEOREM OF THE CALCULUS. Let function f be continuous in a closed interval $[a,b]$.

(1) If function F is defined by

$$F(x) = \int_a^x f(t)\,dt, \quad \text{domain } F = [a,b],$$

then $F'(x) = f(x)$ in $[a,b]$.

(2) If g is any antiderivative of f in $[a,b]$, then

$$\int_a^b f(t)\,dt = g(b) - g(a).$$

Proof of (2): By **6.18**, there exists a constant k such that

$$g(x) - F(x) = k \quad \text{for every } x \text{ in } [a,b].$$

Evidently, $F(a) = 0$ and therefore

$$g(a) = k.$$

Thus $g(b) - F(b) = k = g(a)$ and $F(b) = g(b) - g(a)$; i.e.,

$$F(b) = \int_a^b f(t)\,dt = g(b) - g(a).$$

This completes the proof of **7.19.**

EXAMPLE 1. Find $\int_{-3}^{0} x^2\,dx$.

Solution: If $f(x) = x^2$, then f is continuous and has g defined by

$$g(x) = \tfrac{1}{3}x^3$$

as an antiderivative. Hence, by the fundamental theorem of the calculus,

$$\int_{-3}^{0} x^2\,dx = g(0) - g(-3) = 0 - \frac{1}{3}(-3)^3 = 9.$$

EXAMPLE 2. Find $\int_1^3 (3 - 2x + x^2)\,dx$.

Solution: The function f defined by

$$f(x) = 3 - 2x + x^2$$

is continuous and has antiderivative g defined by

$$g(x) = 3x - x^2 + \tfrac{1}{3}x^3.$$

Therefore, by the fundamental theorem of the calculus,

$$\begin{aligned}\int_1^3 (3 - 2x + x^2)\,dx &= g(3) - g(1)\\ &= (9 - 9 + 9) - (3 - 1 + \tfrac{1}{3})\\ &= \tfrac{20}{3}\end{aligned}$$

EXAMPLE 3. Find $\int_4^9 t\sqrt{t}\,dt$.

Solution: The function f defined by

$$f(t) = t\sqrt{t} = t^{3/2}$$

is continuous and increasing in $[0, \infty)$ and has antiderivative

$$g(t) = \frac{2}{5}t^{5/2} = \frac{2}{5}t^2\sqrt{t}$$

in $(0, \infty)$. Therefore

$$\begin{aligned}\int_4^9 t\sqrt{t}\,dt &= g(9) - g(4)\\ &= \frac{2}{5}(81\sqrt{9} - 16\sqrt{4})\\ &= \frac{358}{5}.\end{aligned}$$

EXERCISES

I

Evaluate each of the following integrals by finding an antiderivative g of the integrand f.

1. $\int_2^5 2x\,dx.$
2. $\int_{-1}^3 7\,dx.$
3. $\int_{-2}^0 3x^2\,dx.$
4. $\int_{-10}^{10} x^3\,dx.$
5. $\int_{-6}^6 (4x^2 + 1)\,dx.$
6. $\int_{-100}^{100} (2x^5 - 3x^3 + 2x + 1)\,dx.$
7. $\int_4^9 2(\sqrt{x} - x)\,dx.$
8. $\int_1^5 \frac{1}{\sqrt{5t}}\,dt.$
9. $\int_3^6 \sqrt{y-2}\,dy.$
10. $\int_0^1 \frac{1}{\sqrt{z+1}}\,dz.$
11. Show that $D\sqrt{2x+1} = 1/\sqrt{2x+1}$. Then find

$$\int_0^4 \frac{1}{\sqrt{2x+1}}\,dx,$$

12. Show that $D\sqrt{1+2x^2} = \frac{2x}{\sqrt{1+2x^2}}$. Then find

$$\int_0^2 \frac{x}{\sqrt{1+2x^2}}\,dx.$$

II

Evaluate each of the following integrals.

1. $\int_{-1}^1 |x|\,dx.$
2. $\int_0^3 |x^3 - 2|\,dx.$
3. $\int_{-2}^4 (|x-1| + |x+1|)\,dx.$
4. $\int_0^2 \max(3x, 4 - x^2)\,dx.$

7 INTEGRATION FORMULAS

We know antiderivatives of many continuous functions, and therefore we can actually compute integrals of such functions. Some examples will be given in this section. But before giving examples, let us introduce the convenient notation

$$g(x)\Big|_a^b = g(b) - g(a).$$

Thus, if g is an antiderivative of f,

$$\int_a^b f(x)\,dx = g(x)\Big|_a^b$$

according to the fundamental theorem of the calculus.

It is also convenient to use the notation

$$\int f(x)\,dx$$

for an antiderivative of f. This integral without an interval $[a,b]$ of integration is called an *indefinite integral* of the function f. An integral with an interval of integration,

$$\int_a^b f(x)\,dx,$$

is commonly called a *definite integral.*

If f is a continuous function in a closed interval I and g is an antiderivative of f in I, then, by **6.18**, every antiderivative of f in I has the form $g + C$ for some constant function C. This fact is usually expressed by writing

$$\int f(x)\,dx = g(x) + C.$$

The interval I in which f is taken is not usually explicitly stated. Any interval in which the *integrand* f is continuous will suffice. By the fundamental theorem of the calculus,

$$D\int f(x)\,dx = f(x), \qquad \int Df(x)\,dx = f(x) + C.$$

Corresponding to the power differentiation formula (**5.17**) is the following *power integration formula.*

7.20 $$\int x^r\,dx = \frac{x^{r+1}}{r+1} + C, \qquad (r \text{ a rational number} \neq -1).$$

That is, if functions f and g are defined by

$$f(x) = x^r, \qquad g(x) = \frac{x^{r+1}}{r+1},$$

then

$$Dg(x) = f(x).$$

We must exclude the case $r = -1$ in **7.20** since the right side of this equation involves the impossible operation of division by zero when $r = -1$. However, this does not mean that $\int x^{-1}\,dx$ does not exist. Actually, this integral does exist in every interval I not containing 0. We shall discuss its value in Chapter 10.

If in **7.20** r is a negative rational number other than -1, then x^r is undefined if $x = 0$. Since the definite integral of f from a to b is defined only if the closed interval $[a,b]$ is contained in the domain of f, we must take a and b to be both positive or both negative in this case.

EXAMPLE 1. Find $\int_2^4 x^3\,dx.$

Solution: By **7.20**,

$$\int_2^4 x^3\,dx = \left.\frac{x^4}{4}\right|_2^4 = \frac{1}{4}(4^4 - 2^4) = 60.$$

EXAMPLE 2. Find $\int_1^4 \sqrt{u}\,du.$

Solution: Since $\sqrt{u} = u^{1/2}$, we have, by **7.20**,

$$\int_1^4 u^{1/2}\,du = \left.\frac{u^{3/2}}{3/2}\right|_1^4 = \frac{2}{3}(4^{3/2} - 1^{3/2}) = \frac{14}{3}.$$

EXAMPLE 3. Find $\int \frac{1}{x^3}\,dx.$

Solution: Since $1/x^3 = x^{-3}$, we have, by **7.20**,

$$\int x^{-3}\,dx = \frac{x^{-2}}{-2} + C = -\frac{1}{2x^2} + C.$$

If a function f is continuous, then so is cf for any constant function c, and

7.21
$$\int cf(x)\,dx = c\int f(x)\,dx.$$

By this equation we mean that c times an antiderivative of f is an antiderivative of cf. It is true because $D(cg) = cDg$ for any differentiable function g.

If functions F and G are respective antiderivatives of functions f and g, then $F + G$ is an antiderivative of $f + g$, since

$$D(F + G) = DF + DG = f + g.$$

This proves the following integration formula for continuous functions:

7.22 $$\int [f(x) + g(x)]\,dx = \int f(x)\,dx + \int g(x)\,dx.$$

Using **7.20–7.22**, we can easily integrate any polynomial function, as illustrated in the following examples.

EXAMPLE 4. Find $\int_{-1}^{1} (x^2 + 2x - 3)\,dx$.

Solution:

$$\int_{-1}^{1} (x^2 + 2x - 3)\,dx = (\tfrac{1}{3}x^3 + x^2 - 3x)\Big|_{-1}^{1} = (\tfrac{1}{3} + 1 - 3) - (-\tfrac{1}{3} + 1 + 3) = -\tfrac{16}{3}.$$

EXAMPLE 5. Find $\int (15u^4 - 12u^3 + 3u^2 + 6u + 1)\,du$.

Solution:

$$\int (15u^4 - 12u^3 + 3u^2 + 6u + 1)\,du = (3u^5 - 3u^4 + u^3 + 3u^2 + u) + C.$$

EXAMPLE 6. Find $\int \frac{x^2 + 2}{x^2}\,dx$.

Solution: We note that

$$\frac{x^2 + 2}{x^2} = \frac{x^2}{x^2} + \frac{2}{x^2} = 1 + 2x^{-2}.$$

Therefore

$$\int \frac{x^2 + 2}{x^2}\,dx = \int (1 + 2x^{-2})\,dx = (x - 2x^{-1}) + C = \left(x - \frac{2}{x}\right) + C.$$

EXERCISES

I

In each of Exercises 1–10, evaluate the integral.

1. $\int_0^2 (x^3 - 1)\,dx.$

2. $\int_{-1}^{1} (x + 1)\,dx.$

3. $\int_1^4 (u^2 - 2u + 3)\,du.$

4. $\int_0^5 (-3u^2 + 2u + 5)\,du.$

5. $\int_{-5}^{-1} (t^2 + 1)\,dt.$

6. $\int_0^1 (\sqrt{x} + 1)^2\,dx.$

7. $\int_4^1 x(\sqrt{x} - 3)\,dx.$

8. $\int_{-1}^{-8} z(\sqrt[3]{z} - 2z)\,dz.$

9. $\int_4^9 \left(\sqrt{x} - \frac{1}{\sqrt{x}}\right) dx.$ 10. $\int_1^4 \frac{x^2 - 3x + 4}{\sqrt{x}} dx.$

II

Evaluate the following integrals:

1. $\int_{-2}^{3} |x^3 - x| \, dx.$ 2. $\int_{-4}^{4} \sqrt{1 + 2|x|} \, dx.$

3. Show by using upper and lower sums that

$$\int_n^{n+1} [x] \, dx = n \quad \text{for every integer } n.$$

4. Show that

$$\int_0^n [x] \, dx = \frac{n(n-1)}{2}.$$

8 CHANGE OF VARIABLE

Integrals that cannot be evaluated directly by known formulas may sometimes be evaluated after a "change of variable." A formula for this transformation follows directly from the chain rule.

By the chain rule, $DF(g(x)) = F'(g(x))g'(x)$; hence

$$\int F'(g(x))g'(x) \, dx = F(g(x)) + C.$$

If we let $F' = f$, then we get the formula

$$\int f(g(x))g'(x) \, dx = F(g(x)) + C,$$

where F is an antiderivative of f. Letting

$$u = g(x), \qquad du = g'(x) \, dx,$$

we can express the above formula in the following useful form:

7.23 $$\int f(g(x))g'(x) \, dx = \int f(u) \, du \Big|_{u=g(x)}.$$

We call **7.23** the *change of variable* integration formula. The vertical bar followed by $u = g(x)$ indicates that u is to be replaced by $g(x)$ after the integration is performed. Thus, since F is an antiderivative of f,

$$\int f(u) \, du \Big|_{u=g(x)} = F(u) + C \Big|_{u=g(x)} = F(g(x)) + C.$$

For definite integrals 7.23 has the form

7.24
$$\int_a^b f(g(x))g'(x)\,dx = \int_{g(a)}^{g(b)} f(u)\,du,$$

which is easily verified.

We may remember 7.23 and 7.24 in the following way. We "change variables" in the left-hand integral by letting $u = g(x)$ and then by formally letting du be the derivative of g times dx, $du = g'(x)\,dx$. If a and b are thought of as x limits of integration, then the u limits are $g(a)$ and $g(b)$.

Some examples of the usefulness of the change of variable formula are given below.

EXAMPLE 1. Find $\int 2x(x^2 + 1)^3\,dx$.

Solution: Let $u = x^2 + 1$, so that $du = 2x\,dx$. Then, by 7.23,

$$\int 2x(x^2 + 1)^3\,dx = \int u^3\,du\Big|_{u=x^2+1} = \frac{1}{4}u^4 + C\Big|_{u=x^2+1} = \frac{1}{4}(x^2 + 1)^4 + C.$$

EXAMPLE 2. Find $\int_1^3 x\sqrt{x^2 - 1}\,dx$.

Solution: We change variables by letting

$$u = x^2 - 1, \qquad du = 2x\,dx.$$

If we supply a factor of 2 in the integrand and multiply the integral by $\frac{1}{2}$, we have

$$\int_1^3 x\sqrt{x^2 - 1}\,dx = \frac{1}{2}\int_1^3 \sqrt{x^2 - 1}(2x\,dx).$$

Since $u = 0$ when $x = 1$, and $u = 8$ when $x = 3$, we have, by 7.24,

$$\int_1^3 x\sqrt{x^2 - 1}\,dx = \frac{1}{2}\int_0^8 u^{1/2}\,du = \frac{1}{2}\left(\frac{2}{3}u^{3/2}\right)\Big|_0^8 = \frac{1}{3}(8^{3/2} - 0^{3/2}) = \frac{16\sqrt{2}}{3}.$$

A slight change in the integral of Example 2 makes it nonintegrable by the present methods. Thus we cannot evaluate

$$\int_1^3 \sqrt{x^2 - 1}\,dx$$

by use of 7.24. If we proceed as before and let $u = x^2 - 1$, $du = 2x\,dx$, then $u^{1/2}\,du = \sqrt{x^2 - 1}\,(2x\,dx)$. We can supply a factor of 2 in the integrand, but we cannot supply an x. This integral will be evaluated later by other methods.

EXAMPLE 3. Find $\int \frac{u^2}{(u^3 + 1)^2}\,du$.

Solution: Since the variable is already u, let us change the variable to y by letting

$$y = u^3 + 1, \qquad dy = 3u^2\,du.$$

Then

$$\int \frac{u^2}{(u^3+1)^2}\,du = \frac{1}{3}\int \frac{1}{(u^3+1)^2}(3u^2\,du) = \frac{1}{3}\int \frac{1}{y^2}\,dy\,\Big|_{y=u^3+1}$$

$$= \frac{1}{3}\int y^{-2}\,dy\,\Big|_{y=u^3+1} = \frac{1}{3}\frac{y^{-1}}{-1} + C\,\Big|_{y=u^3+1}$$

$$= -\frac{1}{3(u^3+1)} + C.$$

EXERCISES

I

In each of Exercises 1–16, evaluate the integral.

1. $\int_0^3 \sqrt{x+1}\,dx.$
2. $\int 2\sqrt{2x+1}\,dx.$
3. $\int_{-1}^{1} \frac{2x}{(4+x^2)^2}\,dx.$
4. $\int_{-1}^{2} 9x^2(1+3x^3)^2\,dx.$
5. $\int_0^{-5} \sqrt{1-3u}\,du.$
6. $\int \frac{1}{\sqrt{4u+1}}\,du.$
7. $\int_0^1 y\sqrt{1-y^2}\,dy.$
8. $\int_{-1}^{-2} 3z\sqrt[3]{z^2+1}\,dz.$
9. $\int_{-2}^{2} \frac{x}{\sqrt{1+8x^2}}\,dx.$
10. $\int_{-3}^{-1} \frac{1}{(4x-1)^2}\,dx.$
11. $\int_{-3}^{-1} \frac{1}{(2-3t)^3}\,dt.$
12. $\int \frac{t^2}{(1+t^3)^2}\,dt.$
13. $\int_{-1}^{1} u(1-u^2)^5\,du.$
14. $\int_1^2 \frac{1}{x^2}\sqrt{1-\frac{1}{x}}\,dx.$
15. $\int \frac{\sqrt{1+\sqrt{x}}}{\sqrt{x}}\,dx.$
16. $\int_0^1 \sqrt{u}\sqrt{1+u\sqrt{u}}\,du.$

II

Evaluate the following integrals.

1. $\int \frac{x}{\sqrt{1+x}}\,dx.$
2. $\int_0^3 \frac{x^3}{\sqrt{1+x}}\,dx.$

3. $\int_0^1 \frac{1}{\sqrt{1+\sqrt{x}}}\,dx.$ 4. $\int \frac{x}{x+\sqrt{x^2-1}}\,dx.$

5. If $I = \int_{-1}^{1} dy$, then clearly $I = 2$. However, if we first make the change of variable $y = x^{5/2}$ in the integral, we get $I = \frac{5}{2}\int_1^1 x^{3/2}\,dx = 0$. Explain.

9 INTERMEDIATE VALUE THEOREM FOR INTEGRALS

If a function F is continuous in a closed interval $[a,b]$ and if the domain of F' contains the open interval (a,b), then the mean value theorem (6.5) tells us that there exists a number c in (a,b) such that

$$F(b) - F(a) = (b - a)F'(c).$$

Now if f is any function which is continuous in $[a,b]$ then f has an antiderivative F which has the properties stated above. Since $F(b) - F(a)$ is the integral of f from a to b by 7.19 and $F'(c) = f(c)$, we have established the following integral analogue of the mean value theorem.

7.25 INTERMEDIATE VALUE THEOREM FOR INTEGRALS. If function f is continuous in an interval $[a,b]$, then there exists a number c in (a,b) such that

$$\int_a^b f(x)\,dx = (b - a)f(c).$$

EXERCISES

I

1. Find the number c in 7.25 for the function $f(x) = x^n$ in the interval $[a,b]$.

2. If the functions f and g are continuous in $[a,b]$ and if $f(x) \leq g(x)$ in $[a,b]$, prove that

$$\int_a^b f(x)\,dx \leq \int_a^b g(x)\,dx.$$

3. If the function F is continuous in $[a,b]$, prove that

$$\left|\int_a^b F(x)\,dx\right| \leq \int_a^b |F(x)|\,dx.$$

4. Let f be continuous in $[0,1]$ and let $0 \leq f(x) \leq 1$ for every x in $[0,1]$. Prove that there is a number z in $[0,1]$ such that $f(z) = z$. [*Hint:* If $f(0) = 0$ or $f(1) = 1$, the theorem is true. If $f(0) > 0$ and $f(1) < 1$, consider $g(x) = f(x) - x$.]

II

1. If f and p are continuous functions in $[a,b]$ and $p(x) \geq 0$ in $[a,b]$, show that there exists a number c in (a,b) such that

$$\int_a^b f(x)p(x)\,dx = f(c)\int_a^b p(x)\,dx.$$

(This generalizes 7.25.)

REVIEW

Oral Exercises

Explain or define the following:

1. Lower and upper bounds of a set of numbers.
2. Greatest lower bound and least upper bound of a set of numbers.
3. Completeness property of the real number system.
4. A piecewise monotonic function.
5. Upper and lower integrals.
6. Fundamental theorem of the calculus.
7. Area of a plane region.

8. Change of variable integration formula.

9. Intermediate value theorem for functions.

10. Intermediate value theorem for integrals.

I

In each of Exercises 1–6, sketch the graph of f and the graph of g in the given interval using the same coordinate system, where $g(x) = \int_0^x f(t)\,dt$.

1. $f(x) = x + 1$, $[0,4]$.
2. $f(x) = (x - 1)^2$, $[0,3]$.
3. $f(x) = x - 1$, $[0,4]$.
4. $f(x) = x^2 - 4x + 3$, $[0,5]$.
5. $f(x) = x^3 - 4x^2 + 4x$, $[0,4]$.
6. $f(x) = x^4$, $[-2,2]$.

In Exercises 7–18, a, b, c, d are real numbers and m, n are positive integers. Find the integrals.

7. $\int_1^4 \left(\frac{1}{\sqrt{x}} + \frac{1}{\sqrt{2}}\right) dx.$
8. $\int_0^1 (1 - x + x^3)^2(3x^2 - 1)\,dx.$
9. $\int_0^1 (1 + 5x - x^5)^4(x^2 - 1)(x^2 + 1)\,dx.$
10. $\int_0^1 (2ax + b)(ax^2 + bx + c)^n\,dx.$
11. $\int_c^d \sqrt{ax + b}\,dx.$
12. $\int_c^d \frac{1}{\sqrt{ax + b}}\,dx.$
13. $\int_1^a x(x^2 - 1)^n\,dx.$
14. $\int_0^1 x(x^2 + a^2)^n\,dx.$
15. $\int_0^a \frac{x}{(x^2 + a^2)^n}\,dx$, $n > 1$, $a \neq 0$.
16. $\int_0^b x^{m-1}(x^m + b^m)^n\,dx.$
17. $\int_{-1}^1 (x^2 + 2ax + a^2)^n\,dx.$
18. $\int_0^a \frac{x}{\sqrt{1 + x^2}\sqrt{1 + \sqrt{1 + x^2}}}\,dx.$

In each of Exercises 19–22, find the limit if it exists.

19. $\underset{t \to \infty}{\text{limit}} \int_1^t \frac{1}{x^2}\,dx.$
20. $\underset{t \to \infty}{\text{limit}} \int_1^t \frac{1}{\sqrt{x}}\,dx.$
21. $\underset{t \to 0}{\text{limit}} \int_t^1 \frac{1}{x^2}\,dx.$
22. $\underset{t \to 0}{\text{limit}} \int_t^1 \frac{1}{\sqrt{x}}\,dx.$

23. Let f' be continuous in $[a,b]$. State under what conditions

$$D\left(\int_a^x f(t)\,dt\right) = \int_a^x (Df)(t)\,dt.$$

II

1. a. Find $\int_1^x z^2\,dz$. b. Find $\int_x^{x^2} (z - a)^3\,dz$.

   c. Find $\int_a^{x^2} \sqrt[3]{z}\,dz$.

   d. If $H(x) = \int_1^{3x^2} (2z - 3)\,dz$, find $H'(x)$.

   e. Write a formula for $D\left\{\int_a^{g(x)} f(z)\,dz\right\}$ assuming that $g'(x)$ exists and that f is continuous in a closed interval containing a and $g(x)$.

   Using **e**, find

   f. $D\left\{\int_0^{3x} \dfrac{1}{u^4 + 1}\,du\right\}$. g. $D\left\{\int_0^{x^2} \sqrt{1 - z^2}\,dz\right\}$.

   h. $D\left\{\int_{x^2}^{x^3} \dfrac{1}{1 + t^3}\,dt\right\}$.

2. Let $f(x) = \dfrac{1}{x^2}$ and $F(x) = -\dfrac{1}{x}$. Find $F(1) - F(-1)$. Does $\int_{-1}^{1} f(x)\,dx = F(1) - F(-1)$? Explain.

3. Since the integrand of the integral

$$I = \int_{-1}^{1} \frac{1}{1 + x^2}\,dx \text{ is positive, it follows that } I > 0.$$

   However, if we make the change of variable $x = 1/u$, then

$$I = \int_{-1}^{1} \frac{1}{1 + x^2}\,dx = -\int_{-1}^{1} \frac{1}{1 + u^2}\,du = -I,$$

   whence $I = 0$. Explain.

4. Find the value of $f(c)$ in **7.25** for the function $f(x) = kx^2$ in $[a,b]$. At how many points of the interval does the function assume this value?

5. (a) If $|f|$ is integrable in an interval $[a,b]$, show that f need not be integrable in $[a,b]$.
   (b) If both f and $|f|$ are integrable in $[a,b]$, prove that

$$\left|\int_a^b f(x)\,dx\right| \le \int_a^b |f(x)|\,dx.$$

6. If the functions F and H are integrable in $[a,b]$ and if $F(x) \le G(x) \le H(x)$ for every x in $[a,b]$, state whether it follows that

$$\int_a^b F(x)\,dx \le \int_a^b G(x)\,dx \le \int_a^b H(x)\,dx.$$

7. Show that

$$.5 < \int_0^{1/2} \frac{1}{\sqrt{1 - x^n}}\,dx < .586 \quad \text{for every integer } n > 1.$$

8. An ancient approximation for π is $\frac{22}{7}$. We may find bounds on the error for this approximation as follows. Using

$$\int_0^1 \frac{x^4(1-x)^4}{1+x^2}\,dx = \frac{22}{7} - \pi,$$

(subsequently, we will be able to verify this), show that

$$\frac{1}{630} > \frac{22}{7} - \pi > \frac{1}{1260}.$$

9. Determine a polynomial function F satisfying

$$F'(x) - F(x) = x^3 \quad \text{(called a differential equation).}$$

10. Determine a polynomial function G satisfying the differential equation

$$G''(x) + aG'(x) + bG(x) = x^2.$$

11. If F^2, FG, and G^2 are integrable functions in the interval $[a,b]$, show that

$$\int_a^b F^2(x)\,dx \cdot \int_a^b G^2(x)\,dx \geq \left\{\int_a^b F(x)G(x)\,dx\right\}^2$$

with equality if and only if $F = kG$ (k a constant). (This is the very useful Schwarz-Buniakowsky inequality). [*Hint:* Start with the obvious inequality

$$\int_a^b (mF + nG)^2\,dx = m^2 \int_a^b F^2\,dx + 2mn \int_a^b FG\,dx + n^2 \int_a^b G^2\,dx \geq 0,$$

which holds for all real numbers m and n.]

12. Using Exercise 11, with $F^2(x) = \dfrac{1}{1+x^2}$, $G^2(x) = 1 + x^2$, show that

$$\int_0^1 \frac{1}{1+x^2}\,dx > \frac{3}{4}.$$

(Subsequently, we will be able to show that the integral $= \pi/4$.)

13. Prove that

$$1 > \int_0^1 \frac{1}{1+x^n}\,dx > \frac{n+1}{n+2} \quad (n > 0).$$

14. Find the function y having a continuous derivative in $[0,1]$ for which the integral $I = \int_0^1 y'^2(x)\,dx$ takes on its least value, if y is subject to the boundary conditions

a. $y(0) = y(1) = 0$; b. $y(0) = 0$, $y(1) = 1$.

[*Hint:* Use Exercise 11.]

8

THEORY OF THE INTEGRAL

IN THIS CHAPTER the basic properties of a function which is continuous in a closed interval are proved. Our primary aim is to show that such a function is bounded and integrable. We also introduce sequences in this chapter, and then prove that an integral can be considered to be the limit of a sequence.

1 BOUNDEDNESS OF A CONTINUOUS FUNCTION

A set C of open intervals is called an (open) *covering* of an interval I if every number x in I is also in some open interval of C.

For example, if $C = \{(-1,0), (-\frac{1}{2},1), (\frac{1}{3},2), (\frac{3}{2},3)\}$, then C is a covering of the interval $[0,2]$. Thus each number x, $(0 \leq x \leq 2)$, is in one or more of the open intervals of C. In particular, 0 is in $(-\frac{1}{2},1)$, $\frac{1}{2}$ is in both $(-\frac{1}{2},1)$ and $(\frac{1}{3},2)$, and $\frac{7}{4}$ is in $(\frac{3}{2},3)$.

As another example, let us associate with each rational number r, $(0 \leq r \leq 1)$, the open interval $(r - .01, r + .01)$. The set C of all such open intervals is a covering of the closed interval $[0,1]$. Thus each real number x in $[0,1]$ is within .01 of a unit of some rational number r, and therefore x is in $(r - .01, r + .01)$. For example, $\sqrt{2} - 1$ is in $(.41, .43)$. Since there are infinitely many rational numbers in $(0,1)$, there are infinitely many open intervals in the covering C of $[0,1]$. However, we can find a finite subset C' of C that is also a covering of $[0,1]$. For example, let

$$C' = \{(-.01,.01), (0,.02), (.01,.03), \cdots, (.98,1), (.99,1.01)\}.$$

Since any two adjacent intervals of C' overlap, it is clear that C' is a covering of $[0,1]$. Evidently, C' contains 100 open intervals.

The example above illustrates the following fundamental property of coverings.

8.1 **THEOREM.** If a set C of open intervals is a covering of a closed interval $[a,b]$, then some finite subset C' of C is also a covering of $[a,b]$.

Proof: Let A be the set consisting of every number x of $[a,b]$ such that the interval $[a,x]$ is covered by some finite subset of C, and let

$$c = \text{l.u.b. } A.$$

Clearly, $c \leq b$ by the definition of A. By assumption, some interval (e,f) of C contains c. Since $c = \text{l.u.b. } A$, necessarily some number x of A is also in (e,f).

Let B be a finite subset of C covering $[a,x]$. Then

$$C' = B \cup \{(e,f)\}$$

is a finite covering of $[a,c]$ (see Figure 8.1). Therefore c is in set A. Actually, $c = b$ and C' is a covering of $[a,b]$. For if $c < b$ and d is in $(c,b) \cap (e,f)$ (see Figure 8.1), then d is in A since $[a,d]$ is also covered by C'. However, this contradicts the fact that $c = \text{l.u.b. } A$. This proves **8.1**.

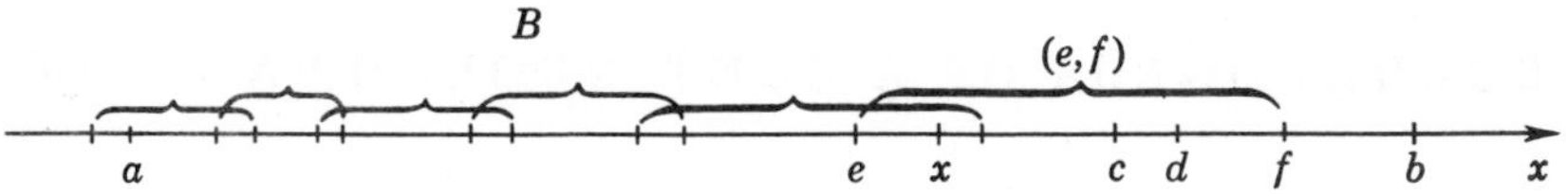

FIGURE 8.1

We shall use **8.1** in discussing the boundedness of a continuous function. Thus let f be a continuous function in a closed interval $[a,b]$. For each number c in $[a,b]$, there is a neighborhood N_c of c (depending on c) such that

$$f(c) - 1 < f(x) < f(c) + 1 \quad \text{for every } x \text{ in } N_c \cap [a,b].$$

We note that f is *bounded* in each interval N_c, having lower bound $f(c) - 1$ and upper bound $f(c) + 1$.

The set $C = \{N_c \mid c \text{ in } [a,b]\}$ is an infinite covering of $[a,b]$ by open intervals. Hence, by **8.1**, some finite subset C' of C is also a covering of $[a,b]$. Since f is bounded in each of the intervals of C', it is bounded in $[a,b]$. For if $k_1, k_2, \cdots, k_n$ are the lower bounds of f in the intervals of C', then the least of the numbers $k_1, k_2, \cdots, k_n$ is a lower bound of f in $[a,b]$; and similarly for upper bounds. This proves the following result.

8.2 THEOREM. A function that is continuous in a closed interval is bounded in that interval.

We should realize that **8.2** is not true for open intervals. For example, the function f defined by $f(x) = 1/x$ is continuous but not bounded in the open interval $(0,1)$.

Knowing that a continuous function f is bounded in a closed interval $[a,b]$, we can prove even more, namely that f assumes a maximum value and a minimum value. We state this result as follows.

8.3 THEOREM. If a function f is continuous in a closed interval $[a,b]$, then there exist numbers u and v in $[a,b]$ such that $f(u)$ is the minimum value and $f(v)$ is the maximum value of f in $[a,b]$.

Proof: Let $R = \{f(x) \mid x \text{ in } [a,b]\}$ be the range of f in $[a,b]$. By **8.2**, R has both an upper bound and a lower bound. Hence R has a l.u.b. and a g.l.b. Let

$$k = \text{l.u.b. } R.$$

If $k = f(v)$ for some v in $[a,b]$, then $f(v)$ is the maximum value of f in $[a,b]$ and the desired conclusion follows.

On the other hand, if $f(x) \neq k$ for every x in $[a,b]$, then $k - f(x) > 0$ for every x in $[a,b]$. The function g defined by

$$g(x) = \frac{1}{k - f(x)}, \qquad (\text{domain } g = [a,b]),$$

is continuous in $[a,b]$. Hence, by **8.2**, g has an upper bound w in $[a,b]$, so that

$$0 < \frac{1}{k - f(x)} \leq w \quad \text{for every } x \text{ in } [a,b].$$

Solving this inequality for $f(x)$, we have

$$f(x) \leq k - \frac{1}{w} \quad \text{for every } x \text{ in } [a,b].$$

Thus $k - 1/w$ is an upper bound of R less than l.u.b. R. This contradiction shows that $f(x)$ cannot be different from k for every x in $[a,b]$. Hence f assumes a maximum value in $[a,b]$.

The existence of the minimum value of f in $[a,b]$ is established in an analogous way. This proves **8.3**.

This theorem was of basic importance (6.1) in our discussion of extrema of a function in Chapter 6. With the aid of **8.3**, we were able to prove such fundamental results as Rolle's theorem (6.4) and the mean value theorem (6.5).

EXERCISES

I

In each of Exercises 1–6 the function is continuous in the given interval. Find numbers in the interval at which the function assumes its maximum and minimum values in that interval. Sketch the graph of the function in the given interval.

1. $f(x) = x^2 + 9$, $[-3,3]$.
2. $g(x) = -x^2 + x + 2$, $[-2,2]$.
3. $g(x) = 2x^3 - 3x^2 - 12x$, $[-2,3]$.
4. $g(x) = |x^2 - 1|$, $[-2,1]$.
5. $F(x) = |x|$, $[-2,3]$.
6. $G(x) = \dfrac{x+1}{x-1}$, $(1,100]$.
7. Let the function f be defined as follows:

$$f(x) = x \text{ for every } x \text{ in the open interval } (0,1), \quad f(0) = f(1) = \tfrac{1}{2}.$$

   a. Is f continuous in the closed interval $[0,1]$?
   b. Is f bounded in $[0,1]$? If so, what are l.u.b. and g.l.b. for f in this interval?
   c. Does f attain either a maximum or a minimum value in $[0,1]$?

8. Give an example of a function which is not continuous in the closed interval $[0,1]$ but is bounded and attains its maximum and minimum values in $[0,1]$.
9. Given $F(x) = x^3$ in $(-1,1)$, what are the g.l.b. and l.u.b. of F in this interval? Does the function F have a maximum or minimum in the given interval?
10. Show that the function F defined by

$$F(x) = \begin{cases} x^{-2}, & (x \neq 0) \\ 0, & (x = 0) \end{cases}$$

is unbounded in $[-1,1]$.

II

1. Show that the function F defined by $F(x) = [x] - x$ in the interval $[0,3]$ has a maximum value and a lower bound, but not a minimum value.
2. If f is continuous at a and g is not continuous at a, then show that $f + g$ is not continuous at a. If $f + g$ is continuous at a, must f and g both be continuous at a? Prove your answer.

3. Prove that if f is continuous and periodic with period k, then

$$\int_a^{a+k} f(x)\,dx = \int_0^k f(x)\,dx \quad \text{for every number } a.$$

Express this result in another form by making the change of variable $y = x - a$ in the first integral.

4. State and prove a converse of the result of Exercise 3.

5. If the function F is continuous in [0,2] and assumes only rational values, show that if $F(1) = \frac{1}{2}$, then $F(x) = \frac{1}{2}$ for every x in [0,2].

6. Prove that if f is a continuous function with domain $[a,b]$ and range contained in $[a,b]$, then $f(x) = x$ for some x in $[a,b]$.

2 SEQUENCES

The functions known as sequences are of particular interest in mathematics.

8.4 **DEFINITION.** A sequence is a function having as its domain the set of positive integers.

In order to define any function, we must somehow describe the correspondence that associates with each number in the domain of the function a number in its range. This may be done by means of a table, an equation, or a combination of a table and an equation.

The customary way to define a sequence a is to list in order the values of a at the successive positive integers, as indicated below.

$$a(1), a(2), a(3), \cdots .$$

The dots are used to suggest that the "table" is an infinite one. A further convention is the use of subscripts rather than the usual functional notation. Thus the sequence above will be written

$$a_1, a_2, a_3, \cdots .$$

The numbers a_1, a_2, a_3, and so on, are called the *elements* of the sequence a, a_k being the kth element.

In essence, a sequence is just an unending succession of numbers described by some rule of formation. The following are examples of sequences:

$$(1) \quad \frac{2}{1}, \frac{2}{2}, \frac{2}{3}, \frac{2}{4}, \cdots ; \qquad a_n = \frac{2}{n}.$$

(2) $1^2, 2^2, 3^2, 4^2, \cdots;$ $\qquad a_n = n^2.$

(3) $-1, -2, -3, -4, \cdots;$ $\qquad a_n = -n.$

(4) $2, 4, 6, 8, \cdots;$ $\qquad a_n = 2n.$

(5) $1, \sqrt{2}, \sqrt{3}, \sqrt{4}, \cdots;$ $\qquad a_n = \sqrt{n}.$

(6) $2, 2, 2, 2, \cdots;$ $\qquad a_n = 2.$

(7) $-2, 2, -2, 2, \cdots;$ $\qquad a_n = (-1)^n 2.$

(8) $\frac{1}{2}, \frac{2}{3}, \frac{3}{4}, \frac{4}{5}, \cdots;$ $\qquad a_n = \frac{n}{n+1}.$

(9) $-\frac{1}{2}, \frac{1}{4}, -\frac{1}{8}, \frac{1}{16}, \cdots;$ $\qquad a_n = \left(-\frac{1}{2}\right)^n.$

(10) $2, \frac{5}{2}, \frac{8}{3}, \frac{11}{4}, \cdots;$ $\qquad a_n = 3 - \frac{1}{n}.$

In each of these examples we have displayed the nth element in order to give the general rule of formation of the sequence. For example, in (1), knowing that $a_n = 2/n$, we find

$$a_1 = \frac{2}{1}, \quad a_2 = \frac{2}{2}, \quad a_3 = \frac{2}{3}, \quad a_4 = \frac{2}{4}, \quad a_5 = \frac{2}{5},$$

and so on. Thus the 32nd element of the sequence is $a_{32} = \frac{2}{32} = \frac{1}{16}$. In most of the examples above we could guess the rule of formation used just by looking at the first few elements of the sequence. However, given that a sequence starts out as follows,

$$5, 7, 7, 3, \cdots,$$

we would not be able to continue it without some clue as to how the first four elements were chosen. The rule we used in forming this sequence was to let a_n be the nth digit in the decimal expansion of $\sqrt{3}/3$,

$$\frac{\sqrt{3}}{3} = .577350 \cdots.$$

It is important to distinguish between a sequence and the *set of elements* of the sequence. For example, the set of elements of sequence (5) above is the set of square roots of all the positive integers. An entirely different sequence is the following:

$$1, \sqrt{2}, 1, \sqrt{3}, 1, \sqrt{4}, \cdots; \qquad a_n = \begin{cases} 1, & n \text{ odd} \\ \sqrt{\frac{n}{2} + 1}, & n \text{ even.} \end{cases}$$

Although these two sequences are different, they consist of the same set of elements. In other words, the ranges of the two sequences are the same. The set of elements in sequence (7) above consists of two elements, -2 and 2.

The nth element $2/n$ of sequence (1) above is close to zero if n is large. For this reason, we shall say that the limit of sequence (1) is zero.

The limit of sequence (6) is 2, since the nth element is equal to 2 (and hence close to 2) when n is large.

Since the nth element of sequence (10) above is $3 - 1/n$, evidently the nth element is close to 3 when n is large. Thus the limit of this sequence is 3, according to the following definition of the limit of a sequence.

8.5 DEFINITION. The sequence

$$a_1, a_2, \cdots, a_n, \cdots$$

has limit b if for every neighborhood N of b there exists a positive number k such that a_n is in N for every integer n in (k, ∞).

If the sequence with nth element a_n has limit b, then we write

$$\operatorname*{limit}_{n \to \infty} a_n = b.$$

It should be noted that the definition of the limit of a sequence is almost word for word the same as the definition of

$$\operatorname*{limit}_{x \to \infty} f(x)$$

given in **4.19**. Hence we can expect the methods used in Chapter 4 for infinite limits of functions to carry over to limits of sequences.

Let us use **8.5** to prove that sequence (10) above has limit 3, i.e., that

$$\operatorname*{limit}_{n \to \infty} \left(3 - \frac{1}{n}\right) = 3.$$

We must show that for every neighborhood N of 3 there exists a positive number k such that $3 - (1/n)$ is in N for every integer n in (k, ∞). If $N = (3 - \epsilon, 3 + \epsilon)$, then $3 - \epsilon < 3 - (1/n) < 3 + \epsilon$ if and only if $-\epsilon < -1/n < \epsilon$, or $\epsilon > 1/n$. Thus we need only select $k = 1/\epsilon$ in order that $3 - (1/n)$ be in N for every n in (k, ∞).

Of the ten examples of sequences listed at the beginning of this section, it is intuitively clear that (2), (3), (4), (5), and (7) do not have limits. Each of the other sequences has a limit.

The sequence

$$\frac{d}{1^p}, \frac{d}{2^p}, \frac{d}{3^p}, \cdots, \frac{d}{n^p}, \cdots$$

has the limit 0 for any real number d and any positive rational number p, i.e.,

8.6 $$\lim_{n \to \infty} \frac{d}{n^p} = 0, \qquad p > 0.$$

We shall not prove **8.6**, since its proof is almost identical with that of **4.20**. As a consequence of **8.6** each of the following sequences has zero as its limit:

$$1, \frac{1}{2}, \frac{1}{3}, \frac{1}{4}, \cdots, \frac{1}{n}, \cdots,$$

$$-2, \frac{-2}{\sqrt{2}}, \frac{-2}{\sqrt{3}}, \frac{-2}{\sqrt{4}}, \cdots, \frac{-2}{\sqrt{n}}, \cdots,$$

$$3, \frac{3}{2^2}, \frac{3}{3^2}, \frac{3}{4^2}, \cdots, \frac{3}{n^2}, \cdots.$$

Limits of sequences have many of the properties of limits of functions given in Chapter 4. Before stating these properties, we observe that from the sequences

$$a_1, a_2, \cdots, a_n, \cdots,$$

$$b_1, b_2, \cdots, b_n, \cdots,$$

we can form many new sequences; for example,

$$a_1 + b_1, a_2 + b_2, \cdots, a_n + b_n, \cdots,$$

$$a_1b_1, a_2b_2, \cdots, a_nb_n, \cdots,$$

$$\frac{a_1}{b_1}, \frac{a_2}{b_2}, \cdots, \frac{a_n}{b_n}, \cdots \quad \text{(if each } b_n \neq 0\text{)},$$

$$|a_1|, |a_2|, \cdots, |a_n|, \cdots,$$

and so on.

The constant sequence $c, c, \cdots, c, \cdots$ has c as its limit; i.e.,

8.7 $$\lim_{n \to \infty} c = c.$$

If

$$\lim_{n \to \infty} a_n = a, \qquad \lim_{n \to \infty} b_n = b,$$

then

8.8 $$\lim_{n \to \infty} (a_n + b_n) = a + b,$$

8.9 $$\lim_{n\to\infty} a_n b_n = ab,$$

8.10 $$\lim_{n\to\infty} \frac{a_n}{b_n} = \frac{a}{b}, \qquad b_n \neq 0,\ b \neq 0.$$

Since the proofs of these limit theorems are similar to the corresponding ones for functions, they will be omitted.

Some useful limit theorems of a slightly different nature are as follows:

8.11 **THEOREM.** If $a_n \leq c_n \leq b_n$ for each integer n and if $\lim_{n\to\infty} a_n = \lim_{n\to\infty} b_n = a$, then $\lim_{n\to\infty} c_n = a$.

8.12 **THEOREM.** If $\lim_{n\to\infty} a_n = a$, then $\lim_{n\to\infty} |a_n| = |a|$.

8.13 **THEOREM.** If $\lim_{n\to\infty} |a_n| = 0$, then $\lim_{n\to\infty} a_n = 0$.

Proof of **8.11** For every neighborhood N of a, there must exist some positive number k such that a_n and b_n are in N for every integer n in (k, ∞). Hence c_n is in N for every n in (k, ∞). This proves **8.11**.

The proofs of **8.12** and **8.13** are left for the reader to supply.

A sequence $a_1, a_2, \cdots, a_n, \cdots$ is said to be *increasing* if $a_1 \leq a_2 \leq a_3 \leq \cdots \leq a_n \leq \cdots$ and *decreasing* if $a_1 \geq a_2 \geq a_3 \geq \cdots \geq a_n \geq \cdots$. As for other functions, a sequence is called *monotonic* if it is either increasing or decreasing. A number M is called an *upper bound* of a sequence $a_1, a_2, \cdots, a_n, \cdots$ if $a_n \leq M$ for every n, and similarly for a lower bound. We call a sequence *bounded* if it has both an upper bound and a lower bound.

8.14 **THEOREM.** Every bounded monotonic sequence has a limit.

Proof: Assume that $a_1, a_2, \cdots, a_n, \cdots$ is a bounded increasing sequence. Hence, the set $S = \{a_n \mid n = 1, 2, \cdots\}$ has a l.u.b., which we denote by a. For every number $\epsilon > 0$, $a - \epsilon$ is not an upper bound of S and therefore $a_N > a - \epsilon$ for some integer N. Since the sequence is increasing, $a_n \geq a_N$ for every $n > N$. Thus, for every $\epsilon > 0$ there exists an integer N such that

$$0 \leq a - a_n < \epsilon \quad \text{for every } n > N.$$

This proves that

$$\lim_{n\to\infty} a_n = a.$$

A similar proof holds if the sequence is decreasing. This completes the proof of **8.14**.

Since the sequence $\{d/n^p\}$ of **8.6** is monotonic, it has a limit by **8.14.** Its limit is 0 because $0 = \text{g l.b. } \{d/n^p \mid n = 1, 2, \cdots\}$ if $d > 0$ and $0 = \text{l.u.b. } \{d/n^p|n = 1, 2, \cdots\}$ if $d < 0$.

With the aid of the above limit theorems, it is possible to evaluate directly the limits of many sequences, as shown in the following examples.

EXAMPLE 1. Find $\underset{n\to\infty}{\text{limit}} \dfrac{n}{n+1}$.

Solution: Since

$$\frac{n}{n+1} = \frac{1}{1 + 1/n}.$$

the given sequence is the quotient of two sequences having nth terms 1 and $1 + 1/n$, respectively. Thus, by **8.10**,

$$\underset{n\to\infty}{\text{limit}} \frac{n}{n+1} = \underset{n\to\infty}{\text{limit}} \frac{1}{1+1/n} = \frac{\underset{n\to\infty}{\text{limit}}\ 1}{\underset{n\to\infty}{\text{limit}}\ (1 + 1/n)}.$$

However, by **8.6**, **8.7**, and **8.8**,

$$\underset{n\to\infty}{\text{limit}} \left(1 + \frac{1}{n}\right) = \underset{n\to\infty}{\text{limit}}\ 1 + \underset{n\to\infty}{\text{limit}} \frac{1}{n} = 1.$$

We conclude that

$$\underset{n\to\infty}{\text{limit}} \frac{n}{n+1} = 1.$$

EXAMPLE 2. Find $\underset{n\to\infty}{\text{limit}} \dfrac{1 - 2n + 3n^2}{5n^2}$.

Solution: We note that

$$\frac{1 - 2n + 3n^2}{5n^2} = \frac{\frac{1}{5}}{n^2} - \frac{\frac{2}{5}}{n} + \frac{3}{5}.$$

Hence

$$\underset{n\to\infty}{\text{limit}} \frac{1 - 2n + 3n^2}{5n^2} = \underset{n\to\infty}{\text{limit}} \frac{\frac{1}{5}}{n^2} - \underset{n\to\infty}{\text{limit}} \frac{\frac{2}{5}}{n} + \underset{n\to\infty}{\text{limit}} \frac{3}{5}$$
$$= 0 - 0 + \frac{3}{5} = \frac{3}{5}.$$

EXAMPLE 3. Find $\underset{n\to\infty}{\text{limit}} \dfrac{5n}{n^2+1}$.

Solution: We again change $5n/(n^2 + 1)$ into a form containing powers of $1/n$:

$$\frac{5n}{n^2+1} = \frac{5/n}{1 + 1/n^2}.$$

Hence

$$\lim_{n\to\infty} \frac{5n}{n^2+1} = \frac{\lim_{n\to\infty} (5/n)}{\lim_{n\to\infty} 1 + \lim_{n\to\infty} (1/n^2)} = \frac{0}{1+0} = 0.$$

EXERCISES

I

In each of Exercises 1–13 the nth element a_n of a sequence is given. Write down the first five numbers of the sequence, and then find $\lim_{n\to\infty} a_n$, if it exists. (You may use any of the limit theorems.)

1. $a_n = \dfrac{3}{n}$.
2. $a_n = 1 - \dfrac{2}{n}$.
3. $a_n = \dfrac{2n}{n+3}$.
4. $a_n = \dfrac{1-2n}{1+n}$.
5. $a_n = \dfrac{(-1)^n}{n^2}$.
6. $a_n = \dfrac{(-1)^{n+1}(n+1)}{2n}$.
7. $a_n = \dfrac{n^2-2}{n^2+2}$.
8. $a_n = \dfrac{n^3-1}{n^3+1}$.
9. $a_n = \dfrac{2n}{n+1} - \dfrac{n+1}{2n}$.
10. $a_n = \dfrac{n^2}{2n+1} - \dfrac{n^2}{2n-1}$.
11. $a_n = \dfrac{n^3}{n^2+2} - \dfrac{n^3}{n^2-2}$.
12. $a_n = \dfrac{n^2+5n-2}{2n^2}$.
13. $a_n = \dfrac{1}{\sqrt{n^2+1}}$.

II

1. Show that **8.13** does not necessarily hold if the two zeros are replaced by any positive number a.
2. Let $a_1, a_2, \ldots, a_n, \ldots$ be a sequence such that $\lim_{n\to\infty} a_n = b$. Let f be a function

such that for every positive integer n greater than some integer N all a_n are in the domain of f and f is continuous at b. Prove that

$$\lim_{n\to\infty} f(a_n) = f(b).$$

In each of Exercises 3–10, write down the first few terms of the given sequence $\{a_n\}$, $(n = 1, 2, 3, \ldots)$. Where appropriate, show that a limit exists and find it.

3. $a_n = k^n$.

4. $a_n = \sqrt[n]{2}$.

5. $a_n = \sqrt{n+2} - \sqrt{n+1}$.

6. $a_n = \sqrt[3]{n+2} - \sqrt[3]{n+1}$.

7. $a_n = \dfrac{10{,}000^n}{n!}$.

8. $a_n = n^{1/n}$.

9. $a_n = \dfrac{n!}{n^n}$.

10. $a_n = \sqrt[n]{a^n + b^n}$ $(a,b > 0)$.

11. $a_n = (n+1)^{-2} + (n+2)^{-2} + \cdots + (n+n)^{-2}$.

12. $a_n = \dfrac{1}{\sqrt{n^2+1}} + \dfrac{1}{\sqrt{n^2+2}} + \cdots + \dfrac{1}{\sqrt{n^2+n}}$.

3 RIEMANN SUMS

If f is an integrable function in a closed interval $[a,b]$, $P = \{x_0, x_1, \cdots, x_n\}$ is a partition of $[a,b]$, and z_i is a number in the ith subinterval $[x_{i-1},x_i]$ of P, $i = 1, 2, \cdots, n$, then

$$R(P) = \sum_{i=1}^{n} f(z_i)\,\Delta x_i$$

is called a *Riemann* sum* of f over $[a,b]$. We recall that the upper sum $S(P)$ and lower sum $T(P)$ of f over $[a,b]$ are defined by

$$S(P) = \sum_{i=1}^{n} m_i\,\Delta x_i, \quad T(P) = \sum_{i=1}^{n} M_i\,\Delta x_i$$

where m_i is the g.l.b. and M_i the l.u.b. of f in $[x_{i-1}, x_i]$. Clearly $m_i \leq f(z_i) \leq M_i$ for each i, and therefore for every partition P and every choice of the z_i in $R(P)$, we have

8.15 $$S(P) \leq R(P) \leq T(P).$$

* Georg Friedrich Riemann was a famous German mathematician of the nineteenth century. In one of his early papers on the foundations of analysis (1850) is given the first rigorous definition of an integral as a limit of a sum.

The fact that f is integrable in $[a,b]$ means (7.16) that for every $\epsilon > 0$ there exists a partition P of $[a,b]$ such that $0 \leq T(P) - S(P) < \epsilon$. If $R(P)$ is a Riemann sum, then both $R(P)$ and $\int_a^b f(x)\,dx$ lie between $S(P)$ and $T(P)$, so that

$$-\epsilon < R(P) - \int_a^b f(x)\,dx < \epsilon.$$

Thus the Riemann sums of f over $[a,b]$ are close to the integral of f from a to b if the partitions of $[a,b]$ over which the Riemann sums are defined are properly chosen.

What we wish to indicate in this section is how $\int_a^b f(x)\,dx$ may be expressed as a limit of a sequence of Riemann sums. Before stating the theorem, let us define the *norm* of a partition $P = \{x_0, x_1, \cdots, x_n\}$ of $[a,b]$. It is simply the largest of the lengths $\Delta x_1, \Delta x_2, \cdots, \Delta x_n$ of the subintervals of P. Denoting the *norm* of P by $||P||$,

$$||P|| = \text{max. } \{\Delta x_1, \Delta x_2, \cdots, \Delta x_n\}.$$

Thus $||P|| \geq \Delta x_i$ for every i, with $||P|| = \Delta x_i$ for some i.

8.16 **THEOREM.** Let f be integrable in $[a,b]$ and $P_1, P_2, \cdots, P_n, \cdots$ be a sequence of partitions of $[a,b]$ for which

$$\operatorname*{limit}_{n \to \infty} ||P_n|| = 0.$$

If $R(P_1), R(P_2), \cdots, R(P_n), \cdots$ is any sequence of Riemann sums of f associated with the given sequence of partitions, then

$$\operatorname*{limit}_{n \to \infty} R(P_n) = \int_a^b f(x)\,dx.$$

Proof: We need only show that for every $\epsilon > 0$ there exists a number N such that $0 \leq T(P_n) - S(P_n) < \epsilon$ for every $n > N$. This will imply

$$-\epsilon < R(P_n) - \int_a^b f(x)\,dx < \epsilon \quad \text{for every } n > N.$$

To this end, we know by 7.16 that for every $\epsilon > 0$ there exists a partition $P = \{x_0, x_1, \cdots, x_k\}$ of $[a,b]$, such that

$$0 \leq T(P) - S(P) < \frac{\epsilon}{2}.$$

Clearly we can choose P so that $k > 1$. Since f is bounded, there exists a positive number M such that

$$-M \leq f(x) \leq M \quad \text{for every } x \text{ in } [a,b].$$

For each P_n, $k - 1$ or fewer of the subintervals of P_n contain the numbers $x_1, x_2, \cdots, x_{k-1}$ of P and the rest of the subintervals of P_n are contained in subintervals of P. Now each term of $T(P_n) - S(P_n)$ has the form $(M_i - m_i)\,\Delta u_i$, where m_i is the g.l.b. and M_i the l.u.b. of f in the ith subinterval $[u_{i-1},u_i]$ of P_n. Since $-M \leq m_i \leq M_i \leq M$ and $\Delta u_i \leq ||P_n||$, each term of $T(P_n) - S(P_n)$ is less than or equal to $2M||P_n||$. Hence, the sum of the terms of $T(P_n) - S(P_n)$ which correspond to subintervals containing the numbers $x_1, x_2, \cdots, x_{k-1}$ is at most $2M(k - 1)||P_n||$.

For each subinterval $[u_{i-1},u_i]$ of P_n which is contained in a subinterval $[x_{j-1},x_j]$ of P, the term $(M_i - m_i)\,\Delta u_i$ of $T(P_n) - S(P_n)$ is less than or equal to the corresponding term $(M'_j - m'_j)\,\Delta x_j$ of $T(P) - S(P)$ because $M' \geq M$, $m' \leq m$, and $\Delta u_i \leq \Delta x_j$. Hence, the sum of the terms of $T(P_n) - S(P_n)$ which do not involve the numbers $x_1, x_2, \cdots, x_k$ is at most $T(P) - S(P)$.

Combining the two types of subintervals of P_n discussed above, we obtain

$$0 \leq T(P_n) - S(P_n) \leq [T(P) - S(P)] + 2M(k - 1)||P_n||.$$

Since $\lim_{n\to\infty} ||P_n|| = 0$, for every $\epsilon > 0$ there exists a number N such that

$$||P_n|| < \frac{\epsilon}{4M(k - 1)} \quad \text{for every } n > N.$$

Hence $2M(k - 1)||P_n|| < \epsilon/2$ for every $n > N$ and

$$0 \leq T(P_n) - S(P_n) < \frac{\epsilon}{2} + \frac{\epsilon}{2} = \epsilon \quad \text{for every } n > N.$$

This proves **8.16**.

The conclusion of **8.16** may be expressed in the following form if P_n is the regular partition of $[a,b]$ into n subintervals:

8.17
$$\int_a^b f(x)\,dx = \lim_{n\to\infty} \sum_{i=1}^{n} f(z_i)\,\Delta x.$$

In this notation $\sum_{i=1}^{n} f(z_i)\,\Delta x$ represents a Riemann sum of f relative to $P_n = \{x_0,x_1, \cdots, x_n\}$, with

$$x_{i-1} \leq z_i \leq x_i \quad \text{and} \quad \Delta x = x_i - x_{i-1} = \frac{b - a}{n},$$

$(i = 1, 2, \cdots, n)$.

Let us illustrate with an example how **8.17** might be used to compute an integral.

EXAMPLE. Find $\int_0^2 x^2\,dx$ by use of **8.17**.

Solution: The function f defined by

$$f(x) = x^2$$

is continuous in [0,2]. For each positive integer n, the regular partition P_n is given by

$$P_n = \{0,\Delta x, 2\Delta x, \cdots, (n-1)\Delta x, 2\}$$

where $\Delta x = 2/n$. Hence

$$\int_0^2 x^2\,dx = \lim_{n\to\infty} \sum_{i=1}^{n} f(z_i)\,\Delta x$$

for any choice of $z_1, z_2, \cdots, z_n$, one in each of the subintervals of P_n. If, for example, we choose $z_1 = \Delta x$, $z_2 = 2\,\Delta x, \cdots, z_n = n\,\Delta x$, then we have

$$\int_0^2 x^2\,dx = \lim_{n\to\infty} \sum_{i=1}^{n} f(i\,\Delta x)\,\Delta x.$$

We may compute the above sum as follows:

$$\begin{aligned}\sum_{i=1}^{n} f(i\,\Delta x)\,\Delta x &= \sum_{i=1}^{n}\left(i\cdot\frac{2}{n}\right)^2\frac{2}{n}\\ &= \frac{8}{n^3}\sum_{i=1}^{n} i^2\\ &= \frac{8}{n^3}\,\frac{n(n+1)(2n+1)}{6} \qquad \text{(by } \mathbf{8.14}\text{)}\\ &= \frac{4}{3}\left(2+\frac{3}{n}+\frac{1}{n^2}\right).\end{aligned}$$

Therefore

$$\int_0^2 x^2\,dx = \lim_{n\to\infty}\frac{4}{3}\left(2+\frac{3}{n}+\frac{1}{n^2}\right) = \frac{8}{3}.$$

This result naturally checks with that obtained by using the fundamental theorem of the calculus:

$$\int_0^2 x^2\,dx = \left.\frac{x^3}{3}\right|_0^2 = \frac{8}{3}.$$

EXERCISES

I

Evaluate the definite integrals of the following functions over the indicated interval by using **8.17**:

1. $F(x) = x^2$, [0,3].
2. $F(x) = x(x+1)$, [0,1].

3. $G(x) = x(x + 1)(x + 2)$, $[0,a]$.

4. $G(x) = x(x^2 + 1)$, $[2,5]$.

II

1. By extending Exercise II-3, Section 3, Chapter 7, show that

$$\lim_{n \to \infty} \sum_{i=1}^{n} i^p/n^{p+1} = \frac{1}{p+1} \quad (p \text{ an integer}).$$

2. Using the previous exercise and **8.17**, show that

$$\int_0^a x^p\,dx = \frac{a^{p+1}}{p+1} \quad (p \text{ an integer}).$$

3. Using **8.17**, express the following limits as definite integrals:

a. $\lim_{n \to \infty} \left[\frac{1}{n} + \frac{1}{n+1} + \frac{1}{n+2} + \cdots + \frac{1}{n+n}\right]$.

b. $\lim_{n \to \infty} \left[\frac{n}{n^2+1^2} + \frac{n}{n^2+2^2} + \frac{n}{n^2+3^2} + \cdots + \frac{1}{n^2+4n^2}\right]$.

4. a. Show by induction that $\sum_{k=n+1}^{2n} \frac{1}{k} = \sum_{m=1}^{2n} \frac{(-1)^{m+1}}{m}$.

b. Using a and the previous exercise, express

$$\lim_{m \to \infty} \sum_{m=1}^{2n} \frac{(-1)^{m+1}}{m}$$

as a definite integral.

4 INTEGRABILITY OF CONTINUOUS FUNCTIONS

Each continuous function f in a closed interval $[a,b]$ is bounded. Therefore, f has a lower integral and an upper integral in $[a,b]$. In this section we will prove that the lower and upper integrals of a continuous function f are equal, which will prove that f is integrable in $[a,b]$.

The following property of coverings of a closed interval will be used in proving the main result of this section.

8.18 **THEOREM.** If $C = \{N_1, N_2, \cdots, N_k\}$ is a finite covering of interval $[a,b]$ by open intervals, then there exists a number* $\delta > 0$ such that for every c in $[a,b]$ the neighborhood $(c - \delta, c + \delta)$ of c is contained in N_i for some i.

* Such a number is often called a *Lebesgue number* of C in honor of the French mathematician Henri Lebesgue (1875–1941).

Proof: For each x in $[a,b]$, we can select an N_j from C containing x. In fact, since N_j is an open interval, we can select a number $\alpha > 0$ (depending on x and j) such that the neighborhood $(x - 2\alpha, x + 2\alpha)$ of x is contained in N_j. Let B be the set of all open intervals of the form $(x - \alpha, x + \alpha)$, one such interval associated with each x in $[a,b]$. Since B is a covering of $[a,b]$ by open intervals, some finite subset $B' = \{(x_1 - \alpha_1, x_1 + \alpha_1), (x_2 - \alpha_2, x_2 + \alpha_2), \cdots, (x_n - \alpha_n, x_n + \alpha_n)\}$ of B is also a covering of $[a,b]$, by **8.1**.

Now let us select δ to be the least of the positive numbers $\alpha_1, \alpha_2, \cdots, \alpha_n$. For each c in $[a,b]$ there exists an $(x_i - \alpha_i, x_i + \alpha_i)$ in B' containing c. In turn, there exists some N_j in C such that $(x_i - 2\alpha_i, x_i + 2\alpha_i)$ is contained in N_j. Since $0 < \delta \leq \alpha_i$ and $x_i - \alpha_i < c < x_i + \alpha_i$, we have

$$x_i - 2\alpha_i < c - \alpha_i \leq c - \delta < c + \delta \leq c + \alpha_i < x_i + 2\alpha_i,$$

and therefore $(c - \delta, c + \delta)$ is contained in N_j. This proves **8.18**.

We recall that a function f is said to be continuous in an interval I if for every c in I and every $\epsilon > 0$ there exists some $\delta > 0$ (depending on both c and ϵ) such that $f(x)$ is in $(f(c) - \epsilon, f(c) + \epsilon)$ for every x of I in $(c - \delta, c + \delta)$. A function f is said to be *uniformly continuous* in an interval I if for every number $\epsilon > 0$ there exists some number $\delta > 0$ such that $f(x)$ is in $(f(c) - \epsilon, f(c) + \epsilon)$ for every x of I in $(c - \delta, c + \delta)$ and every c in I. The difference between continuity and uniform continuity is that in uniform continuity the number δ does not depend on both c and ϵ but only on ϵ. The main result of interest to us on uniform continuity is given below.

8.19 THEOREM. A function f that is continuous in a closed interval $[a,b]$ is uniformly continuous in $[a,b]$.

Proof: For every number $\epsilon > 0$ and every c in $[a,b]$, there exists some number $\alpha > 0$ (depending on ϵ and c) such that $f(x)$ is in $(f(c) - \epsilon/2, f(c) + \epsilon/2)$ for every x of $[a,b]$ in $(c - \alpha, c + \alpha)$. The set

$$C = \{(c - \alpha, c + \alpha) \mid c \text{ in } [a,b]\}$$

is a covering of $[a,b]$ by open intervals. Hence, by **8.1**, there is a finite subset

$$C' = \{(c_1 - \alpha_1, c_1 + \alpha_1), (c_2 - \alpha_2, c_2 + \alpha_2), \cdots, (c_n - \alpha_n, c_n + \alpha_n)\}$$

of C that is also a covering of $[a,b]$. In turn, by **8.18** there exists a number $\delta > 0$ such that for every c in $[a,b]$ the interval $(c - \delta, c + \delta)$ is contained in $(c_i - \alpha_i, c_i + \alpha_i)$ for some i. If x is in $(c - \delta, c + \delta)$, then both x and c are in $(c_i - \alpha_i, c_i + \alpha_i)$, and therefore $f(x)$ and $f(c)$ are in the interval $(f(c_i) - \epsilon/2, f(c_i) + \epsilon/2)$ by the choice of α_i. Since this latter interval has length ϵ, evidently $f(x)$ is within ϵ of $f(c)$; i.e., $f(x)$ is in $(f(c) - \epsilon, f(c) + \epsilon)$. Clearly, δ depends only on ϵ. This proves **8.19**.

We are now ready to prove the following important result.

8.20 **THEOREM.** A function f that is continuous in a closed interval $[a,b]$ is integrable in $[a,b]$.

Proof: To prove that f is integrable in $[a,b]$, we must show by 7.16 that for every $\epsilon > 0$ there exists a partition P of $[a,b]$ such that $0 \leq T(P) - S(P) < \epsilon$.

By the uniform continuity of f, for every $\epsilon > 0$ there exists some $\delta > 0$ such that $f(x)$ is in $(f(c) - \epsilon/(b-a), f(c) + \epsilon/(b-a))$ for every c in $[a,b]$ and every x in $(c - \delta, c + \delta) \cap [a,b]$. If $P = \{x_0, x_1, \cdots, x_n\}$ is any partition of $[a,b]$ for which $||P|| < \delta$, and $f(u_i)$ is the minimum value and $f(v_i)$ the maximum value of f in $[x_{i-1}, x_i]$, then

$$T(P) - S(P) = \sum_{i=1}^{n} [f(v_i) - f(u_i)]\,\Delta x_i$$

Since u_i and v_i are in $[x_{i-1}, x_i]$ and $x_i - x_{i-1} < \delta$, we know that $f(v_i)$ is in $(f(u_i) - \epsilon/(b-a),\ f(u_i) + \epsilon/(b-a))$. Hence $f(v_i) - f(u_i) < \epsilon/(b-a)$ for each i, and

$$0 \leq T(P) - S(P) < \sum_{i=1}^{n} \frac{\epsilon}{b-a}\Delta x_i = \frac{\epsilon}{b-a}\sum_{i=1}^{n} \Delta x_i = \frac{\epsilon}{b-a}\cdot(b-a) = \epsilon.$$

This proves 8.20.

EXERCISES

I

In each of Exercises 1–6 show that each function F defined is uniformly continuous in the given interval by finding *a* function δ of ϵ only such that $|F(x) - F(y)| < \epsilon$ whenever $|x - y| < \delta(\epsilon)$.

[Although it would be simpler to establish uniform continuity from continuity using 8.19, there are times when one needs to use an appropriate $\delta(\epsilon)$ explicitly.]

1. $F(x) = 2x^2$, $[-3,3]$.
2. $F(x) = 3x^3$, $[-2,2]$.
3. $F(x) = ax^n$, (n-integer), $[c,d]$.
4. $F(x) = x^2 - x$, $[-1,1]$.
5. $F(x) = \sqrt{x}$, $[1,5]$.
6. $F(x) = 2/x$, $[1, \infty)$.

In each of Exercises 7–10 show that the given function is not uniformly continuous in the given interval.

7. $F(x) = \dfrac{1}{x}$, $(0,1)$.
8. $F(x) = 2x^2$, $[1, \infty)$.
9. $F(x) = \dfrac{x+1}{x-1}$, $(1,2)$.
10. $F(x) = x^3$, $(0, \infty)$.

II

For Exercises 1–4, determine whether or not the given function is uniformly continuous in the given interval by finding (or attempting to find) a function $\delta(\epsilon)$ such that $|F(x) - F(y)| < \epsilon$ whenever $|x - y| < \delta(\epsilon)$.

1. $F(x) = \sqrt{x}$, $[0,1]$.
2. $F(x) = \dfrac{x^3 + 2}{x + 1}$, $[0, \infty)$.
3. $F(x) = \sqrt{1 - x^2}$, $[0,1]$.
4. $F(x) = \sqrt[3]{1 - x^2}$, $[-1,1]$.
5. Show that for every continuous function f with domain $[a,b]$ and every number $\epsilon > 0$, there exists a polygonal function g (one whose graph is a simple polygonal figure) such that

$$|f(x) - g(x)| < \epsilon \text{ for all } x \text{ in } [a,b].$$

REVIEW

Oral Exercises

1. What is an (open) covering of an interval?
2. If a function is continuous in an interval, must it be bounded in that interval? Why?

Explain or define the following:

3. Sigma notation.
4. A sequence.
5. A bounded sequence.
6. A monotone sequence.
7. Limit of a sequence.
8. Riemann sum.
9. Uniform continuity.
10. The theorem on the integrability of a continuous function.

I

In each of Exercises 1–6, find the limit, if it exists.

1. $\displaystyle\lim_{n\to\infty}\left(\frac{n^2+1}{n+1} - \frac{n^2+2}{n+2}\right)$.
2. $\displaystyle\lim_{n\to\infty}\left(\frac{n^2+1}{n+1}\right) \div \left(\frac{n^2+2}{n+2}\right)$.
3. $\displaystyle\lim_{n\to\infty}\frac{1/(n^2-4)}{1/n^2}$.
4. $\displaystyle\lim_{n\to\infty}\frac{(a+1/n)^2 - a^2}{1/n}$.
5. $\displaystyle\lim_{n\to\infty}\frac{\sqrt{n^3+n}}{n}$.
6. $\displaystyle\lim_{n\to\infty}[2 - (-1)^n/n]^3$.

7. a. If $a_n = (3n^2 - 1)/(5n^2 + 1)$ and $b_n = a_{2n+1}$, $c_n = a_{n^2+1}$, then find $\lim_{n\to\infty} a_n$, $\lim_{n\to\infty} b_n$, and $\lim_{n\to\infty} c_n$.

   b. Let u be a function such that $u(n)$ is a positive integer for every positive integer n and $u(m) > u(n)$, if $m > n$. Prove that if $\lim_{n\to\infty} a_n = L$, then $\lim_{n\to\infty} a_{u(n)} = L$.

8. For the function $F(x) = x^2 - [x]^2$ in $[0, \infty)$, sketch the graph and determine the greatest lower bound and the least upper bound if they exist.

9. Using upper and lower Riemann sums for the integral $\int_0^{1000} x^{10}\,dx$, determine an approximate value for the sum $1^{10} + 2^{10} + 3^{10} + \cdots + 1000^{10}$.

10. Using upper and lower Riemann sums for the integral $\int_2^{1000} x^{-10}\,dx$, determine an approximate value for the sum $2^{-10} + 3^{-10} + 4^{-10} + \cdots + 1000^{-10}$.

11. Show that $\displaystyle\int_0^{10} \frac{x\,dx}{x^3 + 16} < \frac{144}{160}$ or less by breaking up the integration into two intervals [0,1] and [1,10] and using appropriate approximations for the integrand.

12. Show that $F(x) = \sqrt[3]{x}$ is uniformly continuous in the interval [1,10] (by finding an appropriate $\delta(\epsilon)$).

13. Show that $G(x) = \sqrt[3]{x} + \sqrt{x}$ is uniformly continuous in the interval [1,10] (by finding an appropriate $\delta(\epsilon)$).

14. If $F(x)$ and $G(x)$ are uniformly continuous in $[a,b]$, prove that so also is $F(x) \pm G(x)$ (by finding an appropriate $\delta(\epsilon)$).

15. Find the maximum and minimum values, whenever they exist, for the function

$$F(x) = \frac{2}{x^4 - 5x^2 + 4}$$

in each of the following intervals, and discuss the continuity of F in that interval. Sketch the graph of F.

   a. $(-1,1)$. b. $[0,1]$. c. $[-\frac{1}{2},\frac{1}{2}]$. d. $[1,2]$.

II

1. If the sequence $a_1, a_2, \cdots, a_n, \cdots$ is monotonic, show that the sequence with nth term $(a_1 + a_2 + \cdots + a_n)/n$ is also monotonic and in the same sense.

2. If $a_{n+1} = (a_n + b_n)/2$ and $a_{n+1}b_{n+1} = a_nb_n$, show that the sequences with nth terms a_n and b_n, respectively are both monotonic and converge to the same limit $(a_0, b_0 \geq 0)$. Find their common limit.

3. Find $\displaystyle\lim_{k\to\infty} \sum_{n=1}^{k} \frac{1}{n(n+1)(n+2)}$.

4. Prove that $\lim_{n \to \infty} \sqrt[n]{a^n + b^n + c^n} = \max(a,b,c)$ where $a, b, c \geq 0$.

5. Prove that $\lim_{n \to \infty} \left(1 + \frac{1}{n^2}\right)^n = 1$.

6. Find $\lim_{n \to \infty} \sum_{k=1}^{n} \frac{kn^2}{(n^2 + k^2)^2}$.

7. Show that if $F(x)$ and $G(x)$ are uniformly continuous in $[a,b]$, then so also is $F(x)G(x)$ (by finding an appropriate $\delta(\epsilon)$).

9

APPLICATIONS OF THE INTEGRAL

LIKE THE DERIVATIVE, the integral has many interesting applications to geometrical and physical problems. Some of these applications are given in the present chapter.

1 AREAS

If f is a continuous, positive-valued function in a closed interval $[a,b]$, then the lines $x = a$, $x = b$, the x axis, and the graph of f bound a region R of the plane (Figure 9.1). As we saw in Section 2 of Chapter 7, each lower sum $S(P)$ of f over $[a,b]$ is the area of a polygon inscribed in R and each upper sum $T(P)$ is the area

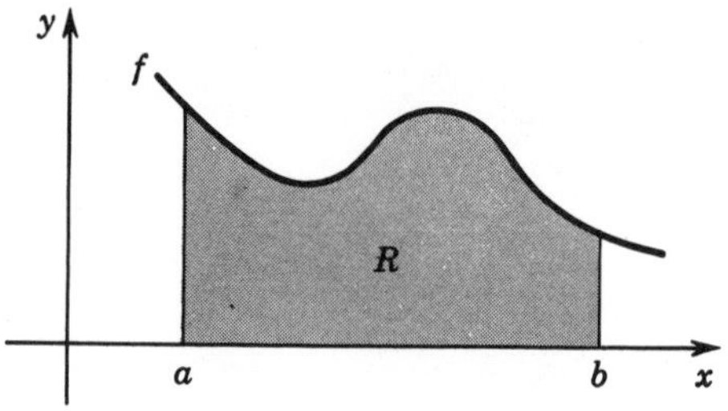

FIGURE 9.1

of a polygon circumscribed about R. Therefore, it is natural to consider the area $A(R)$ of region R, if it exists, to be between $S(P)$ and $T(P)$,

$$S(P) \leq A(R) \leq T(P)$$

However, there is precisely one number which is between $S(P)$ and $T(P)$ for every partition P of $[a,b]$, namely $\int_a^b f(x)\,dx$. This fact suggests the following definition for area.

9.1 **DEFINITION OF AREA.** If a region R of the plane is bounded by the lines $x = a$, $x = b$, the x axis, and the graph of a continuous, positive-valued function f (Figure 9.1), then the area $A(R)$ of R is defined to be

$$A(R) = \int_a^b f(x)\,dx.$$

We call the region R of Figure 9.1 *the region under the graph of f between a and b.*

EXAMPLE 1. If function g is defined by

$$g(x) = \sqrt[3]{x},$$

find the area of the region R under the graph of g from 1 to 8.

Solution: The region R, shown in Figure 9.2, has area

$$A(R) = \int_1^8 \sqrt[3]{x}\,dx = \int_1^8 x^{1/3}\,dx = \frac{3}{4}x^{4/3}\Big|_1^8$$

$$= \frac{3}{4}(8^{4/3} - 1^{4/3}) = \frac{45}{4}.$$

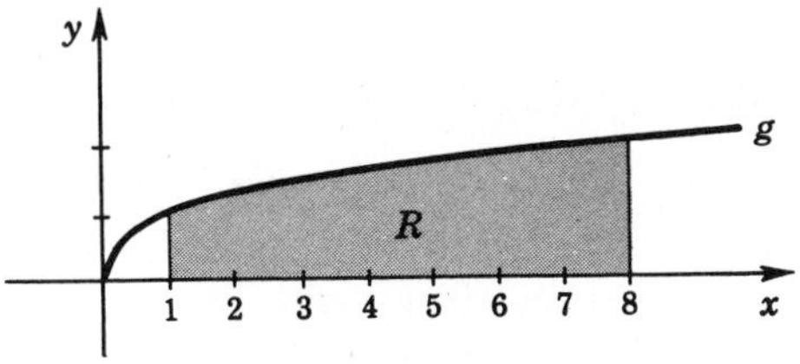

FIGURE 9.2

Is our answer reasonable? Clearly, R can be inscribed in a rectangle of base 7 and height 2, so that we expect $A(R)$ to be less than 14. On the other hand, a trapezoid of height 7 and bases 1 and 2 can be inscribed in R. Thus we expect $A(R)$ to be greater than $\frac{1}{2}7\cdot(1 + 2)$, or $21/2$. Since

$$\tfrac{42}{4} < \tfrac{45}{4} < \tfrac{56}{4},$$

our answer seems reasonable.

If f is a continuous, negative-valued function in an interval $[a,b]$, then $\int_a^b f(x)\,dx < 0$ and the area of the region R bounded by the lines $x = a$, $x = b$, the x axis, and the graph of f is given by

$$A(R) = -\int_a^b f(x)\,dx.$$

More generally, if f and g are continuous functions in $[a,b]$ and

$$f(x) \geq g(x) \quad \text{for every } x \text{ in } [a,b],$$

then there is a region R of the coordinate plane whose boundaries are the graph of f, the graph of g, and the lines $x = a$, $x = b$. (See Figure 9.3.)

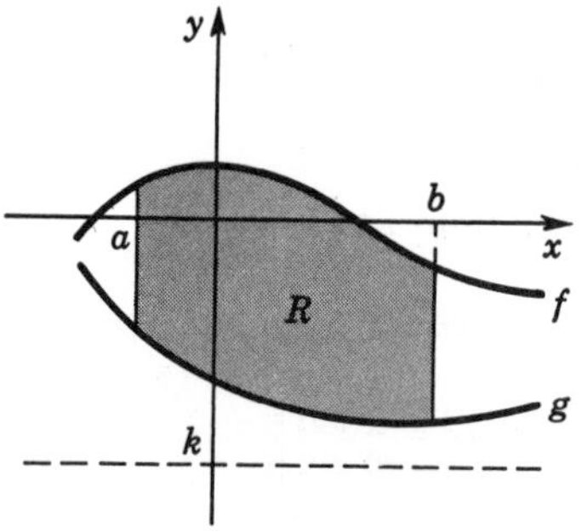

FIGURE 9.3

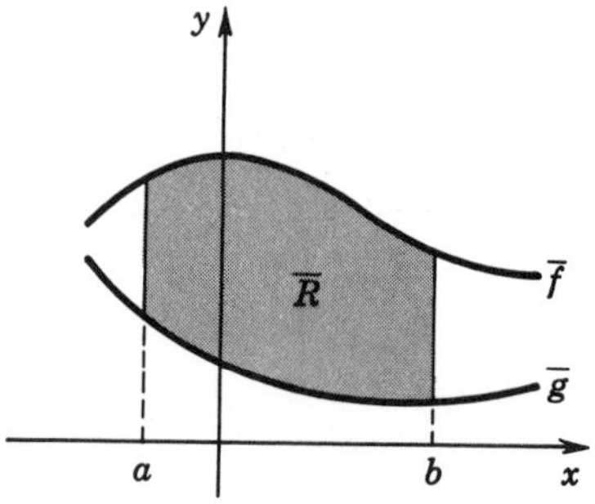

FIGURE 9.4

Let us choose a constant k less than the minimum value of g in $[a,b]$. Then $g(x) - k > 0$ for every x in $[a,b]$ and, since $f(x) \geq g(x)$, $f(x) - k > 0$ for every x in $[a,b]$. Hence the functions $\overline{f}$ and $\overline{g}$ defined by

$$\overline{f}(x) = f(x) - k, \qquad \overline{g}(x) = g(x) - k$$

are continuous and positive-valued in $[a,b]$. If k is chosen as in Figure 9.3, then the graphs of $\overline{f}$ and $\overline{g}$ are as shown in Figure 9.4.

The area of the region $\overline{R}$ between the graphs of $\overline{f}$ and $\overline{g}$ is the same as that of R, since the regions are congruent. Thus the area of $\overline{R}$, and hence also that of R, is seen to be the difference of the areas of the regions under the graphs of $\overline{f}$ and $\overline{g}$ from a to b,

$$A(R) = \int_a^b \overline{f}(x)\,dx - \int_a^b \overline{g}(x)\,dx.$$

However,

$$\int_a^b \bar{f}(x)\,dx - \int_a^b \bar{g}(x)\,dx = \int_a^b [\bar{f}(x) - \bar{g}(x)]\,dx,$$

$$= \int_a^b \{[f(x) - k] - [g(x) - k]\}\,dx,$$

$$= \int_a^b [f(x) - g(x)]\,dx.$$

Hence, if f and g are continuous functions in $[a,b]$ and if $f(x) \geq g(x)$ for every x in $[a,b]$, then the area $A(R)$ of the region R between the graphs of f and g from a to b is given by the formula

$$A(R) = \int_a^b [f(x) - g(x)]\,dx.$$

EXAMPLE 2. Find the area of the region over the graph of f between -1 and 2 if

$$f(x) = x^3 - 3x - 3.$$

Solution: The graph of f has a maximum point at $(-1,-1)$ and a minimum point at $(1,-5)$, as shown in Figure 9.5. The area $A(R)$ of the shaded region R is given by

$$A(R) = -\int_{-1}^{2} (x^3 - 3x - 3)\,dx = -\left(\frac{x^4}{4} - 3\frac{x^2}{2} - 3x\right)\Bigg|_{-1}^{2} = \frac{39}{4}.$$

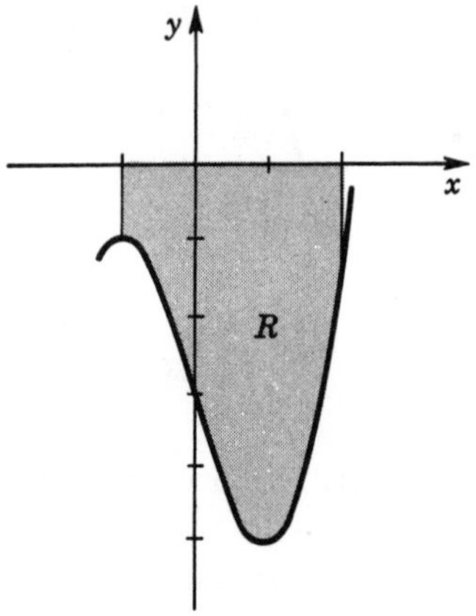

FIGURE 9.5

EXAMPLE 3. Find the area of the region between the graphs of the equations

$$y = x - 2 \quad \text{and} \quad y = 2x - x^2.$$

Solution: The graphs will intersect in those points whose coordinates are the simultaneous solutions of the given equations. Eliminating y between these equations, we have

$$x - 2 = 2x - x^2,$$
$$\text{or} \quad x^2 - x - 2 = (x - 2)(x + 1) = 0.$$

Thus $x = 2$ or $x = -1$, and the common points of the two graphs are (2,0) and $(-1,-3)$.

The graph of $y = x - 2$ is a straight line. The graph of $y = 2x - x^2$ is a parabola that is concave downward and has its vertex at (1,1). The region R whose area is sought is shaded in Figure 9.6. This area is given by

$$A(R) = \int_{-1}^{2} [(2x - x^2) - (x - 2)]\, dx = \int_{-1}^{2} (-x^2 + x + 2)\, dx$$
$$= \left(-\frac{1}{3}x^3 + \frac{1}{2}x^2 + 2x\right)\Bigg|_{-1}^{2} = \frac{9}{2}.$$

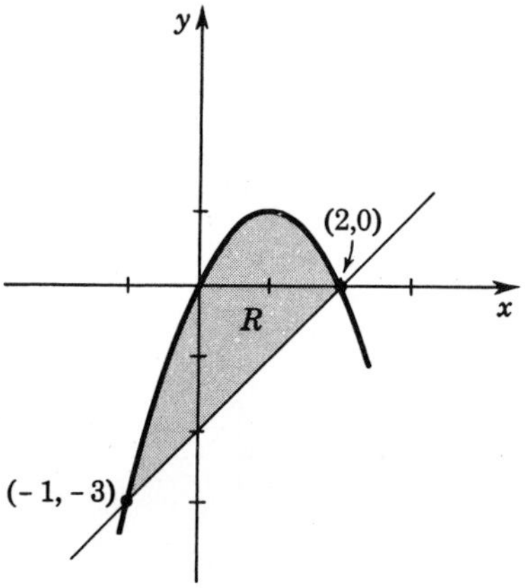

FIGURE 9.6

EXAMPLE 4. Find the area of the region bounded by one loop of the graph of the equation

$$y^2 = 4x^2 - x^4.$$

Solution: The graph is symmetric to both axes. Since

$$y = \pm x\sqrt{4 - x^2},$$

it is clear that the total graph lies between $x = -2$ and $x = 2$. The point $(\sqrt{2},2)$ is a maximum point on the graph. We can plot a few points and sketch the rest of the curve by symmetry, as indicated in Figure 9.7.

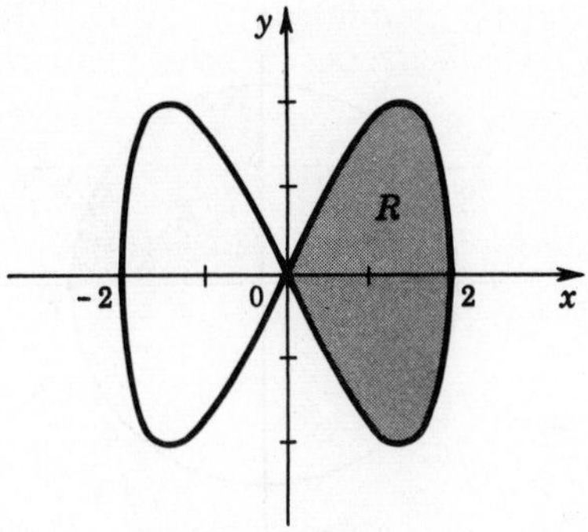

FIGURE 9.7

Let us find the area of the shaded region R bounded by the loop between $x = 0$ and $x = 2$. The equation of the top half of this loop is

$$y = x\sqrt{4 - x^2},$$

whereas that of the lower half is

$$y = -x\sqrt{4 - x^2}.$$

Thus

$$A(R) = \int_0^2 [(x\sqrt{4 - x^2}) - (-x\sqrt{4 - x^2})]\, dx = \int_0^2 2x\sqrt{4 - x^2}\, dx.$$

In order to evaluate this integral, we let

$$u = 4 - x^2, \qquad du = -2x\, dx.$$

Then $u = 4$ when $x = 0$, and $u = 0$ when $x = 2$. Hence

$$A(R) = -\int_4^0 u^{1/2}\, du = -\frac{2}{3}u^{3/2}\Big|_4^0 = \frac{16}{3}.$$

EXAMPLE 5. Find the area of a circle C_r of radius r.

Solution: Evidently, the area of C_r is four times the area of region R in Figure 9.8.

$$A(C_r) = 4A(R).$$

Now the curved boundary of R has equation

$$y = \sqrt{r^2 - x^2},$$

so that

$$A(C_r) = 4\int_0^r \sqrt{r^2 - x^2}\, dx.$$

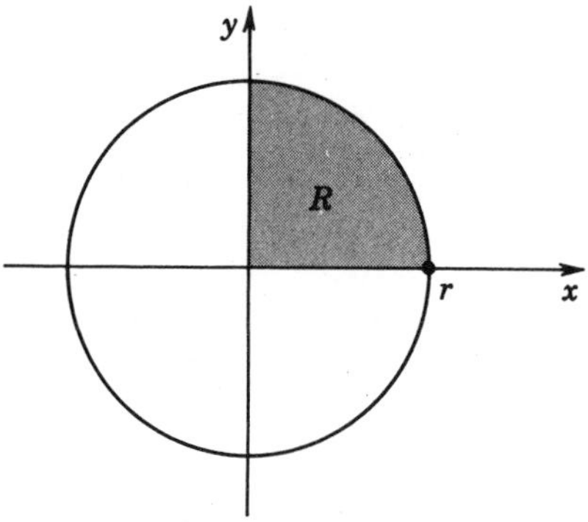

FIGURE 9.8

We cannot evaluate this integral in the sense that we can find an antiderivative. However, we can do the following. We may change variables by letting

$$u = \frac{1}{r}x, \qquad du = \frac{1}{r}dx.$$

Then

$$A(C_r) = 4\int_0^r r\sqrt{1 - \left(\frac{x}{r}\right)^2}\,dx$$

$$= 4r^2\int_0^r \sqrt{1 - \left(\frac{x}{r}\right)^2}\left(\frac{1}{r}dx\right) = 4r^2\int_0^1 \sqrt{1 - u^2}\,du.$$

After the number π is defined in Chapter 11 (as the circumference of a unit circle), we will show that

$$\pi = 4\int_0^1 \sqrt{1 - u^2}\,du.$$

Hence we obtain the familiar formula

$$A(C_r) = \pi r^2$$

for the area of a circle of radius r.

EXERCISES

I

Find the area of the region bounded by the graphs of the following equations. Sketch each region.

1. $y = x^3$, $y = 0$, $x = 1$, $x = 3$.

2. $y = 9 - x^2$, $y = 0$, $x = -2$, $x = 1$.

3. $y = \sqrt{x}, y = -\sqrt{x}, x = 4.$

4. $y = \sqrt{x+4}, y = 0, x = 0.$

5. $y = x^2 - 4, y = 4 - x^2.$

6. $y = \sqrt[3]{x^2}, y = 0, x = 8.$

7. $y = x^2, y = 1.$

8. $4y = x^2, x - 4y + 2 = 0.$

9. $x^2y = 4, 3x + y - 7 = 0.$

10. $y = x(x-2)^2, y = 0.$

11. $y^2 = 4x, x = 1.$

12. $y = x^3 - x, y = 0$, in fourth quadrant.

II

1. Sketch and find the area of the region bounded by the parabola $y = -x^2 + 4x - 3$ and the tangents to it at the points $(0, -3)$ and $(4, -3)$.
2. Sketch and find the area of the loop of the graph of $y^2 = x(x-a)^2 (a > 0)$.
3. Sketch and find the area of the region bounded by the graph of $y^2 = a^2x^6 - x^8$.

2 VOLUME

Just as integrals can be used to find areas of certain regions in a plane, so they can be used to find volumes of certain regions in space, as we shall show in this section.

We shall call a solid C a *cylinder* if C is bounded by two congruent regions R_1 and R_2 lying in parallel planes and by a lateral surface S composed of line segments that connect corresponding points of the boundaries of R_1 and R_2 and that are perpendicular to the planes of R_1 and R_2 (Figure 9.9). Each of the

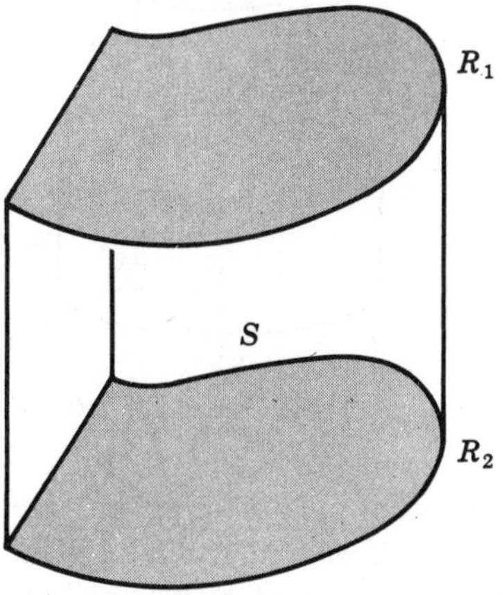

FIGURE 9.9

regions R_1 and R_2 is called a *base* of cylinder C and the distance between the planes of R_1 and R_2 is called the *height* of C.

The common right circular cylinder is, of course, a cylinder having a circle as base. A rectangular paralellepiped is also, according to our general definition, a cylinder having a rectangle as base.

If C is a cylinder with base B and height h, then we define the *volume* $V(C)$ of C to be the area of the base $A(B)$ times the height h; i.e.,

9.2 $$V(C) = A(B)\cdot h,$$

Formula 9.2 yields the familiar formula $V(C) = \pi r^2 h$ for the volume of a right circular cylinder of radius r and height h. Also, the volume of a rectangular parallelepiped P with edges of length a, b, and c is given by

$$V(P) = abc,$$

as we expected.

If a solid S is a composite of cylinders $C_1, C_2, \cdots, C_n$, then we define the volume $V(S)$ of S to be

$$V(S) = V(C_1) + V(C_2) + \cdots + V(C_n).$$

For example, the solid S of Figure 9.10 is composed of three right circular cylinders and has volume

$$V(S) = \pi r_1^2 h_1 + \pi r_2^2 h_2 + \pi r_3^2 h_3.$$

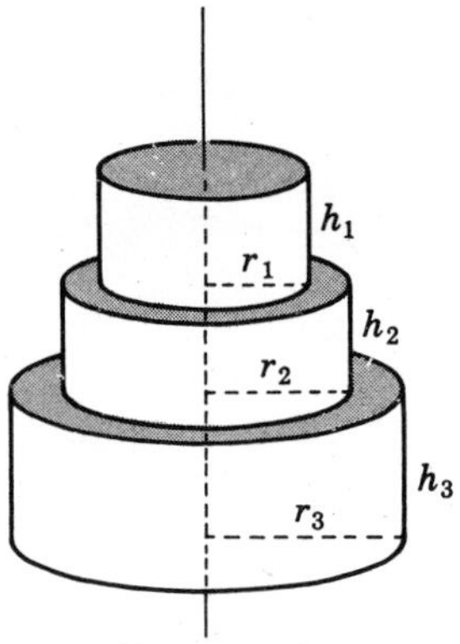

FIGURE 9.10

We turn now to the problem of defining the volume of a solid S which is not composed of cylinders. First, we remark that a plane intersecting S cuts S in a plane region called a *cross section* of S. We shall attempt to define the volume of S only under the added assumption that the areas of all cross sections of S

perpendicular to some fixed line are known and change continuously. That is, there exists a coordinate line L such that the solid S lies between the planes drawn perpendicular to L at some numbers a and b, and the cross section of S in the plane perpendicular to L at each number x in $[a,b]$ has a known area $A(x)$ (see Figure 9.11) such that the area function A is continuous in $[a,b]$.

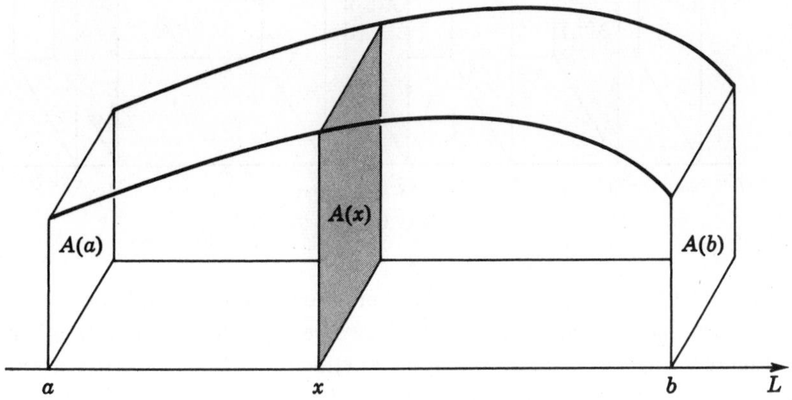

FIGURE 9.11

For each partition $P = \{x_0,x_1, \cdots, x_k\}$ of $[a,b]$, we can approximate the volume $V(S)$ of solid S (Figure 9.11) by selecting numbers $z_1, z_2, \cdots, z_k$ in $[x_0,x_1]$, $[x_1,x_2]$, $\cdots$, $[x_{k-1},x_k]$, respectively, and then constructing cylinders of heights $\Delta x_1 = x_1 - x_0$, $\Delta x_2 = x_2 - x_1$, $\cdots$, $\Delta x_k = x_k - x_{k-1}$ and respective cross section areas $A(z_1), A(z_2), \cdots, A(z_k)$. Then the Riemann sum

9.3 $$R(P) = \sum_{i=1}^{k} A(z_i)\,\Delta x_i$$

is an approximation of $V(S)$. The solid S of Figure 9.11 is approximated by the three cylinders shown in Figure 9.12.

If we select a sequence of partitions $P_1, P_2, \cdots, P_n, \cdots$ of $[a,b]$ such that

$$\operatorname*{limit}_{n\to\infty} \|P_n\| = 0,$$

and if $R(P_1), R(P_2), \cdots, R(P_n), \cdots$ is a corresponding sequence of Riemann sums of the area function A of type **9.3**, then we can define the volume $V(S)$ of solid S to be

$$V(S) = \operatorname*{limit}_{n\to\infty} R(P_n)$$

By **8.17**, the limit above exists and equals $\int_a^b A(x)\,dx$. Thus the volume of S may be defined as follows.

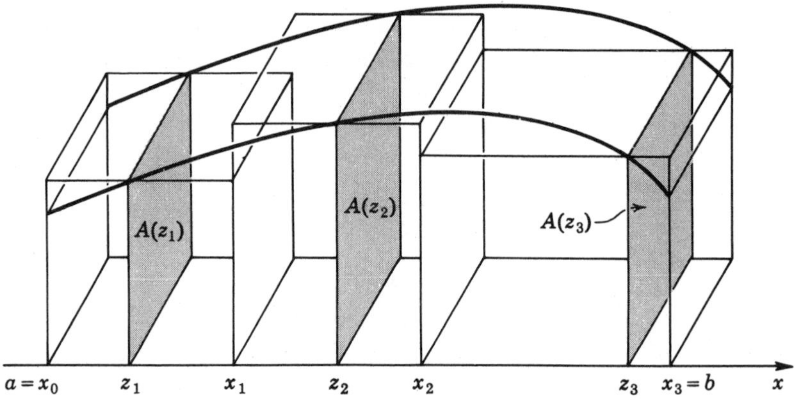

FIGURE 9.12

9.4 DEFINITION OF VOLUME. Let S be a bounded solid and L a coordinate line such that S lies between planes drawn perpendicular to L at numbers a and b (Figure 9.11). For each x in $[a,b]$ let $A(x)$ be the area of the cross section of S in the plane drawn perpendicular to L at x. If the function A is continuous in $[a,b]$, then the volume $V(S)$ of S is given by

$$V(S) = \int_a^b A(x)\, dx.$$

Let us use this definition to find the volumes of some easily described solids.

EXAMPLE 1. Find the volume of a sphere S of radius r.

Solution: We select coordinate axes as shown in Figure 9.13. For each number x in $[-r,r]$ the area $A(x)$ of the circular cross section of S perpendicular to the x axis is given by $A(x) = \pi y^2$. However, $x^2 + y^2 = r^2$ for every point (x,y) on the circle in the planes of the axes. Thus

$$A(x) = \pi(r^2 - x^2) \quad \text{for every } x \text{ in } [-r,r].$$

Evidently, A is a continuous function. Hence, by **9.4**,

$$\begin{aligned} V(S) &= \int_{-r}^{r} \pi(r^2 - x^2)\, dx \\ &= \pi\left(r^2x - \frac{x^3}{3}\right)\Big|_{-r}^{r} = \pi\left(r^3 - \frac{r^3}{3}\right) - \pi\left(-r^3 + \frac{r^3}{3}\right) \\ &= \frac{4}{3}\pi r^3. \end{aligned}$$

This is the usual formula for the volume of a sphere.

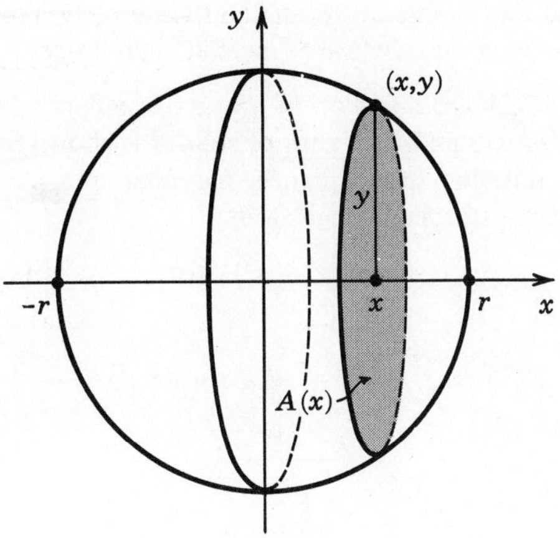

FIGURE 9.13

EXAMPLE 2. Find the volume of the solid generated by rotating about the x axis the region bounded by the line $x = 4$ and the parabola

$$y^2 = x.$$

Solution: This solid of revolution S, shaped somewhat like a headlight of a car, is shown in Figure 9.14. For each x in $[0,4]$, evidently

$$A(x) = \pi y^2 = \pi x.$$

Hence

$$V(S) = \int_0^4 \pi x \, dx = 8\pi.$$

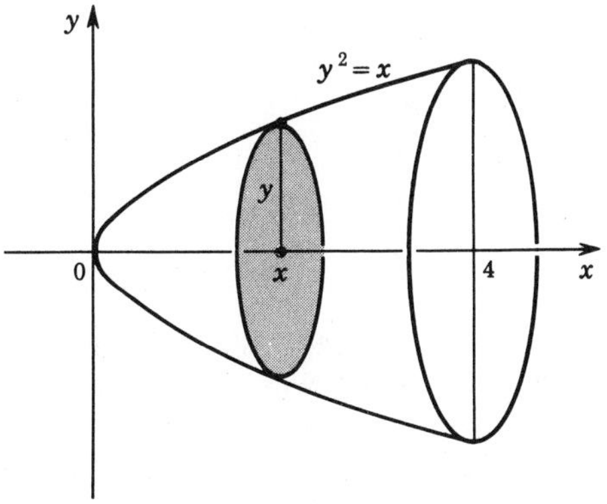

FIGURE 9.14

EXAMPLE 3. Find the volume of the solid S of intersection of two right circular cylinders of radius r, assuming that their axes meet at right angles.

Solution: Each cross section of S in a plane parallel to both axes is a square. A quarter of this square and an eighth of solid S is shown in Figure 9.15. This quarter-square, in the notation of the figure, has area $y^2 = yz = z^2 = r^2 - x^2$. Hence the cross-sectional area of solid S is given by

$$A(x) = 4(r^2 - x^2) \quad \text{for each } x \text{ in } [-r,r].$$

By 9.4,

$$V(S) = \int_{-r}^{r} 4(r^2 - x^2)\,dx = 4\left(r^2x - \frac{x^3}{3}\right)\Bigg|_{-r}^{r} = \frac{16}{3}r^3.$$

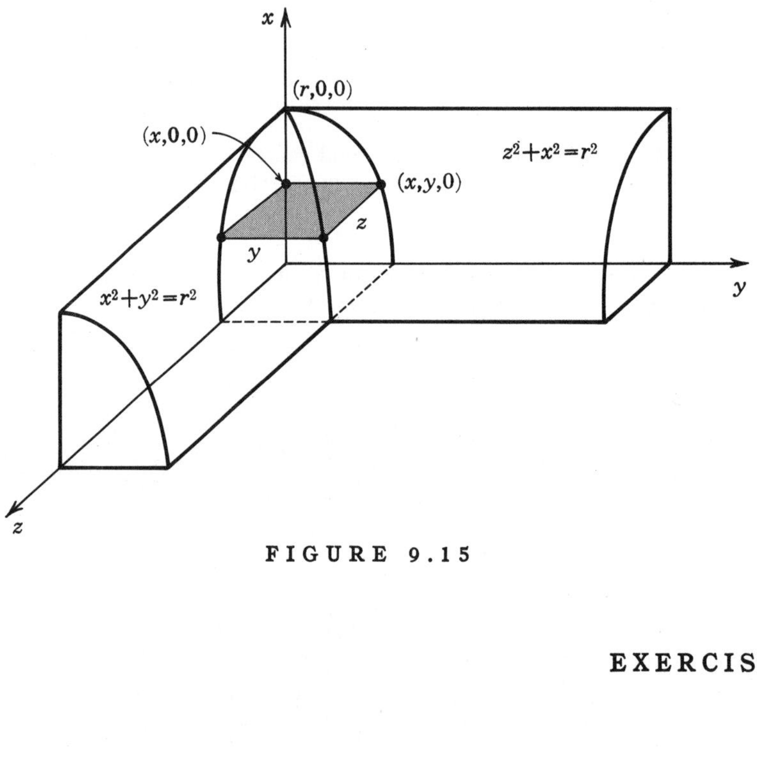

FIGURE 9.15

EXERCISES

I

In each of Exercises 1–10 the graphs of the given equations bound a region of the plane. Find the volume of the solid obtained by rotating the region about the x axis. Sketch the solid.

1. $y = x^2, \quad y = 0, \quad x = 2.$
2. $y = 2x^2, \quad y = 0, \quad x = 3.$
3. $y = \sqrt{4 + x}, \quad x = 0, \quad y = 0.$
4. $y = 4 - x^2, \quad y = 0.$

5. $y = \frac{1}{x}$, $x = 1$, $x = 3$, $y = 0$.

6. $y = \sqrt{9 - x}$, $x = 0$, $y = 0$.

7. $y = x^2 - x$, $y = 0$.

8. $y = \frac{4}{x + 1}$, $x = -5$, $x = -2$, $y = 0$.

9. $y = \frac{1}{(x - 1)^3}$, $x = -1$, $x = 0$, $y = 0$.

10. $y = \sqrt[3]{x}$, $x = 0$, $x = 8$, $y = 0$.

11. Find the volume of a frustum of a cone by the methods of this section. Take the radius of the upper base to be r, of the lower base to be R, and the altitude to be h.

12. Let a sphere of radius r be cut by a plane, thereby forming a segment of the sphere of height h. Prove that the volume of the segment is $\pi h^2(r - h/3)$.

13. Find the volume of a parabolic disc formed by rotating the region bounded by a parabola and its latus rectum about the latus rectum. Let p be the distance between the focus and the vertex of the parabola.

14. The base of a solid is a circle of radius r. All cross sections of the solid perpendicular to a fixed diameter of the base are squares. Find the volume of the solid.

II

1. Prove Cavalieri's theorem, i.e., if in two solids of equal altitude the cross sections made by planes parallel to and at the same distance from their respective bases have equal area, then the two volumes are equal. (It should be noted that there are pathological "solids" where the set does not have a volume and the theorem breaks down; see R. Agnew, *Analytic Geometry and Calculus*, McGraw-Hill, 1962, p. 283.)

2. Extend Exercise 1 to the case where the ratio of corresponding cross-sectional area is not 1 but some other constant λ.

3. Apply Exercise 2 to redo Example 3, page 258, by considering an inscribed sphere and comparing corresponding cross sections.

4. We define a prismatoid as a solid such that the area of a cross section, $A(h)$, parallel to and at distance h from a fixed plane can be expressed as a quadratic polynomial,

$$A(h) = ah^2 + bh + c.$$

Show that the volume V of a prismatoid is given by

$$V = (B_1 + B_2 + 4M)\frac{H}{6},$$

where B_1 and B_2 are the area of the bases, M is the area of a cross section parallel to the bases and midway between them, and H is the height of the solid (formulated by Newton in 1711).

5. Show that the following solids are prismatoids and use Exercise 4 to determine their volumes:
   a. Sphere.
   b. Segment of a sphere.
   c. Frustrum of a cone.
   d. Pyramid.

6. Show that the formula in Exercise 4 also holds for solids called *general prismatoids* whose cross-sectional area is given by

$$A(h) = ah^2 + bh + c + dh^3.$$

3 WORK

If a constant force of F lb is applied to an object in moving it a distance of d ft, then the *work* done on the object has magnitude W defined by

$$W = Fd.$$

If the unit of force is pounds and the unit of distance is feet, then the unit of work is foot-pounds. Other possible units of work are inch-pounds, foot-tons, and the like.

EXAMPLE 1. An object of weight 110 lb is lifted (at a constant velocity) a distance of 23 ft. Find the amount of work done on the object.

Solution: Since a force of 110 lb is needed to lift the object, the amount of work done on the object in lifting it 23 ft is given by

$$W = 110 \cdot 23 = 2530 \text{ ft-lb}.$$

The calculus comes into play when we wish to define the work done on an object by a variable force. Let us assume that an object A is being moved along a coordinate line L (Figure 9.16), and a force of $F(x)$ units is being applied to A when A is at the point with coordinate x on L. We assume that the object A

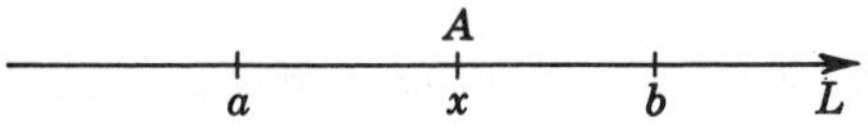

FIGURE 9.16

moves from a to b and that the force function F so defined is continuous in the interval $[a,b]$.

In order to define the amount of work done on the object A as it moves from a to b, we select a partition

$$P = \{x_0, x_1, \cdots, x_m\}$$

of $[a,b]$. In each subinterval $[x_{i-1}, x_i]$ of P, let $F(u_i)$ be the minimum and $F(v_i)$ be the maximum value of the force F. It is reasonable to assume that the amount W_i of work done on A as it moves from x_{i-1} to x_i is between the minimum value of the force times the distance Δx_i and the maximum value of the force times Δx_i:

(1) $$F(u_i)\,\Delta x_i \leq W_i \leq F(v_i)\,\Delta x_i.$$

Since the total amount W of work done on A as it moves from a to b is the sum of the W_i,

$$W = \sum_{i=1}^{m} W_i,$$

we obtain from (1) that

(2) $$\sum_{i=1}^{m} F(u_i)\,\Delta x_i \leq W \leq \sum_{i=1}^{m} F(v_i)\,\Delta x_i.$$

The inequality (2) holds for every partition P of $[a,b]$. If we take a sequence of partitions $P_1, P_2, \cdots, P_n, \cdots$ with norms of limit zero, then the limit of each sum in (2) as n approaches infinity is equal to

$$\int_a^b F(x)\,dx,$$

according to **8.17**. Their common limit must be W. This leads us to the following definition.

The amount W of work done on an object in moving it from a to b along a coordinate line is given by

9.5 $$W = \int_a^b F(x)\,dx,$$

where $F(x)$ is the force applied to the object at position x.

EXAMPLE 2. Find the amount of work done in stretching a spring from its natural length of 6 in. to double that length if a force of 20 lb is needed to hold the spring at double its natural length.

Solution: The force $F(x)$ required to hold a spring extended (within its elastic limit) x units beyond its natural length is given by

$$F(x) = kx, \qquad (k \text{ a constant}),$$

according to *Hooke's law*. We are given that $F(6) = 20$; therefore

$$20 = k \cdot 6 \qquad \text{and} \qquad k = \tfrac{10}{3}.$$

Thus

$$F(x) = \tfrac{10}{3}x$$

for this particular spring.

The amount W of work done in stretching the spring from its natural length ($x = 0$) to double its natural length ($x = 6$) is given by

$$W = \int_0^6 \frac{10}{3} x \, dx = \frac{5}{3} x^2 \Big|_0^6 = 60 \text{ in.-lb.}$$

If we wish to find the amount of work done in stretching this spring from a position already 2 in. extended to a position 4 in. extended, we evaluate the integral

$$\int_2^4 \frac{10}{3} x \, dx = 20 \text{ in.-lb},$$

and so on.

EXAMPLE 3. Find the amount W of work done in removing all the water at the top from a vertical cylindrical tank 4 ft in diameter and 6 ft high.

Solution: Let us think of the water as being pushed out of the tank by a piston starting out from the bottom of the tank (Figure 9.17). The force $F(x)$ on the piston

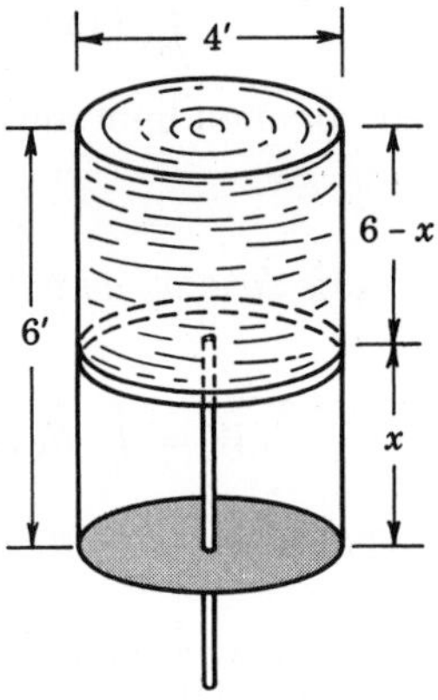

FIGURE 9.17

after it has moved a distance of x ft is the weight of the water remaining in the tank, i.e.,

$$F(x) = \pi \cdot 2^2 \cdot (6 - x) \cdot k,$$

where $k = 62.5$ lb, the weight of a cubic foot of water. Hence

$$W = \int_0^6 4\pi k(6 - x)\,dx = 4\pi k\left(6x - \frac{x^2}{2}\right)\Bigg|_0^6$$

$$= 72\pi k \doteq 14{,}140 \text{ ft-lb.}$$

EXAMPLE 4. Water is to be pumped out of the conical tank in Figure 9.18 to a point 10 ft above the top of the tank. Find the amount of work required to pump out 4 ft of water.

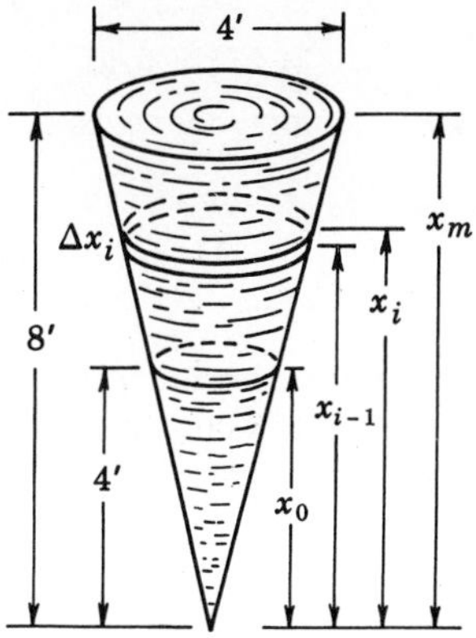

FIGURE 9.18

Solution: Let us think of the mass of water in the tank as cut up into m disc-shaped pieces. One such piece is shown in Figure 9.18. The weight M_i of this piece satisfies the inequality

$$62.5\pi r_{i-1}^2\,\Delta x_i \leq M_i \leq 62.5\pi r_i^2\,\Delta x_i.$$

This slice must be lifted a distance between $10 + (8 - x_i)$ and $10 + (8 - x_{i-1})$ ft. Hence the work W_i done in emptying the water from this slice satisfies the inequality

$$62.5\pi r_{i-1}^2(18 - x_i)\,\Delta x_i \leq W_i \leq 62.5\pi r_i^2(18 - x_{i-1})\,\Delta x_i.$$

The total work W done in emptying the tank therefore satisfies the inequality

(1) $$\sum_{i=1}^{m} 62.5\pi r_{i-1}^2(18 - x_i)\,\Delta x_i \leq W \leq \sum_{i=1}^{m} 62.5\pi r_i^2(18 - x_{i-1})\,\Delta x_i.$$

It is evident by similar triangles that

$$\frac{r_i}{x_i} = \frac{2}{8} \quad \text{or} \quad r_i = \frac{x_i}{4}.$$

If we take a sequence of partitions $P_1, P_2, \cdots, P_n, \cdots$ of [4,8] with norms having limit zero, each partition P_n of the sequence leads to an inequality of form (1). Taking the limit of each sum in (1) as n approaches infinity, we obtain the same value

$$\int_4^8 62.5\pi \left(\frac{x}{4}\right)^2 (18 - x)\, dx,$$

according to **8.17**. Thus

$$\begin{aligned} W &= \frac{62.5\pi}{16} \int_4^8 (18x^2 - x^3)\, dx \\ &= \frac{125\pi}{32} \left(6x^3 - \frac{x^4}{4}\right)\Big|_4^8 \\ &= 6750\pi \text{ ft-lb.} \end{aligned}$$

EXERCISES

1. Find the work done in stretching a spring from its natural length of 12 in. to a length of 18 in. if a force of 4 lb is needed to hold the spring extended 1 in.

2. A spring of natural length 5 in. requires a force of 9 oz to hold it at a length of 7 in. Find the work done in stretching the spring from a length of 7 in. to a length of 10 in.

3. A vertical cylindrical tank 6 ft in diameter and 10 ft high is half full of water. Find the amount of work done in pumping all the water out at the top of the tank.

4. A vertical cylindrical tank 6 ft in diameter and 10 ft high is full of water. Find the amount of work done in pumping half the water out at the top of the tank.

5. Any two electrons repel each other with a force inversely proportional to the square of the distance between them. If two electrons are held stationary at the points $(\pm 10,0)$ on the x axis, find the work done in moving a third electron:
   a. from (8,0) to $(-2,0)$ along the x axis;
   b. from (7,0) to $(-7,0)$ along the x axis.

6. Water is being pumped into the conical tank of Example 4 (Figure 9.18) at the bottom. Find the amount of work required to fill the tank.

7. Water is being pumped into the cylindrical tank of Example 3 above (Figure 9.17) at the bottom. Find the amount of work required to fill the tank half full.

8. A tank has the shape of a paraboloid of revolution. The radius of the circular top is 4 ft and its depth is 10 ft. If the tank is full of water, find the work required to empty the water from the tank at a point 5 ft above the top of the tank. [*Hint:* If the parabola has its vertex at the origin, its equation is $y = kx^2$ for some determinable number k. Then "slice" the water into discs as in Example 4 above.]

If a gas in a cylinder expands against a piston head from a volume of v_0 ft³ to v_1 ft³, the external work in ft-lb is given by

$$W = \int_{v_0}^{v_1} P\,dv$$

where P denotes the pressure in lb/ft.² Under isothermal expansion Pv remains constant.

9. A quantity of air with an initial volume of 200 ft³ and pressure 15 lb/in.² is compressed isothermally to 80 lb/in.² Determine the work done and the final volume.

10. Repeat Exercise 9 if the compression is adiabatic. Here, Pv^n remains constant. (Assume $n = 1.4$.)

4 ARC LENGTH

It is common practice to call a function f *smooth* if f' exists and is continuous. Thus, if f is smooth in $[a,b]$, the graph of f has a tangent line at each number in $[a,b]$ and, furthermore, tangent lines at nearby points have nearly equal slopes.

If f is a smooth function in a closed interval $[a,b]$, then it is possible to assign a meaningful length to the graph of f between $(a,f(a))$ and $(b,f(b))$. In order to describe how this is done, let us first simplify our notation. For each number x in the domain of f, let $P(x)$ denote the point $(x,f(x))$ on the graph of f. If $P(c)$ and $P(d)$ are two distinct points on the graph of f, let $\overparen{P(c)P(d)}$ designate the piece, or *arc*, of the graph between c and d.

An obvious way to approximate the length of arc $\overparen{P(a)P(b)}$ is to inscribe a broken line in the arc and measure its length. Thus, if $p = \{x_0, x_1, \cdots, x_n\}$ is a partition of $[a,b]$, the broken line $P(x_0)P(x_1) \cdots P(x_n)$ made up of n line segments (indicated in Figure 9.19 for $n = 4$) is denoted by I_p and is called an

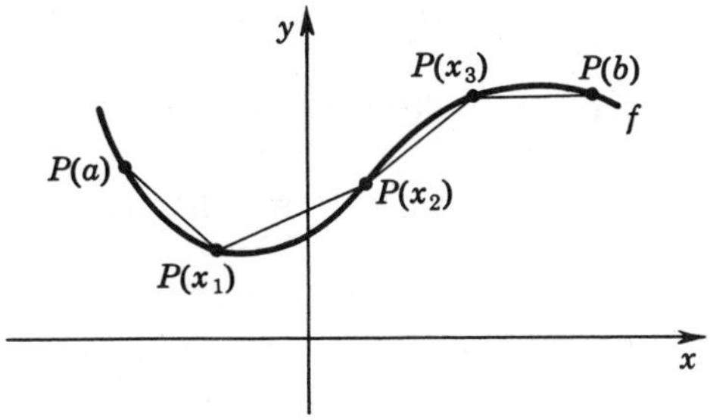

FIGURE 9.19

inscripture of arc $\widehat{P(a)P(b)}$. The length of I_p is denoted by $|I_p|$ and is clearly given by

$$|I_p| = \sum_{i=1}^{n} |P(x_{i-1})P(x_i)|.$$

Using the distance formula, this may be expressed in the form

(1) $$|I_p| = \sum_{i=1}^{n} \sqrt{(x_i - x_{i-1})^2 + [f(x_i) - f(x_{i-1})]^2}.$$

We may put (1) in a more useful form with the aid of the mean value theorem. Thus, for each subinterval $[x_{i-1},x_i]$ of p,

$$f(x_i) - f(x_{i-1}) = (x_i - x_{i-1})f'(z_i)$$

for some number z_i in (x_{i-1},x_i). Letting $x_i - x_{i-1} = \Delta x_i$ as usual, we now obtain

(2) $$|I_p| = \sum_{i=1}^{n} \sqrt{1 + f'^2(z_i)}\, \Delta x_i.$$

It is geometrically clear that $|I_p|$ is less than or equal to the number we wish to assign as the length of arc $\widehat{P(a)P(b)}$. Furthermore, we expect $|I_p|$ to be close to the length of this arc if $|p|$ is small. Therefore, if $p_1, p_2, \cdots, p_m, \cdots$ is any sequence of partitions of $[a,b]$ such that limit $\|p_m\| = 0$, we might reasonably expect

(3) $$\operatorname*{limit}_{m\to\infty} |I_{p_m}|$$

to be called the length of arc $\widehat{P(a)P(b)}$, provided that this limit exists.

We can easily evaluate (3) once we observe that $|I_p|$ in (2) is a Riemann sum, not of the function f but of the function

$$\sqrt{1 + f'^2}.$$

This function is continuous because of our assumption that f is smooth. Hence, by **8.17**,

(4) $$\operatorname*{limit}_{m\to\infty} |I_{p_m}| = \int_a^b \sqrt{1 + f'^2(x)}\, dx.$$

This leads us to make the following definition.

9.6 DEFINITION OF ARC LENGTH. If function f is smooth in the closed interval $[a,b]$, then the length of arc $\widehat{P(a)P(b)}$ of the graph of f is given by

$$L = \int_a^b \sqrt{1 + f'^2(x)}\, dx.$$

A further discussion of arc length is presented in Chapter 16.

EXAMPLE 1. Find the arc length of the graph of the function

$$f(x) = x^{3/2}$$

over the interval [0,4].

Solution: Since $f'(x) = \frac{3}{2}x^{1/2}$, the arc length is given by

$$L = \int_0^4 \sqrt{1 + \tfrac{9}{4}x}\, dx.$$

We may evaluate this integral by making the change of variable

$$u = 1 + \tfrac{9}{4}x, \qquad du = \tfrac{9}{4}\, dx.$$

This gives

$$L = \frac{4}{9}\int_1^{10} \sqrt{u}\, du = \frac{4}{9}\cdot\frac{2}{3}u^{3/2}\Big|_1^{10} = \frac{8}{27}(10\sqrt{10} - 1).$$

EXAMPLE 2. Find the length of an arc $\widehat{P(a)P(b)}$ of a parabola

$$x^2 = 4py.$$

Solution: We have

$$\frac{dy}{dx} = \frac{x}{2p}.$$

Therefore the arc length of the parabola joining the points $(a,a^2/4p)$ and $(b,b^2/4p)$ (assuming $a > b$) is given by

$$L = \int_a^b \sqrt{1 + \frac{x^2}{4p^2}}\, dx = \frac{1}{2p}\int_a^b \sqrt{4p^2 + x^2}\, dx.$$

We cannot evaluate this integral by means of the formulas available to us at this time. However, in Chapter 12 we shall develop methods for evaluating such integrals.

EXERCISES

I

Find the arc length of the graph of each of the following equations between the indicated points:

1. $y = 4 - 2\sqrt{x^3}$, (0,4) to (4,−12).
2. $y = x^{2/3}$, (−1,1) to (1,1).
3. $y = \dfrac{x^3}{6} + \dfrac{1}{2x}$, $(1,\frac{2}{3})$ to $(3,\frac{14}{3})$.
4. $y = \dfrac{x^6 + 2}{8x^2}$, $x = a$ to $x = b$, where $0 < a < b$.

5. Find the length of arc of the semicubical parabola $5y^3 = x^2$ lying inside the circle $x^2 + y^2 = 6$.

II

1. Sketch and find the length of the loop of the graph of

$$3ay^2 = x(x - a)^2.$$

2. Sketch and find the length of the hypocycloid

$$x^{2/3} + y^{2/3} = a^{2/3}.$$

5 APPROXIMATIONS BY THE TRAPEZOIDAL RULE

If no antiderivative of f is known, then we cannot evaluate

$$\int_a^b f(x)\,dx$$

by use of the fundamental theorem of the calculus. However, it is possible to approximate the value of this integral as closely as we desire. An obvious approximation method will be given in this section, and a subtler one will be developed in Section 6.

Let f be a continuous function in a closed interval $[a,b]$, and let $P_1, P_2, \cdots, P_n, \cdots$ be any sequence of partitions of $[a,b]$ such that

$$\operatorname*{limit}_{n\to\infty} \|P_n\| = 0.$$

If $R(P_1), R(P_2), \cdots, R(P_n), \cdots$ is any sequence of Riemann sums associated with the given sequence of partitions, then, by **8.17**,

$$\operatorname*{limit}_{n\to\infty} R(P_n) = \int_a^b f(x)\,dx.$$

Hence for every number $\epsilon > 0$ there exists a number k such that

$$R(P_n) \text{ is in } \left(\int_a^b f(x)\,dx - \epsilon,\ \int_a^b f(x)\,dx + \epsilon\right) \quad \text{for every } n \text{ in } (k,\infty).$$

That is, $R(P_n)$ is an approximation within ϵ of $\int_a^b f(x)\,dx$ for every n in (k,∞).

In an actual example we can let $P_1, P_2, \cdots, P_n, \cdots$ be the sequence of regular partitions of $[a,b]$. If $P_n = \{x_0, x_1, \cdots, x_n\}$, then we could select either

$$R(P_n) = \sum_{i=1}^{n} f(x_{i-1})\,\Delta x \qquad \text{or} \qquad \bar{R}(P_n) = \sum_{i=1}^{n} f(x_i)\,\Delta x,$$

where $\Delta x = (b - a)/n$ for the nth Riemann sum. We know that for a large enough integer n, both $R(P_n)$ and $\bar{R}(P_n)$ are close approximations of $\int_a^b f(x)\,dx$. It seems reasonable that the arithmetic average of $R(P_n)$ and $\bar{R}(P_n)$, $[R(P_n) + \bar{R}(P_n)]/2$, might often be a better approximation of $\int_a^b f(x)\,dx$ than either $R(P_n)$ or $\bar{R}(P_n)$. Now,

$$\tfrac{1}{2}[R(P_n) + \bar{R}(P_n)] = \frac{\Delta x}{2}\left[\sum_{i=1}^{n} f(x_{i-1}) + \sum_{i=1}^{n} f(x_i)\right]$$
$$= \frac{\Delta x}{2}\left[f(x_0) + \sum_{i=1}^{n-1} 2f(x_i) + f(x_n)\right].$$

Therefore, if $P_n = \{x_0, x_1, \cdots, x_n\}$ is a regular partition of $[a,b]$, then

9.7 $$\int_a^b f(x)\,dx \doteq \frac{b-a}{2n}[f(x_0) + 2f(x_1) + \cdots + 2f(x_{n-1}) + f(x_n)].$$

The above approximation formula for the integral is called the *trapezoidal rule*.

If the graph of f is above the x axis between $x = a$ and $x = b$, then the right side of **9.7** is the sum of the areas of n trapezoids, each of thickness Δx, as indi-

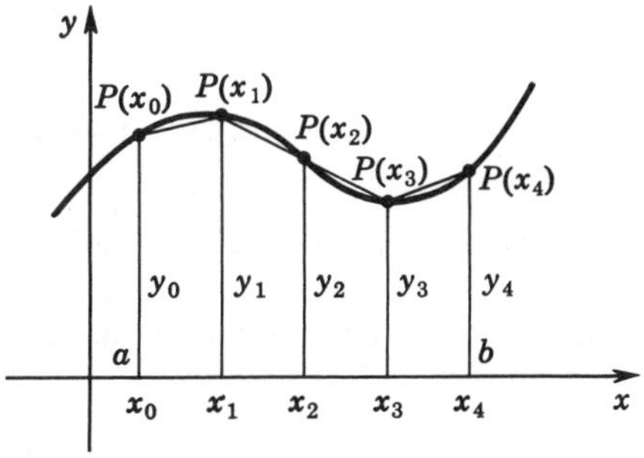

FIGURE 9.20

cated in Figure 9.20. Thus, if $n = 4$ as in the figure, the sum S of the areas of the four trapezoids is given by

$$S = \frac{y_0 + y_1}{2}\Delta x + \frac{y_1 + y_2}{2}\Delta x + \frac{y_2 + y_3}{2}\Delta x + \frac{y_3 + y_4}{2}\Delta x,$$

where $y_i = f(x_i)$ and $\Delta x = (b - a)/4$. We may reduce S to the form

$$S = \frac{b-a}{8}(y_0 + 2y_1 + 2y_2 + 2y_3 + y_4),$$

which is the right side of **9.7** if $n = 4$.

EXAMPLE. Use the trapezoidal rule to approximate the area of the region under the graph of the equation

$$y = \sqrt{x^2+1}$$

between $x = 0$ and $x = 3$.

Solution: The area in question is given by the integral

$$\int_0^3 \sqrt{x^2+1}\,dx,$$

an integral that cannot be evaluated exactly by any of our previous methods.

If we let

$$f(x) = \sqrt{x^2+1} \quad \text{and} \quad n = 6,$$

then the partition P_6 of [0,3] is given by

$$P_6 = \{0,\tfrac{1}{2},1,\tfrac{3}{2},2,\tfrac{5}{2},3\}.$$

The following table of values of f is approximated to two decimal places of accuracy:

x	0	.5	1	1.5	2	2.5	3
$f(x)$	1	1.12	1.41	1.80	2.24	2.69	3.16

If we let $n = 6$ in **9.7**, we get

$$\int_0^3 \sqrt{x^2+1}\,dx \doteq \frac{1}{4}[1 + 2.24 + 2.82 + 3.60 + 4.48 + 5.38 + 3.16],$$

$$\text{or} \quad \int_0^3 \sqrt{x^2+1}\,dx \doteq 5.67.$$

It may be shown that the correct result is 5.65, accurate to two decimal places.

EXERCISES

Use the trapezoidal rule to approximate each of the following integrals, taking the suggested value of n:

1. $\int_1^3 \frac{1}{x}\,dx, \quad n = 8.$

2. $\int_{-4}^{-1} \frac{1}{x}\,dx, \quad n = 6.$

3. $4\int_0^1 \sqrt{1-x^2}\,dx, \quad n = 4.$

4. $\int_0^1 \frac{4}{1+x^2}\,dx, \quad n = 4.$

5. $\int_{-1}^3 \sqrt{4+x^3}\,dx, \quad n = 4.$

6. Sketch the graph of

$$x^2 + 16y^2 = 25,$$

and find the length of the arc in the first quadrant between (3,1) and (5,0), using the trapezoidal rule with $n = 4$.

6 APPROXIMATIONS BY SIMPSON'S RULE

Simpson's rule is as easy to apply as the trapezoidal rule and is generally more accurate.

9.8 SIMPSON'S RULE. If f is a continuous function in an interval $[a,b]$, if n is an even integer, and if $P_n = \{x_0, x_1, \cdots, x_n\}$ is the regular partition of $[a,b]$ into n subintervals, then

$$\int_a^b f(x)\,dx \doteq \frac{b-a}{3n}[f(x_0) + 4f(x_1) + 2f(x_2) + 4f(x_3) + \cdots + 2f(x_{n-2}) + 4f(x_{n-1}) + f(x_n)].$$

This rule might well be called the *parabolic rule*, since the basic idea behind the rule is the approximating of the graph of f by arcs of parabolas. Before proving **9.8**, let us make a few preliminary remarks on parabolas.

There is a unique curve with equation of the form

$$y = ax^2 + bx + c$$

passing through the three points $(-\Delta x, y_0)$, $(0, y_1)$, and $(\Delta x, y_2)$. That is, the three equations

$$\begin{aligned} y_0 &= a\,(-\Delta x)^2 + b(-\Delta x) + c, \\ y_1 &= c, \\ y_2 &= a(\Delta x)^2 + b\,\Delta x + c, \end{aligned} \tag{1}$$

have a unique solution for a, b, and c. The area under this curve from $-\Delta x$ to Δx (see Figure 9.21) is given by

$$\int_{-\Delta x}^{\Delta x} (ax^2 + bx + c)\,dx = \frac{ax^3}{3} + \frac{bx^2}{2} + cx\,\Bigg|_{-\Delta x}^{\Delta x}$$

$$= \frac{\Delta x}{3}\,[2a\,(\Delta x)^2 + 6c].$$

From Equations (1) it is easily verified that

$$y_0 + 4y_1 + y_2 = 2a\,(\Delta x)^2 + 6c.$$

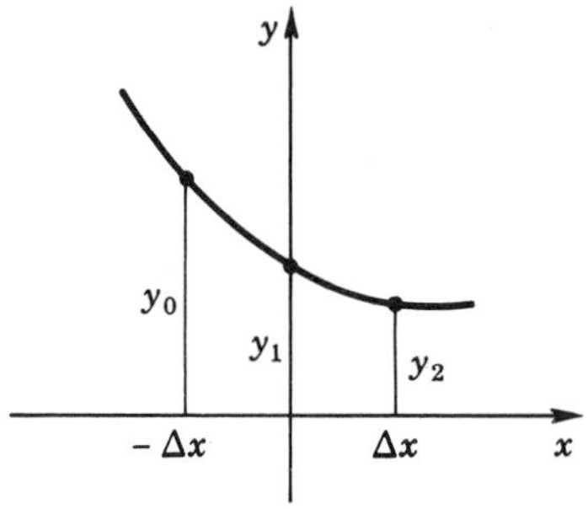

FIGURE 9.21

Thus

$$\int_{-\Delta x}^{\Delta x} (ax^2 + bx + c)\, dx = \frac{\Delta x}{3}(y_0 + 4y_1 + y_2)$$

gives the area under the parabola of Figure 9.21.

If a congruent parabola is located elsewhere in the plane, as in Figure 9.22, say a parabola of the form

$$y = ax^2 + bx + c$$

passing through the three points (x_0,y_0), (x_1,y_1), and (x_2,y_2), where $\Delta x = x_2 - x_1 = x_1 - x_0$, then it is clear that the area under the parabola is the same; i.e.,

$$\int_{x_0}^{x_2} (ax^2 + bx + c)\, dx = \frac{\Delta x}{3}(y_0 + 4y_1 + y_2).$$

We are now ready to prove Simpson's rule.

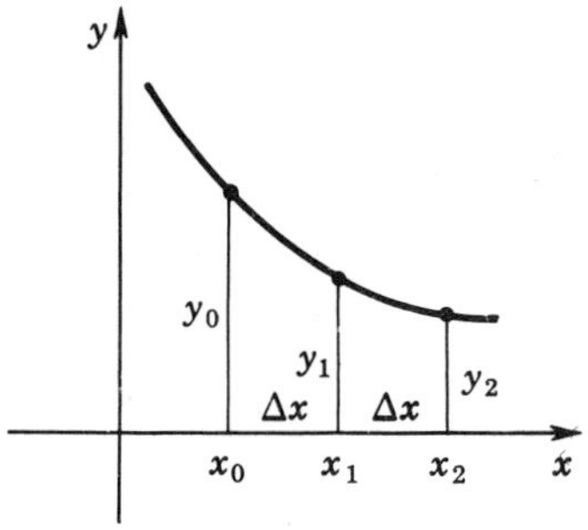

FIGURE 9.22

Proof: Let $\Delta x = (b - a)/n$, the norm of P_n. Since n is even, we may write

$$\int_a^b f(x)\,dx = \int_{x_0}^{x_2} f(x)\,dx + \int_{x_2}^{x_4} f(x)\,dx + \cdots + \int_{x_{n-4}}^{x_{n-2}} f(x)\,dx + \int_{x_{n-2}}^{x_n} f(x)\,dx.$$

Each of the integrals

$$\int_{x_i}^{x_{i+2}} f(x)\,dx$$

may be approximated by the area under a parabola through the three points $(x_i, f(x_i))$, $(x_{i+1}, f(x_{i+1}))$, and $(x_{i+2}, f(x_{i+2}))$. (See Figure 9.23.) Thus by our remarks above we have

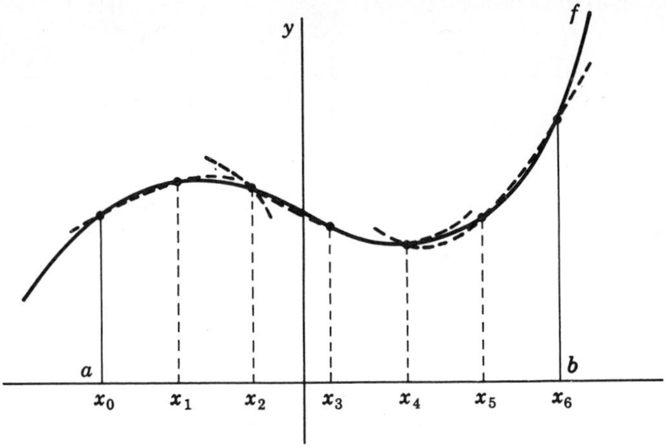

FIGURE 9.23

$$\int_{x_0}^{x_2} f(x)\,dx \doteq \frac{\Delta x}{3}[f(x_0) + 4f(x_1) + f(x_2)],$$

$$\int_{x_2}^{x_4} f(x)\,dx \doteq \frac{\Delta x}{3}[f(x_2) + 4f(x_3) + f(x_4)],$$

$$\vdots$$

$$\int_{x_{n-4}}^{x_{n-2}} f(x)\,dx \doteq \frac{\Delta x}{3}[f(x_{n-4}) + 4f(x_{n-3}) + f(x_{n-2})],$$

$$\int_{x_{n-2}}^{x_n} f(x)\,dx \doteq \frac{\Delta x}{3}[f(x_{n-2}) + 4f(x_{n-1}) + f(x_n)].$$

Adding these together, we obtain **9.8.**

We shall not give the proof, but it may be shown that the error E incurred by the use of Simpson's rule satisfies the inequality

9.9
$$E \leq \frac{(b-a)^5 K}{180 n^4},$$

where the number K is chosen so that $K \geq |f^{[4]}(x)|$ for every x in $[a,b]$.

EXAMPLE 1. With $n = 4$, approximate $\int_0^1 \sqrt{1-x^2}\,dx$ by Simpson's rule.

Solution: Clearly, $P_4 = \{0,\frac{1}{4},\frac{1}{2},\frac{3}{4},1\}$. We make the following table of values, accurate to three decimal places:

x	0	$\frac{1}{4}$	$\frac{1}{2}$	$\frac{3}{4}$	1
$\sqrt{1-x^2}$	1	.968	.866	.661	0

Then, by Simpson's rule,

$$\int_0^1 \sqrt{1-x^2}\,dx \doteq \tfrac{1}{12}[1 + 4(.968) + 2(.866) + 4(.661) + 0]$$
$$\doteq .771.$$

By Example 5, page 251, the given integral equals $\pi/4$. Hence $4.(.771) = 3.084$ is an approximation of π. A better approximation could be obtained by letting $n = 8$ or a larger integer.

EXAMPLE 2. With $n = 6$, approximate $\int_1^4 \frac{1}{x}\,dx$ by Simpson's rule.

Solution: Using the following table of values,

x	1	$\frac{3}{2}$	2	$\frac{5}{2}$	3	$\frac{7}{2}$	4
$1/x$	1	$\frac{2}{3}$	$\frac{1}{2}$	$\frac{2}{5}$	$\frac{1}{3}$	$\frac{2}{7}$	$\frac{1}{4}$

we have, by Simpson's rule,

$$\int_1^4 \frac{1}{x}\,dx \doteq \tfrac{3}{18}(1 + 4\cdot\tfrac{2}{3} + 2\cdot\tfrac{1}{2} + 4\cdot\tfrac{2}{5} + 2\cdot\tfrac{1}{3} + 4\cdot\tfrac{2}{7} + \tfrac{1}{4})$$
$$\doteq 1.388.$$

We shall find the antiderivative of this function in Chapter 10. It can be shown that our approximation above is within .002 of the value of the integral.

EXAMPLE 3. Approximate the arc length of the graph of

$$y = \frac{1}{x}$$

between the points $(1,1)$ and $(5,\frac{1}{5})$.

Solution: Since $dy/dx = -1/x^2$, evidently (9.6)

$$L = \int_1^5 \sqrt{1 + \frac{1}{x^4}}\, dx = \int_1^5 \frac{\sqrt{1 + x^4}}{x^2}\, dx.$$

Using the following table of values, we may approximate L by Simpson's rule.

x	1	2	3	4	5
$\sqrt{1 + x^4}/x^2$	1.414	1.031	1.007	1.002	1.001

Thus

$$L \doteq \tfrac{1}{3}[1.414 + 4.124 + 2.014 + 4.008 + 1.001],$$

or $L \doteq 4.187$. This answer seems reasonable, since the chord joining (1,1) and $(5,\frac{1}{5})$ has length approximately equal to 4.08.

EXERCISES

I

In each of Exercises 1–6, use Simpson's rule to approximate the integral.

1. Exercise 1, Section 5, $n = 8$.
2. Exercise 2, Section 5, $n = 6$.
3. $\int_1^{10} \frac{dx}{x}$, $n = 10$.
4. $\int_0^1 \sqrt{1 + x^4}\, dx$, $n = 10$.
5. Exercise 4, Section 5 with $n = 4$ (the exact answer is π which will be shown subsequently and $\doteq 3.14159265$ to 8 decimal places).
6. Redo Exercise 5, using $n = 10$.
7. Redo Exercise 5, using the trapezoidal rule and $n = 10$.
8. Approximate the area of the region bounded by the hypocycloid $x^{2/3} + y^{2/3} = a^{2/3}$ by using Simpson's rule with $n = 6$ for one quarter of the region. [*Hint:* First show that the area is proportional to a^2 and then approximate the constant of proportionality.]
9. Approximate the arc length of the graph of the equation $5y = \sqrt{x^5}$ between $x = 0$ and $x = 1$ by using Simpson's rule with $n = 4$.

II

1. Show that the approximation

$$\int_a^b F(x)\, dx \doteq \frac{b - a}{6}\left[F(a) + 4F\left(\frac{a + b}{2}\right) + F(b)\right],$$

which is Simpson's rule for $n = 2$, is exact for $F(x)$ a cubic polynomial. How is this connected with the prismatoid formula in Exercises 4 and 6, p. 259?

2. Consider Exercise 1 for the symmetric interval $[-h,h]$,

$$\int_{-h}^{h} F(x)\,dx \doteq \frac{h}{3}[F(-h) + 4F(0) + F(h)].$$

Determine a class of functions F other than cubics for which Simpson's rule gives the exact answer. [*Hint:* Express F as the sum of an even and an odd function and differentiate with respect to h. Solve the resulting equation by assuming that F is a polynomial function.]

Oral Exercises

In each of Exercises 1–4 explain how to obtain the

1. Area of a region.
2. Volume of a solid of revolution.
3. Work done on a moving object in a force field.
4. Arc length of a curve.
5. What is the trapezoidal rule?
6. What is Simpson's rule?
7. Give some other ways than Exercises 5 and 6 for approximating a definite integral.

I

In each of Exercises 1–4 find the area of the region bounded by the graphs of the given equations. Sketch.

1. $y = x^2 - 4x + 1, \quad x + y = 5.$
2. $y = 3 - 2x - x^2, \quad x + y = 1.$
3. $y^2(4 - x^2) = x^2, \quad x = 1.$
4. $y = (x - 1)/\sqrt{x^2 - 2x + 4}, \quad x = 0, \quad y = 0.$

In each of Exercises 5–8, find the volume of the solid generated by revolving the region with given boundaries about the given line.

5. The region with boundaries $x^2 = 4py$ and $y = b$ (p and b positive) about the x axis.
6. The region in Exercise 5 about the line $y = b$.

7. The region with boundaries $x^2 = 4py$, $y = 0$, and $x = a$ (p and a positive) about the x axis.

8. The region in Exercise 7 about the line $x = a$.

9. Do Exercise 14, p. 259, if all the cross sections are regular pentagons instead of squares.

10. The base of a solid is a segment of a parabola cut off by a chord perpendicular to its axis. The chord has length $2L$ and is at a distance of L from the vertex. Find the volume of the solid if every cross section perpendicular to the axis of the parabola is (a) a semicircle; (b) an equilateral triangle.

11. Find the volume of the solid generated by revolving the region bounded by the hypocycloid $x^{2/3} + y^{2/3} = a^{2/3}$ about the y axis; about the x axis.

12. A parabolic mirror, hollowed out of a cylindrical piece of glass of radius 4 in. and height 2 in., is 1 in. thick at the center. Find the volume of the mirror and the position of the focal point.

13. Find the approximate length of the curve $y^2 = x^5/25$ from $x = 0$ to $x = 2$, using Simpson's rule, with $n = 4$.

14. Find the approximate length of the curve $y = x^3/3$ from (0,0) to (1,1/3), using Simpson's rule.

15. Find the length of the curve $y = (\frac{4}{9}x^2 + 1)^{3/2}$ between (0,1) and $(2,\frac{125}{27})$.

II

1. The contour of a small island at height h ft above sea level is given by the circle

$$x^2 + y^2 - 2h(x - 100) = 6400.$$

Find the volume of the island above water.

2. a. Show that the area of the region bounded by the ellipse $x^2/a^2 + y^2/b^2 = 1$ is ab times the area of the region bounded by the circle $x^2 + y^2 = 1$.
   b. Show that the volume of the ellipsoid $x^2/a^2 + y^2/b^2 + z^2/c^2 = 1$ is abc times the volume of the sphere $x^2 + y^2 + z^2 = 1$.

3. Find the volume of the solid remaining after a cylindrical hole is drilled out of a sphere of radius r along a diameter if the length of the hole is h. Check some special cases (such as $h = 0$ and $h = 2r$) to see if your answer is reasonable.

4. Three holes are in the form of (1) a square of side $2r$, (2) a circle of radius r, and (3) an isosceles triangle of base $2r$ and altitude $2r$. Design a solid that will completely stop each hole and yet pass through each hole, and set up an integral for finding its volume. What other kind of a hole might be used in place of (3)?

For Exercises 5 and 6, find an equation of a curve whose arc length between $x = 0$ and $x = a$ (for all $0 \leq a \leq M$) is given by

5. $L = \frac{2}{3}[(1 + a)^{3/2} - 1]$.

6. $L = \dfrac{a^3}{6} - \dfrac{1}{2a} + \dfrac{1}{3}$.

7. A chain 100 ft long and weighing p lb/ft is completely suspended from a windlass situated on the 10th floor of a building under construction. Find the work required to wind up the chain if there is also a weight of 500 lb attached to the end of the chain.

8. Same as the previous exercise except that the windlass is on the 6th floor which is 60 ft high and, consequently, 40 ft of chain and bucket are resting on the ground.

The arithmetic mean of a set of numbers $x_1, x_2, \cdots, x_n$ is defined as $\bar{x} = (x_1 + x_2 + \cdots + x_n)/n$. Similarly, the (arithmetic) mean of an integrable function $F(x)$ in the interval $[a,b]$ is defined as

$$\bar{F} = \frac{\int_a^b F(x)\,dx}{b - a}.$$

Geometrically, $\bar{F}$ denotes the height of a rectangle with base $b - a$, having the same area as the region underneath $y = F(x)$ between a and b. That the value $\bar{F}$ exists follows from the intermediate value theorem for integrals.

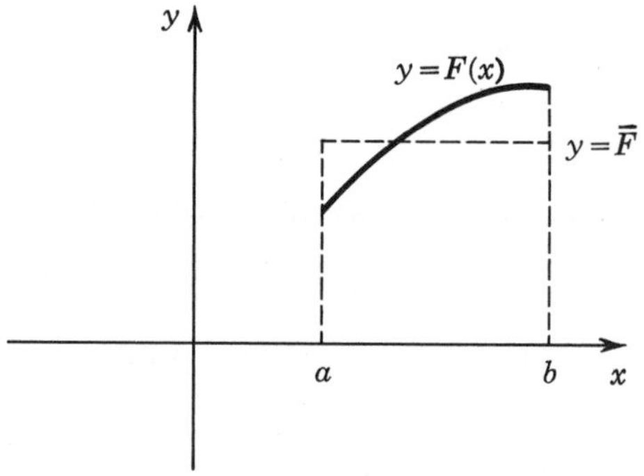

As a generalization, we have the mean value of $F(x)$ with respect to the weighting function $w(x)$ in $[a,b]$ as

$$\bar{F} = \frac{\int_a^b F(x)w(x)\,dx}{\int_a^b w(x)\,dx}.$$

[See also Exercise II-1, Chapter 7, Section 9].
Interpretations of this mean value will occur subsequently in the section dealing with centroids, center of pressure, and the like.

9. Determine the mean square distance from the point (h,k) to points of the segment $y = 0, 0 \leq x \leq a$.

10. Determine the mean distance from the point $(0,k)$ to the points of the segment $y = 0, 0 \leq x \leq a$, with respect to the weighting function $w(x) = x$.

10

EXPONENTIAL AND LOGARITHMIC FUNCTIONS

ALTHOUGH THE THEORY of the derivative and the integral developed in the previous chapters holds for many functions, the examples illustrating the theory have been drawn from the set of algebraic functions.

We shall enlarge our set of functions in this and the next chapter to include the elementary transcendental functions. Thus our new set of functions will include the algebraic, exponential, logarithmic, trigonometric, and inverse trigonometric functions.

1 INTUITIVE APPROACH

For a given positive number a, $a \neq 1$, the function f defined by

$$f(x) = a^x$$

is called the *exponential function* with base a. Thus

$$f(2) = a^2, f(\tfrac{2}{3}) = a^{2/3} = \sqrt[3]{a^2}, f(0) = a^0 = 1, f(-7) = a^{-7} = 1/a^7,$$

and so on. While it might not be clear what $f(\sqrt{3}) = a^{\sqrt{3}}$ means, we assume that this is a definite number. In fact, let us assume that a^x is defined for every real number x, so that the domain of f is $(-\infty, \infty)$. We shall also assume that the usual laws of exponents hold for all numbers x and y:

$$a^x a^y = a^{x+y}$$

$$\frac{a^x}{a^y} = a^{x-y}$$

$$(a^x)^y = a^{xy}$$

The derivative of the exponential function f is given by

$$Da^x = \lim_{h \to 0} \frac{a^{x+h} - a^x}{h}$$

$$= \lim_{h \to 0} \frac{a^x(a^h - 1)}{h}$$

$$= a^x \lim_{h \to 0} \frac{a^h - 1}{h}$$

provided the latter limit exists. Note that the expression $(a^h - 1)/h$ does not involve x, so that this limit, if it exists, is simply some number k (depending only on the base a),

10.1 $$\lim_{h \to 0} \frac{a^h - 1}{h} = k.$$

Therefore

10.2 $$Da^x = ka^x$$

provided the limit **10.1** exists.

If $a > 1$, then it is intuitively clear that a^x increases with x—that is, that the function $f(x) = a^x$ is strictly increasing. For example, if $a = 2$ we have

$$2^{-2} < 2^0 < 2^1 < 2^5 < 2^{100}.$$

Thus it is evident that the number k in **9.2** is positive if $a > 1$. Similarly, f is strictly decreasing and $k < 0$ if $0 < a < 1$.

A function f is called a 1–1 *function* (one-to-one function) if unequal numbers in the domain of f are mapped into unequal numbers in the range, i.e., if for all b, c in domain f, $f(b) \neq f(c)$ whenever $b \neq c$. Every 1–1 function f has an *inverse function* f^{-1} defined

$$y = f^{-1}(x) \text{ if and only if } x = f(y).$$

The domain of f^{-1} is the range of f, and the range of f^{-1} is the domain of f. A strictly monotonic function, such as the exponential function above, is a 1–1 function and hence has an inverse. Inverse functions are discussed in some detail in the next chapter.

The exponential function $f(x) = a^x$ appears to have domain $(-\infty, \infty)$ and range $(0, \infty)$. Its inverse function is called the *logarithm* to the base a, abbreviated $\log_a$. Thus

10.3 $$y = \log_a x \text{ if and only if } x = a^y.$$

The domain of $\log_a$ is $(0, \infty)$ and the range of $\log_a$ is $(-\infty, \infty)$. If we replace x by a^y in the first equation of **10.3** and y by $\log_a x$ in the second, we see that

10.4 $$\log_a a^y = y \quad \text{and} \quad a^{\log_a x} = x \text{ for all } x \text{ in } (0, \infty) \text{ and } y \text{ in } (-\infty, \infty).$$

If the logarithm function has a derivative, then it can be found from **10.4** by implicit differentiation. Thus the second equation of **10.4** has the form

$$x = f(g(x))$$

where $f(y) = a^y$ and $g(x) = \log_a x$. Hence, by the chain rule,

$$Dx = f'(g(x))g'(x)$$

Since $f'(y) = ka^y$ by **10.2**, the equation above is equivalent to

$$1 = ka^{\log_a x} D \log_a x.$$

Using **10.4**, this gives

10.5 $$D \log_a x = \frac{1}{kx} \qquad \text{for all } x \text{ in } (0, \infty).$$

Since $a^0 = 1$, $\log_a 1 = 0$ by **10.3**. Therefore, we can use the fundamental theorem of the calculus to express **10.5** in the integral form

10.6 $$\log_a x = \frac{1}{k} \int_1^x \frac{1}{t}\, dt \qquad \text{for all } x \text{ in } (0, \infty),$$

where k is given by **10.1**.

Equation **10.6** gives us a clue as to how we might *define* the logarithm function other than as the inverse of the exponential function. The rational function $F(t) = 1/t$ is continuous in $(0, \infty)$ by **4.12**, and therefore the integral in **10.6** exists for all x in $(0, \infty)$. Hence we can *define* $\log_a x$ by **10.6**, and the resulting function $\log_a$ is differentiable in its domain $(0, \infty)$. Its derivative is given by **10.5**. This approach to the logarithm function is used in the next section.

2 THE NATURAL LOGARITHM

It is reasonable to suspect that for some choice of a in **10.6** k equals 1. This leads us to make the following definition.

10.7 DEFINITION OF THE NATURAL LOGARITHM. The natural logarithm function, denoted by ln, is defined by

$$\ln x = \int_1^x \frac{1}{t}\, dt, \qquad \text{domain ln} = (0, \infty).$$

We have immediately from 10.7 that

$$\ln 1 = 0.$$

Since $1/t > 0$ for all $t > 0$, it is clear that

$$\ln x > 0 \qquad \text{if } x \text{ is in } (1, \infty),$$

and $\ln x$ is the area of region R in Figure 10.1. On the other hand, if $0 < x \leq 1$ then

$$\int_1^x \frac{1}{t}\, dt = -\int_x^1 \frac{1}{t}\, dt.$$

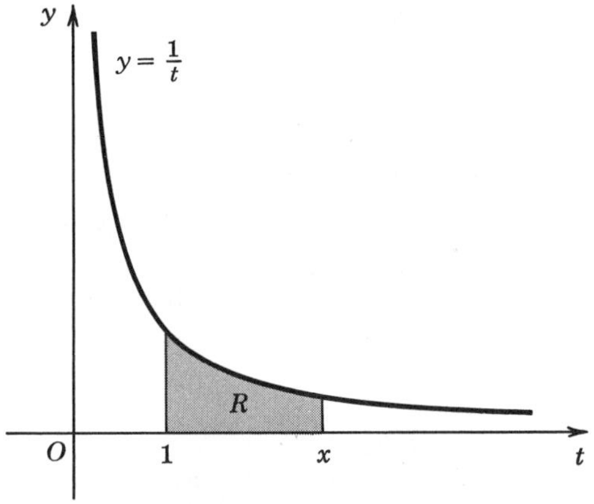

FIGURE 10.1

We conclude that

$$\ln x < 0 \qquad \text{if } x \text{ is in } (0,1),$$

and that $-\ln x$ is the area of region R in Figure 10.2.

We can easily approximate $\ln x$ by inscribing rectangles in region R or circumscribing rectangles about region R in Figures 10.1 or 10.2. The case ln 2 is

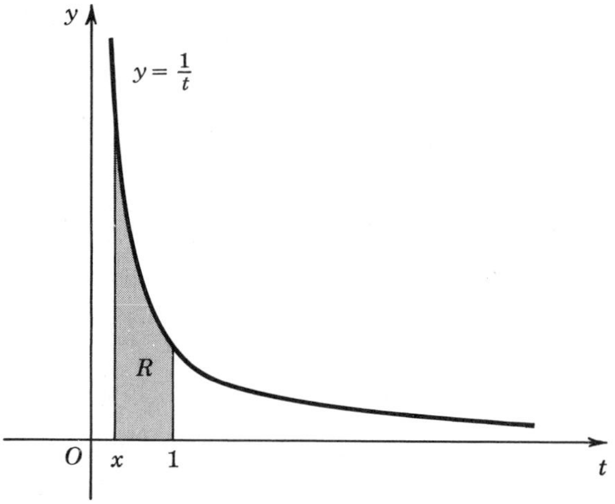

FIGURE 10.2

illustrated in the enlarged Figure 10.3. The two inscribed rectangles have total area 7/12, the two circumscribed 5/6. Therefore

$$\frac{7}{12} < \ln 2 < \frac{5}{6}.$$

A more accurate estimate is that $\ln 2 \doteq .69$.

By the fundamental theorem of the calculus **(7.19)**,

10.8 $$D \ln x = \frac{1}{x} \qquad \text{for all } x \text{ in } (0, \infty).$$

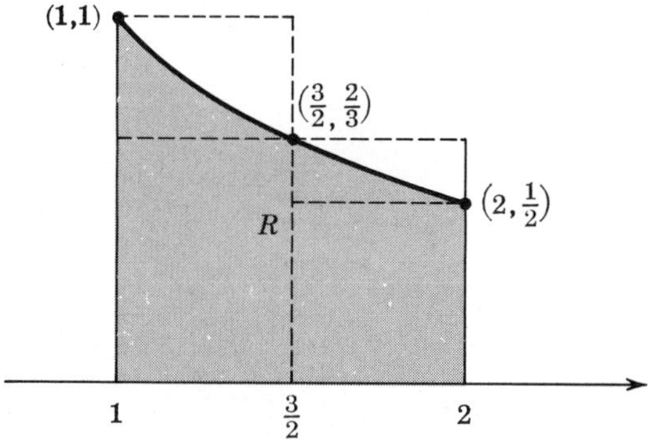

FIGURE 10.3

Since $1/x > 0$ in $(0, \infty)$, we have by **6.6** that the function ln is *strictly increasing* in its domain $(0, \infty)$. The second derivative of ln is as follows:

10.9 $$D^2 \ln x = -\frac{1}{x^2} \qquad \text{for all } x \text{ in } (0, \infty).$$

Thus, $D^2 \ln x < 0$ and the graph of ln is concave downward at every point $(x, \ln x)$ by **6.11**. A rough sketch of the graph of ln is given in Figure 10.4.

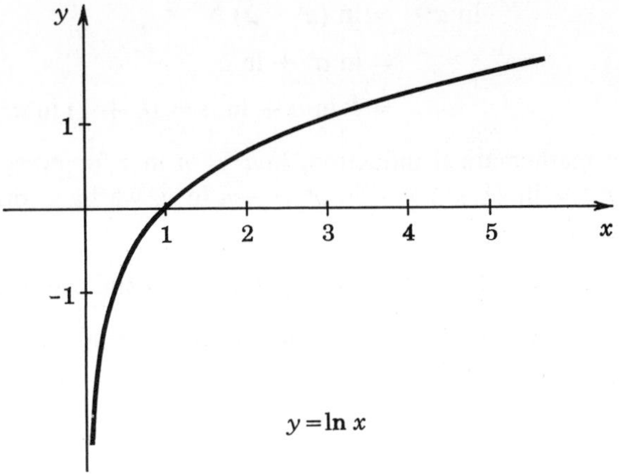

FIGURE 10.4

For each number $a > 0$, the function f defined by

$$f(x) = \ln (ax), \qquad \text{domain} f = (0, \infty),$$

has derivative

$$f'(x) = \frac{1}{ax} D(ax) = \frac{1}{ax} \cdot a = \frac{1}{x}$$

according to the chain rule and **10.8**. Since f and ln have the same derivative, they differ by a constant (**6.18**):

$$f(x) = \ln x + c \qquad \text{for some number } c.$$

Letting $x = 1$ in this equation, we get $\ln (a \cdot 1) = \ln 1 + c$, or $\ln a = c$ Thus, we have proved that

$$\ln (ax) = \ln x + \ln a.$$

We state this basic result in the following way.

10.10 $$\ln ab = \ln a + \ln b \qquad \text{for all } a, b \text{ in } (0, \infty).$$

If in **10.10** we let $a = 1/b$, then we get $\ln 1 = \ln(1/b) + \ln b$, or $\ln(1/b) = -\ln b$. Therefore, $\ln(a/b) = \ln a + \ln(1/b) = \ln a - \ln b$:

10.11 $$\ln \frac{a}{b} = \ln a - \ln b \qquad \text{for all } a, b \text{ in } (0, \infty)$$

If in **10.10** we let $b = a$, then we see that $\ln a^2 = \ln a + \ln a = 2 \ln a$. In turn, $\ln a^3 = \ln a^2 \cdot a = \ln a^2 + \ln a = 2 \ln a + \ln a = 3 \ln a$. If k is a positive integer for which $\ln a^k = k \ln a$, then

$$\begin{aligned} \ln a^{k+1} &= \ln(a^k \cdot a) \\ &= \ln a^k + \ln a \\ &= k \ln a + \ln a = (k+1) \ln a. \end{aligned}$$

Hence, by mathematical induction, $\ln a^n = n \ln a$ for every positive integer n. Since $\ln a^{-n} = \ln(1/a^n) = -\ln a^n = -n \ln a$, we have proved the following property of ln.

$$\ln a^n = n \ln a \qquad \text{for every } a \text{ in } (0, \infty) \text{ and every integer } n.$$

Each positive number a has a unique positive nth root $b = \sqrt[n]{a}$ for every integer $n \geq 2$ (see Exercises 5, 6, p. 189). Since $b^n = a$, we have $\ln b^n = \ln a$, $n \ln b = \ln a$, and $\ln b = (1/n) \cdot \ln a$. Hence

$$\ln \sqrt[n]{a} = \frac{1}{n} \ln a.$$

Every rational number has the form $r = m/n$ for some integers m and n, with $n > 0$. Hence, by definition, $a^r = a^{m/n} = (\sqrt[n]{a})^m$ and

$$\ln a^r = \ln(\sqrt[n]{a})^m = m \ln \sqrt[n]{a} = \frac{m}{n} \ln a$$

by our results above; that is,

10.12 $$\ln a^r = r \ln a \qquad \text{for every } a \text{ in } (0, \infty) \text{ and every rational number } r.$$

By definition, the domain of the function ln is $(0, \infty)$. What is its range? To answer this question, we first observe that $\ln a$ is large when a is large. Thus, from the fact that $\ln 2 > 1/2$, we have $\ln 4 = \ln 2^2 = 2 \ln 2 > 1$ and

$$\ln 4^r > r \qquad \text{for every rational number } r.$$

Now every positive number c is between $0 = \ln 1$ and some rational number r, $0 < c \leq r$. Hence

$$\ln 1 < c < \ln 4^r.$$

Since the function ln is continuous, there exists a number a, $1 < a < 4^n$, such that

$\ln a = c$ by the intermediate value theorem (7.3). This shows that every positive number is in the range of ln. If $c < 0$, then it can be shown similarly that

$$\ln 4^r < c < \ln 1$$

for some negative rational number r (since $\ln 4^{-1} < -1$). Hence, $c = \ln b$ for some number b, $4^r < b < 1$. Therefore every negative number is also in the range of ln. This completes the answer to our question, namely, that the *range of the ln function is* $(-\infty, \infty)$. Since the function ln is strictly increasing, we can state our conclusions in the following form.

10.13 **THEOREM.** For every number y there exists a *unique* positive number x such that

$$y = \ln x.$$

The unique number x such that $\ln x = 1$ is universally denoted by e:

10.14 $$\ln e = 1.$$

Since $\ln 2 < 1 < \ln 4$, $2 < e < 4$. A better approximation to be obtained later is

$$e \doteq 2.71828.$$

Other than roots of rational numbers, e and π are the two most important irrational numbers of mathematics.

By **10.12** and **10.14**, $\ln e^r = r$ for every rational number r. Even if r is an irrational number, there exists a unique number b such that $\ln b = r$. This fact gives us a natural way of *defining* e^r in case r is irrational, namely $e^r = b$ when $\ln b = r$. Having defined e^r in this manner when r is irrational, we then have

10.15 $$\ln e^r = r \qquad \text{for every real number } r.$$

Similarly, for every a in $(0, \infty)$ and every r in $(-\infty, \infty)$, we *define* a^r so that $\ln a^r = r \ln a$. Then we have

10.16 $$\ln a^r = r \ln a \qquad \text{for every } a \text{ in } (0,\infty) \text{ and every } r \text{ in } (-\infty,\infty).$$

The three equations **10.10**, **10.11**, and **10.16** are called the *laws of logarithms*. These laws together with a table of logarithms allowed early astronomers to reduce complicated calculations to a manageable form.

EXERCISES

I

1. Make a table of values for $\ln x$ with x taking on the following values:

$$e,\ e^2,\ e^3,\ e^4,\ 1/e,\ 1/e^2,\ 1/e^3,\ \sqrt{e},\ 1/\sqrt[3]{e}.$$

2. Make a table of values for $\ln x$ with x taking on the following values:

$$10, 4, \tfrac{5}{2}, .5, .2, .1, .25, .01, .001, .0001,$$

given that $\ln 2 \doteq .693$, $\ln 5 \doteq 1.609$. [*Hint:* $\ln 20 = \ln (2^2 \cdot 5) = \ln 2^2 + \ln 5 = 2 \ln 2 + \ln 5 \doteq 2.995$, etc.)

3. Solve each of the following equations:

a. $\ln x = 0$.
b. $\ln x = 1$.
c. $\ln x = -1$.
d. $\ln x = -3$.
e. $\ln (x - 2) = 3$.
f. $\ln (5 - x^2) = -2$.

4. Solve each of the following inequalities:

a. $\ln x > 2$.
b. $\ln x < -3$.
c. $\ln |x| < -1$.
d. $\ln (x + 2) < 0$.

In each of Exercises 5–8 sketch the graph of the equation.

5. $y = \ln (-x)$, $(x < 0)$.
6. $y = \ln |x|$, $(x \neq 0)$.
7. $y = \ln (1 + x)$, $(x > -1)$.
8. $y = \ln (1 - x)$, $(x < 1)$.
9. Prove that there exists a unique number u such that $\ln u + u = 0$.
10. Find $D^n \ln x$ for any positive integer n.
11. If $x < 0$, express $\int_{-1}^{x} \frac{1}{t}\, dt$ in terms of the ln function.
12. If $x > -1$, express $\int_{0}^{x} \frac{1}{1 + t}\, dt$ in terms of the ln function.
13. Prove that $\int_{a}^{ax} \frac{1}{u}\, du = \int_{1}^{x} \frac{1}{t}\, dt$. [*Hint:* Make an appropriate change of variable in the first integral]. Use this to give another proof that $\ln ax = \ln a + \ln x$.
14. Approximate ln 3 using Simpson's rule.

II

1. Show that for each integer $m > 1$,

$$\frac{1}{2} + \frac{1}{3} + \cdots + \frac{1}{m} < \ln m < 1 + \frac{1}{2} + \cdots + \frac{1}{m - 1}.$$

2. Find $\lim_{r \to \infty} \left[\frac{1}{r + 1} + \frac{1}{r + 2} + \cdots + \frac{1}{r + nr}\right]$, ($n$-positive integer).

3. Verify by differentiating that

$$\int \ln x\, dx = x \ln x - x + c.$$

4. Using the previous exercise show that for each integer $m > 1$,

$$\ln 1 + \ln 2 + \cdots + \ln (m - 1) < m \ln m - m + 1 < \ln 2 + \ln 3 + \cdots + \ln m.$$

5. Using the preceding exercise, show that

$$e\left(\frac{m+1}{e}\right)^{m+1} > m! > e\left(\frac{m}{e}\right)^{m}.$$

6. Prove that

$$\frac{x}{1+x} \leq \ln (1 + x) \leq x \qquad \text{for } x \geq 0.$$

(Use mean value theorem.)

7. Starting from

$$\frac{1}{1+x} - 1 + x - x^2 + \cdots + x^{2n-1} = \frac{x^{2n}}{1+x},$$

show that

$$t - \frac{t^2}{2} + \frac{t^2}{3} - \cdots - \frac{t^{2n}}{2n} \leq \ln (1 + t) \leq t - \frac{t^2}{2} + \frac{t^3}{3} - \cdots + \frac{t^{2n+1}}{2n+1}$$

for $t \geq 0$.

8. Prove $\lim_{x \to 0} \dfrac{\ln (1 + x)}{x} = 1.$

3 THE NATURAL EXPONENTIAL FUNCTION

The *natural exponential function* is denoted by exp and defined by

10.17 $$\exp x = e^x, \qquad \text{domain } \exp = (-\infty, \infty).$$

If $y = e^x$, then $\ln y = \ln e^x = x$ by **10.15**. On the other hand, if $\ln y = x$ then $y = e^x$ because $\ln y = \ln e^x = x$ and ln is a 1–1 function. Thus, *the function* exp *is the inverse of the function* ln.

Since ln is a strictly increasing function, it is clear that the function exp is also strictly increasing. When x is large $\exp x$ is large, and when x is negative but $|x|$ is large, $\exp x$ is small. The graph of exp is sketched in Figure 10.5.

The familiar laws of exponents stated below can be derived from the laws of logarithms (**10.10**, **10.11**, **10.16**):

$$a^r a^s = a^{r+s}, \qquad \frac{a^r}{a^s} = a^{r-s}$$

$$a^r b^r = (ab)^r, \qquad \frac{a^r}{b^r} = \left(\frac{a}{b}\right)^r$$

$$(a^r)^s = a^{rs}$$

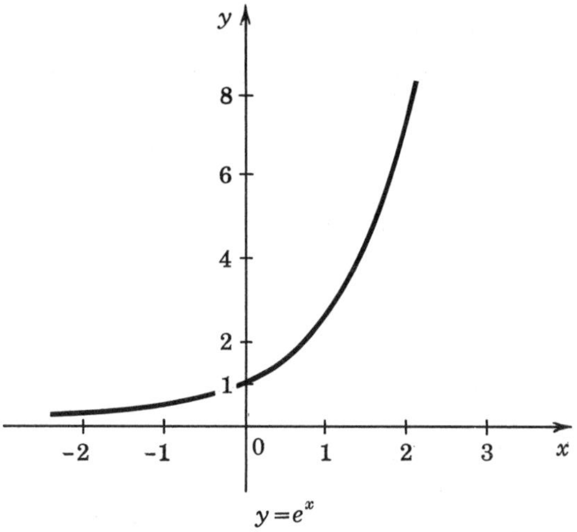

FIGURE 10.5

For example, to prove $a^r a^s = a^{r+s}$, we need only show that $\ln (a^r a^s) = \ln a^{r+s}$ because ln is a 1–1 function. This is done as follows.

$$\ln (a^r a^s) = \ln a^r + \ln a^s = r \ln a + s \ln a$$
$$= (r + s) \ln a = \ln a^{r+s}.$$

The others are proved similarly.

The inverse of a differentiable function is also differentiable by a result we shall prove in Chapter 11. If $f(x) = \ln x$ and $g(x) = \exp x$, then the derivative of g is given by

$$g'(x) = \frac{1}{f'(g(x))},$$

according to **11.36**. Since $f'(g(x)) = 1/g(x)$ by **10.8**, we have $g'(x) = g(x)$. That is, $D \exp x = \exp x$ for every x in $(-\infty, \infty)$.

In exponential notation,

10.18 $$De^x = e^x.$$

Thus we have a function exp which is its own derivative.

EXERCISES

I

1. Prove the laws of exponents.

2. Prove that the function exp is strictly increasing.

3. Prove $\lim_{h\to 0} \frac{e^h - 1}{h} = 1$. [*Hint:* Consider the derivative of e^x at $x = 0$.]

4. Sketch the graphs of the functions e^x, e^{2x}, e^{3x}, e^{-x}, e^{-2x}, e^{-3x} using only one set of coordinate axes.

5. Evaluate $\int_0^2 e^{-x}\,dx$.

6. a. Verify by differentiation that

$$\int x\,e^x\,dx = xe^x - e^x + c.$$

b. Obtain $\int xe^{ax}\,dx$ from a.

7. Determine the maximum and minimum points and point of inflection (if any) of $F(x) = xe^x$. Sketch the graphs of F, DF, and D^2F on the same set of coordinate axes.

8. Find

a. $D^n xe^x$. b. $D^n x^2e^x$.

9. Using the mean value theorem, show that

$$e^x \geq 1 + x, \quad e^{-x} \geq 1 - x \qquad \text{for all } x \geq 0.$$

10. If $Df(x) = f(x)$ for all x in $(-\infty, \infty)$, is $f(x) = e^x$?

II

1. Find $\lim_{n\to\infty} \frac{1}{n}\{e^{-a/n} + e^{-2a/n} + \cdots + e^{-na/n}\}$.

2. By integrating the result of Exercise 9 above, show that

$$e^x \geq 1 + x + \frac{x^2}{2!} + \cdots + \frac{x^n}{n!} \quad (n \text{ an arbitrary integer}),$$

$$1 - x + \frac{x^2}{2!} - \frac{x^3}{3!} + \cdots + \frac{x^{2n}}{(2n)!} \geq e^{-x}$$

$$\geq 1 - x + \frac{x^2}{2!} - \frac{x^3}{3!} + \cdots + \frac{x^{2n}}{(2n)!} - \frac{x^{2n+1}}{(2n+1)!}$$

3. Using the preceding exercise, show that

$$2.727 > e > 2.708.$$

4. If $x \geq 0$, and m is any positive integer, show that

$$e^x \geq \left(1 + \frac{x}{m}\right)^m$$

and that if also $x < m$, then

$$e^x \leq \left(1 - \frac{x}{m}\right)^{-m}.$$

5. One of the famous limits of mathematics is as follows:

$$e = \lim_{h \to 0} (1 + h)^{1/h}.$$

Prove it. [*Hint:* Use Exercise II-8, sec. 2.]

4 DERIVATIVES AND INTEGRALS

Knowing the derivatives of ln and exp, we can find derivatives of composites of these functions with other differentiable functions by use of the chain rule. However, in working with a function of the form $f(x) = \ln g(x)$, we must restrict x so that $g(x) > 0$. This suggests that we consider $\ln |g(x)|$ rather than $\ln g(x)$. Actually, $D|g(x)|$ exists whenever $Dg(x)$ exists, as long as $g(x) \neq 0$:

$$D|g(x)| = Dg(x) \qquad \text{if } g(x) > 0$$

$$D|g(x)| = D[-g(x)] = -Dg(x) \qquad \text{if } g(x) < 0.$$

From these equations and the chain rule, we have

$$D \ln |g(x)| = \frac{1}{|g(x)|} D|g(x)| = \frac{Dg(x)}{g(x)} \qquad \text{if } g(x) \neq 0.$$

Thus we have the formulas

10.19 $$D \ln |g(x)| = \frac{Dg(x)}{g(x)} \qquad \text{if } g(x) \neq 0.$$

10.20 $$\int \frac{g'(x)}{g(x)} dx = \ln |g(x)| + C.$$

In using the definite integral analogue of **10.20**, we must always remember to integrate over an interval $[a,b]$ in which g is differentiable and $g(x) \neq 0$.

EXAMPLE 1. Find $D \ln |x^2 - 5x + 4|$.

Solution: We have, by **10.19**,

$$D \ln |x^2 - 5x + 4| = \frac{D(x^2 - 5x + 4)}{x^2 - 5x + 4} = \frac{2x - 5}{x^2 - 5x + 4}$$

as long as $x^2 - 5x + 4 \neq 0$. Since

$$x^2 - 5x + 4 = (x - 1)(x - 4)$$

the derivative above is valid for all x except 1 and 4.

EXAMPLE 2. Find $D \ln \sqrt{\dfrac{x^2 + 1}{x^2 - 1}}$.

Solution: Clearly, the domain of the function being differentiated is $(-\infty, -1) \cup (1, \infty)$. Before differentiating, we algebraically simplify the given function as follows:

$$\ln \sqrt{\frac{x^2 + 1}{x^2 - 1}} = \ln \left(\frac{x^2 + 1}{x^2 - 1}\right)^{1/2} = \frac{1}{2} \ln \left(\frac{x^2 + 1}{x^2 - 1}\right)$$

$$= \frac{1}{2} [\ln (x^2 + 1) - \ln (x^2 - 1)].$$

Therefore

$$D \ln \sqrt{\frac{x^2 + 1}{x^2 - 1}} = \frac{1}{2} [D \ln (x^2 + 1) - D \ln (x^2 - 1)]$$

$$= \frac{1}{2} \left[\frac{2x}{x^2 + 1} - \frac{2x}{x^2 - 1}\right] = \frac{-2x}{x^4 - 1}.$$

EXAMPLE 3. Find $\displaystyle\int \frac{x}{x^2 - 1}\, dx$.

Solution: If we multiply the integral by $\frac{1}{2}$ and the integrand by 2, then we can use **10.20** directly.

$$\int \frac{x}{x^2 - 1}\, dx = \frac{1}{2} \int \frac{2x}{x^2 - 1}\, dx$$

$$= \tfrac{1}{2} \ln |x^2 - 1| + C.$$

This is well defined over any interval not containing -1 or 1.

At times it is convenient to make a change of variables before integrating, as illustrated below.

EXAMPLE 4. Find $\displaystyle\int_{-3}^{-1} \frac{x^2}{3x - 1}\, dx$.

Solution: If we let

$$u = 3x - 1, \qquad du = 3\, dx,$$

then

$$x = \tfrac{1}{3}(u + 1)$$

and
$$\int_{-3}^{-1} \frac{x^2}{3x-1}\,dx = \frac{1}{27}\int_{-10}^{-4} \frac{(u+1)^2}{u}\,du$$
$$= \frac{1}{27}\int_{-10}^{-4}\left(u + 2 + \frac{1}{u}\right) du$$
$$= \frac{1}{27}\left(\frac{u^2}{2} + 2u + \ln|u|\right)\Bigg|_{-10}^{-4}$$
$$= -\frac{1}{27}\left(30 + \ln\frac{5}{2}\right).$$

If $f(x) = \exp x$, then $f(g(x)) = \exp g(x)$
$$Df(g(x)) = f'(g(x))g'(x) = [\exp g(x)]g'(x)$$
This proves the following formulas.

10.21
$$De^{g(x)} = e^{g(x)} Dg(x)$$

10.22
$$\int e^{g(x)} g'(x)\,dx = e^{g(x)} + C.$$

EXAMPLE 5. Find $D(e^{3x} + e^{-3x})$.

Solution: By **10.21**,
$$D(e^{3x} + e^{-3x}) = De^{3x} + De^{-3x}$$
$$= e^{3x}\cdot 3 + e^{-3x}\cdot(-3)$$
$$= 3(e^{3x} - e^{-3x})$$

EXAMPLE 6. Find Dxe^{x^2}.

Solution: We have
$$Dxe^{x^2} = (Dx)(e^{x^2}) + x(De^{x^2})$$
$$= e^{x^2} + x(e^{x^2}Dx^2)$$
$$= e^{x^2} + 2x^2e^{x^2}$$
$$= e^{x^2}(1 + 2x^2)$$

EXAMPLE 7. Find $\int xe^{x^2}\,dx$.

Solution: We have by **10.22**:
$$\int xe^{x^2}\,dx = \frac{1}{2}\int (2x)e^{x^2}\,dx$$
$$= \tfrac{1}{2}e^{x^2} + C.$$

It is not necessary to remember **10.22** if we use the change of variable formula (**7.23** or **7.24**).

EXAMPLE 8. Evaluate $\int (x^2 - 2)\exp(x^3 - 6x)\,dx$.

Solution: Letting $u = x^3 - 6x$, we have $du = (3x^2 - 6)\,dx$. Hence

$$\int (x^2 - 2)\exp(x^3 - 6x)\,dx = \int \frac{1}{3} \exp u\,du \Big|_{u=x^3-6x}$$
$$= \tfrac{1}{3} \exp u + C \Big|_{u=x^3-6x}$$
$$= \tfrac{1}{3} \exp(x^3 - 6x) + C.$$

EXERCISES

I

Differentiate each of the following functions.

1. $f(x) = x^2e^{2x}$.
2. $g(x) = \sqrt{1 + e^x}$.
3. $G(x) = (1 + e^{-3x^2})^3$.
4. $F(x) = \dfrac{e^x}{\sqrt{e^{2x} - 1}}$.
5. $(x + 1)\ln|x^2 - 1|$.
6. $\ln\sqrt{x^4 + 4}$.
7. $\dfrac{x^2}{\ln x}$.
8. $e^x \ln x$.
9. $\ln(e^x + 1)$.
10. $\ln\sqrt{e^x + 1}$.

In each of Exercises 11–14 find all maximum points, minimum points and points of inflection (if any) of the graph of the given function and sketch it.

11. $F(x) = x \ln x$.
12. $g(x) = x^2e^{-x}$.
13. $F(x) = e^{-a^2x^2} (a > 0)$.
14. $G(x) = \dfrac{e^{2x} - 1}{e^{2x} + 1}$.

In each of Exercises 15–22 evaluate the given integral.

15. $\int_0^2 e^{-5x}\,dx$.
16. $\int_0^1 x^2 \exp(-x^3)\,dx$.
17. $\int \dfrac{e^{\sqrt{x}}}{\sqrt{x}}\,dx$.
18. $\int (x + 2)\exp(x^2 + 4)\,dx$.
19. $\int \dfrac{x^3}{x + a}\,dx$.
20. $\int_0^3 \dfrac{x}{2x^2 + 3}\,dx$.
21. $\int \dfrac{\ln x}{x}\,dx$.
22. $\int \dfrac{e^x}{1 - e^x}\,dx$.

II

Sketch the graph of each of the following equations and determine y' and y''.

1. $y = \exp(e^x)$.
2. $y = \exp(e^{-x})$.
3. $y = \exp(-e^x)$.
4. $y = \exp(-e^{-x})$.
5. $y = \ln(\ln x)$.

In each of Exercises 6–9 determine $f'(x)$ by first taking logs of both sides of the equation and then differentiating implicitly. This is known as *logarithmic differentiation*.

6. $f(x) = e^{\ln^2 x}$.
7. $f(x) = x^x$.
8. $f(x) = x^{x^2} \cdot e^{x^3}$.
9. $f(x) = \dfrac{(x^3 - 1)^4(\sqrt{x} + 1)^3(e^{x^2} + 1)^{1/2}}{(x^2 + 1)^{1/3}}$.

In each of Exercises 10–13 evaluate the integral.

10. $\displaystyle\int \frac{1}{1 + e^x}\,dx$.
11. $\displaystyle\int \frac{1}{x \ln x \ln \ln x}\,dx$.
12. $\displaystyle\int \frac{1}{e^x + e^{-x} + 2}\,dx$.
13. $\displaystyle\int \exp(x + e^x)\,dx$.
14. Find the arc length of the graph of the equation $y = \ln(x^2 - 1)$ between $x = 2$ and $x = 3$. $\left[\textit{Hint:}\ \dfrac{2}{x^2 - 1} = \dfrac{1}{x - 1} - \dfrac{1}{x + 1}\right]$.

5 HYPERBOLIC FUNCTIONS

Some simple combinations of exponential functions have proved useful in physical applications of mathematics. These are the hyperbolic functions discussed below.

The *hyperbolic sine*, designated by *sinh*, and the *hyperbolic cosine*, designated by *cosh*, are defined as follows:

10.23 $$\sinh x = \frac{e^x - e^{-x}}{2}, \qquad \cosh x = \frac{e^x + e^{-x}}{2}.$$

Each function has $(-\infty, \infty)$ as its domain, whereas sinh has $(-\infty, \infty)$ and cosh has $(0, \infty)$ as its range. Clearly, sinh is an odd function (i.e., $\sinh - x = -\sinh x$)

and cosh is an even function (i.e., $\cosh - x = \cosh x$). An easy computation shows that

10.24 $$e^x = \sinh x + \cosh x$$

In functional notation, $\exp = \sinh + \cosh$.

By adding ordinates of the graphs of $y = e^x/2$ and $y = -e^{-x}/2$, we can easily sketch the graph of sinh, as shown in Figure 10.6. The graph of cosh is sketched in Figure 10.7 in a similar way.

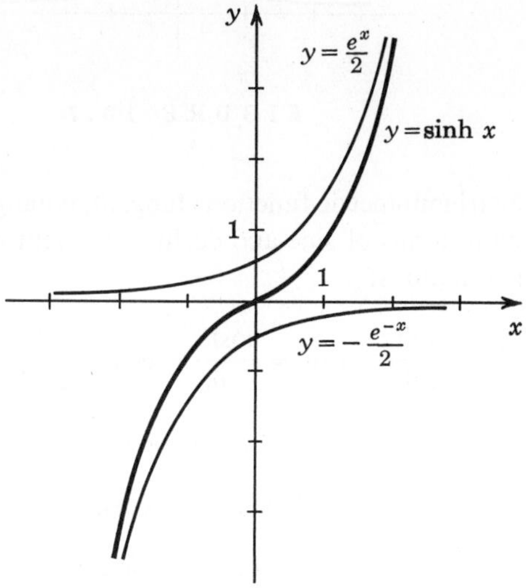

FIGURE 10.6

As is indicated by their names, the hyperbolic functions are related to both the hyperbola (which will be discussed in Chapter 13) and the trigonometric functions. Corresponding to the trigonometric identity

$$\sin^2 x + \cos^2 x = 1$$

is the identity

10.25 $$\cosh^2 x - \sinh^2 x = 1.$$

This identity is easily proved from the definitions of sinh and cosh. Other identities that are similar to trigonometric identities are as follows:

10.26 $$\sinh (x + y) = \sinh x \cosh y + \cosh x \sinh y,$$
$$\cosh (x + y) = \cosh x \cosh y + \sinh x \sinh y.$$

Proofs of these identities will be left as exercises.

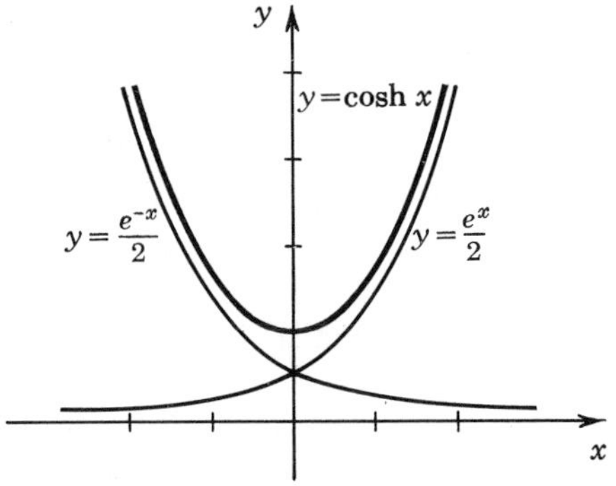

FIGURE 10.7

Just as the trigonometric functions tangent, cotangent, secant, and cosecant may be defined in terms of sine and cosine, so might we define the corresponding hyperbolic functions:

$$\tanh = \frac{\sinh}{\cosh}, \quad \coth = \frac{\cosh}{\sinh}, \quad \operatorname{sech} = \frac{1}{\cosh}, \quad \operatorname{csch} = \frac{1}{\sinh}.$$

Since $D \exp(-x) = -\exp(-x)$, evidently

10.27 $$D \sinh x = \cosh x.$$

10.28 $$D \cosh x = \sinh x.$$

As we shall see in Chapter 11, these formulas are closely related to the formulas for the derivatives of the sine and the cosine. The integral analogues of **10.27** and **10.28** are as follows:

10.29 $$\int \sinh x\, dx = \cosh x + C.$$

10.30 $$\int \cosh x\, dx = \sinh x + C.$$

EXAMPLE. Find (a) $D \tanh x$; (b) $\int \frac{\sinh x}{\cosh^2 x}\, dx$.

Solution: (a) We have

$$D \tanh x = D\frac{\sinh x}{\cosh x} = \frac{\cosh x\, D \sinh x - \sinh x\, D \cosh x}{\cosh^2 x}$$

$$= \frac{\cosh^2 x - \sinh^2 x}{\cosh^2 x} = \frac{1}{\cosh^2 x} = \operatorname{sech}^2 x.$$

(b) Letting $u = \cosh x$ and $du = \sinh x\, dx$, we have

$$\int \frac{\sinh x}{\cosh^2 x}\, dx = \int u^{-2}\, du \Big|_{u=\cosh x}$$

$$= -\frac{1}{u} + C \Big|_{u=\cosh x}$$

$$= -\operatorname{sech} x + C.$$

EXERCISES

I

Sketch the graph of each of the following equations and find y' and y''.

1. $y = \sinh x$.
2. $y = \cosh x$.
3. $y = \tanh x$.
4. $y = \coth x$.
5. $y = \operatorname{csch} x$.
6. $y = \operatorname{sech} x$.

Establish the following identities.

7. $\cosh^2 x - \sinh^2 x = 1$.
8. $\operatorname{sech}^2 x + \tanh^2 x = 1$.
9. $\sinh (x - y) = \sinh x \cosh y - \cosh x \sinh y$.
10. $\cosh (x - y) = \cosh x \cosh y - \sinh x \sinh y$.
11. $(\cosh x + \sinh x)^n = \cosh nx + \sinh nx$ for every integer n.

Evaluate the following integrals:

12. $\int \sinh x \cosh x\, dx$.
13. $\int \tanh x \operatorname{sech} x\, dx$.
14. $\int \coth hx \operatorname{csch} x\, dx$.
15. $\int \tanh x \operatorname{sech}^2 x\, dx$.
16. Find the arc length of the catenary $y = \cosh x$ from $x = 0$ to $x = a$.
17. Find the volume of the solid generated by revolving the region bounded by the catenary $y = a/2 \cosh x/a$, $x = a$, $x = -a$, and $y = 0$ about the x axis.
18. Using Simpson's rule with $n = 4$, approximate the volume of the solid generated by revolving the region bounded by $y = \sinh x$, $y = \sinh 1$, and $x = 0$, about the y axis.

II

Establish the following identities:

1. $\sinh 2x = 2 \sinh x \cosh x$.

2. $\cosh 2x = 2\cosh^2 x - 1 = 1 + 2\sinh^2 x = \cosh^2 x + \sinh^2 x.$

3. $\tanh 2x = \dfrac{2\tanh x}{1 + \tanh^2 x}.$

4. $\sinh 3x = 3\sinh x + 4\sinh^3 x.$

5. $\cosh 3x = 4\cosh^3 x - 3\cosh x.$

6. a. $\cosh nx = C^n + \binom{n}{2} C^{n-2}S^2 + \binom{n}{4} C^{n-4}S^4 + \cdots,$

b. $\sinh nx = \binom{n}{1} C^{n-1}S + \binom{n}{3} C^{n-3}S^3 + \binom{n}{5} C^{n-5}S^5 + \cdots,$

where $C = \cosh x$, $S = \sinh x$.

[*Hint:* use Exercise 11, I.]

Evaluate the following integrals:

7. $\int \sinh^2 x\, dx.$

8. $\int \cosh^2 x\, dx.$

9. $\int \sinh^3 x\, dx.$

10. $\int \cosh^3 x\, dx.$

11. $\int \operatorname{sech}^2 x\, dx.$

12. $\int \operatorname{csch}^2 x\, dx.$

6 CHANGE OF BASE

Given any positive number $a \neq 1$, a^x is defined for every real number x by **10.16.** Thus

10.31 $$a^x = e^{x \ln a} \quad \text{for every } x \text{ in } (-\infty, \infty).$$

This defines the *exponential function* $f(x) = a^x$ with domain $(-\infty, \infty)$ and range $(0, \infty)$. Since the function f is a 1–1 function, it has an inverse which we call the *logarithm function to the base a* and denote by $\log_a$. Thus

10.32 $$y = \log_a x \quad \text{if and only if} \quad x = a^y.$$

The laws of exponents and logarithms hold for the base a just as they do for the base e. Since $x = a^y$ if and only if $\ln x = y \ln a$, we have by **10.31** that

10.33 $$\log_a x = \frac{\ln x}{\ln a}.$$

We can use **10.31** and **10.33** to differentiate a^x and $\log_a x$. Thus, by **10.21**, $Da^x = a^x D(x \ln a) = a^x \cdot \ln a$:

10.34 $$Da^x = (\ln a)a^x.$$

This proves that the constant k we encountered in **10.1** and **10.2** is given by $k = \ln a$. From **10.33**, $D \log_a x = (D \ln x)/\ln a = 1/x \ln a$:

10.35 $$D \log_a x = \frac{1}{x \ln a}.$$

EXAMPLE 1. Find $D \log_{10} |3x + 1|$.

Solution: By **10.35** and **10.19**,

$$D \log_{10} |3x + 1| = \frac{1}{\ln 10} D \ln |3x + 1|$$
$$= \frac{1}{\ln 10} \frac{3}{3x + 1}.$$

We recall that a function f defined by an equation of the form

$$f(x) = x^r$$

is called a *power function*. In view of the results of the present chapter, this is a well-defined function even if r is an irrational number, in which case the domain of f is the set of all positive numbers.

The derivative of f in case r is rational is given by the familiar formula

$$D\, x^r = rx^{r-1}.$$

Let us prove that this formula is valid even if r is an irrational number. Thus, since

$$x^r = e^{r \ln x},$$

we have

$$D\, x^r = e^{r \ln x} D\,(r \ln x) = x^r \cdot \frac{r}{x} = rx^{r-1}.$$

EXAMPLE 2. Find $\int 10^x\, dx$.

Solution: We have by **10.31**

$$\int 10^x\, dx = \int e^{x \ln 10}\, dx.$$

This may be evaluated by letting

$$u = x \ln 10, \qquad du = \ln 10\, dx,$$

so that

$$\begin{aligned}\int 10^x\,dx &= \frac{1}{\ln 10}\int e^u\,du\Big|_{u=x\ln 10}\\ &= \frac{1}{\ln 10}e^u + C\Big|_{u=x\ln 10}\\ &= \frac{1}{\ln 10}e^{x\ln 10} + C = \frac{10^x}{\ln 10} + C.\end{aligned}$$

EXERCISES

Differentiate the following.

1. $\log_2|5 - 2x|$.
2. $\log_{10}(x^2 + 2)$.
3. $x^2\log_{10}(3 + 2x^2)$.
4. $\dfrac{\log_{10} x}{x}$.
5. $(\ln x + 1)^\pi$.
6. $\left(\dfrac{x}{x^2+1}\right)^e$.
7. $(1 + \sqrt{x})^{1+e}$.
8. $(1 + e)^{1+\sqrt{x}}$.
9. 2^{2x}.
10. $\exp(e^x)$.

Find the following integrals.

11. $\int_1^2 2^x\,dx$.
12. $\int_{-1}^1 (1 + e)^x\,dx$.
13. $\int_{-3}^{-1} 10^{-x}\,dx$.
14. $\int x3^{x^2}\,dx$.
15. Prove that

    a. $\log_a x = (\log_a b)(\log_b x)$.

    b. $\log_a x = \dfrac{\log_b x}{\log_b a}$.

7 EXPONENTIAL LAWS OF GROWTH AND DECAY

It sometimes happens that the rate of change of the amount of a given substance at any time is proportional to the amount of the substance present at that time. The first example that comes to mind is the decomposition of a radioactive substance, the rate of decomposition being proportional to the amount of radioactive substance present. The growth of a culture of bacteria obeys this same law under ideal conditions.

In order to give a mathematical analysis of this phenomenon, let $f(t) > 0$ be the amount of a substance present at time t. Then to say that the rate of change of f at time t is proportional to $f(t)$ is to say that

10.36 $$f'(t) = kf(t)$$

for some constant k and every time t in some interval. This differential equation may be solved for f in the following way.

We first put **10.36** in the form

$$\frac{f'(t)}{f(t)} = k,$$

and then integrate as follows:

$$\int_0^t \frac{f'(t)}{f(t)}\,dt = \int_0^t k\,dt,$$

[changing variables by letting $u = f(t)$, $du = f'(t)\,dt$]

$$\int_{f(0)}^{f(t)} \frac{1}{u}\,du = \int_0^t k\,dt,$$

$$\ln u \Big|_{f(0)}^{f(t)} = kt \Big|_0^t,$$

$$\ln f(t) - \ln f(0) = kt,$$

$$\ln \frac{f(t)}{f(0)} = kt,$$

$$\frac{f(t)}{f(0)} = e^{kt},$$

$$f(t) = f(0)e^{kt}.$$

According to this equation, the amount $f(t)$ present at time t equals the initial amount $f(0)$ (at time $t = 0$) times e^{kt}. The constant k depends on the substance in question, and can be found if sufficient data are given. It is permissible to express the equation above in the form

10.37 $$f(t) = f(0)a^{ct}$$

using any base a we wish. Evidently, $c = k \log_a e$.

EXAMPLE 1. The half-life of radium is approximately 1600 years (i.e., a given amount of radium will be half gone after 1600 years). Starting with 150 mg of pure radium, find the amount left after t years. After how many years is only 30 mg left?

Solution: Using **10.37** with $a = 2$, and the unit of time a year, we have

$$f(t) = 150 \cdot 2^{ct}.$$

Since $f(1600) = 75$,

$$75 = 150 \cdot 2^{1600c},$$
$$\tfrac{1}{2} = 2^{1600c}.$$

Thus $1600c = -1$ and $c = -1/1600$. It is evident now that the base 2 was chosen so as to make the evaluation of c easy. We have proved that the amount $f(t)$ of radium left after t years is given by

$$f(t) = 150 \cdot 2^{-t/1600}.$$

The solution of the equation

$$30 = 150 \cdot 2^{-t/1600}$$

or

$$\tfrac{1}{5} = 2^{-t/1600}$$

will give the number t of years that must elapse before only 30 mg is left. We solve this equation by logarithms, obtaining

$$t = \frac{1600 \log_{10} 5}{\log_{10} 2} \doteq 3715 \text{ years.}$$

The above is an example of an exponential law of decay. The following example is an exponential law of growth.

EXAMPLE 2. The number of bacteria in a culture was 1000 at a certain instant and 8000 two hours later. Assuming ideal conditions for growth, how many bacteria are there after t hours?

Solution: The number $f(t)$ of bacteria after t hours is given by (using $a = 8$ in **10.37**)

$$f(t) = 1000 \cdot 8^{ct}.$$

It is given that $f(2) = 8000$; thus

$$8000 = 1000 \cdot 8^{2c}$$
$$8 = 8^{2c}$$

and $2c = 1$. Hence

$$f(t) = 1000 \cdot 8^{t/2}.$$

After five hours, for example,

$$f(5) = 1{,}000 \cdot 8^{5/2} = 64{,}000\sqrt{8} \doteq 180{,}000.$$

EXERCISES

I

1. Show that the law of decay for radium may be written in the form

$$A = A_0\left(\frac{1}{2}\right)^{t/1600},$$

where A_0 is the initial amount of radium and A is the amount left after t years. The percentage of radium left at any time t is $100A/A_0$. Find the percentage of radium left after 800 years; after 6400 years. In how many years is 10 percent of the radium decomposed?

2. When bacteria grow under ideal circumstances, their rate of growth is proportional to the number of bacteria present. Express the number of bacteria present in terms of time t. In a certain culture of bacteria the number of bacteria present at a certain instant was 1000 and the number present 10 hours later was 8000. Find the law of growth for this culture, and find the number of bacteria present 15 hours after the first count.

3. a. Under normal conditions the rate of change of population is considered to be proportional to the population at any time. If P_0 is the population at time $t = 0$, express the population P in terms of time t.
   b. A town had a population of 18,000 in 1945 and 25,000 in 1955. Assuming the exponential law of growth, what population was expected in 1965?

4. The radioactive element polonium has a half-life of 140 days. Express the amount A of polonium left after t days in terms of the initial amount A_0 of polonium and t. Approximately what percentage of a given supply of polonium is left after one year?

5. In solution, sugar decomposes into other substances at a rate proportional to the amount x still unchanged. Show that

$$x = x_0e^{kt}$$

where x_0 is the amount unchanged at time $t = 0$. If 30 lb of sugar reduces to 10 lb in four hours, when will 95 percent of the sugar be decomposed?

A function y satisfies the differential equation $y' = ky$. In each of Exercises 6–9, find $y = y(x)$ if the initial condition given is satisfied.

6. $y(0) = 1, \quad y(1) = e^2$.
7. $y(0) = 1, \quad y(1) = e^{-2}$.
8. $y(0) = 100, \quad y(1) = 200$.
9. $y(0) = 100, \quad y(1) = 50$.
10. Find $y(5)$ in Exercise 8 above.
11. Find $y(5)$ in Exercise 9 above.

II

1. When a resistance R (ohms) and a capacitance C (farads) are connected in series with an electromotive force (emf) E (volts), the current I (amperes) is given by

$$R\frac{dI}{dt} + \frac{I}{C} = \frac{dE}{dt}.$$

Solve for I, assuming that E, R, and C are all constant and that, at the instant the switch in the circuit is closed, $t = 0$, $I = I_0$. Sketch the graph of I and find its limiting value as $t \to \infty$.

2. If in Exercise 1 the capacitance is replaced by a coil of inductance L (henries) the current is given by

$$L\frac{dI}{dt} + RI = E.$$

Solve for I if, at $t = 0$, $I = 0$. Sketch the graph of I and find its limiting value as $t \to \infty$. [*Hint:* Let $x = E - RI$.]

3. A mass of m lb is being drawn across a rough surface by a constant force of F lb. The force of friction retarding the motion is um, where u is the coefficient of friction (assumed to be constant). Also retarding the motion is air resistance, which is proportional to the velocity kv. If the body starts from rest at time $t = 0$, what will the velocity and the displacement from the initial position be at time t? [*Hint:* Solve as in Exercise 2.]

REVIEW

Oral Exercises

1. Define the natural logarithm function. What is its domain? What is its range? What is its derivative?
2. What is the inverse of the natural logarithm function called? What is its domain and range? What is its derivative and integral?
3. What is the definition of e?
4. What are the laws of exponents?
5. Define the six hyperbolic functions. What are their domains and ranges? What are their derivatives?

I

In each of Exercises 1–4 sketch the graph and find dy/dx.

1. a. $y = x^2 \ln x$.

2. a. $y = \dfrac{\ln x}{\sqrt{x}}$.

b. $y = \ln^2 x$

b. $y = \dfrac{\ln x}{x}$.

c. $y = \sqrt{x} \ln x$.

c. $y = \dfrac{\ln x}{x^2}$.

3. $y = \ln (x + \sqrt{x^2 - 1})$, $(x \geq 1)$.

4. $y = \ln (x + \sqrt{x^2 + 1})$.

In each of Exercises 5–10 find dy/dx by logarithmic differentiation (see Section 4, Exercises II.).

5. $y = \sqrt{\dfrac{1 - x^2}{1 + x^2}}$.

6. $y = (x^2 + 1)^x$.

7. $xe^y y^2 = 1$.

8. $y = \sqrt{\dfrac{(a - x)(b - x)}{(a + x)(b + x)}}$.

9. $y = (x)^{10^x} - (10)^{x^{10}}$

10. $y = (x)^{x^x}$.

11. Find the area of the region bounded by the curve $y = a \cosh x/a$, the x axis, and the lines $x = \pm a$.

12. Find the area of the region bounded by the curve $y = a \tanh x/a$, the x axis, and the lines $x = m$ and $x = n$.

13. Find the volume of the solid generated by rotating the region bounded by $y = ae^{bx}$, $x = 0$, $x = c$, $y = 0$ about the x axis.

14. Find the arc length of the graph of the equation $y = x^2/4 - \frac{1}{2} \ln x$ between $x = 1$ and $x = 2$.

In each of Exercises 15–18, evaluate the integral.

15. $\displaystyle\int \frac{x}{x + a}\, dx$.

16. $\displaystyle\int \frac{x^3 - a^3}{x + a}\, dx$.

17. $\displaystyle\int \frac{e^{-3x} - 1}{e^{-3x} + 1}\, dx$.

18. $\displaystyle\int_e^{e^3} \frac{\ln x}{x}\, dx$.

19. A man keeps his money in a savings bank where he draws interest at the rate of 4 percent compounded quarterly. How long will it take for his money to double?

20. A person has invested \$1000 in each of two savings banks. One bank gives interest at 4 percent compounded quarterly and the other gives $4\frac{1}{8}$ percent compounded annually. Which bank pays out more interest after an integral number of years? What is a good reason then for splitting his savings (assuming both banks are insured, so there is no need to worry about bank failures)?

21. Prove that $\tanh (x \pm y) = \dfrac{\tanh x \pm \tanh y}{1 \pm \tanh x \tanh y}$.

22. Express $\tanh 3x$ as a function of $\tanh x$.

II

Find:

1. $\displaystyle\int \frac{\ln(\ln x^2)}{x \ln x^2}\,dx.$

2. $\displaystyle\int x^{4x}(1 + \ln x)\,dx.$

3. Prove that $\displaystyle\lim_{x\to\infty} \frac{\ln x}{x^h} = 0 \quad (h > 0).$

4. Find $\displaystyle\lim_{n\to\infty} n(\sqrt[n]{a} - 1)$, where $a > 0$.

5. How can Exercise 4 be used to compute logarithms?

6. Verify the recursion formula

$$\int x^r \ln^s x\,dx = \frac{x^{r+1}\ln^s x}{r+1} - \frac{s}{r+1}\int x^r \ln^{s-1} x\,dx.$$

Using the preceding exercise, find

7. $\displaystyle\int x^2 \ln^3 x\,dx.$

8. $\displaystyle\int \ln^4 x\,dx.$

9. Find $\int x^3e^x\,dx$ by assuming that the answer has the form $P(x)e^x$ for some polynomial function P. Generalize your result.

10. Find the arc length of the graph of the equation $e^y = (e^x + 1)/(e^x - 1)$ between $x = a$ and $x = b$, $(0 < a < b)$.

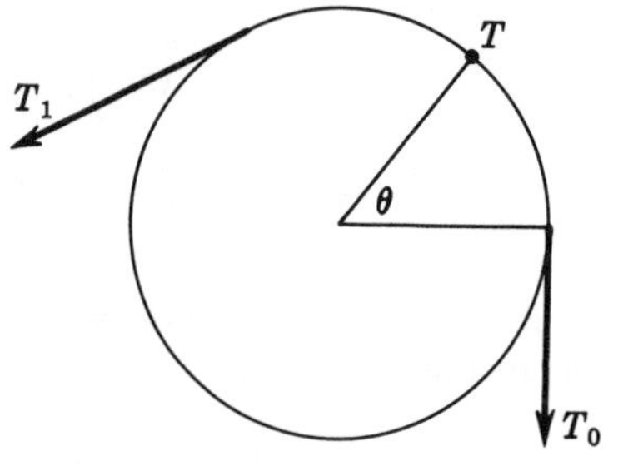

11. A rope is wound around a rough circular cylinder. Ignoring the weight of the rope, the tension T at any point (given by angle θ) satisfies the differential equation

$$\frac{dT}{d\theta} = uT$$

when the rope is on the point of slipping (u = coefficient of friction). If a boat exerting a pull of 10 tons (T_1) is to be held by a rope wrapped around a hawser and held by a man who can exert a pull of 50 lb (T_0), at least how many times around the hawser must the rope be wound? Take $u = .2$.

12. A tank initially contains 1000 gal of fresh water. Brine containing 3 lb/gal of salt flows into the tank at a rate of 2 gal/min, and the mixture, kept uniform by stirring, runs out at the same rate. How long will it take for the quantity of salt in the tank to reach 100 lb? To reach 90 percent of maximum?

13. Approximate $\int_0^{100} x^x\,dx$ to within 10%. [*Hint:* Use $Dx^x = x^x(1 + \ln x)$].

14. a. Verify that

$$\int e^{x^3}\,dx = \frac{e^{x^3}}{3x^2} + \frac{2}{3}\int \frac{e^{x^3}}{x^3}\,dx.$$

b. Approximate $\int_0^{100} e^{x^3}\,dx$ to within 10%.

11

TRIGONOMETRIC AND INVERSE TRIGONOMETRIC FUNCTIONS

WE CONTINUE in this chapter the study of the elementary transcendental functions started in Chapter 10. The emphasis in the present chapter is on the trigonometric functions.

1 RADIAN MEASURE

It is clear that an arc of a circle has length. Thus an arc smaller than a semicircle can be considered the graph of a smooth function and hence, by **9.6**, has length. An arc that is a semicircle or larger can be considered to be a union of smaller arcs, and its length to be the sum of the lengths of these smaller arcs.

If $\widehat{A_1B_1}$ and $\widehat{A_2B_2}$ are arcs of concentric circles subtending the same central angle (Figure 11.1), then the lengths s_1 and s_2 of $\widehat{A_1B_1}$ and $\widehat{A_2B_2}$ are proportional to the corresponding radii of the circles

$$\frac{s_1}{s_2} = \frac{r_1}{r_2}.$$

This may be proved in the manner suggested by Figure 11.1.

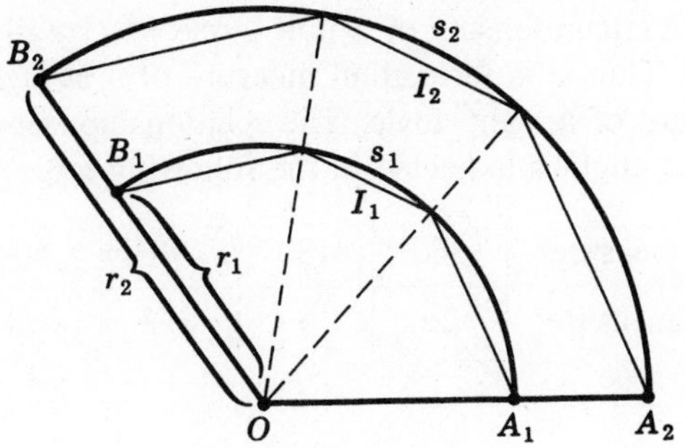

FIGURE 11.1

As is the usual practice, we designate the length of the circumference of a circle of diameter 1 by π. Then if C is the length of a circle of radius r, we have $C/\pi = r/\frac{1}{2}$, or

$$C = 2\pi r,$$

in view of our remarks above. This is the usual formula for the length of the circumference of a circle of radius r.

We can think of an angle OAB as being swept out by rotating its initial side OA, perhaps more than a complete revolution, to its terminal side OB. Under such a rotation the point A travels on the circumference of a circle having center O and radius $|OA|$ to the point B. We shall speak of the length of the arc of the circle traversed by the point A as the distance traveled by A.

11.1 DEFINITION. Let OAB be a central angle of a circle of radius 1 having initial side OA and terminal side OB (Figure 11.2). The *radian measure* of angle OAB is the distance θ traveled on the unit circle by the point A under the rota-

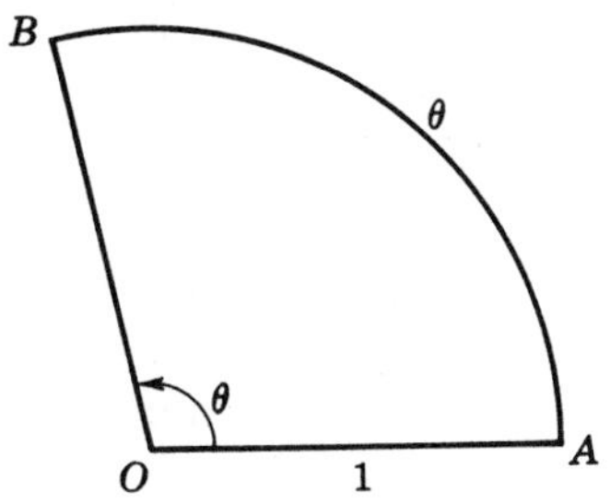

FIGURE 11.2

tion of the angle. The number θ is taken to be positive if the rotation is counterclockwise; otherwise, θ is taken to be negative.

Since the circumference of a unit circle has length 2π, a semicircular arc has length π. Thus π is the radian measure of a straight angle and $\pi/2$ is the radian measure of a right angle. The relationship between degree and radian measure of an angle is indicated in the following table.

Degree measure	360	180	90	60	45	30
Radian measure	2π	π	$\pi/2$	$\pi/3$	$\pi/4$	$\pi/6$

2 THE SINE AND COSINE FUNCTIONS

For each real number s, $\sin s$ and $\cos s$ are defined as shown in Figure 11.3. Thus, starting from the point $A(1,0)$ on the unit circle with center at the origin O, we traverse the circumference of the circle in a counterclockwise direction a distance s to the point P if $s \geq 0$; and a distance $|s|$ in a clockwise direction to the point P if $s < 0$. If we think of s as the radian measure of the central angle subtended by arc $\widehat{AP}$, we see that $\sin s = \overline{BP}$ and $\cos s = \overline{OB}$ in Figure 11.3. Since $|OP| = 1$, these are the usual definitions of sine and cosine for acute angles. The sine and cosine functions have the set of all real numbers as their domain and the interval $[-1,1]$ as their range.

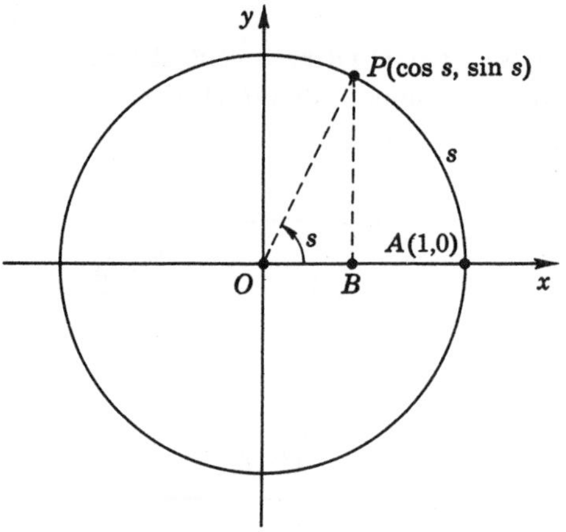

FIGURE 11.3

An important property of the sine and cosine is that they are *periodic functions*, with period 2π. Thus

$$\sin(s + 2\pi) = \sin s, \qquad \cos(s + 2\pi) = \cos s$$

for every real number s, and 2π is the least positive number for which each of these equations is true for every s. Some of the basic trigonometric identities are listed in the Appendix (page 808).

If the sine is a differentiable function, then its derivative may be found as follows:

$$D\sin(x) = \lim_{h\to 0} \frac{\sin(x+h) - \sin x}{h}.$$

Replacing $\sin(x + h)$ by $\sin x \cos h + \cos x \sin h$ and rearranging terms, we see that

$$D\sin(x) = (\sin x) \lim_{h\to 0} \frac{\cos h - 1}{h} + (\cos x) \lim_{h\to 0} \frac{\sin h}{h}.$$

Since

11.2 $$D\sin(0) = \lim_{h\to 0} \frac{\sin h - \sin 0}{h} = \lim_{h\to 0} \frac{\sin h}{h},$$

11.3 $$D\cos(0) = \lim_{h\to 0} \frac{\cos h - \cos 0}{h} = \lim_{h\to 0} \frac{\cos h - 1}{h},$$

we have

11.4 $$D\sin(x) = (\sin x)\, D\cos(0) + (\cos x)\, D\sin(0).$$

Thus the problem of finding the derivative of the sine function at each number x reduces to the problem of finding the derivatives of sine and cosine at 0.

By the same process we may show that

11.5 $$D\cos(x) = (\cos x)\, D\cos(0) - (\sin x)\, D\sin(0).$$

To find $D\sin(0)$, we must evaluate

$$\lim_{h\to 0} \frac{\sin h}{h}.$$

Let us first find

(1) $$\lim_{h\to 0^+} \frac{\sin h}{h}.$$

In evaluating (1), we might as well restrict h to be small, say $0 < h < \pi/2$. So select an arc $\widehat{AP}$ of length $h < \pi/2$ and construct the tangent lines PC and AC, and the point D as shown in Figure 11.4. Evidently, $\sin h = \overline{BP} = |BP|$, $\cos h = \overline{OB} = |OB|$, and $|BP| < |AP| \leq h$. Thus

$$\sin h < h. \tag{2}$$

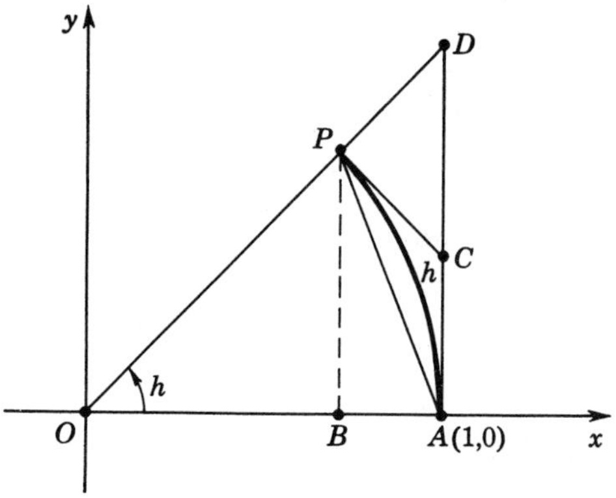

FIGURE 11.4

On the other hand, $h \leq |AC| + |CP| < |AC| + |CD| = |AD|$ and $(\sin h)/(\cos h) = |BP|/|OB| = |AD|/|OA| = |AD|$. Hence

$$h < (\sin h)/(\cos h)$$

and

$$\cos h < \frac{\sin h}{h}. \tag{3}$$

We can approximate the size of $\cos h$ by the half-angle formula,

$$\sin^2\left(\frac{h}{2}\right) = \frac{1 - \cos h}{2}.$$

Thus, since $\sin(h/2) < h/2$ by (2),

$$\frac{1 - \cos h}{2} < \frac{h^2}{4}. \tag{4}$$

We easily derive from (4) that

$$1 - \frac{h^2}{2} < \cos h. \tag{5}$$

From (2)–(5), we quickly arrive at the following inequality:

$$1 - \frac{h^2}{2} < \frac{\sin h}{h} < 1 \quad \text{for every } h \text{ in } \left(0, \frac{\pi}{2}\right). \tag{6}$$

Since $\lim_{h\to 0} [1 - (h^2/2)] = 1$, it is easily shown from (6) that

(7) $$\lim_{h\to 0^+} \frac{\sin h}{h} = 1.$$

The sine function is an *odd function;* i.e., $\sin(-x) = -\sin x$ for every x. Hence

$$\frac{\sin(-x)}{-x} = \frac{\sin x}{x} \quad \text{for every } x \neq 0.$$

In particular, we see that (6) holds for every h in $(-\pi/2,0)$. This implies that

(8) $$\lim_{h\to 0^-} \frac{\sin h}{h} = 1.$$

Together, (7) and (8) yield

11.6 $$\lim_{h\to 0} \frac{\sin h}{h} = 1.$$

Hence, from **11.2**,

11.7 $$D \sin(0) = 1.$$

From (4), we derive

(9) $$0 < 1 - \cos h < \frac{h^2}{2}.$$

Now, the cosine function is an *even function;* i.e., $\cos(-x) = \cos x$ for every x. Hence (9) holds for h in either $(0,\pi/2)$ or $(-\pi/2,0)$. Thus

(10) $$0 < \frac{1 - \cos h}{h} < \frac{h}{2} \quad \text{if } h \text{ is in } \left(0, \frac{\pi}{2}\right),$$

(11) $$\frac{h}{2} < \frac{1 - \cos h}{h} < 0 \quad \text{if } h \text{ is in } \left(\frac{-\pi}{2}, 0\right).$$

Together, (10) and (11) prove the following limit:

11.8 $$\lim_{h\to 0} \frac{1 - \cos h}{h} = 0.$$

Hence, by **11.3**,

11.9 $$D \cos(0) = 0.$$

Substituting the values from **11.7** and **11.9** in **11.4** and **11.5**, we get

11.10 $$D \sin(x) = \cos x,$$

11.11 $$D \cos(x) = -\sin x.$$

Thus we also have

11.12 $$\int \sin x\, dx = -\cos x + C,$$

11.13 $$\int \cos x\, dx = \sin x + C.$$

If in place of $\sin x$ we have $\sin f(x)$, then we can differentiate the resulting function by use of the chain rule:

11.14 $$D \sin f(x) = \cos f(x)\, D f(x)$$

11.15 $$D \cos f(x) = -\sin f(x)\, D f(x).$$

EXAMPLE 1. Find (a) $D \sin (3x - 1)$; (b) $D \cos^2 2x$.

Solution: (a) By **11.14**,

$$D \sin (3x - 1) = \cos (3x - 1) D(3x - 1) = 3 \cos (3x - 1).$$

(b) We have

$$\begin{aligned} D (\cos 2x)^2 &= 2(\cos 2x)^1 D \cos 2x \\ &= 2 \cos 2x(-\sin 2x \cdot 2) \\ &= -4 \sin 2x \cos 2x. \end{aligned}$$

EXAMPLE 2. Find the extrema in one period of the function

$$f(x) = \sin^2 x - \cos x.$$

Solution: The period of f is clearly 2π. We have

$$\begin{aligned} f'(x) &= D (\sin x)^2 - D \cos x \\ &= 2 \sin x \cos x + \sin x \\ &= 2 \sin x(\cos x + \tfrac{1}{2}). \end{aligned}$$

Hence $f'(x) = 0$ if and only if $\sin x = 0$ or $\cos x = -\frac{1}{2}$. Therefore

$$\left\{0, \pi, \frac{2\pi}{3}, \frac{4\pi}{3}\right\}$$

is the set of critical numbers of f in $[0,2\pi)$.

The second derivative of f is given by

$$\begin{aligned} f''(x) &= 2D (\sin x \cos x) + D \sin x \\ &= 2[\cos x \cdot \cos x + \sin x \cdot (-\sin x)] + \cos x \\ &= 2(\cos^2 x - \sin^2 x) + \cos x. \end{aligned}$$

We easily verify that $f''(0) = 3$, $f''(\pi) = 1$, $f''(\frac{2}{3}\pi) = -\frac{3}{2}$, $f''(\frac{4}{3}\pi) = -\frac{3}{2}$. Therefore $f(0) = -1$ and $f(\pi) = 1$ are minimum values of f and $f(\frac{2}{3}\pi) = \frac{5}{4}$ and $f(\frac{4}{3}\pi) = \frac{5}{4}$ are maximum values of f. The graph of f in one period is sketched in Figure 11.5 from the following table of values.

x	0	$\frac{1}{2}\pi$	$\frac{2}{3}\pi$	π	$\frac{4}{3}\pi$	$\frac{3}{2}\pi$	2π
$f(x)$	-1	1	$\frac{5}{4}$	1	$\frac{5}{4}$	1	-1

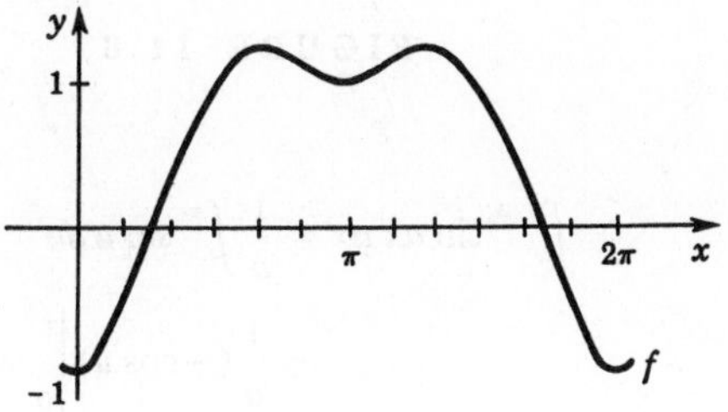

FIGURE 11.5

EXAMPLE 3. Find $\int \sin^3 2x \cos 2x \, dx$.

Solution: If we let

$$u = \sin 2x, \qquad du = 2 \cos 2x \, dx,$$

then

$$\int \sin^3 2x \cos 2x \, dx = \frac{1}{2} \int u^3 \, du \Big|_{u = \sin 2x}$$

$$= \frac{1}{8} u^4 + C \Big|_{u = \sin 2x}$$

$$= \frac{1}{8} \sin^4 2x + C.$$

EXAMPLE 4. Find the area of the region R bounded by the x axis and one arch of the graph of $y = \sin ax$, a a positive number.

Solution: The function f defined by

$$f(x) = \sin ax$$

has period $2\pi/a$. One arch of the graph of f occurs in the interval $[0,\pi/a]$, as shown in Figure 11.6. The area of R is given by

$$A(R) = \int_0^{\pi/a} \sin ax \, dx.$$

We can evaluate this integral directly or by changing variables as follows. Let

$$u = ax, \qquad du = a \, dx.$$

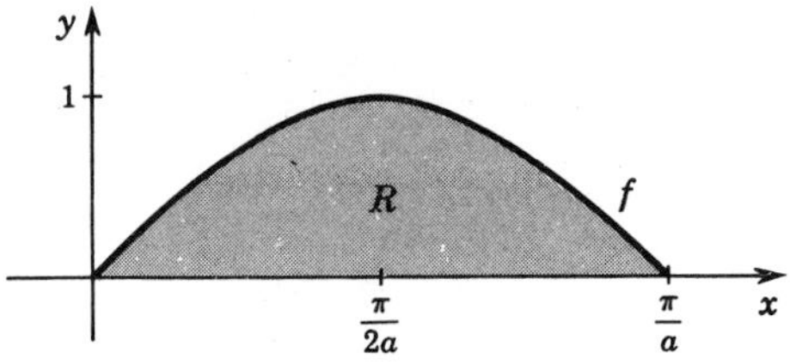

FIGURE 11.6

Then

$$\int_0^{\pi/a} \sin ax\,dx = \frac{1}{a}\int_0^{\pi} \sin u\,du$$
$$= \frac{1}{a}(-\cos u)\Big|_0^{\pi} = \frac{2}{a}.$$

Thus $A(R) = 2/a$. For example, if $a = 1$, then we see that the area of the region under an arch of the sine curve is 2.

3 THE OTHER TRIGONOMETRIC FUNCTIONS

The other trigonometric functions, tangent, cotangent, secant, and cosecant, are simple combinations of sine and cosine. Thus

$$\tan = \frac{\sin}{\cos}, \quad \cot = \frac{\cos}{\sin}, \quad \sec = \frac{1}{\cos}, \quad \csc = \frac{1}{\sin}.$$

The domain of tangent and secant is the set of all real numbers except the zeros of cosine, $\{\pm\frac{1}{2}\pi, \pm\frac{3}{2}\pi, \pm\frac{5}{2}\pi, \cdots\}$; that of cotangent and cosecant the set of all real numbers except the zeros of sine, $\{0, \pm\pi, \pm 2\pi, \pm 3\pi, \cdots\}$.

We can find the derivatives of tangent, cotangent, secant, and cosecant in a straightforward manner. Thus

$$D\tan = D\frac{\sin}{\cos} = \frac{\cos D\sin - \sin D\cos}{\cos^2}$$
$$= \frac{\cos^2 + \sin^2}{\cos^2} = \frac{1}{\cos^2} = \sec^2.$$

Also,

$$D\sec = D(\cos)^{-1} = -1\,(\cos)^{-2}\,D\cos$$
$$= \frac{\sin}{\cos^2} = \frac{\sin}{\cos}\,\frac{1}{\cos} = \tan\cdot\sec.$$

In this way we derive the following formulas.

11.16 $$D \tan(x) = \sec^2 x.$$

11.17 $$D \cot(x) = -\csc^2 x.$$

11.18 $$D \sec(x) = \sec x \tan x.$$

11.19 $$D \csc(x) = -\csc x \cot x.$$

EXAMPLE 1. Find $D(\sec 2x + \tan 2x)^2$.

Solution: We proceed as follows:

$$\begin{aligned} D(\sec 2x + \tan 2x)^2 &= 2(\sec 2x + \tan 2x)\, D(\sec 2x + \tan 2x) \\ &= 2(\sec 2x + \tan 2x)(\sec 2x \tan 2x\, D\, 2x + \sec^2 2x\, D\, 2x) \\ &= 2(\sec 2x + \tan 2x)\, 2 \sec 2x(\tan 2x + \sec 2x) \\ &= 4 \sec 2x(\sec 2x + \tan 2x)^2. \end{aligned}$$

Corresponding to the differentiation formulas **11.16–11.19** are the following integration formulas:

11.20 $$\int \sec^2 x\, dx = \tan x + C,$$

11.21 $$\int \csc^2 x\, dx = -\cot x + C,$$

11.22 $$\int \sec x \tan x\, dx = \sec x + C,$$

11.23 $$\int \csc x \cot x\, dx = -\csc x + C.$$

EXAMPLE 2. Find $\int \sec^3 3x \tan 3x\, dx$.

Solution: If we let

$$u = \sec 3x, \quad du = \sec 3x \tan 3x\, D\, 3x = 3 \sec 3x \tan 3x\, dx,$$

then

$$\begin{aligned} \int \sec^3 3x \tan 3x\, dx &= \frac{1}{3} \int \sec^2 3x(3 \sec 3x \tan 3x\, dx) \\ &= \frac{1}{3} \int u^2\, du \Big|_{u = \sec 3x} \\ &= \frac{1}{3} \cdot \frac{u^3}{3} + C \Big|_{u = \sec 3x} \\ &= \frac{1}{9} \sec^3 3x + C. \end{aligned}$$

EXERCISES

I

Differentiate the following:

1. $2 \sin x \cos x$.
2. $\tan 4x$.
3. $\dfrac{\sin 2x}{1 + \cos 2x}$.
4. $\dfrac{\sec 3x}{1 + \tan 3x}$.
5. $\tan^3 \dfrac{x}{2}$.
6. $3 \sin^2 \dfrac{x}{3}$.
7. $\sec^2 x \tan^2 x$.
8. $\sin^3 x \cos^2 x$.
9. $\dfrac{\cot 2x - 1}{\csc 2x}$.
10. $(\csc 3x - \cot 3x)^2$.
11. $\ln |\sec x + \tan x|$.
12. $\ln |\csc x - \cot x|$.
13. $e^{2x} \cos 2x$.
14. $e^{ax}(a \sin bx - b \cos bx)$.
15. $x \sin x + \cos x$.
16. $x \sin \dfrac{1}{x}$.
17. $\sqrt{1 - \tan^2 2x}$.
18. $\tan \sqrt{x}$.
19. $\sec x^3$.
20. $x^2 \cot x^2$.

Find $\dfrac{dy}{dx}$ and $\dfrac{d^2y}{dx^2}$ if:

21. $y = \csc^3 2x$.
22. $y = \dfrac{1 - \sin x}{1 + \sin x}$.
23. $y = \tan x \sec^2 x$.
24. $y = x^2 \tan^2 2x$.
25. $y = x^2 \sin \dfrac{1}{x}$.
26. $y = \csc 2x^3$.
27. $y = \cos^2 2x - \sin^2 2x$.
28. $y = \sin x + \sin x \cos x$.

Find $\dfrac{dy}{dx}$ if:

29. $x = \sin y$.
30. $x = \tan y$.
31. $x = \sec y$.
32. $e^x \sin 2y = x + y$.
33. $\cos (x + y) = y \sin x$.
34. $\tan (x^2 + y) = 4 + \cot y$.

Find the extrema of the following functions and sketch their graphs for $0 \leq x \leq 2\pi$:

35. $f(x) = \sin x + \cos x$.
36. $g(x) = 2\cos x + \cos 2x$.
37. $F(x) = \sin^2 x + \cos x$.
38. $f(x) = \tan x - 2x$.
39. $g(x) = 2\sec x - \tan x$.
40. $F(x) = \sec x + 2\cos x$.

In each of Exercises 41–57 find the integral.

41. $\int_0^{\pi/2} \sin x\, dx$.
42. $\int_0^{\pi/2} \cos x\, dx$.
43. $\int_0^{\pi/4} \sec^2 \theta\, d\theta$.
44. $\int_{-\pi/4}^{\pi/4} \sec^2 \theta\, d\theta$.
45. $\int \sin(2z + \pi/2)\, dz$.
46. $\int_{-\pi/4}^{0} \sec x \tan x\, dx$.
47. $\int \cot \theta\, d\theta$.
48. $\int (\cos x)\, e^{\sin x}\, dx$.
49. $\int_0^{\pi/2} \frac{\sin x}{1 + \cos x}\, dx$.
50. $\int_1^2 \csc^2 \frac{\pi\theta}{4}\, d\theta$.
51. $\int \csc \frac{\pi\theta}{4} \cot \frac{\pi\theta}{4}\, d\theta$.
52. $\int_0^{\pi/3} \sin^2 \theta \cos \theta\, d\theta$.
53. $\int \cos^3 x \sin x\, dx$.
54. $\int \sec^2 x \tan^2 x\, dx$.
55. $\int \csc^2 x \cot x\, dx$.
56. $\int e^x \sin(\pi e^x)\, dx$.
57. $\int_a^b x \sin(x^2 + 1)\, dx$.
58. Find the area of the region bounded by the graph of $y = \tan x$, the line $x = \pi/4$, and the x axis.
59. The sine and cosine curves together bound certain regions. Discuss these regions and their areas.
60. Find the area of one of the regions bounded by the graphs of the equations $y = \sec^2 x$ and $y = 2$.
61. Find the area of the region in the first quadrant bounded by the graph of the equation $y = \sin x/(1 + \cos x)$, the x axis and the line $x = \pi/2$.
62. Using Simpson's rule with $n = 6$, approximate the length of one arch of the sine curve.

II

Starting with the identities $\sin(x + y) = \sin x \cos y + \cos x \sin y$ and $\cos(x + y) = \cos x \cos y - \sin x \sin y$, prove each of the following identities:

1. $\tan(x + y) = \dfrac{\tan x + \tan y}{1 - \tan x \tan y}$.
2. $2\sin^2 x = 1 - \cos 2x$.

3. $2\cos^2 x = 1 + \cos 2x$.

4. $\sin 3x = 3\sin x - 4\sin^3 x$.

5. $\cos 3x = 4\cos^3 x - 3\cos x$.

Using Exercises 1–5, evaluate the integrals in Exercises 6–11.

6. $\int \sin^2 ax\,dx$.

7. $\int x\cos^2 ax^2\,dx$.

8. $\int \sin^3 bx\,dx$.

9. $\int x^2\cos^3 2x^3\,dx$.

10. $\int \frac{1-\cos 2x}{1+\cos 2x}\,dx$.

11. $\int \cos^4 ax\,dx$.

12. If the position function s of a moving point on a line satisfies the differential equation $d^2s/dt^2 = -k^2s$, (k a constant), then the point is said to undergo *simple harmonic motion*. Show that $s(t) = A\sin kt + B\cos kt$ satisfies the differential equation for any constants A and B.

13. Determine the constants A and B in Exercise 12 if s and $v = ds/dt$ have the following values when $t = 0$: (a) $s = 0$, $v = v_0$; (b) $s = s_0$, $v = 0$; (c) $s = s_0$, $v = v_0$.

14. Without using the calculus, find the extrema of the function F defined by $F(x) = a\sin x + b\cos x$.

15. In Exercise 13(c) determine the maximum displacement and maximum speed of the moving point.

16. Prove that the function f defined by $f(x) = \sin \pi/x$, domain $f = (0,1]$, has an infinite number of extrema. Prove that it is not possible to define $f(0)$ so that f is continuous in the closed interval $[0,1]$.

17. Prove that the function g defined by $g(x) = x\sin \pi/x$, domain $g = (0,1]$, has an infinite number of extrema. Prove that it is possible to define $g(0)$ so that g is continuous in the closed interval $[0,1]$. Having defined $g(0)$ so that g is continuous in $[0,1]$, determine whether $D^+g(0)$ exists. If it does, find it.

18. Do Exercise 17 for the function h defined by $h(x) = x^2\sin \pi/x$, domain $h = (0,1]$.

4 INVERSE TRIGONOMETRIC FUNCTIONS

Since the sine function is differentiable, it is everywhere continuous. As we remarked previously, its range is the closed interval $[-1,1]$. From the periodicity of the sine (graphed in Figure 11.7), it is clear that for each number y in $[-1,1]$

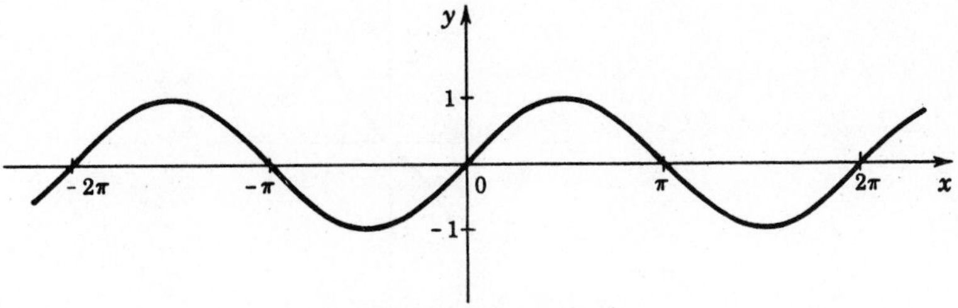

FIGURE 11.7

there exist infinitely many numbers x such that $\sin x = y$. In fact, for each y in $[-1,1]$ there exists a unique number x in each of the intervals

11.24 $$\ldots, \left[\frac{-3\pi}{2}, \frac{-\pi}{2}\right], \left[\frac{-\pi}{2}, \frac{\pi}{2}\right], \left[\frac{\pi}{2}, \frac{3\pi}{2}\right], \ldots$$

of length π such that $y = \sin x$.

We now ask if the sine function has an inverse, i.e., if there exists a function f with domain $[-1,1]$ and range the set of all real numbers such that

$$y = f(x) \text{ if and only if } x = \sin y.$$

Since the sine is not a 1–1 function, it is evident that the answer to this question is no. However, if we restrict the sine function to one of the intervals listed in **11.24**, then it is strictly monotone and hence has an inverse. It is common practice to restrict the sine to the interval $[-\pi/2, \pi/2]$ in defining its inverse; however, we must realize that any other interval of **11.24** would be equally suitable.

11.25 **DEFINITION.** The *inverse sine function* is designated by $\sin^{-1}$ and is defined as follows:

$$y = \sin^{-1} x \text{ if and only if } x = \sin y \text{ and } -\frac{\pi}{2} \leq y \leq \frac{\pi}{2}.$$

By this definition, the function $\sin^{-1}$ has domain $[-1,1]$ and range $[-\pi/2,\pi/2]$. Its graph is sketched in Figure 11.8.

Because of the possible confusion between the two totally different concepts of

$$\sin^{-1} x, \quad (\sin x)^{-1},$$

we shall sometimes call the inverse sine function the *arcsine function*, and write

$$\arcsin x$$

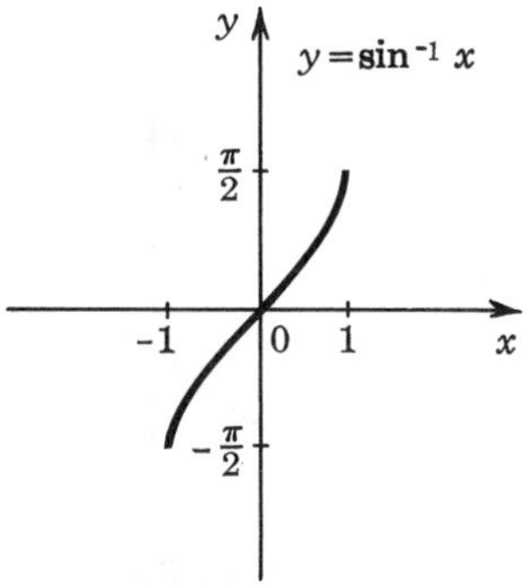

FIGURE 11.8

for $\sin^{-1} x$. By definition,

11.26
$$\sin(\sin^{-1} x) = \sin(\arcsin x) = x, \qquad x \text{ in } [-1,1].$$
$$\sin^{-1}(\sin y) = \arcsin(\sin y) = y, \qquad y \text{ in } \left[\frac{-\pi}{2}, \frac{\pi}{2}\right].$$

The other inverse trigonometric functions may be defined similarly. Let us carry through the definition of one other such function, namely the inverse tangent.

The tangent function is continuous at every number other than an odd multiple of $\pi/2$. The lines

$$\ldots, \quad x = -\frac{3\pi}{2}, \quad x = -\frac{\pi}{2}, \quad x = \frac{\pi}{2}, \quad x = \frac{3\pi}{2}, \quad \ldots$$

are vertical asymptotes of the graph of the tangent function, as indicated in Figure 11.9. Since the tangent is not a 1–1 function, it doesn't have an inverse. However, if we restrict the tangent function to the interval $(-\pi/2, \pi/2)$, then it is strictly increasing and hence has an inverse. Thus, we may make the following definition.

11.27 **DEFINITION.** The *inverse tangent function*, designated $\tan^{-1}$, is defined by

$$y = \tan^{-1}x \quad \text{if and only if} \quad x = \tan y \text{ and } -\frac{\pi}{2} < y < \frac{\pi}{2}.$$

By definition, the domain of the inverse tangent function is the set of all real numbers and its range is the open interval $(-\pi/2, \pi/2)$. Its graph is sketched in Figure 11.10. Again, we shall sometimes call the inverse tangent function the *arctangent*. By definition,

11.28
$$\tan(\tan^{-1} x) = \tan(\arctan x) = x, \qquad x \text{ in } (-\infty, \infty).$$
$$\tan^{-1}(\tan y) = \arctan(\tan y) = y, \qquad y \text{ in } \left(-\frac{\pi}{2}, \frac{\pi}{2}\right).$$

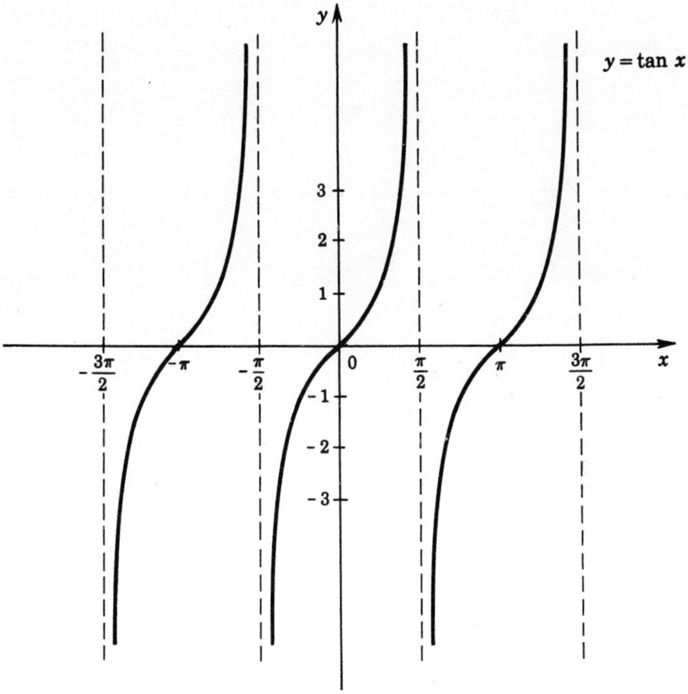

FIGURE 11.9

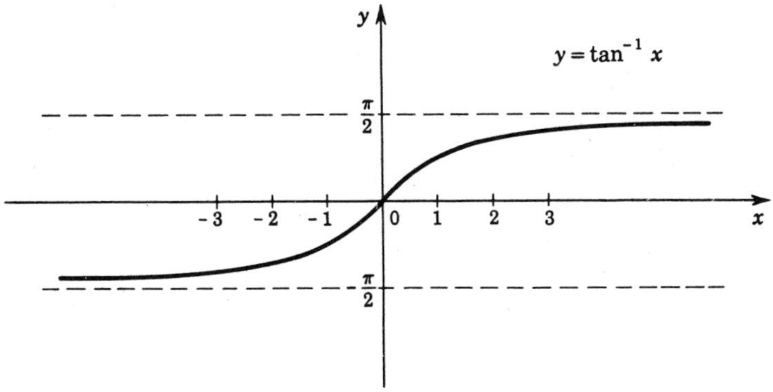

FIGURE 11.10

EXERCISES

I

Find the following:

1. $\sin^{-1} \frac{1}{2}$.
2. $\tan^{-1} 1$.
3. $\sin^{-1} \frac{\sqrt{2}}{2}$.
4. $\tan^{-1} - \frac{1}{\sqrt{3}}$.
5. $\arctan - 1$.
6. $\arcsin - \frac{\sqrt{3}}{2}$.
7. $\sin (\arctan 1)$.
8. $\tan \left(\sin^{-1} \frac{\sqrt{3}}{2} \right)$.
9. $\csc (\tan^{-1} - \sqrt{3})$.

II

Simplify the following:

1. $\tan (\sin^{-1} x)$.
2. $\cos (2 \tan^{-1} x)$.
3. $\sin (3 \sin^{-1} x)$.
4. $\cot (4 \cos^{-1} 2x)$.

Show:

5. $\sin^{-1} x + \sin^{-1} y = \sin^{-1} (x\sqrt{1 - y^2} + y\sqrt{1 - x^2})$.
6. $\cos^{-1} x + \cos^{-1} y = \cos^{-1} (xy - \sqrt{1 - x^2} \cdot \sqrt{1 - y^2})$.
7. $\tan^{-1} x + \tan^{-1} y = \tan^{-1} \frac{x + y}{1 - xy}$.

5 DERIVATIVES OF INVERSE TRIGONOMETRIC FUNCTIONS

Since

$$\sin (\sin^{-1} x) = x \quad \text{for every } x \text{ in } [-1,1],$$

implicit differentiation may be used to find the derivative of $\sin^{-1}$, if indeed it has a derivative. Thus

$$D \sin (\sin^{-1} x) = Dx,$$

$$\cos (\sin^{-1} x)\, D \sin^{-1} x = 1,$$

$$D \sin^{-1} x = \frac{1}{\cos (\sin^{-1} x)} \qquad \text{if } \cos (\sin^{-1} x) \neq 0.$$

Since $\sin^{-1} x$ is in the interval $[-\pi/2,\pi/2]$ and $\cos y \geq 0$ for every y in this interval, evidently

$$\cos(\sin^{-1} x) = \sqrt{1 - \sin^2(\sin^{-1} x)} = \sqrt{1 - x^2}$$

for every x in $[-1,1]$. We note that $\cos(\sin^{-1} x) \neq 0$ if x is in the open interval $(-1,1)$. Therefore, if $\sin^{-1}$ has a derivative, it is given by

11.29 $$D \sin^{-1}(x) = \frac{1}{\sqrt{1 - x^2}}, \qquad x \text{ in } (-1,1).$$

The proof that $\sin^{-1}$ has a derivative is similar to that for the function ln. First, let us define the function F as follows:

$$F(x) = \int_0^x \frac{1}{\sqrt{1 - t^2}}\, dt, \qquad \text{domain of } F = (-1,1).$$

Then

$$DF(x) = \frac{1}{\sqrt{1 - x^2}} \quad \text{for every } x \text{ in } (-1,1).$$

Let us prove that $F(x) = \sin^{-1} x$ for every x in $(-1,1)$, which will show that $\sin^{-1}$ is differentiable.

According to the chain rule,

$$\begin{aligned} DF(\sin y) &= F'(\sin y)\, D \sin y = F'(\sin y) \cos y \\ &= \frac{1}{\sqrt{1 - \sin^2 y}} \cos y = 1 \quad \text{if } -\frac{\pi}{2} < y < \frac{\pi}{2}. \end{aligned}$$

Since $DF(\sin y) = 1$,

$$F(\sin y) = y + C$$

for some constant C. However, $F(\sin 0) = F(0) = 0 = 0 + C$ and $C = 0$. Therefore $F(\sin y) = y$. Letting $y = \sin^{-1} x$, we have $\sin y = x$ and

$$F(x) = \sin^{-1} x.$$

This proves that $\sin^{-1}$ is differentiable in the interval $(-1,1)$.

If the function $\tan^{-1}$ has a derivative, then it may be found from the equation

$$\tan(\tan^{-1} x) = x$$

by implicit differentiation. Thus

$$\begin{aligned} D \tan(\tan^{-1} x) &= Dx, \\ \sec^2(\tan^{-1} x)\, D \tan^{-1} x &= 1, \\ D \tan^{-1} x &= \frac{1}{\sec^2(\tan^{-1} x)}. \end{aligned}$$

Since $\sec^2(\tan^{-1} x) = 1 + \tan^2(\tan^{-1} x) = 1 + x^2$, we have

11.30
$$D \tan^{-1}(x) = \frac{1}{1 + x^2}.$$

The domain of $D \tan^{-1}$ is the set of all real numbers.

The proof that the inverse tangent function has a derivative is omitted, since it is similar to that given above for $\sin^{-1}$.

Inspection of **11.29** and **11.30** shows a remarkable feature of the functions $\sin^{-1}$ and $\tan^{-1}$: their derivatives are *algebraic functions*. Actually, each of the inverse trigonometric functions has this property.

We shall briefly mention one other inverse trigonometric function, namely $\sec^{-1}$, which has domain $(-\infty,-1] \cup [1,\infty)$ and range

$$[0,\pi/2) \cup [\pi,3\pi/2)$$

(see Figure **11.11**). Its derivative is given by

11.31
$$D \sec^{-1}(x) = \frac{1}{x\sqrt{x^2 - 1}}.$$

The domain of $D \sec^{-1}$ is $(-\infty,-1) \cup (1,\infty)$.

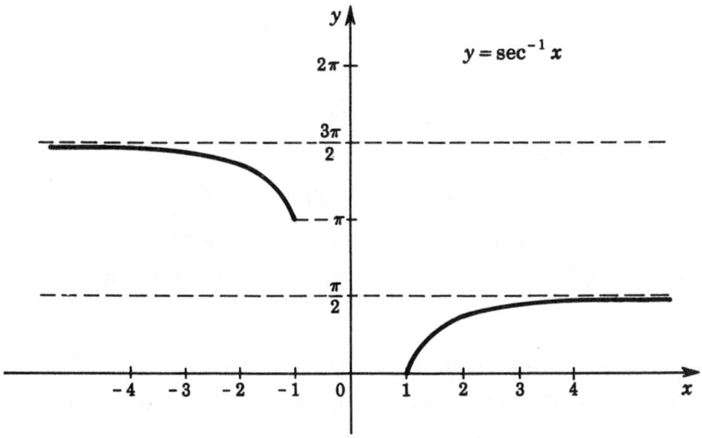

FIGURE 11.11

Since the inverse trigonometric functions have algebraic derivatives, they will themselves be integrals of algebraic functions. It is convenient to state these integrals in the following forms:

11.32
$$\int \frac{1}{\sqrt{a^2 - x^2}}\,dx = \sin^{-1}\frac{x}{a} + C.$$

11.33 $$\int \frac{1}{a^2 + x^2}\,dx = \frac{1}{a}\tan^{-1}\frac{x}{a} + C.$$

11.34 $$\int \frac{1}{x\sqrt{x^2 - a^2}}\,dx = \frac{1}{a}\sec^{-1}\frac{x}{a} + C.$$

Proof of **11.32***:* By **11.29** and the chain rule, we have

$$D\sin^{-1}\frac{x}{a} = \frac{1}{\sqrt{1-(x/a)^2}}\,D\frac{x}{a}$$
$$= \frac{1}{a}\,\frac{1}{\sqrt{1-(x^2/a^2)}} = \frac{1}{\sqrt{a^2 - x^2}}.$$

The proofs of **11.33** and **11.34** are similar and hence are omitted.

EXAMPLE 1. Find $D\tan^{-1} 1/x$.

Solution: By **11.30** and the chain rule,

$$D\tan^{-1}\frac{1}{x} = \frac{1}{1+(1/x)^2}\,D\frac{1}{x} = \frac{1}{1+(1/x^2)}\left(-\frac{1}{x^2}\right)$$
$$= -\frac{1}{1+x^2}.$$

Since $D\tan^{-1} 1/x = -D\tan^{-1} x$, we must have

$$\tan^{-1}\frac{1}{x} = -\tan^{-1} x + C$$

for some constant C. Since $\tan^{-1} 1 = \pi/4$, we see that $C = \pi/2$. Hence

$$\tan^{-1}\frac{1}{x} = -\tan^{-1} x + \frac{\pi}{2} \quad \text{for every } x \neq 0.$$

To approximate values of inverse trigonometric functions, we can use the fact that each inverse trigonometric function is an integral of an algebraic function. Consider the following example.

EXAMPLE 2. Approximate π.

Solution: We know that $\sin^{-1}\frac{1}{2} = \pi/6$ so that

$$\int_0^{1/2} \frac{1}{\sqrt{1-x^2}}\,dx = \sin^{-1}\frac{1}{2} - \sin^{-1} 0 = \frac{\pi}{6}.$$

Also, $\tan^{-1} 1 = \pi/4$ so that

$$\int_0^1 \frac{1}{1+x^2}\,dx = \tan^{-1} 1 - \tan^{-1} 0 = \frac{\pi}{4}.$$

Thus, if we can approximate one of these integrals, say by Simpson's rule, we can approximate π. Clearly, the inverse tangent integral is easier to approximate, since the integrand does not involve square roots.

Let us approximate $\int_0^1 \frac{1}{1+x^2}\,dx$ by Simpson's rule with $n = 4$. Thus we first make the following table of values.

x	0	$\frac{1}{4}$	$\frac{1}{2}$	$\frac{3}{4}$	1
$\frac{1}{1+x^2}$	1	$\frac{16}{17}$	$\frac{4}{5}$	$\frac{16}{25}$	$\frac{1}{2}$

Then, by **9.8**,

$$\int_0^1 \frac{1}{1+x^2}\,dx \doteq \frac{1}{12}\left[1 + 4\left(\frac{16}{17}\right) + 2\left(\frac{4}{5}\right) + 4\left(\frac{16}{25}\right) + \frac{1}{2}\right] \doteq .785392.$$

We know that

$$\int_0^1 \frac{1}{1+x^2}\,dx = \tan^{-1} 1 = \frac{\pi}{4}.$$

Thus we have an approximation of π,

$$4(.785392) = 3.141568,$$

accurate, as we know, to four decimal places.

EXAMPLE 3. Find $\int \frac{x}{\sqrt{4 - x^4}}\,dx.$

Solution: If we make a change of variables

$$u = x^2, \qquad du = 2x\,dx,$$

then

$$\int \frac{x}{\sqrt{4-x^4}}\,dx = \frac{1}{2}\int \frac{1}{\sqrt{4-u^2}}\,du\Big|_{u=x^2}$$
$$= \frac{1}{2}\sin^{-1}\frac{u}{2}\Big|_{u=x^2} + C$$
$$= \frac{1}{2}\sin^{-1}\frac{x^2}{2} + C.$$

EXAMPLE 4. Find $D \sec^{-1}\sqrt{x}$.

Solution: Using **11.31** and the chain rule, we have

$$D \sec^{-1}\sqrt{x} = \frac{1}{\sqrt{x}\sqrt{(\sqrt{x})^2 - 1}}\,D\sqrt{x} = \frac{1}{\sqrt{x}\sqrt{x-1}}\,\frac{1}{2}\,\frac{1}{\sqrt{x}}$$
$$= \frac{1}{2x\sqrt{x-1}}.$$

EXERCISES

I

1. Define the inverse cosine function with the equation $\cos y = x$, $0 \leq y \leq \pi$. Sketch its graph and find its derivative.

2. Define the inverse cotangent function with the equation $\cot y = x$, $0 < y < \pi$. Sketch its graph and find its derivative.

3. Define the inverse secant function with the equation $\sec y = x$, where either $0 \leq y < \pi/2$ or $\pi \leq y < 3\pi/2$. Sketch its graph and verify 11.31.

4. How would you define the function $\csc^{-1}$? Sketch its graph and find its derivative.

In each of Exercises 5–24, differentiate.

5. $\sin^{-1} 2x$.

6. $\tan^{-1} (x + 1)$.

7. $\sec^{-1} 4x$.

8. $\sin^{-1} e^x$.

9. $(1 + \arcsin 3x)^2$.

10. $\arctan \dfrac{1}{x}$.

11. $\dfrac{\arctan e^{2x}}{e^{2x}}$.

12. $2x \arctan x - \ln (1 + x^2)$.

13. $x \sin^{-1} x + \sqrt{1 - x^2}$.

14. $\operatorname{arcsec} \sqrt{x^2 - 1}$.

15. $\tan^{-1} \sqrt{x^2 - 1}$.

16. $\sin^{-1} \sqrt{1 - x^2}$.

17. $\sec^{-1} \sqrt{x}$.

18. $\sqrt{\sin^{-1} 3x}$.

19. $\ln \arctan x$.

20. $\sqrt{1 - x^2} + \arcsin x$.

21. $\arcsin x - x\sqrt{1 - x^2}$.

22. $\tan^{-1} \dfrac{1 + 2x}{2 - x}$.

23. $2x^3 \tan^{-1} x + \ln (1 + x^2) - x^2$.

24. $\sec \dfrac{1}{x}$.

25. Prove that $\tan^{-1} \dfrac{x + 1}{x - 1} + \tan^{-1} x = c$, a constant, and find c. [*Hint:* Differentiate or use Exercise II-7, page 326.]

26. Prove that $\sec^{-1} x = \dfrac{\pi}{2} - \sin^{-1} \dfrac{1}{x}$ for every $x \geq 1$.

Find the following integrals.

27. $\displaystyle\int_0^{\sqrt{3}/2} \frac{1}{\sqrt{1 - x^2}}\, dx$.

28. $\displaystyle\int_0^3 \frac{1}{x^2 + 9}\, dx$.

29. $\int_{\sqrt{3}}^{3\sqrt{3}} \frac{1}{x^2+9}\,dx.$

30. $\int \frac{e^x}{e^{2x}+1}\,dx.$

31. $\int_{2/\sqrt{3}}^{\sqrt{2}} \frac{1}{x\sqrt{x^2-1}}\,dx.$

32. $\int_{-6}^{-3\sqrt{2}} \frac{1}{x\sqrt{x^2-9}}\,dx.$

33. $\int \frac{\cos x}{1+\sin^2 x}\,dx.$

34. $\int \frac{1}{x\sqrt{1-\ln^2 x}}\,dx.$

II

1. Show that if $\ln(x^2+y^2) + 2\tan^{-1}\frac{x}{y} = 0$ then $\frac{dy}{dx} = \frac{x+y}{x-y}$.

2. Show that if $y = \sin(a\tan^{-1}x)$ then

$$(1+x^2)^2\frac{d^2y}{dx^2} + 2x(1+x^2)\frac{dy}{dx} + a^2y = 0.$$

3. Show that if $y = \sin(a\sin^{-1}x)$ then

$$(1-x^2)\frac{d^2y}{dx^2} - x\frac{dy}{dx} + a^2y = 0.$$

In each of Exercises 4–9 find the integral.

4. $\int_0^1 \frac{\tan^{-1}x}{1+x^2}\,dx.$

5. $\int \frac{1}{x\sqrt{x-a^2}}\,dx$ (see Example 4, page 330).

6. $\int \frac{1}{\sqrt{e^{2x}-1}}\,dx.$

7. $\int_0^2 \frac{1}{(x^2+1)(x^2+4)}\,dx.$

8. $\int_0^a \operatorname{sech} x\,dx$ (let $e^x = y$).

9. $\int \frac{x^2}{\sqrt{1-x^6}}\,dx.$

10. Find $\lim_{n\to\infty} \sum_{k=1}^{n} \frac{n}{n^2+k^2}$.

6 THE INVERSE OF A FUNCTION

If f is a 1–1 function, then another function g may be defined from f as follows:

$$g(y) = x \quad \text{if and only if} \quad y = f(x).$$

The domain of g is the range of f, and the range of g is the domain of f. By this definition,

$$f(g(y)) = y \quad \text{and} \quad g(f(x)) = x$$

for every y in domain g and every x in domain f. The function g so defined is called the *inverse function* of f and is usually designated by f^{-1}. Actually, f and g are inverses of each other. Any strictly monotonic function has an inverse.

We now give some examples of inverse functions.

EXAMPLE 1. If $f(x) = \sqrt{x}$ with domain $f = [0, \infty)$, then f is a 1–1 function since it is strictly increasing. Find its inverse.

Solution: Since $y = f(x)$ if and only if $x = f^{-1}(y)$, evidently $y = \sqrt{x}$, $x = y^2$ and

$$f^{-1}(y) = y^2, \qquad \text{domain } f^{-1} = [0, \infty).$$

EXAMPLE 2. The function g defined by

$$g(x) = x^3 + 1$$

is strictly increasing and hence is 1–1. Find its inverse.

Solution: If $y = x^3 + 1$, then $x^3 = y - 1$ and $x = \sqrt[3]{y - 1}$. Hence

$$g^{-1}(y) = \sqrt[3]{y - 1}, \qquad \text{domain } g^{-1} = (-\infty, \infty).$$

EXAMPLE 3. The function cosh is strictly decreasing in the interval $(-\infty, 0]$ and strictly increasing in the interval $[0, \infty)$. Find the inverse of the function defined by

$$y = \cosh x, \qquad x \text{ in } [0, \infty).$$

Solution: We have $2y = e^x + e^{-x}$ and

$$e^{2x} - 2ye^x + 1 = 0.$$

We can solve this equation for e^x by the quadratic formula,

$$e^x = \frac{2y \pm \sqrt{4y^2 - 4}}{2} = y \pm \sqrt{y^2 - 1}.$$

Since $y - \sqrt{y^2 - 1} \leq 1$ whereas $e^x \geq 1$ if x is in $[0, \infty)$, evidently we must have

$$e^x = y + \sqrt{y^2 - 1}$$

$$\text{and} \qquad x = \ln (y + \sqrt{y^2 - 1}).$$

Thus

$$\cosh^{-1} y = \ln (y + \sqrt{y^2 - 1})$$

if we take $[0, \infty)$ as the domain of cosh. The domain of $\cosh^{-1}$ clearly is $[1, \infty)$.

If we had taken $(-\infty, 0]$ as the domain of cosh, then we would have obtained $\cosh^{-1} y = \ln (y - \sqrt{y^2 - 1})$.

Some other examples of inverse functions are: ln is the inverse of exp; $\sin^{-1}$ is the inverse of sine if the domain of sine is limited to $[-\pi/2, \pi/2]$.

If f is a strictly increasing function, then so is f^{-1}; similarly, f^{-1} is strictly decreasing if f is. For if f is strictly increasing and x_1 and x_2 are in domain f^{-1} with $x_1 < x_2$, then $f(f^{-1}(x_1)) < f(f^{-1}(x_2))$ so that

$$f^{-1}(x_1) < f^{-1}(x_2).$$

If a continuous function f is strictly monotonic in a closed interval $[a,b]$, then for every number y between $f(a)$ and $f(b)$ there exists a number x in $[a,b]$, such that $y = f(x)$ by the intermediate-value theorem (7.3). Hence f maps the closed interval $[a,b]$ into either the closed interval $[f(a),f(b)]$ or $[f(b),f(a)]$, depending on whether f is increasing or decreasing. For any function f which has an inverse f^{-1}, necessarily f is strictly monotonic in any interval in which it is continuous (6.7).

11.35 **THEOREM.** Let f be a 1–1 function. If f is continuous in a closed interval $[a,b]$, then f^{-1} is continuous in the corresponding closed interval $[f(a),f(b)]$ or $[f(b),f(a)]$.

Proof: Let us assume f is strictly increasing in $[a,b]$, so that f^{-1} is strictly increasing in $[f(a),f(b)]$, and that c is in $[a,b]$. If c is in the open interval (a,b), then $f(c)$ is in the open interval $(f(a),f(b))$. We shall have proved that f^{-1} is continuous at $f(c)$ when we have shown that for every neighborhood N of $f^{-1}(f(c)) = c$, there exists a neighborhood D of $f(c)$ such that $f^{-1}(y)$ is in N for every y in D. This is easily accomplished by letting $D = \{f(x) \mid x \text{ in } N \cap [a,b]\}$. If $c = a$ or $c = b$, then we can similarly show that f^{-1} is continuous at $f(c)$ by using one-sided limits. Clearly an analogous argument holds if f is decreasing in $[a,b]$.

If a strictly monotonic function is differentiable, then so is its inverse according to the following result.

11.36 **THEOREM.** If f and g are inverse functions and if f is differentiable, then g is differentiable at each x for which $f'(g(x)) \neq 0$ and $g'(x)$ is given by

$$g'(x) = \frac{1}{f'(g(x))} \quad \text{if } f'(g(x)) \neq 0.$$

Proof: Let c be chosen in the domain of g so that $f'(g(c))$ exists and is nonzero. By definition,

$$g'(c) = \operatorname*{limit}_{x \to c} \frac{g(x) - g(c)}{x - c}.$$

We introduce the new function F, defined as follows:

$$F(y) = \frac{y - g(c)}{f(y) - f(g(c))}, \qquad \text{if } y \neq g(c),$$

$$F(g(c)) = \frac{1}{f'(g(c))}.$$

The domain of F is the same as that of f. Since

$$\lim_{y \to g(c)} \frac{f(y) - f(g(c))}{y - g(c)} = f'(g(c)),$$

evidently

$$\lim_{y \to g(c)} F(y) = \frac{1}{f'(g(c))}.$$

Thus the function F is continuous at $g(c)$.

We may now use **4.26** to draw the desired conclusion. Thus g is continuous at c by **11.35** and

$$\lim_{x \to c} F(g(x)) = F(g(c)) = \frac{1}{f'(g(c))}$$

according to **4.26**, whereas

$$F(g(x)) = \frac{g(x) - g(c)}{x - c}$$

by the definition of the function F. Hence

$$\lim_{x \to c} \frac{g(x) - g(c)}{x - c} = \frac{1}{f'(g(c))},$$

and the theorem is proved.

EXAMPLE 4. Find the derivative of the function $\cosh^{-1}$, assuming cosh has domain $[0, \infty)$.

Solution: Since cosh is differentiable, so is $\cosh^{-1}$ by **11.36**. If we let $y = \cosh^{-1} x$, so that $x = \cosh y$, then by **11.36** and **10.28**,

$$D \cosh^{-1} x = \frac{1}{D \cosh y} = \frac{1}{\sinh y}.$$

By **10.25**, $\sinh y = \sqrt{\cosh^2 y - 1} = \sqrt{x^2 - 1}$ if $y \geq 0$. Therefore

$$D \cosh^{-1} x = \frac{1}{\sqrt{x^2 - 1}}.$$

EXERCISES

I

In each of Exercises 1–10 find the inverse of the function and give its domain.

1. $f(x) = \sqrt[3]{x}$.
2. $g(x) = x^2$, $(x \leq 0)$.
3. $F(x) = \tan x, \left(-\frac{\pi}{2} < x < \frac{\pi}{2}\right)$.
4. $f(x) = \log_a x$, $(x > 0)$.
5. $f(x) = x + 2$.
6. $F(x) = 3 - x$.
7. $g(x) = 2x$.
8. $f(x) = 2 - 3x$.
9. $F(x) = a^x$.
10. $g(x) = e^{3x}$.
11. Show that the hyperbolic sine is an increasing function, and hence that it has an inverse function $\sinh^{-1}$. Thus $y = \sinh^{-1} x$ if and only if $x = \sinh y$. Find the domain of $\sinh^{-1}$, and prove that $\sinh^{-1} x = \ln (x + \sqrt{x^2 + 1})$. [*Hint:* Solve $x = \sinh y = (e^y - e^{-y})/2$ for y.]
12. Show that the hyperbolic tangent is an increasing function, and hence that it has an inverse function $\tanh^{-1}$. Find the domain of $\tanh^{-1}$, and prove that

$$\tanh^{-1} x = \frac{1}{2} \ln \left(\frac{1 + x}{1 - x}\right), \qquad (|x| < 1).$$

13. Show that the hyperbolic cosine is a decreasing function if $x < 0$ and an increasing function if $x > 0$. If $f(x) = \cosh x$, $(x \geq 0)$, prove that $f^{-1}(x) = \ln (x + \sqrt{x^2 - 1})$, $(x \geq 1)$; if $f(x) = \cosh x$, $(x \leq 0)$, prove that $f^{-1}(x) = -\ln (x + \sqrt{x^2 - 1})$, $(x \geq 1)$.
14. For the function $\sinh^{-1}$ defined in Exercise 11, show that $D \sinh^{-1} x = 1/\sqrt{x^2 + 1}$.
15. For the function $\tanh^{-1}$ defined in Exercise 12, show that $D \tanh^{-1} x = 1/(1 - x^2)$.

II

1. If $\int F(x)\, dx = G(x)$, show that $\int F^{-1}(x)\, dx = xF^{-1}(x) - G(F^{-1}(x))$, assuming that all the functions appearing are well defined.

Using Exercise 1, evaluate the following integrals.

2. $\int \sin^{-1} x\, dx$.
3. $\int \tan^{-1} 3x\, dx$.
4. $\int \cosh^{-1} ax\, dx$.
5. $\int \ln x\, dx$.
6. $\int \ln (x + \sqrt{x^2 + a^2})\, dx$ (see Exercise I–11).

REVIEW

Oral Exercises

Explain or define each of the following.

1. Radian measure of an angle.
2. The relationship between radian measure and degree measure.
3. The trigonometric functions.
4. The derivatives of the trigonometric functions.
5. The inverse trigonometric functions.
6. The derivatives of the inverse trigonometric functions.
7. The inverse of a strictly monotonic function.
8. The derivative of the inverse of a strictly monotonic function.

I

In each of Exercises 1–8 find dy/dx.

1. $y = \ln |\sin x|$.
2. $y = \sin \ln |x|$.
3. $y = \tan \ln x^2$.
4. $y = (\sin x^2)^{\exp x^2}$.
5. $y = \arcsin (m \sin x)$.
6. $y = \arcsin \sqrt{\sin x}$.
7. $y = x - \sqrt{1 - x^2} \arcsin x$.
8. $y = \frac{2}{3} \arctan x + \frac{1}{3} \arctan \frac{x}{1 - x^2}$.

In each of Exercises 9–14 find the limit.

9. $\lim_{x \to 0} x \sin \frac{1}{x}$.
10. $\lim_{y \to 0} \frac{\arcsin ky}{y}$.
11. $\lim_{x \to 0} \frac{\sin x^2}{x}$.
12. $\lim_{y \to 0} \frac{\sin ay}{\sin by}$.
13. $\lim_{t \to 0} \left[\frac{1 - \cos 2t}{t^2}\right]^2$.
14. $\lim_{n \to \infty} 2n \sin \frac{\pi}{n}$. (Also, interpret this in terms of regular polygons inscribed in a unit circle.)
15. Find the period of each of the following periodic functions:

   a. $f(x) = \sin 3x$.

   b. $g(x) = \sin \frac{x}{3}$.

c. $F(x) = \sin 2x + 2\cos 4x$.

d. $G(x) = 2\sin\frac{x}{3} - \cos\frac{x}{5}$.

e. $h(x) = \sin\frac{x}{3} - \cos\frac{x}{6} + \tan\frac{x}{9}$.

f. $H(t) = A\sin\omega t + B\cos\omega t$ (A, B, ω are constants).

16. Find the extrema of the function f defined by $f(x) = \sin x + \frac{1}{2}\sin 2x$ and sketch the graph of the function.

17. Determine the maximum, minimum, and inflection points of the graph of the equation $y = x + \sin x$. Sketch the graph.

In each of Exercises 18–23 evaluate the integral.

18. $\int \frac{\sin\sqrt{2x}}{\sqrt{x}}\,dx$.

19. $\int \frac{1}{x\sqrt{x^4 - 1}}\,dx$.

20. $\int \tan 2x\,dx$.

21. $\int \tan^2\frac{x}{3}\,dx$.

22. $\int \frac{1 - \cos z}{\sin z}\,dz$.

23. $\int \frac{x^2}{9x^2 + 1}\,dx$.

24. Find the length of the curve

$$y = \sqrt{x - x^2} + \arcsin\sqrt{x}.$$

25. Find the length of the curve

$$y = \arcsin x \pm \sqrt{1 - x^2}.$$

26. The region bounded by the curve $y = \sec x$, the x axis and $x = \pm\frac{\pi}{4}$ is rotated around the x axis. Find the volume of the solid generated.

27. The region bounded by the x axis and one arc of the curve $y = \sin ax$ is rotated around the x axis. Find the volume of the solid-generated. [*Hint:* See Exercise II-2, page 321.]

II

1. Show directly from the definitions of the sine and cosine that:

a. $\sin x = -\sin(-x)$.

b. $\cos x = \cos(-x)$.

c. $\cos x = \sin\left(\frac{\pi}{2} \pm x\right)$.

d. $\sin(\pi - x) = \sin x$.

e. $\sin(\pi + x) = -\sin x$.

f. $\cos(\pi \pm x) = -\cos x$.

2. Show how to obtain the derivative of the cosine directly from that of the sine.

3. Knowing that $D \sin = \cos$ and $D \cos = -\sin$, we can derive the basic addition formula $\sin(x + y) = \sin x \cos y + \cos x \sin y$ as follows: For each number y we can define the function S by $S(x) = \sin(x + y)$. Verify that S is a solution of the differential equation $S'' + S = 0$. It may be shown that every solution of this differential equation has the form $A \sin + B \cos$ for some constants A and B. It follows that $\sin(x + y) = A(y) \sin x + B(y) \cos x$. Now derive the addition formula by giving special values to x.

4. Obtain the addition formula for $\cos(x + y)$ from that of $\sin(x + y)$.

5. Find all zeros of the equation $\sin^m x + \cos^m x = 1$, where m is a positive integer and $0 \leq x \leq 2\pi$.

6. Since $\sin x < x$ for $x > 0$ (give a geometric interpretation of this fact), it follows that

$$\int_0^x \sin t\, dt \leq \int_0^x t\, dt \qquad \text{or} \qquad 1 - \frac{x^2}{2!} \leq \cos x \leq 1.$$

In a similar fashion show that $x - (x^3/3!) \leq \sin x \leq x$.

7. Show that $D^n \sin ax = a^n \sin(ax + n\pi/2)$.

8. Find the derivative of the function g defined by $g(x) = \dfrac{x^2}{2} \sin \dfrac{1}{x^2}$ if $x \neq 0$, $g(0) = 0$, domain $[-1,1]$. In particular, does $g'(0)$ exist?

9. Give examples, if possible, of periodic functions f and g with periods m and n, respectively, $(m < n)$, such that the functions $f + g$ and fg are periodic with periods s and t, respectively, and (a) $s < m$; (b) $s > n$; (c) $t < m$; (d) $t > n$.

10. Same as Exercise 9, except that $m = n$.

11. If F and G are two periodic functions with integral periods m and n, respectively, can the period of the composite function $F \circ G$ be smaller than either m or n?

12. a. Evaluate the integral $\int e^{ax} \sin bx\, dx$ by first assuming the answer has the form

$$e^{ax}(A \sin bx + B \cos bx) + C$$

and then finding the constants A and B.

b. Evaluate $\int e^{ax} \cos bx\, dx$.

13. A particle travels around a circle with uniform speed. Prove that the projection of the particle on any diameter moves in simple harmonic motion (see Exercise II-12, page 322).

14. The differential equation for the motion of a simple pendulum *in vacuo* is

$$\frac{d^2x}{dt^2} + \frac{g}{L} \sin x = 0,$$

where L is the length of the pendulum and g is the gravitational constant 32.2 ft/sec^2. If the pendulum starts at rest from an initial angle $x = x_0$, solve the equation for small vibrations; i.e., make the approximation $\sin x \doteq x$ (see Exercise II-6, page 339 and Exercises II-12, 13, page 322). What is the period of this motion? Is this answer larger or smaller than the period obtained without making the approximation $\sin x \doteq x$? [*Hint:* Use a physical argument.]

15. Consider a particle of mass m lb which is dropped in a straight tunnel bored through the center of the earth (assumed spherical with a radius of $R = 3960$ miles). Since the gravitational attraction between two external homogeneous spheres is proportional to their masses and inversely proportional to the square of the distance between their centers, it can be shown that the gravitational force being exerted on the particle at point P in the tunnel depends only on the attraction of a sphere concentric to the earth passing through P. Now show that the force F of attraction at P is given by $F(P) = -mgr/R$. Next show that, neglecting air resistance, the particle moves in simple harmonic motion (see Exercise II-12, page 322), and that the time T it takes the particle to drop to the other side of the earth is given by

$$T = \pi\sqrt{\frac{R}{g}} \doteq 42.2 \text{ min.}$$

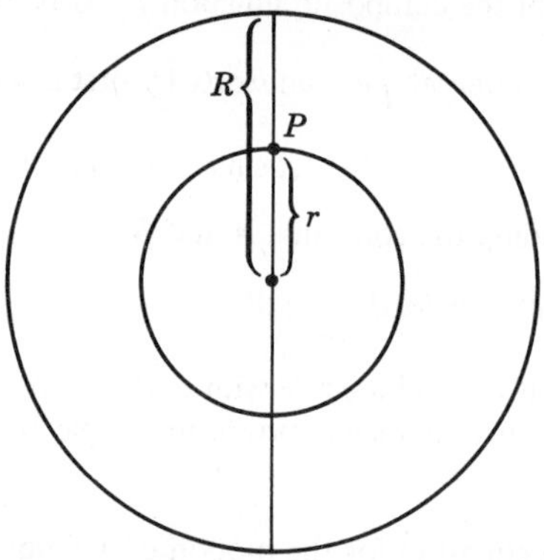

16. A function F is defined to be algebraic if it satisfies a polynomial equation of the form

$$P_0(x)F^n + P_1(x)F^{n-1} + \cdots + P_{n-1}(x)F + P_n(x) = 0, \quad (P_0(x) \neq 0),$$

where the $P_i(x)$ $(i = 0,1,\ldots,n)$ are polynomials in x. A function which is not algebraic is defined to be *transcendental*. $\sqrt{x}$ and $\sqrt[3]{x+1}$ are algebraic since they satisfy $F^2 - x = 0$ and $F^3 - x - 1 = 0$ respectively.

Prove that e^x is a transcendental function by using an indirect proof—i.e., assume that e^x is algebraic and thus satisfies some equation of the form

$$P_0(x)e^{nx} + P_1(x)e^{(n-1)x} + \cdots + P_{n-1}(x)e^x + P_n(x) = 0,$$

and obtain a contradiction by using the fact that $\lim_{x\to\infty} e^{-x}x^n = 0$ for every integer n.

17. Prove that the inverse of an algebraic function is algebraic. Then use Exercise 16 to show that the function ln is transcendental.

18. Show that the six trigonometric functions and their inverses are transcendental functions. [*Hint:* Show that no periodic function other than a constant can be algebraic. Use the fact that a nonzero polynomial function of one variable has only a finite number of zeros.]

12

FORMAL INTEGRATION

IN THIS CHAPTER we shall develop methods for finding integrals of some common types of algebraic and transcendental functions.

1 ELEMENTARY INTEGRATION FORMULAS

Several integration formulas were derived in the last five chapters. For example,

$$\int \frac{1}{x}\,dx = \ln|x| + C, \qquad \int \sin x\,dx = -\cos x + C.$$

These and all the others studied so far are tabulated as the first 15 formulas in the Table of Integrals (page 000).

We are faced with two problems in this chapter. The first is that of extending our basic list of 15 formulas. Although any given (exact) integration formula may be verified by differentiation, we also wish to indicate how the formula might be developed in the first place.

The second problem is that of the use of the formulas. For example, the integral

$$\int \frac{e^x}{e^x + 1}\,dx$$

will not be found in the Table of Integrals. Nevertheless, this integral may easily be evaluated from the table.

The familiar change of variable formula (No. 3 in the table) is one of the important tools available to us:

$$\int f(g(x))g'(x)\,dx = \int f(u)\,du\bigg|_{u=g(x)}$$

It may be used to evaluate the integral above if we let

$$u = e^x + 1, \qquad du = e^x\,dx.$$

Then, using No. 5 of the table, we have

$$\int \frac{e^x}{e^x+1}\,dx = \int \frac{1}{u}\,du\bigg|_{u=e^x+1} = \ln|u| + C\bigg|_{u=e^x+1}$$
$$= \ln(e^x+1) + C.$$

Another example of the use of the change of variable formula is given below.

EXAMPLE 1. Find $\int x\sqrt{ax+b}\,dx$, $(a \neq 0)$.

Solution: If we let

$$u = ax + b, \qquad du = a\,dx,$$

then $x = (u - b)/a$ and

$$\int x\sqrt{ax+b}\,dx = \frac{1}{a^2}\int (u-b)\sqrt{u}\,du\bigg|_{u=ax+b}$$
$$= \frac{1}{a^2}\int (u^{3/2} - bu^{1/2})\,du\bigg|_{u=ax+b}$$
$$= \frac{1}{a^2}\left(\frac{2}{5}u^{5/2} - \frac{2b}{3}u^{3/2}\right) + C\bigg|_{u=ax+b}$$
$$= \frac{1}{a^2}\left[\frac{2}{5}(ax+b)^{5/2} - \frac{2b}{3}(ax+b)^{3/2}\right] + C.$$

Using the same technique, we could evaluate such integrals as

$$\int x^2\sqrt{ax+b}\,dx, \qquad \int x(ax+b)^{3/2}\,dx,$$

and so on.

The trigonometric identity

$$\sin\theta\cos\varphi = \tfrac{1}{2}[\sin(\theta+\varphi) + \sin(\theta-\varphi)]$$

and similar ones given in the appendix, Facts and Formulas from Trigonometry (page 000), may be used to evaluate integrals of the type given in the following example.

EXAMPLE 2. Find $\int \sin 7x \cos 3x \, dx$.

Solution: Using the identity above, we have

$$\begin{aligned}\int \sin 7x \cos 3x \, dx &= \frac{1}{2}\left(\int \sin 10x \, dx + \int \sin 4x \, dx\right)\\ &= \frac{1}{2}\left(\frac{1}{10}\int \sin u \, du \Big|_{u=10x} + \frac{1}{4}\int \sin v \, dv \Big|_{v=4x}\right)\\ &= -\frac{1}{20}\cos 10x - \frac{1}{8}\cos 4x + C.\end{aligned}$$

The quadratic polynomial $x^2 + ax + b$ can be expressed as the sum or difference of two squares by the usual process of the completion of squares. This is useful in evaluating certain integrals, as illustrated in the next examples.

EXAMPLE 3. Find $\int \frac{1}{x^2 + 4x + 5} dx$.

Solution: Since

$$x^2 + 4x + 5 = (x + 2)^2 + 1,$$

we have

$$\begin{aligned}\int \frac{1}{x^2 + 4x + 5} dx &= \int \frac{1}{(x + 2)^2 + 1} dx\\ &= \int \frac{1}{u^2 + 1} du \Big|_{u=x+2}\\ &= \tan^{-1} u + C \Big|_{u=x+2} = \tan^{-1}(x + 2) + C.\end{aligned}$$

EXAMPLE 4. Find $\int \frac{x}{\sqrt{7 + 2x - x^2}} dx$.

Solution: Since

$$7 + 2x - x^2 = -(x^2 - 2x + 1) + 8 = 8 - (x - 1)^2,$$

we have

$$\begin{aligned}\int \frac{x}{\sqrt{7 + 2x - x^2}} dx &= \int \frac{x}{\sqrt{8 - (x - 1)^2}} dx\\ &= \int \frac{u + 1}{\sqrt{8 - u^2}} du \Big|_{u=x-1}\\ &= \left\{\int u(8 - u^2)^{-1/2} du + \int \frac{1}{\sqrt{(\sqrt{8})^2 - u^2}} du\right\} \Big|_{u=x-1}\end{aligned}$$

$$= -\sqrt{8-u^2} + \sin^{-1}\frac{u}{\sqrt{8}} + C\Big|_{u=x-1}$$

$$= -\sqrt{7+2x-x^2} + \sin^{-1}\frac{x-1}{\sqrt{8}} + C.$$

Formula No. 64 of the Table of Integrals may be developed as in the following example.

EXAMPLE 5. Find $\int \sec x \, dx$.

Solution: We can change variables by letting

$$u = \sec x + \tan x,$$

in which case

$$\begin{aligned} du &= (\sec x \tan x + \sec^2 x)\, dx \\ &= \sec x(\sec x + \tan x)\, dx \\ &= u \sec x \, dx. \end{aligned}$$

Hence $(1/u)\, du = \sec x \, dx$ and

$$\begin{aligned} \int \sec x \, dx &= \int \frac{1}{u}\, du \Big|_{u=\sec x + \tan x} \\ &= \ln|\sec x + \tan x| + C. \end{aligned}$$

EXERCISES

I

In each of Exercises 1–22 find the integral.

1. $\int x(x-2)^{3/2}\, dx.$

2. $\int x^2\sqrt{ax+b}\, dx.$

3. $\int \sin^3 x \, dx$ [*Hint:* let $\sin^2 x = 1 - \cos^2 x$].

4. $\int \tan^3 x \, dx$ [*Hint:* let $\tan^2 x = \sec^2 x - 1$].

5. $\int \sin\frac{x}{2}\cos\frac{3x}{2}\, dx.$

6. $\int \cos(x-1)\cos(x+1)\, dx.$

7. $\int \frac{x^2}{x+2}\, dx.$

8. $\int \csc x \, dx.$

9. $\int \sqrt{x}(2x+1)^2\,dx.$

10. $\int \cos^3 x\,dx.$

11. $\int \frac{1}{x^2-4x+13}\,dx.$

12. $\int \frac{x-2}{\sqrt{x^2-4x+13}}\,dx.$

13. $\int \frac{1}{\sqrt{2x-x^2}}\,dx.$

14. $\int \frac{x}{3x^2-2x+1}\,dx.$

15. $\int \frac{x}{3x^4-2x^2+1}\,dx.$

16. $\int x\sqrt[3]{2x+1}\,dx.$

17. $\int \frac{\sin^3 x}{\cos x}\,dx.$

18. $\int \sec^2 x\sqrt{\tan x}\,dx.$

19. $\int \frac{\tan^3 x}{\sec x}\,dx.$

20. $\int \sin^3 x\cos^2 x\,dx.$

21. $\int \frac{1}{e^x+1}\,dx$ [*Hint:* $e^x+1=e^x(1+e^{-x})$].

22. $\int \frac{e^{2x}-1}{e^{2x}+1}\,dx$ [*Hint:* $e^{2x}-1=e^x(e^x-e^{-x})$, etc.].

23. According to a trigonometric identity, $\sin 2x = 2\sin x\cos x$. However,

$$\int \sin 2x\,dx = -\frac{1}{2}\cos 2x + C_1,$$

whereas

$$\int 2\sin x\cos x\,dx = \sin^2 x + C_2.$$

Explain the difference in answers.

24. We may evaluate the integral of $\sec^2 x\tan x$ in two ways, namely

$$\int \sec^2 x\tan x\,dx = \int u\,du\,\bigg|_{u=\tan x} = \frac{1}{2}\tan^2 x + C_1,$$

$$\int \sec^2 x\tan x\,dx = \int u\,du\,\bigg|_{u=\sec x} = \frac{1}{2}\sec^2 x + C_2.$$

Explain the difference in answers.

25. Verify that, for any positive integer n, $\int_0^{\pi} \sin^2 nx\,dx = \frac{\pi}{2}$.

[*Hint:* $\sin^2\theta = (1-\cos 2\theta)/2$.]

26. Verify that, for any positive integer n,

$$\int_0^{\pi/n} \sin nx\cos nx\,dx = 0.$$

II

In each of Exercises 1–9 find the integral.

1. $\int \sin^5 \theta \, d\theta$.

2. $\int \sin^{2n+1} \theta \, d\theta$ (n a positive integer), (see Exercise I-3).

3. $\int \sin (ax + b) \sin (cx + d) \, dx$.

4. $\int \sin ax \sin bx \cos cx \, dx$.

5. $\int \cos x \sqrt{1 - \cos x} \, dx$.

6. $\int \sin^2 y \cos^2 y \, dy$.

7. $\int \frac{1}{x^2 + 2px + q} \, dx$. (Consider the three cases $q - p^2 > 0, = 0, < 0$).

8. $\int \frac{ax + b}{\sqrt{x^2 + 2px + q}} \, dx$. (Consider the same cases as in Exercise 7).

9. In Exercises 7 and 8, state what integrals are obtained by making the change of variable $x = 1/y$.

2 INTEGRATION BY PARTS

We have not as yet given the integral analogue of the product differentiation formula:

$$D f(x)g(x) = f(x)g'(x) + g(x)f'(x).$$

This is easily done by integrating each side of the equation above, yielding

$$f(x)g(x) = \int f(x)g'(x) \, dx + \int g(x)f'(x) \, dx,$$

or

12.1 $$\int f(x)g'(x) \, dx = f(x)g(x) - \int g(x)f'(x) \, dx.$$

This formula (No. 16 of the Table of Integrals), called the formula for *integration by parts*, holds for all smooth functions f and g. For definite integrals 12.1 has the form

$$\int_a^b f(x)g'(x) \, dx = f(x)g(x) \Big|_a^b - \int_a^b g(x)f'(x) \, dx.$$

If we let

$$u = f(x), \qquad v = g(x),$$

and

$$du = f'(x) \, dx, \qquad dv = g'(x) \, dx,$$

then 12.1 can be written in the condensed form

12.2 $$\int u\,dv = uv - \int v\,du.$$

The formula for integration by parts allows us to change certain integrals into forms that can be evaluated by previously developed methods. The use of this formula is illustrated by the following examples.

EXAMPLE 1. Find $\int \ln x\,dx$.

Solution: According to 12.1, we must express the integrand $\ln x$ in the form

$$\ln x = f(x)g'(x)$$

for some functions f and g. The simplest way of doing this is to let

$$f(x) = \ln x \qquad \text{and} \qquad g'(x) = 1,$$

so that

$$f'(x) = \frac{1}{x} \qquad \text{and} \qquad g(x) = x.$$

It would not be sensible to let $f(x) = 1$ and $g'(x) = \ln x$, since the problem of finding g is the problem of finding an antiderivative of the logarithmic function, which is equivalent to that of evaluating the given integral.

Furthermore, we note that the logarithm has an algebraic derivative and hence the choice $f(x) = \ln x$ effects a simplification. (Other transcendental functions with algebraic derivatives are the inverse trigonometric functions.)

In the u, v notation, we let

$$u = \ln x, \qquad dv = dx,$$

so that

$$du = \frac{1}{x}\,dx, \qquad v = x.$$

Hence, by 12.12,

$$\int \ln x\,dx = x\ln x - \int x\frac{1}{x}\,dx = x\ln x - x + C.$$

This is essentially No. 72 of the Table of Integrals.

EXAMPLE 2. Find $\int_0^{\pi} x\sin x\,dx$.

Solution: These are two obvious choices for u and v, namely

(1) $$u = x, \qquad dv = \sin x\,dx,$$

(2) $$u = \sin x, \qquad dv = x\,dx.$$

In case (1) we have

$$(3) \qquad du = dx, \qquad v = -\cos x;$$

in case (2),

$$(4) \qquad du = \cos x\, dx, \qquad v = \frac{x^2}{2}.$$

Integrating by parts in case (1), we have

$$\begin{aligned} \int_0^\pi x \sin x\, dx &= -x \cos x \Big|_0^\pi - \int_0^\pi (-\cos x)\, dx \\ &= -\pi \cos \pi + 0 \cos 0 + \sin \pi - \sin 0 \\ &= \pi. \end{aligned}$$

Integrating by parts in case (2), we get

$$\int_0^\pi x \sin x\, dx = \frac{x^2}{2} \sin x \Big|_0^\pi - \frac{1}{2} \int_0^\pi x^2 \cos x\, dx.$$

This latter integral certainly is no easier to evaluate than the given one. Clearly case (1) is the better choice of u and v. Note that we have essentially established No. 48 of the Table of Integrals.

EXAMPLE 3. Find $\displaystyle\int \frac{x^3}{\sqrt{1 + x^2}}\, dx.$

Solution: If we let

$$u = x^3, \qquad dv = \frac{1}{\sqrt{1 + x^2}}\, dx,$$

then the new integral $\int v\, du$ is no easier to evaluate than the given one. However, if we let

$$u = x^2, \qquad dv = \frac{x}{\sqrt{1 + x^2}}\, dx = x(1 + x^2)^{-1/2}\, dx,$$

then

$$du = 2x\, dx, \qquad v = \int x(1 + x^2)^{-1/2}\, dx = \sqrt{1 + x^2},$$

and

$$\begin{aligned} \int \frac{x^3}{\sqrt{1 + x^2}}\, dx &= x^2\sqrt{1 + x^2} - \int 2x\sqrt{1 + x^2}\, dx \\ &= x^2\sqrt{1 + x^2} - \frac{2}{3}(1 + x^2)^{3/2} + C = \frac{x^2 - 2}{3}\sqrt{1 + x^2} + C. \end{aligned}$$

EXAMPLE 4. Find $\int e^x \cos x\, dx$.

Solution: If we let

$$u = e^x, \qquad dv = \cos x\, dx,$$

then

$$du = e^x\, dx, \qquad v = \sin x,$$

and

(1) $$\int e^x \cos x\, dx = e^x \sin x - \int e^x \sin x\, dx.$$

Clearly, the new integral is of the same type as the given one, and cannot be evaluated by known methods.

If we try to integrate by parts

$$\int e^x \sin x\, dx$$

by letting

$$u = e^x, \qquad dv = \sin x\, dx,$$

then

$$du = e^x\, dx, \qquad v = -\cos x,$$

and we get

(2) $$\int e^x \sin x\, dx = -e^x \cos x + \int e^x \cos x\, dx.$$

Substituting (2) in (1), we have

$$\begin{aligned}\int e^x \cos x\, dx &= e^x \sin x - \left(-e^x \cos x + \int e^x \cos x\, dx\right)\\ &= e^x \sin x + e^x \cos x - \int e^x \cos x\, dx.\end{aligned}$$

Transposing the latter integral to the other side of the equation, we get

$$2\int e^x \cos x\, dx = e^x \sin x + e^x \cos x,$$

and thus

$$\int e^x \cos x\, dx = \frac{e^x}{2}(\sin x + \cos x) + C.$$

This is a special case of No. 71 of the Table of Integrals.

EXAMPLE 5. Prove that if the integer $n > 1$,

12.3 $$\int \sec^n x\, dx = \frac{1}{n-1}\left[\sec^{n-2} x \tan x + (n-2)\int \sec^{n-2} x\, dx\right].$$

Solution: The easy power of the secant to integrate is $\sec^2 x$; thus let

$$u = \sec^{n-2} x, \qquad dv = \sec^2 x\, dx,$$

so that

$$du = (n-2)\sec^{n-3} x \sec x \tan x\, dx = (n-2)\sec^{n-2} x \tan x\, dx, \qquad v = \tan x.$$

Hence

$$(1) \qquad \int \sec^n x\, dx = \sec^{n-2} x \tan x - (n-2)\int \sec^{n-2} x \tan^2 x\, dx.$$

In order to put this equation into the desired form, let us replace $\tan^2 x$ by $\sec^2 x - 1$ in the new integral to yield

$$-(n-2)\int \sec^{n-2} x \tan^2 x\, dx = -(n-2)\int \sec^n x\, dx + (n-2)\int \sec^{n-2} x\, dx.$$

On substituting this in (1) and collecting the integrals involving $\sec^n x$, we get

$$(n-1)\int \sec^n x\, dx = \sec^{n-2} x \tan x + (n-2)\int \sec^{n-2} x\, dx.$$

This easily reduces to **12.3**.

Formula **12.3** (No. 65 of the Table of Integrals) is known as a *reduction formula* for the reason that the integral of a power of the secant has been expressed in terms of an integral of a reduced power of the secant. Many other reduction formulas are to be found in the table.

With the aid of **12.3**, perhaps using it several times, we can integrate any positive integral power of the secant. For example, letting $n = 3$, we get

$$\int \sec^3 x\, dx = \frac{1}{2}\left(\sec x \tan x + \int \sec x\, dx\right)$$

$$= \frac{1}{2}(\sec x \tan x + \ln|\sec x + \tan x|) + C;$$

letting $n = 4$, we get

$$\int \sec^4 x\, dx = \frac{1}{3}\left(\sec^2 x \tan x + 2\int \sec^2 x\, dx\right)$$

$$= \frac{1}{3}(\sec^2 x \tan x + 2\tan x) + C;$$

and so on.

EXAMPLE 6. Find a reduction formula for $\int \sin^m x \cos^n x\, dx$, $(m + n \neq 0)$.

Solution: If we let

$$u = \sin^{m-1} x \cos^n x, \qquad dv = \sin x\, dx,$$

then

$$du = [(m-1)\sin^{m-2} x \cos^{n+1} x - n \sin^m x \cos^{n-1} x]\, dx, \qquad v = -\cos x,$$

and

$$\int \sin^m x \cos^n x\, dx = -\sin^{m-1} x \cos^{n+1} x + (m-1)\int \sin^{m-2} x \cos^{n+2} x\, dx - n\int \sin^m x \cos^n x\, dx.$$

If in the next to the last integral we replace $\cos^2 x$ by $1 - \sin^2 x$, then this integral becomes

$$(m-1)\int \sin^{m-2} x \cos^n x\,(1-\sin^2 x)\, dx = (m-1)\int \sin^{m-2} x \cos^n x\, dx - (m-1)\int \sin^m x \cos^n x\, dx.$$

Substituting this in the preceding equation, we get

$$\int \sin^m x \cos^n x\, dx = -\sin^{m-1} x \cos^{n+1} x + (m-1)\int \sin^{m-2} x \cos^n x\, dx - (m-1)\int \sin^m x \cos^n x\, dx - n\int \sin^m x \cos^n x\, dx.$$

Transposing the integrals of $\sin^m x \cos^n x$ to the left side and simplifying, we finally get

$$\int \sin^m x \cos^n x\, dx = \frac{1}{m+n}\left[-\sin^{m-1} x \cos^{n+1} x + (m-1)\int \sin^{m-2} x \cos^n x\, dx\right].$$

This is part of No. 52 of the Table of Integrals. It is clear why we must assume $m + n \neq 0$.

Let us use this reduction formula to find the following integral:

$$\int \sin^3 x \cos^2 x\, dx = \frac{1}{5}\left[-\sin^2 x \cos^3 x + 2\int \sin x \cos^2 x\, dx\right]$$
$$= \frac{1}{5}\left[-\sin^2 x \cos^3 x - \frac{2}{3}\cos^3 x\right] + C.$$

EXERCISES

I

In each of Exercises 1–22, find the integral.

1. $\int x \ln x\, dx.$

2. $\int x^2 \ln x\, dx.$

3. $\int_1^2 \sqrt{x} \ln x\, dx.$

4. $\int_0^1 \tan^{-1} x\, dx.$

5. $\int x \tan^{-1} x \, dx.$

6. $\int x^2 \sin x \, dx.$

7. $\int x \cos x \, dx.$

8. $\int_{-1}^{1} xe^x \, dx.$

9. $\int_{-1}^{0} \sin^{-1} x \, dx.$

10. $\int \sec^5 x \, dx.$

11. $\int x^2 e^x \, dx.$

12. $\int_0^{\sqrt{3}/2} \frac{x^3}{\sqrt{1 - x^2}} \, dx.$

13. $\int \frac{x}{\sqrt{2x + 1}} \, dx.$

14. $\int \frac{x \ln x}{(x^2 - 1)^{3/2}} \, dx.$

15. $\int e^{2x} \sin 3x \, dx.$

16. $\int e^{-x} \cos x \, dx.$

17. $\int_0^1 x^3 \sqrt{1 - x^2} \, dx.$

18. $\int x \sec^2 x \, dx.$

19. $\int \ln (x^2 + 1) \, dx.$

20. $\int \frac{x^3}{e^{x^2}} \, dx.$

21. $\int x^r \ln x \, dx, \ (r \neq -1).$

22. $\int x^{-1} \ln x \, dx.$

In each of Exercises 23–28 integrate by parts (for a general method see Exercise II-1 below).

23. $\int \sin^{-1} ax \, dx.$

24. $\int \sinh^{-1} ax \, dx.$

25. $\int \tan^{-1} ax \, dx.$

26. $\int \tanh^{-1} ax \, dx.$

27. $\int x \tanh^{-1} ax \, dx.$

28. $\int x \sin^{-1} bx \, dx.$

29. In Example 6 make the alternate substitution $u = \sin^m x \cos^{n-1} x$, $dv = \cos x \, dx$ to arrive at the other part of No. 52 in the Table of Integrals.

30. Show that Exercise 29 can be done much more easily by making the substitution $x = (\pi/2) - y$.

II

1. If $\int F(x) \, dx = G(x)$, show that $\int F^{-1}(x) \, dx$ can be explicitly integrated by parts to give $\int F^{-1}(x) \, dx = xF^{-1}(x) - G(F^{-1}(x))$ (assuming all the indicated functions exist and are continuous).

2. Using Exercise 1, find $\int \operatorname{sech}^{-1} ax \, dx.$

3. Show that a generalization of Example 2 is given by $\int_0^{2a} xF(x) \, dx = a \int_0^{2a} F(x) \, dx$, where $F(x) = F(2a - x)$. Prove the result and give a geometric interpretation.

In each of Exercises 4–7, establish a reduction formula.

4. $\int x^n e^x \, dx.$

5. $\int x^n \cos x \, dx.$

6. $\int \sin^n x \, dx.$

7. $\int \cos^n x \, dx$ (obtain directly from the result of Exercise 6).

3 TRIGONOMETRIC SUBSTITUTIONS

If in the change of variable formula (No. 3 of the Table of Integrals) the function g has an inverse in some interval, then the integral of $f(g(x))g'(x)$ becomes the integral of $f(u)$ if we let $x = g^{-1}(u)$; i.e.,

$$\int f(u) \, du = \int f(g(x))g'(x) \, dx \Big|_{x = g^{-1}(u)}.$$

For convenience, let us interchange x and u in this formula, obtaining

12.4 $$\int f(x) \, dx = \int f(g(u))g'(u) \, du \Big|_{u = g^{-1}(x)}.$$

Written in this form, the change of variable formula has many uses, as illustrated below.

We may remember the form of **12.4** by a substitution of $g(u)$ for x,

$$x = g(u),$$

and then substituting in place of dx the derivative of g times du,

$$dx = g'(u) \, du.$$

After the new integral in u is evaluated, u is replaced by $g^{-1}(x)$.

An integral of an algebraic function involving square roots of the form

$$\sqrt{a^2 - x^2} \qquad \text{or} \qquad \sqrt{x^2 \pm a^2}, \qquad (a > 0),$$

can often be evaluated by changing the integrand into a trigonometric form. This technique is illustrated below.

EXAMPLE 1. Given a circle of radius r, the shaded region S of Figure 12.1 is called a *sector with central angle* α. Find the area of S, assuming $0 < \alpha \leq \pi/2$.

Solution: The region S is the union of a triangle OPC and the region CPB. Hence $A(S) = A(OPC) + A(CPB)$. Since point P has coordinates $(r \cos \alpha, r \sin \alpha)$, evidently

$$A(OPC) = \frac{1}{2}(r \cos \alpha)(r \sin \alpha) = \frac{r^2}{2} \sin \alpha \cos \alpha.$$

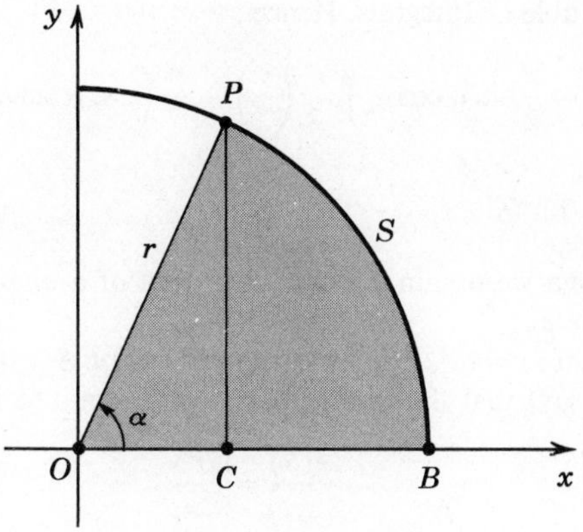

FIGURE 12.1

The circle has equation $x^2 + y^2 = r^2$, and therefore

$$A(CPB) = \int_{r\cos\alpha}^{r} \sqrt{r^2 - x^2}\, dx.$$

Hence

$$A(S) = \frac{r^2}{2}\sin\alpha\cos\alpha + \int_{r\cos\alpha}^{r} \sqrt{r^2 - x^2}\, dx.$$

We evaluate the above integral by letting

$$x = r\sin u, \qquad u \text{ in} \left[-\frac{\pi}{2}, \frac{\pi}{2}\right].$$

Then

$$\sqrt{r^2 - x^2} = \sqrt{r^2(1 - \sin^2 u)} = r\sqrt{\cos^2 u} = r|\cos u| = r\cos u.$$

We now use 12.4 with

$$x = r\sin u, \quad dx = r\cos u\, du, \quad u = \sin^{-1}\frac{x}{r}.$$

Since $u = \sin^{-1} 1 = \pi/2$ when $x = r$ and $u = \sin^{-1}(\cos\alpha) = \pi/2 - \alpha$ [for, $\sin(\sin^{-1}(\cos\alpha)) = \cos\alpha = \sin(\pi/2 - \alpha)$], we have

$$\begin{aligned} A(S) &= \frac{r^2}{2}\sin\alpha\cos\alpha + \int_{(\pi/2)-\alpha}^{\pi/2} (r\cos u) r\cos u\, du \\ &= \frac{r^2}{2}\sin\alpha\cos\alpha + r^2\int_{(\pi/2)-\alpha}^{\pi/2} \cos^2 u\, du \\ &= \frac{r^2}{2}\sin\alpha\cos\alpha + \frac{r^2}{2}(\sin u\cos u + u)\Bigg|_{(\pi/2)-\alpha}^{\pi/2} \end{aligned}$$

by No. 56 of the Table of Integrals. Hence

$$A(S) = \frac{r^2}{2}\sin\alpha\cos\alpha + \frac{r^2}{2}\left(\frac{\pi}{2}\right) - \frac{r^2}{2}\left(\cos\alpha\sin\alpha + \frac{\pi}{2} - \alpha\right)$$
$$= \alpha\frac{r^2}{2}.$$

If $\alpha = \pi/2$, then we obtain $\pi r^2/4$ for the area of a quarter-circle, and hence πr^2 for the area of a circle.

The formula $A(S) = \alpha r^2/2$ for the area of sector S with central angle α is the expected result; it says that the area of S is proportional to its central angle; i.e.,

$$\frac{A(S)}{\alpha} = \frac{\pi r^2}{2\pi}.$$

The trigonometric identities

$$\sin^2\theta + \cos^2\theta = 1, \qquad \sec^2\theta = \tan^2\theta + 1$$

play a basic role in determining the proper substitution for a change of variable. However, since we are employing **12.4** with g as a trigonometric function, we must remember to restrict sufficiently the domain of g so that its inverse g^{-1} exists.

We note in passing that the hyperbolic functions could be used in a similar fashion, using the identity

$$\cosh^2 x - \sinh^2 x = 1.$$

If the integrand of an integral involves $\sqrt{a^2 - x^2}$, $(a > 0)$, then for

$$x = a\sin\theta, \qquad \theta \text{ in } \left[\frac{-\pi}{2}, \frac{\pi}{2}\right],$$

we have $\cos\theta \geq 0$ and

$$\sqrt{a^2 - x^2} = \sqrt{a^2 - a^2\sin^2\theta} = a\cos\theta,$$

as in Example 1. We may solve for θ, getting $g^{-1}(x)$ to be

$$\theta = \sin^{-1}\frac{x}{a}.$$

If the integrand involves $\sqrt{x^2 - a^2}$, $(a > 0)$, then let

$$x = a\sec\theta, \qquad \left(0 \leq \theta < \frac{\pi}{2} \quad \text{or} \quad \pi \leq \theta < \frac{3\pi}{2}\right).$$

In this range of θ, $\tan\theta \geq 0$ and

$$\sqrt{x^2 - a^2} = \sqrt{a^2\sec^2\theta - a^2} = a\sqrt{\sec^2\theta - 1} = a\tan\theta.$$

We may again solve for θ in this range,

$$\theta = \sec^{-1}\frac{x}{a}.$$

The third possible case is illustrated by the following example.

EXAMPLE 2. Verify formula No. 29 of the Table of Integrals.

Solution: We evaluate

$$\int \frac{x^2}{\sqrt{x^2+a^2}}\,dx$$

by letting

$$x = a\tan\theta, \quad dx = a\sec^2\theta\,d\theta, \quad -\frac{\pi}{2} < x < \frac{\pi}{2}.$$

Then

$$\sqrt{x^2+a^2} = \sqrt{a^2(1+\tan^2\theta)} = a|\sec\theta| = a\sec\theta,$$

and

$$\begin{aligned}\int \frac{x^2}{\sqrt{x^2+a^2}}\,dx &= \int \frac{a^2\tan^2\theta}{a\sec\theta}\,a\sec^2\theta\,d\theta\,\Big|_{\theta=\tan^{-1}x/a}\\ &= a^2\int \tan^2\theta\sec\theta\,d\theta\,\Big|_{\theta=\tan^{-1}x/a}\\ &= a^2\int(\sec^2\theta-1)\sec\theta\,d\theta\,\Big|_{\theta=\tan^{-1}x/a}\\ &= a^2\left\{\int\sec^3\theta\,d\theta-\int\sec\theta\,d\theta\right\}\Big|_{\theta=\tan^{-1}x/a}\\ &= a^2\left\{\frac{1}{2}\sec\theta\tan\theta+\frac{1}{2}\int\sec\theta\,d\theta-\int\sec\theta\,d\theta\right\}\Big|_{\theta=\tan^{-1}x/a}\\ &= \frac{a^2}{2}(\sec\theta\tan\theta-\ln|\sec\theta+\tan\theta|)+C\,\Big|_{\theta=\tan^{-1}x/a}\\ &= \frac{x}{2}\sqrt{x^2+a^2}-\frac{a^2}{2}\ln\left|\frac{\sqrt{x^2+a^2}}{a}+\frac{x}{a}\right|+C\\ &= \frac{x}{2}\sqrt{x^2+a^2}-\frac{a^2}{2}\ln|\sqrt{x^2+a^2}+x|+C',\end{aligned}$$

where $C' = C + (a^2 \ln a)/2$.

If we use the minus sign in No. 29, then we must use the substitution $x = a\sec\theta$ and proceed as above.

We could solve Example 2 by using the hyperbolic functions. Thus, letting

$$x = a \sinh \theta, \qquad dx = a \cosh \theta \, d\theta,$$

we obtain

$$\begin{aligned}\int \frac{x^2}{\sqrt{x^2 + a^2}}\, dx &= \int a^2 \sinh^2 \theta \, d\theta \Big|_{\theta = \sinh^{-1} x/a} \\ &= \frac{a^2}{2} \int (\cosh 2\theta - 1)\, d\theta \Big|_{\theta = \sinh^{-1} x/a} \\ &= \frac{a^2}{2}\left(\frac{1}{2}\sinh 2\theta - \theta\right) + C \Big|_{\theta = \sinh^{-1} x/a},\end{aligned}$$

and so on.

EXERCISES

I

Find the following integrals.

1. $\int \sqrt{25 - x^2}\, dx.$
2. $\int \frac{\sqrt{25 - x^2}}{x}\, dx.$
3. $\int \frac{1}{\sqrt{25 - x^2}}\, dx.$
4. $\int \sqrt{x^2 - 4}\, dx.$
5. $\int \sqrt{9x^2 - 4}\, dx.$
6. $\int x\sqrt{9x^2 - 4}\, dx.$
7. $\int \frac{1}{x\sqrt{x^2 + 9}}\, dx.$
8. $\int \frac{1}{(x^2 + 9)^2}\, dx.$
9. $\int \frac{1}{(x^2 - 4)^2}\, dx.$
10. $\int \frac{x}{(x^2 - 4)^2}\, dx.$

The following integrals are listed in the Table of Integrals. Develop them by the methods of this section.

11. $\int \frac{\sqrt{x^2 - a^2}}{x}\, dx.$
12. $\int \frac{\sqrt{x^2 - a^2}}{x^2}\, dx.$
13. $\int \frac{\sqrt{a^2 - x^2}}{x^2}\, dx.$
14. $\int x^2\sqrt{a^2 - x^2}\, dx.$
15. $\int \sqrt{x^2 + a^2}\, dx.$
16. $\int \frac{\sqrt{a^2 + x^2}}{x^2}\, dx.$

17. $\int \frac{x^2}{\sqrt{x^2 - a^2}}\,dx.$

18. $\int \frac{x^2}{\sqrt{a^2 - x^2}}\,dx.$

19. $\int \frac{1}{x\sqrt{a^2 - x^2}}\,dx.$

20. $\int \frac{1}{x\sqrt{a^2 + x^2}}\,dx.$

Find the following integrals.

21. $\int \frac{1}{(x^2 - 4x + 5)^2}\,dx.$

22. $\int (x + 3)^2\sqrt{x^2 + 6x + 8}\,dx.$

II

In each of Exercises 1–3 find the integral.

1. $\int \sqrt{x^2 + 2px + q}\,dx$ (consider the cases $q - p^2 > 0, =0, <0$).

2. $\int \frac{\sqrt{x^2 + 2px + q}}{x^3}\,dx$ (obtain from Exercise 1).

3. $\int \frac{x^2}{\sqrt{x^2 + 2px + q}}\,dx$ (obtain from Exercise 1 above and Exercise II-8, Section 1).

4. Given the result of Exercise I-11, show how to obtain Exercise I-13.

5. What is the relationship between the following pairs of integrals:

a. $\int \frac{1}{x\sqrt{a^2 + x^2}}\,dx$ and $\int \frac{1}{\sqrt{a^2 + x^2}}\,dx.$

b. $\int \frac{x^2}{\sqrt{a^2 - x^2}}\,dx$ and $\int \frac{1}{x^3\sqrt{x^2 - a^2}}\,dx.$

4 INTEGRATION OF RATIONAL FUNCTIONS

Let us consider as an example the problem of evaluating the integral

(1) $$\int \frac{2x^4 + 3x^3 - x^2 + x - 1}{x^3 - x}\,dx.$$

By long division we can show that

(2) $$\frac{2x^4 + 3x^3 - x^2 + x - 1}{x^3 - x} = 2x + 3 + \frac{x^2 + 4x - 1}{x^3 - x},$$

and hence

(3) $$\int \frac{2x^4 + 3x^3 - x^2 + x - 1}{x^3 - x}\,dx = x^2 + 3x + \int \frac{x^2 + 4x - 1}{x^3 - x}\,dx.$$

The integrand of (1) is of the form

$$f(x) = \frac{F(x)}{G(x)},$$

where F and G are polynomial functions. Such a function f is called a rational function. Equation (2) illustrates a general theorem which states that

$$\frac{F(x)}{G(x)} = Q(x) + \frac{R(x)}{G(x)},$$

where $Q(x)$ (the quotient) and $R(x)$ (the remainder) are polynomials and $R(x)$ is of degree less than the degree of $G(x)$. If $F(x)$ is of degree less than that of $G(x)$, then $Q(x) = 0$, and $R(x) = F(x)$. Thus the problem of integrating a rational function can always be reduced to one of integrating a quotient of two polynomials where the degree of the numerator is less than the degree of the denominator [as in (3)].

It is easy to verify that

$$\text{(4)} \qquad \frac{x^2 + 4x - 1}{x^3 - x} = \frac{1}{x} + \frac{2}{x - 1} - \frac{2}{x + 1},$$

and therefore

$$\begin{aligned}\int \frac{x^2 + 4x - 1}{x^3 - x}\,dx &= \int \frac{1}{x}\,dx + 2\int \frac{1}{x - 1}\,dx - 2\int \frac{1}{x + 1}\,dx \\ &= \ln|x| + 2\ln|x - 1| - 2\ln|x + 1| + C \\ &= \ln\left|\frac{x(x - 1)^2}{(x + 1)^2}\right| + C,\end{aligned}$$

so that the integral (1) has the value

$$x^2 + 3x + \ln\left|\frac{x(x - 1)^2}{(x + 1)^2}\right| + C.$$

In equation (4) we have reduced the quotient $(x^2 + 4x - 1)/(x^3 - x)$ to a sum of *partial fractions*. Obviously, it is this equation which allows us to proceed with the evaluation of (1). It is our purpose in this section to give methods by which these partial fractions may be determined.

Although we shall not give the proof, it can be proved that every polynomial $G(x)$ with real number coefficients can be expressed as a product of linear and quadratic polynomials. For example,

$$\begin{aligned} x^3 - x &= x(x - 1)(x + 1), \\ x^3 + 8 &= (x + 2)(x^2 - 2x + 4), \\ x^4 + 4x^2 + 4 &= (x^2 + 2)^2. \end{aligned}$$

Therefore, starting with a quotient

$$\frac{F(x)}{G(x)}$$

of two polynomials, with the degree of $F(x)$ less than that of $G(x)$, we can first of all factor $G(x)$ into linear and quadratic factors. Having done so, we can hope to express the given quotient as a sum of partial fractions having as denominators factors of $G(x)$.

If $(ax + b)^r$, $(r \geq 1)$, is the highest power of the linear polynomial $ax + b$ that is a factor of $G(x)$, then included in the sum of partial fractions of $F(x)/G(x)$ will be r terms of the form

$$\frac{A_1}{ax + b} + \frac{A_2}{(ax + b)^2} + \cdots + \frac{A_r}{(ax + b)^r},$$

where $A_1, A_2, \cdots, A_r$ are constants. There will be such a sum associated with each different linear factor of $G(x)$.

If $ax^2 + bx + c$ is a quadratic factor of $G(x)$ that cannot be further factored, and if $(ax^2 + bx + c)^s$, $(s \geq 1)$, is the highest power of it that is a factor of $G(x)$, then in the sum of partial fractions of $F(x)/G(x)$ there will be included s terms of the form

$$\frac{B_1x + C_1}{ax^2 + bx + c} + \frac{B_2x + C_2}{(ax^2 + bx + c)^2} + \cdots + \frac{B_sx + C_s}{(ax^2 + bx + c)^s},$$

where the B_i and C_i are constants. Such a sum will be associated with each distinct quadratic factor of $G(x)$.

We shall see in the examples below how the numerators of these partial fractions are determined.

EXAMPLE 1. Establish formula No. 21 of the Table of Integrals.

Solution: According to the discussion above,

$$\frac{1}{x^2 - a^2} = \frac{A}{x - a} + \frac{B}{x + a}$$

for some constants A and B. Adding fractions, we have

$$\frac{1}{x^2 - a^2} = \frac{A(x + a) + B(x - a)}{x^2 - a^2}.$$

Since these fractions have the same denominator, their numerators must be equal,

$$1 = A(x + a) + B(x - a),$$
$$1 = (A + B)x + (A - B)a.$$

The two sides of this equation are equal for every number x if and only if

$$A + B = 0,$$
$$(A - B)a = 1.$$

A simultaneous solution of these two equations is easily found to be

$$A = \frac{1}{2a}, \qquad B = -\frac{1}{2a}.$$

Hence

$$\frac{1}{x^2 - a^2} = \frac{1}{2a}\left(\frac{1}{x - a} - \frac{1}{x + a}\right),$$

and

$$\begin{aligned}\int \frac{1}{x^2 - a^2}\,dx &= \frac{1}{2a}\left(\int \frac{1}{x - a}\,dx - \int \frac{1}{x + a}\,dx\right)\\ &= \frac{1}{2a}(\ln|x - a| - \ln|x + a|) + C\\ &= \frac{1}{2a}\ln\left|\frac{x - a}{x + a}\right| + C.\end{aligned}$$

This proves No. 21 of the table.

EXAMPLE 2. Find $\int \frac{x^2 + x + 1}{(2x + 1)(x^2 + 1)}\,dx.$

Solution: We have that

$$\frac{x^2 + x + 1}{(2x + 1)(x^2 + 1)} = \frac{A}{2x + 1} + \frac{Bx + C}{x^2 + 1}$$

for some constants A, B, and C, according to our previous discussion. To determine A, B, and C, we multiply out the right side of the above equation, obtaining

$$\frac{x^2 + x + 1}{(2x + 1)(x^2 + 1)} = \frac{(A + 2B)x^2 + (B + 2C)x + (A + C)}{(2x + 1)(x^2 + 1)}.$$

In order for these fractions to be identically the same, their numerators must be equal:

$$x^2 + x + 1 = (A + 2B)x^2 + (B + 2C)x + (A + C).$$

In turn, these two polynomials are identically the same if the corresponding powers of x have the same coefficients, i.e., if

$$A + 2B = 1, \quad B + 2C = 1, \quad A + C = 1.$$

These three equations in the three unknowns A, B, and C may be solved in the usual way to yield

$$A = \tfrac{3}{5}, \quad B = \tfrac{1}{5}, \quad C = \tfrac{2}{5}.$$

Hence

$$\frac{x^2 + x + 1}{(2x + 1)(x^2 + 1)} = \frac{1}{5}\left(\frac{3}{2x + 1} + \frac{x + 2}{x^2 + 1}\right),$$

and

$$\int \frac{x^2 + x + 1}{(2x + 1)(x^2 + 1)}\,dx = \frac{1}{5}\left(\int \frac{3}{2x + 1}\,dx + \int \frac{x}{x^2 + 1}\,dx + \int \frac{2}{x^2 + 1}\,dx\right)$$

$$= \frac{1}{5}\left[\frac{3}{2}\ln|2x + 1| + \frac{1}{2}\ln(x^2 + 1) + 2\tan^{-1} x\right] + C.$$

EXAMPLE 3. Find $\int \frac{2x^2 - 3x - 2}{x^3 + x^2 - 2x}\,dx.$

Solution: The denominator factors as $x(x + 2)(x - 1)$; hence

$$\frac{2x^2 - 3x - 2}{x^3 + x^2 - 2x} = \frac{A}{x} + \frac{B}{x + 2} + \frac{C}{x - 1}.$$

On multiplying out the right side of this equation and equating numerators, we get

(1) $$2x^2 - 3x - 2 = A(x + 2)(x - 1) + Bx(x - 1) + Cx(x + 2).$$

We can use the method of Example 2 to determine A, B, and C. However, there is an easier way for this example. Since Equation (1) is an identity, it holds for every number x. In particular, it holds for $x = 0, 1, -2$. (Note that these are the numbers that make the denominator equal zero.) If we let $x = 0$ in (1), we get

$$-2 = A(2)(-1),$$

and therefore $A = 1$. If we let $x = 1$ in (1), we get

$$-3 = C(1)(3),$$

and hence $C = -1$. When $x = -2$, we have

$$12 = B(-2)(-3),$$

and $B = 2$.

Thus

$$\int \frac{2x^2 - 3x - 2}{x^3 + x^2 - 2x}\,dx = \int \frac{1}{x}\,dx + \int \frac{2}{x + 2}\,dx - \int \frac{1}{x - 1}\,dx$$

$$= \ln|x| + 2\ln|x + 2| - \ln|x - 1| + C$$

$$= \ln\left|\frac{x(x + 2)^2}{x - 1}\right| + C.$$

EXAMPLE 4. Find $\int \frac{x}{(x-1)^2}\,dx$.

Solution: Here for the first time we have a repeated factor in the denominator. For a repeated linear factor, we have the following sum of partial fractions:

$$\frac{x}{(x-1)^2} = \frac{A}{x-1} + \frac{B}{(x-1)^2}.$$

Equating numerators of each side of this equation, we get

$$x = A(x-1) + B = Ax + (-A + B).$$

Thus we must have

$$A = 1, \qquad -A + B = 0,$$

or $A = 1, B = 1$. Hence

$$\int \frac{x}{(x-1)^2}\,dx = \int \frac{1}{x-1}\,dx + \int \frac{1}{(x-1)^2}\,dx$$

$$= \ln|x-1| - \frac{1}{x-1} + C.$$

EXAMPLE 5. Find $\int \frac{x^3 - 3x^2 + 2x - 3}{(x^2+1)^2}\,dx$.

Solution: In this example there is a repeated quadratic polynomial in the denominator. Hence, according to our previous discussion,

$$\frac{x^3 - 3x^2 + 2x - 3}{(x^2+1)^2} = \frac{A_1x + B_1}{x^2+1} + \frac{A_2x + B_2}{(x^2+1)^2}$$

for some constants A_1, B_1, A_2, and B_2.

An easy way to determine these constants is as follows. By long division,

$$\frac{x^3 - 3x^2 + 2x - 3}{x^2+1} = x - 3 + \frac{x}{x^2+1},$$

and therefore

$$\frac{x^3 - 3x^2 + 2x - 3}{(x^2+1)^2} = \frac{x-3}{x^2+1} + \frac{x}{(x^2+1)^2}.$$

Thus $A_1 = 1$, $B_1 = -3$, $A_2 = 1$, and $B_2 = 0$.

We now have

$$\int \frac{x^3 - 3x^2 + 2x - 3}{(x^2+1)^2}\,dx = \int \frac{x}{x^2+1}\,dx - \int \frac{3}{x^2+1}\,dx + \int \frac{x}{(x^2+1)^2}\,dx$$

$$= \frac{1}{2}\ln(x^2+1) - 3\tan^{-1}x - \frac{1}{2(x^2+1)} + C.$$

EXERCISES

I

Find the following integrals.

1. $\int \frac{x+1}{x^2-x}\,dx.$

2. $\int \frac{x}{x^2-5x+6}\,dx.$

3. $\int \frac{x^3}{x^2-2x-3}\,dx.$

4. $\int \frac{6x^2+1}{2-x-6x^2}\,dx.$

5. $\int \frac{3x-1}{4x^2-4x+1}\,dx.$

6. $\int \frac{1}{4x^2+12x+9}\,dx.$

7. $\int \frac{x^2+1}{x^3+x^2-2x}\,dx.$

8. $\int \frac{4x^2-3x}{(x+2)(x^2+1)}\,dx.$

9. $\int \frac{x^2}{x^4-16}\,dx.$

10. $\int \frac{1}{x^3-x^2}\,dx.$

11. $\int \frac{x^3+1}{x^3-4x}\,dx.$

12. $\int \frac{x^3+1}{x^3-1}\,dx.$

13. $\int \frac{2x^2+1}{(x-2)^3}\,dx.$

14. $\int \frac{x^2+x+1}{(x+1)^3}\,dx.$

15. $\int \frac{2x^3+x^2+5x+4}{x^4+8x^2+16}\,dx.$

16. $\int \frac{x^4+x^3+18x^2+10x+81}{(x^2+9)^3}\,dx.$

17. $\int \frac{3x+1}{(x^2-4)^2}\,dx.$

18. $\int \frac{x^3+1}{(4x^2-1)^2}\,dx.$

The following integrals are listed in the Table of Integrals. Establish them by the methods of this section.

19. $\int \frac{1}{(ax+b)(cx+d)}\,dx.$

20. $\int \frac{x}{(ax+b)(cx+d)}\,dx.$

21. $\int \frac{x}{(ax+b)^2(cx+d)}\,dx.$

22. $\int \frac{1}{(ax+b)^2(cx+d)}\,dx.$

II

Find the following integrals.

1. $\int \frac{x}{(x-a)^2(x-b)^2}\,dx.$

2. $\int \frac{1}{(x-a)^2(x-b)^2}\,dx.$

3. $\int \frac{1}{(x-a)(x-b)(x-c)}\,dx.$

4. $\int \frac{1}{(x-a_1)(x-a_2)\cdots(x-a_n)}\,dx.$

5. $\int \frac{x^4}{x^2-1}\,dx.$

6. $\int \frac{x^4}{x^2+1}\,dx.$

7. $\int \frac{x^7}{x^4+a^4}\,dx.$

8. $\int \frac{x^7}{(x^4+a^4)^2}\,dx.$

9. $\int \frac{1}{x^4+x^6}\,dx.$

10. $\int \frac{x^2}{x^4-1}\,dx.$

11. $\int \frac{1}{x^3+1}\,dx.$

5 SEPARABLE DIFFERENTIAL EQUATIONS

Given an equation in x and y such as, for example,

$$\sin x + y^3 = C,$$

C a constant, it is evident that every differentiable function f such that $y = f(x)$ satisfies this equation also satisfies the differential equation

$$\cos x + 3y^2 \frac{dy}{dx} = 0.$$

We wish to show in this section that, starting with a differential equation such as the one above, we can find an equation in x and y satisfied by any solution of the differential equation.

The above differential equation is of the type

12.5 $$M(x) + N(y)\frac{dy}{dx} = 0,$$

or, letting $y = f(x)$,

12.6 $$M(x) + N(f(x))f'(x) = 0,$$

where M and N are continuous functions. Such an equation as **12.5** is called a *separable differential equation* (since the variables x and y appear in separate terms). In solving **12.6** we shall seek only smooth solutions f.

If we let

$$F(x) = M(x) + N(f(x))f'(x),$$

then, by 12.6, $F(x) = 0$ and

$$\int F(x)\,dx = C$$

for some constant C. Since

$$\int F(x)\,dx = \int M(x)\,dx + \int N(f(x))f'(x)\,dx,$$

and, by No. 3 of the Table of Integrals,

$$\int N(f(x))f'(x)\,dx = \int N(y)\,dy\,\Big|_{y=f(x)},$$

the solution of 12.5 is given by

12.7
$$\int M(x)\,dx + \int N(y)\,dy = C.$$

Thus for every smooth function f such that $y = f(x)$ satisfies 12.5 there is a choice of the constant C such that $y = f(x)$ satisfies 12.7.

For example, the differential equation

$$\cos x + 3y^2 \frac{dy}{dx} = 0$$

has as its solution the equation

$$\int \cos x\,dx + \int 3y^2\,dy = C,$$

or

$$\sin x + y^3 = C.$$

Separable differential equations appear in a natural way in many applications of mathematics. As a matter of fact, the differential equation

$$\frac{dy}{dt} = ky, \qquad (y > 0),$$

studied in Section 7 of Chapter 10 is separable, since it can be written in the form

$$k - \frac{1}{y}\frac{dy}{dt} = 0.$$

Let us solve this equation by our present methods.

EXAMPLE 1. Solve the differential equation

$$k - \frac{1}{y}\frac{dy}{dt} = 0, \qquad (y > 0).$$

Solution: By 12.7,

$$\int k\,dt - \int \frac{1}{y}\,dy = C,$$

or

$$kt - \ln y = C.$$

Thus $\ln y = kt - C$, and

$$y = e^{kt-C} = Ae^{kt},$$

where A is a constant (e^{-C}).

EXAMPLE 2. Solve the differential equation

$$(x + \sec^2 x) + (y - e^y)\frac{dy}{dx} = 0.$$

Solution: For this equation, the functions M and N are defined by

$$M(x) = x + \sec^2 x, \qquad N(y) = y - e^y.$$

By **12.7**, its solution is

$$\int (x + \sec^2 x)\,dx + \int (y - e^y)\,dy = C,$$

or

$$\frac{x^2}{2} + \tan x + \frac{y^2}{2} - e^y = C.$$

EXAMPLE 3. Solve the differential equation

$$\frac{1}{\sqrt{1 - x^2}} + \frac{1}{y}\frac{dy}{dx} = 0, \qquad (y > 0).$$

Solution: By **12.7**, the solution is

$$\int \frac{1}{\sqrt{1 - x^2}}\,dx + \int \frac{1}{y}\,dy = C,$$

or

$$\sin^{-1} x + \ln y = C.$$

Thus $\ln y = C - \sin^{-1} x$, and

$$y = Ae^{-\sin^{-1} x},$$

where A is a constant (e^C).

In Examples 1 and 3 the solution is given explicitly in the form $y = f(x)$. The solution is given *implicitly* in Example 2 in that the equation is not solved for y in terms of x. It is desirable to give the explicit solution of a differential equation whenever possible. However, the explicit determination of $f(x)$ can offer great difficulties, as it would in the solution of Example 2.

A physical problem that has as its solution a separable differential equation is as follows. Let y be the temperature at time t of a body immersed in a bath of constant temperature a. We shall assume that $y > a$ and hence that the body is being cooled. It is a physical law that the temperature of the body decreases at a rate proportional to the difference between its temperature and the temperature of the surrounding medium (Newton's law of cooling). This law leads to the differential equation

12.8 $$\frac{dy}{dt} = k(y - a), \qquad (y > a),$$

for some constant k.

EXAMPLE 4. A body is immersed in water having a constant temperature of 20°C. The body has initial temperature of 40° and a temperature of 35°C two minutes later. What will its temperature be at the end of 10 minutes?

Solution: Employing **12.8** with $a = 20$, we have the separable differential equation

$$\frac{1}{y - 20}\frac{dy}{dt} = k, \qquad (y - 20 > 0),$$

whose solution is

$$\int \frac{1}{y - 20}\, dy = \int k\, dt + C,$$

or $$\ln (y - 20) = kt + C.$$

Thus

$$y - 20 = e^{kt+C} = Ae^{kt},$$

and

(1) $$y = Ae^{kt} + 20.$$

We determine A and k as follows. Since $y = 40$ at $t = 0$,

$$40 = A + 20,$$

and $A = 20$. Thus (1) becomes

(2) $$y = 20e^{kt} + 20.$$

Next, it is given that $y = 35$ when $t = 2$, so that

$$35 = 20e^{2k} + 20.$$

Thus

$$e^{2k} = \tfrac{3}{4},$$

and $$k = \tfrac{1}{2} \ln \tfrac{3}{4}.$$

On substituting k in (2), we get

(3) $$y = 20e^{(1/2 \ln 3/4)t} + 20$$

as the solution of the given problem.

Solution (3) may be written in a more usable form if we observe that

$$e^{\ln 3/4} = \tfrac{3}{4}.$$

Then (3) becomes

(4) $$y = 20(\tfrac{3}{4})^{t/2} + 20.$$

The temperature y when $t = 10$ is given by

$$y = 20\,(\tfrac{3}{4})^5 + 20 \doteq 24.7^\circ\ \text{C}.$$

EXERCISES

I

In each of Exercises 1–10 solve the differential equation.

1. $\dfrac{1}{x} + \dfrac{1}{y}\dfrac{dy}{dx} = 0.$

2. $\dfrac{1-x}{x^3} - \dfrac{1}{y^2}\dfrac{dy}{dx} = 0.$

3. $\dfrac{dy}{dx} = xy^2.$

4. $\dfrac{dy}{dx} = y^2.$

5. $\dfrac{y}{y-1}\dfrac{dy}{dx} - \dfrac{x+1}{x} = 0.$

6. $e^{3x} + 1 + \sin y \dfrac{dy}{dx} = 0.$

7. $e^{x-y}\dfrac{dy}{dx} + 1 = 0.$

8. $\dfrac{dy}{dx} = \dfrac{1-x}{1-y}.$

9. $\sec x + \tan y \dfrac{dy}{dx} = 0.$

10. $\dfrac{dy}{dx} = \cos^2 y.$

11. A thermometer reading 80°F is placed in a room whose temperature is 50°F. After 1 min the reading on the thermometer is 70°F.
    a. What is the reading on the thermometer after 3 min?
    b. At what time is the reading on the thermometer 56°F?

II

1. a. If $v = \dfrac{dx}{dt}$, show that $a = \dfrac{dv}{dt} = \dfrac{d^2x}{dt^2} = v\dfrac{dv}{dx}.$

   b. Using a, solve the equation for simple harmonic motion,

$$\frac{d^2x}{dt^2} + w^2x = 0, \qquad (w \text{ a constant}),$$

(see Exercise II-12, page 322).

2. In a certain chemical reaction $A + B = C$, one molecule of A combines with one molecule of B to form one molecule of C. If the initial amounts of A and B are a and b, respectively, then the amount y of C at any time t is given by

$$\frac{dy}{dt} = k(a - y)(b - y), \qquad (k \text{ a constant}).$$

(This follows from the law of mass action.) Find the amount of C present at the end of 60 min if initially $y = 0$ and

a. $a = 10, b = 10.$
b. $a = 10, b = 5.$
c. $a = 10, b = 1.$

3. A tank of cross-sectional area $A(h)$ ft² at water level has an orifice of area A_0 ft² at the bottom. If h ft is the depth of the liquid in the tank at any time t sec, it can be shown that the rate of flow ft³/sec is given approximately by

$$\frac{dv}{dt} = A(h)\frac{dh}{dt} = -\frac{\pi A_0}{\pi + 2}\sqrt{2gh}, \qquad (g = 32.2 \text{ ft/sec}^2).$$

Find the time required to empty a full cylindrical tank (with its axis vertical) whose dimensions are diameter 10 ft and length 20 ft, and whose orifice has a $\frac{1}{2}$-ft diameter.

REVIEW

Oral Exercises

Explain and illustrate by means of a specific example each of the following seven methods for integrating.

1. Table of integrals.
2. Change of variables.
3. Integration by parts.
4. Reduction formulae.
5. Trigonometric substitution for integrands involving square roots.
6. Hyperbolic substitution for integrands involving square roots.
7. Partial fractions.
8. What is a differential equation?
9. What is meant by a separable differential equation?

I

Find the following integrals.

1. $\int \left(\frac{x - 1}{x + 1}\right)^3 dx.$
2. $\int x^2 \ln (x^3 + 1)\, dx.$

3. $\int (\ln x)^3\, dx.$

4. $\int \ln(1 + x^2)\, dx.$

5. $\int e^{\sqrt{t}}\, dt.$

6. $\int \ln(x + \sqrt{x^2 + 1})\, dx.$

7. $\int \ln(x + \sqrt{x^2 - a^2})\, dx.$

8. $\int \frac{(2 + \sqrt{x})^3}{\sqrt[3]{x}}\, dx.$

9. $\int \frac{1}{\sin^2 x + \cos 2x}\, dx.$

10. $\int \sin 2x \cos^3 x\, dx.$

11. $\int \frac{(\arctan x)^2}{x^2 + 1}\, dx.$

12. $\int \frac{1}{(1 - \sin^2 x)\sqrt{1 + \tan x}}\, dx.$

13. $\int e^x (\sin e^x)\, dx.$

14. $\int \frac{1}{1 + \sin x}\, dx.$

15. $\int \cos 2x \cos 3x\, dx.$

16. $\int \sin 2x \sin 5x\, dx.$

17. $\int x \cdot 5^x\, dx.$

18. $\int \arctan \sqrt{x}\, dx.$

19. $\int x^2 \ln(1 + x)\, dx.$

20. $\int \cos \ln x\, dx.$

21. $\int \sqrt{x}\, e^{\sqrt{x}}\, dx.$

22. $\int \sin \sqrt[3]{x}\, dx.$

II

In each of Exercises 1–6 find the integral.

1. $\int \sqrt{1 + e^{2x}}\, dx.$

2. $\int \sqrt{e^{2x} + e^x + 1}\, dx.$

3. $\int \left(\frac{x - 1}{x + 1}\right)^n dx,$ (n an integer).

4. $\int x \ln(x^3 + 1)\, dx.$

5. $\int x^5 e^{-x^2}\, dx.$

6. $\int x^5 e^{ax^3}\, dx.$

7. Let $R(x,y)$ be a rational expression in x and y; i.e., $R(x,y)$ is a quotient of two polynomials in x and y. Show that $\int R(\sin\theta, \cos\theta)\, d\theta$ can be evaluated by the change of variable $z = \tan \theta/2$. [*Hint:* Show that $\sin\theta = 2z/(1 + z^2)$, $\cos\theta = (1 - z^2)/(1 + z^2)$, and $d\theta = 2dz/(1 + z^2)$.]

Use Exercise 7 or otherwise to find the following integrals.

8. $\int_0^{\pi/2} \frac{1}{a + b\sin\theta}\, d\theta, \quad (a > b > 0).$

9. $\int_0^{\pi/2} \frac{1}{a + b\cos\theta}\, d\theta, \quad (b > a > 0).$

10. $\displaystyle\int \frac{1}{a\sin\theta + b\cos\theta}\,d\theta.$

11. $\displaystyle\int \frac{1}{a^2\sin^2\theta + b^2\cos^2\theta}\,d\theta.$

In each of Exercises 12–17 establish a reduction formula for the integral (the exponents are positive integers).

12. $\displaystyle\int (\ln x)^m\,dx.$

13. $\displaystyle\int x^n(\ln x)^m\,dx.$

14. $\displaystyle\int \tan^n x\,dx.$

15. $\displaystyle\int \operatorname{sech}^n x\,dx.$

16. $\displaystyle\int \frac{1}{(x^2+a^2)^n}\,dx.$

17. $\displaystyle\int x^n \sin^2 x\,dx.$

18. Prove

$$\int_0^{\pi/2} \sin^{2m-1}\theta\cos^{2n-1}\theta\,d\theta = \frac{(m-1)!(n-1)!}{2(m+n-1)!}, \quad m, n > 0.$$

[*Hint:* Use mathematical induction and the result of Example 6, page 351.]

19. Redo Exercise II-3, page 371, if the tank is horizontal instead of vertical.

20. Shown below are two identical tanks which are frustums of a right circular cone. If both tanks are initially full of water, which tank will empty out first? (Assume that the orifice areas are the same and that the tanks start discharging at the same time.)

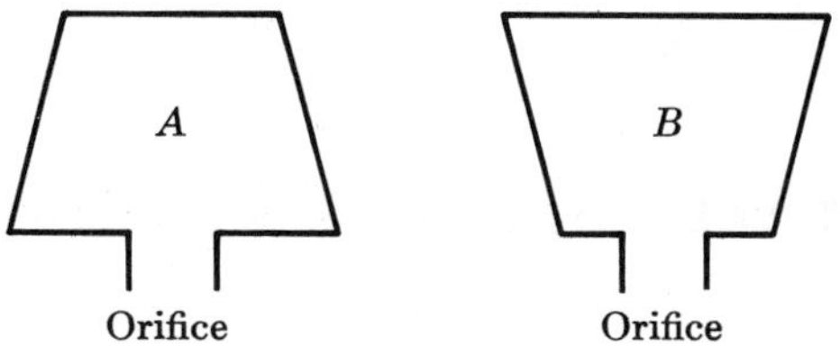

21. Water is slightly compressible. If sea water weighs $64(1 + 2 \times 10^{-8}P)$ lb/ft^3 under a pressure of P lb/ft^2, find the weight of a cubic foot of water at a depth of (a) 1 mile below sea level; (b) 5 miles below sea level.

13

FURTHER APPLICATIONS OF THE CALCULUS

APPLICATIONS OF THE calculus to such problems as finding the center of gravity of a body and the force of water against a dam will be given in this chapter. Before giving these applications, however, we shall further study conic sections. The conic sections already discussed are the circle and the parabola.

1 THE CENTRAL CONICS; THE ELLIPSE

If a right circular cone of two nappes is cut by a plane not parallel to an edge of the cone and not passing through the vertex of the cone, the resulting curve is either an ellipse (if the plane intersects only one nappe) or a hyperbola (if the plane cuts both nappes). Each of these curves may be defined in an alternate way as follows.

13.1 DEFINITION. An *ellipse* is the set of all points in a plane the sum of whose distances from two fixed points (the foci) in the plane is a constant. A *hyperbola* is the set of all points in a plane the difference of whose distances from two fixed points (the foci) in the plane is a constant.

An ellipse can be constructed from a loop of string in the following way. Place two thumbtacks F and F' (the foci) in the paper and loop the piece of string over them. Then pull the string taut with your pencil point P, as shown in Figure 13.1. Now move the pencil, always keeping the string taut. Since $|FP| + |F'P|$ is always a constant, the curve traced out will be an ellipse, according to **13.1**. If F and F' coincide, clearly the ellipse becomes a circle.

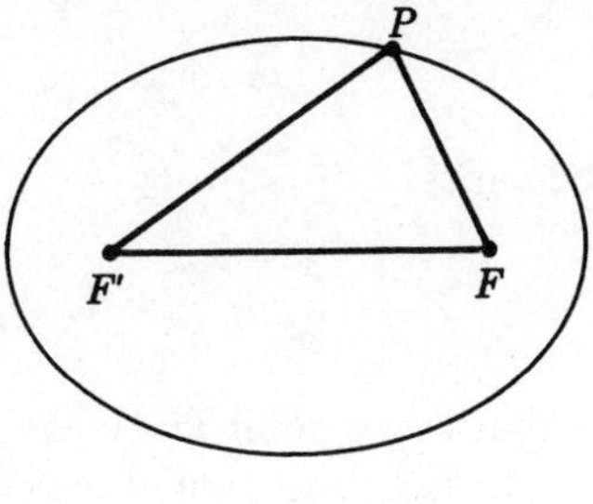

FIGURE 13.1

By placing coordinate axes in the plane, we can find an equation for an ellipse or a hyperbola in much the same way that we found an equation for a parabola. An obvious choice for one axis is the line through the foci and for the other axis is the perpendicular bisector of the segment joining the foci. If the x axis is the axis containing the foci, then the foci will have coordinates $F(c,0)$ and $F'(-c,0)$ for some number $c > 0$.

To find an equation of an ellipse, let $2a$ designate the constant sum of the distances from a point P on the ellipse to the foci F and F'. Evidently, $a > c$. Then a point $P(x,y)$ of the plane is on the ellipse if and only if

$$|FP| + |F'P| = 2a,$$

(see Figure 13.2), i.e., if and only if

$$\sqrt{(x-c)^2 + y^2} + \sqrt{(x+c)^2 + y^2} = 2a.$$

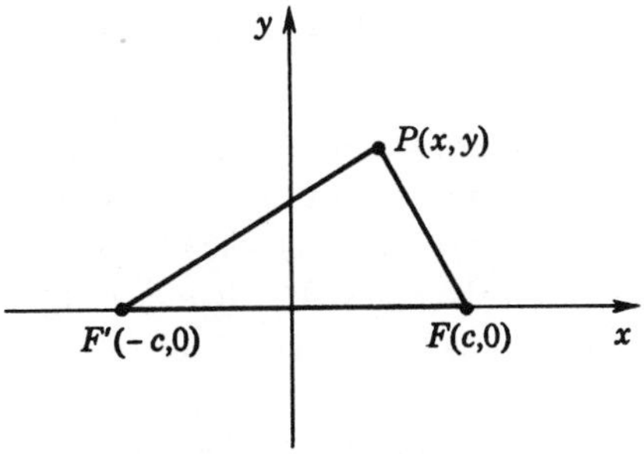

FIGURE 13.2

If this equation is rationalized by transposing one of the radicals and then squaring both sides, and similarly for one more step, it reduces to

$$\frac{x^2}{a^2} + \frac{y^2}{a^2 - c^2} = 1.$$

If we let

13.2 $$b^2 = a^2 - c^2,$$

the above equation becomes

13.3 $$\frac{x^2}{a^2} + \frac{y^2}{b^2} = 1.$$

We have proved that every point $P(x,y)$ on the given ellipse satisfies **13.3**. In order to prove that **13.3** is an equation of the ellipse, we must show conversely that every point $P(x,y)$ satisfying **13.3** lies on the given ellipse. The proof of this is left as an exercise for the reader (Exercise 15, page 379).

For each point $P(x,y)$ on the ellipse with Equation **13.3**, the points $P_1(-x,y)$, $P_2(x,-y)$, and $P_3(-x,-y)$ are also on the ellipse (Figure 13.3), since their co-

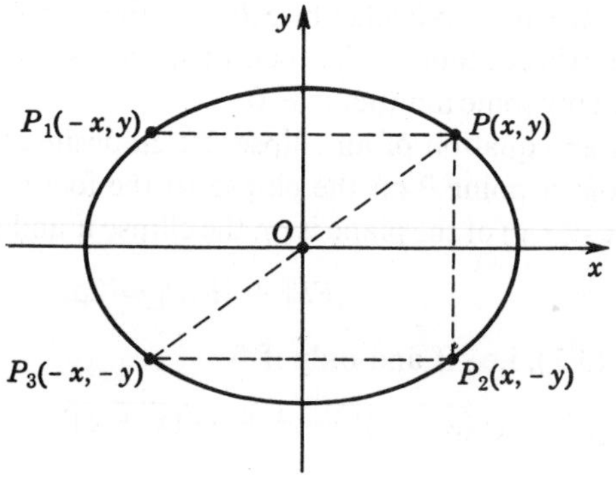

FIGURE 13.3

ordinates again are solutions of **13.3**. Since P_1 is the image of P in the x axis, evidently the ellipse is symmetric to the x axis. For a similar reason the ellipse is symmetric to the y axis. It follows that the ellipse is also symmetric to the origin; i.e., for each point P on the ellipse the diametrically opposite point P_3 is also on the ellipse. The origin is called the *center* of the ellipse. In **13.3**, if $y = 0$, then $x = \pm a$; if $x = 0$, $y = \pm b$. Thus the ellipse cuts the x axis at $(\pm a,0)$ and the y axis at $(0,\pm b)$, as indicated in Figure 13.4. The points $V(a,0)$ and $V'(-a,0)$ are called the *vertices* of the ellipse, the segment VV' is called the *major axis* of the

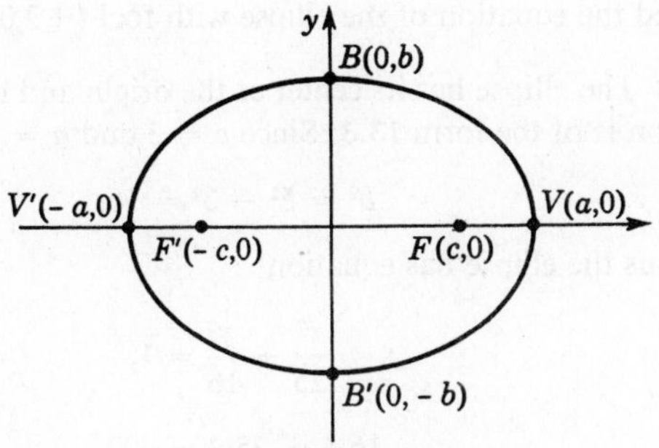

FIGURE 13.4

ellipse, and the segment BB' is called the *minor axis* of the ellipse. The major axis of the ellipse contains the foci and is of length $2a$, whereas the minor axis is of length $2b$. From **13.2** it is clear that $a > b$, and therefore the major axis of an ellipse is actually longer than the minor axis (unless the ellipse is a circle).

If the foci of an ellipse are on the y axis and equispaced from the origin, and if $2a$ again designates the sum of the distances of the foci from each point on the ellipse, then the equation of the ellipse is **13.3** with x and y interchanged; i.e.,

13.4
$$\frac{y^2}{a^2} + \frac{x^2}{b^2} = 1.$$

The vertices and major axis are now on the y axis, as shown in Figure 13.5.

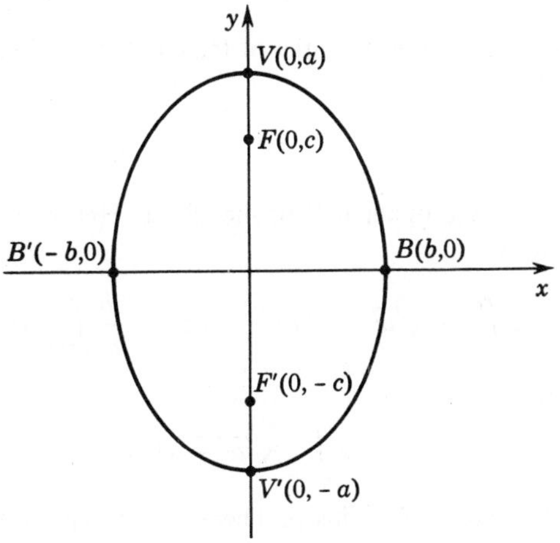

FIGURE 13.5

EXAMPLE 1. Find the equation of the ellipse with foci $(\pm 3,0)$ and vertices $(\pm 5,0)$.

Solution: The ellipse has its center at the origin and its foci on the x axis; therefore its equation is of the form **13.3**. Since $c = 3$ and $a = 5$, we have **(13.2)**

$$b^2 = 5^2 - 3^2 = 16,$$

and $b = 4$. Thus the ellipse has equation

$$\frac{x^2}{25} + \frac{y^2}{16} = 1,$$

or

$$16x^2 + 25y^2 = 400.$$

EXAMPLE 2. Discuss the grapn of the equation

$$4x^2 + y^2 = 4.$$

Solution: If we divide each member of this equation by 4, we get the equation

$$\frac{x^2}{1} + \frac{y^2}{4} = 1.$$

This equation is of the form **13.4** with $a^2 = 4$ and $b^2 = 1$. Thus the graph is an ellipse with major axis on the y axis and minor axis on the x axis. The vertices are $(0, \pm 2)$, and the ends of the minor axis are $(\pm 1,0)$. Since

$$c^2 = a^2 - b^2 = 3,$$

$c = \sqrt{3}$ and the foci are the points $(0, \pm\sqrt{3})$.

EXAMPLE 3. Find the area of an elliptical region of the plane.

Solution: Let us find the area of the elliptical region of Figure 13.4. On solving **13.3** for y, we get

$$y = \frac{b}{a}\sqrt{a^2 - x^2}$$

as an equation of the upper half of the ellipse. Hence, by symmetry, the area of the ellipse is given by

$$2\int_{-a}^{a} \frac{b}{a}\sqrt{a^2 - x^2}\,dx \qquad \text{or} \qquad \frac{2b}{a}\int_{-a}^{a} \sqrt{a^2 - x^2}\,dx.$$

We know that

$$2\int_{-a}^{a} \sqrt{a^2 - x^2}\,dx = \pi a^2$$

is the area of a circle of radius a. Therefore the ellipse with semimajor axis a and semiminor axis b has area $(b/a)(\pi a^2)$, or

$$\pi ab.$$

EXERCISES

I

Discuss and sketch the graph of each of the following equations.

1. $x^2 + 4y^2 = 4.$
2. $25x^2 + 16y^2 = 400.$
3. $25x^2 + 9y^2 = 225.$
4. $4x^2 + 9y^2 = 16.$
5. $16x^2 + 25y^2 = 9.$
6. $x^2 + 2y^2 = 1.$
7. $4x^2 + y^2 = 1.$
8. $3x^2 + 4y^2 = 7.$

In each of Exercises 9–14 find an equation of the ellipse satisfying the given conditions.

9. Foci $(\pm 4,0)$, vertices $(\pm 5,0)$.
10. Foci $(0,\pm 2)$, ends of minor axis $(\pm 1,0)$.
11. Foci $(0,\pm\sqrt{21})$, end of minor axis $(2,0)$.
12. Vertices $(\pm 6,0)$, focus $(-3\sqrt{3},0)$.
13. Vertices $(0,\pm 3)$, passing through the point $(\frac{2}{3},2\sqrt{2})$.
14. Foci $(\pm\sqrt{5},0)$, passing through the point $(\frac{3}{2},\sqrt{3})$.
15. Prove that for every point $P(x,y)$ satisfying 13.3

$$|PF| + |PF'| = 2a$$

(notation of Figure 13.2). [*Hint:* Multiply each side of the equation $\sqrt{(x-c)^2 + y^2} + \sqrt{(x+c)^2 + y^2} = 2a$ by a, then replace a^2y^2 under each radical by $a^2b^2 - b^2x^2$. By 13.2, the resulting equation reduces to $|a^2 - cx| + |a^2 + cx| = 2a^2$. But $x \leq a$, etc.]

16. Show that

$$\frac{x_1x}{a^2} + \frac{y_1y}{b^2} = 1$$

is an equation of the tangent line to the ellipse 13.3 at $P(x_1,y_1)$.

17. Define the latus rectum for an ellipse as for a parabola. Show that its length is $2b^2/a$.
18. A *diameter* of an ellipse is any chord through its center. Show that the minor axis is the shortest and the major axis is the longest diameter if the axes are of unequal lengths.

II

1. Prove that the longest chord of an ellipse is the major axis. Note that this problem generalizes Exercise 18 above.

2. Conjecture a generalization of Exercise 1 and prove it if you can.

3. Many results concerning ellipses can be deduced rather simply from the corresponding results for circles by means of a transformation called orthogonal projection. The orthogonal projection of a figure onto a plane is the graph of the feet of

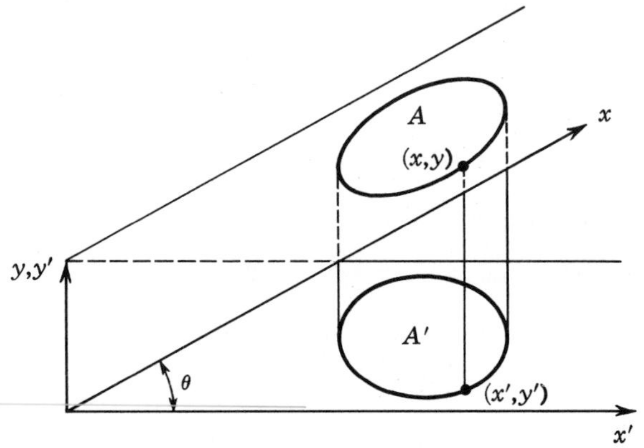

the perpendiculars from points of the figure onto the plane. Physically, this corresponds approximately to the shadow of a figure cast on the ground when the sun is directly overhead. Analytically, the transformation is given by

a. $$y' = y, \quad x' = x\cos\theta.$$

From a, or else geometrically, the following properties hold for this transformation:

b. Straight lines project into straight lines.
c. Parallel lines project into parallel lines.
d. The ratio of lengths of two segments of a given line or parallel lines projects into the same ratio of lengths for the projected segments.
e. The ratio of areas of two figures in the same plane projects into the same ratio of areas for the projected figures. In particular, if A and A' denote the areas of the figures above, then $A' = A\cos\theta$.
f. Tangent curves project into tangent curves.
g. Conics project into conics.
h. Centroids project into centroids.

Now show that all rectangles inscribed in a proper ellipse (i.e., one with unequal axes) have their sides parallel to the axes.

4. Show that the graph of the set of midpoints of all chords of an ellipse parallel to a given chord is a diameter of the ellipse (see Exercise I–18).

5. Derive the area of an ellipse from the area formula of a circle.

6. What is the maximum area of any rectangle inscribed in the ellipse $x^2/a^2 + y^2/b^2 = 1$? (Use Exercise 3.)

7. Show that there is exactly one square that can be inscribed in a proper ellipse and find its area.

8. Sketch the graph of the equation

$$x^2 + xy + y^2 = 3.$$

9. Given the ellipse $\dfrac{x^2}{a^2} + \dfrac{y^2}{b^2} = 1$ with circumference L, show that:

a. $L = 4a \displaystyle\int_0^{\pi/2} \sqrt{1 - e^2 \sin^2 u}\, du,$
where $e = \sqrt{a^2 - b^2}/a$. (e is called the eccentricity of the ellipse.)

b. Using the Schwarz-Buniakowsky inequality (Exercise II-11, Review, Chapter 7), or otherwise, show that

$$L \leq \pi\sqrt{2(a^2 + b^2)}.$$

c. Using the trapezoidal rule with $n = 2$, show that

$$L > \frac{\pi}{2}\left(a + b + \sqrt{(a^2 + b^2)/2}\right).$$

2 THE HYPERBOLA

Let us determine the equation of a hyperbola just as we did that of the ellipse by placing the foci on the x axis equispaced from the origin (Figure 13.6). The point O midway between the foci is called the *center* of the hyperbola. Again, as in the

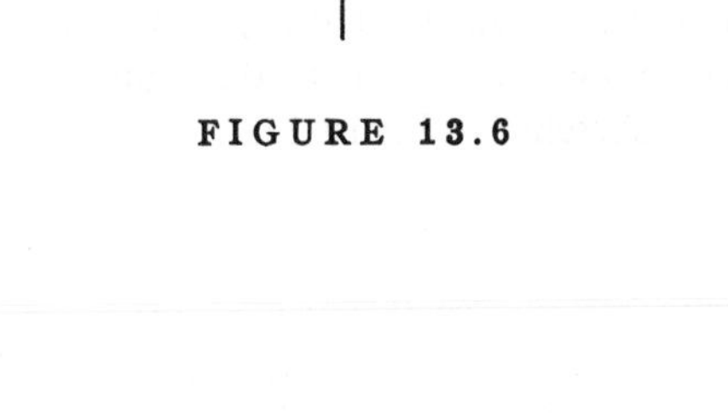

FIGURE 13.6

ellipse, we let the coordinates of the foci be $(\pm c,0)$, and we designate the difference of the distances of the foci from a point on the hyperbola by $2a$. Thus the point $P(x,y)$ will be on the hyperbola if and only if

$$|FP| - |F'P| = \pm 2a,$$

(Figure 13.6), i.e., if and only if

$$\sqrt{(x-c)^2+y^2} - \sqrt{(x+c)^2+y^2} = \pm 2a.$$

The plus or minus sign on the right side of the equation is necessitated by the fact that we allow either $|FP|$ or $|F'P|$ to be the larger number, and insist only that the larger number minus the smaller number be $2a$.

In order for the hyperbola to have some point P on it that is not on the x axis, we must have $|F'F| + |FP| > |F'P|$ (i.e., the sum of the lengths of two sides of a triangle exceeds the length of the third side) and $|F'F| + |F'P| > |FP|$. Thus $|F'F| > |F'P| - |FP|$ and $|F'F| > |FP| - |F'P|$, and since $|F'F| = 2c$, $2c > 2a$ and $c > a$. So we insist henceforth that $c > a$.

If we rationalize the above equation of the hyperbola, we obtain the equation

$$\frac{x^2}{a^2} - \frac{y^2}{c^2 - a^2} = 1,$$

or, on letting

13.5 $$b^2 = c^2 - a^2,$$

we get

13.6 $$\frac{x^2}{a^2} - \frac{y^2}{b^2} = 1.$$

Every point on the hyperbola satisfies this equation. That, conversely, every point P satisfying **13.6** is on the hyperbola is left as an exercise for the reader. Thus **13.6** is an equation of the given hyperbola.

It is evident from its equation that the hyperbola is symmetric to both axes and its center (the origin in this case). If $y = 0$, then $x = \pm a$, and the hyperbola cuts the x axis at the points $V(a,0)$ and $V'(-a,0)$, called the *vertices* of the hyperbola. The hyperbola does not intersect the y axis. The segment VV' connecting the vertices is called the *transverse axis* of the hyperbola.

Solving **13.6** for y, we obtain

13.7 $$y = \pm \frac{b}{a}\sqrt{x^2 - a^2},$$

from which equation it is evident that the curve does not exist if $x^2 < a^2$. Thus the hyperbola has two branches, one to the right of $x = a$ and the other to the left of $x = -a$. It is sketched in Figure 13.7.

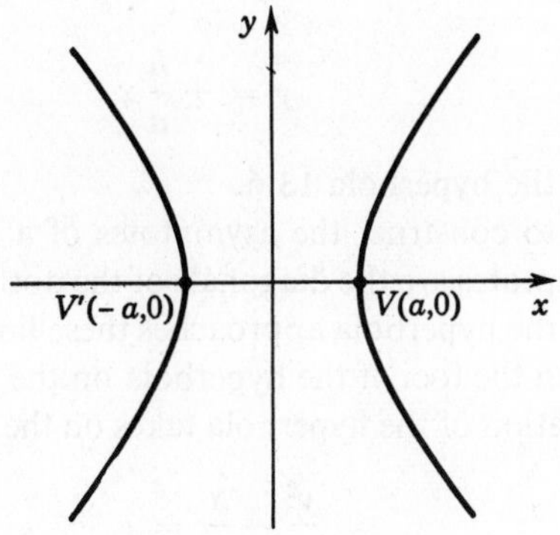

FIGURE 13.7

The hyperbola 13.6 has asymptotes, as we shall now show. It is intuitively clear that $\sqrt{x^2 - a^2}$ and x are approximately equal when x is a large positive number. Hence y, given by 13.7, should be approximately equal to

$$y = \pm \frac{b}{a} x.$$

To be more precise, let us prove that

$$\operatorname*{limit}_{x \to \infty} \left(\frac{b}{a} x - \frac{b}{a} \sqrt{x^2 - a^2} \right) = 0,$$

which will prove that the line $y = bx/a$ is an asymptote of the hyperbola. Since

$$(x - \sqrt{x^2 - a^2})(x + \sqrt{x^2 - a^2}) = a^2,$$

evidently

$$\operatorname*{limit}_{x \to \infty} \frac{b}{a} (x - \sqrt{x^2 - a^2}) = \operatorname*{limit}_{x \to \infty} \frac{ab}{x + \sqrt{x^2 - a^2}} = 0.$$

It can also be shown that

$$\operatorname*{limit}_{x \to -\infty} \left(-\frac{b}{a} x - \frac{b}{a} \sqrt{x^2 - a^2} \right) = 0,$$

which proves that the line $y = -bx/a$ is an asymptote. In a similar manner, it can be shown that the lines $y = \pm bx/a$ are asymptotes of the graph of

$$y = -\frac{b}{a} \sqrt{x^2 - a^2}.$$

Thus the lines

$$y = \pm \frac{b}{a} x$$

are asymptotes of the hyperbola **13.6.**

An easy way to construct the asymptotes of a hyperbola is shown in Figure 13.8. The asymptotes are the diagonals of the dotted rectangle. Having drawn in the asymptotes, the hyperbola approaches these lines as indicated in the figure.

If we start with the foci of the hyperbola on the y axis and equispaced from the origin, the equation of the hyperbola takes on the form

13.8
$$\frac{y^2}{a^2} - \frac{x^2}{b^2} = 1,$$

where, again, $b^2 = c^2 - a^2$. The vertices of this hyperbola have coordinates $(0, \pm a)$ and the transverse axis is along the y axis. The asymptotes have equations

$$x = \pm \frac{b}{a} y.$$

The hyperbola **13.8** is shown in Figure 13.9.

The ellipse and hyperbola are called *central conics* for the reason that each has a center of symmetry.

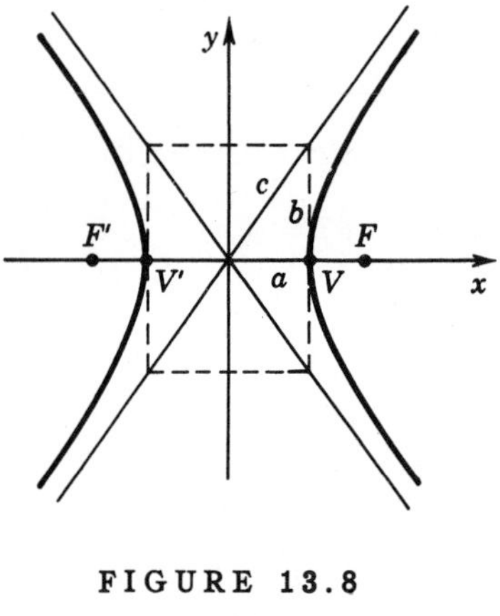

FIGURE 13.8

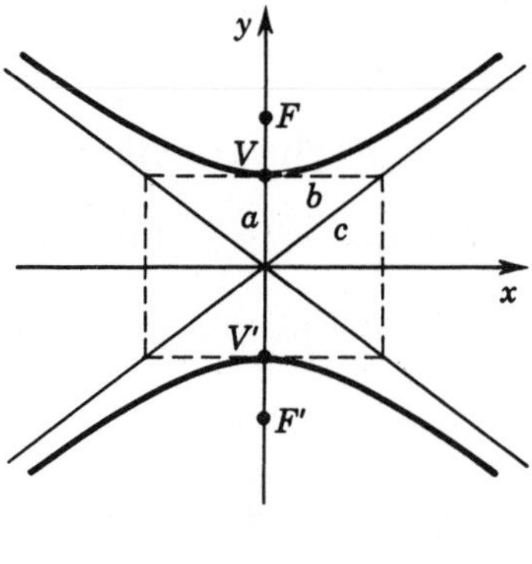

FIGURE 13.9

EXAMPLE 1. Find an equation of the hyperbola with foci $(\pm 5,0)$ and vertices $(\pm 4,0)$.

Solution: The center of this hyperbola is the origin and the transverse axis is along the x axis. Therefore its equation has the form **13.6.** Clearly, $c = 5$ and $a = 4$, so that

$$b^2 = c^2 - a^2 = 9.$$

Thus the equation is

$$\frac{x^2}{16} - \frac{y^2}{9} = 1,$$

or

$$9x^2 - 16y^2 = 144.$$

The asymptotes of this hyperbola are the lines

$$y = \tfrac{3}{4}x \quad \text{and} \quad y = -\tfrac{3}{4}x.$$

EXAMPLE 2. Discuss the graph of the equation

$$4x^2 - 5y^2 + 20 = 0.$$

Solution: If we divide each member of this equation by 20, we obtain the equation

$$\frac{y^2}{4} - \frac{x^2}{5} = 1.$$

This equation has the form **13.8** with $a^2 = 4$ and $b^2 = 5$. Thus

$$c^2 = a^2 + b^2 = 9,$$

and $a = 2$, $b = \sqrt{5}$, and $c = 3$. The transverse axis is along the y axis, the vertices are the points $(0, \pm 2)$, the foci the points $(0, \pm 3)$, and the asymptotes the lines

$$x = \pm \frac{\sqrt{5}}{2} y.$$

EXERCISES

I

Discuss and sketch the graph of each of the following equations.

1. $x^2 - 4y^2 = 4$.
2. $25x^2 - 16y^2 = 400$.
3. $9x^2 - 16y^2 + 144 = 0$.
4. $16x^2 - 9y^2 + 144 = 0$.
5. $x^2 - y^2 = 4$.
6. $4x^2 - 4y^2 + 1 = 0$.
7. $4x^2 - 9y^2 + 16 = 0$.
8. $144x^2 - 25y^2 = 3600$.

In each of Exercises 9–14, find an equation of the hyperbola satisfying the given conditions.

9. Foci $(\pm 4,0)$, vertices $(\pm 2,0)$.
10. Foci $(0, \pm 13)$, vertices $(0, \pm 5)$.
11. Foci $(\pm 10,0)$, vertices $(\pm 6,0)$.
12. Foci $(0, \pm \sqrt{2})$, vertices $(0, \pm 1)$.
13. Vertices $(\pm 2,0)$, asymptotes $y = \pm 2x$.

14. Vertices $(0, \pm 4)$, asymptotes $y = \pm 2x/3$.

15. Prove that for every point $P(x,y)$ satisfying Equation 13.6

$$|FP| - |F'P| = \pm 2a$$

(notation of Figure 13.6). [*Hint:* See Exercise I-15, page 379.]

16. Show that

$$\frac{x_1 x}{a^2} - \frac{y_1 y}{b^2} = 1$$

is an equation of the tangent line to the hyperbola 13.7 at the point $P(x_1,y_1)$.

17. If A and B are the points at which the tangent line to a hyperbola at any point P intersects the asymptotes, show that P is the midpoint of AB.

II

1. Discuss and sketch the graphs of

$$\frac{x^2}{25 + \lambda} + \frac{y^2}{9 + \lambda} = 1,$$

where λ is a variable parameter.

2. On a level meadow the crack of a rifle is heard at the same instant as the thud of the bullet striking the target. Show that the hearer must be located on a fixed hyperbola.

3. Show that the tangent at any point of a hyperbola cuts off a triangle of constant area with its asymptotes.

4. Compare the areas of the shaded sectors of an ellipse and a hyperbola as shown in the figures.

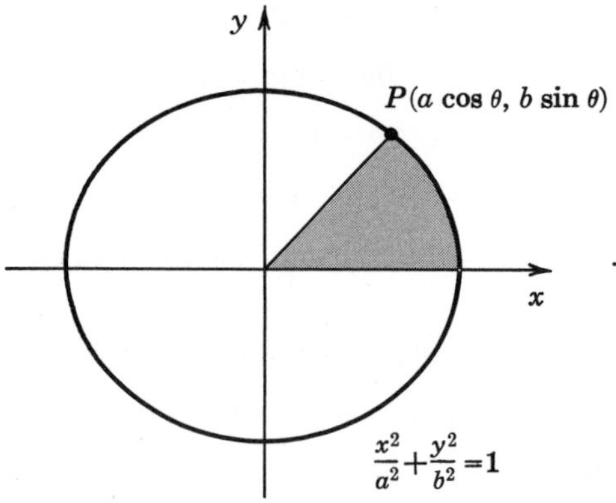

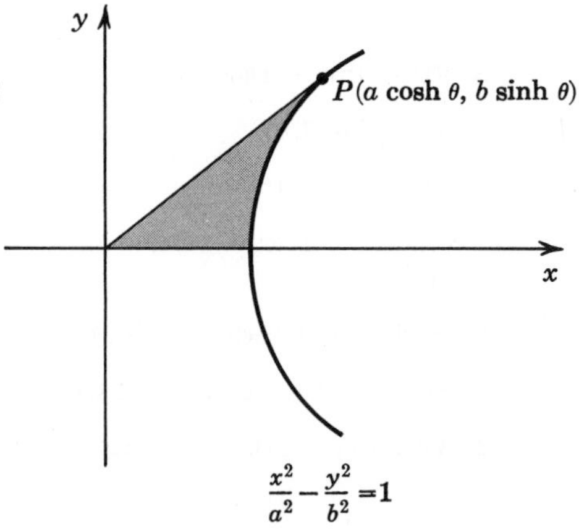

5. a. Show that the arc length of the hyperbola $x^2/a^2 - y^2/b^2 = 1$ between $x = a$ and $x = a \cosh k$, $(k > 0)$, is given by

$$L = 2a \int_0^k \sqrt{e^2 \cosh^2 u - 1}\, du.$$

where $e = \sqrt{a^2 + b^2}/a$ is called the eccentricity.

b. Show that $L < ak\sqrt{2e^2 - 4 + (e^2/k) \sinh 2k}$ (see Exercise II–9, Section 1.)

6. What is the condition that the graphs of the equations

$$\frac{x^2}{a^2} + \frac{y^2}{b^2} = 1 \qquad \text{and} \qquad \frac{x^2}{c^2} - \frac{y^2}{d^2} = 1$$

intersect orthogonally?

7. By considering the midpoints of parallel chords, show how to construct the center of a given hyperbola with straightedge and compass.

8. Describe the graph of the set of points of intersection of the pair of lines

$$\frac{x}{a} - \frac{y}{b} = m, \qquad \frac{x}{a} + \frac{y}{b} = \frac{1}{m},$$

where m is a variable parameter and a and b are constants.

3 TRANSLATION OF AXES

If, in the coordinate plane with given x and y axes, new coordinate axes are chosen parallel to the given ones, then we shall say that there has been a *translation of axes* in the plane. In Figure 13.10 the given x and y axes have been trans-

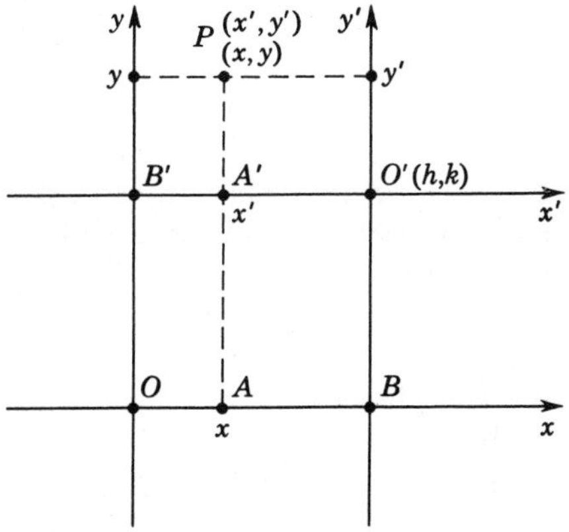

FIGURE 13.10

lated to the x' and y' axes with origin (h,k) relative to the given axes. The positive numbers are assumed to be on the same side of the origin on the new axes as they were on the given axes.

A point P with coordinates (x,y) relative to the given coordinate axes will also have coordinates, say $(x',y')'$, relative to the new axes. These coordinates of P are related to each other by the equations

13.9 $$x' = x - h, \qquad y' = y - k,$$

or

13.10 $$x = x' + h, \qquad y = y' + k.$$

To prove these, let the points O, A, B, O', A', and B' be selected as in Figure 13.10. Then $x = \overline{OA}$, $x' = \overline{O'A'}$, $h = \overline{OB}$, and $k = \overline{OB'}$. Since

$$\overline{OB} = \overline{OA} + \overline{AB} = \overline{OA} + \overline{A'O'} = \overline{OA} - \overline{O'A'},$$

we have

$$h = x - x' \qquad \text{or} \qquad x' = x - h.$$

The other part of **13.9** is proved similarly, whereas **13.10** is just **13.9** written in a slightly different way.

From a given equation in x and y we may derive an equation in x' and y' simply by replacing x by $x' + h$ and y by $y' + k$ as in **13.10**. The graph of the given equation relative to the x and y axes must coincide with the graph of the new equation (in x' and y') relative to the new x' and y' axes, since the point (x,y) satisfies the given equation if and only if $(x',y')'$ satisfies the new equation. We now give an example to illustrate these ideas.

EXAMPLE 1. Let the given coordinate axes be translated to the new origin (2,3). Find an equation relative to the new x' and y' axes of the graph of the equation

$$x^2 - 4x - 3y + 13 = 0$$

relative to the x and y axes.

Solution: The old and new coordinate axes are shown in Figure 13.11. A point P with coordinates $(x',y')'$ relative to the new coordinate axes has coordinates (x,y) relative to the old axes given by

$$x = x' + 2, \qquad y = y' + 3,$$

according to **13.10**. By replacing x by $x' + 2$, and y by $y' + 3$ in the given equation, we obtain the equation

$$(x' + 2)^2 - 4(x' + 2) - 3(y' + 3) + 13 = 0.$$

This simplifies to the equation

$$x'^2 = 3y'.$$

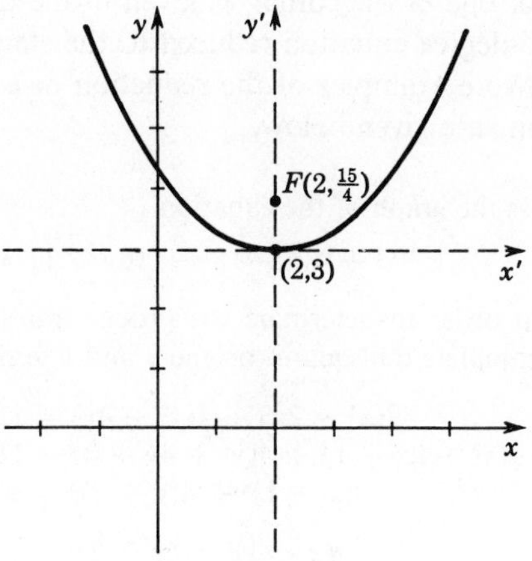

FIGURE 13.11

The graph of this equation relative to the x' and y' axes is a parabola with $p = \frac{3}{4}$. It is sketched in Figure 13.11. Thus the graph of the given equation relative to the x and y axes is a parabola with vertex the point (2,3), focus the point $(2,\frac{15}{4})$, and directrix the line $y = \frac{9}{4}$.

This example illustrates an important use of translation of axes, namely to reduce an equation to a simpler form so as to facilitate the graphing of the given equation.

The second degree equation in x and y,

$$x^2 + y^2 + 2 = 0,$$

has no graph at all, since $x^2 \geq 0$, $y^2 \geq 0$, and $x^2 + y^2 + 2 > 0$ for every real number x and y. The equation

$$4(x - 2)^2 + 9(y + 3)^2 = 0$$

has a graph consisting of one point, namely the point $(2,-3)$. The equation

$$y^2 - x^2 = 0$$

has as its graph the two straight lines $y = \pm x$. From these examples it is evident that the graph of a second-degree equation in x and y might not exist, or might consist of just a point or of (one or two) straight lines.

The graph of a second-degree equation of the form

13.11 $$Ax^2 + Cy^2 + Dx + Ey + F = 0,$$

if it exists and is not made up of just a point or straight lines, is necessarily one of the conic sections. A proper translation of axes will reduce the equation into a standard form of one of the conics as given in the previous sections. In Example 1 the second-degree equation reduced to the standard form of the equation of a parabola. More examples of the reduction of equations of the form **13.11** to standard forms are given below.

EXAMPLE 2. Discuss the graph of the equation

$$9x^2 + 4y^2 - 18x + 16y - 11 = 0.$$

Solution: In order to determine the proper translation of axes to reduce this equation, let us complete the squares on the x and y terms as follows:

$$9(x^2 - 2x) + 4(y^2 + 4y) = 11,$$
$$9(x^2 - 2x + 1) + 4(y^2 + 4y + 4) = 11 + 9 + 16,$$
$$9(x - 1)^2 + 4(y + 2)^2 = 36,$$

$$\frac{(x-1)^2}{4} + \frac{(y+2)^2}{9} = 1.$$

If we let

$$x' = x - 1, \qquad y' = y + 2,$$

so that $h = 1$ and $k = -2$ in **13.9**, the given equation reduces to the standard form of an ellipse (**13.4**)

$$\frac{x'^2}{4} + \frac{y'^2}{9} = 1.$$

Thus a translation of axes to the new origin $(1,-2)$ shows that the graph of the given equation is an ellipse with axes parallel to the coordinate axes. It is sketched in Figure 13.12.

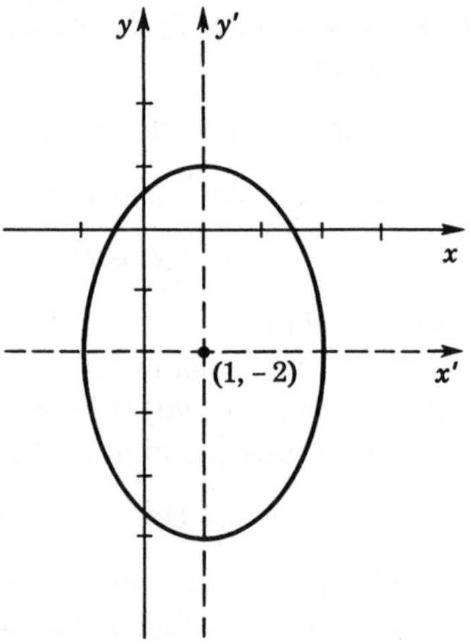

FIGURE 13.12

EXAMPLE 3. Discuss the graph of the equation

$$x^2 - 4y^2 + 6x + 24y - 31 = 0.$$

Solution: We first complete the squares as follows:

$$(x^2 + 6x + 9) - 4(y^2 - 6y + 9) = 31 + 9 - 36,$$
$$(x + 3)^2 - 4(y - 3)^2 = 4,$$
$$\frac{(x + 3)^2}{4} - \frac{(y - 3)^2}{1} = 1.$$

Letting

$$x' = x + 3, \qquad y' = y - 3,$$

so that $h = -3$ and $k = 3$ in **13.9**, the given equation reduces to the standard form of a hyperbola (13.6),

$$\frac{x'^2}{4} - \frac{y'^2}{1} = 1.$$

Hence a translation of axes to the new origin $(-3,3)$ shows that the graph of the given equation is a hyperbola. The graph is sketched in Figure 13.13.

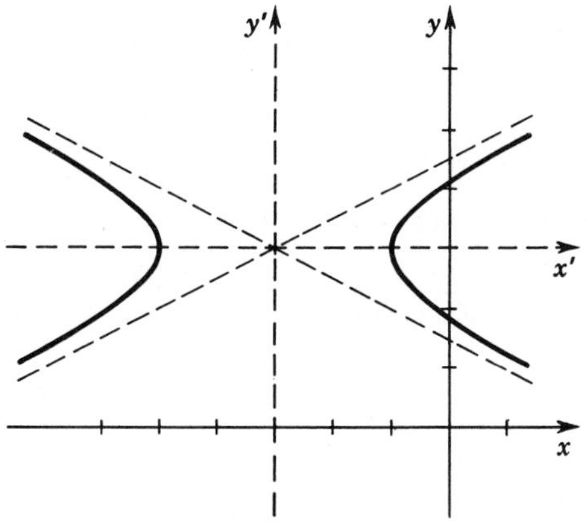

FIGURE 13.13

EXERCISES

I

In each of Exercises 1–12, discuss and sketch the graph of the equation.

1. $x^2 - 6x - 4y + 1 = 0.$
2. $y^2 + 2y + 8x - 15 = 0.$
3. $x^2 + 9y^2 - 4x - 18y + 4 = 0.$
4. $2x^2 + 8y^2 - 8x - 16y + 9 = 0.$

5. $2x^2 + 3y^2 - 4x + 12y + 8 = 0$.

6. $4x^2 - y^2 - 24x - 4y + 36 = 0$.

7. $x^2 - y^2 + 4x - 4y + 1 = 0$.

8. $x^2 + y^2 + 6x + 5 = 0$.

9. $y^2 + 8x - 6 = 0$.

10. $x^2 + 2x - 2y + 2 = 0$.

11. $9x^2 - 4y^2 - 54x + 45 = 0$.

12. $9x^2 - 25y^2 - 90x - 50y - 25 = 0$.

13. Find an equation of the parabola with vertex (h,k) and focus $(h + p,k)$.

14. Find an equation of the parabola with vertex (h,k) and focus $(h,k + p)$.

15. Find an equation of the ellipse with center (h,k), foci $(h \pm c,k)$, and vertices $(h \pm a,k)$.

16. Find an equation of the ellipse with center (h,k), foci $(h,k \pm c)$, and vertices $(h,k \pm a)$.

17. Find an equation of the hyperbola with center (h,k), foci $(h \pm c,k)$, and vertices $(h \pm a,k)$.

18. Find an equation of the hyperbola with center (h,k), foci $(h,k \pm c)$, and vertices $(h,k \pm a)$.

19. Find the maximum or minimum point (vertex) of the parabola $y = ax^2 + bx + c$ by a translation of axes.

20. Show how to solve the quadratic equation $ax^2 + bx + c = 0$ by means of Exercise 19.

II

1. Find the shortest distance from the point $(-1,-1)$ to the graph of $9x^2 - 16y^2 + 36x - 32y = 124$.

2. Find the shortest distance from the point $(4,-6)$ to the graph of $81x^2 + 16y^2 - 648x - 32y + 16 = 0$.

3. Show that the two congruent ellipses

$$\frac{x^2}{a^2} + \frac{y^2}{b^2} = 1 \quad \text{and} \quad \frac{(x-h)^2}{a^2} + \frac{(y-k)^2}{b^2} = 1 \quad (h,k \neq 0)$$

intersect in at most two points (real).

4. To provide for generalizations of Exercise 3 and Exercise 7 to follow as well as other subsequent ones, we briefly introduce the notion of convexity. This topic has many applications throughout geometry, analysis and algebra; much current research is being done in this field and it provides an easy source to discover new challenging problems.

A set of points is defined to be *convex*, if for any two points of the set, the line segment joining the two points belong to the set, as shown in the figure. With respect to a plane convex figure, the points of the plane can be divided into three

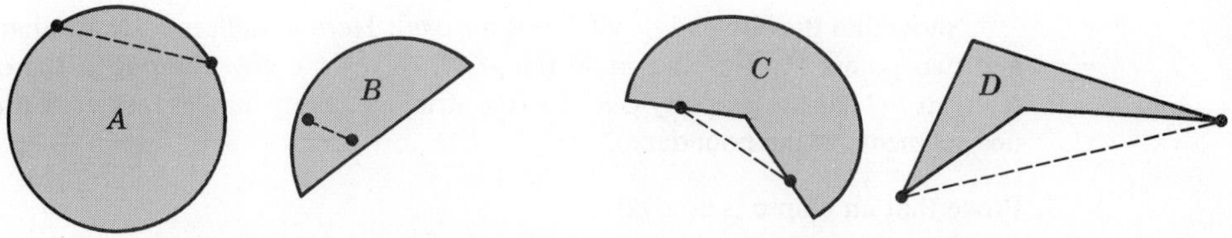

Convex **Non-convex**

classes: interior points, exterior points and boundary points. A point of the figure is called an *interior* point if it is the center of a circle (with sufficiently small radius) which belongs entirely to the figure, e.g., points E and F in the figure. A point is called an *exterior* point with respect to a figure if it is the center of a circle containing no point of the figure, e.g., point G. Finally, a point is called a *boundary* point of a figure if every circle about the point always contains both interior and exterior

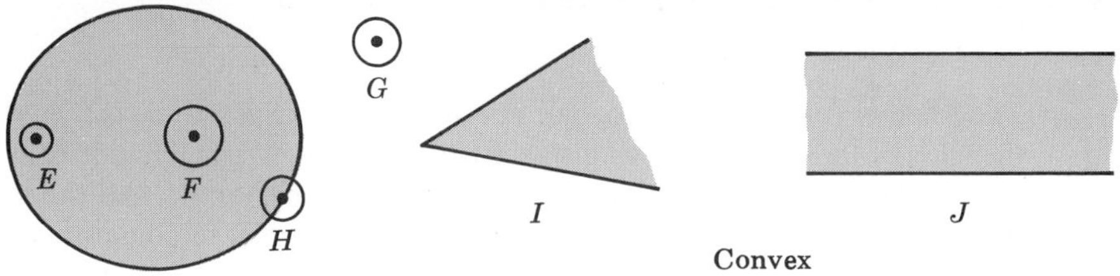

Convex

points, e.g., point H. The figure is said to be *bounded* if it can be enclosed in a circle of finite radius, e.g., figure B above is bounded, whereas figures I and J are unbounded. A figure is said to be *closed* if it contains all its boundary points. From now on, we will use *convex figure* to designate a plane convex closed bounded figure. A *strictly* convex figure is defined as one which contains no line segments in its boundary and will be called an *oval*, e.g., figure A is strictly convex (an oval), whereas figure B is just convex.

It follows from the definition of convexity that the intersection of two or more convex figures is also a convex figure where by the intersection of two (or more) figures, we mean the figure composed of all points lying in both (or all) of the figures, as in figure K.

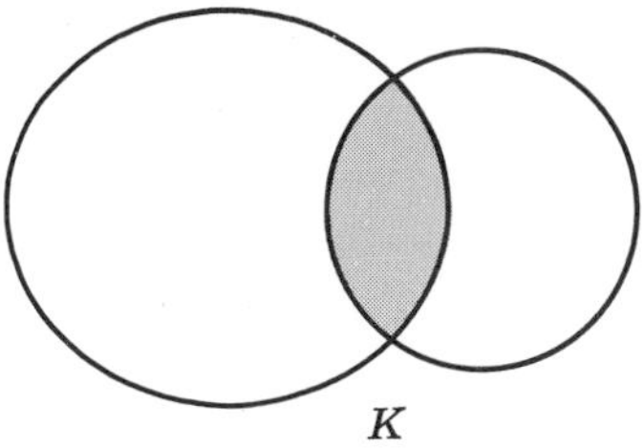

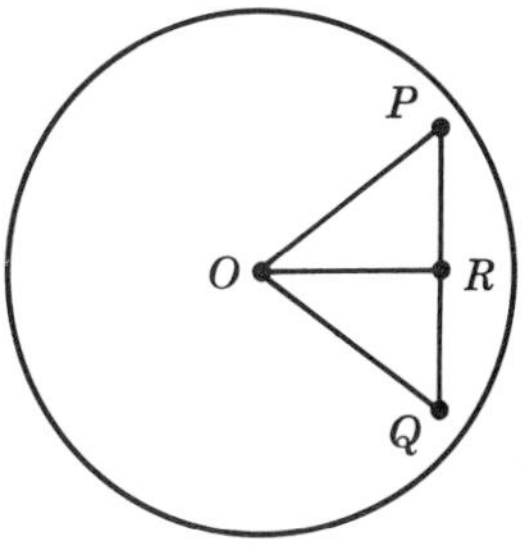

Show that the circle $x^2 + y^2 \leq r^2$ is an oval. Here it suffices to show that for any two points P, Q of the circle (i.e., OP, $OQ \leq r$), any point R in the open segment PQ has the property $OR < r$ (the strict inequality implies that there are no line segments in the boundary).

5. Prove that an ellipse is an oval.

6. Conjecture a generalization of Exercise 3 using ovals and prove it if you can.

7. For the ellipses in Exercise 3 show that the segment joining their centers and their common chord bisect each other.

8. Repeat Exercise 6 for Exercise 7.

4 MOMENTS AND CENTERS OF MASS

The *moment* (of force) of a particle about a line is defined to be the product of the mass of the particle and its distance from the line. We shall find it convenient to consider the particle located on a coordinate plane, and to find the moment of the particle about a coordinate axis (or a line parallel to a coordinate axis). Also, directed distances will be used so that the moment will be positive, negative, or zero, depending on whether the point is on the positive or negative side of the axis, or is on the axis.

In Figure 13.14 the particle of mass m is at the point (x,y) in a coordinate plane. Its moments M_x and M_y about the x and y axes, respectively, are given by

$$M_x = my, \qquad M_y = mx.$$

If the particle is in the second quadrant, as in Figure 13.14, then $M_x > 0$ and $M_y < 0$.

Moments are used to find the *center of mass* of a physical object. As an illustration, consider a seesaw with boys of masses m_1 and m_2 on it. For conveni-

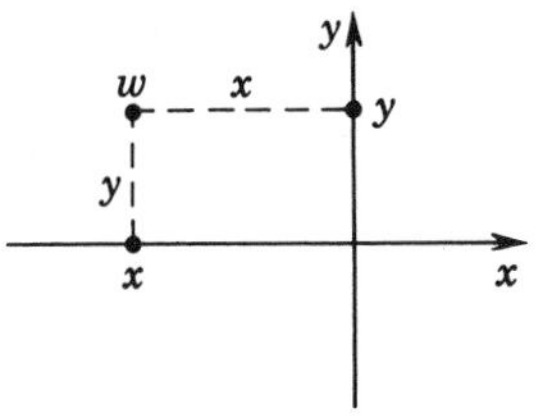

FIGURE 13.14

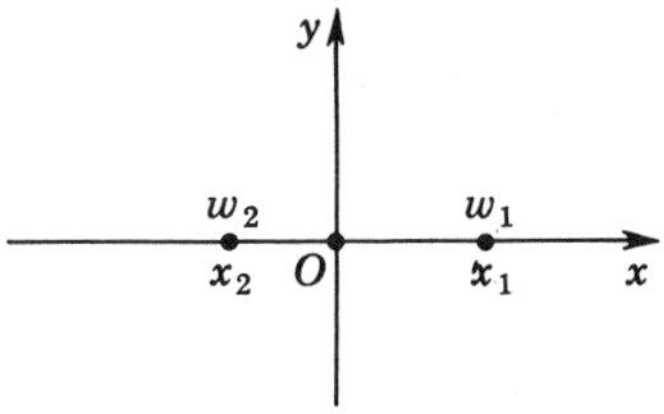

FIGURE 13.15

ence, we think of the seesaw as being on the x axis with balance point at the origin O (Figure 13.15). The moments of the two boys about the y axis are

$$M_1 = m_1x_1, \qquad M_2 = m_2x_2.$$

The two boys will balance each other provided the sum of their moments is zero, i.e.,

$$m_1x_1 + m_2x_2 = 0.$$

If they balance each other, the balance point O is called the center of mass of the physical system made up of the two boys.

The moments of a system of n particles located in a coordinate plane are defined similarly. Thus if the particles of masses $m_1, m_2, \cdots, m_n$ are at the respective points (x_1,y_1), (x_2,y_2), $\cdots$, (x_n,y_n) (Figure 13.16), then the moments M_x and M_y of the system of n particles are defined as follows:

$$M_x = \sum_{i=1}^{n} m_iy_i, \qquad M_y = \sum_{i=1}^{n} m_ix_i.$$

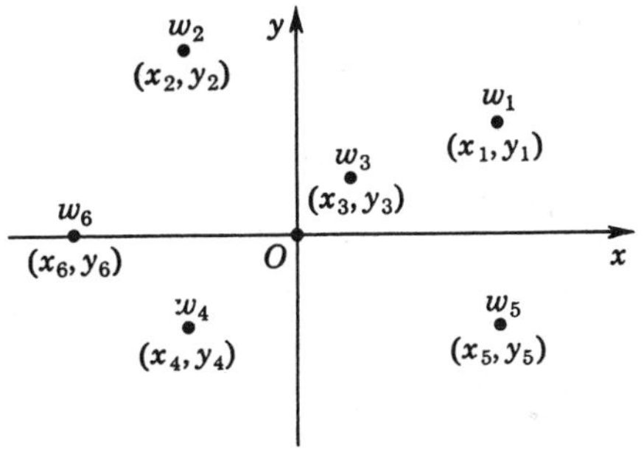

FIGURE 13.16

If $M_x = M_y = 0$, the origin is the center of mass of this system. However, even if $M_x \neq 0$ or $M_y \neq 0$, the given system still has a center of mass, namely the point O' such that relative to the translated axes with center at O', $M_{x'} = M_{y'} = 0$. The following theorem gives the location of the point O'.

13.12 THEOREM. Consider a physical system made up of n particles of masses $m_1, m_2, \cdots, m_n$ located at the respective points (x_1,y_1), (x_2,y_2), $\cdots$, (x_n,y_n). If M_x and M_y are the moments of the system and $m = \sum_{i=1}^{n} m_i$ is its mass, then the center of mass of this system is the point $(\bar{x},\bar{y})$ given by

$$\bar{x} = \frac{M_y}{m}, \qquad \bar{y} = \frac{M_x}{m}.$$

Proof: Let us translate the coordinate axes to a new origin $O'(h,k)$. Relative to the new x' and y' axes, the given particles have coordinates $(x_1',y_1')'$, $(x_2',y_2')'$, $\cdots$, $(x_n',y_n')'$, where

$$x_i' = x_i - h, \qquad y_i' = y_i - k, \qquad (i = 1, 2, \cdots, n).$$

Hence

$$M_x' = \sum_{i=1}^{n} m_i y_i' = \sum_{i=1}^{n} m_i(y_i - k) = \sum_{i=1}^{n} m_i y_i - k \sum_{i=1}^{n} m_i,$$

and therefore

$$M_x' = M_x - km.$$

Similarly,

$$M_y' = M_y - hm.$$

Now the new origin $O'(h,k)$ will be the center of mass of the given system provided that $M_x' = M_y' = 0$, i.e.,

$$M_x - km = 0 \qquad \text{and} \qquad M_y - hm = 0.$$

On solving these equations for h and k, we get $h = M_y/m$ and $k = M_x/m$, as stated in the theorem.

An interesting conclusion that can be drawn from this theorem is that the given system of n particles has the same moments relative to the x and y axes as a system made up of one particle of mass $m = m_1 + m_2 + \cdots + m_n$ and located at the point $(\bar{x},\bar{y})$. This follows immediately from the equations

$$M_x = m\bar{y}, \qquad M_y = m\bar{x}$$

of the theorem. Thus each moment of the system may be found by assuming that its mass is concentrated at the center of mass of the system.

The center of mass of a thin homogeneous sheet of substance, called a *lamina*, may be thought of as the balance point of the lamina. If the lamina has a geometric center, then this point will also be the center of mass. For example, the center of mass of a rectangular lamina is the point of intersection of the diagonals of the rectangle.

The moment of a lamina about a line in the plane of the lamina may be defined with the aid of the calculus. We assume that the moment M_L of a lamina of mass m about an axis L is between md_1 and md_2,

$$md_1 \leq M_L \leq md_2,$$

where d_1 is the minimum (directed) distance of any point of the lamina from L, and d_2 is the maximum (directed) distance of any point of the lamina from L

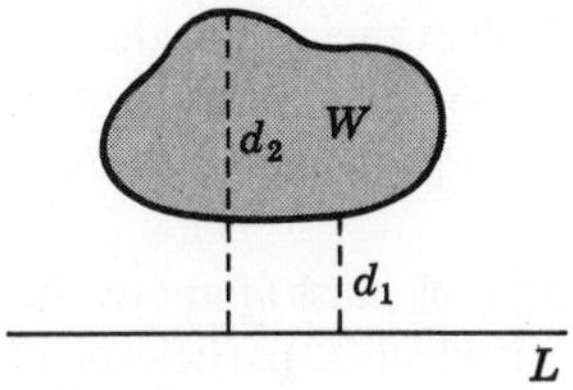

FIGURE 13.17

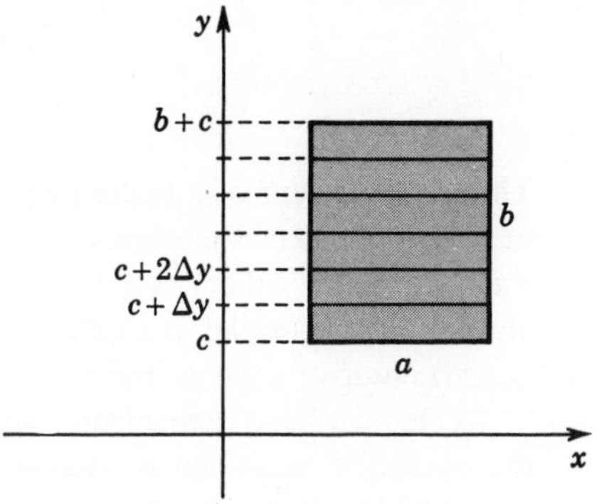

FIGURE 13.18

(Figure 13.17). We also assume that if the lamina is cut up into pieces, the moment of the lamina is the sum of the moments of its pieces.

Let us illustrate the use of these two assumptions in finding the moment of a rectangular lamina of density ρ about an axis parallel to a side of the lamina.* We divide the given rectangle into n congruent rectangles as in Figure 13.18. The height of each smaller rectangle is $\Delta y = b/n$ and its mass is $\rho a\,\Delta y$.

The moment about the x axis of the first rectangle is between $(\rho a\,\Delta y)c$ and $(\rho a\,\Delta y)(c + \Delta y)$; of the second rectangle it is between $(\rho a\,\Delta y)(c + \Delta y)$ and $(\rho a\,\Delta y)(c + 2\,\Delta y)$; and so on. Hence the moment M_x of the given rectangle satisfies the inequality

$$\sum_{i=1}^{n} (\rho a\,\Delta y)[c + (i-1)\,\Delta y] \le M_x \le \sum_{i=1}^{n} (\rho a\,\Delta y)(c + i\,\Delta y).$$

Using **7.4**, we may simplify this as follows $(n\,\Delta y = b)$:

$$\sum_{i=1}^{n} (\rho a\,\Delta y)c + \sum_{i=1}^{n} (\rho a\,\Delta y^2)(i-1) \le M_x \le \sum_{i=1}^{n} (\rho a\,\Delta y)c + \sum_{i=1}^{n} (\rho a\,\Delta y^2)i,$$

$$n(\rho a\,\Delta y)c + \rho a\,\Delta y^2\,\frac{(n-1)n}{2} \le M_x \le n(\rho a\,\Delta y)c + \rho a\,\Delta y^2\,\frac{n(n+1)}{2},$$

$$\rho abc + \rho ab\,\frac{b - \Delta y}{2} \le M_x \le \rho abc + \rho ab\,\frac{b + \Delta y}{2}.$$

The limit of each side of this inequality is the same as n approaches ∞ (and

---

* The mass of a square unit of a lamina is called its density. The mass of a (homogeneous) lamina is ρA, where ρ is its density and A is its area.

Δy approaches 0). Therefore this common limit must be M_x,

$$M_x = \rho ab\left(c + \frac{b}{2}\right).$$

Thus the moment of a rectangular lamina about an axis parallel to a side is the mass ρab of the lamina times the distance $c + b/2$ from the axis to the center of the lamina. In other words, the moment of a rectangular lamina of mass m about an axis parallel to a side is the same as that of a particle of mass m located at the center of mass of the lamina.

Once we have defined the moments of a lamina of mass m about the axes, the center of mass can be defined as the point at which a particle of mass m would be located so that the moments of the particle about the axes would equal the moments of the lamina.

EXAMPLE. Find the center of mass of a lamina of density ρ lb/in.^{2} having the shape of Figure 13.19.

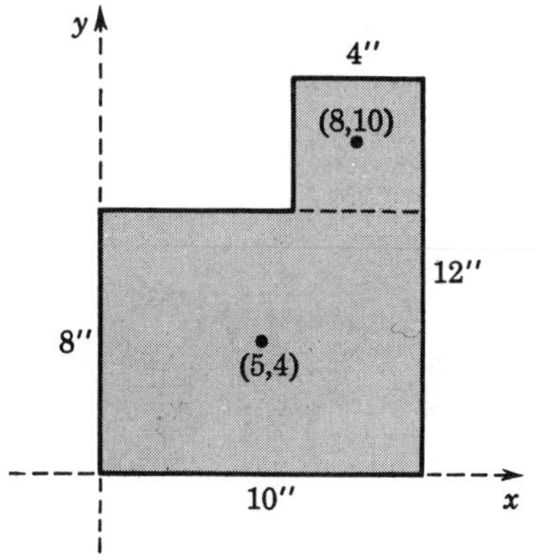

FIGURE 13.19

Solution: The lamina is made up of two rectangles and has a total area of 96 in.^{2} If we place coordinate axes as indicated in the figure, then the centers of mass of the two rectangles are (5,4) and (8,10). Thus the moments of the lamina about the axes are as follows:

$$M_x = (80\rho)4 + (16\rho)10 = 480\rho.$$

$$M_y = (80\rho)5 + (16\rho)8 = 528\rho.$$

Therefore the center of mass $(\bar{x},\bar{y})$ is given by

$$\bar{x} = \frac{M_y}{m} = \frac{528\rho}{96\rho} = \frac{11}{2}, \qquad \bar{y} = \frac{M_x}{m} = \frac{480\rho}{96\rho} = 5,$$

i.e., by $(\frac{11}{2},5)$.

EXERCISES

I

In the following exercises, the notation $m(x,y)$ signifies that a particle of mass m is located at the point (x,y). Find the center of mass of each of the given systems of particles.

1. 3(2,2), 4(2,−2), 5(−2,2), 2(−2,−2).
2. 8(4,4), 6(4,−4), 3(−4,4), 5(−4,−4).
3. 6(0,0), 6(8,0), 6(0,8), 6(8,8), 3(4,4).

In Exercises 4 and 5 find the center of mass of the lamina of density ρ having the shape in the given figure.

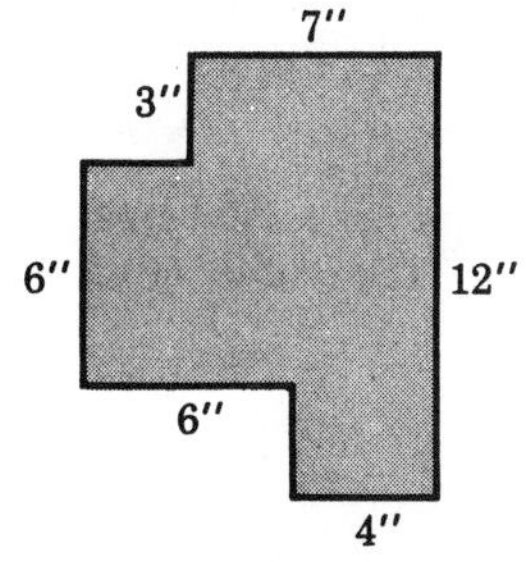

4.

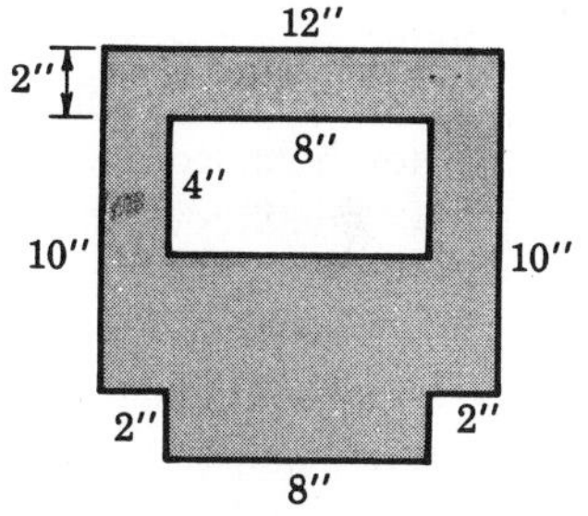

5.

6. Assume that for a given system of n particles $M_x = 0$ and $M_y = 0$. Prove that $M_L = 0$ for every line L passing through the origin.

II

In Exercises 1 and 2, find the center of mass of the lamina of density P having the shape in the given figure.

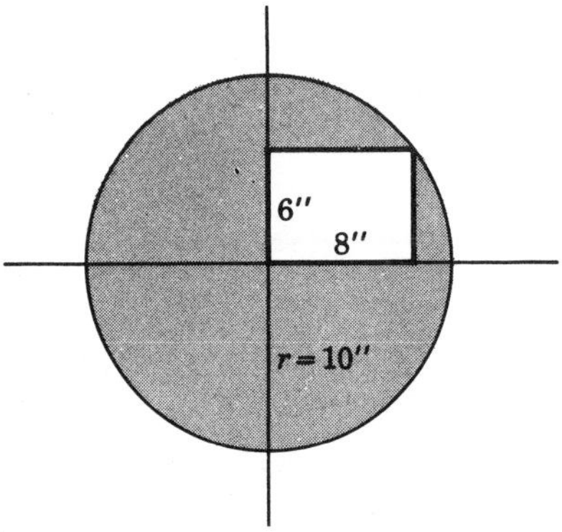

1.

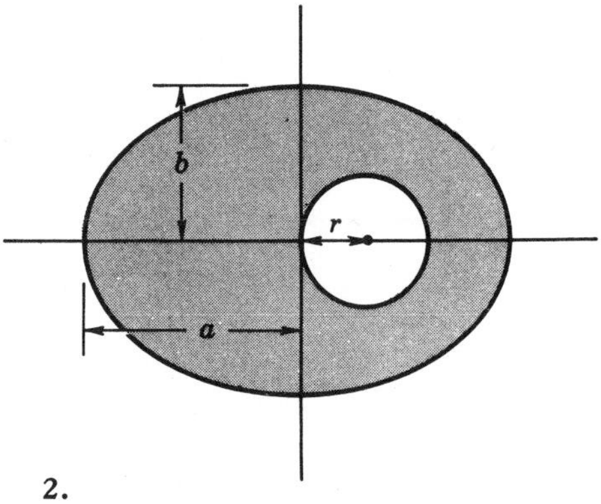

2.

5 CENTROID OF A PLANE REGION

We turn now to the problem of finding the center of mass of a lamina with a curved boundary. In order to make the problem mathematically solvable, we assume that the boundary of the lamina is made up of graphs of continuous functions.

For simplicity, we first assume that a lamina L of density ρ has the shape of a region bounded by the lines $x = a$ and $x = b$, $(a < b)$, the x axis, and the graph of a continuous nonnegative function f, as shown in Figure 13.20. We may approximate the moments of L by selecting a partition $P = \{x_0,x_1, \cdots, x_n\}$ of $[a,b]$ and constructing a rectangular polygon relative to P as follows. Let $z_1, z_2, \cdots, z_n$ be the midpoints of segments $[x_0,x_1], [x_1,x_2], \cdots, [x_{n-1},x_n]$, respectively, and $f(z_1), f(z_2), \cdots, f(z_n)$ be the heights of n rectangles with respective bases $[x_0,x_1], [x_1,x_2], \cdots, [x_{n-1},x_n]$. The case $n = 3$ is illustrated in Figure 13.21. A lamina having the shape of the polygon made up of these n rectangles has the following moments about the axes:

$$M_x = \sum_{i=1}^{n} \tfrac{1}{2} f(z_i)[\rho f(z_i)\,\Delta x_i], \qquad M_y = \sum_{i=1}^{n} z_i[\rho f(z_i)\,\Delta x_i],$$

where $\Delta x_i = x_i - x_{i-1}$, $i = 1, \cdots, n$.

It is clear that M_x is a Riemann sum, not for the function f but for the function $\frac{1}{2}\rho f^2$, and that M_y is a Riemann sum for the function g defined by $g(x) =$

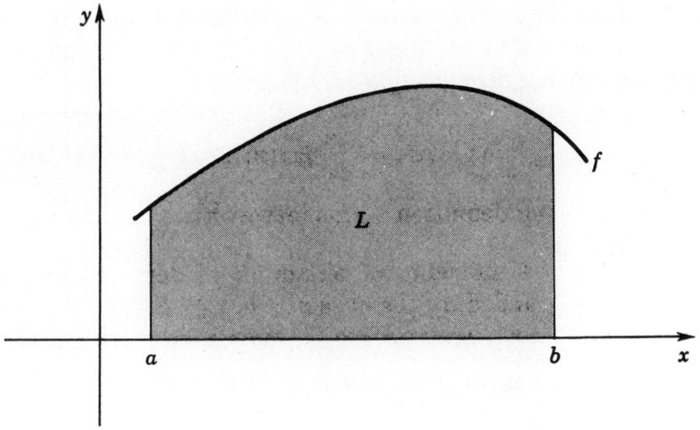

FIGURE 13.20

$\rho xf(x)$. If we take a sequence of partitions $P_1, P_2, \cdots, P_n, \cdots$ of $[a,b]$ for which

$$\operatorname*{limit}_{n\to\infty} \|P_n\| = 0,$$

and define $(M_n)_x$ and $(M_n)_y$ as above relative to partition P_n, then, by **8.16**,

$$\operatorname*{limit}_{n\to\infty} (M_n)_x = \int_a^b \frac{1}{2}\rho f^2(x)\,dx$$

$$\operatorname*{limit}_{n\to\infty} (M_n)_y = \int_a^b \rho xf(x)\,dx.$$

Therefore the following definition seems reasonable.

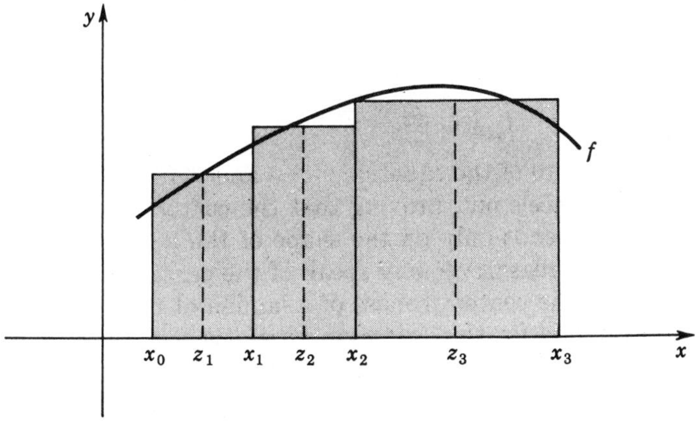

FIGURE 13.21

13.13 DEFINITION. The moments of a lamina of density ρ having the shape of the region bounded by the lines $x = a$, $x = b$, and $y = 0$, and by the graph of a continuous nonnegative function f are given by

$$M_x = \frac{\rho}{2}\int_a^b f^2(x)\,dx, \qquad M_y = \rho\int_a^b xf(x)\,dx.$$

Having defined the moments of a lamina, it is natural to define the center of mass of the lamina of mass m to be the point $(\bar{x},\bar{y})$, where

13.14
$$\bar{x} = \frac{M_y}{m}, \qquad \bar{y} = \frac{M_x}{m}.$$

Incidentally, the mass m of the lamina of **13.13** is ρA, where A is the area of the lamina; i.e.,

$$m = \rho\int_a^b f(x)\,dx.$$

Note that

$$M_x = m\bar{y}, \qquad M_y = m\bar{x},$$

according to **13.14**. Thus, again, the moments of the lamina may be found by assuming that the mass of the lamina is concentrated at the center of mass of the lamina.

For the lamina of **13.13** we may write the coordinates of the center of mass in the form

$$\bar{x} = \frac{\int_a^b xf(x)\,dx}{\int_a^b f(x)\,dx}, \qquad \bar{y} = \frac{1}{2}\,\frac{\int_a^b f^2(x)\,dx}{\int_a^b f(x)\,dx}.$$

An interesting feature of the equations for $\bar{x}$ and $\bar{y}$ in this form is that the density factor ρ cancels out, proving that the center of mass of a homogeneous lamina depends only on the shape of the lamina and not on its substance. For this reason we may speak of the center of mass of a plane region in place of the center of mass of a lamina of that shape. We shall use the term *centroid* for the center of mass of a plane region, reserving the term *center of mass* for a material object.

By mathematical arguments similar to those above, we may find the moments and centroids of many different plane regions. If, for example, a region is bounded by the graphs of two functions, then we can imagine the region as being the difference between two regions, one under the graph of each function. Hence its moments will be the difference of two moments, and so on.

A mnemonic device for finding moments of a region such as in Figure 13.22 is as follows. We assume that the region is between the lines $y = a$ and $y = b$, and that for every y in the interval $[a,b]$ the width $W(y)$ of the region is known, W being a continuous function. We imagine the region as being approximated

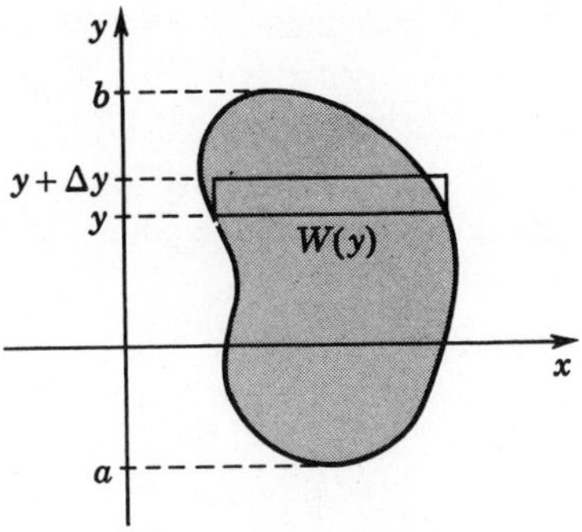

FIGURE 13.22

by a polygon made up of n rectangles, a representative one of which, shown in the figure, has the approximate moment $yW(y)\,\Delta y$ about the x axis. By summing up the moments of the n rectangles and taking a limit, we eventually obtain

13.15
$$M_x = \int_a^b yW(y)\,dy$$

for the moment of the given region about the x axis. If the region has area A, then $\bar{y} = M_x/A$ is the y coordinate of its centroid. A similar device may be used to find $\bar{x}$.

EXAMPLE 1. Find the centroid of the region bounded by the lines $x = -1$ and $y = 0$, and the graph of the equation $y = 4 - x^2$.

Solution: For this region, sketched in Figure 13.23, we have, by **13.13** (with $\rho = 1$),

$$M_x = \frac{1}{2}\int_{-1}^{2} (4 - x^2)^2\,dx = \frac{153}{10}, \qquad M_y = \int_{-1}^{2} x(4 - x^2)\,dx = \frac{9}{4}.$$

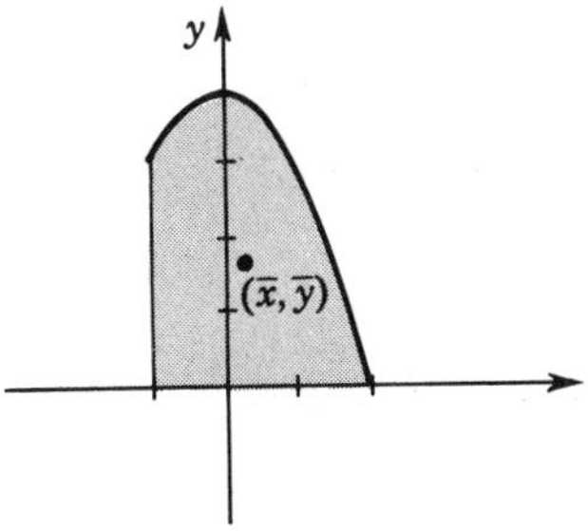

FIGURE 13.23

The area $A = 9$, as may be easily verified. Hence

$$\bar{x} = \frac{M_y}{A} = .25, \qquad \bar{y} = \frac{M_x}{A} = 1.7,$$

and the centroid of the given region is the point (.25,1.7).

EXAMPLE 2. Find the centroid of a triangle.

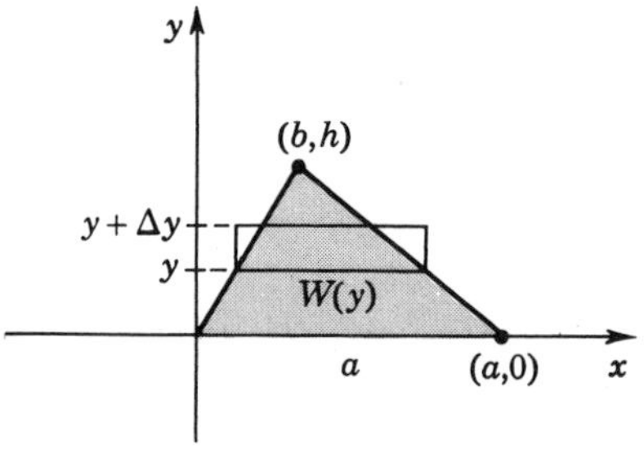

FIGURE 13.24

Solution: Let the coordinate axes be chosen as in Figure 13.24. By similar triangles,

$$\frac{W(y)}{h - y} = \frac{a}{h},$$

$$\text{or} \qquad W(y) = \frac{a}{h}(h - y).$$

Hence, by **13.15**,

$$M_x = \frac{a}{h}\int_0^h (h - y)\,dy = \frac{ah^2}{6}.$$

Since the triangle has area $A = ah/2$,

$$\bar{y} = \frac{M_x}{A} = \frac{h}{3}.$$

We could have chosen the x axis on any one of the three sides of the triangle. In each case we would get that the centroid was one-third the altitude above the base. Hence the centroid is the unique point one-third the altitude above each base. By elementary geometry, this is the point of intersection of the medians of the triangle.

EXERCISES

I

In each of Exercises 1–10 find the centroid of the region bounded by the graphs of the given equations. Sketch each region.

1. $y = \sqrt{x}, \quad y = 0, \quad x = 4.$

2. $y = 1/(x + 1), \quad x = 0, \quad x = 4, \quad y = 0.$

3. $y = x^3, \quad x = 0, \quad x = 2, \quad y = 0.$

4. $y = \sin x, \quad x = 0, \quad x = \pi, \quad y = 0.$

5. $y = \cos x, \quad x = 0, \quad x = \pi/2, \quad y = 0.$

6. $y = e^x, \quad x = 0, \quad x = 2, \quad y = 0.$

7. $y = \ln x, \quad x = 1, \quad x = e, \quad y = 0.$

8. $y = \sec^2 x, \quad x = -\pi/4, \quad x = \pi/4, \quad y = 0.$

9. $y = 1/\sqrt{x^2 + 1}, \quad x = 0, \quad x = 1, \quad y = 0.$

10. $x^2 - y^2 = 1, \quad x = 3.$

11. Find the centroid of a semicircle of radius a.

12. a. Find the centroid of the semielliptic region

$$\frac{x^2}{a^2} + \frac{y^2}{b^2} \leq 1, \quad y \geq 0.$$

    b. The solution of Exercise 11 can be obtained from this one by merely letting $b = a$. Show how to obtain the solution of Part a from that of Exercise 11.

13. Find the centroid of the region bounded by the x axis, the curve $y = \sinh x$, and the line $x = a$, $(a > 0)$.

14. Find the centroid of the region bounded by the x axis, the curve $y = \cosh x$, and the lines $x = -a$ and $x = a$.

II

1. Using the result of Exercise I-11, find the centroid of a quarter-circle of radius a.

2. Find the centroid of a circular segment of radius r and height h.

3. Find the centroid of a sector of a circle of radius r and angle 2θ. Find the limit of the position of the centroid as θ approaches zero.

6 CENTROIDS OF SOLIDS OF REVOLUTION

The general problem of finding the center of mass of a solid object will be considered in Chapter 19. However, we can find the center of mass of a homogeneous object having the shape of a solid of revolution, assuming that the center of mass is on the axis of revolution.

Let us assume that a homogeneous object of density* ρ has the shape of a solid generated by rotating about the x axis the region under the graph of a continuous, non-negative function f between $x = a$ and $x = b$ (Figure 13.25).

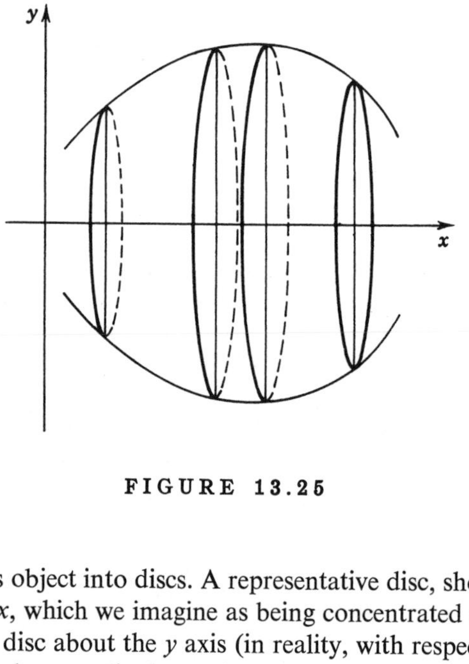

FIGURE 13.25

We "slice" this object into discs. A representative disc, shown in the figure, has mass $\rho\pi f^2(x)\,\Delta x$, which we imagine as being concentrated at its center. The moment M_y of this disc about the y axis (in reality, with respect to a plane containing the y axis and perpendicular to the x axis) is $x[\rho\pi f^2(x)\,\Delta x]$. Summing up the moments of all the discs and taking a limit, just as in Chapter 8, we finally get

$$M_y = \rho\pi \int_a^b x f^2(x)\,dx.$$

---

* Density now means the mass of a cubic unit of the substance.

Clearly, the object has mass $m = \rho V$, where V is its volume. Hence the center of mass, $(\bar{x},0)$, of the object is given by

$$\bar{x} = \frac{M_y}{\rho V} = \frac{\int_a^b x f^2(x)\, dx}{\int_a^b f^2(x)\, dx}.$$

We see from the above equation that the center of mass of the homogeneous object depends only on the shape of the object and not on its substance. Thus we may speak of the center of mass of this geometric solid; this point, as in the case of a region, is called the *centroid* of the solid of revolution.

EXAMPLE. Find the centroid of a hemisphere.

Solution: Let the hemisphere be generated by rotating about the x axis the quarter-circle of radius r having equation

$$y = \sqrt{r^2 - x^2}, \qquad (0 \le x \le r).$$

Then

$$M_y = \pi \int_0^r x(\sqrt{r^2 - x^2})^2\, dx = \frac{\pi r^4}{4},$$

$$x = \frac{M_y}{V} = \frac{\pi r^4}{4} \cdot \frac{3}{2\pi r^3} = \frac{3r}{8},$$

and the centroid is the point $(3r/8,0)$.

EXERCISES

I

In each of Exercises 1–6, the region bounded by the graphs of the given equations is rotated about the x axis. Find the centroid of the solid generated.

1. $y = \sqrt{x}, \quad y = 0, \quad x = 4.$
2. $y = 1/(x + 1), \quad x = 0, \quad x = 4, \quad y = 0.$
3. $y = \sin x, \quad x = 0, \quad x = \pi/2, \quad y = 0.$
4. $y = \sec x, \quad x = 0, \quad x = \pi/6, \quad y = 0.$
5. $y = 1/\sqrt{x^2 + 1}, \quad x = 0, \quad x = 2, \quad y = 0.$
6. $x^2 - y^2 = 4, \quad x = 4.$
7. Find the centroid of a right circular cone having radius of base r and altitude h.

8. The region in the first quadrant bounded by the ellipse $x^2/a^2 + y^2/b^2 = 1$ is rotated about the x axis. Find the centroid of the solid generated.

9. The region bounded by a parabola and its latus rectum is rotated about the axis of the parabola. Find the centroid of the solid generated.

II

1. Prove the following *first theorem of Pappus:* If a plane region, lying on one side of a line L in its plane, is revolved about L, then the volume of the solid generated is equal to the product of the area of the region and the distance traveled by the centroid of the region.

Use Exercise 1 to work each of the following exercises.

2. Find the volume of a torus (doughnut-shaped solid) generated by rotating the circle $x^2 + (y - b)^2 = r^2$, $(b > r)$, about the x axis.

3. Find the centroid of a semicircular region.

4. Find the volume of a right circular cone of radius r and height h.

5. Find the volume of the ellipsoid of revolution

$$\frac{x^2}{a^2} + \frac{y^2}{b^2} + \frac{z^2}{b^2} = 1.$$

7 FORCE ON A DAM

A liquid in a container exerts a force on the bottom of the container, namely the weight of the liquid therein. The force per square unit of the bottom is called the *pressure* of the liquid at the bottom. Actually, the pressure exerted by a liquid of density ρ at a point d units below the surface is ρd; and this pressure is the same in all directions.

In this section we are interested in finding the total force of a liquid of density ρ against a vertical dam. Let us introduce a coordinate system on a blueprint of the dam, placing the x axis along the line of the surface of the liquid and the positive y axis downward as illustrated in Figure 13.26. In order to make the problem mathematically solvable, we assume that the width $W(y)$ of the dam at depth y is given by a continuous function W.

For each partition $P = \{y_0, y_1, \cdots, y_n\}$ of the interval $[0,h]$, let us approximate the region of the dam by a polygon made up of rectangles associated with P in the usual way. The force against the ith rectangle (see Fig-

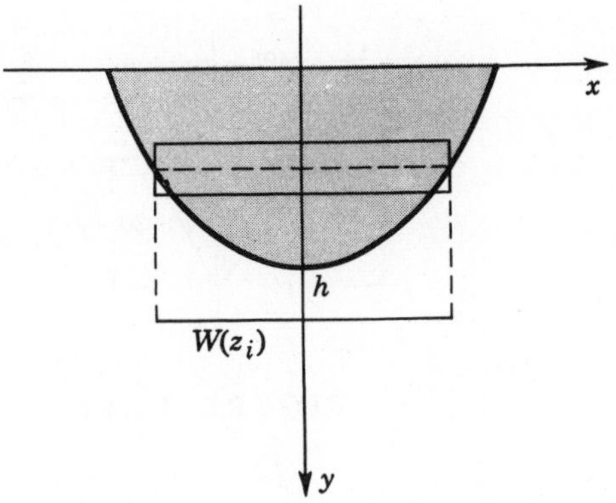

FIGURE 13.26

ure 13.26) is approximately equal to $\rho z_i W(z_i)\,\Delta y_i$. Hence the force against the dam is approximately equal to

$$\sum_{i=1}^{n} \rho z_i W(z_i)\,\Delta y_i.$$

On taking a sequence of partitions of $[0,h]$ with disappearing norms and finding the limit of the above sum relative to the sequence of partitions, it seems plausible that the force F against the dam is given by the integral

13.16 $$F = \rho \int_0^h yW(y)\,dy.$$

Thus **13.16** is taken to be the definition of the force F. Note that this integral is precisely the moment about the x axis of a lamina of density ρ having the shape of the dam **(13.13)**.

EXAMPLE 1. Find the force of water against a triangular dam 40 ft wide and 30 ft deep.

Solution: Let the coordinate axes be selected as in Figure 13.27. By similar triangles,

$$\frac{W(y)}{30 - y} = \frac{40}{30}, \qquad \text{or} \qquad W(y) = \frac{4}{3}(30 - y).$$

The density of water is 62.5 lb/ft³. Hence, by **13.16**,

$$F = 62.5 \int_0^{30} y \cdot \frac{4}{3}(30 - y)\,dy = 3.75 \cdot 10^5 \text{ lb}.$$

EXAMPLE 2. A cylindrical tank 4 ft in diameter and 6 ft long is half full of oil. If the tank is lying on its side, find the force exerted by the oil on one end (assume $\rho = 60$ lb/ft³).

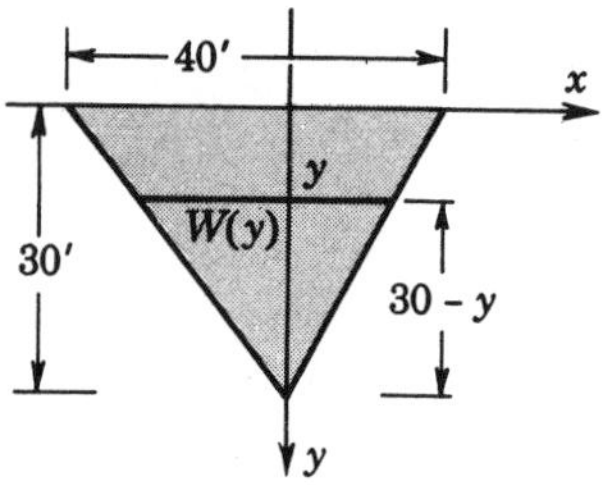

FIGURE 13.27

Solution: If the coordinate axes are chosen on an end of the tank as in Figure 13.28, then the semicircle has equation $y = \sqrt{4 - x^2}$ and

$$W(y) = 2x = 2\sqrt{4 - y^2}$$

for each y. Hence, by **13.16**,

$$F = 60 \int_0^2 2y\sqrt{4 - y^2}\, dy$$

$$= -40(4 - y^2)^{3/2} \Big|_0^2 = 320 \text{ lb.}$$

Note that the length of the tank is immaterial.

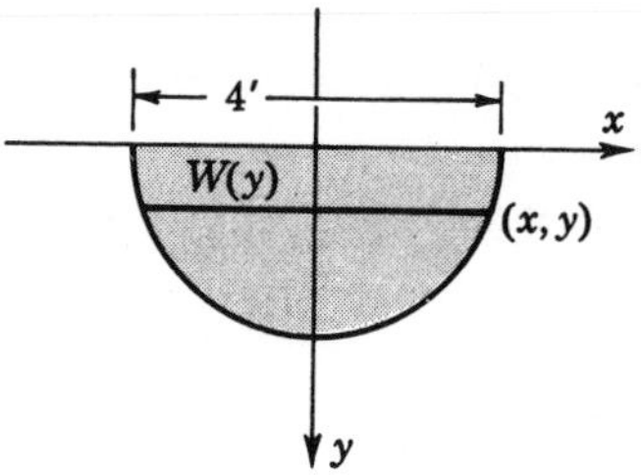

FIGURE 13.28

We need not choose a coordinate axis at the surface of the liquid if it is more convenient to do otherwise. If, for example, we wish to find the force F against the shaded region of Figure 13.29, and if the axes are chosen as in the figure, with the x axis d units above the water level, then by the same reasoning as above,

$$F = \rho \int_a^{a+h} (y - d)W(y)\, dy.$$

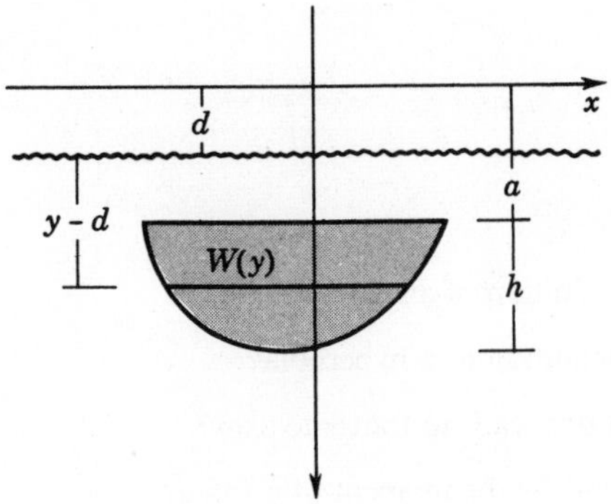

FIGURE 13.29

EXERCISES

I

1. Find the force of water against an elliptical dam if the major axis of length 50 ft is at the surface of the water and if the semiminor axis has length 20 ft.
2. Find the force of water against a rectangular gate in a dam, if the gate is 6 ft wide and 4 ft high, with the top of the gate parallel to the surface of water and 10 ft below the surface.
3. Find the force of water against the lower half of the gate in Exercise 2.
4. The gate of Exercise 2 is cut into two triangular gates by a diagonal of the gate. Find the force of water against each triangular gate.
5. A dam has a parabolic shape, with the axis of the parabola vertical. If the dam is 50 ft across at the water level and is 60 ft deep, find the force of water against the dam.
6. A trough has a trapezoidal cross section and is 4 ft wide at the top, 2 ft wide at the bottom, and 2 ft deep. Find the force against an end of the trough if it is full of water.
7. A cylindrical tank 6 ft long and 4 ft in diameter is lying on its side. Find the force against the end of the tank if there is 1 ft of water in the tank.

II

1. a. Show that the force against any vertical region under water of a dam is the product of the density of the liquid, the area of the region, and the depth to the centroid of the region.
   b. Use this result to mentally obtain the solution of Exercise I-2.

REVIEW

Oral Exercises

1. What is a definition of an ellipse?
2. What is a definition of a hyperbola?
3. Why would one want to translate axes?
4. What is meant by the moment of a force?
5. What is meant by a centroid?
6. If a uniform body has an axis of symmetry, why does the centroid lie on the axis?
7. How can Exercise 6 be used to find the centroid of bodies with more than one axis of symmetry?
8. What is the first theorem of Pappus? (See Exercise II-1, Section 6.)
9. How can the theorem of Pappus be used to find centroids of certain plain figures?
10. How does one compute the hydrostatic force on the face of a dam?

I

1. How many tangent lines can be drawn from a given point to an ellipse?
2. How many tangent lines can be drawn from a given point to a hyperbola?
3. What is the maximum number of points of intersection of the ellipse $x^2/a^2 + y^2/b^2 = 1$ and the hyperbola

$$\frac{(x-h)^2}{c^2} - \frac{(y-k)^2}{d^2} = 1?$$

4. By sketching the graphs accurately on ruled paper, determine how the graphs of the following equations are related:

$$x^2 - y^2 = a^2, \qquad 2xy = a^2.$$

5. Discuss the graph of a point which moves in such a way that its distance from a fixed line is some constant times its distance from a fixed point.

The mean value M of a function f in the interval $[a,b]$ is defined to be

$$M = \frac{\int_a^b f(x)\,dx}{b-a}.$$

In each of Exercises 6–9, find the mean value of the function in the given interval, sketch the graph, and interpret the mean value of f geometrically.

6. $f(x) = x^2$; $[0,3]$.
7. $f(x) = x^2$; $[-3,0]$.
8. $f(x) = \sin x$; $[0,\pi]$.
9. $f(x) = xe^x$; $[0,1]$.
10. What is a physical interpretation for the mean value of each of the following functions: (a) $xF(x)$; (b) $F^2(x)$ for a unit interval?

In each of Exercises 11–14, find the centroid of the region with the given boundaries.

11. $y = xe^x$, $y = 0$, $x = 1$.
12. $y = xe^x$, $y = 0$, $x = -1$.
13. $y = \text{arc sinh } x$, $y = 0$, $x = \pm e$.
14. $y = \cosh x$, $y = 0$, $x = -1$, $x = 1$.

In each of Exercises 15–17, find the volume of the solid generated by revolving the given region about the x axis by the method of the first theorem of Pappus (Exercise II-1, Section 6).

15. Region of Exercise 11.
16. Region of Exercise 12.
17. Region of Exercise 14.

In each of Exercises 18–20, find the centroid of the solid generated by revolving the given region about the x axis.

18. Region of Exercise 11.
19. Region of Exercise 12.
20. Region of Exercise 14.

II

1. Show that the tangent and normal lines to an ellipse or hyperbola at a given point bisect the internal and external angles formed by the focal radii to the given point.
2. Find the length of a common tangent to the two curves

$$\frac{x^2}{a^2} - \frac{y^2}{b^2} = 1 \quad \text{and} \quad \frac{y^2}{a^2} - \frac{x^2}{b^2} = 1.$$

3. Show that, from each point of a certain circle surrounding the ellipse $\frac{x^2}{a^2} + \frac{y^2}{b^2} = 1$, the angle subtended by the ellipse (i.e., the angle between the two tangent lines from the point) is a right angle.
4. Show how to construct the center of a given ellipse with straightedge and compass (see solution of Exercise II-7, Section 2).
5. Show that a regular pentagon cannot be inscribed in a proper ellipse (one with unequal axes).

6. Find the volume of the solid of revolution formed by rotating the loop of the curve $y^2 = \dfrac{x^2(a - x)}{a + x}$ about the x axis.

7. A solid of revolution is obtained by rotating a square about an axis lying in its plane and passing through one of its corners. Determine the maximum volume of the solid.

8. Repeat Exercise 7 for a triangle instead of a square.

9. A square plate of side a ft is submerged vertically in water so that a diagonal is parallel to the water surface. If one corner of the square lies at the water surface determine the hydrostatic force on each side of the plate.

10. Show that the centroid of an arbitrary trapezoid $ABCD$ is given by the point of intersection of the three lines EF, HI, and GJ, where E and F are the midpoints of the parallel sides AB and CD, respectively; G, A, B, H are collinear in that order and $GA = BH = DC$; and I, D, C, J are collinear in that order and $ID = CJ = AB$

14

INDETERMINATE FORMS, IMPROPER INTEGRALS, AND TAYLOR'S FORMULA

A GENERALIZATION of the mean value theorem, called *Cauchy's formula*, allows us to find limits of so-called indeterminate forms. Another topic to be considered concerns a generalization of the integral to improper integrals. Finally, polynomial approximations of functions are studied.

1 CAUCHY'S FORMULA

We recall that Rolle's theorem and the mean value theorem, proved in Chapter 6, had to do with a function f continuous in a closed interval $[a,b]$. Rolle's theorem stated that if $f(a) = f(b)$ then f has a critical number z in (a,b). Hence, if $f'(z)$ exists, necessarily $f'(z) = 0$. The mean value theorem stated that if f' exists in (a,b) then, even if $f(a) \neq f(b)$, there exists a number z in (a,b) such that

$$f(b) - f(a) = (b - a)f'(z).$$

A useful generalization of these theorems is the following result.

14.1 CAUCHY'S FORMULA.* If f and g are functions defined in the closed interval $[a,b]$ such that

(1) f and g are continuous in $[a,b]$,
(2) f' and g' exist in (a,b),
(3) $g'(x) \neq 0$ for every x in (a,b),

then there exists a number z in (a,b) such that

$$\frac{f(b) - f(a)}{g(b) - g(a)} = \frac{f'(z)}{g'(z)}.$$

Proof: Clearly, $g(b) \neq g(a)$, for otherwise $g'(z) = 0$ for some z in (a,b) by Rolle's theorem, contrary to property (3).

Let the function F be defined as follows:

$$F(x) = [f(b) - f(a)]g(x) - [g(b) - g(a)]f(x).$$

Then $F'(x)$ exists for every x in (a,b) and is given by

$$F'(x) = [f(b) - f(a)]g'(x) - [g(b) - g(a)]f'(x).$$

Also, the function F is continuous at both a and b, since the functions f and g appearing in the definition of F are continuous at a and b. Finally, we may easily show that

$$F(a) = F(b) = f(b)g(a) - f(a)g(b).$$

The function F satisfies all the conditions of Rolle's theorem, and therefore there exists a number z in (a,b) such that $F'(z) = 0$. Thus

$$[f(b) - f(a)]g'(z) - [g(b) - g(a)]f'(z) = 0,$$

and, since both $g(b) - g(a)$ and $g'(z)$ are unequal to zero,

$$\frac{f(b) - f(a)}{g(b) - g(a)} = \frac{f'(z)}{g'(z)}.$$

This proves Cauchy's formula.

We note that Cauchy's formula is just the mean value theorem when

$$g(x) = x,$$

for then $g'(x) = 1$ and Cauchy's formula becomes

$$\frac{f(b) - f(a)}{b - a} = f'(z).$$

---

* Augustin Louis Cauchy (1789–1857) was a French mathematician who had much to do with the modern rigorous development of the calculus.

EXAMPLE. Prove that, for every $x > 0$, $\dfrac{x}{x^2+1} < \tan^{-1} x < x$.

Solution: By Cauchy's formula (or the mean value theorem),

$$\frac{\tan^{-1} x - 0}{x - 0} = \frac{1/(1+z^2)}{1}$$

for some number z, $(0 < z < x)$. Thus

$$\tan^{-1} x = \frac{x}{1+z^2}$$

for some z, $(0 < z < x)$. Since $z > 0$, $1 + z^2 > 1$ and $x/(1+z^2) < x$. On the other hand, $z < x$ and $z^2 < x^2$. Hence $x/(1+z^2) > x/(1+x^2)$. Thus

$$\frac{x}{1+x^2} < \tan^{-1} x < x,$$

as desired.

For example, if $x = .1$, this inequality states that

$$.099 < \tan^{-1} .1 < .1.$$

EXERCISES

I

In each of Exercises 1–5, use Cauchy's formula to show that there exists a number z satisfying the given condition.

1. a. $\dfrac{\sin x}{x} = \cos z$, $(0 < z < x)$. b. $\dfrac{\sin x}{x} = \cos z$, $(x < z < 0)$.

2. a. $\dfrac{\tan x}{x} = \sec^2 z$, $\left(0 < z < x < \dfrac{\pi}{2}\right)$. b. $\dfrac{\tan x}{x} = \sec^2 z$, $\left(-\dfrac{\pi}{2} < x < z < 0\right)$.

3. a. $\dfrac{\tan^{-1} x}{x} = \dfrac{1}{1+z^2}$, $(0 < z < x)$. b. $\dfrac{\tan^{-1} x}{x} = \dfrac{1}{1+z^2}$, $(x < z < 0)$.

4. a. $\dfrac{\sin b - \sin a}{b - a} = \cos z$, $(0 < a < z < b)$.

   b. Use a to prove that $\sin b - \sin a < b - a$ if $0 < a < b < \dfrac{\pi}{2}$.

5. $\dfrac{\sin x - x}{x^3} = -\dfrac{1}{6}\cos z$, $(0 < z < x)$. [*Hint:* Cauchy's formula will have to be used several times.]

6. Show that if $x > 0$, then $\frac{x}{x+1} < \ln(x+1) < x$. [*Hint:* Prove that $\frac{\ln(x+1)}{x} = \frac{1}{z+1}$ for some z, $(0 < z < x)$.]

7. Show that $e^x > 1 + x$ for every $x \neq 0$.

II

1. The function F defined by $F(x) = 1 - x^{2/5}$ is continuous in $[-1,1]$ and $F(1) = F(-1) = 0$. Why isn't $F'(x) = 0$ for some x in $[-1,1]$?

2. If $F'(x) < 1$, show that there is at most one number x in $(\frac{1}{2},1)$ for which $F(x) = x^2$.

3. Show that the equation

$$x^n - nx + a = 0,$$

where n is an integer, $n > 2$, and a is an arbitrary number, cannot have more than one real root in $[-1,1]$.

4. Prove the following generalization of Cauchy's formula. If (1) F, G, and H are continuous functions in $[a,b]$, and (2) F', G', and H' exist in (a,b), then there is a number λ in (a,b) such that

$$\begin{vmatrix} F'(\lambda) & G'(\lambda) & H'(\lambda) \\ F(a) & G(a) & H(a) \\ F(b) & G(b) & H(b) \end{vmatrix} = 0.$$

[*Hint:* Consider the same determinant with the first row replaced by $(F(x), G(x), H(x))$.]

5. Obtain Cauchy's formula from Exercise 4.

6. If F and G are continuous in $[a,b]$, show that

$$G(\lambda) \int_a^b F(t)\,dt = F(\lambda) \int_a^b G(t)\,dt$$

for some number λ in (a,b).

2 INDETERMINATE FORMS

If we define the function H by

$$H(x) = \frac{\ln(x+1)}{x}, \qquad (x \geq -1, \quad x \neq 0),$$

then

$$H(x) = \frac{f(x)}{g(x)},$$

where $f(x) = \ln(x + 1)$, $g(x) = x$. We cannot evaluate

$$\lim_{x\to 0} H(x)$$

by use of the quotient limit theorem

$$\lim_{x\to 0} H(x) = \frac{\lim_{x\to 0} f(x)}{\lim_{x\to 0} g(x)},$$

since

$$\lim_{x\to 0} g(x) = 0.$$

However, in addition,

$$\lim_{x\to 0} f(x) = 0,$$

and therefore

$$\lim_{x\to 0} H(x)$$

still might exist. [If $\lim_{x\to 0} g(x) = 0$ and $\lim_{x\to 0} f(x) \neq 0$, $\lim_{x\to 0} H(x)$ cannot possibly exist.] Let us show how Cauchy's formula can be used to evaluate this limit.

Since $f(0) = 0$ and $g(0) = 0$,

$$H(x) = \frac{g(x) - g(0)}{f(x) - f(0)}.$$

Therefore by Cauchy's formula,

$$H(x) = \frac{f'(z)}{g'(z)}$$

for some number z between 0 and x. Since $f'(x) = 1/(x + 1)$ and $g'(x) = 1$,

$$H(x) = \frac{1}{z + 1}.$$

Actually, we might better write

$$H(x) = \frac{1}{z(x) + 1}$$

to show that z depends on x, and consider z as a function. Since $0 < z(x) < x$ if $x > 0$ and since $x < z(x) < 0$ if $x < 0$, clearly

$$\lim_{x\to 0} z(x) = 0.$$

Hence

$$\underset{x\to 0}{\text{limit}} \frac{\ln(x+1)}{x} = \underset{x\to 0}{\text{limit}} \frac{1}{z(x)+1} = 1.$$

The fraction $[\ln(x+1)]/x$ is an example of an indeterminate form at 0. We call a quotient f/g of functions f and g an *indeterminate form* at a number c if either

$$\underset{x\to c}{\text{limit}} f(x) = 0 \quad \text{and} \quad \underset{x\to c}{\text{limit}} g(x) = 0 \qquad \left(\text{type } \frac{0}{0}\right)$$

or

$$\underset{x\to c}{\text{limit}} f(x) = \pm\infty \quad \text{and} \quad \underset{x\to c}{\text{limit}} g(x) = \pm\infty \qquad \left(\text{type } \frac{\infty}{\infty}\right).$$

If f/g is an indeterminate form at c, then we cannot evaluate

$$\underset{x\to c}{\text{limit}} \frac{f(x)}{g(x)}$$

by the quotient limit theorem. However, this limit still might exist, as the example above shows.

The following rule can be used in evaluating certain limits of indeterminate forms.

14.2 L'HOSPITAL'S RULE.* Let the functions f and g be differentiable at every number other than c in some interval, with $g'(x) \neq 0$ if $x \neq c$. If $\underset{x\to c}{\text{limit}} f(x) = \underset{x\to c}{\text{limit}} g(x) = 0$, or if $\underset{x\to c}{\text{limit}} f(x) = \pm\infty$ and $\underset{x\to c}{\text{limit}} g(x) = \pm\infty$, then

$$\underset{x\to c}{\text{limit}} \frac{f(x)}{g(x)} = \underset{x\to c}{\text{limit}} \frac{f'(x)}{g'(x)},$$

provided this latter limit exists or is infinite.

Proof: (0/0). Assume that

$$\underset{x\to c}{\text{limit}} f(x) = \underset{x\to c}{\text{limit}} g(x) = 0.$$

If we define the functions F and G as follows,

$$F(x) = f(x) \text{ if } x \neq c; \quad F(c) = 0,$$
$$G(x) = g(x) \text{ if } x \neq c; \quad G(c) = 0,$$

---

* Guillaume François Marquis de l'Hospital (1661–1704) was a French mathematician who made several contributions to the calculus in its early formative stage. He wrote the first textbook on the calculus.

then the functions F and G are continuous at c as well as being differentiable elsewhere in the given interval. Hence, by Cauchy's formula, for every $x \neq c$ in the given interval there exists a number z between x and c such that

$$\frac{F(x) - F(c)}{G(x) - G(c)} = \frac{F'(z)}{G'(z)}.$$

Since $F(c) = G(c) = 0$ and $F(x) = f(x)$, $G(x) = g(x)$, $F'(x) = f'(x)$, $G'(x) = g'(x)$ if $x \neq c$, we have shown that

$$\frac{f(x)}{g(x)} = \frac{f'(z)}{g'(z)}$$

for some number z between c and x.

As above, z depends on x (assuming that c is unchanged throughout our argument), and we indicate this fact by writing

$$\frac{f(x)}{g(x)} = \frac{f'(z(x))}{g'(z(x))}.$$

Since $z(x)$ is always between x and c,

$$\underset{x \to c}{\text{limit}}\, z(x) = c.$$

If

$$\underset{x \to c}{\text{limit}} \frac{f'(x)}{g'(x)} = k,$$

then also

$$\underset{x \to c}{\text{limit}} \frac{f'(z(x))}{g'(z(x))} = k.$$

For if N is a neighborhood of k and D is a deleted neighborhood of c such that $f'(x)/g'(x)$ is in N for each x in D, then $f'(z(x))/g'(z(x))$ is in N for each x in D, because $z(x)$ is also in D. Thus

$$\underset{x \to c}{\text{limit}} \frac{f(x)}{g(x)} = \underset{x \to c}{\text{limit}} \frac{f'(z)}{g'(z)} = k,$$

and l'Hospital's rule is proved.

If

$$\underset{x \to c}{\text{limit}} \frac{f'(x)}{g'(x)} = \infty \quad (\text{or } -\infty),$$

then, by the same reasoning as above,

$$\underset{x \to c}{\text{limit}} \frac{f(x)}{g(x)} = \infty \quad (\text{or } -\infty).$$

This shows that l'Hospital's rule holds for infinite limits also.

We will not offer a proof here of the more difficult case (∞/∞) when

$$\lim_{x\to c} f(x) = \pm\infty \qquad \text{and} \qquad \lim_{x\to c} g(x) = \pm\infty.$$

This may be found in many books on advanced calculus.

EXAMPLE 1. Find $\displaystyle\lim_{x\to\pi} \frac{\sin x}{x-\pi}$.

Solution: Since

$$\lim_{x\to\pi} \sin x = \lim_{x\to\pi} (x-\pi) = 0,$$

we apply l'Hospital's rule to obtain

$$\lim_{x\to\pi} \frac{\sin x}{x-\pi} = \lim_{x\to\pi} \frac{\cos x}{1} = -1.$$

EXAMPLE 2. Find $\displaystyle\lim_{x\to 0^+} \frac{\ln x}{1/x}$.

Solution: Since

$$\lim_{x\to 0^+} \ln x = -\infty \qquad \text{and} \qquad \lim_{x\to 0^+} \frac{1}{x} = \infty,$$

we may apply l'Hospital's rule to get

$$\lim_{x\to 0^+} \frac{\ln x}{1/x} = \lim_{x\to 0^+} \frac{1/x}{-1/x^2} = \lim_{x\to 0^+} (-x) = 0.$$

The fraction $(1/x)/-(1/x^2)$ is also an indeterminate form (∞/∞), but we have chosen to reduce the fraction algebraically rather than to employ l'Hospital's rule, which, as is easily seen, would lead us to no conclusion.

In the following example we see that l'Hospital's rule may profitably be applied more than once in certain instances.

EXAMPLE 3. Find $\displaystyle\lim_{x\to 0} \frac{\sin x - x}{x^3}$.

Solution: We may use l'Hospital's rule, since

$$\lim_{x\to 0} (\sin x - x) = \lim_{x\to 0} x^3 = 0.$$

Hence

$$\lim_{x\to 0} \frac{\sin x - x}{x^3} = \lim_{x\to 0} \frac{\cos x - 1}{3x^2},$$

if the latter limit exists.

Since

$$\lim_{x\to 0} (\cos x - 1) = \lim_{x\to 0} 3x^2 = 0,$$

we may again use l'Hospital's rule to obtain

$$\lim_{x\to 0} \frac{\cos x - 1}{3x^2} = \lim_{x\to 0} \frac{-\sin x}{6x}.$$

The fraction $-\sin x/6x$ is still indeterminate (0/0), so we reapply the rule to get finally

$$\lim_{x\to 0} \frac{-\sin x}{6x} = \lim_{x\to 0} \frac{-\cos x}{6} = -\frac{1}{6}.$$

We might equally well have recalled in the final step that $\lim_{x\to 0} \sin x/x = 1$ by **11.6.** Thus

$$\lim_{x\to 0} \frac{\sin x - x}{x^3} = -\frac{1}{6}.$$

As indicated in Example 2, l'Hospital's rule applies equally well to the evaluation of one-sided limits such as

$$\lim_{x\to c^+} \frac{f(x)}{g(x)} \quad \text{and} \quad \lim_{x\to c^-} \frac{f(x)}{g(x)}.$$

EXAMPLE 4. Find $\lim_{\theta\to\pi/2^-} \frac{\sec\theta}{\tan\theta}$.

Solution: This is an ∞/∞ form to which we apply l'Hospital's rule as follows.

$$\lim_{\theta\to\pi/2^-} \frac{\sec\theta}{\tan\theta} = \lim_{\theta\to\pi/2^-} \frac{\sec\theta\tan\theta}{\sec^2\theta} = \lim_{\theta\to\pi/2^-} \frac{\tan\theta}{\sec\theta}.$$

Reapplying the rule, we get

$$\lim_{\theta\to\pi/2^-} \frac{\tan\theta}{\sec\theta} = \lim_{\theta\to\pi/2^-} \frac{\sec\theta}{\tan\theta}.$$

Clearly, l'Hospital's rule gives us no information in this example. However, since $\sec\theta/\tan\theta = 1/\sin\theta$,

$$\lim_{\theta\to\pi/2^-} \frac{\sec\theta}{\tan\theta} = \lim_{\theta\to\pi/2^-} \frac{1}{\sin\theta} = 1.$$

EXERCISES

I

Evaluate, if possible, each of the following limits.

1. $\lim_{x\to 0} \frac{\tan x}{x}$.

2. $\lim_{x\to 2} \frac{x^2 - 4}{x - 2}$.

3. $\lim_{x\to 0} \frac{e^x - 1}{x}$.

4. $\lim_{y\to 0} \frac{\tan^{-1} y}{y}$.

5. $\lim_{t\to 0} \frac{\sqrt{1+t} - \sqrt{1-t}}{t}$.

6. $\lim_{z\to \pi} \frac{\ln \cos 2z}{(\pi - z)^2}$.

7. $\lim_{\theta\to \pi/2} \frac{\ln |\theta - \pi/2|}{\tan \theta}$.

8. $\lim_{x\to 0} \frac{\tan x - x}{x - \sin x}$.

9. $\lim_{x\to 0} \frac{e^x - 2\cos x + e^{-x}}{x \sin x}$.

10. $\lim_{x\to 0} \frac{1 - \cos x}{x^2}$.

11. $\lim_{x\to -1} \frac{\ln |x|}{x + 1}$.

12. $\lim_{t\to 0} \frac{t \sin t}{1 - \cos t}$.

13. $\lim_{\theta\to \pi/2} \frac{\ln |\sin \theta|}{\cot \theta}$.

14. $\lim_{y\to 0} \frac{\tan^{-1} y - y}{y^3}$.

15. $\lim_{y\to 0} \frac{\sin^{-1} y - y}{y^3}$.

16. $\lim_{x\to 0} \frac{\sin^{-1} x}{\sin^{-1} 3x}$.

17. $\lim_{x\to \pi/2} \frac{\sec^2 3x}{\sec^2 x}$.

18. $\lim_{x\to 0} \frac{e^x - 2 + e^{-x}}{1 - \cos 2x}$.

19. $\lim_{x\to 0} \frac{\cot 3x}{\cot 2x}$.

20. $\lim_{u\to 0} \frac{\tan 2u}{u \sec u}$.

21. $\lim_{x\to 0} \frac{10^x - e^x}{x}$.

22. $\lim_{x\to 0} \frac{x - \tan^{-1} x}{\sin^{-1} x - x}$.

II

Find each of the following limits.

1. $\lim_{x\to 0} \frac{\sin x - x + (x^3/6)}{x^5}$.

2. $\lim_{x\to 0} \frac{x^2 + 2x + 2\ln(1 - x)}{x^3}$.

3. $\lim_{x\to 0} \frac{x^3 + 6x - 6\sin^{-1} x}{-x^5}$.

4. $\lim_{y\to 0} y^{\epsilon}(\ln y)^n$, $(\epsilon, n > 0)$.

5. $\lim_{t\to 1} \dfrac{nt^{n+1} - (n+1)t^n + 1}{(t-1)^2}.$

6. $\lim_{x\to 1} \dfrac{\sum_{k=1}^{n} x^k - n}{x - 1}.$ How is this problem related to Exercise 5?

7. $\lim_{x\to 0} \dfrac{\sum_{k=1}^{n} k^x - n}{x}.$

8. $\lim_{\lambda\to 0} \dfrac{1}{\ln \lambda} \int_{\lambda}^{a} \dfrac{\cos x}{x}\, dx.$

9. $\lim_{\lambda\to 0} \int_{\lambda}^{2\lambda} \dfrac{e^{-x}}{x}\, dx.$

3 FURTHER INDETERMINATE FORMS

L'Hospital's rule may be used in the evaluation of limits of the form

$$\lim_{x\to\infty} \frac{f(x)}{g(x)},$$

as we shall now prove.

14.3 L'HOSPITAL'S SECOND RULE. Let the functions f and g be differentiable at every x greater than some number a, with $g'(x) \neq 0$. If $\lim_{x\to\infty} f(x) = \lim_{x\to\infty} g(x) = 0$, or $\lim_{x\to\infty} f(x) = \pm\infty$ and $\lim_{x\to\infty} g(x) = \pm\infty$, then

$$\lim_{x\to\infty} \frac{f(x)}{g(x)} = \lim_{x\to\infty} \frac{f'(x)}{g'(x)},$$

provided this latter limit exists or is infinite.

Proof: We shall prove the (0/0) case and omit the proof of the other one. So let us assume that

$$\lim_{x\to\infty} f(x) = \lim_{x\to\infty} g(x) = 0.$$

If we let $x = 1/y$, then

$$\lim_{x\to\infty} \frac{f(x)}{g(x)} = \lim_{y\to 0^+} \frac{f(1/y)}{g(1/y)}.$$

Since

$$Df\left(\frac{1}{y}\right) = f'\left(\frac{1}{y}\right) D\left(\frac{1}{y}\right) = -\frac{f'(1/y)}{y^2},$$

and similarly for $Dg\left(\frac{1}{y}\right)$, we may apply the first l'Hospital rule to obtain

$$\operatorname*{limit}_{y\to 0^+} \frac{f(1/y)}{g(1/y)} = \operatorname*{limit}_{y\to 0^+} \frac{[f'(1/y)]/y^2}{[g'(1/y)]/y^2} = \operatorname*{limit}_{y\to 0^+} \frac{f'(1/y)}{g'(1/y)} = \operatorname*{limit}_{x\to\infty} \frac{f'(x)}{g'(x)}.$$

This proves **14.3.**

Rule **14.3** also applies to the evaluation of

$$\operatorname*{limit}_{x\to -\infty} \frac{f(x)}{g(x)}.$$

EXAMPLE 1. Find $\operatorname*{limit}_{x\to\infty} \frac{\ln x}{x}$.

Solution: This limit is indeterminate of the form ∞/∞. Thus we may use **14.3** to obtain

$$\operatorname*{limit}_{x\to\infty} \frac{\ln x}{x} = \operatorname*{limit}_{x\to\infty} \frac{1/x}{1} = 0.$$

If

$$\operatorname*{limit}_{x\to a} f(x) = 0 \quad \text{and} \quad \operatorname*{limit}_{x\to a} g(x) = \pm\infty,$$

then $f(x)g(x)$ is indeterminate of the form $0\cdot\infty$. We can change it to either the form $(0/0)$ or (∞/∞) as follows:

$$\operatorname*{limit}_{x\to a} f(x)g(x) = \operatorname*{limit}_{x\to a} \frac{f(x)}{1/g(x)} = \operatorname*{limit}_{x\to a} \frac{g(x)}{1/f(x)}.$$

L'Hospital's rule is applicable to these latter two limits. For example,

$$\operatorname*{limit}_{x\to 0^+} x \ln x = \operatorname*{limit}_{x\to 0^+} \frac{\ln x}{1/x} = 0,$$

by Example 2 of Section 2.

Other indeterminate forms are encountered in evaluating limits of the form

$$\operatorname{limit}\, [f(x)]^{g(x)}.$$

If $\operatorname{limit} f(x) = \operatorname{limit} g(x) = 0$, we have the 0^0 form; other forms are 1^∞ and ∞^0. Each of these types is attacked by writing

$$[f(x)]^{g(x)} = \exp[g(x) \ln f(x)]$$

By the continuity of the exponential function (and **4.26**), we have, for instance, that

$$\operatorname*{limit}_{x\to a} \exp[g(x) \ln f(x)] = \exp\,[\operatorname*{limit}_{x\to a} g(x) \ln f(x)]$$

Thus we have only to evaluate

$$\lim_{x \to a} g(x) \ln f(x)$$

in order to find the desired limit.

EXAMPLE 2. Find $\lim_{x \to 0^+} x^x$.

Solution: This 0^0 indeterminate form is evaluated as follows:

$$\lim_{x \to 0^+} x^x = \lim_{x \to 0^+} \exp(x \ln x)$$
$$= \exp\left(\lim_{x \to 0^+} x \ln x\right) = e^0 = 1.$$

EXAMPLE 3. Find $\lim_{h \to 0^+} (1 + ah)^{1/h}$.

Solution: Since $1 + ah$ has limit 1 and $1/h$ has limit ∞ as h approaches 0^+, we have the indeterminate form 1^∞. We evaluate this limit as follows:

$$\lim_{h \to 0^+} (1 + ah)^{1/h} = \lim_{h \to 0^+} \exp\left[\frac{1}{h} \ln(1 + ah)\right] = \exp \lim_{h \to 0^+} \frac{\ln 1 + ah}{h}.$$

By l'Hospital's first rule,

$$\lim_{h \to 0^+} \frac{\ln(1 + ah)}{h} = \lim_{h \to 0^+} \frac{a/(1 + ah)}{1} = a.$$

Hence

$$\lim_{h \to 0^+} (1 + ah)^{1/h} = e^a.$$

EXAMPLE 4. Sketch the graph of the function f defined by

$$f(x) = x \ln x.$$

Solution: The domain of f is the set of positive real numbers. Since

$$\lim_{x \to 0^+} x \ln x = 0,$$

the graph approaches the origin when x approaches zero. Now

$$f'(x) = 1 + \ln x,$$

and $f'(x) = 0$ if and only if $\ln x = -1$. Thus $e^{-1} = 1/e$ is the only critical number of f. Since $f''(x) = 1/x$, $f''(1/e) > 0$, and the point $(1/e, -1/e)$ is a minimum point on the graph. Clearly, $f(1) = 0$. The graph is shown in Figure 14.1.

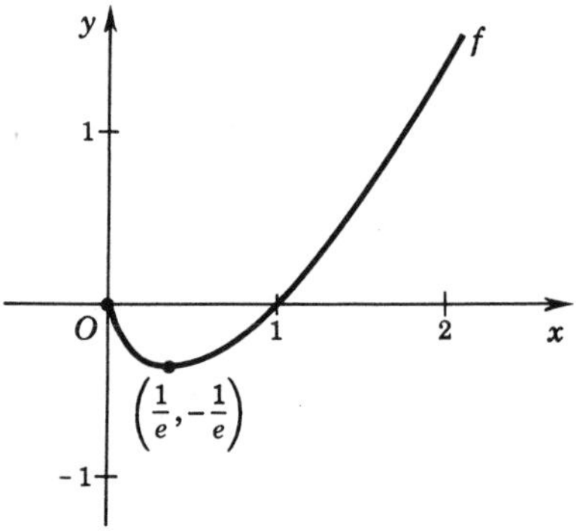

FIGURE 14.1

EXERCISES

I

In each of Exercises 1–18, evaluate the limit, if possible.

1. $\lim_{x\to\infty} xe^{-x}$.

2. $\lim_{x\to\infty} \frac{\ln x}{\sqrt{x}}$.

3. $\lim_{x\to\infty} \frac{x^n}{e^x}$, ($n$ a positive integer).

4. $\lim_{x\to-\infty} x^2e^x$.

5. $\lim_{x\to\infty} \frac{\ln x}{x^a}$, ($a > 0$).

6. $\lim_{x\to0^+} \left(1 + \frac{1}{x}\right)^x$.

7. $\lim_{x\to0} (1 - x)^{1/x}$.

8. $\lim_{x\to\infty} x^{1/x}$.

9. $\lim_{x\to0^+} \left(\frac{1}{\sin x} - \frac{1}{x}\right)$.

10. $\lim_{x\to\pi/2} (\sec x - \tan x)$.

11. $\lim_{x\to\pi/2} (\sin x)^{\tan x}$.

12. $\lim_{x\to0} (1 + 2\sin x)^{\cot x}$.

13. $\lim_{x\to0} (x + e^{2x})^{1/x}$.

14. $\lim_{x\to0^+} (\sin x)^x$.

15. $\lim_{x\to0^+} x^{\sin x}$.

16. $\lim_{x\to0} \left(\frac{1}{x} - \frac{1}{\tan^{-1} x}\right)$.

17. $\lim_{x\to0^+} x^{a/\ln x}$.

18. $\lim_{x\to1} x^{1/(1-x)}$.

19. If $a > 0$, prove that there exists a number N such that $\ln x < x^a$ for every $x > N$.

20. If $a > 1$ and n is a positive integer, prove that there exists a number N such that $x^n < a^x$ for every $x > N$.

II

In each of Exercises 1–9 evaluate the limit.

1. $\lim_{x \to 0^+} (\sin x)^{\sin x - x}$.
2. $\lim_{x \to 0^+} (\sin x)^{\csc x}$.
3. $\lim_{y \to 0} (1 - \sin y^2)^{\csc y^2}$.
4. $\lim_{x \to 0^-} (1 + x - \sin x)^{\tan^{-3} x}$.
5. $\lim_{x \to 0} \left(\frac{1}{x \sin^{-1} x} - \frac{1}{x^2}\right)$.
6. $\lim_{x \to 0} \left(\frac{\operatorname{csch} x}{x} - \frac{1}{x^2}\right)$.
7. $\lim_{\lambda \to 0} \left[\lim_{x \to \infty} \left(\frac{\left[1 + \frac{a\lambda}{x}\right]^x - \left[1 + \frac{b\lambda}{x}\right]^x}{\lambda} \right) \right]$.
8. Redo Exercise 7 but reverse the order of the limits.
9. $\lim_{x \to \infty} xe^{-x^2} \int_0^x e^{t^2}\, dt$.
10. For what value of n does $x^n e^{-x^4} \int_0^x e^{t^4}\, dt$ have a finite limit as $x \to \infty$? Find the limit in this case.

4 IMPROPER INTEGRALS

If

$$f(x) = xe^{-x},$$

then

$$\lim_{x \to \infty} f(x) = \lim_{x \to \infty} \frac{x}{e^x} = \lim_{x \to \infty} \frac{1}{e^x} = 0.$$

The part of the graph of f in the first quadrant is sketched in Figure 14.2.

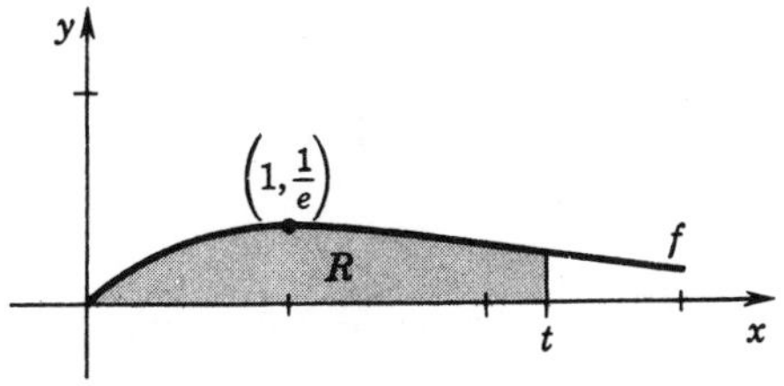

FIGURE 14.2

The region R between the graph of f and the positive x axis is a region of infinite extent. Let us show how we can assign a finite area to this region.

Consider the area $A(t)$ of the shaded region under the graph of f between 0 and t; clearly,

$$A(t) = \int_0^t xe^{-x}\,dx = (-xe^{-x} - e^{-x})\Big|_0^t$$
$$= -te^{-t} - e^{-t} + 1.$$

Now

$$\lim_{t\to\infty} A(t) = \lim_{t\to\infty}\left(-\frac{t}{e^t} - \frac{1}{e^t} + 1\right) = 1.$$

Hence we assign to the region R the area 1.

It is convenient to introduce the following definitions.

14.4 $$\int_a^\infty f(x)\,dx = \lim_{t\to\infty}\int_a^t f(x)\,dx, \text{ if this limit exists.}$$

14.5 $$\int_{-\infty}^a f(x)\,dx = \lim_{t\to-\infty}\int_t^a f(x)\,dx, \text{ if this limit exists.}$$

Thus the area of the region R above is given by

$$\int_0^\infty xe^{-x}\,dx = \lim_{t\to\infty}\int_0^t xe^{-x}\,dx.$$

The integrals defined in **14.4** and **14.5** are called *improper integrals*. They differ from ordinary definite integrals in that they are evaluated over infinite intervals.

EXAMPLE 1. The graph of the function f defined by

$$f(x) = \frac{1}{x}$$

is sketched in the first quadrant in Figure 14.3. Can an area be assigned to the shaded region R? If the region R is rotated about the x axis, can a volume be assigned to the solid so formed?

Solution: If R is to have an area consistent with the area of a finite region, it must be given by

$$\int_1^\infty \frac{1}{x}\,dx.$$

However,

$$\int_1^\infty \frac{1}{x}\,dx = \lim_{t\to\infty}\int_1^t \frac{1}{x}\,dx = \lim_{t\to\infty} \ln t = \infty.$$

Thus R does not have a finite area.

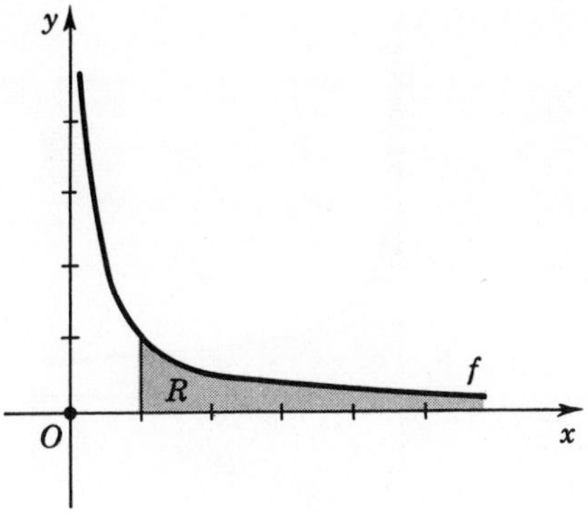

FIGURE 14.3

The volume of the solid obtained by rotating R about the x axis must be given by

$$\pi \int_1^\infty \frac{1}{x^2}\, dx.$$

Since

$$\int_1^\infty \frac{1}{x^2}\, dx = \operatorname*{limit}_{t\to\infty} \int_1^t \frac{1}{x^2}\, dx$$

$$= \operatorname*{limit}_{t\to\infty} \left(-\frac{1}{t} + 1 \right) = 1,$$

the volume assigned to this solid is π.

A function might be integrable in $[a,b)$ (i.e., integrable in the interval $[a,t]$ for every t in (a,b)) but not even bounded in $[a,b)$. However, the integral of f in $[a,b]$ might exist according to the following definition.

14.6 DEFINITION. (1) If the function f is integrable in the half-open interval $[a,b)$, then

$$\int_a^b f(x)\, dx = \operatorname*{limit}_{t\to b^-} \int_a^t f(x)\, dx, \text{ if this limit exists.}$$

(2) If f is integrable in $(a,b]$, then

$$\int_a^b f(x)\, dx = \operatorname*{limit}_{t\to a^+} \int_t^b f(x)\, dx, \text{ if this limit exists.}$$

EXAMPLE 2. Find $\displaystyle\int_0^4 \frac{1}{\sqrt{x}}\, dx.$

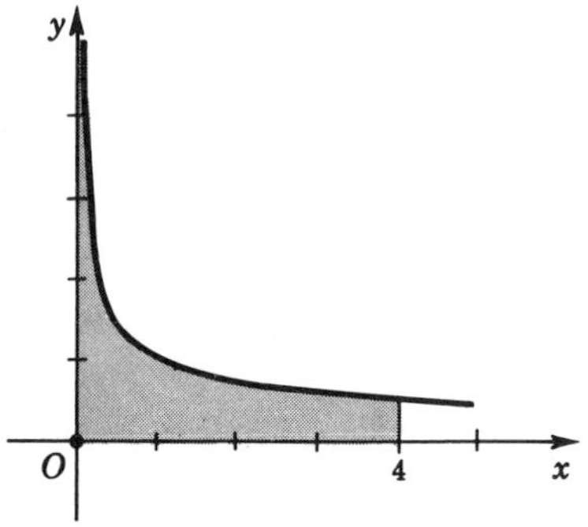

FIGURE 14.4

Solution: Evidently the function $f(x) = 1/\sqrt{x}$ is unbounded in (0,4], but is continuous and hence integrable in $[t,4]$ for $0 < t < 4$. This is an improper integral of type 14.6(2). Hence

$$\int_0^4 \frac{1}{\sqrt{x}}\,dx = \underset{t\to 0^+}{\text{limit}} \int_t^4 x^{-1/2}\,dx$$

$$= \underset{t\to 0^+}{\text{limit}}\ 2x^{1/2}\Big|_t^4 = \underset{t\to 0^+}{\text{limit}}\ (4 - 2\sqrt{t}) = 4.$$

Geometrically, we have shown that the shaded region of Figure 14.4, a region of infinite extent, has a finite area of 4 square units.

EXAMPLE 3. Find $\int_1^0 x \ln x\,dx$. (This is the area of the region bounded by the graph of $y = x \ln x$ and the x axis sketched in Figure 14.1.)

Solution: The integrand has a discontinuity at 0 since ln 0 does not exist. Hence

$$\int_1^0 x \ln x\,dx = \underset{t\to 0^+}{\text{limit}} \int_1^t x \ln x\,dx$$

$$= \underset{t\to 0^+}{\text{limit}}\ \tfrac{1}{4}(2x^2 \ln x - x^2)\Big|_1^t$$

$$= \underset{t\to 0^+}{\text{limit}}\ \tfrac{1}{4}(2t^2 \ln t - t^2 + 1).$$

By l'Hospital's first rule,

$$\underset{t\to 0^+}{\text{limit}}\ t^2 \ln t = \underset{t\to 0^+}{\text{limit}} \frac{\ln t}{1/t^2}$$

$$= \underset{t\to 0^+}{\text{limit}} \frac{1/t}{-2/t^3} = \underset{t\to 0^+}{\text{limit}} \left(-\frac{t^2}{2}\right) = 0.$$

Thus

$$\lim_{t\to 0^+} \frac{1}{4}(2t^2 \ln t - t^2 + 1) = \frac{1}{4},$$

and

$$\int_1^0 x \ln x \, dx = \frac{1}{4}.$$

EXERCISES

I

In each of Exercises 1–16 find the value of the improper integral, if it exists.

1. $\int_1^\infty \frac{1}{x\sqrt{x}}\, dx.$

2. $\int_{-\infty}^4 \frac{1}{(5-x)^2}\, dx.$

3. $\int_{-\infty}^3 \frac{1}{\sqrt{7-x}}\, dx.$

4. $\int_0^\infty \frac{x}{1+x^2}\, dx.$

5. $\int_3^4 \frac{1}{\sqrt{x-3}}\, dx.$

6. $\int_{-2}^0 \frac{1}{\sqrt{4-x^2}}\, dx.$

7. $\int_0^\infty \frac{1}{\sqrt{e^x}}\, dx.$

8. $\int_0^\infty e^{-ax}\, dx,\ (a > 0).$

9. $\int_0^1 \frac{1}{\sqrt[3]{x}}\, dx.$

10. $\int_0^4 \frac{1}{x\sqrt{x}}\, dx.$

11. $\int_1^\infty \frac{1}{1+x^2}\, dx.$

12. $\int_3^\infty \frac{1}{x^2-2x}\, dx.$

13. $\int_{\pi/4}^{\pi/2} \sec x\, dx.$

14. $\int_0^{\pi/2} \frac{1}{1-\sin x}\, dx.$

15. $\int_{-1}^\infty \frac{x}{e^{x^2}}\, dx.$

16. $\int_2^\infty \frac{1}{x^2-1}\, dx.$

17. If f is continuous at each real number x, define

(1) $$\int_{-\infty}^\infty f(x)\, dx = \int_{-\infty}^0 f(x)\, dx + \int_0^\infty f(x)\, dx$$

provided each integral on the right side of (1) exists.

a. Show that if the integral (1) exists then

$$\int_{-\infty}^\infty f(x)\, dx = \int_{-\infty}^a f(x)\, dx + \int_a^\infty f(x)\, dx$$

for every real number a.

b. Show by example that $\lim_{t\to\infty} \int_{-t}^{t} f(x)\,dx$ can exist even though $\int_{-\infty}^{\infty} f(x)\,dx$ does not exist.

Find the integrals in Exercises 18 and 19.

18. $\displaystyle\int_{-\infty}^{\infty} \frac{1}{1+x^2}\,dx.$

19. $\displaystyle\int_{-\infty}^{\infty} \frac{1}{e^x+e^{-x}}\,dx.$

20. If f is continuous at each number in the closed interval $[a,b]$ except c, $(a < c < b)$, then define

(1) $$\int_a^b f(x)\,dx = \int_a^c f(x)\,dx + \int_c^b f(x)\,dx,$$

provided each integral on the right side of (1) exists.

a. Does

$$\int_a^b f(x)\,dx = \lim_{\epsilon\to 0^+}\left[\int_a^{c-\epsilon} f(x)\,dx + \int_{c+\epsilon}^b f(x)\,dx\right]?$$

b. What is wrong with the reasoning,

$$\int_{-1}^{1} \frac{1}{x}\,dx = \ln|x|\,\Big|_{-1}^{1} = \ln 1 - \ln 1 = 0?$$

Find the integrals in Exercises 21 and 22, if they exist.

21. $\displaystyle\int_{-2}^{1} \frac{1}{\sqrt[3]{x^2}}\,dx.$

22. $\displaystyle\int_{0}^{4} \frac{1}{(x-2)^2}\,dx.$

23. Show that $\displaystyle\int_0^1 \frac{1}{\sqrt[3]{x^2}}\,dx$ exists but that $\displaystyle\int_0^1 \frac{1}{\sqrt[3]{x^4}}\,dx$ does not, and interpret the result geometrically.

24. Show that

$$\int_0^4 \frac{1}{(x+4)\sqrt{x}}\,dx = \frac{\pi}{4}, \qquad \int_4^{\infty} \frac{1}{(x+4)\sqrt{x}}\,dx = \frac{\pi}{4}.$$

Hence find

$$\int_0^{\infty} \frac{1}{(x+4)\sqrt{x}}\,dx.$$

Find the following integrals.

25. $\displaystyle\int_1^{\infty} \frac{\ln x}{x^2}\,dx.$

26. $\displaystyle\int_1^{\pi/2} \left(\frac{1}{x^2} - \csc x \cot x\right) dx.$

27. $\displaystyle\int_0^{\pi/2} (\sec x \tan x - \sec^2 x)\,dx.$

28. $\displaystyle\int_0^{e} x^2 \ln x\,dx.$

II

For what values of a and b do the following improper integrals exist?

1. $\int_0^1 x^a\,dx.$ 2. $\int_1^\infty x^a\,dx.$ 3. $\int_0^\infty \frac{x^a}{1+x^b}\,dx.$

In each of Exercises 4–6, find the values of n for which the given improper integral exists and evaluate the integral.

4. $\int_0^1 x^n \ln x\,dx.$ 5. $\int_0^1 x^n \ln^2 x\,dx.$ 6. $\int_1^\infty \frac{\ln x}{x^n}\,dx.$

7. Evaluate $\int_0^\infty x^n e^{ax}\,dx$ if n is a positive integer and $a < 0$.

8. Prove $\lim_{\lambda\to\infty} \int_0^\infty \frac{1}{1+\lambda x^4}\,dx = 0.$

5 TAYLOR'S FORMULA

Let f be a function for which the nth derivative $f^{[n]}$ exists at some number c. The polynomial*

14.7 $$P_n(x) = f(c) + f'(c)(x-c) + \frac{f''(c)}{2!}(x-c)^2 + \cdots + \frac{f^{[n]}(c)}{n!}(x-c)^n,$$

of degree n in x, is called the nth-degree *Taylor's*† *polynomial* of f at c. Using the $\sum$ notation, with $0! = 1$ and $f^{[0]} = f$,

$$P_n(x) = \sum_{k=0}^{n} \frac{f^{[k]}(c)}{k!}(x-c)^k.$$

Since

$$D\frac{f^{[k]}(c)}{k!}(x-c)^k = \frac{kf^{[k]}(c)}{k!}(x-c)^{k-1} = \frac{f^{[k]}(c)}{(k-1)!}(x-c)^{k-1},$$

evidently

$$P_n'(x) = \sum_{k=1}^{n} \frac{f^{[k]}(c)}{(k-1)!}(x-c)^{k-1},$$

and, in general,

* $n!$, read "n factorial," equals $n(n-1)(n-2)\cdots 1$.
† Brook Taylor (1685–1731) gave methods of expanding a function in a series in his book *Methodus Incrementorum Directa et Inversa*, published in 1715. His methods were made mathematically rigorous a century later, notably by Gauss and Cauchy.

14.8 $$P_n^{[j]}(x) = \sum_{k=j}^{n} \frac{f^{[k]}(c)}{(k-j)!}(x-c)^{k-j}, \qquad 0 \le j \le n.$$

Since $P_n(x)$ is a polynomial of degree n [or less if $f^{[n]}(c) = 0$], clearly

$$P_n^{[j]}(x) = 0, \qquad j > n.$$

If we replace x by c in **14.7**, each term becomes zero with the exception of the first one; thus

$$P_n(c) = f(c).$$

Similarly, each term of the right side of **14.8** after the first one becomes zero if we replace x by c; i.e.,

14.9 $$P_n^{[j]}(c) = f^{[j]}(c), \qquad 0 \le j \le n.$$

Thus not only does the Taylor's polynomial $P_n(x)$ have the same value as f at c, but also each derivative of P_n through the nth has the same value as the corresponding derivative of f at c.

EXAMPLE 1. Find the fourth-degree Taylor's polynomial of the sine function at $\pi/2$.

Solution: If $f(x) = \sin x$, then, by **14.7**,

$$P_4(x) = f\left(\frac{\pi}{2}\right) + f'\left(\frac{\pi}{2}\right)\left(x - \frac{\pi}{2}\right) + \frac{f''(\pi/2)}{2}\left(x - \frac{\pi}{2}\right)^2$$
$$+ \frac{f'''(\pi/2)}{3!}\left(x - \frac{\pi}{2}\right)^3 + \frac{f^{[4]}(\pi/2)}{4!}\left(x - \frac{\pi}{2}\right)^4.$$

Since

$$f(x) = \sin x, \quad f\left(\frac{\pi}{2}\right) = 1,$$

$$f'(x) = \cos x, \quad f'\left(\frac{\pi}{2}\right) = 0,$$

$$f''(x) = -\sin x, \quad f''\left(\frac{\pi}{2}\right) = -1,$$

$$f'''(x) = -\cos x, \quad f'''\left(\frac{\pi}{2}\right) = 0,$$

$$f^{[4]}(x) = \sin x, \quad f^{[4]}\left(\frac{\pi}{2}\right) = 1,$$

we obtain

$$P_4(x) = 1 - \frac{1}{2}\left(x - \frac{\pi}{2}\right)^2 + \frac{1}{24}\left(x - \frac{\pi}{2}\right)^4.$$

We come now to the fundamental Taylor's formula, relating a function to its Taylor's polynomials.

14.10 **TAYLOR'S FORMULA.** Let f be a function and n an integer such that $f^{[n+1]}(x)$ exists for every number x in a closed interval $[a,b]$ containing the number c. Then if $P_n(x)$ is the nth-degree Taylor's polynomial of f at c, there exists some number z (depending on x) between x and c such that

$$f(x) = P_n(x) + \frac{f^{[n+1]}(z)}{(n+1)!}(x-c)^{n+1}, \qquad a \leq x \leq b.$$

Proof: We shall consider x a constant, distinct from c, in the arguments that follow. Define the functions F and G by

$$F(t) = f(x) - \sum_{k=0}^{n} \frac{f^{[k]}(t)}{k!}(x-t)^k, \qquad a \leq t \leq b,$$

$$G(t) = (x-t)^{n+1}.$$

It is evident that

(1) $$F(c) = f(x) - P_n(x), \qquad F(x) = f(x) - f(x) = 0.$$

Although $F(t)$ is a sum of $n+2$ terms, the derivative of F is very simply given by

(2) $$F'(t) = -\frac{f^{[n+1]}(t)}{n!}(x-t)^n.$$

To prove (2), we note that each term of the summation in F involves a product of two functions. Thus [since $Df(x) = 0$]

$$F'(t) = -\sum_{k=0}^{n} \frac{f^{[k+1]}(t)}{k!}(x-t)^k - \sum_{k=0}^{n} \frac{f^{[k]}(t)}{k!} k(x-t)^{k-1}(-1).$$

The limits of summation can always be changed as follows:

$$\sum_{k=0}^{n} a_k = \sum_{k=1}^{n+1} a_{k-1}.$$

Making such a change in the first summation of $F'(t)$, we have

(3) $$F'(t) = -\sum_{k=1}^{n+1} \frac{f^{[k]}(t)}{(k-1)!}(x-t)^{k-1} + \sum_{k=1}^{n} \frac{f^{[k]}(t)}{(k-1)!}(x-t)^{k-1}.$$

The lower limit of the second summation was made 1, since the term for $k = 0$ is zero. The two summations in (3) are identical except that the first summation has one more term for $k = n + 1$. Thus all the terms cancel except for the last term of the first summation. This proves (2).

Let us now use Cauchy's formula with the functions F and G. Thus

$$\frac{F(c) - F(x)}{G(c) - G(x)} = \frac{F'(z)}{G'(z)}$$

for some number z between c and x, according to Cauchy's formula. Since $G'(t) = -(n + 1)(x - t)^n$ and $G(x) = 0$, we have by (1) and (2) that

$$\frac{f(x) - P_n(x)}{(x - c)^{n+1}} = \frac{-\dfrac{f^{[n+1]}(z)}{n!}(x - z)^n}{-(n + 1)(x - z)^n} = \frac{f^{[n+1]}(z)}{(n + 1)!},$$

and

$$f(x) = P_n(x) + \frac{f^{[n+1]}(z)}{(n + 1)!}(x - c)^{n+1}.$$

This proves Taylor's formula.

The term

14.11 $$R_n(x) = \frac{f^{[n+1]}(z)}{(n + 1)!}(x - c)^{n+1}$$

appearing in Taylor's formula is called the nth *remainder term* of f at c. Using **14.11**, we may write Taylor's formula in the form

$$f(x) = P_n(x) + R_n(x).$$

We shall soon show that under certain conditions the remainder term is very small; hence

$$f(x) \doteq P_n(x).$$

EXAMPLE 2. Write Taylor's formula for the sine function of Example 1.

Solution: Since $f^{[5]}(x) = \cos x$, we have

$$R_4(x) = \frac{f^{[5]}(z)}{5!}\left(x - \frac{\pi}{2}\right)^5 = \frac{\cos z}{120}\left(x - \frac{\pi}{2}\right)^5.$$

Hence, using P_4 from Example 1,

$$\sin x = 1 - \frac{1}{2}\left(x - \frac{\pi}{2}\right)^2 + \frac{1}{24}\left(x - \frac{\pi}{2}\right)^4 + \frac{\cos z}{120}\left(x - \frac{\pi}{2}\right)^5$$

for some number z between x and $\pi/2$.

If $c = 0$, Taylor's formula becomes

14.12 $$f(x) = f(0) + f'(0)x + \frac{f''(0)}{2!}x^2 + \cdots + \frac{f^{[n]}(0)}{n!}x^n + \frac{f^{[n+1]}(z)}{(n + 1)!}x^{n+1},$$

with z a number between 0 and x. This form of Taylor's formula is called *Maclaurin's formula.**

EXAMPLE 3. Write Maclaurin's formula for the exponential function.

Solution: If $f(x) = e^x$, then $f^{[k]}(x) = e^x$ for each k and therefore $f^{[k]}(0) = e^0 = 1$. Thus Maclaurin's formula becomes

$$e^x = 1 + x + \frac{x^2}{2!} + \frac{x^3}{3!} + \cdots + \frac{x^n}{n!} + \frac{e^z}{(n+1)!}x^{n+1},$$

with z a number between 0 and x.

EXERCISES

In each of the following exercises, find $P_n(x)$, $R_n(x)$, and write the Taylor's formula for the given function, value of n, and value of c.

1. $f(x) = \cos x$, $n = 5$, $c = \frac{\pi}{2}$.
2. $g(x) = \ln x$, $n = 5$, $c = 1$.
3. $F(x) = \tan^{-1} x$, $n = 3$, $c = 1$.
4. $G(x) = e^x$, $n = 4$, $c = -1$.
5. $f(x) = \sec x$, $n = 3$, $c = \frac{\pi}{4}$.
6. $h(x) = \frac{1}{x+1}$, $n = 6$, $c = -2$.

In each of the following exercises, write the Maclaurin's formula for the given function and value of n.

7. $f(x) = \sin x$, $n = 6$.
8. $f(x) = \cos x$, $n = 5$.
9. $g(x) = \ln (x + 1)$, $n = 5$.
10. $F(x) = \tan^{-1} x$, $n = 4$.
11. $F(x) = \sin^{-1} x$, $n = 3$.
12. $g(x) = \sqrt{1 + x}$, $n = 5$.
13. $f(x) = \frac{1}{\sqrt{1 - x}}$, $n = 4$.
14. $f(x) = e^{-x}$, $n = 5$.
15. $g(x) = \tan x$, $n = 4$.
16. $g(x) = \frac{1}{(1 - x)^2}$, $n = 4$.
17. $F(x) = \frac{1}{1 + e^x}$, $n = 3$.
18. $g(x) = x^5$, $n = 6$.

---

* Colin Maclaurin (1698–1746), a Scotch mathematician and contemporary of Taylor, gave this formula in his *Treatise of Fluxions* in 1742. However, this formula had appeared 25 years earlier in a publication by Stirling.

I

1. Many calculus textbooks state that Maclaurin's formula is a special case of Taylor's formula. Show that they are equivalent.

2. Find the Maclaurin expansion of y up to the x^3 term if

$$y^3 + xy = 1 \quad \text{and} \quad y = 1 \quad \text{for } x = 0.$$

(*Suggestion:* Use implicit differentiation).

3. Same as Exercise 2, except that

$$e^x - e^y = xy \quad \text{and} \quad y = 0 \quad \text{for } x = 0.$$

6 APPROXIMATIONS BY TAYLOR'S POLYNOMIALS

One of the easiest functions with which to compute values is the polynomial function. Thus it is an easy matter to find values of

$$f(x) = x - \frac{x^3}{6}$$

corresponding to various choices of x. For example,

$$f(.2) = .2 - \frac{.008}{6} \doteq .19867.$$

The theory of Section 6 allows us to approximate many functions by polynomial functions. Thus, if $P_n(x)$ and $R_n(x)$ are the Taylor's polynomial and the remainder term for a function f at c,

$$f(x) = P_n(x) + R_n(x), \quad \text{and} \quad |f(x) - P_n(x)| = |R_n(x)|.$$

If we can find a number d such that

$$|R_n(x)| \leq d,$$

then we will have $|f(x) - P_n(x)| \leq d$, or

$$P_n(x) - d \leq f(x) \leq P_n(x) + d.$$

We shall write

$$f(x) = P_n(x) \pm d$$

in this case, with the understanding that this equation means $f(x) \doteq P_n(x)$, with an error of not more than d units.

EXAMPLE 1. Approximate $\sin x$ by a fourth-degree polynomial in x, if $0 \leq x \leq .2$.

Solution: If $f(x) = \sin x$, then

$$f(0) = 0,\ \ f'(0) = 1,\ \ f''(0) = 0,\ \ f'''(0) = -1,\ \ f^{[4]}(0) = 0,\ \ f^{[5]}(x) = \cos x.$$

Hence the fourth-degree Taylor's polynomial of f at 0 is given by

$$P_4(x) = x - \frac{x^3}{3!}.$$

Note that this polynomial is actually of the third degree, since the coefficient $f^{[4]}(0)$ of the term of fourth degree is zero. Also,

$$R_4(x) = \frac{\cos z}{5!}\, x^5,$$

where $0 < z < .2$.

Since $\cos z \leq 1$,

$$0 < R_4(x) \leq \frac{(.2)^5}{5!} < .000003$$

in the given range $0 \leq x \leq .2$. Thus

$$\sin x = x - \frac{x^3}{6} \pm .000003, \qquad (0 \leq x \leq .2).$$

For example,

$$\sin .2 \doteq .19867,$$

accurate to five decimal places.

If we increase the range of x in the above example to $0 \leq x \leq .5$, then it is easily shown that $R_4(x) < .0003$. Hence

$$\sin x = x - \frac{x^3}{3!} \pm .0003, \qquad (0 \leq x \leq .5).$$

We still have accuracy to three decimal places, allowing x to range up to .5 radian (about 28°). Thus

$$\sin .5 \doteq .479,$$

accurate to three decimal places. The accuracy could be increased by choosing a Taylor's polynomial of higher degree.

EXAMPLE 2. Approximate $\ln x$ by a fifth-degree polynomial in x, if $1 \leq x \leq 1.2$.

Solution: Let us find $P_5(x)$ and $R_5(x)$ for $f(x) = \ln x$ at $c = 1$. Since

$$f'(x) = \frac{1}{x},\ \ f''(x) = -\frac{1}{x^2},\ \ f'''(x) = \frac{2}{x^3},\ \ f^{[4]}(x) = -\frac{6}{x^4},\ \ f^{[5]}(x) = \frac{24}{x^5},$$

we have

$$f(1) = 0,\ f'(1) = 1,\ f''(1) = -1,\ f'''(1) = 2,\ f^{[4]}(1) = -6,\ f^{[5]}(1) = 24.$$

Thus

$$P_5(x) = (x-1) - \frac{1}{2!}(x-1)^2 + \frac{2}{3!}(x-1)^3 - \frac{6}{4!}(x-1)^4 + \frac{24}{5!}(x-1)^5,$$

or

$$P_5(x) = (x-1) - \frac{1}{2}(x-1)^2 + \frac{1}{3}(x-1)^3 - \frac{1}{4}(x-1)^4 + \frac{1}{5}(x-1)^5.$$

The remainder term is given by

$$R_5(x) = \frac{f^{[6]}(z)}{6!}(x-1)^6 = -\frac{(x-1)^6}{6z^6}$$

for some number z, $1 < z < 1.2$. Since $1/z < 1$,

$$|R_5(x)| < \frac{(.2)^6}{6} < .000011.$$

Thus

$$\ln x = (x-1) - \tfrac{1}{2}(x-1)^2 + \tfrac{1}{3}(x-1)^3 - \tfrac{1}{4}(x-1)^4 + \tfrac{1}{5}(x-1)^5 \pm .000011,$$

if $1 \le x \le 1.2$.

For example,

$$\ln 1.2 = .2 - \frac{(.2)^2}{2} + \frac{(.2)^3}{3} - \frac{(.2)^4}{4} + \frac{(.2)^5}{5} \pm .000011,$$

and

$$\ln 1.2 \doteq .18233,$$

with a possible error of 1 in the fifth decimal place.

EXAMPLE 3. Find $\sqrt[3]{e}$ to an accuracy of five decimal places.

Solution: By Example 3 of Section 5,

$$e^x = 1 + x + \frac{x^2}{2!} + \frac{x^3}{3!} + \cdots + \frac{x^n}{n!} + R_n(x),$$

where

$$R_n(x) = \frac{e^z}{(n+1)!}x^{n+1}, \qquad (0 < z < x \text{ if } x > 0).$$

We wish to choose n so that $\left|R_n\left(\frac{1}{3}\right)\right| < 10^{-5}$. Clearly $e^{1/3} < 2$; therefore

$$\left|R_n\left(\frac{1}{3}\right)\right| < \frac{2}{3^{n+1}(n+1)!}.$$

If $n = 5$,

$$\left|R_5\left(\frac{1}{3}\right)\right| < \frac{2}{3^6\,6!} = \frac{1}{729 \times 360} < 10^{-5}.$$

Thus

$$\sqrt[3]{e} \doteq 1 + \frac{1}{3} + \frac{1}{2}\left(\frac{1}{3}\right)^2 + \frac{1}{6}\left(\frac{1}{3}\right)^3 + \frac{1}{24}\left(\frac{1}{3}\right)^4 + \frac{1}{120}\left(\frac{1}{3}\right)^5,$$

$$\text{or} \qquad \sqrt[3]{e} \doteq 1.39563.$$

EXERCISES

I

In each of Exercises 1–4 approximate the given function by a polynomial of given degree n in the given interval. State the error of approximation and compute the value of the function at the given number d as accurately as possible with the polynomial at hand.

1. $f(x) = \sin x, \quad 0 \le x \le .5, \quad n = 6, \quad d = .5.$
2. $g(x) = \cos x, \quad 0 \le x \le .2, \quad n = 3, \quad d = .2.$
3. $F(x) = e^x, \quad 0 \le x \le 1, \quad n = 5, \quad d = 1.$
4. $G(x) = e^{-x}, \quad 0 \le x \le 1, \quad n = 6, \quad d = 1.$
5. Show that if $F(x)$ is a polynomial in x of degree n then $F(x) = P_n(x)$, the Taylor's polynomial of F at any number c.
6. Write the general Maclaurin's formula for $\ln(1 - x)$ and for $\ln(1 + x)$.

II

In each of Exercises 1–4 determine Maclaurin's formula.

1. $\ln \dfrac{1 - x^2}{1 + x^2}.$
2. $e^{x^2}.$
3. $\cos^2 x.$
4. $\sin^3 wx.$
5. Obtain Newton's recursion scheme for approximating the roots of an equation $F(x) = 0$ (see Review, part II, 5) by means of the first few terms of the Taylor expansion of F.
6. If the mean value theorem is expressed in the form

$$F(x) = F(0) + xF'(\theta x),$$

where θ depends on x, $0 < \theta < 1$, find $\lim_{x \to 0} \theta$ [assume $F''(0) \neq 0$].

7. In a right triangle of sides a, b, c where $a \leq b < c$, show that angle A has measure approximately $172a/(2c + b)$ degrees. Check this approximation for the two cases $a = 1$, $b = \sqrt{3}$, $c = 2$, and $a = 1$, $b = 1$, $c = \sqrt{2}$. What, in general, is the approximate error in using this approximation? (R. A. Johnson, *Amer. Math. Monthly*, vol. 27, 368–369.)

8. The nth-derivative test for extrema of a function may be stated as follows: Let c be a critical number of the function f such that

$$f'(c) = 0, \quad f''(c) = 0, \quad \cdots, f^{[n-1]}(c) = 0, \quad f^{[n]}(c) \neq 0.$$

Assume that $f^{[n]}$ exists in some interval containing c and that $f^{[n]}$ is continuous at c. Then

(a) $f(c)$ is a maximum value of f if n is even and $f^{[n]}(c) < 0$,
(b) $f(c)$ is a minimum value of f if n is even and $f^{[n]}(c) > 0$,
(c) $f(c)$ is not an extrema of f if n is odd.

REVIEW

Oral Exercises

1. What is Cauchy's formula?
2. What is an indeterminate form?
3. Are 1^0, 0^1, and 0^∞ indeterminate forms?
4. What are l'Hospital's rules?
5. What is an improper integral?
6. What is the relationship between Taylor's formula and Maclaurin's formula?
7. How could one approximate a transcendental function by means of a polynomial?

I

Find each of the following limits.

1. $\displaystyle \operatorname*{limit}_{x\to 1} \frac{\ln x}{x^2 - x}$.
2. $\displaystyle \operatorname*{limit}_{x\to 0} \frac{e^x - e^{-x}}{\sin x}$.
3. $\displaystyle \operatorname*{limit}_{\theta\to\pi/2^-} (\sec \theta)^{\cos \theta}$.
4. $\displaystyle \operatorname*{limit}_{\alpha\to\pi/2} (1 - \sin \alpha)\tan \alpha$.
5. $\displaystyle \operatorname*{limit}_{x\to 0^+} x \ln (\sin x)$.
6. $\displaystyle \operatorname*{limit}_{z\to 0^+} \frac{\ln z}{\cot z}$.

7. $\lim_{x \to \infty} (\sqrt{x^2 + 2} - \sqrt{x^2 - 2})$.

8. $\lim_{x \to \infty} x^{3/2} (\sqrt{x^3 + a} - \sqrt{x^3 - a})$.

In each of Exercises 9–14 find the integral if it exists.

9. $\int_0^\infty e^{-ax} \sin bx \, dx, \ (a > 0)$.

10. $\int_0^\infty e^{-ax} \cos bx \, dx, \ (a > 0)$.

11. $\int_0^1 \frac{1}{e^x - e^{-x}} \, dx$.

12. $\int_{-\infty}^\infty \frac{1}{e^x - e^{-x}} \, dx$.

13. $\int_0^\infty \frac{1}{e^x + e^{-x}} \, dx$.

14. $\int_0^a \frac{1}{\sqrt{ax - x^2}} \, dx, \ (a > 0)$.

In each of Exercises 15 and 16 find $P_n(x)$, $R_n(x)$ and write the Taylor's formula for the given function and given values of n and c.

15. $F(x) = \frac{1}{2 + x}, \quad n = 4, \quad c = -1.$

16. $F(x) = \begin{cases} \dfrac{e^x - 1}{x} & \text{for } x \neq 0 \\ 1 & \text{for } x = 0, \end{cases} \quad n = 4, \quad c = 0.$

17. Calculate $\int_0^{1/4} \frac{2e^{-x^2}}{\sqrt{\pi}} \, dx$ accurate to five decimal places.

18. Calculate the smallest positive root of the equation $e^x + 10x = 2.216$ accurate to three decimal places by use of Maclaurin's formula.

19. If $|F'(x)| < M$ for every x in (a,b), then prove that

$$|F(b) - F(a)| < M(b - a).$$

20. In the mean value theorem,

$$F(b) - F(a) = (b - a)F'(c) \quad \text{for some } c \text{ in } (a,b).$$

Show that if $F(x)$ is a quadratic polynomial then $c = (a + b)/2$.

21. Give a geometric interpretation for the number λ in Exercise II-6, Section 1, if $G(x) = 1$ for all x in $[a,b]$.

22. Comment on the following student's proof of l'Hospital's rule:

Given that functions F and G are differentiable at every number other than c in some interval, with $G'(x) \neq 0$ if $x \neq c$. If $\lim_{x \to c} F(x) = \lim_{x \to c} G(x) = 0$, then

$$\lim_{x \to c} \frac{F(x)}{G(x)} = \lim_{x \to c} \frac{F'(x)}{G'(x)}$$

provided this latter limit exists or is infinite.

Proof: Let $\dfrac{F(x)}{G(x)} = H(x)$. Then $F'(x) = G'(x)H(x) + G(x)H'(x)$. Dividing by $G'(x)$,

$$\frac{F'(x)}{G'(x)} = H(x) + \frac{G(x)H'(x)}{G'(x)} = \frac{F(x)}{G(x)} + G(x)\frac{H'(x)}{G'(x)}.$$

Since $\operatorname*{limit}_{x\to c} G(x) = 0$ and $G'(x) \neq 0$ if $x \neq c$, it follows that

$$\operatorname*{limit}_{x\to c} \frac{F'(x)}{G'(x)} = \operatorname*{limit}_{x\to c} \frac{F(x)}{G(x)}.$$

II

If F and G are functions and a is a number (or $a = \infty$), then we will write

$$F(x) = O(G(x)) \quad \text{as } x \to a$$

if there exists a constant K and a deleted neighborhood N of a, [$N = (c, \infty)$ for some number c if $a = \infty$], such that

$$|F(x)| \leq KG(x) \quad \text{for every } x \text{ in } N.$$

We then say that *F is big O of G at a.* Some examples are:

$$\sin x = O(x) \quad \text{as } x \to 0,$$
$$x^3 + x = O(x^3) \quad \text{as } x \to \infty.$$

Similarly, we will write

$$F(x) = o(G(x)) \quad \text{as } x \to a$$

if

$$\operatorname*{limit}_{x\to a} \frac{F(x)}{G(x)} = 0.$$

We then say *F is little o of G at a.* Some examples are:

$$1 - \cos x = o(x) \quad \text{as } x \to 0,$$
$$\ln x = o(x^c),\ (c > 0), \quad \text{as } x \to \infty.$$

Also, we shall write $F(x) \sim G(x)$ at a if $\operatorname*{limit}_{x\to a} \dfrac{F(x)}{G(x)}$ exists and is nonzero.

1. Show that big O and little o of two functions F and G at a satisfy:

   a. $O(F) + O(G) = O(F + G)$.
   b. $O(F)\cdot O(G) = O(FG)$.
   c. $O(F)\cdot o(G) = o(FG)$.
   d. If $F \sim G$, then $F + o(G) \sim G$.

2. If $F(x) = O(G(x))$ at a, then prove that

$$\int_0^x F(\lambda)\, d\lambda = O\left\{\int_0^x G(\lambda)\, d\lambda\right\} \text{at } a.$$

3. Show:

a. $\sin x = x + O(x^3)$ as $x \to 0$.

b. $\cos x = 1 - \dfrac{x^2}{2} + O(x^4)$ as $x \to 0$.

c. $e^x = 1 + x + O(x^2)$ as $x \to 0$.

d. $\ln(1 + x) = x + O(x^2)$ as $x \to 0$.

e. $\left(1 + \dfrac{a}{x}\right)^x = e^a\left\{1 - \dfrac{a^2}{2x} + O\left(\dfrac{1}{x^2}\right)\right\}$ as $x \to \infty$.

4. Use Exercise 3(a) to solve Exercise I-9, Section 3.

5. Use Exercise 3(e) to find $\lim_{x\to\infty} x\left[\left(1 + \dfrac{1}{x}\right)^x - e\right]$.

6. What is the interpretation of:

a. $F(x) = O(1)$ at a?

b. $F(x) = o(1)$ at a?

7. If $\lim_{x\to\infty} F(x) = \lim_{x\to\infty} F'(x) = \lim_{x\to\infty} F''(x) = \infty$ and $\lim_{x\to\infty} \dfrac{xF'''(x)}{F''(x)} = 1$, find $\lim_{x\to\infty} \dfrac{xF'(x)}{F(x)}$.

8. It is known that $\int_0^\infty e^{-x^2}\,dx = \dfrac{\sqrt{\pi}}{2}$. Determine

$$\int_0^5 e^{-x^2}\,dx \div \int_0^\infty e^{-x^2}\,dx$$

correct to five decimal places.

9. If $F'(x) > 0$ for every x in (a,b), then prove that there is at most one root of the equation $F(x) = 0$ in this interval.

10. If $|F'(x)| < 1$ for all x, then prove that the equation $F(x) = x$ has at most one real root.

11. The functions $F(x)$ and $G(x)$ are such that $F(0) = G(0) = 0$. By considering the case where $F(x) = x^2 \sin 1/x$, $G(x) = \tan x$, show that $\lim_{x\to 0} \dfrac{F(x)}{G(x)}$ may exist even though $\lim_{x\to 0} \dfrac{F'(x)}{G'(x)}$ does not exist.

12. If F is a continuous function and

$$F(x) = \int_0^x F(t)\,dt,$$

show that $F(x) = 0$ for every x.

15

INFINITE SERIES

ONCE TAYLOR'S polynomial $P_n(x)$ is defined for a function f, it is natural to ask if $\lim_{n\to\infty} P_n(x)$ exists. This leads to a study of the infinite series

$$a_1 + a_2 + \cdots + a_n + \cdots$$

associated with each sequence $a_1, a_2, \cdots, a_n, \cdots$.

1 CONVERGENCE AND DIVERGENCE

Associated with an infinite series $a_1 + a_2 + \cdots + a_n + \cdots$ are its *partial sums*

$$\begin{aligned} S_1 &= a_1, \\ S_2 &= a_1 + a_2, \\ S_3 &= a_1 + a_2 + a_3, \\ &\cdots \\ &\cdots \\ S_n &= a_1 + a_2 + \cdots + a_n, \\ &\cdots \\ &\cdots \end{aligned}$$

If the sigma notation is used, we write

$$\sum_{k=1}^{\infty} a_k$$

for the given infinite series (or at times just Σa_k without limits) and

$$S_n = \sum_{k=1}^{n} a_k$$

for the nth partial sum.

An infinite series need not have a sum. As a matter of fact, we must define what we mean by a sum of an infinite sequence of numbers, since the usual operation of addition applies only to a finite set of numbers. Thus, whereas the sum of an infinite sequence of numbers is as yet undefined, each partial sum of the infinite series is a sum of a finite set of numbers and hence is itself a well-defined number. It is natural to define the sum of an infinite series as the number approached by the partial sum S_n as n gets large.

15.1 **DEFINITION.** An infinite series

$$a_1 + a_2 + \cdots + a_n + \cdots$$

with partial sums $S_1, S_2, \cdots, S_n, \cdots$ is said to be *convergent* if and only if

$$\operatorname*{limit}_{n \to \infty} S_n$$

exists. If this limit does not exist, the infinite series is said to be *divergent*. The number

$$S = \operatorname*{limit}_{n \to \infty} S_n$$

is called the *sum* of a convergent infinite series. A divergent infinite series does not have a sum.

If a convergent infinite series Σa_k has sum S, then we shall write

$$S = \sum_{k=1}^{\infty} a_k.$$

An infinite series of the form

$$\sum_{k=1}^{\infty} ar^{k-1} = a + ar + ar^2 + \cdots + ar^{n-1} + \cdots$$

is called a *geometric series*. From the identity

$$1 - r^n = (1 - r)(1 + r + r^2 + \cdots + r^{n-1}),$$

we easily deduce that the nth partial sum S_n of the geometric series is given by

$$S_n = a \sum_{k=1}^{n} r^{k-1} = \frac{a(1 - r^n)}{1 - r},$$

$$\text{or} \quad S_n = \frac{a}{1 - r} - \frac{ar^n}{1 - r}, \qquad (r \neq -1).$$

Since
$$\lim_{n \to \infty} r^n = 0 \quad \text{if} \quad |r| < 1,$$
evidently
$$\lim_{n \to \infty} S_n = \frac{a}{1-r} - \frac{a}{1-r} \lim_{n \to \infty} r^n = \frac{a}{1-r}$$
if $|r| < 1$. This proves that the geometric series converges and has sum $a/(1-r)$ if $|r| < 1$; i.e.,

15.2
$$\sum_{k=1}^{\infty} ar^{k-1} = \frac{a}{1-r}, \qquad |r| < 1.$$

(It is a corollary of the next theorem that the geometric series diverges if $|r| \geq 1$.)

For example,
$$1 + \frac{1}{2} + \frac{1}{4} + \cdots + \frac{1}{2^{n-1}} + \cdots = \frac{1}{1 - \frac{1}{2}} = 2,$$
$$.3 + .03 + .003 + \cdots + \frac{3}{10^n} + \cdots = \frac{.3}{1 - 10^{-1}} = \frac{1}{3}.$$
We recognize this latter series to be $.3333\cdots$, the infinite decimal representation of $\frac{1}{3}$.

We can, conversely, use **15.2** to obtain an infinite series expansion for fractions such as $1/(c - x)$. For example, if we let $a = 1$ and $r = -x^2$ in **15.2**, we obtain
$$\begin{aligned} \frac{1}{1+x^2} = \frac{1}{1-(-x^2)} &= 1 + (-x^2) + (-x^2)^2 + (-x^2)^3 + \cdots \\ &= 1 - x^2 + x^4 - x^6 + \cdots \\ &= \sum_{k=1}^{\infty} (-1)^{k-1} x^{2k-2} \\ &= \sum_{k=0}^{\infty} (-1)^k x^{2k}. \end{aligned}$$
The series converges if $x^2 < 1$, i.e., $|x| < 1$.

Every sequence of numbers
$$S_1, S_2, \cdots, S_n, \cdots$$
is the sequence of partial sums of some infinite series, namely the series
$$a_1 + a_2 + a_3 + \cdots + a_n + \cdots$$
where
$$a_1 = S_1,\ a_2 = S_2 - S_1,\ a_3 = S_3 - S_2,\ \cdots,\ a_n = S_n - S_{n-1},\ \cdots.$$

Clearly

$$S_n = a_1 + a_2 + a_3 + \cdots + a_n$$
$$= S_1 + (S_2 - S_1) + (S_3 - S_2) + \cdots + (S_n - S_{n-1})$$

for every positive integer n.

For example,

$$\frac{1}{2}, \frac{2}{3}, \cdots, \frac{n}{n+1}, \cdots$$

is the sequence of partial sums of the infinite series

$$\frac{1}{2} + \left(\frac{2}{3} - \frac{1}{2}\right) + \cdots + \left(\frac{n}{n+1} - \frac{n-1}{n}\right) + \cdots,$$

or

$$(1) \qquad \frac{1}{1\cdot 2} + \frac{1}{2\cdot 3} + \cdots + \frac{1}{n(n+1)} + \cdots.$$

Since

$$\operatorname*{limit}_{n\to\infty} S_n = \operatorname*{limit}_{n\to\infty} \frac{n}{n+1} = \operatorname*{limit}_{n\to\infty} \frac{1}{1 + 1/n} = 1,$$

series (1) is convergent with sum equal to 1,

$$\sum_{k=1}^{\infty} \frac{1}{k(k+1)} = 1.$$

It is an immediate consequence of the definition of the limit of a sequence that if the sequence

$$S_1, S_2, \cdots, S_n, \cdots$$

has a limit, then so does the sequence

$$S_m, S_{m+1}, \cdots, S_{m+n}, \cdots$$

obtained by deleting the first $m - 1$ elements of the first sequence. Furthermore, the two sequences have the same limit,

$$\operatorname*{limit}_{n\to\infty} S_n = \operatorname*{limit}_{n\to\infty} S_{m+n}.$$

In particular, if S_n is the nth partial sum of the convergent infinite series Σa_k, then

$$a_n = S_n - S_{n-1}$$

and **(8.8)**,

$$\operatorname*{limit}_{n\to\infty} a_n = \operatorname*{limit}_{n\to\infty} S_n - \operatorname*{limit}_{n\to\infty} S_{n-1} = 0.$$

Thus we have the following result.

15.3 THEOREM. If the infinite series Σa_k converges, then

$$\lim_{n\to\infty} a_n = 0.$$

The contrapositive of **15.3** is the following result.

15.4 THEOREM. If $\lim\limits_{n\to\infty} a_n \neq 0$, then the infinite series Σa_k diverges.

We may use this theorem to prove that the geometric series Σar^{k-1}, $(a \neq 0)$, diverges if $|r| \geq 1$. Thus

$$\lim_{n\to\infty} r^n \neq 0 \quad \text{if} \quad |r| \geq 1,$$

and the divergence of the geometric series if $|r| \geq 1$ follows from **15.4**.

If the infinite series Σa_k with nth partial sum S_n converges and has sum S, then for every number $\epsilon > 0$ there exists a number N such that

$$|S - S_n| < \epsilon \quad \text{for every } n > N.$$

Consequently,

$$|S_n - S_m| \leq |S_n - S| + |S - S_m| < 2\epsilon \quad \text{if } m, n > N.$$

In words, the difference between any two partial sums S_m and S_n is small if $m > N$ and $n > N$. This fact may be used at times to prove the divergence of an infinite series, as is shown below.

The series

$$\sum_{k=1}^{\infty} \frac{1}{k} = 1 + \frac{1}{2} + \cdots + \frac{1}{n} + \cdots$$

is called the *harmonic series*. For this series,

$$S_{2n} - S_n = \frac{1}{n+1} + \frac{1}{n+2} + \cdots + \frac{1}{2n} > \frac{1}{2n} + \frac{1}{2n} + \cdots + \frac{1}{2n} = \frac{1}{2},$$

i.e.,

$$S_{2n} - S_n > \frac{1}{2}$$

for every integer $n > 1$. Since $S_{2n} - S_n < \frac{1}{2}$ for n large enough if a series is convergent, we conclude that the *harmonic series* $\Sigma 1/k$ *is divergent.*

The harmonic series is an example of a divergent series whose nth term has limit zero,

$$\lim_{n\to\infty} \frac{1}{n} = 0.$$

This example shows that an infinite series Σa_k for which $\lim_{n\to\infty} a_n = 0$ need not be convergent. Therefore the converse of theorem **15.3** or **15.4** is false.

EXERCISES

I

Find the sum of each of the following convergent series.

1. $5 + \frac{5}{7} + \cdots + \frac{5}{7^{n-1}} + \cdots.$

2. $5 - \frac{5}{7} + \cdots + \frac{(-1)^{n-1}\,5}{7^{n-1}} + \cdots.$

3. $\pi + \frac{\pi}{\sqrt{2}} + \cdots + \frac{\pi}{\sqrt{2^{n-1}}} + \cdots.$

4. $.\overline{23}2323\cdots$ (the bar over the number 23 means that 23 is to be repeated indefinitely).

5. $.\overline{612}612612\cdots.$

6. $1 - \frac{1}{4} + \frac{1}{16} - \frac{1}{64} + \cdots + \frac{(-1)^{n-1}}{4^{n-1}} + \cdots.$

Each of the following is the nth partial sum of an infinite series. Find the infinite series, tell whether it is convergent or divergent, and if convergent, find its sum.

7. $S_n = \frac{n}{2n+1}.$

8. $S_n = \frac{3n}{4n+1}.$

9. $S_n = \frac{n^2}{n+1}.$

10. $S_n = \ln(n+1).$

11. $S_n = \frac{1}{2^n}.$

12. $S_n = 2^n.$

13. $S_n = \frac{n^2}{n^2+1}.$

14. $S_n = \frac{n^3-1}{n^3}.$

In each of Exercises 15–20, show that the infinite series diverges.

15. $\frac{1}{2} + \frac{2}{3} + \cdots + \frac{n}{n+1} + \cdots.$

16. $-1 + 1 + \cdots + (-1)^n + \cdots.$

17. $1 + \frac{1}{\sqrt{2}} + \cdots + \frac{1}{\sqrt{n}} + \cdots.$

18. $\sum_{n=0}^{\infty} \sum_{i=0}^{2^n} 2^{-n}.$

19. $\frac{3}{2} + \frac{9}{4} + \cdots + \left(\frac{3}{2}\right)^n + \cdots$.

20. $\frac{1}{\ln 2} + \frac{1}{\ln 3} + \cdots + \frac{1}{\ln n} + \cdots$.

21. If Σa_k is a convergent infinite series and

$$R_n = a_{n+1} + a_{n+2} + \cdots,$$

the *remainder* of the series after n terms, then prove that

$$\lim_{n\to\infty} R_n = 0.$$

22. Let $b_1, b_2, \cdots, b_n, \cdots$ be a sequence of nonzero numbers such that $\lim_{n\to\infty} b_n = \pm\infty$. Prove that the infinite series $\Sigma(b_{k+1} - b_k)$ diverges whereas the series $\Sigma(1/b_k - 1/b_{k+1})$ converges.

23. Using Exercise 22, show that the infinite series

$$\sum_{k=1}^{\infty} \ln\left(1 + \frac{1}{k}\right)$$

diverges.

In each of the following series, find for what x the series converges, and then find the sum of the series.

24. $\sum_{n=1}^{\infty} x^{3n-1}$.

25. $\sum_{n=0}^{\infty} (2x)^{2n+1}$.

26. $\sum_{j=2}^{\infty} (-1)^j(2x-1)^{2j-4}$.

27. $\sum_{m=0}^{\infty} \left(\frac{x^2-1}{2}\right)^m$.

II

In each of Exercises 1–6, find the sum of the convergent series. Note that in $S = \sum_{n=1}^{\infty} a_n$, if we can express a_n in the form $a_n = F(n) - F(n-1)$, then $S = -F(0)$ provided $\lim_{n\to\infty} F(n) = 0$. For example,

$$\sum_{n=1}^{\infty} \frac{1}{n(n+1)} = \sum_{n=1}^{\infty} \left(\frac{1}{n} - \frac{1}{n+1}\right) = \left(\frac{1}{1} - \frac{1}{2}\right) + \left(\frac{1}{2} - \frac{1}{3}\right) + \cdots = 1.$$

1. $\sum_{n=1}^{\infty} \frac{n}{(n+1)!}$.

2. $\sum_{n=1}^{\infty} \frac{n^2-n-1}{n!}$.

3. $\sum_{n=1}^{\infty} \frac{1}{(2n-1)(2n+1)}$.

4. $\sum_{n=1}^{\infty} \frac{1}{n(n+1)(n+2)}$.

5. $\sum_{n=1}^{\infty} \frac{(n-1)!}{(n+p)!}$.

6. $\sum_{n=1}^{\infty} \arctan \frac{1}{n^2+n+1}$.

7. Show that the series $\sum_{r=1}^{\infty} ra^r$ converges if $|a| < 1$ and find its sum.

[*Hint:* Consider

$$S_n = a + 2a^2 + 3a^3 + \cdots + na^n$$

and

$$aS_n = \quad a^2 + 2a^3 + \cdots + (n-1)a^n + na^{n+1},$$

and subtract.]

8. Redo Exercise 7 for the series $\sum_{r=1}^{\infty} r^2a^r$.

9. Show that the series $\sum_{n=1}^{\infty} a_n r^n$ converges if $|r| < \frac{1}{2}$ and find its sum where $a_1 = 1$, $a_2 = 1$, and, in general, $a_{n+1} = a_n + a_{n-1}$.

[*Hint:* Consider

$$\begin{aligned} S_n &= a_1r + a_2r^2 + a_3r^3 + \cdots + a_nr^n, \\ rS_n &= \quad a_1r^2 + a_2r^3 + \cdots + a_{n-1}r^n + a_nr^{n+1}, \\ r^2S_n &= \quad a_1r^3 + \cdots + a_{n-2}r^n + a_{n-1}r^{n+1} + a_nr^{n+2}, \end{aligned}$$

and form $S_n - rS_n - r^2S_n$. Also note that $a_{n+1} < 2a_n$, $n > 2$, and thus $a_{n+2} < 2^n$, $n > 1$, and $\lim_{n\to\infty} a_nr^n = 0$.]

2 POSITIVE TERM SERIES

The convergence or divergence of an infinite series Σa_k is not changed by modifying a finite number of its terms. Thus, if the two series

$$\sum_{k=1}^{\infty} a_k, \qquad \sum_{k=1}^{\infty} b_k,$$

with nth partial sums S_n and T_n, respectively, differ only in their first m terms (i.e., $a_k = b_k$ if $k > m$), then

$$S_n - T_n = S_m - T_m$$

for every integer $n \geq m$. Hence

$$\lim_{n\to\infty} S_n = (S_m - T_m) + \lim_{n\to\infty} T_n,$$

and either both limits exist or both limits do not exist; i.e., the series Σa_k and Σb_k

either both converge or both diverge. If the series converge, their sums differ by $S_m - T_m$. In particular, if $b_1 = b_2 = \cdots = b_m = 0$, then

$$\sum_{k=1}^{\infty} a_k \quad \text{and} \quad \sum_{k=m+1}^{\infty} a_k = \sum_{k=1}^{\infty} b_k$$

either both converge or both diverge.

Another useful fact is that if either of the infinite series Σa_k and $\Sigma c a_k$, $(c \neq 0)$, converges, then so does the other and

15.5 $$\sum_{k=1}^{\infty} c a_k = c \sum_{k=1}^{\infty} a_k, \qquad c \neq 0.$$

We prove **15.5** by noting that if S_n is the nth partial sum of Σa_k then cS_n is the nth partial sum of $\Sigma c a_k$, and

$$\lim_{n\to\infty} cS_n = c \lim_{n\to\infty} S_n,$$

where either both limits exist or both do not exist.

Using similar arguments, it can easily be proved that if Σa_k and Σb_k are convergent infinite series then so are the series $\Sigma(a_k + b_k)$ and $\Sigma(a_k - b_k)$, and

15.6 $$\sum_{k=1}^{\infty} (a_k \pm b_k) = \sum_{k=1}^{\infty} a_k \pm \sum_{k=1}^{\infty} b_k.$$

The following theorem on sequences may be used to establish the convergence of certain infinite series. It follows from **8.14**.

15.7 **THEOREM.** If $S_1, S_2, \cdots, S_n, \cdots$ is a sequence for which $S_1 \leq S_2 \leq \cdots \leq S_n \leq \cdots$, and if there exists a number K such that every $S_n \leq K$, then the given sequence has a limit, and

$$\lim_{n\to\infty} S_n \leq K.$$

A series Σa_k with each $a_k > 0$ is called a *positive term series*. For such a series, evidently

$$S_1 < S_2 < \cdots < S_n < \cdots.$$

We can use **15.7** to prove the following result on positive term series.

15.8 **THEOREM.** If the positive term series Σa_k has nth partial sum S_n, then Σa_k converges if there exists a number K such that every $S_n < K$ and diverges otherwise.

Proof: If every $S_n < K$, then $\lim_{n\to\infty} S_n$ exists by **15.7** and hence Σa_k is convergent. If there exists no such K, then

$$\operatorname*{limit}_{n \to \infty} S_n = \infty$$

and Σa_k diverges.

A partial converse of **15.8**, whose proof we leave to the reader, is as follows.

15.9 THEOREM. If the positive term series Σa_k converges and has sum S, then $S_n < S$ for every partial sum S_n of Σa_k.

From a given positive term series Σa_k, we may form other series by grouping the terms in some order. For example, we might form the series

$$a_1 + (a_2 + a_3) + (a_4 + a_5 + a_6) + (a_7 + a_8 + a_9 + a_{10}) + \cdots.$$

Designating this series by Σb_k, we have

$$b_1 = a_1, \quad b_2 = a_2 + a_3, \quad b_3 = a_4 + a_5 + a_6, \quad \cdots.$$

It is evident that each partial sum of the series Σb_k is also a partial sum of the series Σa_k. Thus, if the series Σa_k converges, so does the series Σb_k and their sums are equal. Similar remarks hold for any grouping of the terms of Σa_k.

We may also form a new series from a series Σa_k by rearranging the terms. For example, we might form the sum

$$a_3 + a_1 + a_5 + a_2 + a_7 + a_4 + \cdots.$$

If the series Σa_k is convergent with sum S and if T_n is the nth partial sum of a series Σb_k formed by rearranging the terms of Σa_k, then $T_n < S$ since T_n is a sum of terms of the series Σa_k. Hence Σb_k converges and has a sum $T \leq S$ by **15.7**. Since the series Σa_k may be obtained by rearranging the terms of Σb_k, we have $S \leq T$ by the same reasoning. Thus $S = T$, and we have proved that each rearrangement of a positive term convergent series is a convergent series having the same sum.

The theory of improper integrals may be used to give the following test for convergence of an infinite series.

15.10 INTEGRAL TEST. If f is a positive-valued, continuous, and decreasing function, then the infinite series

$$f(1) + f(2) + \cdots + f(n) + \cdots$$

converges or diverges according as the improper integral

$$\int_1^\infty f(x)\, dx$$

exists or is infinite.

Proof: It is clear from Figure 15.1 that

$$f(2) + f(3) + \cdots + f(n)$$

is a lower sum and

$$f(1) + f(2) + \cdots + f(n-1)$$

is an upper sum of f over the interval $[1,n]$. Hence

$$\sum_{k=2}^{n} f(k) \leq \int_1^n f(x)\,dx \leq \sum_{k=1}^{n-1} f(k). \tag{1}$$

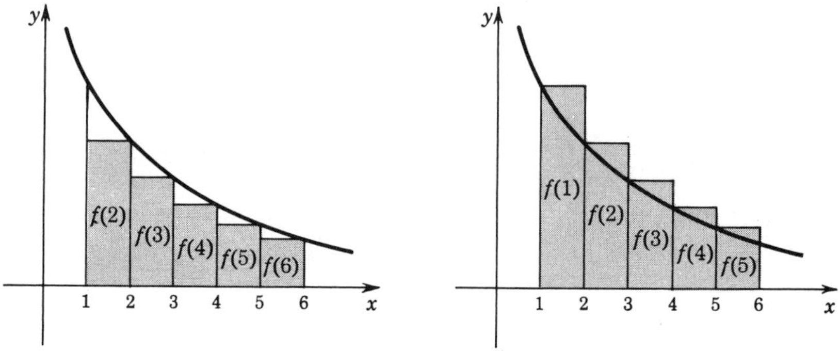

FIGURE 15.1

If the given improper integral exists, then

$$\sum_{k=2}^{n} f(k) \leq \int_1^n f(x)\,dx < \int_1^\infty f(x)\,dx$$

and the infinite series $\Sigma f(k)$ converges by **15.8.** If the given improper integral is infinite, then clearly $\Sigma f(k) = \infty$ also by (1) above. This proves the integral test.

If we let

$$f(x) = \frac{1}{x^p}, \quad p > 0,$$

then the series $\Sigma f(k)$ is simply the *p series*

$$1 + \frac{1}{2^p} + \frac{1}{3^p} + \cdots + \frac{1}{n^p} + \cdots.$$

We easily verify that

$$\int_1^\infty \frac{1}{x^p}\,dx = \operatorname*{limit}_{t\to\infty} \int_1^t x^{-p}\,dx$$

$$= -\frac{1}{p-1} \operatorname*{limit}_{t\to\infty} \left(\frac{1}{t^{p-1}} - 1\right)$$

$$= \frac{1}{p-1} \text{ if } p > 1, \quad \text{or} \quad \infty \text{ if } p < 1.$$

Hence the p series converges by the integral test if $p > 1$ and diverges if $p < 1$. If $p = 1$, the series is the harmonic series which we previously showed diverged. Thus, we have the following result.

15.11 THEOREM. The p series $\Sigma 1/k^p$ converges if $p > 1$ and diverges if $p \leq 1$.

EXAMPLE 1. Test the series

$$\sum_{k=1}^{\infty} \frac{k}{e^k}$$

for convergence.

Solution: If we let $f(x) = x/e^x = xe^{-x}$, then $f(x) > 0$ and $f'(x) = e^{-x} - xe^{-x} < 0$ if $x > 1$. Hence f is a decreasing function in $[1, \infty)$. By formula **6.8** of the Table of Integrals,

$$\int_1^t xe^{-x}\,dx = 2e^{-1} - (t+1)e^{-t}$$

Since

$$\int_1^\infty xe^{-x}\,dx = \operatorname*{limit}_{t\to\infty} [2e^{-1} - (t+1)e^{-t}] = 2e^{-1}$$

the given series converges by the integral test.

EXAMPLE 2. Test the series

$$\sum_{k=2}^{\infty} \frac{1}{k \ln k}$$

for convergence.

Solution: If we let $f(x) = 1/x \ln x$, then

$$f'(x) = -\frac{1 + \ln x}{(x \ln x)^2}.$$

Since $f(x) > 0$ and $f'(x) < 0$ if $x > 1$, f is decreasing in the interval $[2, \infty)$ and the integral test can be applied to $\Sigma 1/k \ln k$. Now

$$\int_2^t \frac{1}{x \ln x}\,dx = \ln(\ln t) - \ln(\ln 2)$$

and therefore

$$\int_2^\infty \frac{1}{x \ln x}\,dx = \lim_{t\to\infty} [\ln(\ln t) - \ln(\ln 2)] = \infty.$$

Hence the series $\Sigma 1/k \ln k$ diverges according to the integral test.

EXERCISES

I

In each of Exercises 1–14, determine whether the series is convergent or divergent.

1. $1 + \frac{1}{2^3} + \frac{1}{3^3} + \cdots + \frac{1}{n^3} + \cdots.$

2. $1 + \frac{1}{2\sqrt{2}} + \frac{1}{3\sqrt{3}} + \cdots + \frac{1}{n\sqrt{n}} + \cdots.$

3. $\frac{1}{3} + \frac{1}{5} + \frac{1}{11} + \cdots + \frac{1}{3^{n-1} + 2} + \cdots.$

4. $\frac{1}{4} + \frac{1}{7} + \frac{1}{10} + \cdots + \frac{1}{3n + 1} + \cdots.$

5. $\sum_{k=1}^{\infty} \frac{k}{k^2 + 10^6}.$

6. $\sum_{k=1}^{\infty} \frac{\ln k}{k}.$

7. $\sum_{i=3}^{\infty} \frac{1}{\sqrt[i]{2}}.$

8. $\sum_{j=4}^{\infty} \frac{\sqrt{j}}{j^2 - 4}.$

9. $\sum_{k=3}^{\infty} \frac{\ln k}{k^2}.$

10. $\sum_{m=2}^{\infty} \frac{1}{m \ln m}.$

11. $\sum_{n=1}^{\infty} n^2 e^{-n}.$

12. $\sum_{r=1}^{\infty} \frac{\tan^{-1} r}{r^2 + 1}.$

13. $\sum_{m=0}^{\infty} \frac{m + 1}{(m + 2)2^m}.$

14. $\sum_{r=0}^{\infty} \frac{1}{\sqrt{r^3 + 1}}.$

II

1. Show that $\sum_{n=1}^{\infty} \frac{P(n)}{Q(n)}$ converges where $P(n)$ and $Q(n)$ are polynomials [$Q(n) \neq 0$ for every n] such that the degree of $Q(n)$ is at least two more than that of $P(n)$.

The result is valid more generally if $O\left(\frac{P(n)}{Q(n)}\right) = n^{-1-\epsilon}$, $\epsilon > 0$ as $n \to \infty$. In this case $P(n)$ and $Q(n)$ need not be polynomials. (For O-notation, see Chapter 14, Review, II). If $\epsilon \leq 0$, the series diverges.

2. To which Exercises of Section 2, Part I does the preceding exercise immediately apply?

3. For what values of r does $\sum_{n=2}^{\infty} \frac{1}{n(\log n)^r}$ converge?

4. In the previous exercises and in the p series it was tacitly assumed that the parameters involved are constant, e.g., in Exercise 3, r = constant; in the p series, p = constant. Now show that the series $\sum_{n=1}^{\infty} \frac{1}{n^{1+\theta(n)}}$ converges if $\lim_{n\to\infty} \theta(n) = L > 0$, whereas the series diverges if $\lim_{n\to\infty} \theta(n) = L < 0$. What can one say if $L = 0$? [*Hint:* Consider the preceding exercise.]

5. Find $\lim_{n\to\infty} \frac{1/\sqrt{1} + 1/\sqrt{2} + \cdots + 1/\sqrt{n}}{\sqrt{n}}$.

6. Prove that $-\frac{\pi}{2} < \sum_{n=1}^{\infty} \frac{a}{n^2 + a^2} < \frac{\pi}{2}$.

7. Use the methods of the proof of the integral test to show that

$$\frac{1}{(p-1)(n+1)^{p-1}} < \sum_{k=1}^{\infty} \frac{1}{k^p} - \sum_{k=1}^{n} \frac{1}{k^p} < \frac{1}{(p-1)n^{p-1}}$$

if $p > 1$.

a. How good an approximation of the infinite series $\Sigma 1/k^2$ is its nth partial sum when $n = 10$? $n = 1000$?

b. How good an approximation of the infinite series $\Sigma 1/k^3$ is its nth partial sum when $n = 10$? $n = 1000$?

8. By using the method of the integral test on the series $S_n = \sum_{r=1}^{n} \ln r$, show that

$$\left(\frac{n}{e}\right)^n e < n! < n\left(\frac{n}{e}\right)^n e.$$

These inequalities give a rough estimate for the order of $n!$. A much better estimate is given by Stirling's formula

$$\left(\frac{n}{e}\right)^n \sqrt{2\pi n} < n! < \left(\frac{n}{e}\right)^n \sqrt{2\pi n}\left(1 + \frac{1}{4n}\right),$$

and thus

$$n! \sim \left(\frac{n}{e}\right)^n \sqrt{2\pi n}.$$

3 COMPARISON TEST

Another useful test for convergence and divergence of a positive term series is as follows.

15.12 COMPARISON TEST I. Let Σa_k and Σb_k be positive term series.

(1) If Σa_k converges and if $b_k \leq a_k$ for every integer k, then the series Σb_k converges.
(2) If Σa_k diverges and if $b_k \geq a_k$ for every integer k, then the series Σb_k diverges.

Proof: Designate the nth partial sums of Σa_k and Σb_k by S_n and T_n, respectively. If Σa_k converges and every $b_k \leq a_k$, then

$$T_n \leq S_n < \sum_{k=1}^{\infty} a_k$$

for every integer n. Hence the series Σb_k converges by **15.8**. We omit the proof of (2) because of its similarity to that of (1).

If $0 < b_k \leq a_k$ for every integer k, then the series Σa_k is said to *dominate* the series Σb_k. According to the theorem above, every infinite series dominated by a convergent series also is convergent.

In view of the fact that a finite number of terms of a series may be changed without affecting the convergence or divergence of the series, it is clear that comparison test I need only hold from the mth term on, where m is any positive integer.

EXAMPLE 1. Test the series

$$\frac{1}{2} + \frac{1}{3} + \frac{1}{5} + \cdots + \frac{1}{2^{n-1} + 1} + \cdots$$

for convergence.

Solution: We compare the given series with the convergent geometric series $\Sigma \frac{1}{2^{k-1}}$. Thus

$$\frac{1}{2^{k-1} + 1} < \frac{1}{2^{k-1}}$$

for every integer k, and the given series must converge.

EXAMPLE 2. Test the series

$$\sum_{k=2}^{\infty} \frac{1}{\ln k}$$

for convergence.

Solution: Since $\ln k < k$ for every $k \geq 2$,

$$\frac{1}{\ln k} > \frac{1}{k} \qquad \text{for every } k \geq 2.$$

Hence, $\Sigma 1/\ln k$ diverges by **15.12(2)**.

The following test is essentially a corollary of comparison test I.

15.13 COMPARISON TEST II. If $c_1, c_2, \cdots, c_n, \cdots$ is a sequence of positive numbers such that

$$\operatorname*{limit}_{n \to \infty} c_n = c, \qquad c > 0,$$

then the two positive term series

$$\sum_{k=1}^{\infty} a_k, \qquad \sum_{k=1}^{\infty} c_k a_k$$

either both converge or both diverge.

Proof: Since $\operatorname*{limit}_{n \to \infty} c_n = c > 0$, there exists an integer N such that

$$\frac{c}{2} < c_k < \frac{3c}{2} \qquad \text{for every integer } k \geq N.$$

Hence

$$\frac{c}{2} a_k < c_k a_k < \frac{3c}{2} a_k \quad \text{if } k \geq N,$$

and if the series Σa_k converges, then so does the series $\Sigma c_k a_k$ since it is dominated by a convergent series $\Sigma(3c/2)a_k$. Conversely, if the series $\Sigma c_k a_k$ is convergent, then so is the series $\Sigma(c/2)a_k$ and in turn $\Sigma a_k = (2/c)\Sigma(c/2)a_k$. This proves that Σa_k converges if and only if $\Sigma c_k a_k$ converges. In turn, this implies that Σa_k diverges if and only if $\Sigma c_k a_k$ diverges. Thus the theorem is proved.

EXAMPLE 3. Test the series

$$\sum_{k=1}^{\infty} \frac{k+1}{k(2k-1)}$$

for convergence.

Solution: We may put the given series in the form

$$\sum_{k=1}^{\infty} \left(\frac{1 + 1/k}{2 - 1/k}\right) \frac{1}{k}.$$

Since

$$\operatorname*{limit}_{n \to \infty} \frac{1 + 1/n}{2 - 1/n} = \frac{1}{2}$$

and the harmonic series $\Sigma 1/k$ diverges, the given series diverges by **15.13**.

EXAMPLE 4. Test the series

$$\sum_{k=1}^{\infty} \frac{k}{\sqrt{k^5+1}}$$

for convergence.

Solution: The series can be put in the form

$$\sum_{k=1}^{\infty} \frac{1}{\sqrt{1+1/k^5}}\,\frac{1}{k^{3/2}}.$$

Since

$$\operatorname*{limit}_{n\to\infty} \frac{1}{\sqrt{1+1/n^5}} = 1,$$

and the p series $\Sigma 1/k^{3/2}$ converges by **15.11**, the given series converges by **15.13**.

I

In each of Exercises 1–10 determine whether the series is convergent or divergent, using the methods of this section.

1. $\displaystyle\sum_{k=0}^{\infty} \frac{k+1}{(k+2)2^k}.$

2. $\displaystyle\sum_{k=1}^{\infty} \frac{2+10^6 \sin^2 3k}{k^2}.$

3. $\displaystyle\sum_{k=1}^{\infty} \frac{k+1}{\ln(k+2)}.$

4. $\displaystyle\sum_{k=1}^{\infty} \frac{k^2}{k^3+1000}.$

5. $\displaystyle\sum_{k=1}^{\infty} ke^{-k^2}.$

6. $\displaystyle\sum_{k=1}^{\infty} \frac{1}{\sqrt[3]{k(k+1)(k+2)}}.$

7. $\displaystyle\sum_{k=1}^{\infty} \frac{1}{\sqrt{k(k+1)(k+2)}}.$

8. $\displaystyle\sum_{k=1}^{\infty} k^2 2^{-k}.$

9. $\displaystyle\sum_{k=2}^{\infty} \frac{\sqrt{k}}{k^2-\sin^2 100k}.$

10. $\displaystyle\sum_{k=1}^{\infty} \frac{\tan^{-1} k}{k^2+1}.$

II

By methods of this section, establish the convergence or divergence of the series in each of Exercises 1–5.

1. $\displaystyle\sum_{n=1}^{\infty} \frac{1}{n^{1+1/n}}.$ After you have obtained your answer, compare it with criteria for the convergence and divergence of the p series and explain.

2. $\displaystyle\sum_{n=1}^{\infty} \frac{n!}{n^n}.$

3. $\displaystyle\sum_{n=1}^{\infty} \frac{1}{(\ln n)^{\ln n}}.$

4. $\displaystyle\sum_{n=3}^{\infty} \frac{1}{(\ln n)^{\ln \ln n}}.$

5. $\displaystyle\sum_{n=1}^{\infty} \left(1-\frac{1}{n}\right)^{n^2}.$

6. Prove that if $a_n \geq 0$ and $\sum_{n=1}^{\infty} a_n$ converges, then so does $\sum_{n=1}^{\infty} a_n^2$.

7. Prove that if $a_n \geq 0$ and $\sum_{n=1}^{\infty} a_n^2$ converges, then so does $\sum_{n=1}^{\infty} \frac{a_n}{n}$.

8. Generalize the preceding exercise.

9. If $\sum_{n=1}^{\infty} \frac{1}{n}$ converges, then

$$1 + \tfrac{1}{2} + \tfrac{1}{3} + \cdots = (1 + \tfrac{1}{3} + \tfrac{1}{5} + \cdots) + \tfrac{1}{2}(1 + \tfrac{1}{2} + \tfrac{1}{3} + \cdots)$$

or $$\tfrac{1}{2} + \tfrac{1}{4} + \tfrac{1}{6} + \cdots = 1 + \tfrac{1}{3} + \tfrac{1}{5} + \cdots.$$

Show from this that $\sum_{n=1}^{\infty} \frac{1}{n}$ diverges.

4 ALTERNATING SERIES

An infinite series of the form

$$a_1 - a_2 + a_3 - a_4 + \cdots + (-1)^{n-1}a_n + \cdots,$$

each $a_n > 0$, having alternating positive and negative terms is called an *alternating series.* A classical example of an alternating series is the alternating harmonic series

$$1 - \frac{1}{2} + \frac{1}{3} - \frac{1}{4} + \cdots + \frac{(-1)^{n-1}}{n} + \cdots,$$

which we shall show presently to be convergent with sum ln 2. A simple test for the convergence of an alternating series is as follows.

15.14 ALTERNATING SERIES TEST. If (1) $a_{n+1} \leq a_n$ for each n, and (2) $\lim_{n \to \infty} a_n = 0$, then the alternating series $\Sigma(-1)^{k-1}a_k$ is convergent.

Proof: The partial sums of $\Sigma(-1)^{k-1}a_k$ having an even number of terms may be written as follows:

$$S_2 = (a_1 - a_2), \qquad S_4 = (a_1 - a_2) + (a_3 - a_4),$$

and, in general,

$$S_{2n} = (a_1 - a_2) + (a_3 - a_4) + \cdots + (a_{2n-1} - a_{2n}).$$

By assumption, $a_1 - a_2 \geq 0$, $a_3 - a_4 \geq 0$, and, in general, $a_{2n-1} - a_{2n} \geq 0$. Thus it is clear that

$$0 \leq S_2 \leq S_4 \leq \cdots \leq S_{2n} \leq \cdots.$$

On the other hand, S_{2n} may also be written in the form

$$S_{2n} = a_1 - (a_2 - a_3) - (a_4 - a_5) - \cdots - (a_{2n-2} - a_{2n-1}) - a_{2n},$$

from which it is clear that, for every integer n,

$$S_{2n} \leq a_1.$$

That

$$\lim_{n\to\infty} S_{2n}$$

exists and is less than or equal to a_1 now follows from **15.7**.

Since $S_{2n+1} = S_{2n} + a_{2n+1}$,

$$\lim_{n\to\infty} S_{2n+1} = \lim_{n\to\infty} S_{2n} + \lim_{n\to\infty} a_{2n+1} = \lim_{n\to\infty} S_{2n}.$$

Thus

$$\lim_{n\to\infty} S_n = \lim_{n\to\infty} S_{2n} = \lim_{n\to\infty} S_{2n+1} = S,$$

and $S \leq a_1$. This proves **15.14.**

If $\Sigma(-1)^{k-1}a_k$ is an alternating series with the properties of **15.14**, then the remainder R_n of this series after n terms,

$$R_n = (-1)^n(a_{n+1} - a_{n+2} + a_{n+3} - \cdots),$$

is again an alternating series with these same properties. Clearly,

$$|R_n| = a_{n+1} - a_{n+2} + a_{n+3} - \cdots,$$

and therefore

$$|R_n| \leq a_{n+1}$$

as shown in the proof of **15.14.** If S is the sum of $\Sigma(-1)^{k-1}a_k$, then $S = S_n + R_n$ and

$$|S - S_n| = |R_n| \leq a_{n+1}.$$

This proves the following result.

15.15 THEOREM. If $\Sigma(-1)^{k-1}a_k$ is an alternating series having the properties stated in **15.14**, and if S_n and S are, respectively, the nth partial sum and the sum of this series, then $S \doteq S_n$ with an error of no more than a_{n+1}.

EXAMPLE 1. Show that the alternating series

$$1 - \frac{1}{1!} + \frac{1}{2!} - \frac{1}{3!} + \cdots + \frac{(-1)^n}{n!} + \cdots$$

is convergent. Approximate its sum S to three decimal places.

Solution: Since

$$\frac{1}{n!} > \frac{1}{(n+1)!} \quad \text{and} \quad \lim_{n\to\infty} \frac{1}{n!} = 0,$$

the series converges by **15.14.** We easily verify that

$$\frac{1}{7!} < .0002.$$

Hence

$$S \doteq 1 - 1 + \tfrac{1}{2} - \tfrac{1}{6} + \tfrac{1}{24} - \tfrac{1}{120} + \tfrac{1}{720} \doteq .368,$$

accurate to three decimal places. We shall show presently that this alternating series has sum $1/e$, so $1/e \doteq .368$.

EXAMPLE 2. Test the alternating series

$$1 - \frac{2}{3} + \frac{3}{5} - \cdots + \frac{(-1)^{n-1}n}{2n-1} + \cdots$$

for convergence.

Solution: If $f(x) = x/(2x-1)$ then $f'(x) = -1/(2x-1)^2$ and hence f is a decreasing function. Therefore, **15.14**(1) is satisfied. However,

$$\lim_{n\to\infty} \frac{n}{2n-1} = \lim_{n\to\infty} \frac{1}{2 - 1/n} = \frac{1}{2}$$

and **15.14**(2) is not satisfied. Since the nth term of the series is not approaching 0, the series diverges by **15.4.**

EXAMPLE 3. Test the alternating series

$$\sum_{k=1}^{\infty} (-1)^k \frac{k}{k^2+1}$$

for convergence.

Solution: If $f(x) = x/(x^2+1)$ then $f'(x) = (1-x^2)/(x^2+1)^2 < 0$ for $x > 1$. Hence, f is a decreasing function in the interval $[1, \infty)$, and $f(1) \geq f(2) \geq f(3) \geq \cdots$. Thus, **15.14**(1) is satisfied. Since

$$\lim_{n\to\infty} \frac{n}{n^2+1} = \lim_{n\to\infty} \frac{1/n}{1+1/n^2} = 0,$$

15.14(2) is also satisfied. Therefore, the series converges.

EXERCISES

I

Test each of the following alternating series for convergence.

1. $1 - \frac{1}{\sqrt{2}} + \frac{1}{\sqrt{3}} - \cdots + \frac{(-1)^{n-1}}{\sqrt{n}} + \cdots.$

2. $\frac{2}{\ln 2} - \frac{2}{\ln 3} + \cdots + \frac{2(-1)^{n-1}}{\ln (n+1)} + \cdots.$

3. $\frac{2}{3} - \frac{1}{2} + \frac{4}{9} - \cdots + \frac{(n+1)(-1)^{n-1}}{3n} + \cdots.$

4. $-\frac{1}{3} + \frac{1}{3} - \frac{3}{11} + \cdots + \frac{(-1)^n n}{n^2+2} + \cdots.$

5. $\sum_{k=1}^{\infty} \frac{(-1)^k}{2k-1}.$

6. $\sum_{k=1}^{\infty} \frac{k(-1)^{k-1}}{2^k}.$

7. $\sum_{k=2}^{\infty} \frac{k(-1)^{k-1}}{\ln k}.$

8. $\sum_{k=1}^{\infty} \frac{(2k-1)(-1)^k}{5k+1}.$

9. $\sum_{k=1}^{\infty} \frac{\sqrt{k}(-1)^{k-1}}{2k+1}.$

10. $\sum_{k=1}^{\infty} \frac{(-1)^{k-1} \ln k}{k}.$

11. Consider the alternating series $\sum_{k=1}^{\infty} (-1)^k a_k$, where

$$\left.\begin{aligned} a_{2k-1} &= \frac{1}{k} \\ a_{2k} &= \frac{1}{k^2} \end{aligned}\right\} \quad k = 1,2,3, \cdots.$$

It is obvious that $\lim_{k \to \infty} a_k = 0$ and $a_{2k} \le a_{2k-1}$ for all k. Show that the series does not converge and explain why the alternating series test does not apply.

12. If $\sum_{n=1}^{\infty} (-1)^{n+1}(a_n - b_n)$ is an alternating decreasing series which converges, what can be said about the convergence of $\sum_{n=1}^{\infty} (-1)^{n+1} a_n$? Illustrate by specific examples.

Approximate the sum of each of the following series to three decimal places.

13. $1 - \frac{1}{2^2} + \frac{1}{2^4} - \cdots + \frac{(-1)^{n-1}}{2^{2(n-1)}} + \cdots.$

14. $1 - \frac{1}{2!} + \cdots + \frac{(-1)^{n-1}}{(2n-2)!} + \cdots.$

15. $1 - \frac{1}{3^3} + \cdots + \frac{(-1)^{n-1}}{(2n-1)^3} + \cdots.$

16. $\frac{1}{3} - \frac{1}{2\cdot 3^2} + \cdots + \frac{(-1)^{n-1}}{n\cdot 3^n} + \cdots.$

II

In each of Exercises 1–5 test the series for convergence or divergence.

1. $\sum_{r=1}^{\infty} \frac{(-1)^{r+1}\ln^2 r}{r}.$

2. $\sum_{r=1}^{\infty} \frac{(-1)^{r+1}\ln^p r}{\sqrt{r}}, p \geq 1.$

3. $\sum_{n=1}^{\infty} (-1)^{n+1} \operatorname{arccot} n.$

4. $\sum_{n=1}^{\infty} (-1)^{n+1} n \arctan \frac{1}{n^2}.$

5. $\sum_{n=1}^{\infty} (-1)^n \left\{\frac{1\cdot 3\cdot 5 \cdots (2n-1)}{2\cdot 4\cdot 6 \cdots (2n)}\right\}$ (use Exercise II-8, Section 2).

6. For what r does the following series converge?

$$1 - \frac{1}{2^r} + \frac{1}{3} - \frac{1}{4^r} + \cdots + \frac{1}{2n-1} - \frac{1}{(2n)^r} + \cdots.$$

(*Suggestion:* Use the method of the integral test to obtain bounds on the sums of the first n even terms and the first n odd terms.)

7. Show that $\lim_{n\to\infty} \left(1 + \frac{1}{2} + \frac{1}{3} + \cdots + \frac{1}{n} - \log n\right)$ exists and lies in (0,1). This important limit is called *Euler's constant* and is denoted by γ, $\gamma \doteq 0.577216$, accurate to six decimal places.

(*Suggestion:* Use the method of the integral test and show that the term in the parenthesis is strictly decreasing.)

In Exercises 8 and 9 show that the given rearrangements of the alternating harmonic series converge and find their sums [use the result of the preceding exercise and that

$$\lim_{n\to\infty} \left\{\frac{1}{n+1} + \frac{1}{n+2} + \cdots + \frac{1}{n+bn}\right\} = \ln(1+b)$$

(Exercise II-13 Review, Chapter 10.)]

8. $1 + \frac{1}{3} - \frac{1}{2} + \frac{1}{5} + \frac{1}{7} - \frac{1}{4} + \cdots + \frac{1}{4n-3} + \frac{1}{4n-1} - \frac{1}{2n} + \cdots.$

9. $1 - \frac{1}{2} - \frac{1}{4} + \frac{1}{3} - \frac{1}{6} - \frac{1}{8} + \cdots + \frac{1}{2n-1} - \frac{1}{4n-2} - \frac{1}{4n} + \cdots.$

10. Generalize the results of Exercises 8 and 9.

11. Discuss the convergence of the series resulting when every rth term is struck out of the alternating harmonic series. Find its sum when it is convergent.

12. Let $\{a_n\}$ and $\{b_n\}$ be two sequences such that $a_n \geq a_{n+1} \geq 0$, $b_n \geq 0$ for all $n \geq 1$,

$$\operatorname*{limit}_{n\to\infty} a_n = 0, \qquad \text{and} \qquad \operatorname*{limit}_{n\to\infty} \frac{a_n}{b_n} = 1.$$

Since $\sum_{n=1}^{\infty} (-1)^n a_n$ converges, it seems reasonable to suppose that $\sum_{n=1}^{\infty} (-1)^n b_n$ also converges. Prove or disprove.

5 ABSOLUTE CONVERGENCE

We shall consider in this section series having negative as well as positive terms. Associated with each infinite series Σa_k is its series of absolute values

$$\sum_{k=1}^{\infty} |a_k| = |a_1| + |a_2| + \cdots + |a_n| + \cdots.$$

A series Σa_k is called *absolutely convergent* if its series of absolute values $\Sigma|a_k|$ converges. Let us prove the following theorem on absolutely convergent series.

15.16 THEOREM. Every absolutely convergent series Σa_k is convergent, and

$$\left|\sum_{k=1}^{\infty} a_k\right| \leq \sum_{k=1}^{\infty} |a_k|.$$

Proof: Consider the three infinite series Σa_k, $\Sigma|a_k|$, and $\Sigma(a_k + |a_k|)$ having respective nth partial sums S_n, T_n, and U_n. Clearly,

$$S_n + T_n = U_n.$$

Since $0 \leq a_k + |a_k| \leq 2|a_k|$,

$$0 \leq U_n \leq 2T_n \leq 2T$$

for every integer n, where T is the sum of $\Sigma|a_k|$. Since $U_1 \leq U_2 \leq \cdots \leq U_n \leq \cdots \leq 2T$, we have by **15.7** that

$$\operatorname*{limit}_{n\to\infty} U_n = U \leq 2T.$$

Thus

$$\operatorname*{limit}_{n\to\infty} S_n = \operatorname*{limit}_{n\to\infty} U_n - \operatorname*{limit}_{n\to\infty} T_n = U - T,$$

and the series Σa_k is convergent with sum $S = U - T \leq T$.

The series $\Sigma(-a_k)$ has sum $-S$, and, since $T = \Sigma|-a_k|$, we have $-S \leq T$ by the same argument as above with the series Σa_k replaced by $\Sigma(-a_k)$. Since both S and $-S$ are less than or equal to T, then $|S| \leq T$ and the theorem is proved.

Not every convergent series is absolutely convergent. Thus, by the alternating series test, the alternating harmonic series

$$1 - \tfrac{1}{2} + \tfrac{1}{3} - \tfrac{1}{4} + \tfrac{1}{5} - \cdots$$

is convergent, whereas its series of absolute values is the divergent harmonic series. A series such as the alternating harmonic series that is convergent without being absolutely convergent is called *conditionally convergent.*

We may easily prove the following results on absolutely convergent series. (Compare these results with 15.5 and 15.6.)

15.17 THEOREM. If the series Σa_k and Σb_k are absolutely convergent, then so are the series $\Sigma(a_k + b_k)$ and $\Sigma c a_k$ for any constant c.

Proof: These follow readily from the inequalities

$$\sum_{k=1}^{n} |a_k \pm b_k| \leq \sum_{k=1}^{n} |a_k| + \sum_{k=1}^{n} |b_k| \leq \sum_{k=1}^{\infty} |a_k| + \sum_{k=1}^{\infty} |b_k|,$$

$$\sum_{k=1}^{\infty} |ca_k| = |c| \sum_{k=1}^{\infty} |a_k|,$$

and from 15.7.

A very useful test for absolute convergence of a series is the ratio test that follows.

15.18 RATIO TEST. The series Σa_k is:

(1) absolutely convergent if $\displaystyle\lim_{n\to\infty} \left|\frac{a_{n+1}}{a_n}\right| = L < 1$;

(2) divergent if $\displaystyle\lim_{n\to\infty} \left|\frac{a_{n+1}}{a_n}\right| = \begin{cases} L > 1 \\ \infty. \end{cases}$

Proof: To prove (1), let r be any number such that

$$0 \leq L < r < 1.$$

Since the limit of $|a_{n+1}/a_n|$ as n approaches ∞ is L, there exists a positive integer N such that

$$\left|\frac{a_{n+1}}{a_n}\right| < r \quad \text{for every integer } n \geq N.$$

Thus

$$|a_{N+1}| < r|a_N|,$$
$$|a_{N+2}| < r|a_{N+1}| < r^2|a_N|,$$
$$|a_{N+3}| < r|a_{N+2}| < r^2|a_{N+1}| < r^3|a_N|,$$

and, in general,

$$|a_{N+k}| < r^k|a_N| \quad \text{for every integer } k > 0.$$

Hence the series

$$|a_{N+1}| + |a_{N+2}| + \cdots + |a_{N+n}| + \cdots$$

is convergent, since it is dominated by the convergent geometric series

$$|a_N|r + |a_N|r^2 + \cdots + |a_N|r^n + \cdots.$$

Therefore the series

$$\sum_{k=1}^{\infty} |a_k| = \sum_{k=1}^{N} |a_k| + \sum_{k=1}^{\infty} |a_{N+k}|$$

is convergent, and the given series Σa_k is absolutely convergent.

To prove (2), if $L > 1$, then there exists a number N such that

$$\left|\frac{a_{n+1}}{a_n}\right| > 1 \quad \text{for every integer } n > N.$$

Thus $|a_{n+1}| > |a_n|$ for every $n > N$, and

$$\lim_{n \to \infty} |a_n|$$

cannot equal zero. Hence, by **8.12**,

$$\lim_{n \to \infty} a_n \neq 0,$$

and therefore the series Σa_k is divergent by **15.4**. An analogous argument proves the other part of (2).

If

$$\lim_{n \to \infty} \left|\frac{a_{n+1}}{a_n}\right| = 1,$$

nothing can be said directly about the convergence of the series Σa_k. For example,

$$\lim_{n \to \infty} \frac{1/(n+1)^p}{1/n^p} = \lim_{n \to \infty} \left(\frac{n}{n+1}\right)^p = 1$$

for every p series $\Sigma 1/k^p$. We have already shown that the p series converges if $p > 1$ and diverges if $p \leq 1$. The ratio test is of no help in testing series similar to the p series for convergence.

EXAMPLE 1. Test the convergence of the series

$$1 + \frac{1}{2!} + \frac{1}{3!} + \cdots + \frac{1}{n!} + \cdots.$$

Solution: Since

$$\lim_{n\to\infty} \frac{1/(n+1)!}{1/n!} = \lim_{n\to\infty} \frac{1}{n+1} = 0,$$

the series converges by the ratio test.

EXAMPLE 2. Test the convergence of the series

$$\frac{1}{5} - \frac{2}{5^2} + \frac{3}{5^3} - \cdots + \frac{n(-1)^{n-1}}{5^n} + \cdots.$$

Solution: We have

$$\lim_{n\to\infty} \left| \frac{(n+1)(-1)^n/5^{n+1}}{n(-1)^{n-1}/5^n} \right| = \lim_{n\to\infty} \frac{n+1}{5n} = \frac{1}{5},$$

and therefore the series converges absolutely by the ratio test.

EXAMPLE 3. Test the convergence of the series

$$1 + \frac{2^2}{2!} + \frac{3^3}{3!} + \cdots + \frac{n^n}{n!} + \cdots.$$

Solution: The ratio a_{n+1}/a_n for this series is given by

$$\frac{a_{n+1}}{a_n} = \frac{(n+1)^{n+1}}{(n+1)!} \cdot \frac{n!}{n^n} = \frac{(n+1)^n \cdot (n+1) \cdot n!}{(n+1)! \cdot n^n} = \left(\frac{n+1}{n}\right)^n,$$

or

$$\frac{a_{n+1}}{a_n} = \left(1 + \frac{1}{n}\right)^n.$$

Since

$$\lim_{n\to\infty} \left(1 + \frac{1}{n}\right)^n = e$$

and $e > 1$ (see p. 000) the series diverges by the ratio test.

EXERCISES

I

In each of Exercises 1–16 test the given series for convergence or divergence. In case of convergence, determine whether the series converges absolutely.

1. $1 - \frac{1}{3!} + \cdots + \frac{(-1)^{n-1}}{(2n-1)!} + \cdots.$

2. $2 - \frac{2^2}{2!} + \cdots - \frac{(-2)^n}{n!} + \cdots.$

3. $\frac{1}{2} + \frac{3}{5} + \frac{9}{10} + \cdots + \frac{3^{n-1}}{n^2 + 1} + \cdots.$

4. $\frac{1}{9} - \frac{2}{81} + \frac{6}{729} - \cdots + \frac{n!(-1)^{n-1}}{9^n} + \cdots.$

5. $\sum_{k=1}^{\infty} \frac{(-1)^{k+1}}{\sqrt[3]{k}}.$

6. $\sum_{k=1}^{\infty} \frac{(-1)^k(k + 1000)}{k^3}.$

7. $\sum_{k=1}^{\infty} \frac{(-1)^k k^{1000}}{(k + 2)!}.$

8. $\sum_{k=1}^{\infty} (-1)^k \left(\frac{1}{k}\right)^{1/k}.$

9. $\sum_{k=3}^{\infty} \frac{(-1)^k}{\ln k}.$

10. $\sum_{k=1}^{\infty} \frac{(-1)^k k!}{100^k}.$

11. $\sum_{k=2}^{\infty} \frac{(-1)^k(4k + 1)}{7k^2 - 1}.$

12. $\sum_{k=1}^{\infty} \frac{(-1)^{k+1}3^k}{k^3 \cdot 2^{k+3}}.$

13. $\sum_{k=1}^{\infty} \frac{(-1)^k k^7 \cdot 7^{k+3}}{2^{3k}}.$

14. $\sum_{k=1}^{\infty} \frac{(-1)^k k!}{1 \cdot 3 \cdot 5 \cdots (2k - 1)}.$

15. $\sum_{k=1}^{\infty} \frac{(-1)^k}{k \ln^2 k}.$

16. $\sum_{k=1}^{\infty} (-1)^k \frac{\sin 10k}{\sqrt{k^3}}.$

II

In each of Exercises 1–7, test for convergence and absolute convergence.

1. $\sum_{n=1}^{\infty} (-1)^n \frac{\sin (1/n)}{n}.$

2. $\sum_{n=1}^{\infty} (-1)^n \left(n \sin \frac{1}{n} - 1\right).$

3. $\sum_{n=1}^{\infty} (-1)^n \tan \frac{1}{n}.$

4. $\sum_{n=1}^{\infty} (-1)^n \frac{\tan^{-1} n}{\sqrt{n}}.$

5. $\sum_{n=1}^{\infty} \frac{\sin \pi n/3}{n^p}, \quad p > 0.$

6. $\sum_{n=1}^{\infty} (-1)^{n+1}(a^{1/n} - 1), \quad a > 0.$

7. $\sum_{n=1}^{\infty} (-1)^{n+1} \left\{\frac{1 \cdot 3 \cdot 5 \cdots (2n - 1)}{2 \cdot 4 \cdot 6 \cdots (2n)}\right\}^p, \quad p > 0.$

(*Suggestion:* Use Stirling's formula $n! \sim \left(\frac{n}{e}\right)^n \sqrt{2\pi n}$, Exercise II-8, Section 2.)

8. For what values of a and b is the series

$$\frac{a}{1} - \frac{b}{2} + \frac{a}{3} - \frac{b}{4} + \cdots + \frac{a}{2n - 1} - \frac{b}{2n} + \cdots$$

convergent? Absolutely convergent?

9. a. Does the convergence of $\sum_{n=1}^{\infty} a_n$ imply the convergence of $\sum_{n=1}^{\infty} (a_n + a_{n+1})$?

b. Does the convergence of $\sum_{n=1}^{\infty} (a_n + a_{n+1})$ imply the convergence of $\sum_{n=1}^{\infty} a_n$?

c. Does the convergence of $\sum_{n=1}^{\infty} (|a_n| + |a_{n-1}|)$ imply the convergence of $\sum_{n=1}^{\infty} |a_n|$?

6 POWER SERIES

An infinite series of the form

$$\sum_{k=0}^{\infty} a_k x^k = a_0 + a_1 x + a_2 x^2 + \cdots + a_n x^n + \cdots$$

is called a *power series* in x. A power series in x is the infinite series analogue of a polynomial in x.

If the power series $\Sigma a_k x^k$ is absolutely convergent, so that the series $\Sigma |a_k||x|^k$ converges, then it is evident by comparison test I that the power series $\Sigma a_k z^k$ is absolutely convergent for every number z such that $|z| \leq |x|$. Similarly, if the series $\Sigma |a_k||x|^k$ is divergent, then so is the series $\Sigma |a_k||z|^k$ whenever $|z| \geq |x|$.

15.19 DEFINITION. The *radius of convergence* r of a power series $\Sigma a_k x^k$ is the l.u.b. of the set of all numbers x such that the series is absolutely convergent. If the series is absolutely convergent for every number x, let $r = \infty$.

If the power series $\Sigma |a_k||z|^k$ is divergent, then the number $|z|$ is an upper bound of the set S of all numbers x such that the given power series $\Sigma a_k x^k$ is absolutely convergent. Incidentally, the set S has at least one number in it, namely 0. Thus it is clear that the radius of convergence r is well defined by the above definition and that either $r = 0$, r is a positive number, or $r = \infty$.

If r is the radius of convergence of the power series $\Sigma a_k x^k$ and if the series $\Sigma |a_k||z|^k$ diverges, then necessarily $|z| \geq r$, in view of our remarks above. Therefore we conclude that the series $\Sigma a_k x^k$ converges absolutely if $|x| < r$, and we have proved part of the following theorem.

15.20 THEOREM. If r is the radius of convergence of the power series $\Sigma a_k x^k$, then the series converges absolutely if $|x| < r$ and diverges if $|x| > r$.

Proof: The only part of the theorem not proved is that if $|x| > r$ then the series $\Sigma a_k x^k$ diverges. This will be proved by showing that if the series $\Sigma a_k x^k$ converges then $|x| \leq r$. In order to prove that $r \geq |x|$, we will show that for every number z such that $|z| < |x|$ the series $\Sigma a_k z^k$ converges absolutely. Hence the l.u.b. r of the set of all numbers z such that the series $\Sigma a_k z^k$ is absolutely convergent exceeds or is equal to $|x|$.

If $\Sigma a_k x^k$ converges, $(x \neq 0)$, then

$$\operatorname*{limit}_{n \to \infty} |a_n x^n| = 0$$

and there exists a number M such that

$$|a_k x^k| \leq M \quad \text{for every integer } k.$$

Since $|z| < |x|$, the number

$$s = \frac{|z|}{|x|}$$

is less than 1. Evidently,

$$|a_k z^k| = |a_k x^k s^k| \leq M s^k$$

for every k, and therefore the series $\Sigma |a_k||z^k|$ is dominated by the convergent geometric series $\Sigma M s^k$. Thus $\Sigma a_k z^k$ is absolutely convergent, and the proof is completed.

A useful corollary of **15.20** is given below.

15.21 THEOREM. Let r be the radius of convergence of the power series $\Sigma a_k x^k$ and let s be any number such that $0 < s < r$. If $c_1, c_2, \cdots, c_n, \cdots$ is a sequence of numbers such that $|c_k| \leq s$ for every integer k, then the series

$$a_0 + a_1 c_1 + a_2 (c_2)^2 + \cdots + a_n (c_n)^n + \cdots$$

is absolutely convergent.

Proof: Evidently, $\Sigma |a_k||c_k|^k$ is dominated by the convergent series $\Sigma |a_k| s^k$. This proves **15.21.**

If the power series $\Sigma a_k x^k$ has radius of convergence $r > 0$, then by **15.20**, the series converges absolutely for every number x in the open interval $(-r,r)$. The only other numbers for which the series might converge are $x = -r$ and $x = r$. Thus the set of all numbers at which the power series $\Sigma a_k x^k$ converges is either an open interval $(-r,r)$, a half-closed interval $[-r,r)$ or $(-r,r]$, or a closed interval $[-r,r]$. Of course, there are also the two other possibilities: that $r = 0$ or $r = \infty$. The interval in which a power series converges is called the *interval of convergence* of the series.

Knowing the interval of convergence of the power series $\Sigma a_k x^k$, we can easily find the interval of convergence of the power series

$$\sum_{k=0}^{\infty} a_k (x - c)^k = a_0 + a_1 (x - c) + a_2 (x - c)^2 + \cdots + a_n (x - c)^n + \cdots.$$

If, for example, $\Sigma a_k x^k$ has interval of convergence $[-r,r)$, then the series $\Sigma a_k(x-c)^k$ converges for $-r \leq x - c < r$, i.e., for every x in the interval $[c - r, c + r)$. This interval is called the *interval of convergence* of the series $\Sigma a_k(x-c)^k$.

The ratio test may often be used to find the interval of convergence of a power series, as the following example shows.

EXAMPLE. Find the interval of convergence of each of the following power series:

(a) $$1 + x + \frac{x^2}{2!} + \cdots + \frac{x^n}{n!} + \cdots.$$

(b) $$1 - x + \frac{x^2}{2} - \cdots + \frac{(-1)^{n-1}x^n}{n} + \cdots.$$

(c) $$1 + x + 2x^2 + \cdots + nx^n + \cdots.$$

(d) $$\frac{1}{3} + \frac{(x-2)}{36} + \frac{(x-2)^2}{243} + \cdots + \frac{(x-2)^n}{3^n n^2} + \cdots.$$

Solution: (a) Since

$$\operatorname*{limit}_{n\to\infty}\left|\frac{x^{n+1}/(n+1)!}{x^n/n!}\right| = \operatorname*{limit}_{n\to\infty}\frac{|x|}{n+1} = 0$$

for every number x, this series converges for every number x by the ratio test. Its interval of convergence is $(-\infty, \infty)$.

(b) We have

$$\operatorname*{limit}_{n\to\infty}\left|\frac{(-1)^n x^{n+1}/(n+1)}{(-1)^{n-1}x^n/n}\right| = \operatorname*{limit}_{n\to\infty}\frac{n}{n+1}|x| = |x|,$$

and therefore the series converges if $|x| < 1$ and diverges if $|x| > 1$ by the ratio test. Hence $r = 1$ for this series. Clearly, the series converges if $x = 1$ and diverges if $x = -1$. Hence $(-1,1]$ is its interval of convergence.

(c) Since

$$\operatorname*{limit}_{n\to\infty}\left|\frac{(n+1)x^{n+1}}{nx^n}\right| = \operatorname*{limit}_{n\to\infty}\frac{n+1}{n}|x| = |x|,$$

again $r = 1$ by the ratio test. This series evidently diverges if $x = \pm 1$. Hence its interval of convergence is the open interval $(-1,1)$.

(d) We have

$$\operatorname*{limit}_{n\to\infty}\left|\frac{(x-2)^{n+1}}{3^{n+1}(n+1)^2}\cdot\frac{3^n n^2}{(x-2)^n}\right| = \operatorname*{limit}_{n\to\infty}\frac{n^2}{3(n+1)^2}|x-2| = \frac{|x-2|}{3}.$$

Hence the series converges if $|x-2|/3 < 1$, or if

$$|x-2| < 3.$$

If $|x - 2| = 3$, the series is just the p series (or alternating p series) for $p = 2$. Since these series also converge, the interval of convergence of the given series is the set of all x such that $|x - 2| \leq 3$, i.e., the closed interval $[-1,5]$.

The multiplication of a series termwise by a nonzero number does not alter the convergence or divergence of a series **(15.5)**. Thus, for example, the power series

$$a_0x + a_1x^2 + \cdots + a_nx^{n+1} + \cdots$$

has the same interval of convergence as Σa_kx^k, since it is obtained by multiplying Σa_kx^k termwise by x. If we multiply Σa_kx^k termwise by $1/x$ and omit the first term of the resulting series, we obtain the series

$$a_1 + a_2x + \cdots + a_nx^{n-1} + \cdots,$$

which again has the same interval of convergence as Σa_kx^k. The coefficients of a power series may also be altered in certain ways without affecting the radius of convergence of the series, as the following theorem shows.

15.22 THEOREM. If $c_0, c_1, \cdots, c_n, \cdots$ is a sequence of positive numbers for which

$$\lim_{n\to\infty} \sqrt[n]{c_n} = 1,$$

then the two power series Σa_kx^k and $\Sigma c_ka_kx^k$ have the same radius of convergence.

Proof: Let r be the radius of convergence of the series Σa_kx^k and r' that of $\Sigma c_ka_kx^k$. We shall first of all assume that r is a positive number and that x is chosen so that

$$0 < |x| < r.$$

Then $(r - |x|)/|x| > 0$, and we can select a number $\epsilon > 0$ so that $\epsilon < (r - |x|)/|x|$, i.e., so that

$$(1 + \epsilon)|x| < r.$$

Since $\lim_{n\to\infty} \sqrt[n]{c_n} = 1$, we can find an integer N such that

$$1 - \epsilon < \sqrt[n]{c_n} < 1 + \epsilon \quad \text{for every } n \geq N.$$

Hence

$$|c_nx^n| = (\sqrt[n]{c_n}\,|x|)^n < [(1 + \epsilon)|x|]^n \quad \text{for every } n \geq N,$$

and the series

$$\sum_{k=N}^{\infty} |c_ka_kx^k|$$

is dominated by the series

$$\sum_{k=N}^{\infty} |a_k|[(1 + \epsilon)|x|]^k.$$

This latter series converges since $(1 + \epsilon)|x| < r$, and therefore the former series converges also. By adding on N terms to this series, we can conclude that the series $\Sigma c_k a_k x^k$ is absolutely convergent if $|x| < r$. Therefore the series $\Sigma c_k a_k x^k$ has a radius of convergence $r' \geq r$.

Since

$$\sum_{k=0}^{\infty} a_k x^k = \sum_{k=0}^{\infty} \frac{1}{c_k} (c_k a_k x^k),$$

$$\text{and} \qquad \operatorname*{limit}_{n\to\infty} \sqrt[n]{\frac{1}{c_n}} = 1,$$

we may start with the series $\Sigma c_k a_k x^k$, use our arguments above, and end up with the radius of convergence r of the series $\Sigma a_k x^k$ satisfying the inequality $r \geq r'$. This, together with the inequality $r' \geq r$, proves that $r = r'$, as desired.

If $r = \infty$, then we can prove that $r' = \infty$ by a slight modification of our previous proof. If either r or r' is a positive number, then $r = r'$ by our arguments above. Hence, if either r or r' is zero, then both must equal zero. Thus $r = r'$ always, and **15.22** is proved.

15.23 COROLLARY. The series $\Sigma a_k x^k$ and $\Sigma k a_k x^{k-1}$ have the same radius of convergence.

Proof: Since

$$\operatorname*{limit}_{n\to\infty} \sqrt[n]{n} = \operatorname*{limit}_{n\to\infty} e^{(\ln n)/n} = e^0 = 1,$$

we may use **15.22** with $c_k = k$ to conclude that $\Sigma k a_k x^k$, and hence also $\Sigma k a_k x^{k-1}$, has the same radius of convergence as $\Sigma a_k x^k$.

Note that the series

$$a_1 + 2a_2 x + 3a_3 x^2 + \cdots + n a_n x^{n-1} + \cdots$$

of **15.23** is in a formal sense the "derivative" of the power series

$$a_0 + a_1 x + a_2 x^2 + a_3 x^3 + \cdots + a_n x^n + \cdots.$$

That it actually is the derivative will be shown in Section 6.

EXERCISES

I

In each of Exercises 1–20 find the interval of convergence of the power series.

1. $x - \dfrac{x^3}{3!} + \cdots + \dfrac{(-1)^{n-1} x^{2n-1}}{(2n-1)!} + \cdots.$

2. $1 - x + \cdots + (-x)^{n-1} + \cdots$.

3. $1 + x + \frac{x^2}{\sqrt{2}} + \frac{x^3}{\sqrt{3}} + \cdots + \frac{x^n}{\sqrt{n}} + \cdots$.

4. $1 + \frac{x}{2} + \frac{2x^2}{2^2} + \frac{3x^3}{2^3} + \cdots + \frac{nx^n}{2^n} + \cdots$.

5. $\sum_{k=0}^{\infty} \frac{x^{2k}}{k!}$.

6. $\sum_{k=0}^{\infty} \frac{(-1)^k x^k}{(k+1)^2}$.

7. $\sum_{k=0}^{\infty} \frac{(3x)^k}{2^{k+1}}$.

8. $\sum_{k=0}^{\infty} \frac{k!x^k}{10^k}$.

9. $\sum_{k=1}^{\infty} (-1)^k k^2 x^k$.

10. $\sum_{k=1}^{\infty} \frac{(-1)^{k-1} x^{2k-1}}{k+1}$.

11. $\sum_{k=1}^{\infty} \frac{k(x-1)^{k-1}}{3^k}$.

12. $\sum_{k=0}^{\infty} \frac{(x+2)^k}{(k+1)2^k}$.

13. $\sum_{k=0}^{\infty} \frac{(-1)^{k+1}(x+1)^{2k}}{(k+1)^2 5^k}$.

14. $\sum_{k=1}^{\infty} \frac{(-1)^k (2x-1)^k}{k!}$.

15. $\sum_{k=1}^{\infty} \frac{k!^3 x^k}{2k!}$.

16. $\sum_{k=1}^{\infty} \frac{x^k}{\ln(k+1)}$.

17. $\sum_{k=2}^{\infty} \frac{(-1)^k x^k}{k(\ln k)^2}$.

18. $\sum_{k=0}^{\infty} \frac{(2x+1)^k}{3^k}$.

19. $\sum_{k=0}^{\infty} \frac{(x-2)^k}{2^k\sqrt{k+1}}$.

20. $\sum_{k=0}^{\infty} \frac{kx^k}{(k+1)(k+2)2^k}$.

21. Complete the proof of 15.22 by showing that if $\Sigma a_k x^k$ has infinite radius of convergence then so does $\Sigma c_k a_k x^k$.

22. If $a_k = 2^{-k}$, k an even integer, and $a_k = 2^{-k+1}$, k an odd integer, show that the power series $\Sigma a_k x^k$ has the open interval $(-2,2)$ as its interval of convergence. Note that $\lim_{n\to\infty} a_{n+1}/a_n$ does not exist.

II

In each of Exercises 1–8, determine the radius of convergence of the power series.

1. $\sum_{n=1}^{\infty} \frac{n^n}{n!} x^n$.

2. $\sum_{n=1}^{\infty} (a^n + b^n + c^n)x^n$, $a,b,c \geq 0$.

3. $\sum_{n=1}^{\infty} 2^{-n} x^{2^n}$.

4. $\sum_{n=1}^{\infty} \frac{(n!)^3 x^{3n}}{(3n)!}$.

5. $\sum_{n=1}^{\infty} \left(1 + \frac{a}{n} + \frac{b}{n^2}\right)^n x^n$.

6. $\sum_{n=1}^{\infty} e^{(1+1/2+\cdots+1/n)}x^n$ (see Exercise II-7, Section 4).

7. $\sum_{n=0}^{\infty} n!x^{2^n}$.

8. $\sum_{n=0}^{\infty} (2n)!x^{n!}$.

9. Let r be the radius of convergence of the power series $\Sigma a_k x^k$. Show that if there exists a constant M such that $|a_k| \leq M$ for every integer k then $r \geq 1$. Also show that if there exists another constant N such that $0 < N \leq |a_k| \leq M$ for every integer k then $r = 1$.

10. Prove that if $\lim_{n\to\infty} \sqrt[n]{|a_n|} = r > 0$, then the power series $\Sigma a_k x^k$ has radius of convergence $1/r$.

7 DERIVATIVE AND INTEGRAL OF A POWER SERIES

Each power series $\Sigma a_k x^k$ defines a function f,

$$f(x) = \sum_{k=0}^{\infty} a_k x^k.$$

The domain of f is the interval of convergence of the series. Let us show that f is a differentiable function, having as its derivative the formal derivative discussed in Section 6.

15.24 **THEOREM.** If $\Sigma a_k x^k$ is a power series with nonzero radius of convergence r, then the function f defined by

$$f(x) = \sum_{k=0}^{\infty} a_k x^k$$

has a derivative given by

$$f'(x) = \sum_{k=0}^{\infty} k a_k x^{k-1}$$

at every number x in the open interval $(-r,r)$.

Proof: Let x and c be distinct numbers in the open interval $(-r,r)$. By Taylor's formula **(14.10)**, with $n = 1$,

$$(1) \qquad x^k = c^k + kc^{k-1}(x - c) + \frac{k(k-1)}{2}(z_k)^{k-2}(x - c)^2$$

for every integer k, where z_k is always a number between x and c. Now

$$\begin{aligned}\frac{f(x)-f(c)}{x-c} &= \frac{1}{x-c}\left(\sum_{k=0}^{\infty} a_k x^k - \sum_{k=0}^{\infty} a_k c^k\right)\\ &= \frac{1}{x-c}\sum_{k=0}^{\infty} a_k(x^k - c^k)\\ &= \frac{1}{x-c}\sum_{k=0}^{\infty} a_k\left[kc^{k-1}(x-c) + \frac{k(k-1)}{2}(z_k)^{k-2}(x-c)^2\right]\end{aligned}$$

by (1). Hence

$$\frac{f(x)-f(c)}{x-c} = \sum_{k=0}^{\infty} ka_k c^{k-1} + \frac{(x-c)}{2}\sum_{k=0}^{\infty} k(k-1)a_k(z_k)^{k-2}, \tag{2}$$

where each of the above series may be shown to be absolutely convergent by using results of the previous sections.

From (2) we easily derive that

$$\left|\frac{f(x)-f(c)}{x-c} - \sum_{k=0}^{\infty} ka_k c^{k-1}\right| < \frac{|x-c|}{2}\sum_{k=0}^{\infty} k(k-1)|a_k|d^{k-2}, \tag{3}$$

where d is any positive constant such that $|c| < d < r$ and $|x| < d < r$. On taking limits in (3) as x approaches c, the right side has limit 0, and therefore

$$f'(c) = \operatorname*{limit}_{x\to c}\frac{f(x)-f(c)}{x-c} = \sum_{k=0}^{\infty} ka_k c^{k-1}.$$

This proves **15.24.**

If

$$f(x) = \sum_{k=0}^{\infty} a_k x^k, \qquad g(x) = \sum_{k=0}^{\infty} \frac{a_k}{k+1} x^{k+1},$$

then $f(x)$ and $g(x)$ have the same radius of convergence by **15.23**, and $g'(x) = f(x)$ by **15.24.** Since $g(0) = 0$,

$$\int_0^x f(t)\,dt = g(x),$$

and we have proved the following result.

15.25 THEOREM. If the power series $\Sigma a_k x^k$ has nonzero radius of convergence r, then

$$\int_0^x \sum_{k=0}^{\infty} a_k t^k\,dt = \sum_{k=0}^{\infty} \frac{a_k}{k+1} x^{k+1}, \qquad |x| < r.$$

EXAMPLE 1. Show that

$$\tan^{-1} x = x - \frac{x^3}{3} + \frac{x^5}{5} - \frac{x^7}{7} + \cdots, \qquad |x| < 1.$$

Solution: The geometric series

$$\frac{1}{1+x^2} = 1 - x^2 + x^4 - x^6 + \cdots$$

has radius of convergence $r = 1$. Hence we may integrate the series termwise by **15.25** to obtain

$$\int_0^x \frac{1}{1+t^2}\,dt = \tan^{-1} x = x - \frac{x^3}{3} + \frac{x^5}{5} - \frac{x^7}{7} + \cdots, \qquad |x| < 1.$$

EXAMPLE 2. Approximate $\tan^{-1} \frac{1}{2}$ to three decimal places.

Solution: By Example 1,

$$\tan^{-1}\frac{1}{2} \doteq \frac{1}{2} - \frac{1}{3}\left(\frac{1}{2}\right)^3 + \frac{1}{5}\left(\frac{1}{2}\right)^5 - \frac{1}{7}\left(\frac{1}{2}\right)^7 \doteq .463.$$

By **15.15**, the error does not exceed

$$\frac{1}{9}\left(\frac{1}{2}\right)^9 < 3 \times 10^{-4}.$$

If

$$f(x) = \sum_{k=0}^{\infty} a_k(x-c)^k, \qquad g(x) = \sum_{k=0}^{\infty} a_k x^k,$$

then $f(x) = g(x - c)$, and by the chain rule

$$f'(x) = g'(x-c)\,D(x-c) = g'(x-c).$$

Hence

$$f'(x) = \sum_{k=1}^{\infty} k a_k (x-c)^{k-1},$$

and the power series $\Sigma a_k(x-c)^k$ is differentiated just as the power series $\Sigma a_k x^k$. The integral of $f(x)$ is also found by integrating the series termwise.

EXERCISES

I

1. Show that

$$\ln(1+x) = x - \frac{x^2}{2} + \frac{x^3}{3} - \frac{x^4}{4} + \cdots, \qquad |x| < 1.$$

Approximate ln (1.2) to three decimal places.

2. Show that

$$\ln(1-x) = -x - \frac{x^2}{2} - \frac{x^3}{3} - \frac{x^4}{4} - \cdots, \qquad |x| < 1.$$

Approximate $\ln \frac{3}{4}$ to three decimal places.

3. By combining the series in Exercises 1 and 2, show that

$$\ln\left(\frac{1+x}{1-x}\right) = 2\left(x + \frac{x^3}{3} + \frac{x^5}{5} + \cdots\right), \qquad |x| < 1.$$

Approximate ln 3 to three decimal places.

4. Approximate $\int_0^{1/2} \frac{x}{1+x^3}\,dx$ to four decimal places.

5. Find an infinite series for the improper integral

$$\int_0^x \frac{\ln(1+t)}{t}\,dt.$$

6. Find an infinite series for the improper integral

$$\int_0^x \frac{\tan^{-1} t}{t}\,dt.$$

7. Find the sum of the series

$$S(x) = \frac{x^2}{1\cdot 2} + \frac{x^3}{2\cdot 3} + \cdots + \frac{x^n}{(n-1)(n)} + \cdots$$

by first obtaining $S'(x)$ and using Exercise 2.

8. Find the sum of the series

$$S(x) = \frac{x^2}{1\cdot 2} - \frac{x^4}{3\cdot 4} + \cdots + \frac{(-1)^{n-1}x^{2n-2}}{(2n-3)(2n-2)} + \cdots$$

by first obtaining $S''(x)$.

9. Find the sum of the series

$$\sum_{n=2}^{\infty} \frac{x^{3n}}{2n}.$$

II

Find the power series expansion for each of the following functions, and determine the radius of convergence of the series.

1. $\ln(1 + x + x^2)$.
2. $\ln(1 + 3x + 2x^2)$.

3. $\ln(1 - x - 2x^2)$.

4. $\arctan \dfrac{2x}{1 - x^2}$.

5. $\arctan \dfrac{2x^3}{1 + 3x^2}$.

Sum each of the following series.

6. $\sum_{n=1}^{\infty} (-1)^{n+1}(x^{2n-1} + x^{2n})$.

7. $\sum_{n=0}^{\infty} \dfrac{x^{4n}}{2n + 1}$.

8. $\sum_{n=1}^{\infty} \dfrac{x^n}{n(n + 1)}$.

8 BINOMIAL SERIES

According to the binomial theorem,

$$(a + b)^m = a^m + ma^{m-1}b + \frac{m(m - 1)}{2!} a^{m-2}b^2 + \cdots + \frac{m(m - 1)\cdots(m - k + 1)}{k!} a^{m-k}b^k + \cdots + b^m,$$

where m is a positive integer. If we let $a = 1$ and $b = x$, this series has the form

$$(1 + x)^m = 1 + mx + \frac{m(m - 1)}{2!} x^2 + \cdots + \frac{m(m - 1)\cdots(m - k + 1)}{k!} x^k + \cdots + x^m.$$

If m is not a positive integer, we may still formally write the above series, although the series will not terminate as the one above does. The resulting series is called a *binomial series* and has the form (replacing m by a)

15.26 $$\sum_{k=0}^{\infty} c_k x^k = 1 + ax + \frac{a(a - 1)}{2!} x^2 + \cdots + \frac{a(a - 1)\cdots(a - n + 1)}{n!} x^n + \cdots,$$

where

$$c_k = \frac{a(a - 1)(a - 2)\cdots(a - k + 1)}{k!}, \qquad k = 1, 2, \cdots.$$

The binomial series is finite if and only if a is nonnegative integer.

We can find the radius of convergence of **15.26** by the ratio test. Thus

$$\lim_{n\to\infty} \left|\frac{c_{n+1}x^{n+1}}{c_n x^n}\right| = \lim_{n\to\infty} \left|\frac{a-n}{n+1}\right| |x| = |x|,$$

and the series is convergent if $|x| < 1$ and divergent if $|x| > 1$. Hence its radius of convergence is 1.

The binomial series **15.26** defines a function f,

$$f(x) = \sum_{k=0}^{\infty} c_k x^k, \qquad (|x| < 1),$$

for each real number a. If a is a nonnegative integer, the function f is the power function

$$f(x) = (1 + x)^a$$

by the binomial theorem. Let us prove that f is this power function for each real number a, regardless of whether or not a is a nonnegative integer.

We shall prove that $f(x) = (1 + x)^a$ by showing that

$$D[f(x)(1 + x)^{-a}] = f'(x)(1 + x)^{-a} - af(x)(1 + x)^{-a-1} = 0.$$

On multiplying this differential equation throughout by $(1 + x)^{1+a}$, we obtain the differential equation

$$\text{(1)} \qquad f'(x)(1 + x) - af(x) = 0.$$

Let us now prove that (1) holds for the function f defined by the binomial series.

By **15.24**, if $|x| < 1$,

$$f'(x) = \sum_{k=1}^{\infty} kc_k x^{k-1} = \sum_{k=0}^{\infty} (k + 1)c_{k+1}x^k,$$

$$xf'(x) = \sum_{k=1}^{\infty} kc_k x^k = \sum_{k=0}^{\infty} kc_k x^k.$$

Hence

$$f'(x)(1 + x) = \sum_{k=0}^{\infty} [(k + 1)c_{k+1} + kc_k]x^k.$$

Now

$$(k + 1)c_{k+1} + kc_k = \frac{(k + 1)a(a - 1)(a - 2)\cdots(a - k)}{(k + 1)!} + \frac{ka(a - 1)(a - 2)\cdots(a - k + 1)}{k!}$$

$$= \frac{a(a - 1)(a - 2)\cdots(a - k + 1)}{k!}(a - k + k) = ac_k,$$

and therefore

$$f'(x)(1 + x) = \sum_{k=0}^{\infty} ac_k x^k = af(x).$$

This proves that

$$D[f(x)(1 + x)^{-a}] = 0,$$

and hence that

$$f(x)(1 + x)^{-a} = K,$$

for some constant K. Since $f(0) = 1$, it is clear that $K = 1$, and hence that

$$f(x) = (1 + x)^a.$$

Thus we have proved the generalized binomial theorem

15.27 $$(1 + x)^a = 1 + ax + \frac{a(a-1)}{2!}x^2 + \cdots + \frac{a(a-1)\cdots(a-n+1)}{n!}x^n + \cdots,$$

which holds for every real number a and every x such that $|x| < 1$.

EXAMPLE 1. Find the series expansion of $\sqrt{1 + x}$.

Solution: By **15.27** with $a = \frac{1}{2}$, we have

$$\sqrt{1+x} = 1 + \frac{1}{2}x + \frac{\frac{1}{2}(\frac{1}{2}-1)}{2!}x^2 + \cdots + \frac{\frac{1}{2}(\frac{1}{2}-1)\cdots(\frac{1}{2}-n+1)}{n!}x^n + \cdots$$

$$= 1 + \frac{1}{2}x - \frac{1}{2^2 2!}x^2 + \cdots + \frac{(-1)^{n+1}1\cdot 3\cdots(2n-3)}{2^n n!}x^n + \cdots,$$

if $|x| < 1$.

EXAMPLE 2. Find the series expansion of $\ln(x + \sqrt{1 + x^2})$.

Solution: If $f(x) = \ln(x + \sqrt{1 + x^2})$, then

$$f'(x) = \frac{1 + x/\sqrt{1+x^2}}{x + \sqrt{1+x^2}} = \frac{1}{\sqrt{1+x^2}}.$$

Thus to find the series expansion of f we need only find the series expansion of $(1 + t^2)^{-1/2}$ and then integrate it termwise. By **15.27**,

$$(1 + t^2)^{-1/2} = 1 - \frac{1}{2}t^2 + \frac{1\cdot 3}{2^2\cdot 2!}t^4 + \cdots + (-1)^n\frac{1\cdot 3\cdots(2n-1)}{2^n\cdot n!}t^{2n} + \cdots$$

if $t^2 < 1$. Hence, by **15.25**,

$$\ln(x + \sqrt{1 + x^2}) = \int_0^x \frac{1}{\sqrt{1 + t^2}}\, dt$$

$$= x - \frac{1}{2 \cdot 3} x^3 + \frac{1 \cdot 3}{2^2 \cdot 5 \cdot 2!} x^5 + \cdots$$

$$+ (-1)^n \frac{1 \cdot 3 \cdots (2n - 1)}{2^n \cdot (2n + 1) \cdot n!} x^{2n+1} + \cdots,$$

if $|x| < 1$.

EXERCISES

I

In each of Exercises 1–11, find the power series for the function and determine the radius of convergence.

1. $\sqrt{1 - x}$.
2. $\sqrt[3]{1 + z^2}$.
3. $\dfrac{1}{(1 + x)^2}$.
4. $\dfrac{z}{\sqrt{1 - z^3}}$.
5. $\dfrac{1}{\sqrt{1 - x^2}}$.
6. $(1 + 2x)^{-3}$.
7. $x(4 - x)^{3/2}$. [*Hint:* Factor out the number 4.]
8. $\sqrt{2 + z}$.
9. $\sin^{-1} x$.
10. $\ln(\sqrt{1 + x^2} - x)$.
11. $\sec^{-1} \dfrac{1}{x}$.

II

Determine the power series expansion and radius of convergence for each of the following functions.

1. $(1 + x + x^2)^{-1}$.
2. $(1 - x - 2x^2)^{-1}$.
3. Show that

$$\frac{\sin^{-1} x}{\sqrt{1 - x^2}} = x + \frac{2}{3} x^3 + \frac{2 \cdot 4}{3 \cdot 5} x^5 + \frac{2 \cdot 4 \cdot 6}{3 \cdot 5 \cdot 7} x^7 + \cdots = \sum_{n=0}^{\infty} \frac{2^{2n}(n!)^2 x^{2n+1}}{(2n + 1)!}.$$

4. Find the power series expansion of $(\sin^{-1} x)^2$. (Use Exercise 3.)

9 TAYLOR'S SERIES

A function defined by a power series in x possesses derivatives of all orders, obtainable by differentiating the power series termwise according to **15.24**. We might well ask whether, conversely, if a function has derivatives of all orders, it may then be represented by a power series. While this is not true in general, it is true for most of the elementary functions studied in this book.

If

$$f(x) = \sum_{k=0}^{\infty} a_k(x - c)^k$$

has an open interval containing c as its domain, then

$$f'(x) = \sum_{k=1}^{\infty} ka_k(x - c)^{k-1}, \qquad f''(x) = \sum_{k=2}^{\infty} k(k - 1)a_k(x - c)^{k-2},$$

and, in general,

$$f^{[n]}(x) = \sum_{k=n}^{\infty} k(k - 1) \cdots (k - n + 1)a_k(x - c)^{k-n}.$$

The function f and its derivatives have the same radius of convergence according to **15.24**. Evaluating the function f and its derivatives at the number c, we get

$$f(c) = a_0, \quad f'(c) = a_1, \quad f''(c) = 2a_2,$$

and, in general,

$$f^{[n]}(c) = n!a_n.$$

Thus

$$a_n = \frac{f^{[n]}(c)}{n!}$$

for each integer n, and the power series for f is given by

15.28 $$f(x) = f(c) + f'(c)(x - c) + \frac{f''(c)}{2!}(x - c)^2 + \cdots + \frac{f^{[n]}(c)}{n!}(x - c)^n + \cdots.$$

Series **15.28** is called the *Taylor's series of f* at c.

If $c = 0$, then we get the following *Maclaurin's series* **(14.12)** for $f(x)$.

15.29 $$f(x) = f(0) + f'(0)x + \frac{f''(0)}{2!}x^2 + \cdots + \frac{f^{[n]}(0)}{n!}x^n + \cdots.$$

Such series as the binomial series **15.27** and the arctangent series

$$\tan^{-1}x = x - \frac{x^3}{3} + \frac{x^5}{5} - \frac{x^7}{7} + \cdots$$

are examples of Maclaurin's series for these functions.

The nth partial sum of **15.28** is a Taylor's polynomial $P_n(x)$ as defined in **14.7**. The nth-degree remainder term $R_n(x)$ is given by **(14.11)**

$$R_n(x) = \frac{f^{[n+1]}(z)}{(n+1)!}(x-c)^{n+1},$$

where z is some number between x and c, and

$$f(x) = P_n(x) + R_n(x).$$

The fundamental theorem for representing a function by a power series may be stated as follows.

15.30 **THEOREM.** If the function f has derivatives of all orders in an interval containing the number c and if

$$\operatorname*{limit}_{n\to\infty} R_n(x) = 0$$

for every x in the interval, then f is given by **15.28** in this interval.

Proof: Since $P_n(x) = f(x) - R_n(x)$, we have

$$\operatorname*{limit}_{n\to\infty} P_n(x) = f(x) - \operatorname*{limit}_{n\to\infty} R_n(x) = f(x),$$

and the theorem is proved.

The power series $\Sigma z^k/k!$ converges for every number z. Hence the limit of its nth term must be 0,

15.31 $$\operatorname*{limit}_{n\to\infty} \frac{z^n}{n!} = 0.$$

This fact will be used in some of the following examples.

EXAMPLE 1. Find the Maclaurin's series for e^x, and prove that it represents e^x for all x.

Solution: If $f(x) = e^x$, then $f^{[n]}(x) = e^x$ for every n. Thus $f^{[n]}(0) = 1$ and the Maclaurin's series for e^x is as follows:

15.32 $$e^x = 1 + x + \frac{x^2}{2!} + \frac{x^3}{3!} + \cdots + \frac{x^n}{n!} + \cdots.$$

Let us prove that **15.32** is valid for every number x. Evidently,

$$R_n(x) = \frac{e^{z_n}x^{n+1}}{(n+1)!},$$

where each z_n is between 0 and x. If $x > 0$, $e^{z_n} < e^x$ for every integer n, and therefore

$$0 < R_n(x) < \frac{e^x x^{n+1}}{(n+1)!}.$$

Since

$$\lim_{n\to\infty} e^x \frac{x^{n+1}}{(n+1)!} = 0$$

by **15.31**, also

$$\lim_{n\to\infty} R_n(x) = 0.$$

If $x < 0$, each $e^{z_n} < 1$, and the same conclusion holds. Thus **15.32** is valid for every real number x.

If $x = 1$, **15.32** yields the following expression for e:

$$e = 1 + 1 + \frac{1}{2} + \frac{1}{6} + \cdots + \frac{1}{n!} + \cdots.$$

Let us use this infinite series to show that e is an irrational number. Assume, on the contrary, that e is a rational number. We know that $2 < e < 3$, so that e is not an integer. If $e = k/m$, k and m integers with $m \geq 2$, then

$$e = 1 + 1 + \frac{1}{2} + \cdots + \frac{1}{m!} + \frac{e^z}{(m+1)!} \quad \text{for some } z,\ 0 < z < 1.$$

Hence

$$e \cdot m! = p + \frac{e^z}{m+1},$$

where p is an integer. Since $e \cdot m!$ is also an integer, $e^z/(m+1)$ must be an integer. However, this is impossible, since $m + 1 \geq 3$, whereas $e^z < e < 3$. Thus the assumption that e is rational leads to a contradiction, and e is an irrational number.

EXAMPLE 2. Find the Maclaurin's series for $\sin x$, and prove that it represents $\sin x$ for all x.

Solution: If $f(x) = \sin x$, then $f(0) = 0$ and

$$\begin{aligned} f'(x) &= \cos x, & f'(0) &= 1, \\ f''(x) &= -\sin x, & f''(0) &= 0, \\ f'''(x) &= -\cos x, & f'''(0) &= -1, \\ f^{[4]}(x) &= \sin x, & f^{[4]}(0) &= 0, \end{aligned}$$

and so on. Thus

$$\sin x = x - \frac{x^3}{3!} + \frac{x^5}{5!} - \frac{x^7}{7!} + \cdots.$$

Since $|f^{[n]}(x)|$ is either $|\sin x|$ or $|\cos x|$, evidently $|f^{[n]}(x)| \leq 1$ and

$$\lim_{n\to\infty} |R_n(x)| = \lim_{n\to\infty} |f^{[n+1]}(z_n)| \left|\frac{x^{n+1}}{(n+1)!}\right| = 0.$$

Hence the sine series is valid for every number x.

EXAMPLE 3. Find the Taylor's series for $\ln x$ in powers of $x - 1$.

Solution: If $f(x) = \ln x$, then $f(1) = 0$ and

$$f'(x) = \frac{1}{x}, \quad f'(1) = 1,$$

$$f''(x) = -\frac{1}{x^2}, \quad f''(1) = -1,$$

$$f'''(x) = \frac{2}{x^3}, \quad f'''(1) = 2,$$

and, in general,

$$f^{[n+1]}(x) = \frac{(-1)^n n!}{x^{n+1}}, \quad f^{[n+1]}(1) = (-1)^n n!.$$

The Taylor's series for $\ln x$ thus has the form

$$\ln x = (x-1) - \frac{(x-1)^2}{2} + \frac{(x-1)^3}{3} - \cdots + \frac{(-1)^{n-1}(x-1)^n}{n} + \cdots.$$

This series converges for each x in the interval $(0,2]$ and diverges elsewhere. Evidently,

$$R_n(x) = \frac{(-1)^n n!}{(z_n)^{n+1}} \frac{(x-1)^{n+1}}{(n+1)!} = \frac{(-1)^n}{n+1}\left(\frac{x-1}{z_n}\right)^{n+1},$$

where z_n is between 1 and x. If $x > 1$, then $1 < z_n < x \leq 2$ and $0 < x - 1 \leq 1 < z_n$. Hence $(x-1)/z_n < 1$ and

$$\lim_{n\to\infty} |R_n(x)| = \lim_{n\to\infty} \frac{1}{n+1} = 0.$$

Thus this Taylor's series for $\ln x$ has $\ln x$ as its sum if $1 < x \leq 2$. We omit the details, but it may be shown that $\ln x$ is also given by this series if $0 < x \leq 1$.

We remark in passing that it is not true in general that the sum of the Taylor's series of f at c **(15.28)** necessarily equals $f(x)$ for every x in the interval of convergence of this series. Exercise II-7 at the end of this section illustrates this point.

The infinite series expansion of a function may be used to approximate values of the function, as we have illustrated previously in this chapter. Some more examples of this are given below.

EXAMPLE 4. Approximate $\int_0^1 e^{-x^2}\,dx$ to three decimal places.

Solution: Replacing x by $-x^2$ in **15.32**, we get

$$e^{-x^2} = 1 - x^2 + \frac{x^4}{2!} - \frac{x^6}{3!} + \cdots + \frac{(-1)^n x^{2n}}{n!} + \cdots.$$

We may integrate this series termwise according to **15.25**, getting

$$\int_0^1 e^{-x^2}\,dx = 1 - \frac{1}{3} + \frac{1}{10} - \frac{1}{42} + \cdots + \frac{(-1)^n}{(2n+1)n!} + \cdots.$$

Using five terms, we get

$$\int_0^1 e^{-x^2}\,dx \doteq .747,$$

with an error less than the next term, 1/1320, by **15.15**.

EXAMPLE 5. Approximate $\int_0^{1/2} \cos\sqrt{x}\,dx$ to four significant digits.

Solution: We may easily verify that

$$\cos x = 1 - \frac{x^2}{2!} + \frac{x^4}{4!} - \frac{x^6}{6!} + \cdots$$

for every number x. Hence

$$\cos\sqrt{x} = 1 - \frac{x}{2!} + \frac{x^2}{4!} - \frac{x^3}{6!} + \cdots$$

for every nonnegative number x, and

$$\int_0^{1/2} \cos\sqrt{x}\,dx = \frac{1}{2} - \frac{1}{2\cdot 2!}\left(\frac{1}{2}\right)^2 + \frac{1}{3\cdot 4!}\left(\frac{1}{2}\right)^3 - \frac{1}{4\cdot 6!}\left(\frac{1}{2}\right)^4 + \cdots \doteq .4392.$$

with an error less than the fifth term $1/(2^6 \times 6!)$ by **15.15**.

EXERCISES

I

Find an infinite series expansion for each of the following functions. State its radius of convergence.

1. $\cos x$ in powers of $(x - \pi/4)$.
2. xe^x in powers of x.

3. $\ln |x|$ in powers of $(x + 1)$.

4. $\dfrac{\sin x}{x}$ in powers of x.

5. $\sinh x$ in powers of x.

6. $\cosh x$ in powers of x.

7. $\dfrac{1 - \cos x}{x}$ in powers of x.

8. $\sin x$ in powers of $(x + \pi/3)$.

9. $\sin^2 x$ in powers of x. [*Hint:* Use double-angle formula.]

10. $\cos^2 x$ in powers of x.

Approximate each of the following to the stated degree of accuracy.

11. $\sqrt[3]{e}$, five decimal places.

12. $\sin 10°$, four decimal places. [*Hint:* $1° \doteq .017453$ radian.]

13. $\int_0^{.4} \sin x^2\, dx$, six decimal places.

14. $\sinh \frac{1}{2}$, five decimal places.

II

In each of Exercises 1–5, find an infinite series expansion for the function, and state the interval of convergence of the series.

1. $\exp(x^2 - 1)$ in powers of x.

2. $\sinh^4 2x$ in powers of x.

3. $\cos^3 x$ in powers of $x - \pi/3$.

4. $(2 - x - x^2)^{-1}$ in powers of $x - 2$.

5. $\ln(x^2 + 4x + 4)$ in powers of $x + 1$.

6. Approximate (a) $\cos 61°$; (b) $\tan 47°$; (c) $\sin 74°$. Use Taylor expansions, and obtain each answer accurate to four decimal places.

7. Define the function f as follows: $f(x) = e^{-1/x^2}$ if $x \neq 0$, $f(0) = 0$. Show that $f^{[n]}(0)$ exists and equals 0 for every integer n. Prove that the Maclaurin's series for f is not equal to f in any neighborhood of 0.

8. Prove that the closest integer to $n!/e$ is divisible by $n - 1$. [*Hint:* Use the series for $1/e$.]

REVIEW

Oral Exercises

Explain or define the following terms.

1. A convergent infinite series.

2. A divergent infinite series.

3. Sum of an infinite series.

4. The integral test.

5. The comparison test.

6. The p series.

7. The ratio test.

8. Absolute convergence.

9. Taylor series.

10. Radius of convergence.

I

In each of Exercises 1–10, test the series whose nth term is specified for convergence or divergence. In case of convergence, determine whether or not the series converges absolutely.

1. $\dfrac{(-1)^{n+1}n}{1000n + 10^6}$.

2. $\dfrac{\cos n\pi}{\sqrt{n}}$.

3. $\dfrac{(-1)^{n+1}\sqrt{n}}{10^6 n + 1}$.

4. $(-1)^n \ln \dfrac{1}{n}$.

5. $\dfrac{(-1)^{n+1}}{\ln (n + 1)}$.

6. $\dfrac{\sin^3 n\pi/3}{n\sqrt{n}}$.

7. $\dfrac{(-1)^n(\ln n)^{100}}{n^{3/2}}$.

8. $\dfrac{(-1)^n}{n - \ln n}$.

9. $(-1)^{n+1} \dfrac{(\sqrt{n+1} - \sqrt{n})}{n}$.

10. $\dfrac{(-1)^{n+1}(\sqrt{n^2+n+1} - \sqrt{n^2-n+1})}{n}$.

11. If $\sum_{n=1}^{\infty} a_n$ is absolutely convergent, prove that $\sum_{n=1}^{\infty} \dfrac{n+1}{n} a_n$ is also absolutely convergent.

12. If $\sum_{n=1}^{\infty} a_n^2$ and $\sum_{n=1}^{\infty} b_n^2$ are absolutely convergent, prove that $\sum_{n=1}^{\infty} a_n b_n$ is also absolutely convergent.

In each of Exercises 13–18 determine the interval of convergence of the series.

13. $\sum_{n=1}^{\infty} (nx)^n$.

14. $\sum_{n=1}^{\infty} \dfrac{x^n}{n \cdot 5^{n-100}}$.

15. $\sum_{n=1}^{\infty} \dfrac{x^n}{\sqrt{n^2+n}}$.

16. $\sum_{n=1}^{\infty} \dfrac{x^n \ln n}{n}$.

17. $\sum_{n=1}^{\infty} \dfrac{n(x-2)^n}{\sqrt{n^3+1}}$.

18. $\sum_{n=1}^{\infty} \dfrac{n+\sqrt{n}}{n} (x+1)^{3n}$.

In each of Exercises 19–24, expand the given function into a Taylor series about the given point.

19. $\ln x$, $x = 1$.

20. $\sqrt{x^3}$, $x = 1$.

21. $\dfrac{1}{x}$, $x = 2$.

22. $\sin \dfrac{\pi x}{4}$, $x = 2$.

23. $x^2 e^x$, $x = 0$.

24. $(x - 1)^2 \sin x$, $x = 0$.

In each of Exercises 25–28 use Taylor series to evaluate the given limit.

25. $\displaystyle\operatorname*{limit}_{x\to 0} \frac{\sin x - x + \dfrac{x^3}{6}}{x^5}$.

26. $\displaystyle\operatorname*{limit}_{x\to 0} \frac{e^x - 1 - x}{x^2}$.

27. $\displaystyle\operatorname*{limit}_{x\to 0} \frac{\ln (x + \sqrt{1 + x^2}) - x}{x^3}$.

28. $\displaystyle\operatorname*{limit}_{x\to \infty} \left\{x - x^2 \ln \left(1 + \frac{1}{x}\right)\right\}$.

29. Sum the series

$$\frac{x}{1} + \frac{x^5}{5} + \cdots + \frac{x^{4n-3}}{4n - 3} + \cdots. \quad (\textit{Hint: differentiate.})$$

30. Sum the series

$$e^{-x} + 2e^{-2x} + \cdots + ne^{-nx} + \cdots. \quad (\textit{Hint: integrate.})$$

II

In each of Exercises 1–6 determine the interval of convergence of the series whose nth term is specified.

1. x^{n^2}.

2. $\dfrac{1}{1 + x^n}$.

3. $(\ln x)^n$.

4. $\sin \dfrac{x}{2^n}$.

5. $\dfrac{(x/2)^n (2n)!}{(n!)^2}$.

6. $x^n n^{-[1+2(\ln \ln n)/\ln n]}$.

In each of Exercises 7–10 evaluate the indicated derivative at $x = 0$.

7. $D^{10}(x^6 e^{x+1})$.

8. $D^{10}(e^{2x^2})$.

9. $D^{12}\left(\dfrac{x}{1 + x^2}\right)$.

10. $D^5(x^2[1 + x]^{1/4})$.

11. For what values of x does $\displaystyle\sum_{n=1}^{\infty} \frac{x^n}{1 + x^{2n}}$ converge?

12. Show that

$$\sum_{n=0}^{\infty} \frac{x^{2^n}}{1 - x^{2^{n+1}}}$$

converges except when $x = \pm 1$ and its sum equals $\dfrac{x}{1-x}$ for $|x| < 1$ and $-\dfrac{1}{x-1}$ for $|x| > 1$.

13. Show that

$$\sum_{n=1}^{\infty} \frac{a_n}{(1 + a_1)(1 + a_2) \cdots (1 + a_n)}$$

converges if each $a_n > 0$ and $\sum_{n=1}^{\infty} a_n$ diverges, and find its sum.

14. Show that $\sum_{n=2}^{\infty} \ln\left(1 - \dfrac{1}{n^2}\right)$ converges and find its sum.

15. Another comparison test.

a. If $\sum_{n=1}^{\infty} b_n$ is a convergent positive-termed series and if there exists a number N such that

$$\left|\frac{a_{n+1}}{a_n}\right| \leq \frac{b_{n+1}}{b_n} \quad \text{for every } n \geq N,$$

then prove that the series $\sum_{n=1}^{\infty} a_n$ converges absolutely.

b. If $\sum_{n=1}^{\infty} b_n$ is a divergent positive-termed series and if there exists a number N such that

$$\left|\frac{a_{n+1}}{a_n}\right| \geq \frac{b_{n+1}}{b_n} \quad \text{for every } n \geq N,$$

then prove that the series $\sum_{n=1}^{\infty} a_n$ does not converge absolutely.

16. Show that if a positive series $\sum_{n=1}^{\infty} a_n$ is divergent then a second positive divergent series $\sum_{n=1}^{\infty} b_n$ can be found such that $\lim_{n \to \infty} \dfrac{b_n}{a_n} = 0$. Consider

$$b_n = \frac{a_n}{a_1 + a_2 + \cdots + a_n}.$$

17. If the series $\sum_{n=1}^{\infty} |a_n|$ converges and $|a_n| > |a_{n+1}|$ for every n, then prove that $\lim_{n \to \infty} na_n = 0$.

18. A useful test for series of general terms is Abel's test.

Show that if $\{b_n\}$ is a bounded monotonic sequence and if the series $\sum_{n=1}^{\infty} a_n$ converges, then the series $\sum_{n=1}^{\infty} a_n b_n$ also converges. Compare with **15.13**.

19. Prove that if the series $\sum_{n=1}^{\infty} na_n$ converges, so also does the series $\sum_{n=1}^{\infty} a_n$. (*Note:* This result would follow very simply by comparison if all the terms were positive.) (Use preceding Exercise.)

20. Another useful test for series of general terms is Dirichlet's test.

Show that if $\{b_n\}$ is a strictly decreasing sequence with limit zero and if the set of partial sums of the series Σa_n is bounded, then $\sum_{n=1}^{\infty} a_n b_n$ converges.

21. Discuss the convergence of $\sum_{n=1}^{\infty} \frac{\sin n\theta}{n}$. Use the preceding Exercise and that

$$\sum_{n=1}^{N} \sin n\theta = \frac{\sin N\theta/2 \sin (N+1)\theta/2}{\sin \theta/2}$$

which can be gotten by noting that

$$\sin n\theta = \frac{\sin n\theta/2}{\sin \theta/2}\left\{\sin \frac{(n+1)\theta}{2} - \sin \frac{(n-1)\theta}{2}\right\}.$$

22. Discuss the convergence of

a. $\sum_{n=2}^{\infty} \frac{\sin n\theta}{\ln n}$. (See Exercise 21.)

b. $$\frac{1}{2\cdot 1} + \frac{2}{3\cdot 3} - \frac{3}{4\cdot 2} + \frac{4}{5\cdot 5} + \frac{5}{6\cdot 7} - \frac{6}{7\cdot 4} + \cdots + \frac{3n-2}{(3n-1)(4n-3)} + \frac{3n-1}{(3n)(4n-1)} - \frac{3n}{(3n+1)(2n)} + \cdots.$$

(Use Exercise 18 above and Exercise II-8, Section 4.)

23. For what values of a and b does the series

$$\frac{1}{1^a} - \frac{1}{2^b} + \frac{1}{3^a} - \frac{1}{4^b} + \cdots + \frac{1}{(2n-1)^a} - \frac{1}{(2n)^b} + \cdots$$

converge? Why doesn't the ratio test apply here?

24. If $\sum_{r=1}^{\infty} a_r$ converges, and $S_n = a_1 + a_2 + \cdots + a_n$, show that

$$\operatorname*{limit}_{n\to\infty} \frac{S_1 + S_2 + \cdots + S_n}{n} = \sum_{r=1}^{\infty} a_r.$$

25. Using the preceding exercise, find

$$\operatorname*{limit}_{n\to\infty} \frac{\dfrac{1}{2} + \dfrac{2}{3} + \dfrac{3}{4} + \cdots + \dfrac{n}{n+1}}{n}.$$

16

PLANE CURVES, VECTORS, AND POLAR COORDINATES

HERETOFORE WE have considered only real functions, i.e., functions having domains and ranges in the set of real numbers. In this chapter we shall study functions, called curves, that map intervals into sets of points in a coordinate plane. This will allow us to study the motion of particles along much more complicated paths than graphs of functions, such as that shown in Figure 16.1, where a particle might move along the path from time $t = a$ to time $t = b$.

We shall also introduce a two-dimensional vector space and discuss tangent vectors to curves. The useful polar coordinate system in the plane will be described and equations of the conic sections in polar coordinates will be developed. Finally, arc length of a curve and area of a surface of revolution will be discussed.

1 PLANE CURVES

For convenience we shall henceforth designate the set of all real numbers by

$$\mathsf{R}$$

and the set of all points in a rectangular coordinate plane by

$$\mathsf{R}^2.$$

Thus R^2 is the cartesian product $\mathsf{R} \times \mathsf{R} = \{(a,b) \mid a,b \text{ in } \mathsf{R}\}$.

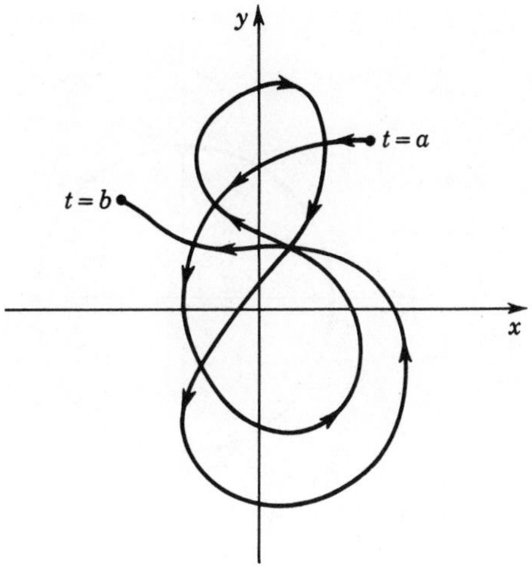

FIGURE 16.1

A mapping λ (lambda) having a subset I of R as its domain and a subset of R^2 as its range is called a *plane curve*, or simply a *curve*. Space curves will be discussed in Chapter 17. The range of a curve λ is called the *trace* of λ.

EXAMPLE 1. Discuss the plane curve λ defined by

$$\lambda(t) = (\cos t, \sin t)$$

when (1) domain $\lambda = [0,\pi]$; (2) domain $\lambda = [-\pi,\pi]$; (3) domain $\lambda = [-2\pi,2\pi]$.

Solution: Since

$$\cos^2 t + \sin^2 t = 1$$

for every number t, evidently the trace of λ lies on the unit circle of Figure 16.2. In case (1), as t varies from 0 to π, clearly $\cos t$ varies from 1 to -1 and $\sin t$ varies from 0 to 1 and back again to 0. Thus the point $\lambda(t)$ moves from A to B on the circle in a counterclockwise direction. In case (2) the point $\lambda(t)$ starts at B when $t = \pi$, moves to A when $t = 0$, and then moves back to B when $t = \pi$. That is, $\lambda(t)$ makes one complete revolution of the circle in a counterclockwise direction starting from B. It is easily seen that in case (3) the point $\lambda(t)$ starts at A when $t = -2\pi$ and makes two complete revolutions of the circle in a counterclockwise direction, ending up at point A when $t = 2\pi$. It is worthwhile noting that the trace of λ is the same in (2) and (3), namely the circle, although the curves clearly are different.

Each curve λ with domain I has the form

$$\lambda(t) = (f(t),g(t)), \qquad (t \text{ in } I),$$

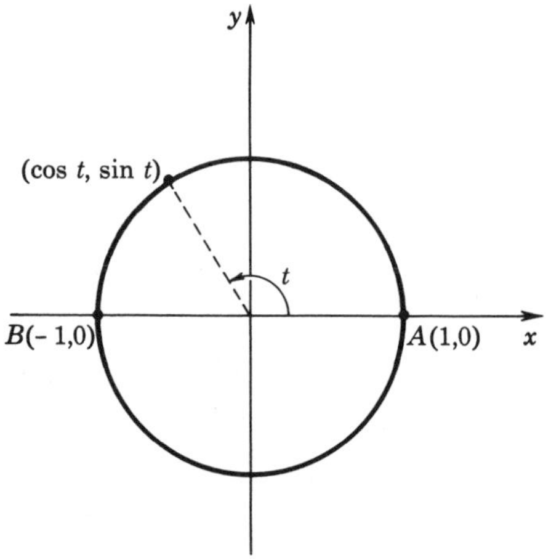

FIGURE 16.2

for some real-valued functions f and g. Thus in Example 1 we have $f(t) = \cos t$ and $g(t) = \sin t$. That is, each point (x,y) of the range of λ is given by

16.1 $$x = f(t), \qquad y = g(t)$$

for some t in I. These equations are usually called *parametric equations* of curve λ and t is called the *parameter.*

EXAMPLE 2. Discuss the curve with parametric equations

$$x = \sin t, \qquad y = \cos^2 t$$

and domain $[0,2\pi]$.

Solution: In our previous notation the curve λ is defined by

$$\lambda(t) = (\sin t, \cos^2 t), \qquad \text{domain } \lambda = [0,2\pi].$$

Since $\sin^2 t + \cos^2 t = 1$, it is evident that the trace of λ lies on the parabola

(1) $$x^2 + y = 1.$$

While the trace of λ is part of the parabola (1), it is not true that the trace of λ is the complete parabola (1). Thus, since $x = \sin t$ and $y = \cos^2 t$, necessarily $-1 \leq x \leq 1$ and $0 \leq y \leq 1$ for every point (x,y) in the trace of λ. Hence the trace of λ consists of at most the part of the parabola (1) on and above the x axis (Figure 16.3).

That the trace of λ is precisely this part of the parabola is seen as follows. Since the sine is continuous in $[0,2\pi]$, for each number x between 1 ($= \sin \pi/2$) and -1 ($= \sin 3\pi/2$) there exists a number t in $[\pi/2,3\pi/2]$ such that $\sin t = x$. Hence the point $(x, 1 - x^2)$ is in the trace of λ for each x in $[-1,1]$.

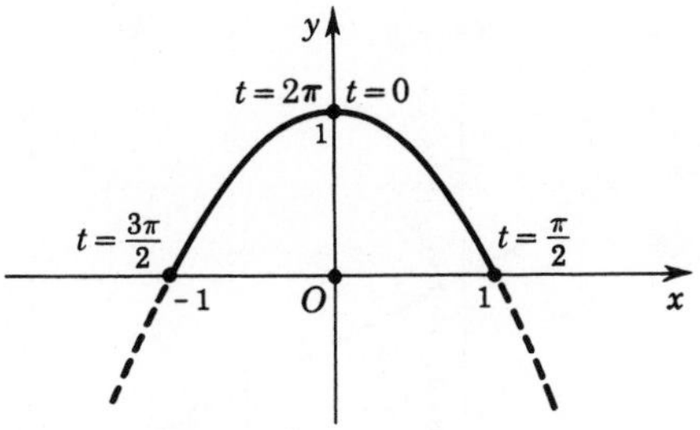

FIGURE 16.3

The point $\lambda(t)$ is at (0,1) when $t = 0$, moves to (1,0) when $t = \pi/2$, moves back to (0,1) when $t = \pi$, moves to $(-1,0)$ when $t = 3\pi/2$, and finally moves back to (0,1) when $t = 2\pi$.

EXAMPLE 3. Describe the curve λ defined by

$$\lambda(t) = (1 + 4t, 3 - 2t), \qquad \text{domain } \lambda = \mathsf{R}.$$

Solution: The curve λ has parametric equations

$$x = 1 + 4t, \qquad y = 3 - 2t.$$

If we solve the first equation for t, obtaining

(1) $$t = \tfrac{1}{4}(x - 1),$$

and substitute this value of t in the second equation, we get the equation

(2) $$y - 3 = -\tfrac{1}{2}(x - 1).$$

Hence the trace of λ is on the line L with equation (2). Since every point (x,y) on L has the form $\lambda(t)$ if we choose t as in (1), it is clear that the trace of λ is the whole line L sketched in Figure 16.4. Furthermore, the line L is traced out only once by λ. As t varies from negative numbers, through 0, and on to positive numbers, the point $\lambda(t)$ moves from left to right on L, being at the point (1,3) when $t = 0$. For example, $\lambda(t)$ is on the y axis when $t = -\frac{1}{4}$ and on the x axis when $t = \frac{3}{2}$.

As the three examples above show, a curve λ has *direction* determined by the order in I, the domain of λ. If I is a closed interval $[a,b]$, then $\lambda(a)$ is called the *initial point* and $\lambda(b)$ the *terminal point* of λ. We think of point $\lambda(t_1)$ preceding point $\lambda(t_2)$ if and only if $t_1 < t_2$. If curve λ has domain $[a,b]$ and $\lambda(a) = \lambda(b)$, then λ is called a *closed curve*. Example 1, cases (2) and (3), and Example 2 are closed curves. A curve λ with domain I is said to be a *one-to-one curve* (or a 1–1 *curve*) if $\lambda(t_1) \neq \lambda(t_2)$ whenever $t_1 \neq t_2$ in I. Finally, a closed curve λ with domain $[a,b]$ is called a *simple closed curve* if $\lambda(t_1) \neq \lambda(t_2)$ whenever $t_1 \neq t_2$, where t_1 is in (a,b) and t_2 in $[a,b]$. Thus the trace of λ is covered only once as t varies from a to

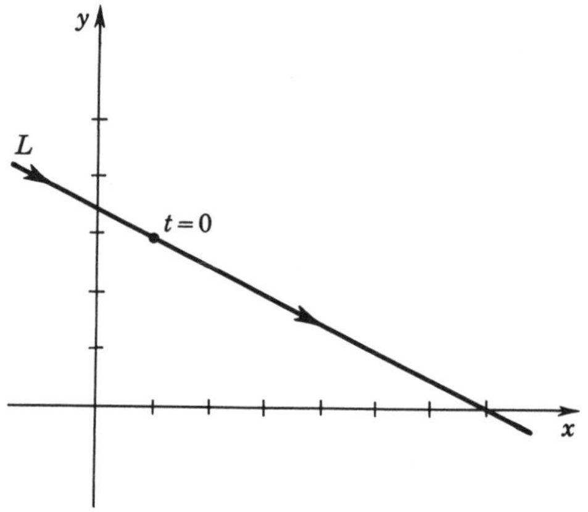

FIGURE 16.4

b if λ is a simple closed curve, except that $\lambda(a) = \lambda(b)$. Example 1, case (2), is a simple closed curve, whereas Example 3 is a 1–1 curve.

EXAMPLE 4. As a circle rolls along a straight line in a plane, the curve described by a fixed point P on the circle is called a *cycloid.* Find parametric equations for the cycloid.

Solution: We shall assume that the circle has radius r, that it rolls along the x axis and above it, and that the origin is so chosen on the x axis that the point P makes contact with the x axis at the origin. Let us choose as parameter the angle t (in radians) of rotation of the circle from the position when P is at the origin (Figure 16.5).

When the circle has revolved through an angle of t radians, it will have rolled a distance $\overline{OA} = rt$ from the origin. Hence the center of the circle will be the point $C(rt,r)$. If we translate axes to the new origin C, then the coordinates of P relative to the new axes will be

(1) $$x' = x - rt, \qquad y' = y - r.$$

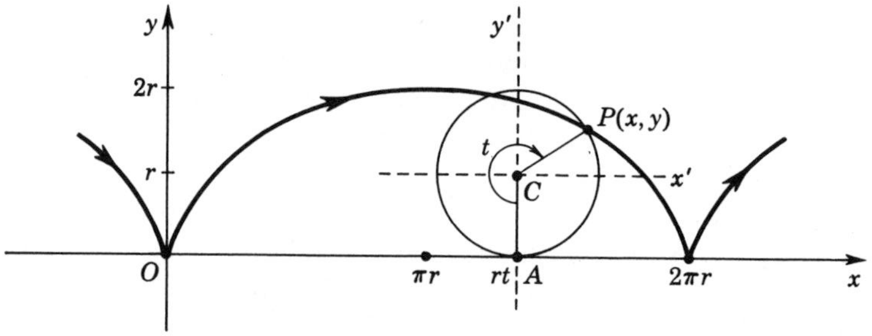

FIGURE 16.5

A close-up view of the new coordinate axes, given in Figure 16.6, shows us that

$$x' = r\cos\left(\frac{3\pi}{2} - t\right) = -r\sin t,$$

(2)

$$y' = r\sin\left(\frac{3\pi}{2} - t\right) = -r\cos t.$$

Finally, on combining (1) and (2), we get

$$x = r(t - \sin t), \qquad y = r(1 - \cos t)$$

as parametric equations of the cycloid.

If we think of the cycloid as a curve λ, then

$$\lambda(t) = (r(t - \sin t), r(1 - \cos t)), \qquad \text{domain } \lambda = \mathsf{R}.$$

The curve is directed from left to right in Figure 16.5.

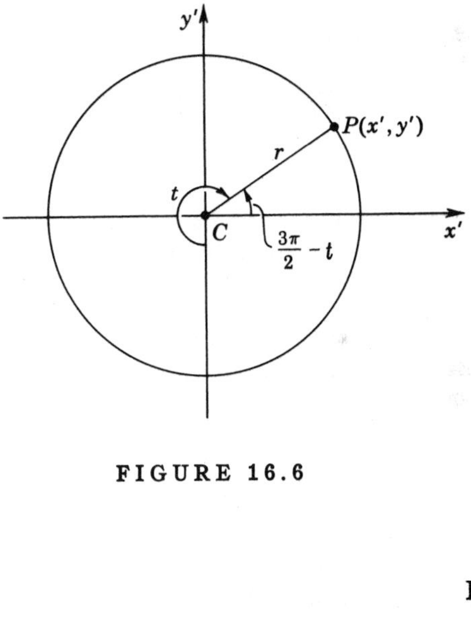

FIGURE 16.6

EXERCISES

I

In each of Exercises 1–10, discuss the curve λ, describe its direction, and sketch its trace.

1. $\lambda(t) = (3t, 2 - t)$, domain $\lambda = \mathsf{R}$.
2. $\lambda(t) = (t^2, t + 1)$, domain $\lambda = \mathsf{R}$.

3. $\lambda(t) = (\sin 2t, 2\sin^2 t)$, domain $\lambda = [0,\pi]$.

4. $\lambda(t) = (\sin 2t, 2\sin^2 t)$, domain $\lambda = [0,2\pi]$.

5. $\lambda(t) = (2\sin t, 3\cos t)$, domain $\lambda = [0,\pi]$.

6. $\lambda(t) = (2\sin t, 3\cos t)$, domain $\lambda = [0,2\pi]$.

7. $\lambda(t) = (2\cos t, 3\sin t)$, domain $\lambda = [0,2\pi]$.

8. $\lambda(t) = (\sinh t, \cosh t)$, domain $\lambda = \mathsf{R}$.

9. $\lambda(t) = (h + a\cosh t, k + b\sinh t)$, domain $\lambda = \mathsf{R}$.

10. $\lambda(t) = (1 + \cos t, 1 - \sin t)$, domain $\lambda = [-\pi,\pi]$.

In each of Exercises 11–18 discuss the curve with the given parametric equations. The domain of each curve is taken to be the set of all real numbers for which the equations are defined.

11. $x = t^3, \quad y = t^2$.

12. $x = \tan s, \quad y = \sec s$.

13. $x = \tan^2 r, \quad y = \sec r$.

14. $x = 3e^t, \quad y = 1 - e^t$.

15. $x = 5\cos s, \quad y = 3\sin s$.

16. $x = 2 + \cos t, \quad y = -1 + \sin t$.

17. $x = a\sec t, \quad y = b\tan t$.

18. $x = 1 + \dfrac{1}{t}, \quad y = t - \dfrac{1}{t}$.

19. Show that the trace of each of the following curves is part or all of the parabola $y = x^2$. Describe the trace in each case.
   a. $\lambda(t) = (t,t^2)$, domain $\lambda = \mathsf{R}$.
   b. $\lambda(t) = (t^2,t^4)$, domain $\lambda = \mathsf{R}$.
   c. $\lambda(t) = (|t|,t^2)$, domain $\lambda = (-\infty,0]$.
   d. $\lambda(t) = (e^t,e^{2t})$, domain $\lambda = [0,\infty)$.
   e. $\lambda(t) = (1 - 1/t^2, 1 - 2/t^2 + 1/t^4)$, domain $\lambda = (-\infty,0) \cup (0,\infty)$.
   f. $\lambda(t) = (\sec t, 1 + \tan^2 t)$, domain $\lambda = \left[0,\dfrac{\pi}{2}\right) \cup \left(\dfrac{\pi}{2},\pi\right]$.

20. Show that $x = x_1 + (x_2 - x_1)t$, $y = y_1 + (y_2 - y_1)t$ are parametric equations of the line passing through the distinct points (x_1,y_1) and (x_2,y_2).

21. Find parametric equations of the circle with center (h,k) and radius r.

22. Show that the curve λ defined by $\lambda(t) = (h + a\cos t, k + b\sin t)$, domain $\lambda = [0,2\pi]$, is an ellipse.

23. Show that the curve λ defined by $\lambda(t) = (h + a\sec t, k + b\tan t)$, domain $\lambda = \left[0,\dfrac{\pi}{2}\right) \cup \left(\dfrac{\pi}{2},\dfrac{3\pi}{2}\right) \cup \left(\dfrac{3\pi}{2},2\pi\right]$, is a hyperbola.

24. A bicycle is proceeding along a straight road at a constant speed of v ft/sec. If each wheel has a radius of r ft, find parametric equations of the motion of a point P on a tire in terms of time t.

II

1. Find parametric equations for the part of the parabola $x^2 + y = 1$ not included in the trace of curve λ in Example 2, page 000.

2. Show how to construct, with straightedge and compass, any number of points on the ellipse $x^2/a^2 + y^2/b^2 = 1$. [*Hint:* Use Exercise I-22.]

3. If a circle of radius r rolls on the inside of a circle of radius R, show that the curve described by a fixed point on the rolling circle has parametric equations

$$x = (R - r)\cos t + r\cos\frac{R - r}{r}t, \qquad y = (R - r)\sin t - r\sin\frac{R - r}{r}t$$

if the coordinate system is properly chosen.

4. Find parametric equations of the curve in Exercise 3 if the circle of radius r rolls on the outside of the other circle.

5. Sketch the trace of the curve of Exercise 3 for $R = 2r$.

6. Sketch the trace of the curve of Exercise 3 for $R = 4r$. Find an equation of the curve in nonparametric form (i.e., in the form $F(x,y) = 0$).

7. If r and R are rational numbers, are the curves of Exercises 3 and 4 closed? If one of r and R is rational and the other is irrational, are these curves closed? Prove your answers.

2 CONTINUITY OF A CURVE

If P and Q are points in R^2, then let us designate the *distance* between P and Q by $d(P,Q)$. We know that if $P = (x_1,y_1)$ and $Q = (x_2,y_2)$ then

$$d(P,Q) = \sqrt{(x_2 - x_1)^2 + (y_2 - y_1)^2}.$$

For each positive number r and each point A in R^2, let us define the *open disc* with center A and radius r to be

$$B(A,r) = \{P \text{ in } \mathsf{R}^2 \mid d(A,P) < r\},$$

and the *closed disc* with center A and radius r to be

$$B[A,r] = \{P \text{ in } \mathsf{R}^2 \mid d(A,P) \le r\}.$$

A subset S of $\mathbb{R}^2$ is called *open* if for each point A in S there exists a positive number r such that the open disc $B(A,r)$ is contained in S. Naturally, $\mathbb{R}^2$ is itself an open set. Another example of an open set in $\mathbb{R}^2$ is

$$H = \{(x,y) \mid x > 0\},$$

the open half-plane to the right of the y axis.

16.2 **DEFINITION.** If λ is a curve with domain I, then λ is said to be *continuous at* c in I if for each open disc $B(\lambda(c),\epsilon)$ there exists a neighborhood N of c such that $\lambda(t)$ is in $B(\lambda(c),\epsilon)$ for every t in $N \cap I$.

As usual, we call a curve λ *continuous* if λ is continuous at each number in its domain. The following result gives us an easy test for continuity of curves.

16.3 **THEOREM.** If λ is a curve given by

$$\lambda(t) = (f(t),g(t)), \qquad \text{domain } \lambda = I,$$

then λ is continuous at c in I if and only if functions f and g are continuous at c.

Proof: Assume that λ is continuous at c. Then for every number $\epsilon > 0$ there exists a neighborhood N of c such that $\lambda(t)$ is in $B(\lambda(c),\epsilon)$ for every t in $N \cap I$. Hence $|f(t) - f(c)| < \epsilon$ for every t in $N \cap I$ (see Figure 16.7). Thus f is continuous at c. A similar argument proves that g is continuous at c.

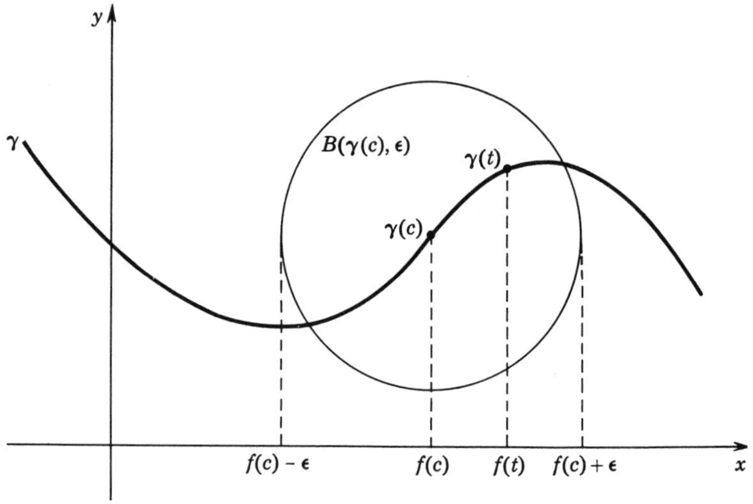

FIGURE 16.7

Conversely, assume that f and g are continuous at c. Then for each number $\epsilon > 0$ there exists a neighborhood N of c such that

$$|f(t) - f(c)| < \frac{\epsilon}{\sqrt{2}} \quad \text{and} \quad |g(t) - g(c)| < \frac{\epsilon}{\sqrt{2}} \quad \text{for every } t \text{ in } N \cap I.$$

Hence

$$[f(t) - f(c)]^2 + [g(t) - g(c)]^2 < \frac{\epsilon^2}{2} + \frac{\epsilon^2}{2} = \epsilon^2$$

for every t in $N \cap I$; i.e.,

$$\lambda(t) \text{ is in } B(\lambda(c),\epsilon) \quad \text{for every } t \text{ in } N \cap I.$$

This proves that λ is continuous at c and completes the proof of **16.3**.

According to **16.3**, each of the curves of Examples 1–4 of Section 1 is continuous, since the functions f and g are continuous in every case.

Given a curve λ and a number c, we can define

$$\operatorname*{limit}_{t \to c} \lambda(t)$$

in an obvious way. That is,

$$\operatorname*{limit}_{t \to c} \lambda(t) = P$$

if λ is continuous at c when we define (or redefine) $\lambda(c) = P$. In view of **16.3**, we have that if

$$\lambda(t) = (f(t),g(t))$$

then

$$\operatorname*{limit}_{t \to c} \lambda(t) = (\operatorname*{limit}_{t \to c} f(t), \operatorname*{limit}_{t \to c} g(t)),$$

provided the latter two limits exist.

3 TWO-DIMENSIONAL VECTOR ALGEBRA

Geometrically speaking, a vector is a directed line segment. Thus a vector has an *initial point* A and a *terminal point* B. Such a vector is denoted by

$$\overrightarrow{AB}.$$

Two vectors $\overrightarrow{AB}$ and $\overrightarrow{CD}$ are considered to be equal, $\overrightarrow{AB} = \overrightarrow{CD}$, if and only if they have equal segments (i.e., $AB = CD$) and the same direction. Otherwise stated, $\overrightarrow{AB} = \overrightarrow{CD}$ if and only if either $A = B$ and $C = D$ or the quadrilateral $ABCD$ is a parallelogram (Figure 16.8).

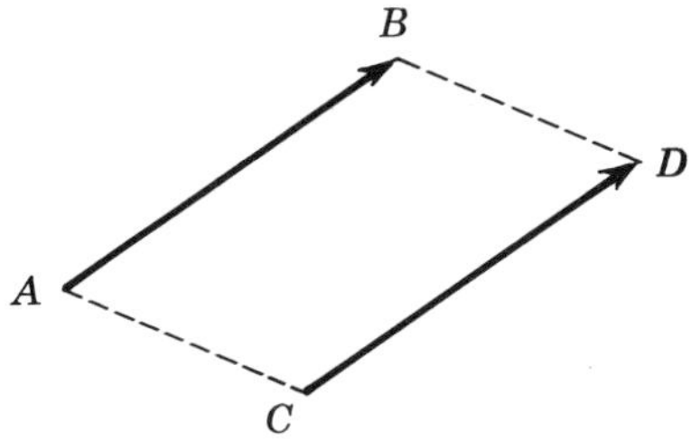

FIGURE 16.8

In this section, all vectors are assumed to lie in a rectangular coordinate plane. Hence, each vector $\overrightarrow{AB}$ has a *length* denoted by $|\overrightarrow{AB}|$ and defined to be the distance between A and B,

$$|\overrightarrow{AB}| = d(A,B).$$

If points A, B, C, and D have respective coordinates (a_1,a_2), (b_1,b_2), (c_1,c_2), and (d_1,d_2), then the equality of vectors $\overrightarrow{AB}$ and $\overrightarrow{CD}$ can be described in terms of coordinates as follows:

$$\overrightarrow{AB} = \overrightarrow{CD} \text{ if and only if } b_1 - a_1 = d_1 - c_1 \text{ and } b_2 - a_2 = d_2 - c_2.$$

That is, in Figure 16.9, $\overrightarrow{AB} = \overrightarrow{CD}$ if and only if $\overline{AE} = \overline{CF}$ and $\overline{EB} = \overline{FD}$.

If $A = (a_1,a_2)$ and $B = (b_1,b_2)$, then the numbers $b_1 - a_1$ and $b_2 - a_2$ are called the *components* of vector $\overrightarrow{AB}$; $b_1 - a_1$ is the *x component* and $b_2 - a_2$ the

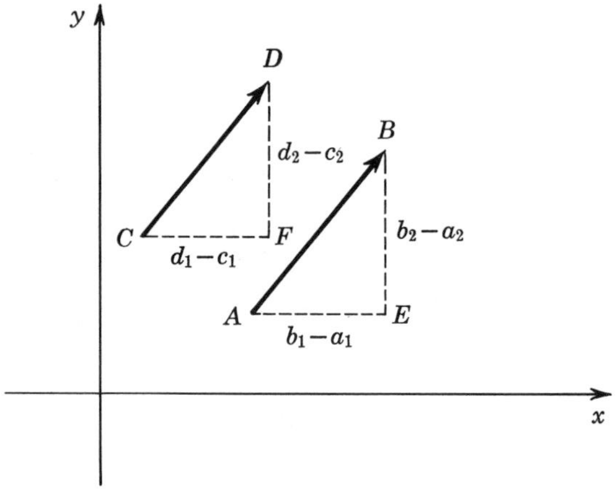

FIGURE 16.9

y component. According to the preceding paragraph, vectors $\overrightarrow{AB}$ and $\overrightarrow{CD}$ are equal if and only if they have the same components. The notation

$$\langle h_1,h_2\rangle$$

will be used for the components of a vector; h_1 being the x component and h_2 the y component.

We shall often use a single letter to designate a vector. When we do, the letter will be printed in boldface, as for example **u**, **v**, and **w**. Since it is difficult to write boldface letters, the reader may wish to use an arrow above a letter, such as $\vec{u}$ or $\vec{v}$, to indicate it denotes a vector. If **u** and **v** denote the vectors of Figure 16.10, for example, then **u** = **v** since they have the same components $\langle 2, -3\rangle$.

Just as we identify a point A with its coordinates (a_1,a_2), so shall we identify a vector **u** with its components $\langle h_1,h_2\rangle$. Corresponding to the notation R^2 for the set of all points in a rectangular coordinate plane, we introduce the notation

$$V_2 = \{\langle h_1,h_2\rangle \mid h_1,h_2 \text{ in } \mathsf{R}\}$$

for the set of all vectors in the plane. Starting with a vector $\mathbf{v} = \langle h_1,h_2\rangle$ and a point $A = (a_1,a_2)$, there is a unique point B such that $\mathbf{v} = \overrightarrow{AB}$, namely $B = (a_1 + b_1,a_2 + b_2)$. Clearly the *length* of **v** is $d(A,B)$, that is,

$$|\langle h_1,h_2\rangle| = \sqrt{h_1^2 + b_2^2}.$$

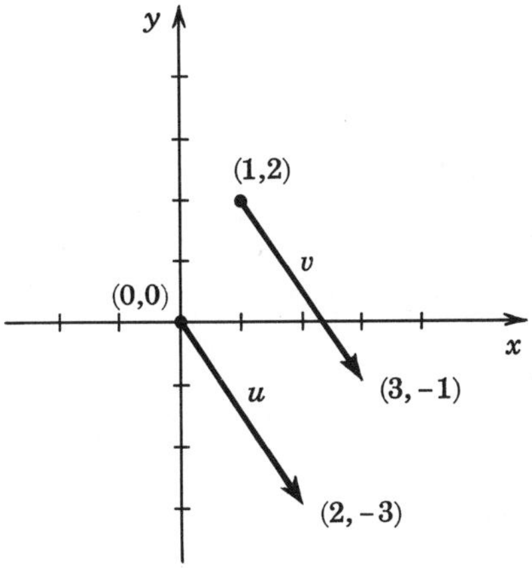

FIGURE 16.10

Operations of addition and subtraction can be defined for vectors in V_2 in a natural way. Thus, we define

$$\langle h_1,h_2\rangle + \langle k_1,k_2\rangle = \langle h_1 + k_1,h_2 + k_2\rangle,$$
$$\langle h_1,h_2\rangle - \langle k_1,k_2\rangle = \langle h_1 - k_1,h_2 - k_2\rangle.$$

Geometrically, vector addition is the familiar triangular addition shown in Figure 16.11. Thus, if $\mathbf{u} = \langle h_1,h_2\rangle$, $\mathbf{v} = \langle k_1,k_2\rangle$, and $A = (a_1,a_2)$, then $\mathbf{u} = \overrightarrow{AB}$ where $B = (a_1 + h_1,a_2 + h_2)$ and $\mathbf{v} = \overrightarrow{BC}$ where $C = ((a_1 + h_1) + k_1, (a_2 + h_2) + k_2)$. On the other hand, $\mathbf{u} + \mathbf{v} = \langle h_1 + k_1, h_2 + k_2\rangle$ and hence $\mathbf{u} + \mathbf{v} = \overrightarrow{AC}$.

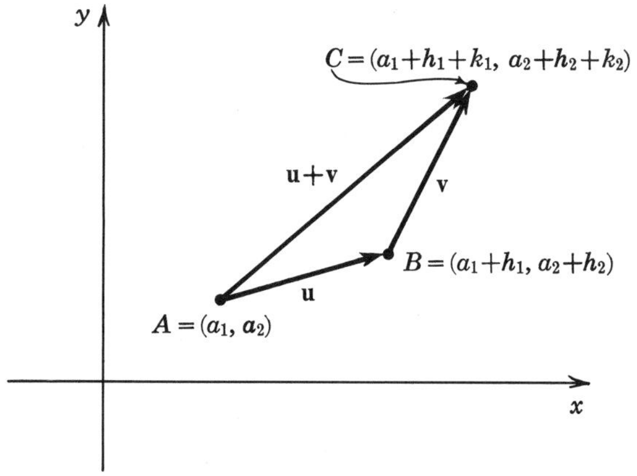

FIGURE 16.11

The usual rules for addition of numbers hold for the addition of vectors. Thus, for all vectors $\mathbf{u}, \mathbf{v}, \mathbf{w}$ in V_2,

$$\mathbf{u} + \mathbf{v} = \mathbf{v} + \mathbf{u} \qquad \text{(commutative law)},$$
$$\mathbf{u} + (\mathbf{v} + \mathbf{w}) = (\mathbf{u} + \mathbf{v}) + \mathbf{w} \qquad \text{(associative law)}.$$

The vector $\langle 0,0\rangle$ is called the *zero vector* and is designated by $\mathbf{0}$,

$$\mathbf{0} = \langle 0,0\rangle.$$

Geometrically, $\mathbf{0} = \overrightarrow{AA}$ for any point A. Clearly

$$\mathbf{v} + \mathbf{0} = \mathbf{v}$$

for every vector $\mathbf{v}$. Each vector $\mathbf{v} = \langle k_1,k_2\rangle$ has a *negative* $-\mathbf{v} = \langle -k_1, -k_2\rangle$ such that

$$\mathbf{v} + (-\mathbf{v}) = \mathbf{0}.$$

We see that

$$\mathbf{u} + (-\mathbf{v}) = \mathbf{u} - \mathbf{v}$$

for all vectors **u** and **v**.

The rules stated above for addition of vectors may be proved from corresponding rules for addition of numbers. For example, if $\mathbf{u} = \langle h_1,h_2\rangle$ and $\mathbf{v} = \langle k_1,k_2\rangle$, then

$$\mathbf{u} + \mathbf{v} = \langle h_1 + k_1, h_2 + k_2\rangle = \langle k_1 + h_1, k_2 + h_2\rangle = \mathbf{v} + \mathbf{u}$$

since $h_1 + k_1 = k_1 + h_1$ and $h_2 + k_2 = k_2 + h_2$ by the commutative law for the real number system. This proves the commutative law for vector addition.

Another useful operation with vectors is that of *scalar multiplication.* For each vector $\mathbf{v} = \langle h,k\rangle$ and each number c (called a *scalar*), the scalar multiple of $\mathbf{v}$ by c is the vector $c\mathbf{v}$ defined as follows:

$$c\langle h,k\rangle = \langle ch,ck\rangle.$$

For example,

$$3\langle 2,-1\rangle = \langle 6,-3\rangle, \qquad (-2)\langle -5,4\rangle = \langle 10,-8\rangle.$$

Geometrically, the vector $c\mathbf{v}$ has the same direction as $\mathbf{v}$ if $c > 0$, and the opposite direction if $c < 0$. The length of $c\mathbf{v}$ is simply the absolute value of c times the length of $\mathbf{v}$,

$$|c\mathbf{v}| = |c||\mathbf{v}|.$$

The following rules hold for scalar multiplication. For all vectors **u** and **v** and scalars c and d,

$$c(\mathbf{u} + \mathbf{v}) = c\mathbf{u} + c\mathbf{v}, \qquad (c + d)\mathbf{v} = c\mathbf{v} + d\mathbf{v},$$

$$(cd)\mathbf{v} = c(d\mathbf{v}), \qquad (-c)\mathbf{v} = -(c\mathbf{v}),$$

$$1\mathbf{v} = \mathbf{v}, \qquad 0\mathbf{v} = \mathbf{0}, \qquad c\mathbf{0} = \mathbf{0}.$$

Proof of $c(\mathbf{u} + \mathbf{v}) = c\mathbf{u} + c\mathbf{v}$: We have

$$\begin{aligned} c(\langle h_1,h_2\rangle + \langle k_1,k_2\rangle) &= c\langle h_1 + k_1, h_2 + k_2\rangle \\ &= \langle c(h_1 + k_1), c(h_2 + k_2)\rangle \\ &= \langle ch_1 + ck_1, ch_2 + ck_2\rangle \\ &= \langle ch_1,ch_2\rangle + \langle ck_1,ck_2\rangle \\ &= c\langle h_1,h_2\rangle + c\langle k_1,k_2\rangle. \end{aligned}$$

The proofs of the other laws are left to the reader.

The *inner product* of two vectors $\mathbf{u}$ and $\mathbf{v}$ is a number denoted by $\mathbf{u}\cdot\mathbf{v}$ and defined as follows. If $\mathbf{u} = \langle h_1,h_2\rangle$ and $\mathbf{v} = \langle k_1,k_2\rangle$, then

$$\mathbf{u}\cdot\mathbf{v} = \langle h_1,h_2\rangle\cdot\langle k_1,k_2\rangle = h_1k_1 + h_2k_2.$$

We emphasize that the inner product of two vectors is a number and not a vector.

For example,

$$\langle 2,-2\rangle\cdot\langle 4,3\rangle = 2\cdot 4 + (-2)\cdot 3 = 2,$$
$$\langle 3,-7\rangle\cdot\langle 7,3\rangle = 3\cdot 7 + (-7)\cdot 3 = 0.$$

The geometric meaning of the inner product is as follows. If $\mathbf{u}$ or $\mathbf{v}$ is $\mathbf{0}$, then $\mathbf{u}\cdot\mathbf{v} = 0$. Otherwise, if $\mathbf{u} = \langle h_1,h_2\rangle \neq \mathbf{0}$ and $\mathbf{v} = \langle k_1,k_2\rangle \neq \mathbf{0}$, then take $\mathbf{u}$ and $\mathbf{v}$ to have the same initial point and let θ be the least angle between $\mathbf{u}$ and $\mathbf{v}$ (Figure 16.12). By the law of cosines (p. 000),

$$|BC|^2 = |\mathbf{u}|^2 + |\mathbf{v}|^2 - 2|\mathbf{u}||\mathbf{v}|\cos\theta.$$

Hence

$$(k_1 - h_1)^2 + (k_2 - h_2)^2 = (h_1^2 + h_2^2) + (k_1^2 + k_2^2) - 2|\mathbf{u}||\mathbf{v}|\cos\theta.$$

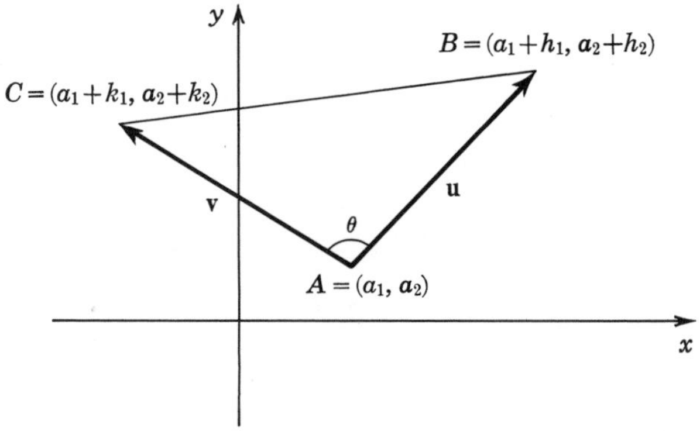

FIGURE 16.12

From this equation and the definition of $\mathbf{u}\cdot\mathbf{v} = h_1k_1 + h_2k_2$, we easily obtain

16.4 $$\mathbf{u}\cdot\mathbf{v} = |\mathbf{u}||\mathbf{v}|\cos\theta.$$

We can use **16.4** to find the angle between two nonzero vectors. For example, if $\mathbf{u} = \langle 1,-1\rangle$ and $\mathbf{v} = \langle 7,1\rangle$, then by **16.4**

$$1\cdot 7 + (-1)\cdot 1 = \sqrt{1^2 + (-1)^2}\,\sqrt{7^2 + 1^2}\cos\theta,$$

where θ is the least angle between $\mathbf{u}$ and $\mathbf{v}$. On solving this equation for $\cos\theta$, we obtain

$$\cos\theta = .6 \qquad \text{and hence } \theta \doteq .53°.$$

Since $0 \le \theta \le \pi$, $\cos\theta = 0$ if and only if $\theta = \pi/2$. This proves the following theorem.

16.5 **THEOREM.** The nonzero vectors $\mathbf{u}$ and $\mathbf{v}$ are perpendicular if and only if $\mathbf{u}\cdot\mathbf{v} = 0$.

Some of the useful properties of the inner product are listed below. For all vectors $\mathbf{u}$, $\mathbf{v}$, and $\mathbf{w}$ and each scalar c,

$$\mathbf{u}\cdot\mathbf{v} = \mathbf{v}\cdot\mathbf{u}, \qquad (\mathbf{u}+\mathbf{v})\cdot\mathbf{w} = \mathbf{u}\cdot\mathbf{w} + \mathbf{v}\cdot\mathbf{w},$$
$$(c\mathbf{u})\cdot\mathbf{v} = \mathbf{u}\cdot(c\mathbf{v}) = c(\mathbf{u}\cdot\mathbf{v}),$$
$$\mathbf{0}\cdot\mathbf{v} = 0, \qquad \mathbf{v}\cdot\mathbf{v} > 0 \;\text{ if }\; \mathbf{v} \ne \mathbf{0}.$$

Proof of $(\mathbf{u}+\mathbf{v})\cdot\mathbf{w} = \mathbf{u}\cdot\mathbf{w} + \mathbf{v}\cdot\mathbf{w}$: If $\mathbf{u} = \langle h_1,h_2\rangle$, $\mathbf{v} = \langle k_1,k_2\rangle$, $\mathbf{w} = \langle l_1,l_2\rangle$, then

$$\begin{aligned}(\mathbf{u}+\mathbf{v})\cdot\mathbf{w} &= \langle h_1 + k_1, h_2 + k_2\rangle\cdot\langle l_1,l_2\rangle\\ &= (h_1 + k_1)l_1 + (h_2 + k_2)l_2\\ &= (h_1l_1 + h_2l_2) + (k_1l_1 + k_2l_2)\\ &= \mathbf{u}\cdot\mathbf{w} + \mathbf{v}\cdot\mathbf{w}.\end{aligned}$$

The proofs of the other properties of the inner product are similar and hence are omitted.

Some other useful properties of the operations with vectors are:

$$|\mathbf{u}\cdot\mathbf{v}| \le |\mathbf{u}||\mathbf{v}| \qquad \text{(Cauchy's inequality)},$$
$$|\mathbf{u}+\mathbf{v}| \le |\mathbf{u}| + |\mathbf{v}| \qquad \text{(triangle inequality)}.$$

These follow geometrically from **16.4** ($|\cos\theta| \le |$) and the fact that the length of a side of a triangle is less than the sum of the lengths of the other two sides. Purely algebraic proofs are as follows.

Proof of Cauchy's inequality: If $\mathbf{u} = \mathbf{0}$, then $|\mathbf{u}\cdot\mathbf{v}| = |\mathbf{u}||\mathbf{v}| = 0$ and the inequality holds. If $\mathbf{u} \ne \mathbf{0}$, define the vector $\mathbf{w}$ as

$$\mathbf{w} = a\mathbf{v} - b\mathbf{u},$$

where $a = \mathbf{u}\cdot\mathbf{u}$ and $b = \mathbf{u}\cdot\mathbf{v}$. Then

$$\begin{aligned}\mathbf{w}\cdot\mathbf{w} &= (a\mathbf{v})\cdot(a\mathbf{v}) + (a\mathbf{v})\cdot(-b\mathbf{u}) + (-b\mathbf{u})\cdot(a\mathbf{v}) + (-b\mathbf{u})\cdot(-b\mathbf{u})\\ &= a^2(\mathbf{v}\cdot\mathbf{v}) - 2ab(\mathbf{u}\cdot\mathbf{v}) + b^2(\mathbf{u}\cdot\mathbf{u}) = a^2(\mathbf{v}\cdot\mathbf{v}) - ab^2\\ &= a[a(\mathbf{v}\cdot\mathbf{v}) - b^2].\end{aligned}$$

Since $a > 0$ and $\mathbf{w}\cdot\mathbf{w} \geq 0$, we have $a(\mathbf{v}\cdot\mathbf{v}) - b^2 \geq 0$, $a(\mathbf{v}\cdot\mathbf{v}) \geq b^2$, and $\sqrt{a}\,\sqrt{\mathbf{v}\cdot\mathbf{v}} \geq |b|$. Thus $|\mathbf{u}||\mathbf{v}| \geq |\mathbf{u}\cdot\mathbf{v}|$, as desired.

Proof of the triangle inequality: Using the Cauchy inequality, we have

$$\begin{aligned}|\mathbf{u} + \mathbf{v}|^2 &= (\mathbf{u} + \mathbf{v})\cdot(\mathbf{u} + \mathbf{v}) = \mathbf{u}\cdot\mathbf{u} + 2\mathbf{u}\cdot\mathbf{v} + \mathbf{v}\cdot\mathbf{v}\\ &\leq |\mathbf{u}|^2 + 2|\mathbf{u}||\mathbf{v}| + |\mathbf{v}|^2 = (|\mathbf{u}| + |\mathbf{v}|)^2.\end{aligned}$$

Hence $|\mathbf{u} + \mathbf{v}| \leq |\mathbf{u}| + |\mathbf{v}|$, as desired.

A vector of length 1 is called a *unit vector*. Special unit vectors are $\mathbf{i}$ and $\mathbf{j}$ defined by

$$\mathbf{i} = \langle 1,0\rangle, \qquad \mathbf{j} = \langle 0,1\rangle$$

Every vector $\mathbf{v} = \langle h_1,h_2\rangle$ is a *linear combination* of $\mathbf{i}$ and $\mathbf{j}$. Thus $\mathbf{v} = \langle h_1,0\rangle + \langle 0,h_2\rangle = h_1\langle 1,0\rangle + h_2\langle 0,1\rangle$, or

$$\langle h_1,h_2\rangle = h_1\mathbf{i} + h_2\mathbf{j}.$$

Geometrically, $\mathbf{v}$ is resolved into *horizontal* and *vertical components*. This is illustrated in Figure 16.13, where

$$\mathbf{v} = \overrightarrow{AB} = \langle -5,2\rangle = -5\mathbf{i} + 2\mathbf{j}.$$

Every nonzero vector $\mathbf{v}$ is a scalar multiple of a unit vector $\mathbf{u}$:

$$\text{If} \quad \mathbf{u} = \frac{1}{c}\,\mathbf{v}, \qquad \text{then} \quad \mathbf{v} = c\mathbf{u} \qquad \text{where} \quad c = |\mathbf{v}|.$$

As we have seen above, the elements of V_2 can be interpreted to be directed line segments in a plane. Another useful interpretation of a vector $\mathbf{v} = \langle h_1,h_2\rangle$ is

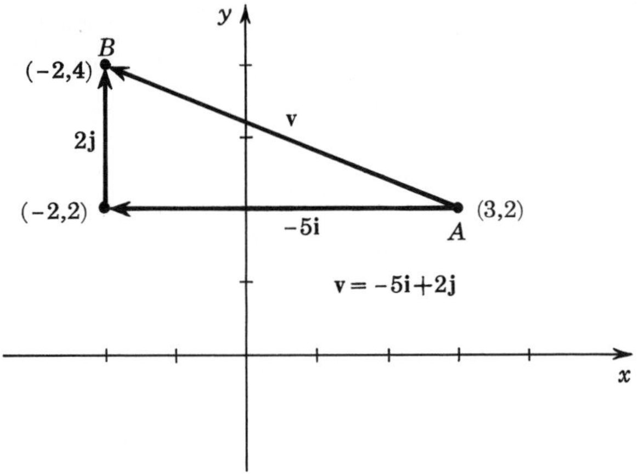

FIGURE 16.13

as a *translation* of R^2. Thus, each point $A = (a_1 \cdot a_2)$ of R^2 is translated into the point $B = (a_1 + h_1, a_2 + h_2)$ by **v**. For example, $\mathbf{v} = \langle 3,1 \rangle$ translates each point 3 units to the right and up 1 unit, as indicated in Figure 16.14.

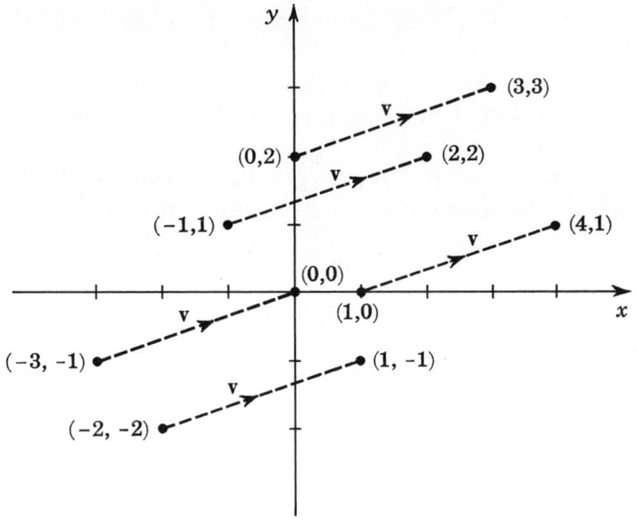

FIGURE 16.14

It is very easy to compute the action of a vector **v** when it is considered as a translation. Thus, we simply add the respective coordinates of point A and vector **v** to obtain the coordinates of the point B into which A is translated. For this reason, we use the notation

$$A + \mathbf{v} = B$$

to indicate that **v** carries point A into point B. In terms of coordinates,

$$(a_1,a_2) + \langle h_1,h_2 \rangle = (a_1 + h_1, a_2 + h_2).$$

For a given point P and a nonzero vector **v**, the set L of all translations of P by scalar multiples of **v** is a line:

$$L = \{P + t\mathbf{v} \mid t \text{ in } \mathsf{R}\}.$$

If $P = (a,b)$ and $\mathbf{v} = \langle h,k \rangle$, then $t\mathbf{v} = \langle th,tk \rangle$ and $P + t\mathbf{v} = (a + th, b + tk)$ so that

$$L = \{(a + th, b + tk) \mid t \text{ in } \mathsf{R}\}.$$

That is, L has *parametric equations*.

16.6 $$x = a + th,\ y = b + tk.$$

We can show that the graph of 16.6 is a line by eliminating t. Thus, if $h \neq 0$, we have $t = (x - a)/h$ and the graph of 16.6 is simply the graph of the equation

$$y - b = \frac{k}{h}(x - a).$$

We recognize the graph to be a line passing through the point (a,b) with slope k/h. If $h = 0$ then $k \neq 0$ and the graph of **16.6** is the vertical line with equation $x = a$.

The line $L = \{P + t\mathbf{v} \mid t \text{ in } \mathsf{R}\}$ has a natural direction assigned to it, namely the direction of the nonzero vector $\mathbf{v}$. We call

$$L_1 = \{P + t\mathbf{v} \mid t > 0\}$$

the *positive half* of L and

$$L_2 = \{P + t\mathbf{v} \mid t < 0\}$$

the *negative half* of L.

For example, $\{(0,0) + t\mathbf{i} \mid t > 0\}$ is the positive x axis and $\{(0,0) + t\mathbf{i} \mid t < 0\}$ is the negative x axis. Similarly, $\{(0,0) + t\mathbf{j} \mid t > 0\}$ is the positive y axis and $\{(0,0) + t\mathbf{j} \mid t < 0\}$ is the negative y axis.

As another example, if $P = (2,-1)$ and $\mathbf{v} = \langle 1,3 \rangle$, then

$$L = \{P + t\mathbf{v} \mid t \text{ in } \mathsf{R}\}$$

is the line shown in Figure 16.15. The positive half, L_1, and the negative half, L_2, of L are also indicated in the figure.

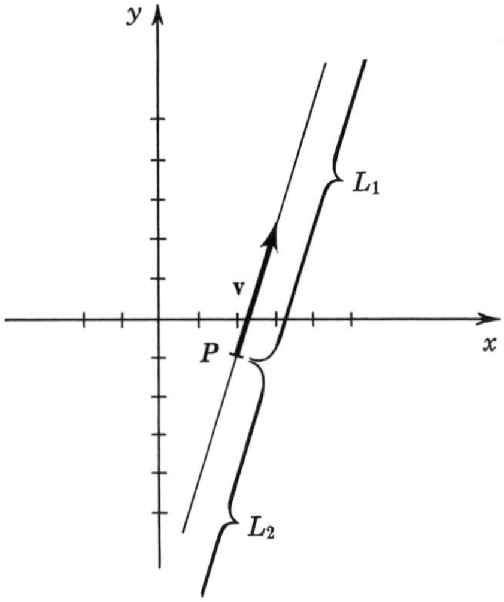

FIGURE 16.15

EXERCISES

I

1. If $\mathbf{u} = \langle 2,3 \rangle$, $\mathbf{v} = \langle 4,6 \rangle$, $\mathbf{w} = \langle -6,4 \rangle$, $\mathbf{z} = \langle 1,-1 \rangle$, determine the following:
   a. $2\mathbf{u} - \mathbf{v}$. b. $\mathbf{u} + \mathbf{v} + 2\mathbf{z}$. c. $\mathbf{u}^2 + \mathbf{v}^2 + \mathbf{w}^2 + \mathbf{z}^2$.
   (*Note:* by $\mathbf{u}^2$, we mean $\mathbf{u} \cdot \mathbf{u}$.)
   d. $\mathbf{u} \cdot \mathbf{w} + \mathbf{v} \cdot \mathbf{w}$. e. $(\mathbf{u} + \mathbf{v} - \mathbf{z}) \cdot (\mathbf{u} - \mathbf{v} + \mathbf{z})$.

2. Determine the angle between the two vectors $\mathbf{u}$ and $\mathbf{v}$ if
   a. $\mathbf{u} = \langle 3,4 \rangle$, $\mathbf{v} = \langle -4,3 \rangle$.
   b. $\mathbf{u} = \langle 1,1 \rangle$, $\mathbf{v} = \langle \sqrt{3},1 \rangle$.
   c. $\mathbf{u} = \langle 1,\sqrt{3} \rangle$, $\mathbf{v} = \langle 2,2 \rangle$.

3. Determine a unit vector perpendicular to $\mathbf{u}$ if
   a. $\mathbf{u} = \langle 3,4 \rangle$. b. $\mathbf{u} = \langle 4,3 \rangle$.
   c. $\mathbf{u} = \langle 2,2 \rangle$. d. $\mathbf{u} = \langle a \cos \theta, a \sin \theta \rangle$.
   e. $\mathbf{u} = \langle a,b \rangle$.

4. When does $|\mathbf{u} \cdot \mathbf{v}| = |\mathbf{u}|\,|\mathbf{v}|$?

5. Prove that $|\mathbf{u}_1| + |\mathbf{u}_2| + \cdots + |\mathbf{u}_n| \geq |\mathbf{u}_1 + \mathbf{u}_2 + \cdots + \mathbf{u}_n|$ and give a geometric interpretation.

6. If $\mathbf{u} \cdot \mathbf{v} = \mathbf{u} \cdot \mathbf{w}$ and $\mathbf{u} \neq \mathbf{0}$, must $\mathbf{v} = \mathbf{w}$?

7. Find parametric equations for the straight lines

$$L = \{P + t\mathbf{v} \mid t \text{ in } \mathsf{R}\}$$

   where
   a. $P = (2,3)$, $\mathbf{v} = \langle 3,4 \rangle$.
   b. $P = (1,2)$, $\mathbf{v} = \langle 1,0 \rangle$.
   c. $P = (0,3)$, $\mathbf{v} = \langle 2,-2 \rangle$.

8. Find the vector form of the equation of the straight line passing through:
   a. the two points (x_1,y_1) and (x_2,y_2).
   b. the point (x_1,y_1) with slope m.

9. Describe the set $\{P + t\mathbf{u} + t^2\mathbf{v} \mid t \text{ in } \mathsf{R}\}$ where $\mathbf{u},\mathbf{v}$ are in V_2 and P is in R^2.

10. Show that the vectors $\mathbf{u} = (\cos \theta)\mathbf{i} + (\sin \theta)\mathbf{j}$ and $\mathbf{v} = (\cos \varphi)\mathbf{i} + (\sin \varphi)\mathbf{j}$ are unit vectors. Derive the addition formula for $\cos(\theta - \varphi)$ by expressing the angle between $\mathbf{u}$ and $\mathbf{v}$ in terms of $\theta - \varphi$ and using the inner product.

Establish each of the following geometric theorems vectorially:

11. The diagonals of a rhombus are perpendicular to each other.

12. In a parallelogram, the sum of the squares of the sides equals the sum of the squares of the diagonals.

13. A man wishes to swim directly across (easterly in a straight line) a river that is flowing south at a rate of $\frac{1}{2}$ mph. If the man's swimming speed in still water is 1 mph, what direction should he swim? Also, if the river is 2 miles wide, how long does it take the man to swim across?

II

1. Give an alternate proof of Cauchy's inequality in V_2 by showing directly that $(a_1b_1 + a_2b_2)^2 \leq (a_1^2 + a_2^2)(b_1^2 + b_2^2)$.

2. Prove that $\max\{|\mathbf{u}|,|\mathbf{v}|\} \leq \max\{|\mathbf{u} - \mathbf{v}|, |\mathbf{u} + \mathbf{v}|\}$ and give a geometric interpretation.

3. If $\mathbf{u} \neq \mathbf{v}$ and $0 < r < 1$, prove that $|r\mathbf{u} + (1 - r)\mathbf{v}| < \max\{|\mathbf{u}|,|\mathbf{v}|\}$ and give a geometric interpretation.

Establish each of the following geometric theorems vectorially:

4. An angle inscribed in a semicircle is a right angle.

5. The sum of the squares of the sides of a quadrilateral equals the sum of the squares of the diagonals plus four times the square of the line segment joining the midpoints of the diagonals.

6. A man walking east at a speed of 4 mph finds that the wind appears to be blowing directly from the north. On doubling his speed, he finds that the wind appears to be blowing from the northeast. What is the velocity of the wind?

7. Prove that there exists a pair of vectors $\mathbf{u},\mathbf{v}$ chosen from the set of vectors $\{\mathbf{w}_1, \mathbf{w}_2, \ldots, \mathbf{w}_n, -(\mathbf{w}_1 + \mathbf{w}_2 + \cdots + \mathbf{w}_n)\}$ such that $|\mathbf{u}|/|\mathbf{v}| \leq 2$. Interpret this result geometrically.

4 TANGENT VECTORS

A function $\mathbf{s}$ having a set of real numbers as its domain and a subset of V_2 as its range is called a *vector-valued function*. Thus, if $\mathbf{s}$ is a vector-valued function with domain I, then

$$\mathbf{s}(t) = \langle F(t),G(t)\rangle, \qquad t \text{ in } I,$$

for some real functions F and G.

Limits are defined for vector-valued functions just as they are for curves, and **16.3** may be shown to hold for vector-valued functions as well as for curves.

Hence, if $\mathbf{s}(t)$ is as given above, then

$$\lim_{t\to c} \mathbf{s}(t) = \langle \lim_{t\to c} F(t), \lim_{t\to c} G(t)\rangle,$$

provided the last two limits exist.

Given two points $P_1 = (a_1,b_1)$ and $P_2 = (a_2,b_2)$ in R^2, there is a unique vector $\mathbf{v}$ which translates P_1 into P_2, namely $\mathbf{v} = \langle a_2 - a_1, b_2 - b_1\rangle$. Thus, $P_1 + \mathbf{v} = P_2$.

In particular, if λ is a curve with domain I and c is a given number in I, then there is a unique vector-valued function $\mathbf{s}(t)$ which translates $\lambda(c)$ into $\lambda(t)$, as shown in Figure 16.16. We call $\mathbf{s}(t)$ a *secant vector* of λ.

If we multiply $\mathbf{s}(t)$ by the scalar $1/(t - c)$, the limit of the resulting vector-valued function as t approaches c, if it exists, is called the *tangent vector of* λ *at* c and is designated by $\lambda'(c)$:

16.7 $$\lambda'(c) = \lim_{t\to c} \frac{1}{t - c}\,\mathbf{s}(t).$$

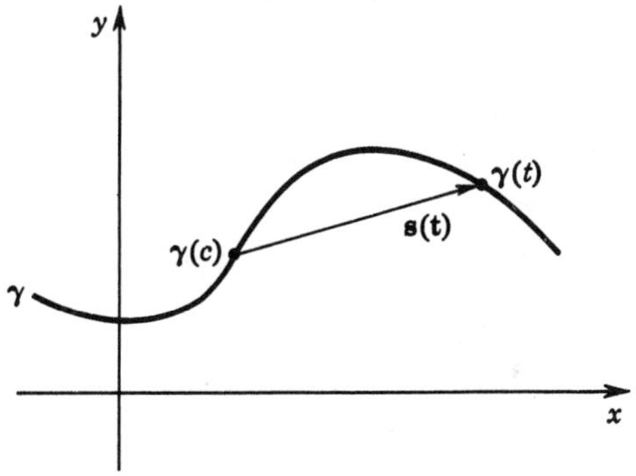

FIGURE 16.16

It will be convenient henceforth when defining a curve λ to use x and y for the real-valued functions in its coordinates,

$$\lambda(t) = (x(t),y(t)), \qquad \text{domain } \lambda = I.$$

Then the secant vector above is given by

$$\mathbf{s}(t) = \langle x(t) - x(c), y(t) - y(c)\rangle$$

and $$\frac{1}{t - c}\,\mathbf{s}(t) = \left\langle \frac{x(t) - x(c)}{t - c}, \frac{y(t) - y(c)}{t - c} \right\rangle.$$

Hence

$$\lambda'(c) = \left\langle \lim_{t \to c} \frac{x(t) - x(c)}{t - c}, \lim_{t \to c} \frac{y(t) - y(c)}{t - c} \right\rangle,$$

or

$$\lambda'(c) = \langle x'(c), y'(c) \rangle.$$

Thus associated with each curve λ is a vector-valued function λ':

16.8 If $\lambda(t) = (x(t),y(t))$, then $\boldsymbol{\lambda}'(t) = \langle x'(t),y'(t)\rangle$.

We shall call λ a *differentiable curve* if λ' exists and λ and λ' have the same domain. If λ is a differentiable curve such that λ' is continuous in its domain, then λ is called a *smooth curve*.

EXAMPLE 1. If $\lambda(t) = (\cos t, \sin t)$, find the function λ' and show that each tangent vector lies along the tangent line in the usual sense.

Solution: By **15.9**,

$$\lambda'(t) = \langle -\sin t, \cos t \rangle.$$

The vector $\mathbf{r}(t)$ translating the origin O into the point $\lambda(t)$ is given by

$$\mathbf{r}(t) = \langle \cos t, \sin t \rangle$$

(see Figure 16.17). To prove that $\lambda'(t)$ lies along the usual tangent line to the trace of λ, a circle, we need only show that $\lambda'(t)$ and $\mathbf{r}(t)$ are perpendicular. However, this follows from **16.5**, since

$$\lambda'(t) \cdot \mathbf{r}(t) = -\sin t \cos t + \cos t \sin t = 0.$$

We note that $\lambda'(t)$ is a unit vector, since

$$|\lambda'(t)| = \sqrt{(-\sin t)^2 + (\cos t)^2} = 1.$$

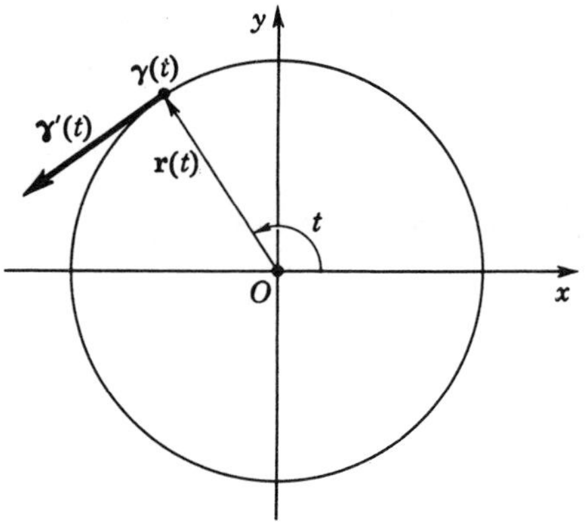

FIGURE 16.17

If λ is a differentiable curve with domain I and if c is a number in I such that $\lambda'(c) \neq 0$, then the line

$$L(\lambda,c) = \{\lambda(c) + t\lambda'(c) \mid t \text{ in } \mathsf{R}\}$$

is called the *tangent line to the curve* λ *at* c. Let us show that $L(\lambda,c)$ closely approximates the trace of λ in the neighborhood of $\lambda(c)$.

16.9 **THEOREM.** If λ is a differentiable curve at c, then

$$\operatorname*{limit}_{t\to 0} \frac{d[\lambda(t+c),\lambda(c)+t\lambda'(c)]}{|t|} = 0.$$

As shown in Figure 16.18, the conclusion of 16.9 is that the distance d between the point $\lambda(t+c)$ on the trace of λ and the corresponding point $\lambda(c) + t\lambda'(c)$ on the tangent line $L(\lambda,c)$ is small in comparison to $|t|$ if t is close to 0.

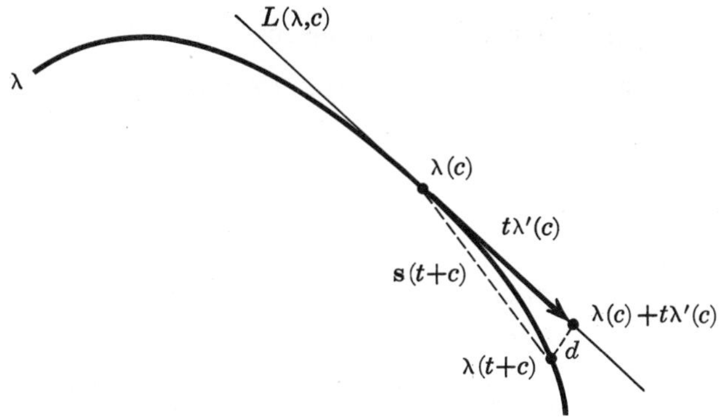

FIGURE 16.18

If $\mathbf{s}(t+c)$ is the secant vector which translates $\lambda(c)$ into $\lambda(t+c)$, then d is the length of the vector $\mathbf{s}(t+c) - t\lambda'(c)$. Since

$$\operatorname*{limit}_{t\to 0} \frac{1}{t}\,\mathbf{s}(t+c) = \operatorname*{limit}_{t\to c} \frac{1}{t-c}\,\mathbf{s}(t) = \lambda'(c)$$

by 16.7, we have

$$\begin{aligned}\operatorname*{limit}_{t\to 0} \frac{d[\lambda(t+c),\lambda(c)+t\lambda'(c)]}{|t|} &= \operatorname*{limit}_{t\to 0} \left|\frac{1}{t}\,\mathbf{s}(t+c) - \lambda'(c)\right| \\ &= |\lambda'(c) - \lambda'(c)| = 0.\end{aligned}$$

This proves 16.9.

If the curve λ defined by

$$\lambda(t) = (x(t),y(t)), \qquad \text{domain } \lambda = I,$$

has a nonzero tangent vector at some t,

$$\boldsymbol{\lambda}'(t) = \langle x'(t),y'(t)\rangle \neq \mathbf{0},$$

then either $x'(t) = 0$, in which case the tangent line $L(\lambda,t)$ is vertical, or $x'(t) \neq 0$, in which case $L(\lambda,t)$ has slope $m(t)$ given by

16.10 $$m(t) = \frac{y'(t)}{x'(t)} \qquad \text{if } x'(t) \neq 0.$$

It might happen that in some interval I the trace of a differentiable curve λ coincides with the graph of a differentiable function f. If $\lambda(t) = (x(t),y(t))$, then this means that

$$y(t) = f(x(t))$$

for every t in I. Hence, by the chain rule,

$$y'(t) = f'(x(t))x'(t)$$

and

16.11 $$f'(x(t)) = \frac{y'(t)}{x'(t)} \qquad \text{if } x'(t) \neq 0.$$

This equation is often written in the abbreviated form

$$\frac{dy}{dx} = \frac{\dfrac{dy}{dt}}{\dfrac{dx}{dt}} \qquad \text{if} \qquad \frac{dx}{dt} \neq 0.$$

Since $f'(x(t))$ is the slope of the tangent line to the graph of f at the point $(x(t),y(t))$, it is clear that the tangent line to the curve λ at t (with slope given by 16.10) coincides with the tangent line to the graph of f at the point $(x(t),y(t))$.

EXAMPLE 2. Describe the tangent lines to the cycloid λ defined by

$$\lambda(t) = (r(t - \sin t), r(1 - \cos t)).$$

Solution: We have

$$\boldsymbol{\lambda}'(t) = \langle r(1 - \cos t), r \sin t\rangle$$

for every t in R. Thus the tangent vector exists at each number t. However, we see that

$$\boldsymbol{\lambda}'(t) = \mathbf{0} \text{ if } t = 2n\pi, n \text{ an integer.}$$

That is, the tangent vectors are zero at each point of the cycloid on the x axis. Hence the slope of the tangent line to the cycloid is given by (16.10)

$$m(t) = \frac{\sin t}{1 - \cos t} \quad \text{if } t \neq 2n\pi, n \text{ an integer.}$$

Although $\lambda'(2n\pi) = 0$, (n an integer), this does not necessarily mean that the cycloid has no tangent line at the point $(2n\pi r,0)$. As usual, we say that the curve has a tangent line at $(2n\pi r,0)$ provided the limit of the slope of the line joining this point to a point $(x(t),y(t))$ as t approaches 0 exists or is infinite. Since

$$\begin{aligned}\lim_{t\to 2n\pi} \frac{y(t)}{x(t) - 2n\pi r} &= \lim_{t\to 2n\pi} \frac{r(1 - \cos t)}{r(t - \sin t - 2n\pi)}\\ &= \lim_{t\to 2n\pi} \frac{\sin t}{(1 - \cos t)}\\ &= \lim_{t\to 2n\pi} \frac{\cos t}{\sin t} = \infty,\end{aligned}$$

by l'Hospital's rule (14.2), the line

$$x = 2n\pi r$$

is tangent to the cycloid at the point $(2n\pi r,0)$.

EXERCISES

I

In each of Exercises 1–4, find the tangent vector to the curve at the specified value of the parameter.

1. $\lambda(t) = (t^2,t^3)$, $(t = 2)$.
2. $\lambda(t) = (e^t,e^{-t})$, $(t = 1)$.
3. $\lambda(r) = (\tan r, \cot r)$, $(r = \frac{3}{4}\pi)$.
4. $\lambda(m) = (3 \cos m, 2 \sin m)$, $(m = \frac{1}{3}\pi)$.

In each of Exercises 5–8, sketch the trace of the curve and find on it each point at which the tangent vector is either horizontal or vertical.

5. $\lambda(t) = (\cos 2t, \cos t)$.
6. $\lambda(s) = (2s - \sin s, 2 - \cos s)$.
7. $\lambda(r) = (a \cos^3 r, a \sin^3 r)$.
8. $\lambda(t) = (2 - 3 \cos t, -1 + 2 \sin t)$.

Sketching the one-parameter family of vectors $\mathbf{v}(t) = \langle x(t),y(t)\rangle$ means sketching the trace of the curve $\delta(t) = (x(t),y(t))$. In each of Exercises 9–12, sketch the family of tangent vectors to the curve.

9. $\lambda(t) = (3t,t^3)$.

10. $\lambda(t) = (e^t,te^{-t})$.

11. $\lambda(r) = (a(r - \sin r), a(1 - \cos r))$.

12. $\lambda(s) = (a \cos^3 s, b \sin^3 s)$.

II

1. Prove that if $x'(a)$ and $y'(a)$ are not both zero then $x = x(a) + x'(a)t$, $y = y(a) + y'(a)t$ are parametric equations of the tangent line to the curve $\lambda(t) = (x(t),y(t))$ at the point $t = a$.
2. Show that the trace of the curve $\lambda(t) = (a \cos^4 t, a \sin^4 t)$, $(a > 0)$, is the same as the graph of the equation $\sqrt{x} + \sqrt{y} = \sqrt{a}$. Sketch this graph.
3. Show that for the curve in Exercise 2 the sum of the x and y intercepts of every tangent line is the constant a.
4. Show that the length of the segment of each tangent line of the curve $\lambda(t) = (a \cos^3 t, a \sin^3 t)$ cut off by the coordinate axes is constant.
5. Show that the tangent and normal lines to the cycloid in Example 4, page 000 pass through the highest and lowest points of the rolling circle at each position.

5 PLANE MOTION

One possible interpretation of a curve λ is as the *motion of a particle* in a coordinate plane. The parameter t is taken to be in time units, so that $\lambda(t)$ is the position of the moving particle at time t.

The tangent vector $\boldsymbol{\lambda}'(t)$ is called the *velocity* of the particle at time t. Its length $|\boldsymbol{\lambda}'(t)|$ is commonly called the *speed* of the particle at time t. Thus the velocity is a vector and the speed is a scalar. If

$$\lambda(t) = (x(t),y(t)),$$

then

$$\boldsymbol{\lambda}'(t) = \langle x'(t),y'(t)\rangle \quad \text{and} \quad |\boldsymbol{\lambda}'(t)| = \sqrt{x'^2(t) + y'^2(t)}.$$

Given a vector-valued function such as $\boldsymbol{\lambda}'$, we can define its derivative $\boldsymbol{\lambda}''(t)$ in the natural way:

$$\boldsymbol{\lambda}''(t) = \operatorname*{limit}_{h\to 0} \frac{1}{h} [\boldsymbol{\lambda}'(t + h) - \boldsymbol{\lambda}'(t)].$$

Since $\boldsymbol{\lambda}'(t + h)$ and $\boldsymbol{\lambda}'(t)$ are vectors, $\boldsymbol{\lambda}'(t + h) - \boldsymbol{\lambda}'(t)$ is also a vector. Thus $\boldsymbol{\lambda}''$ is again a vector-valued function. Actually, since $\boldsymbol{\lambda}'(t) = \langle x'(t),y'(t)\rangle$,

$$\begin{aligned}\boldsymbol{\lambda}''(t) &= \operatorname*{limit}_{h\to 0} \left\langle \frac{x'(t + h) - x'(t)}{h}, \frac{y'(t + h) - y'(t)}{h} \right\rangle \\ &= \langle x''(t),y''(t)\rangle.\end{aligned}$$

The vector $\boldsymbol{\lambda}''(t)$ is called the *acceleration* of the particle at time t.

EXAMPLE 1. Describe the motion of a particle for which

$$\lambda(t) = (2 - t, t^2 - 1).$$

Sketch the velocity and acceleration vectors at $t = 0$ and $t = 1$.

Solution: If we eliminate t from the parametric equations

$$x = 2 - t, \qquad y = t^2 - 1,$$

we see that the path of the particle is the parabola

$$y + 1 = (x - 2)^2$$

sketched in Figure 16.19. The velocity and acceleration vectors are given by

$$\lambda'(t) = \langle -1,2t \rangle, \qquad \lambda''(t) = \langle 0,2 \rangle.$$

Hence

$$\lambda'(0) = \langle -1,0 \rangle, \qquad \lambda''(0) = \langle 0,2 \rangle$$

and

$$\lambda'(1) = \langle -1,2 \rangle, \qquad \lambda''(1) = \langle 0,2 \rangle$$

are the velocity and acceleration vectors at $t = 0$ and $t = 1$, respectively. These are also sketched in Figure 16.19. We note that the acceleration vector is constant. As t increases, the particle moves from right to left along the parabola.

If λ is the motion of a particle of constant mass m, then the vector

$$\mathbf{F}(t) = m\lambda''(t)$$

is called the *force* acting on the particle at time t.

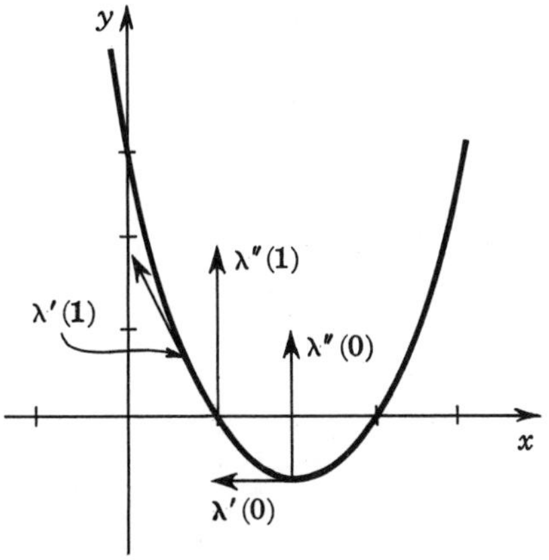

FIGURE 16.19

EXAMPLE 2. Show that if a particle of mass m is moving in a circular path at a constant angular speed of ω revolutions per second, then the (centripetal) force acting on the particle is directed towards the center of the circle.

Solution: The particle sweeps out an angle of $\alpha = 2\pi\omega t$ radians in t seconds (Figure 16.20). Hence the motion function λ is given by

$$\lambda(t) = (r \cos 2\pi\omega t, r \sin 2\pi\omega t),$$

assuming that $\lambda(0) = (r,0)$. We easily compute

$$\begin{aligned} \boldsymbol{\lambda}'(t) &= \langle -2\pi\omega r \sin 2\pi\omega t, 2\pi\omega r \cos 2\pi\omega t\rangle, \\ \boldsymbol{\lambda}''(t) &= -k\langle r \cos 2\pi\omega t, r \sin 2\pi\omega t\rangle, \end{aligned}$$

where $k = 4\pi^2\omega^2$. If we let

$$\mathbf{u}(t) = \langle r \cos 2\pi\omega t, r \sin 2\pi\omega t\rangle,$$

then clearly the vector $\mathbf{u}(t)$ translates the origin O into $\lambda(t)$. Since $\boldsymbol{\lambda}''(t) = -k\mathbf{u}(t)$ and $k > 0$, evidently the force vector

$$\mathbf{F}(t) = m\boldsymbol{\lambda}''(t)$$

has the opposite direction to $\mathbf{u}(t)$. Therefore $\mathbf{F}(t)$ acts on $\lambda(t)$ in the direction of the center O of the circle.

EXERCISES

I

In each of Exercises 1–11, $\lambda(t)$ is the position of a moving particle at time t. Sketch the trace of the particle and find its velocity and acceleration. Sketch the velocity and acceleration of the particle and find its speed at the given time t.

1. $\lambda(t) = (t^2,2t)$, $t = 2$.

2. $\lambda(t) = (2t,t^4)$, $t = 2$.

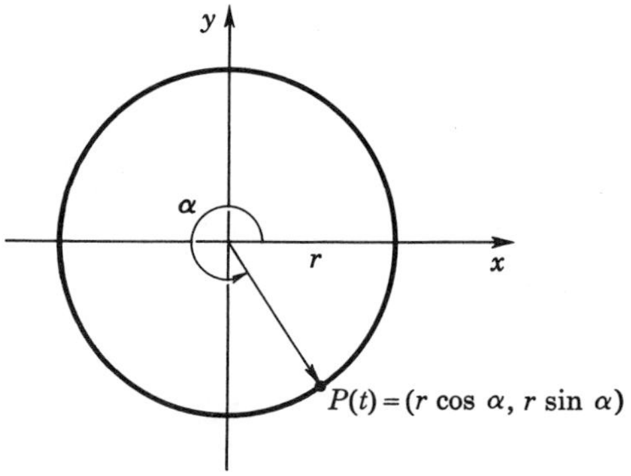

FIGURE 16.20

3. $\lambda(t) = (2 \sin t, 2 \cos t), \quad t = 4\pi.$

4. $\lambda(t) = (\tan t, \cot t), \quad t = \frac{3}{4}\pi.$

5. $\lambda(t) = (\cos t, \cos 2t), \quad t = \frac{1}{2}\pi.$

6. $\lambda(t) = (2t, e^{-t}), \quad t = 0.$

7. $\lambda(t) = (e^t, e^{-t}), \quad t = 0.$

8. $\lambda(t) = (\sin t, \cos^2 t), \quad t = \frac{1}{2}\pi.$

9. $\lambda(t) = (2 \sin t, 2(1 - \cos t)), \quad t = \frac{1}{6}\pi.$

10. $\lambda(t) = (\sqrt{t}, \sqrt{2 - t}), \quad t = 1.$

11. $\lambda(t) = (a \cos bt, a \sin bt), (a > 0, b > 0)$, at time t.

12. Describe the motion of the particle during the time interval $[-2,2]$ if $\lambda(t) = (t^2/2, t^4/4)$. Find $\boldsymbol{\lambda}'(t)$ and $\boldsymbol{\lambda}''(t)$ when $t = -2, -1, 0, 1, 2$.

13. What is the significance of the fact that $\langle 2 \sin t, 2 \cos t\rangle \cdot \boldsymbol{\lambda}'(t) = 0$ in Exercise 3?

14. Show that if $\lambda(t) = (e^t \cos t, e^t \sin t)$ then the acceleration vector $\boldsymbol{\lambda}''(t)$ is perpendicular to the vector $\langle e^t \cos t, e^t \sin t\rangle$ at each time t.

II

1. The position $\lambda(t)$ of a projectile fired with an initial velocity of v_0 ft/sec at an angle α with the horizontal (neglecting air resistance and assuming a constant gravitational deceleration of 32 ft/sec²) is given by $\lambda(t) = (v_0 t \cos \alpha, v_0 t \sin \alpha - 16t^2)$.
   a. What is its range (maximum x)?
   b. What is the maximum height reached?
   c. What is the total time of flight?
   d. What is an equation (in x and y only) of its trajectory?
   e. Determine the angle α for which the range is a maximum, and find this range.
   f. If two projectiles are fired with the same initial velocity at complementary angles with the horizontal, show that their ranges are the same.

2. If $\mathbf{u}$ and $\mathbf{v}$ are vector functions of one variable (i.e., having range in R and domain in V_2), then prove that $D(\mathbf{u} \cdot \mathbf{v}) = \mathbf{u} \cdot D\mathbf{v} + D\mathbf{u} \cdot \mathbf{v}$.

3. If the position of a moving point at time t is given by $\lambda(t) = (x(t), y(t))$ and if $\langle x(t), y(t)\rangle \cdot \boldsymbol{\lambda}'(t) = 0$, what can be said about the motion of the point? (See Exercise I-13.)

4. Solve the vector differential equation $D^2\mathbf{v} + k^2\mathbf{v} = \mathbf{0}$, subject to the initial conditions $\mathbf{v}(0) = \mathbf{a}$, $D\mathbf{v}(0) = \mathbf{b}$.

6 POLAR COORDINATE SYSTEMS

Another convenient way of introducing coordinates in a plane is by the polar coordinate system described below.

We start off with a fixed point O, called the *pole*, and the positive half of a coordinate line, called the *polar axis*, emanating from O. The presence of the polar axis allows us to assign a length to each line segment in the plane.

Each point P in the plane may now be assigned coordinates (r,θ), where r is the length of the segment OP and θ is the measure of an angle with initial side along the polar axis and terminal side along OP (Figure 16.21). We shall also allow the coordinates $(-r,\theta)$ for the point P if $|OP| = r$ and θ is the measure of an angle with initial side along the polar axis and terminal side along the extension of OP through the pole (Figure 16.22). The pole O is assigned coordinates $(0,\theta)$, where θ is any real number.

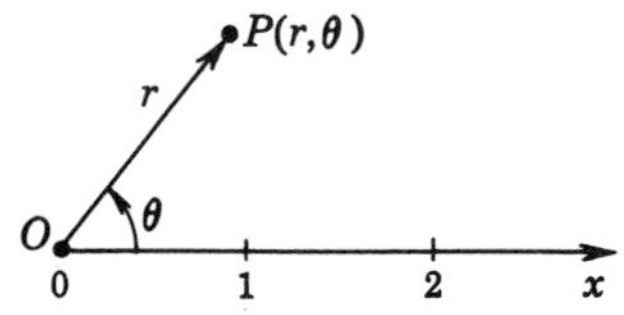

FIGURE 16.21

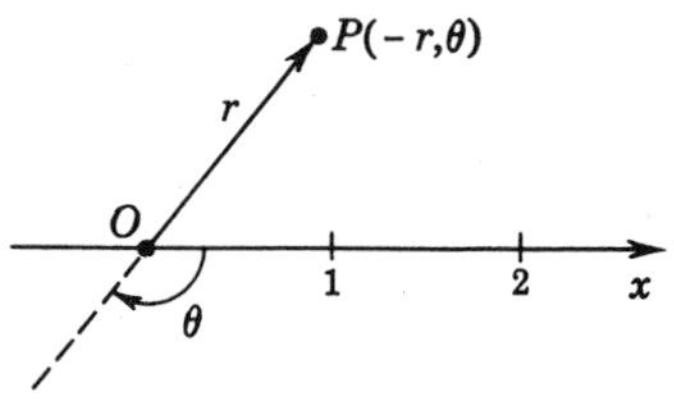

FIGURE 16.22

There certainly is nothing unique about the polar coordinates of a point. The point P of Figure 16.23, for example, has as possible polar coordinates

$$(3,120°),\ (-3,-60°),\ (3,480°),\ (3,-240°),\ (-3,300°),$$

and so on. In general, if P has polar coordinates (r,θ), then P also has polar coordinates $(r,\theta \pm 2n\pi)$ and $(-r,\theta \pm (2n - 1)\pi)$ for every integer n. However, if P is not the pole, P does have a unique set of coordinates (r,θ) where $r > 0$

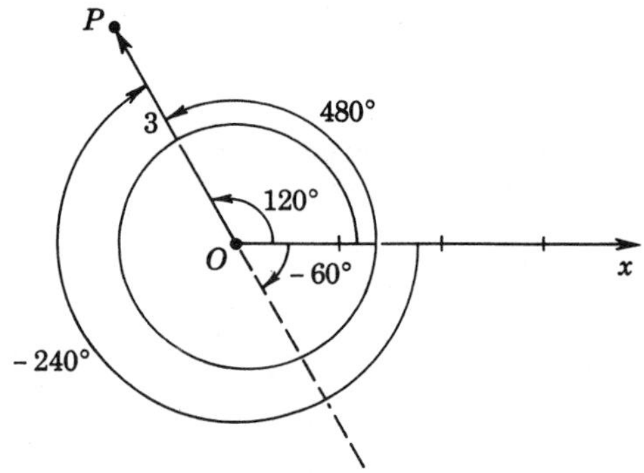

FIGURE 16.23

and $0° \leq \theta < 360°$. The only coordinates of P in Figure 16.23 satisfying these restrictions are $(3,120°)$.

Every pair of numbers (r,θ) determines a unique point P such that $|OP| = |r|$ and θ is the (radian) measure of an angle having initial side along the polar axis and terminal side along OP if $r > 0$ and along OP extended through the origin if $r < 0$. This association of pairs of numbers with points is called a *polar coordinate system* in the plane.

Just as an equation in x and y has a graph in a rectangular coordinate plane, so does an equation in r and θ have a graph in a polar coordinate plane. Thus the graph of an equation in r and θ consists of those and only those points P having some pair of coordinates satisfying the given equation.

The graph of the equation

$$r = c,$$

(c a constant), is a circle of radius $|c|$ having its center at the pole, since each point P on this circle has a pair of coordinates of the form (c,θ) for some θ, whereas each point $P(r,\theta)$ off this circle has $|r| \neq |c|$. The graph of $r = -c$ is the same circle.

The graph of the equation

$$\theta = c,$$

(c a constant), is a straight line passing through the pole and making an angle of measure c with the polar axis. The graph of $\theta = c \pm n\pi$, (n any integer), is the same line.

It is natural to construct coordinate paper for a polar coordinate system, as indicated in Figure 16.24, with each circle having a constant value of r and each line a constant value of θ. Some points are plotted in the figure to indicate how the paper is used.

EXAMPLE 1. Sketch the graph of the equation

$$r = 4 \sin \theta.$$

Solution: We need graph this equation only for $0 \leq \theta \leq 2\pi$, since the sine function has period 2π. Using the accompanying table of values, we sketch the graph as shown in Figure 16.25. The graph is traced out twice, once as θ ranges from 0 to π and

θ	0	$\frac{\pi}{6}$	$\frac{\pi}{4}$	$\frac{\pi}{3}$	$\frac{\pi}{2}$	$\frac{2\pi}{3}$	$\frac{3\pi}{4}$	$\frac{5\pi}{6}$
r	0	2	$2\sqrt{2}$	$2\sqrt{3}$	4	$2\sqrt{3}$	$2\sqrt{2}$	2

π	$\frac{7\pi}{6}$	$\frac{5\pi}{4}$	$\frac{4\pi}{3}$	$\frac{3\pi}{2}$	$\frac{5\pi}{3}$	$\frac{7\pi}{4}$	$\frac{11\pi}{6}$	2π
0	-2	$-2\sqrt{2}$	$-2\sqrt{3}$	-4	$-2\sqrt{3}$	$-2\sqrt{2}$	-2	0

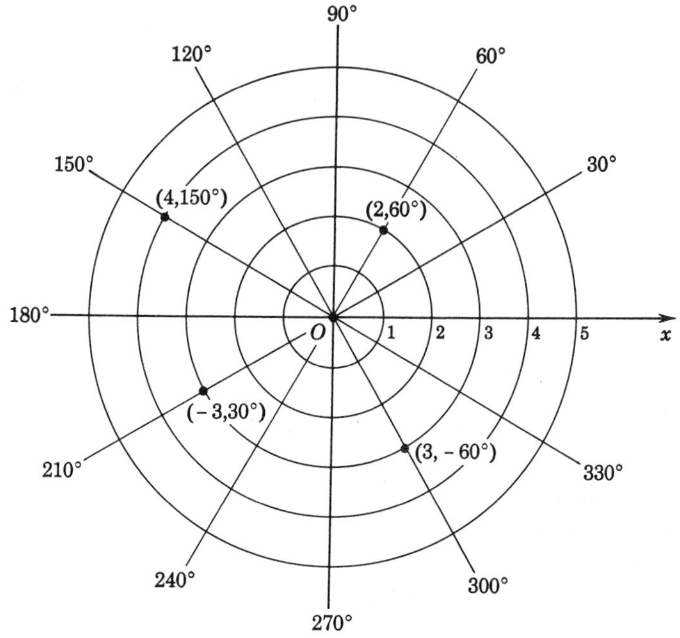

FIGURE 16.24

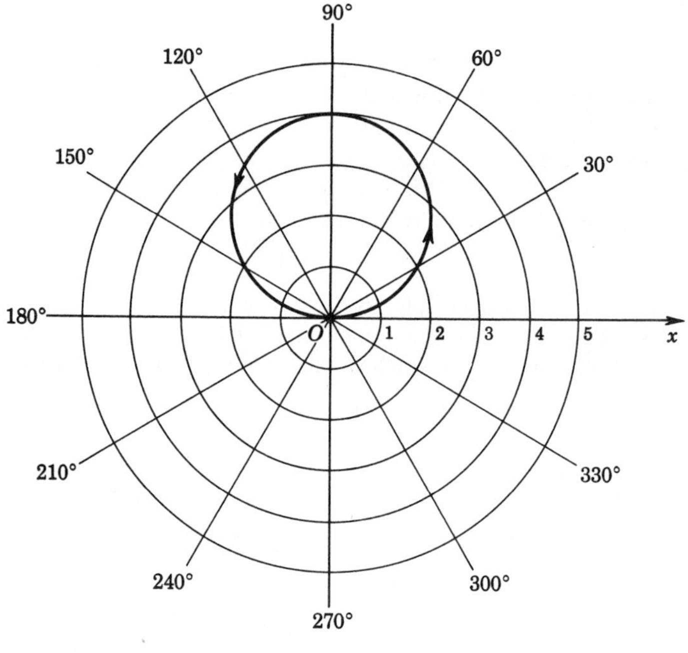

FIGURE 16.25

again as θ ranges from π to 2π. Starting from the pole, the graph is traced out as indicated by the arrowhead. The graph is a circle, as we shall presently show.

EXAMPLE 2. Sketch the graph of the equation

$$r = 2(1 - 2\sin\theta).$$

Solution: We may again limit the range of θ to $0 \leq \theta \leq 2\pi$. The graph is sketched in Figure 16.26 from the accompanying table of values, with r approximated to one decimal place. This curve is called a limacon.

θ	0	$\frac{\pi}{6}$	$\frac{\pi}{4}$	$\frac{\pi}{3}$	$\frac{\pi}{2}$	$\frac{2\pi}{3}$	$\frac{3\pi}{4}$	$\frac{5\pi}{6}$	π	$\frac{7\pi}{6}$	$\frac{5\pi}{4}$	$\frac{4\pi}{3}$	$\frac{3\pi}{2}$	$\frac{5\pi}{3}$	$\frac{7\pi}{4}$	$\frac{11\pi}{6}$	2π
r	2	0	−.8	−1.5	−2	−1.5	−.8	0	2	4	4.8	5.5	6	5.5	4.8	4	2

If a rectangular and a polar coordinate system are placed in the same plane, with the positive x axis of the first the polar axis of the second (Figure 16.27), then each point P in the plane has both rectangular coordinates (x,y) and polar

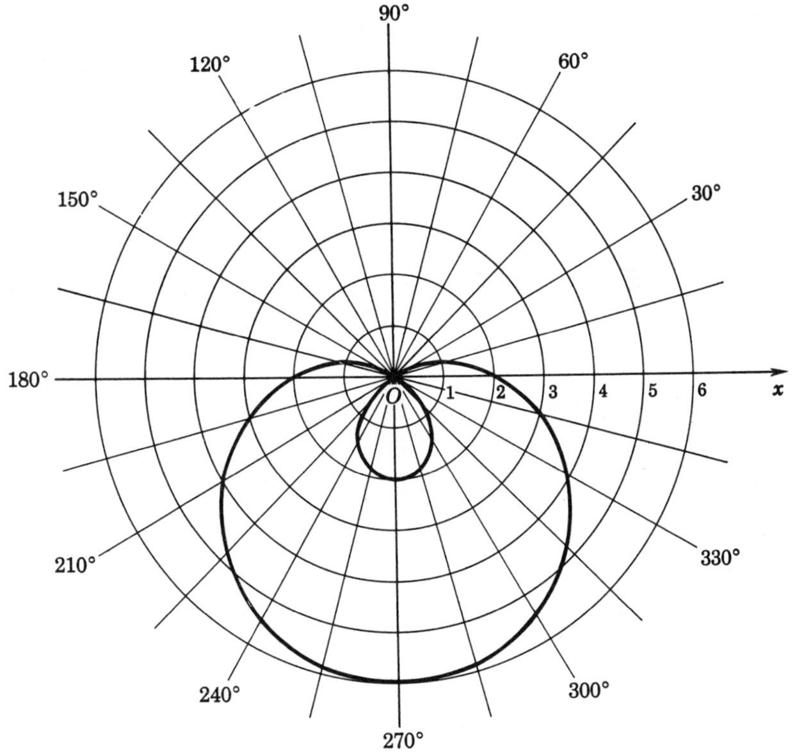

FIGURE 16.26

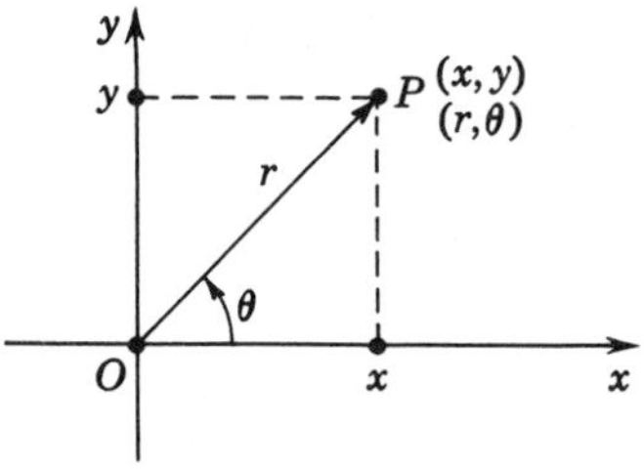

FIGURE 16.27

coordinates (r,θ). If $r > 0$, then, according to the definition of the trigonometric functions,

$$\sin\theta = \frac{y}{r}, \qquad \cos\theta = \frac{x}{r},$$

or

16.12 $$x = r\cos\theta, \qquad y = r\sin\theta.$$

It may be verified that even if $r \leq 0$ **16.12** still holds. Thus the rectangular and polar coordinates of each point in the plane are related by **16.12**. It is clear from **16.12** that x, y, and r are related by the equation

16.13 $$x^2 + y^2 = r^2.$$

In view of **16.12**, the graph of the equation

$$r = f(\theta)$$

in polar coordinates is the same as the graph of the parametric equations (with parameter θ)

$$x = f(\theta)\cos\theta, \qquad y = f(\theta)\sin\theta$$

in rectangular coordinates. Conversely, the graph of a given equation in x and y is the same as the graph of the equation in r and θ obtained by replacing x by $r\cos\theta$ and y by $r\sin\theta$.

EXAMPLE 3. Find an equation in polar coordinates of the hyperbola

$$x^2 - y^2 = 1.$$

Solution: Using **16.12**, we get

$$r^2\cos^2\theta - r^2\sin^2\theta = 1,$$

or, since $\cos^2\theta - \sin^2\theta = \cos 2\theta$,

$$r^2 = \sec 2\theta.$$

EXAMPLE 4. Show that the graph of either $r = a \sin \theta$ or $r = a \cos \theta$, $(a > 0)$, is a circle of diameter a.

Solution: The equation $r = a \sin \theta$ has the same graph as the equation

$$r^2 = ar \sin \theta,$$

since, if $r \neq 0$, we may cancel out an r in the equation above to obtain $r = a \sin \theta$, while the pole is on both graphs. Hence, by **16.12** and **16.13**,

$$x^2 + y^2 = ay$$

is a rectangular-coordinate equation of this graph. This latter equation may be put in the form

$$x^2 + \left(y - \frac{a}{2}\right)^2 = \left(\frac{a}{2}\right)^2,$$

which we recognize as the equation of a circle of radius $a/2$ and with center $(0,a/2)$. Thus the graph of $r = a \sin \theta$ is a circle of diameter a and with center $(a/2,\pi/2)$. By similar arguments, the graph of $r = a \cos \theta$ is a circle of diameter a and with center $(a/2,0)$.

EXERCISES

I

Sketch the graph of each of the following equations.

1. $r = 3$.
2. $\theta = 2\pi/3$.
3. $\theta = -\pi/4$.
4. $r = -4$.
5. $r = 6 \cos \theta$.
6. $r = -2 \sin \theta$.
7. $r = \theta$.
8. $r = 1/\theta$.
9. $r = 2(1 - \cos \theta)$ (cardioid).
10. $r = 2 - \sin \theta$ (limacon).
11. $r = 4 \sin 3\theta$ (three-leaved rose).
12. $r = 2 \cos 2\theta$ (four-leaved rose).
13. $r = 1 + \sin \theta$ (cardioid).
14. $r^2 = a^2 \cos 2\theta$ (lemniscate).
15. $r = 2 \tan \theta$.
16. $r \cos \theta = 3$.
17. $r = 2 \sec \theta + 1$ (conchoid).
18. $r = a(1 + \sin^2 \theta)$.
19. $r = a \csc \theta$.
20. $r = \sin 4\theta$.

Find an equation in polar coordinates of the graph of each of the following rectangular equations.

21. $x^2 + y^2 = 9$.
22. $x = 4$.
23. $xy = 1$.
24. $y^2 = 8x$.
25. $x^2 + y^2 + 4x = 0$.
26. $x^2 + 4y^2 = 4$.

Find an equation in rectangular coordinates of the graph of each of the following polar equations.

27. $r = 2 \sin \theta$.
28. $r = 4$.
29. $r = 1 - \sin \theta$.
30. $r = \sec \theta$.
31. $r = 2 \csc \theta$.
32. $r = 3 \tan \theta$.

II

1. Give two different pairs of polar coordinates for the point Q which is symmetric to the point $P = (r,\theta)$:
   a. with respect to the pole.
   b. with respect to the polar axis.
   c. with respect to the line $\theta = \frac{1}{2}\pi$.
   d. with respect to the line $\theta = \alpha$.

2. Without actually sketching the graph, describe the symmetries of the graph of each of the following equations:
   a. $r^2 = \sin 4\theta$.
   b. $r(1 + \cos \theta) = 2$.
   c. $r = \cos^2 2\theta$.
   d. $r^2 = 4 \sin 2\theta$.

In each of Exercises 3–10, sketch the graph of the equation.

3. $r = \sqrt{1 - \theta}$.
4. $r(1 - \theta) = 4$.
5. $r = 2 + \sin 2\theta$.
6. $r = 1 + \sin 2\theta$.
7. $r = 1 + 2 \sin 2\theta$.
8. $r \sin 2\theta = 1$.
9. $r = \dfrac{3 \sin 2\theta}{\sin^3 \theta + \cos^3 \theta}$.
10. $r^2 \sin 2\theta = 1$.

In each of Exercises 11–15, find all points of intersection of the given pair of equations. [*Hint:* Remember that the polar coordinate representation of a point is not unique.]

11. $r = 2 \sin 2\theta, \quad r = 2 \sin \theta$.
12. $r = 2 \sin \theta, \quad r = \cos \theta - 1$.
13. $r = 2(1 + \cos \theta), \quad r = 2 \cos 2\theta$.
14. $r = 1 - \sin \theta, \quad r = 1 - \cos \theta$.
15. $r = 4(1 + \sin \theta), \quad r(1 - \sin \theta) = 3$.

7 THE CONIC SECTIONS

We recall that the parabola was defined to be the set of all points in a plane equidistant from a fixed point (the focus) and a fixed line (the directrix) of the plane. In like manner, every conic section (other than the circle) may be defined to be the set of all points P in a plane such that the ratio of the distance between P and a fixed point F (the focus) to the distance between P and a fixed line L (the directrix) is a positive constant e, called the *eccentricity* of the conic section.

In order to find an equation in polar coordinates of a conic section defined as above, let us place the focus F at the pole and the directrix L perpendicular to the polar axis, as in Figure 16.28. We let $2p$, $(p > 0)$, be the distance between the directrix and the focus. We limit our discussion to the case

$$e \leq 1,$$

leaving the case $e > 1$ for the reader.

By definition, the point P is on the conic section if and only if (Figure 16.28)

$$\frac{|FP|}{|PQ|} = e.$$

Since $e \leq 1$ by assumption, the point P is necessarily on the same side of the directrix as the focus. If (r,θ) is any pair of coordinates of P with $r > 0$, then $|FP| = r$, $|PQ| = 2p + r \cos \theta$, and r and θ satisfy the equation

$$\frac{r}{2p + r \cos \theta} = e.$$

On solving this equation for r, we get

16.14 $$r = \frac{2ep}{1 - e \cos \theta}$$

as an equation satisfied by every point $P(r,\theta)$, $(r > 0)$, on the conic section.

Conversely, for each point $P(r,\theta)$ satisfying **16.14**, necessarily $r > 0$ (since $1 - e \cos \theta \geq 0$) and a reversal of the argument above proves that P is on the conic section. Thus **16.14** is an equation in polar coordinates of the conic section as defined above. Even if $e > 1$, it may be proved that **16.14** is an equation of a conic section, although in this case $r < 0$ for the points $P(r,\theta)$ on the opposite side of the directrix from the focus.

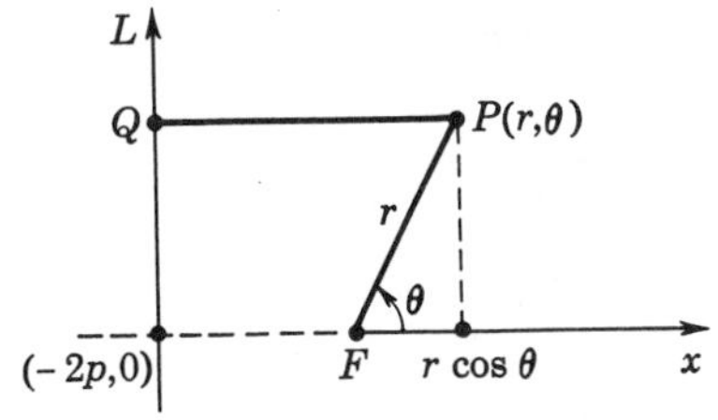

FIGURE 16.28

Let us prove that **16.14** actually is an equation of a conic section by finding an equation in rectangular coordinates of the graph of **16.14.** We shall still assume that $e \leq 1$.

We may write **16.14** in the form

$$r = e(r \cos \theta + 2p),$$

and since $r > 0$, we have by **16.12** and **16.13** that the graph of this equation has equation

$$\sqrt{x^2 + y^2} = e(x + 2p)$$

in rectangular coordinates. In turn, the graph of this equation is the same as the graph of

$$(1) \qquad x^2 + y^2 = e^2(x^2 + 4px + 4p^2).$$

If $e = 1$, (1) becomes

$$y^2 = 4p(x + p),$$

the equation of a parabola with focus at the origin and directrix $x = -2p$.

If $e < 1$, we may complete squares and put (1) in the form

$$(2) \qquad \left(x - \frac{2e^2p}{1 - e^2}\right)^2 + \frac{y^2}{1 - e^2} = \frac{4e^2p^2}{(1 - e^2)^2}.$$

We recognize (2) as an equation of an ellipse with foci on the x axis and with

$$a^2 = \frac{4e^2p^2}{(1 - e^2)^2}, \qquad b^2 = \frac{4e^2p^2}{1 - e^2}, \qquad c^2 = \frac{4e^4p^2}{(1 - e^2)^2}.$$

Since $c = 2e^2p/(1 - e^2)$, the origin is at a focus. The given directrix has equation $x = -2p$. We note incidentally that $e = c/a$.

If $e > 1$, **16.14** may be shown to be an equation of a hyperbola with a focus at the pole.

By keeping the focus at the origin but varying the directrix to either side of the focus or parallel to the polar axis, either above it or below, the conic section may have an equation of the form

$$r = \frac{2ep}{1 \pm e \cos \theta}, \qquad r = \frac{2ep}{1 \pm e \sin \theta}.$$

The conic section is an ellipse if $0 < e < 1$, a parabola if $e = 1$, and a hyperbola if $e > 1$.

EXAMPLE 1. Find an equation of the ellipse with focus at the pole, eccentricity $e = \frac{1}{2}$ and directrix perpendicular to the polar axis at the point $(-4,0)$.

Solution: We let $e = \frac{1}{2}$ and $p = 2$ in 16.14, obtaining

$$r = \frac{4}{2 - \cos\theta}$$

as the desired equation.

EXAMPLE 2. Find an equation of the parabola with focus at the pole and directrix perpendicular to the polar axis at the point $(-3,0)$.

Solution: We let $e = 1$ and $p = \frac{3}{2}$ in 16.14, getting

$$r = \frac{3}{1 - \cos\theta}$$

as an equation of the parabola.

EXAMPLE 3. Describe and sketch the graph of the equation

$$r = \frac{16}{5 + 3\sin\theta}.$$

Solution: We may put this equation in the form

$$r = \frac{\frac{16}{5}}{1 + \frac{3}{5}\sin\theta},$$

which is an equation of an ellipse with focus at the pole and major axis perpendicular to the polar axis. By giving θ the values $\pi/2$ and $3\pi/2$, we find the ends of the major axis to be $(2,\pi/2)$ and $(8,3\pi/2)$. Thus the length of the major axis is 10, and $a = 5$. The center of the ellipse is the point $(3,3\pi/2)$, and $c = 3$. Hence $b^2 = a^2 - c^2 = 16$, and $b = 4$. The ellipse is sketched in Figure 16.29.

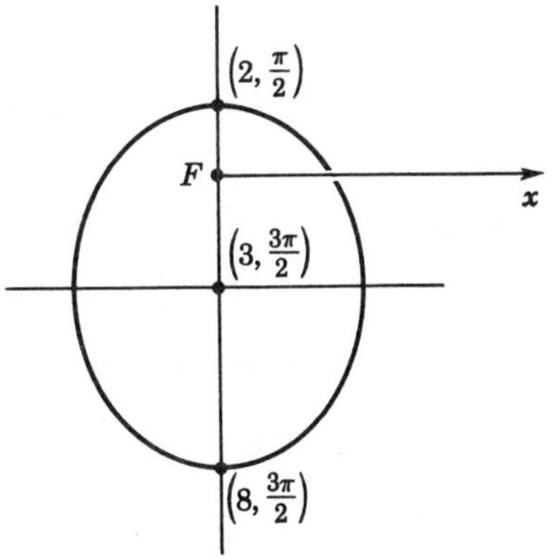

FIGURE 16.29

EXERCISES

I

Describe and sketch the graph of each of the following equations.

1. $r = \dfrac{2}{1 - \cos\theta}$.
2. $r = \dfrac{4}{1 - \sin\theta}$.
3. $r = \dfrac{12}{3 + \cos\theta}$.
4. $r = \dfrac{12}{1 - 3\cos\theta}$.

II

In Exercises 1 and 2, describe and sketch the graph of the given equation.

1. $r = \dfrac{2}{1 - \cos\theta - \sin\theta}$.
2. $r = \dfrac{2}{2 + \cos\theta - \sin\theta}$.
3. Show that if

$$r = \frac{a\,e}{1 - e\cos\theta}$$

is an equation of a hyperbola than the inclination (with the horizontal) of the asymptotes is given by $\cos\theta = 1/e$.

4. Find a polar equation of an ellipse whose center is at the pole.
5. Find a polar equation of a hyperbola whose center is at the pole.

8 TANGENT LINES IN POLAR COORDINATES

The graph of the equation

$$r = f(\theta)$$

in polar coordinates is the same as the trace of the curve λ defined by

16.15 $$\lambda(\theta) = (f(\theta)\cos\theta, f(\theta)\sin\theta)$$

in the associated rectangular coordinate system. Thus we may study tangent lines to the graph of f in polar coordinates by looking at the tangent lines of λ in rectangular coordinates.

If the tangent line to the curve λ of **16.15** at point $\lambda(\theta)$ has slope $m(\theta)$, then

$$m(\theta) = \frac{y'(\theta)}{x'(\theta)} = \frac{f(\theta)\cos\theta + f'(\theta)\sin\theta}{-f(\theta)\sin\theta + f'(\theta)\cos\theta},$$

according to **16.10**. Hence, if α is the inclination of the tangent line, then $\tan\alpha = m(\theta)$, and if $\cos\theta \neq 0$, then

$$\tan\alpha = \frac{f(\theta) + f'(\theta)\tan\theta}{-f(\theta)\tan\theta + f'(\theta)}.$$

We may solve this equation for $f'(\theta)$ (if $\tan\alpha \neq \tan\theta$), obtaining

$$f'(\theta) = \frac{1 + \tan\alpha\tan\theta}{\tan\alpha - \tan\theta} f(\theta).$$

This may be put in the form

16.16 $$f'(\theta) = f(\theta)\cot(\alpha - \theta).$$

Under certain conditions, as indicated in Figure 16.30, $\alpha - \theta = \psi$, an angle between the position vector and tangent line at P. Hence ψ may be computed from the equation

$$\cot\psi = \frac{f'(\theta)}{f(\theta)}.$$

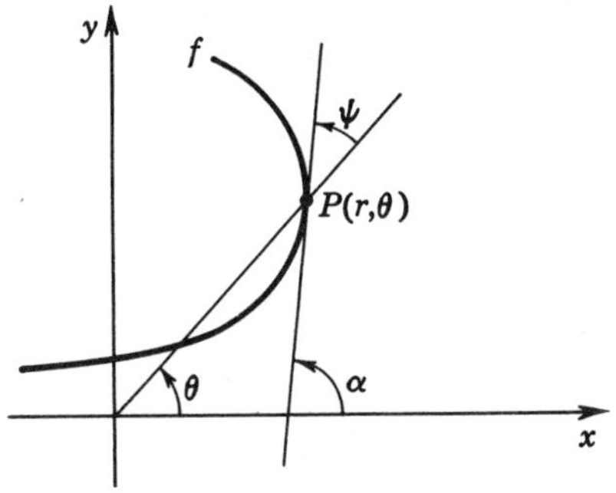

FIGURE 16.30

EXAMPLE. Find the angle ψ for the limacon

$$r = 2(1 - 2\sin\theta),$$

shown in Figure 16.26, at the point (2,0).

Solution: We have $r = f(\theta)$, and

$$\cot(\alpha - \theta) = -\frac{4\cos\theta}{2(1 - 2\sin\theta)},$$

by 16.16. If $\theta = 0$, $\cot(\alpha - \theta) = \cot\alpha = -2$. In this case

$$\alpha = \psi = \tan^{-1}(-\tfrac{1}{2}) \doteq 153°26'.$$

EXERCISES

I

1. Show that the angle ψ is a constant for the logarithmic spiral $r = e^{a\theta}$. Sketch.

In each of Exercises 2–6 find the angle of intersection of the graphs of the given pair of equations. (The angle between the graphs is defined to be the angle between their tangent lines at a point of intersection.)

2. $r\cos\theta = 4$, $r = 10\sin\theta$.
3. $r = a\cos\theta$, $r = -a\sin 2\theta$.
4. $r = 2(1 + \cos\theta)$, $r = -2\sin\theta$.
5. $r = \sec\theta$, $r\sin 2\theta = 2$.
6. $r = a(1 + \sin\theta)$, $r = a(1 - \sin\theta)$.

II

1. If P is a point on the graph of the equation $r^2\sin 2\theta = a^2$, then show that the triangle formed by OP, the polar axis, and the tangent line at P is isosceles.
2. Find equations of all curves such that all rays from the pole intersect the curve at a constant angle α.
3. A point is said to be an equiangular point of a closed curve if the angles of intersection of any chord through the given point with the curve are equal when taken on the same side of the chord. Give an example other than a point within or on a circle.
4. Referring to Exercise 3, show that if one point on a given curve is equiangular then the curve must be a circle.

9 AREAS IN POLAR COORDINATES

We may find the area of a region bounded by the graph of a function in polar coordinates and two radius vectors much as we found areas in rectangular coordinates.

Let f be a continuous, nonnegative function in an interval $[a,b]$, and let R be the region bounded by the graph of f and the lines $\theta = a$ and $\theta = b$ (Figure 16.31). Let $P = \{\theta_0, \theta_1, \cdots, \theta_n\}$ be a partition of $[a,b]$, and, as usual, let $f(u_i)$ be the minimum value and $f(v_i)$ the maximum value of f in the subinterval $[\theta_{i-1}, \theta_i]$.

The region bounded by the lines $\theta = \theta_{i-1}$ and $\theta = \theta_i$ and the graph of f contains the sector of a circle with radius $f(u_i)$ and central angle $\Delta\theta_i = \theta_i - \theta_{i-1}$, and in turn is contained in the sector with radius $f(v_i)$ and central angle $\Delta\theta_i$ (Figure 16.31); thus

$$\tfrac{1}{2}f^2(u_i)\,\Delta\theta_i \le \Delta A_i \le \tfrac{1}{2}f^2(v_i)\,\Delta\theta_i,$$

where ΔA_i designates the area of this region. Since the sum of the ΔA_i, $i = 1, 2, \cdots, n$, is $A(R)$, the area of R, we have

$$\sum_{i=1}^{n} \tfrac{1}{2}f^2(u_i)\,\Delta\theta_i \le A(R) \le \sum_{i=1}^{n} \tfrac{1}{2}f^2(v_i)\,\Delta\theta_i.$$

If now we take a sequence of partitions with norms having limit zero, then each of the above sums approaches the same definite integral, and $A(R)$ must equal this integral; thus the area $A(R)$ of the region R bounded by the graph of f and the lines $\theta = a$ and $\theta = b$ is given by

16.17 $$A(R) = \tfrac{1}{2}\int_a^b f^2(\theta)\,d\theta.$$

EXAMPLE 1. Find the area of the region R bounded by the graph of $r = 1 + \cos\theta$ and the lines $\theta = 0$ and $\theta = \pi/2$ (Figure 16.32).

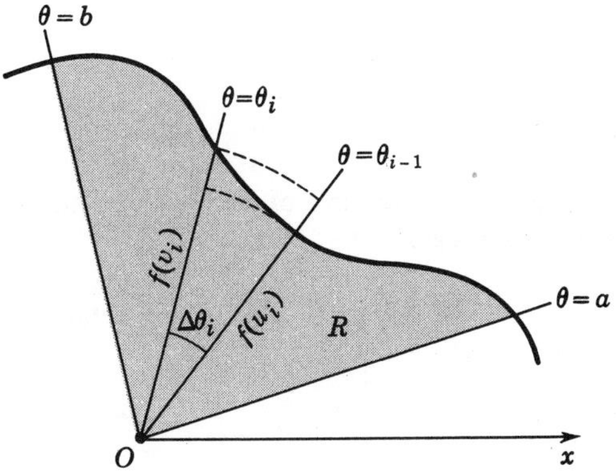

FIGURE 16.31

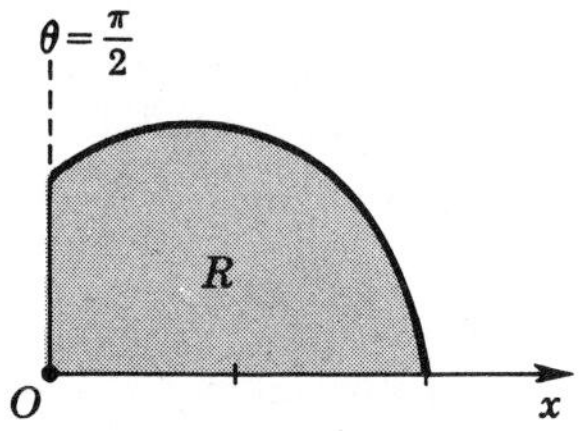

FIGURE 16.32

Solution: By **16.17**,

$$A(R) = \tfrac{1}{2}\int_0^{\pi/2} (1 + \cos\theta)^2\, d\theta = \tfrac{1}{2}\int_0^{\pi/2} (1 + 2\cos\theta + \cos^2\theta)\, d\theta$$

$$= \tfrac{1}{2}\left(\theta + 2\sin\theta + \frac{\theta}{2} + \frac{\sin 2\theta}{4}\right)\Bigg|_0^{\pi/2} = 1 + \frac{3\pi}{8}.$$

EXAMPLE 2. Find the area of one loop of the curve $r = 2\sin 3\theta$.

Solution: The least positive angle θ for which $r = 0$ is $\pi/3$. Thus there is a loop of the curve between $\theta = 0$ and $\theta = \pi/3$ whose area A is given by

$$A = \tfrac{1}{2}\int_0^{\pi/3} (2\sin 3\theta)^2\, d\theta = 2\int_0^{\pi/3} \sin^2 3\theta\, d\theta$$

$$= \frac{2}{3}\left(\frac{3\theta}{3} - \frac{\sin 6\theta}{4}\right)\Bigg|_0^{\pi/3} = \frac{\pi}{3}.$$

EXERCISES

I

In each of Exercises 1–8 find the area of the region bounded by the graphs of the given equations. Sketch each region.

1. $r = \theta;\quad \theta = 0, \theta = \frac{\pi}{2}.$

2. $r = \tan\theta;\quad \theta = \frac{\pi}{6}, \theta = \frac{\pi}{4}.$

3. $r = \frac{1}{\cos\theta};\quad \theta = -\frac{\pi}{4}, \theta = \frac{\pi}{4}.$

4. $r = a\sec^2\frac{\theta}{2};\quad \theta = 0, \theta = \frac{\pi}{2}.$

5. $r = e^{\theta};\quad \theta = 0, \theta = \pi.$

6. $r = \sqrt{\sin\theta};\quad \theta = \frac{\pi}{6}, \theta = \frac{\pi}{2}.$

7. $r = \sqrt{1 - \cos\theta}$; $\theta = \frac{\pi}{2}, \theta = \pi$.

8. $r = \sin\theta + \cos\theta$; $\theta = -\frac{\pi}{4}, \theta = 0$.

In each of Exercises 9–18 find the area of the region bounded by the graph of the equation (find the area of just one loop if there is more than one loop). Sketch each region.

9. $r = 10\cos\theta$.

10. $r = 3\sin\theta$.

11. $r = 1 - \cos\theta$.

12. $r = 2(1 + \sin\theta)$.

13. $r = 2\sin 2\theta$.

14. $r = \cos 4\theta$.

15. $r^2 = \cos 2\theta$.

16. $r^2 = \sin\theta$.

17. $r = a\sin n\theta$, (n a positive integer, $a > 0$).

18. $r^2 = a\cos n\theta$, (n a positive integer, $a > 0$).

In each of Exercises 19–22, find the area of the region common to the two given regions.

19. $r = \cos\theta$, $r = \sin\theta$.

20. $r = 3\cos\theta$, $r = 1 + \cos\theta$.

21. $r = 4(1 + \cos\theta)$, $r = -4\sin\theta$.

22. Find the area of the region between the two loops of the limacon $r = 2 + 4\cos\theta$.

II

1. Find the area of the region inside the graph of the equation $r^2 = 2a^2\cos 2\theta$ and outside the circle $r = a$. Sketch the region.

2. Find the area of the region inside the graph of the equation $r = 3a\sin\theta$ and outside the graph of $r = a(1 + \sin\theta)$. Sketch the region.

3. Find the area of the loop of the graph of the equation $r\cos\theta = a\cos 2\theta$.

4. Find the area of the loop of the curve in Exercise II-9, Section 6.

5. Find the area of the region bounded by the curve in Exercise 4 and its asymptote.

10 ARC LENGTH OF A CURVE

An arc of the graph of a smooth function has length, according to the results of Section 4 of Chapter 9. We shall discuss the more general problem of assigning a length to an arc of a smooth curve in this section.

Given $n + 1$ points $P_0, P_1, P_2, \cdots, P_n$ in the plane, with no two consecutive points the same, we can form the *polygonal curve* having trace $P_0P_1 \cup P_1P_2 \cup \cdots$

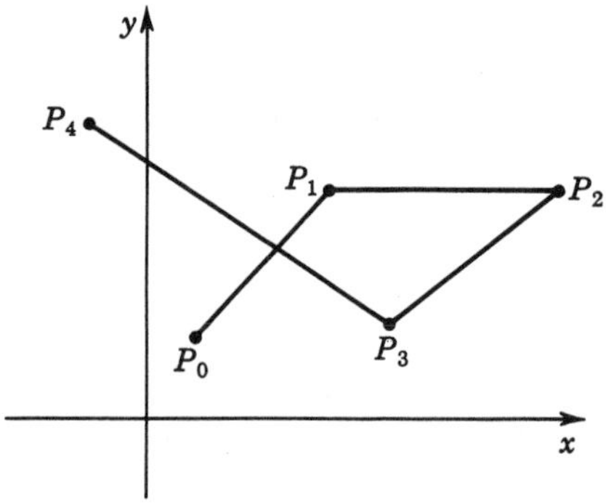

FIGURE 16.33

$\cup\ P_{n-1}P_n$. This is illustrated in Figure 16.33 for $n = 4$. For any given interval $[a,b]$ and any partition $p = \{t_0, t_1, \cdots, t_n\}$ of $[a,b]$ into n subintervals, we can define a curve ρ with domain $[a,b]$ such that ρ is a 1–1curve in each subinterval $[t_{i-1},t_i]$ of p and the trace of ρ over $[t_{i-1},t_i]$ is the line segment $P_{i-1}P_i$. That is, ρ is a polygonal curve having trace $P_0P_1 \cup P_1P_2 \cup \cdots \cup P_{n-1}P_n$.

To see that such a curve can be defined, let A and B be two distinct points in the plane and $\mathbf{v}$ the vector which translates A into B, $B = A + \mathbf{v}$. Then $L = \{A + t\mathbf{v} \mid t \text{ in } \mathsf{R}\}$ is the line passing through A and B, and the segment AB is given by

$$AB = \{A + t\mathbf{v} \mid t \text{ in } [0,1]\}.$$

Thus the curve ρ_1 defined by

$$\rho_1(t) = A + t\mathbf{v}, \qquad \text{domain } \rho_1 = [0,1],$$

is a 1–1 curve and has the segment AB as its trace.

We can easily modify curve ρ_1 to obtain another 1–1 curve ρ_2 whose trace is still AB but whose domain is any prescribed interval $[c,d]$. We define ρ_2 as follows:

$$\rho_2(t) = \rho_1\left(\frac{t-c}{d-c}\right), \qquad \text{domain } \rho_2 = [c,d].$$

To return to the problem stated above, suppose we have constructed 1–1 curves $\rho_1, \rho_2, \cdots, \rho_n$ such that ρ_i has domain $[t_{i-1},t_i]$ and trace $P_{i-1}P_i$, $(i = 1, 2, \cdots, n)$. Then the curve ρ defined by

$$\rho(t) = \rho_i(t) \text{ if } t \text{ is in } [t_{i-1},t_i], \qquad (i = 1, 2, \cdots, n),$$

has domain $[a,b]$ and trace $P_0P_1 \cup P_1P_2 \cup \cdots \cup P_{n-1}P_n$.

EXAMPLE 1. Given points $P_0 = (0,0)$, $P_1 = (1,2)$, $P_2 = (-1,3)$, and $P_3 = (0,0)$, define a polygonal curve ρ with domain $[0,3]$ such that the trace of ρ over $[0,1]$ is P_0P_1, over $[1,2]$ is P_1P_2 and over $[2,3]$ is P_2P_3 (see Figure 16.34).

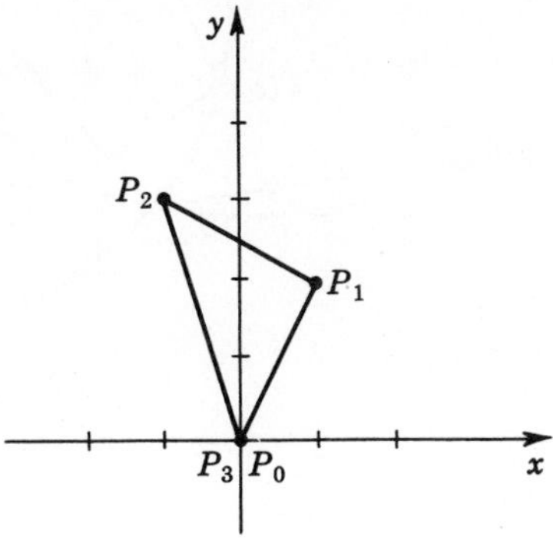

FIGURE 16.34

Solution: If

$$\mathbf{v}_1 = \langle 1,2\rangle, \quad \mathbf{v}_2 = \langle -2,1\rangle, \quad \mathbf{v}_3 = \langle 1,-3\rangle,$$

then $P_0 + \mathbf{v}_1 = P_1$, $P_1 + \mathbf{v}_2 = P_2$, and $P_2 + \mathbf{v}_3 = P_3$. Thus, by our remarks above,

$$\rho(t) = \begin{cases} P_0 + t\mathbf{v}_1 = (t,2t) \text{ if } t \text{ is in } [0,1], \\ P_1 + \left(\dfrac{t-1}{2-1}\mathbf{v}_2\right) = (1 - 2(t-1), 2 + (t-1)) \text{ if } t \text{ is in } [1,2], \\ P_2 + \left(\dfrac{t-2}{3-2}\mathbf{v}_3\right) = (-1 + (t-2), 3 - 3(t-2)) \text{ if } t \text{ is in } [2,3]. \end{cases}$$

If ρ is a polygonal curve with domain $[a,b]$ and trace $P_0P_1 \cup P_1P_2 \cup \cdots \cup P_{n-1}P_n$ as above, then ρ evidently has length $L_a^b(\rho)$ given by

$$L_a^b(\rho) = \sum_{i=1}^{n} d(P_{i-1},P_i).$$

For a nonpolygonal curve λ with domain $[a,b]$, we can approximate the length of the curve by taking a partition $p = \{t_0,t_1, \cdots, t_n\}$ of $[a,b]$ and inscribing a polygonal curve ρ_p in λ, where

$$\rho_p(t_i) = \lambda(t_i), \qquad (i = 0, 1, \cdots, n),$$

and ρ_p is a 1–1 curve and has the line segment $\lambda(t_{i-1})\lambda(t_i)$ for its trace in each interval $[t_{i-1},t_i]$. The case $n = 5$ is illustrated in Figure 16.35. Then the length

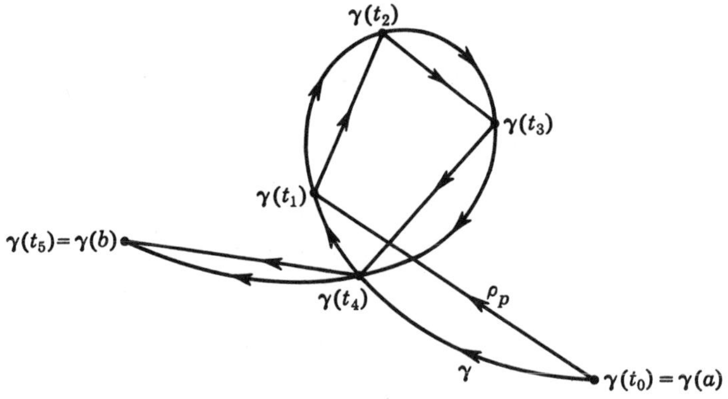

FIGURE 16.35

of λ is approximately equal to the length of ρ_p. It seems clear from Figure 16.35 that $L(^b_a\rho_p)$ is always less than or equal to the length of λ, designated by

$$L_a^b(\lambda).$$

Thus the following definition seems reasonable.

16.18 **DEFINITION.** $L_a^b(\lambda) = \text{l.u.b. } \{L_a^b(\rho_p) \mid p \text{ a partition of } [a,b]\}$.

If the set of all $L_a^b(\rho_p)$ does not have a l.u.b., then the curve λ has no length (or has infinite length).

Let λ be a smooth curve with domain $[a,b]$. For each partition $p = \{t_0,t_1, \cdots, t_n\}$ of $[a,b]$, the polygonal curve ρ_p defined above has length given by

$$L_a^b(\rho_p) = \sum_{i=1}^{n} d(\lambda(t_{i-1}),\lambda(t_i)).$$

If $\lambda(t) = (x(t),y(t))$, then

(1) $$L_a^b(\rho_p) = \sum_{i=1}^{n} \sqrt{[x(t_i) - x(t_{i-1})]^2 + [y(t_i) - y(t_{i-1})]^2}.$$

By the mean value theorem, there exist numbers w_i and z_i in each subinterval $[t_{i-1},t_i]$ of p such that

$$x(t_i) - x(t_{i-1}) = x'(w_i)\,\Delta t_i, \qquad y(t_i) - y(t_{i-1}) = y'(z_i)\,\Delta t_i,$$

where $\Delta t_i = t_i - t_{i-1}$ as usual. With the aid of these equations, (1) may be put in the form

16.19 $$L_a^b(\rho_p) = \sum_{i=1}^{n} \sqrt{x'^2(w_i) + y'^2(z_i)}\,\Delta t_i.$$

Since w_i and z_i need not be the same, the sum above is not a Riemann sum of any function. However, we can imagine taking a sequence of partitions of $[a,b]$ having norm approaching 0, and then taking the limit of the sum in **16.19** relative to this sequence, thereby obtaining the length of curve λ in the form

$$L_a^b(\lambda) = \int_a^b \sqrt{x'^2(t) + y'^2(t)}\, dt.$$

Remembering that $\boldsymbol{\lambda}'(t) = \langle x'(t), y'(t)\rangle$, we are led intuitively to the following result.

16.20 THEOREM. If λ is a smooth curve with domain $[a,b]$, then λ has length $L_a^b(\lambda)$ given by

$$L_a^b(\lambda) = \int_a^b |\boldsymbol{\lambda}'(t)|\, dt.$$

The proof of this theorem will be given in Section 11. In the meantime we shall assume its validity and use it in the examples below.

If λ is the motion of a particle, then $L_a^b(\lambda)$ gives the distance the particle travels from time $t = a$ to time $t = b$. According to **16.20**, the distance traveled is the integral of its speed. When the speed is a constant s, we get the usual formula $L = s(b - a)$ for the distance traveled by the particle.

EXAMPLE 2. Find the length of one arch of the cycloid λ defined by

$$\lambda(t) = (r(t - \sin t), r(1 - \cos t)).$$

Solution: One arch of the cycloid is traced out as t varies from 0 to 2π (see Figure 16.5). Clearly,

$$\boldsymbol{\lambda}'(t) = \langle r(1 - \cos t), r \sin t\rangle$$

and

$$|\boldsymbol{\lambda}'(t)| = \sqrt{r^2(1 - \cos t)^2 + r^2 \sin^2 t} = r\sqrt{2(1 - \cos t)}.$$

Hence

$$L_0^{2\pi}(\lambda) = r\int_0^{2\pi} \sqrt{2(1 - \cos t)}\, dt.$$

Using the identity $1 - \cos t = 2 \sin^2 (t/2)$, we have

$$L_0^{2\pi}(\lambda) = 2r\int_0^{2\pi} \sin \frac{t}{2}\, dt = -4r \cos \frac{t}{2}\Big|_0^{2\pi} = 8r.$$

EXAMPLE 3. The motion of a particle is given by

$$\lambda(t) = (t, 2t\sqrt{t}).$$

Find the distance traveled by the particle from $t = 0$ to $t = 4$.

Solution: Since

$$\lambda'(t) = \langle 1, 3\sqrt{t} \rangle,$$

the speed of the particle is given by

$$|\lambda'(t)| = \sqrt{1+9t}.$$

Hence

$$L_0^4(\lambda) = \int_0^4 \sqrt{1+9t}\,dt = \frac{2}{27}(1+9t)^{3/2}\Big|_0^4 = \frac{2}{27}(37\sqrt{37}-1) \doteq 16.6.$$

If f is a smooth real-valued function in the interval $[a,b]$, then the length L of its graph from a to b was defined in **9.6** to be

$$L = \int_a^b \sqrt{1+f'^2(x)}\,dx.$$

We may obtain this formula from **16.20** by expressing the graph of f as the trace of the curve λ defined by

$$\lambda(t) = (t, f(t)).$$

Then $\lambda'(t) = \langle 1, f'(t)\rangle$ and $|\lambda'(t)| = \sqrt{1+f'^2(t)}$. Thus **16.20** becomes **9.6** if we replace t by x in the integrand.

If the smooth real-valued function f is graphed in a polar coordinate plane, then, by **16.15**, the graph of f is the same as the graph of the curve

$$\lambda(\theta) = (f(\theta)\cos\theta, f(\theta)\sin\theta)$$

in the associated rectangular coordinate plane. We may easily verify that

$$\lambda'(\theta) = \langle -f(\theta)\sin\theta + f'(\theta)\cos\theta, f(\theta)\cos\theta + f'(\theta)\sin\theta\rangle$$

and

$$|\lambda'(\theta)| = \sqrt{f^2(\theta)+f'^2(\theta)}.$$

Hence the length L of the graph of f from $\theta = a$ to $\theta = b$ in polar coordinates is given by

16.21
$$L = \int_a^b \sqrt{f^2(\theta)+f'^2(\theta)}\,d\theta.$$

EXERCISES

I

In each of Exercises 1–5 find the length of the given curve.

1. $\lambda(t) = (t - \sin t, 1 - \cos t)$, domain $\lambda = [0, \pi/3]$.
2. $\lambda(t) = (t^2, t-1)$, domain $\lambda = [-1,1]$.

3. $\lambda(t) = (\ln \sin t, t + 1)$, domain $\lambda = [\pi/6, \pi/2]$.

4. $\lambda(t) = (t, \ln (t^2 - 1))$, domain $\lambda = [-3, -2]$.

5. $\lambda(t) = (\cos t, \cos^2 t)$, domain $\lambda = [0, \pi]$.

In each of Exercises 6–10, find the distance traveled by a particle with the given motion.

6. $\lambda(t) = (3 \cos 2t, 3 \sin 2t)$, between $t = 0$ and $t = 2$.

7. $\lambda(t) = (2t + 1, t^2)$, between $t = 0$ and $t = 2$.

8. $\lambda(t) = (3t^2, 2t^3)$, between $t = 0$ and $t = 3$.

9. $\lambda(t) = (e^t \cos t, e^t \sin t)$, between $t = 0$ and $t = 2$.

10. $\lambda(t) = (3t, t^3)$, between $t = 0$ and $t = 2$. (Approximate by Simpson's rule.)

In each of Exercises 11–15 find the length of the arc given in polar coordinates.

11. $r = e^\theta$, $\theta = 0$ to $\theta = \ln 4$.

12. $r = a(1 - \cos \theta)$, complete curve.

13. $r = \sin^2 \dfrac{\theta}{2}$, $\theta = 0$ to $\theta = \pi$.

14. $r = a\theta^2$, $\theta = 0$ to $\theta = \pi$.

15. $r = \cos^3 \dfrac{\theta}{3}$, complete curve.

16. Show that the length of the graph of the equation $y = \cosh x$ between the points $(0,1)$ and $(x, \cosh x)$, $(x > 0)$, is $\sinh x$.

II

The *centroid* $(\bar{x}, \bar{y})$ of a smooth curve λ given by $\lambda(t) = (x(t), y(t))$, domain $\lambda = [t_1, t_2]$, is defined by

$$\bar{x} = \frac{1}{L} \int_{t_1}^{t_2} x(t)|\lambda'(t)|\, dt, \qquad \bar{y} = \frac{1}{L} \int_{t_1}^{t_2} y(t)|\lambda'(t)|\, dt,$$

where L is the length of the curve. In each of Exercises 1–3, find the centroid of the given curve.

1. $\lambda(t) = (t, t^2)$, domain $\lambda = [-2, 2]$.

2. $\lambda(t) = (r \cos t, r \sin t)$, domain $\lambda = [-a, a]$. (Check your answer for $a \to 0$ and $a = \pi$.)

3. $\lambda(t) = (t, \cosh t)$, domain $\lambda = [-1, 1]$.

4. Determine the integral expressions for the centroid $(\bar{r}, \bar{\theta})$ of an arc given in polar coordinates.

5. Knowing the centroid of a semicircular arc, show how to find the centroid of a quarter-circular arc.

6. As a converse of Exercise I-16, describe the class of curves $\lambda(t) = (t,f(t))$, domain $\lambda = [0,t_0]$, having length $\sinh t_0$.

7. Sketch and find the length of the closed curve with parametric equations $x = a\cos^3 t$, $y = b\sin^3 t$. (Check your answer by letting $a = b$.)

8. Show that the perimeter L of the curve $\lambda(t) = (a\cos t, b\sin t)$, domain $\lambda = [0,2\pi]$, satisfies

$$L = 4\int_0^{\pi/4} \{\sqrt{a^2\cos^2 t + b^2\sin^2 t} + \sqrt{a^2\sin^2 t + b^2\cos^2 t}\}\, dt.$$

Then by considering the minimum and maximum values of each term of the integrand, show also that

$$\pi(b + \sqrt{(a^2 + b^2)/2}) \leq L \leq \pi(a + \sqrt{(a^2 + b^2)/2}), \quad (a \geq b).$$

11 PROOF OF THE ARC-LENGTH FORMULA

As in Section 10, let

$$\lambda(t) = (x(t),y(t)), \qquad \text{domain } \lambda = [a,b],$$

be a smooth curve. Since the functions x' and y' are continuous by assumption, so are the functions x'^2 and y'^2 and each of these functions assumes a maximum value in $[a,b]$. Let $x'^2(u)$ and $y'^2(v)$ be the maximum values of x'^2 and y'^2, respectively, in $[a,b]$.

We recall that corresponding to each partition

$$p = \{t_0, t_1, \cdots, t_n\}$$

of $[a,b]$ is the polygonal curve ρ_p with length given by **16.19**. Since

$$\sqrt{x'^2(w_i) + y'^2(z_i)} \leq \sqrt{x'^2(u) + y'^2(v)}$$

for each number w_i and z_i appearing in **16.19**, evidently

$$L_a^b(\rho_p) \leq \sqrt{x'^2(u) + y'^2(v)} \sum_{i=1}^{n} \Delta t_i.$$

The sum of the Δt_i is $b - a$, and therefore

16.22 $$L_a^b(\rho_p) \leq (b - a)\sqrt{x'^2(u) + y'^2(v)}.$$

Inequality **16.22** holds for every partition p of $[a,b]$. Thus the right side of **16.22** is an upper bound of the set S of all $L_a^b(\rho_p)$. This proves, incidentally, that arc length is well defined by **16.18**, since by **7.2** every set S of numbers with an upper bound has a l.u.b.

In what follows we shall use L_a^b in place of $L_a^b(\lambda)$ for the length of the curve λ from a to b, and L_p for the length of any polygonal curve ρ_p associated with λ. From **16.22** and the definition of L_a^b, we have that

$$L_p \leq L_a^b \leq (b - a)\sqrt{x'^2(u) + y'^2(v)}$$

for every partition p of $[a,b]$.

A desirable property of arc length is that of *additivity*. That is, if a curve is cut into two pieces, then the length of the entire curve is the sum of the lengths of the two pieces.

16.23 If $a < c < b$, then $L_a^b = L_a^c + L_c^b$.

Proof: If p is a partition of $[a,c]$ and q a partition of $[c,b]$, then p and q together form a partition r of $[a,b]$. Clearly, $L_p + L_q = L_r$, and since $L_r \leq L_a^b$, we have

$$L_p \leq L_a^b - L_q$$

for every partition p of $[a,c]$. Thus $L_a^b - L_q$ is an upper bound of the set $\{L_p \mid p \text{ a partition of } [a,c]\}$, and since L_a^c is the l.u.b. of this set, we must have

$$L_a^c \leq L_a^b - L_q.$$

This inequality may be put in the form $L_q \leq L_a^b - L_a^c$, from which we deduce that

$$L_c^b \leq L_a^b - L_a^c,$$

by the same argument as before. Hence we have proved that

$$(1) \qquad L_a^c + L_c^b \leq L_a^b.$$

On the other hand, if r is a partition of $[a,b]$, let us form the partition r' by dividing the subinterval $[t_{i-1},t_i]$ of r containing c into two subintervals $[t_{i-1},c]$ and $[c,t_i]$. Thus r' has one more subinterval than does r, or the same number if $c = t_i$ for some i. In either case, it is clear that

$$L_r \leq L_{r'},$$

as indicated in Figure 16.36. The partition r' of $[a,b]$ is made up of a partition p of $[a,c]$ and a partition q of $[c,b]$, so that

$$L_r \leq L_p + L_q \leq L_a^c + L_c^b.$$

Hence

$$L_a^b \leq L_a^c + L_c^b;$$

this inequality and inequality (1) prove **16.23**.

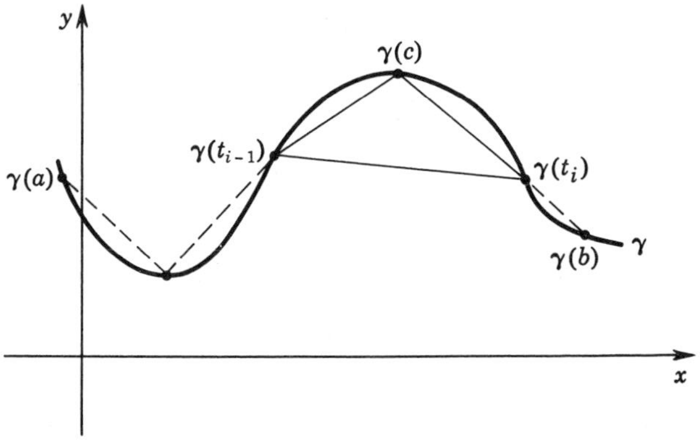

FIGURE 16.36

We may define an *arc-length function* s for the curve λ in the following way:

$$s(t) = L_a^t \text{ if } t > a,$$
$$s(a) = 0.$$

Thus $s(t)$ is the length of the curve λ from a to t. Let us prove now that the function s has a derivative given by

16.24
$$s'(t) = \sqrt{x'^2(t) + y'^2(t)}.$$

Proof: If $h > 0$, then

$$s(t + h) - s(t) = L_t^{t+h},$$

by the additivity of arc length. Hence, by 16.22 (with $a = t, b = t + h$),

(1)
$$s(t + h) - s(t) \leq h\sqrt{x'^2(u) + y'^2(v)}$$

for some numbers u and v in the interval $[t, t + h]$. If we let $p = \{t, t + h\}$, the partition of $[t, t + h]$ into one subinterval, we have, by 16.19,

$$L_p = h\sqrt{x'^2(w) + y'^2(z)}$$

for some numbers w and z in the interval $[t, t + h]$. Since $L_p \leq L_t^{t+h}$, we must have

(2)
$$h\sqrt{x'^2(w) + y'^2(z)} \leq s(t + h) - s(t).$$

We may combine (1) and (2) into one inequality

$$h\sqrt{x'^2(w) + y'^2(z)} \leq s(t + h) - s(t) \leq h\sqrt{x'^2(u) + y'^2(v)}.$$

Dividing throughout this inequality by the positive number h, we get

$$(3) \qquad \sqrt{x'^2(w) + y'^2(z)} \le \frac{s(t+h) - s(t)}{h} \le \sqrt{x'^2(u) + y'^2(v)}.$$

It may be verified that (3) holds even if $h < 0$.

Since the numbers u, v, w, and z are between t and $t + h$,

$$\lim_{h\to 0} x'^2(w) = \lim_{h\to 0} x'^2(u) = x'^2(t),$$

$$\lim_{h\to 0} y'^2(z) = \lim_{h\to 0} y'^2(v) = y'^2(t),$$

and the two extremes of (3) have the same limit as h approaches 0. Thus

$$s'(t) = \lim_{h\to 0} \frac{s(t+h) - s(t)}{h} = \sqrt{x'^2(t) + y'^2(t)},$$

and **16.24** is established.

Theorem **16.20** follows readily from this last result by integration. Thus

$$\int_a^b \sqrt{x'^2(t) + y'^2(t)}\, dt = \int_a^b s'(t)\, dt = s(b) - s(a) = s(b),$$

and $s(b) = L_a^b(\lambda)$, the length of curve λ.

12 AREA OF A SURFACE OF REVOLUTION

If a curve is rotated about a line in its plane, it sweeps out a surface of revolution. The theory of the preceding sections may be used to assign an area to such a surface.

Let λ be a smooth curve with domain $[a,b]$, with $\lambda(t) = (x(t),y(t))$ for every t in $[a,b]$. We shall also assume that the curve λ is above the x axis; i.e., that $y(t) \ge 0$ for every t in $[a,b]$. Let us find the area of the surface swept out by rotating λ about the x axis.

If $p = \{t_0, t_x, \cdots, t_n\}$ is a partition of $[a,b]$, let L_p designate the length of the polygonal curve ρ_p associated with λ, as in the preceding section. It seems reasonable that if ρ_p is rotated about the x axis, it will sweep out a surface with area approximating that of the given surface. The surface generated by ρ_p is made up of n frustums of cones. A frustum of a cone of slant height h and radii of bases r_1 and r_2 (Figure 16.37) has lateral surface area

$$\pi(r_1 + r_2)h,$$

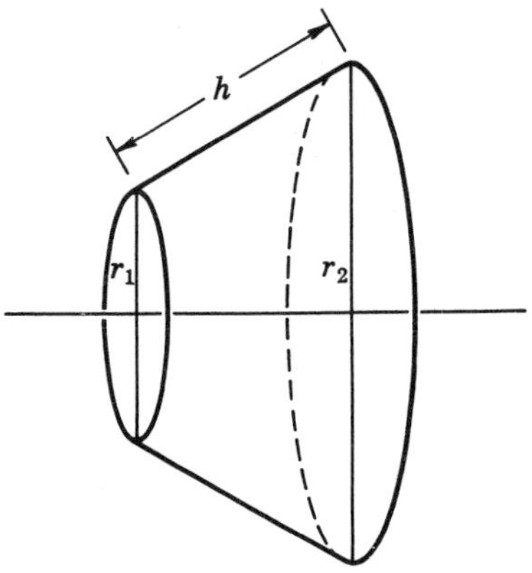

FIGURE 16.37

according to a formula of geometry. Hence the ith segment $\lambda(t_{i-1})\lambda(t_i)$ of ρ_p (Figure 16.38) sweeps out a frustum of a cone of lateral area

$$\pi[y(t_{i-1}) + y(t_i)]d(\lambda(t_{i-1}), \lambda(t_i)).$$

Using the value of $d(\lambda(t_{i-1}), \lambda(t_i))$ given in **16.19**, we find that the total area S_p of the surface swept out by ρ_p is given by

$$S_p = \pi \sum_{i=1}^{n} [y(t_{i-1}) + y(t_i)] \sqrt{x'^2(w_i) + y'^2(z_i)}\, \Delta t_i,$$

where w_i and z_i are numbers in the interval $[t_{i-1},t_i]$.

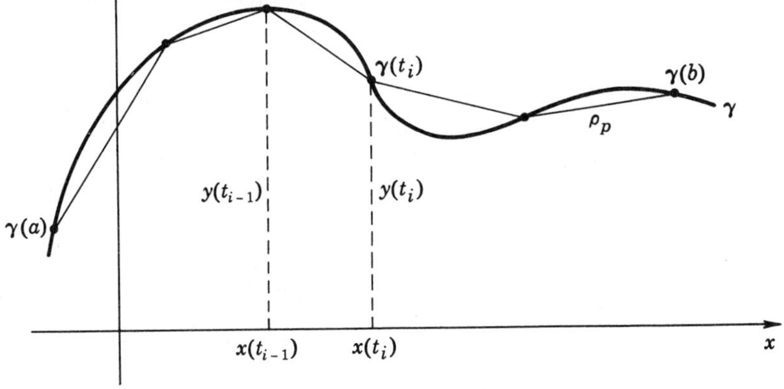

FIGURE 16.38

In the limit as the norm of p approaches zero, we can imagine that the above formula yields

16.25 $$S = 2\pi \int_a^b y(t)|\lambda'(t)|\,dt$$

as the area of the surface swept out by rotating curve λ about the x axis. Although we shall not give a formal proof of **16.25**, we shall nevertheless accept its validity.

If the curve λ is rotated about the y axis, we get the same formula with the factor $y(t)$ replaced by $x(t)$ in the integrand.

If a curve λ is the graph of an equation

$$y = f(x),$$

then **16.25** becomes [letting $x = t$, $y = f(t)$]

16.26 $$S = 2\pi \int_a^b f(x)\sqrt{1 + f'^2(x)}\,dx.$$

EXAMPLE 1. Find the area of the surface generated by rotating the curve

$$\lambda(t) = (t^2, 2t), \qquad \text{domain } \lambda = [0,4].$$

about the x axis.

Solution: By **16.25**,

$$S = 2\pi \int_0^4 2t\sqrt{(2t)^2 + (2)^2}\,dt$$

$$= \frac{8\pi}{3}(t^2 + 1)^{3/2}\Big|_0^4 = \frac{8\pi}{3}(17\sqrt{17} - 1).$$

EXAMPLE 2. Find the area of the surface generated by rotating one arch of the sine curve about its axis.

Solution: If we rotate the graph of the curve $y = \sin x$ between $x = 0$ and $x = \pi$ about the x axis, we obtain a surface with area (using **16.26**)

$$S = 2\pi \int_0^\pi \sin x\sqrt{1 + \cos^2 x}\,dx.$$

This may be integrated by letting $u = \cos x$; thus we obtain

$$S = -2\pi \int_1^{-1} \sqrt{1 + u^2}\,du$$

$$= -2\pi\left[\frac{u}{2}\sqrt{1 + u^2} + \frac{1}{2}\ln\left(u + \sqrt{1 + u^2}\right)\right]\Big|_1^{-1}$$

$$= 2\pi[\sqrt{2} + \ln(\sqrt{2} + 1)].$$

EXERCISES

I

In each of Exercises 1–8 find the area of the surface obtained by rotating the given curve about the x axis.

1. $\lambda(t) = (t^2/2,t)$, domain $\lambda = [1,3]$.
2. $\lambda(t) = (2t^3,3t^2)$, domain $\lambda = [0,2]$.
3. $\lambda(t) = (\cos^2 t, \sin t \cos t)$, domain $\lambda = [0,\pi/2]$.
4. $\lambda(t) = (2 \ln t, t^2)$, domain $\lambda = [1,3]$.
5. $y = x^3$, between $x = 0$ and $x = 2$.
6. $y = \cosh x$, between $x = -1$ and $x = 1$.
7. $y = e^x$, between $x = -2$ and $x = 2$.
8. $y = 2\sqrt{x}$, between $x = 1$ and $x = 4$.
9. Find the surface area of a sphere.
10. The cardioid $r = a(1 + \cos\theta)$ is rotated about the polar axis. Find the area of the surface generated.
11. One loop of the lemniscate $r^2 = a^2 \cos 2\theta$ is rotated about the polar axis. Find the area of the surface generated.
12. Find the area of the surface of an ellipsoid of revolution.

II

1. Prove the following *second theorem of Pappus:* If an arc of a plane curve, lying on one side of a line L in its plane, is revolved about L, then the area of the surface generated is equal to the product of the length of the arc and the distance traveled by the centroid of the arc. (See Exercises II, Section 10, for the definition of the centroid of an arc.)

Use Exercise 1 to work each of Exercises 2–4.

2. Find the surface area of the torus generated by rotating the circle $x^2 + (y - b)^2 = r^2$, $(b > r)$, about the x axis.
3. Find the lateral surface area of a right circular cone of radius r and height h.
4. Find the centroid of a semicircular arc.
5. The part of a sphere between two parallel planes is called a *zone.* Show that the area of a zone of a sphere is $2\pi ah$, where a is the radius of the sphere and h is the height of the zone, i.e., the distance between the parallel planes.

REVIEW

Oral Exercises

1. What is a plane curve?
2. What is a vector?
3. Give a geometric interpretation of the sum and difference of two vectors.
4. Give a geometric or physical interpretation of the inner product of two vectors.
5. What is Cauchy's inequality?
6. What are polar coordinates?
7. How can one transform from polar coordinates to rectangular coordinates and vice versa?
8. How can one determine symmetries of a curve whose equation is given in polar coordinates?
9. What difficulty arises in finding all points of intersection of two curves in polar coordinates?
10. What is the integral for the area of a surface of revolution?

I

In each of Exercises 1–4 discuss the curve λ, describe its direction, and sketch its trace. Also, sketch the velocity and acceleration vectors at the given time t.

1. $\lambda(t) = (\cosh t, \sinh t)$, domain $\lambda = [0,2]$, $t = 1$.
2. $\lambda(t) = (\sec t, \tan t)$, domain $\lambda = [0,\frac{1}{4}\pi]$, $t = \frac{1}{6}\pi$.
3. $\lambda(t) = (t - 3, 3t + 4)$, domain $\lambda = [-4,2]$, $t = 0$.
4. $\lambda(t) = (\cos t^2, \sin t^2)$, domain $\lambda = [0,\sqrt{2\pi}]$, $t = \sqrt{\pi/2}$.
5. Why is the acceleration vector in Exercise 4 not directed toward the origin even though the path is a circle?

In each of Exercises 6–12 sketch a graph of the equation $r = a + b \cos \theta$. (Choose appropriate values for a and b.)

6. $a = b > 0$.
7. $a > b > 0$.
8. $b > a > 0$.
9. $a < b < 0$.
10. $b < a < 0$.
11. $a < 0 < b$.
12. $b < 0 < a$.

13. a. Show that if $A^2 + B^2 = 1$, then there is an angle θ such that $\cos\theta = A$, $\sin\theta = B$. [Consider an angle in standard position whose terminal side is on the point (A,B).]

b. Show that if $P = (x,y)$ is on the graph of the equation $x^2/a^2 + y^2/b^2 = 1$, then there is an angle θ such that $P = (a\cos\theta, a\sin\theta)$.

c. Let $a > b > 0$, and let $c = \sqrt{a^2 - b^2}$. Then $b = \sqrt{a^2 - c^2}$. Consider the points $F_1(-c,0)$, $F_2(c,0)$. Show that $|PF_1| + |PF_2| = 2a$. (This is a solution of Exercise 15, page 000.)

14. Use the method of Exercise 13 to solve Exercise 15, page 000. (Show that if $A^2 - B^2 = 1$, then the angle θ in standard position whose terminal line lies on the point $(1/A, B/A)$ is such that $\sec\theta = A$, $\tan\theta = B$.)

In each of Exercises 15–18 sketch the graph, find the area of the region bounded by the graph, and find the length of the graph.

15. $r = 2 + 2\sin\theta$.

16. $r = \cos\theta - 1$.

17. $r = \cos^2\dfrac{\theta}{2}$.

18. $r = a\cos\theta + b\sin\theta$.

In each of Exercises 19–21, sketch the graphs of the given pair of equations on the same coordinate axes.

19. $r = 1 + \sin\theta, \quad r = \dfrac{1}{1 + \sin\theta}$.

20. $r = 1 + 2\sin\theta, \quad r = \dfrac{1}{1 + 2\sin\theta}$.

21. $r = 1 + \frac{1}{2}\sin\theta, \quad r = \dfrac{1}{1 + \frac{1}{2}\sin\theta}$.

In each of Exercises 22–24 find the area of the surface of revolution generated by revolving the graph of the given equation about the x axis.

22. $x^{2/3} + y^{2/3} = a^{2/3}$.

23. $x^3 = k^2 y$, between $x = 0$ and $x = k$.

24. $y = e^{-x}$ in $[0, \infty]$.

25. If the curve with parametric equations

$$x = x(t), \qquad y = y(t)$$

also has equation $y = f(x)$, then show that

$$\frac{d^2y}{dx^2} = \frac{(d/dt)(dy/dx)}{dx/dt} = \frac{x'(t)y''(t) - y'(t)x''(t)}{(x'(t))^3}.$$

[*Hint:* The derivative f' is given parametrically by

$$x = x(t), \qquad \frac{dy}{dx} = \frac{y'(t)}{x'(t)}.\Big]$$

In each of Exercises 26–30 assume that the curve given parametrically is also the graph of an equation $y = f(x)$. Then use Exercise 25 to find dy/dx and d^2y/dx^2 for each curve.

26. $x = 3t, \quad y = 2t^3$.

27. $x = e^t, \quad y = te^{-t}$.

28. $x = r(\theta - \sin\theta), \quad y = r(1 - \cos\theta)$.

29. $x = a\cos^3\theta, \quad y = a\sin^3\theta$.

30. $x = \ln t, \quad y = t^3$.

II

1. Sketch the folium of Descartes: $x^3 + y^3 - 3axy = 0$. [*Hint:* Obtain a parametric representation by letting $y = tx$.]

2. How is Exercise 1 related to Exercise II-9, Section 6?

3. A thin string is wound about a circular spool. One end of the string is being unwound from the spool, always being kept taut. Show that the curve λ (called the *involute*) traced out by the free end is given by $\lambda(t) = (r\cos t + rt\sin t, r\sin t - rt\cos t)$.

4. Show that if F and G are functions such that $F(\pi + \theta) = -G(\theta)$ for all θ then the graphs of the equations $r = F(\theta)$ and $r = G(\theta)$ are congruent.

5. Which of the following pairs of equations have congruent graphs?

a. $r = a + b\sin\theta, \quad r = -a + b\sin\theta$.

b. $r = a\sin 2\theta, \quad r = a\cos 2\theta$.

c. $r = a\sin 3\theta, r = a\cos 3\theta$.

6. Show that a point (a,α) is a point of intersection of the graphs of the equations $r = F(\theta)$ and $r = G(\theta)$ if, for some integers m and n, either (a), $a = F(\alpha + 2m\pi) = G(\alpha + 2n\pi)$, (b), $a = F(\alpha + 2m\pi) = -G(\alpha + (2n + 1)\pi)$, or (c), $a = F(\alpha + (2m + 1)\pi) = G(\alpha + (2n + 1)\pi)$.

7. Find all points of intersection of the graphs of the equations $r = 2\cos\frac{1}{2}\theta$ and $r = 2\sin\frac{1}{2}\theta$.

8. If a point moves along a curve whose polar equation is $r = f(\theta)$, the motion is completely described by giving θ as a function of the time t.

a. Give a physical interpretation of dr/dt, $d\theta/dt$, and $r\,d\theta/dt$. (In the notation of Newton, $dr/dt = r$, $d\theta/dt = \theta$, $r\,d\theta/dt = r\theta$. Also, $d^2r/dt^2 = r$.)

b. Show that the speed of the moving point is given by $\sqrt{r^2 + r^2\theta^2}$.

c. Prove that the rate of change of the area A swept out by the vector drawn from the origin to the point $(r\cos\theta, r\sin\theta)$ is given by $A = \frac{1}{2}r^2\theta$. (A is called the *areal velocity* of the moving point.)

9. One of Kepler's laws states that each planet moves along an ellipse with the sun at one of the foci and that each planet moves with constant areal velocity. Show that the speed of the planet, when it is furthest from the sun, is given by $2k/a(1 + e)$, where k is the areal velocity, a the semimajor axis, and e the eccentricity of the ellipse.

10. For the moving point in Exercise 8, show that the components of the acceleration along the vector in part **c** and the normal to it are given by $a_r = r - r\theta^2$, and $a_\theta = r\theta + 2r\theta$, respectively.

11. Show that the motion of a particle attracted by a central force has a constant areal velocity. [*Hint:* Use Exercises 8 and 10.]

12. If we represent the position of the moving point in Exercise 8 by the complex number $R = r\,e^{i\theta} = r\cos\theta + i\,r\sin\theta$, show that R and R represent the velocity and acceleration of the moving point in complex form. Then obtain the results of Exercises 8 and 10 from this. [*Hint:* Note that the complex number $e^{i\theta}$ is equivalent to the unit vector $\langle\cos\theta, \sin\theta\rangle$ and that $i\,e^{i\theta}$ is equivalent to a unit vector perpendicular to $\langle\cos\theta, \sin\theta\rangle$.]

13. Referring to Exercise I-25, find: (a), d^3y/dx^3 in parametric form; (b), d^2y/dx^2 and d^3y/dx^3 in terms of dx/dy, d^2x/dy^2, and d^3x/dy^3.

17

THREE-DIMENSIONAL ANALYTIC GEOMETRY

COORDINATE SYSTEMS may be introduced into three-dimensional space much as they are in the plane. It will be convenient to introduce both a three-dimensional space of points and one of vectors, just as was done in Chapter 16 for the plane.

1 THREE-DIMENSIONAL SPACE OF POINTS

Three mutually perpendicular coordinate lines in space allow us to introduce coordinates in space. The three coordinate lines, called the x axis, the y axis, and the z axis, are assumed to have the same scale and to meet at their origins. If the axes are oriented as in Figure 17.1, the coordinate system is said to be right-handed. If the x and y axes were interchanged, it would be left-handed. For the most part, we shall use a right-handed coordinate system. Three coordinate planes are determined by the axes, namely the xy plane containing the x and y axes, the xz plane, and the yz plane.

Each point P in space may be projected onto the coordinate axes. If the projections of P on the x, y, and z axes, respectively, have coordinates x, y, and z, then P itself is said to have coordinates (x,y,z). The three planes through P parallel to the coordinate planes form a parallelepiped with the coordinate planes. The coordinates of the vertices of this parallelepiped are shown in Figure 17.2.

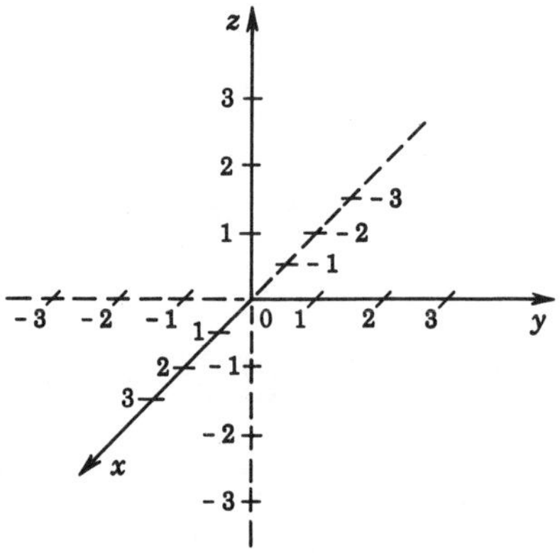

FIGURE 17.1

Just as each point in space has a unique triple of coordinates, so each triple of numbers determines a unique point in space having the triple of numbers as coordinates. This association of triples of numbers with points in space is called a *rectangular coordinate system* in space.

The three coordinate planes separate space into eight parts, called *octants.* We shall need to refer explicitly only to the *first octant*, consisting of all points $P(x,y,z)$ such that $x > 0$, $y > 0$, and $z > 0$.

Distances may be found between points in space by the following analogue of the formula for the plane.

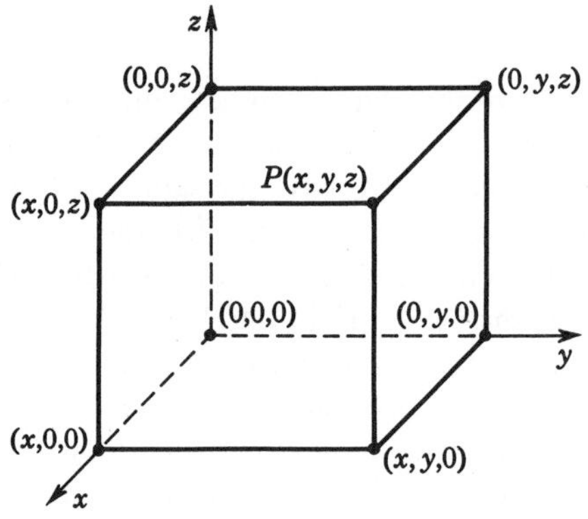

FIGURE 17.2

17.1 **DISTANCE FORMULA.** The distance between the points $P(x_1,y_1,z_1)$ and $Q(x_2,y_2,z_2)$ is given by

$$|PQ| = \sqrt{(x_2 - x_1)^2 + (y_2 - y_1)^2 + (z_2 - z_1)^2}.$$

Proof: Construct a parallelepiped having its faces parallel to the coordinate planes and having P and Q as opposite vertices. If $A(x_2,y_1,z_1)$ and $B(x_2,y_2,z_1)$ are chosen as in Figure 17.3, then

$$|PA| = |x_2 - x_1|, \quad |AB| = |y_2 - y_1|, \quad |BQ| = |z_2 - z_1|.$$

Triangle PAB has a right angle at A, and triangle PBQ has a right angle at B.

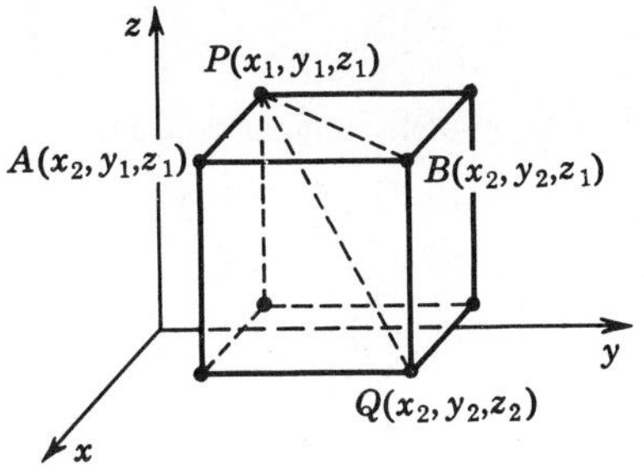

FIGURE 17.3

Hence $|PA|^2 + |AB|^2 = |PB|^2$, $|PB|^2 + |BQ|^2 = |PQ|^2$, and therefore

$$|PQ|^2 = |PA|^2 + |AB|^2 + |BQ|^2 = (x_2 - x_1)^2 + (y_2 - y_1)^2 + (z_2 - z_1)^2.$$

This establishes the distance formula.

The parallelepiped of Figure 17.3 reduces to a rectangle (or a line segment) if P and Q lie in a plane parallel to a coordinate plane. In this case, either $|PA|$, $|AB|$, or $|BQ|$ is zero. However, the distance formula may easily be shown still to hold.

As a particular case of **17.1**, the distance from the origin O to the point $P(x,y,z)$ is given by

$$|OP| = \sqrt{x^2 + y^2 + z^2}.$$

Thus the point $P(x,y,z)$ is on the sphere having radius r and center at the origin O if and only if

$$x^2 + y^2 + z^2 = r^2.$$

Therefore this is an equation of the sphere. A more general consequence of the distance formula is stated without proof below.

17.2 THEOREM. The sphere of radius r having its center at the point (x_0,y_0,z_0) has equation

$$(x - x_0)^2 + (y - y_0)^2 + (z - z_0)^2 = r^2.$$

Since every equation of the form

$$x^2 + y^2 + z^2 + ax + by + cz + d = 0$$

can be put in the form of the equation of 17.2 by completing squares, its graph, if it exists, is a sphere.

EXAMPLE 1. Discuss the graph of the equation

$$x^2 + y^2 + z^2 - 6x + 2y - z - \tfrac{23}{4} = 0.$$

Solution: We first complete squares as follows:

$$(x^2 - 6x + 9) + (y^2 + 2y + 1) + (z^2 - z + \tfrac{1}{4}) = \tfrac{23}{4} + 9 + 1 + \tfrac{1}{4},$$
$$(x - 3)^2 + (y + 1)^2 + (z - \tfrac{1}{2})^2 = 16.$$

Hence the graph is a sphere of radius 4 with center at $(3,-1,\frac{1}{2})$.

In subsequent chapters we shall have occasion to use the set of all points inside a sphere. Such a set is called an *open ball.* If $B(P,r)$ designates the open ball with center $P(x_0,y_0,z_0)$ and radius r, then, by 17.2,

$$B(P,r) = \{(x,y,z) \mid (x - x_0)^2 + (y - y_0)^2 + (z - z_0)^2 < r^2\}.$$

The *closed ball* $B[P,r]$ consists of the open ball together with the sphere,

$$B[P,r] = \{(x,y,z) \mid (x - x_0)^2 + (y - y_0)^2 + (z - z_0)^2 \leq r^2\}.$$

If in Figure 17.3 we imagine a plane parallel to the yz plane cutting the parallelepiped into two equal parts, then this plane will bisect the line segments PA, PB, and PQ. Since the midpoint of PA has x coordinate $(x_1 + x_2)/2$, the midpoint of PQ will also have this x coordinate. A continuation of this argument yields the following result.

17.3 MIDPOINT FORMULA. The segment with endpoints (x_1,y_1,z_1) and (x_2,y_2,z_2) has midpoint

$$\left(\frac{x_1 + x_2}{2}, \frac{y_1 + y_2}{2}, \frac{z_1 + z_2}{2}\right).$$

EXAMPLE 2. Show that $A(2,-1,1)$, $B(5,2,1)$, and $C(1,6,5)$ are the vertices of a right triangle with hypotenuse AC. Find an equation of the sphere having AC as a diameter and passing through the point B.

Solution: We have

$$|AB|^2 = (5-2)^2 + (2+1)^2 = 18,$$
$$|AC|^2 = (1-2)^2 + (6+1)^2 + (5-1)^2 = 66,$$
$$|BC|^2 = (1-5)^2 + (6-2)^2 + (5-1)^2 = 48.$$

Since $|AB|^2 + |BC|^2 = |AC|^2$, then ABC is a right triangle with hypotenuse AC. The point M with coordinates

$$\left(\frac{2+1}{2}, \frac{-1+6}{2}, \frac{1+5}{2}\right),$$

or $(\frac{3}{2},\frac{5}{2},3)$, is the midpoint of AC. Thus

$$\left(x-\frac{3}{2}\right)^2 + \left(y-\frac{5}{2}\right)^2 + (z-3)^2 = \frac{33}{2},$$

$$\text{or} \qquad x^2 + y^2 + z^2 - 3x - 5y - 6z + 1 = 0,$$

is an equation of the sphere with center M and radius $|MB| = \frac{1}{2}|AC| = \sqrt{66}/2$.

EXERCISES

I

In each of Exercises 1–6, A and B are the opposite vertices of a parallelepiped having its faces parallel to the coordinate planes. Sketch the parallelepiped, and find the coordinates of its other vertices.

1. $A(0,0,0)$, $B(7,2,3)$.
2. $A(1,1,1)$, $B(3,4,2)$.
3. $A(-1,1,2)$, $B(2,3,5)$.
4. $A(0,-2,2)$, $B(2,0,-2)$.
5. $A(0,-2,-1)$, $B(3,1,0)$.
6. $A(2,-1,-3)$, $B(4,0,-1)$.

In each of Exercises 7–10 show that the three given points are the vertices of a right triangle, and find the equation of the sphere passing through the three points and having its center on the hypotenuse.

7. $(4,4,1)$, $(1,1,1)$, $(0,8,5)$.
8. $(2,1,3)$, $(0,1,2)$, $(1,3,0)$.
9. $(-3,6,0)$, $(-2,-5,-1)$, $(1,4,2)$.
10. $(2,5,-2)$, $(1,3,0)$, $(4,5,-1)$.

In each of Exercises 11–16 discuss the graph of the equation.

11. $x^2 + y^2 + z^2 - 2x - 24 = 0$.
12. $x^2 + y^2 + z^2 + 6x - 2y + 4z + 13 = 0$.
13. $4x^2 + 4y^2 + 4z^2 + 12y - 4z + 1 = 0$.

14. $x^2 + y^2 + z^2 - 2x + 4y - 8z + 21 = 0$.

15. $x^2 + y^2 + z^2 - 6x + 2y + 11 = 0$.

16. $x^2 + y^2 + z^2 - 3x + 4y - z = 0$.

17. Show that (2,4,2), (2,1,5), (5,1,2), and (1,0,1) are the vertices of a regular tetrahedron, and sketch the tetrahedron.

18. Find an equation of the graph of all points equidistant from the points (3,1,2) and (7,5,6). What is the graph?

19. Find an equation of the graph of all points equidistant from the points $(-1,2,1)$ and $(1,-2,-1)$. What is the graph?

20. Let A, B, C, and D be four points in space, with no three of the points collinear, and let P, Q, R, and S be the midpoints of AB, BC, CD, and DA, respectively. Prove that $PQRS$ is a parallelogram.

II

In each of Exercises 1–6 discuss the graph in space of the given equation or system of equations.

1. $z = 2$.

2. $x = y$.

3. $\begin{cases} x = 0 \\ y = 0. \end{cases}$

4. $\begin{cases} x = z \\ y = z. \end{cases}$

5. $|y| + |z| = 1$.

6. $x^2 + y^2 = 2x + 2y + 2$.

7. Under what conditions on the function F is the graph of the equation $F(x,y,z) = 0$ symmetric with respect to the xy plane? The yz plane? The xz plane?

8. Under what conditions on the function F is the graph of the equation $F(x,y,z) = 0$ symmetric with respect to the x axis? The y axis? The z axis?

9. Under what conditions on the function F is the graph of the equation $F(x,y,z) = 0$ symmetric with respect to the point (h,k,l)?

10. Show that the three lines joining the midpoints of the opposite edges in pairs of a tetrahedron mutually bisect each other.

11. a. Find all axes of symmetry of a cube.
    b. Find all planes of symmetry of a cube.

12. Do Exercise 11 for a regular tetrahedron.

2 THREE-DIMENSIONAL VECTOR SPACE

The notation R was introduced in Chapter 16 to designate the set of all real numbers, R^2 the set of all points in a rectangular coordinate plane, and V_2 the set of all two-dimensional vectors. In the same spirit, let us designate the set of all points in a rectangular coordinate space by R^3 and the set of all three-dimensional vectors by V_3:

$$\mathsf{R}^3 = \{(a,b,c) \mid a, b, c \text{ in } \mathsf{R}\}, \qquad V_3 = \{\langle h,k,l\rangle \mid h,k,l \text{ in } \mathsf{R}\}.$$

Each vector $\mathbf{v} = \langle h,k,l\rangle$ in V_3 can be represented by a directed line segment $\overrightarrow{PQ}$ in R^3, where the initial point P is any point (a,b,c) and the endpoint Q is then the point $(a + h, b + k, c + l)$, as shown in Figure 17.4. If the initial point of $\mathbf{v}$ is taken to be the origin $(0,0,0)$, then the endpoint of $\mathbf{v}$ is simply the point (h,k,l).

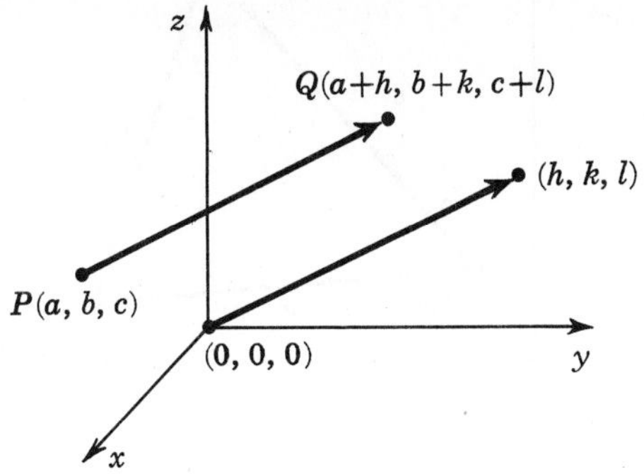

FIGURE 17.4

All the properties of a two-dimensional vector space (Chapter 16, Section 3) carry over to V_3. Thus the operations of addition, scalar multiplication, and inner product are defined by

$$\begin{aligned}\langle h_1,k_1,l_1\rangle + \langle h_2,k_2,l_2\rangle &= \langle h_1 + h_2,\ k_1 + k_2,\ l_1 + l_2\rangle \\ c\langle h,k,l\rangle &= \langle ch,ck,cl\rangle \\ \langle h_1,k_1,l_1\rangle\cdot\langle h_2,k_2,l_2\rangle &= h_1h_2 + k_1k_2 + l_1l_2\end{aligned}$$

and satisfy the associative, commutative, and distributive properties listed in Chapter 16. We denote the zero vector by $\mathbf{0}$,

$$\mathbf{0} = \langle 0,0,0\rangle,$$

and the negative of a vector $\mathbf{v} = \langle h,k,l\rangle$ by $-\mathbf{v}$,

$$-\langle h,k,l\rangle = \langle -h, -k, -l\rangle.$$

The proofs of the various properties of addition, scalar multiplication, and inner product are almost identical with those given in Chapter 16, and hence are omitted.

Geometrically, vector addition is again the familiar triangular addition shown in Figure 17.5, where $\mathbf{u} = \langle h_1,k_1,l_1\rangle$ and $\mathbf{v} = \langle h_2,k_2,l_2\rangle$.

The *length* of a vector $\mathbf{v}$ in V_3 is designated by $|\mathbf{v}|$ and defined to be

$$|\mathbf{v}| = \sqrt{\mathbf{v}\cdot\mathbf{v}}.$$

Thus if $\mathbf{v} = \langle h,k,l\rangle$, then

$$|\mathbf{v}| = \sqrt{h^2 + k^2 + l^2}.$$

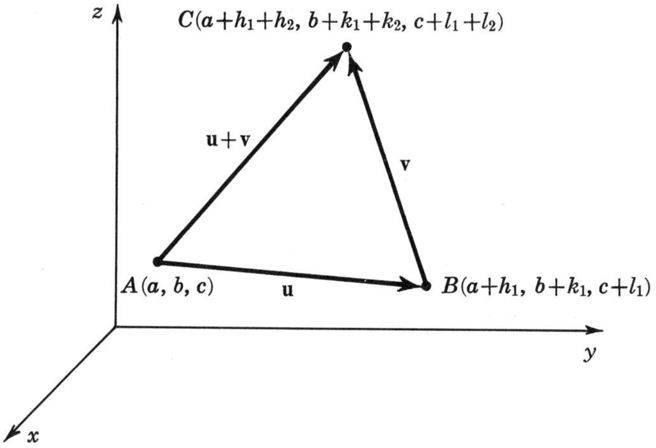

FIGURE 17.5

Clearly, $|\mathbf{v}| \geq 0$, with $|\mathbf{v}| = 0$ if and only if $\mathbf{v} = \mathbf{0}$. The length function has the usual properties stated in Chapter 16:

$$|c\mathbf{v}| = |c||\mathbf{v}|$$

$$|\mathbf{u}\cdot\mathbf{v}| \leq |\mathbf{u}||\mathbf{v}| \qquad \text{(Cauchy inequality)}$$

$$|\mathbf{u} + \mathbf{v}| \leq |\mathbf{u}| + |\mathbf{v}| \qquad \text{(triangle inequality).}$$

These properties hold for all vectors $\mathbf{u}$ and $\mathbf{v}$ in V_3 and for every scalar c.

A vector $\mathbf{v}$ is called a *unit vector* if $|\mathbf{v}| = 1$. The unit vectors along the x axis, the y axis, and the z axis are designated by $\mathbf{i}$, $\mathbf{j}$, and $\mathbf{k}$, respectively, and are defined by

$$\mathbf{i} = \langle 1,0,0\rangle, \quad \mathbf{j} = \langle 0,1,0\rangle, \quad \mathbf{k} = \langle 0,0,1\rangle.$$

Another example of a unit vector is

$$\mathbf{u} = \langle \tfrac{2}{7},-\tfrac{3}{7},\tfrac{6}{7}\rangle,$$

since $(\frac{2}{7})^2 + (-\frac{3}{7})^2 + (\frac{6}{7})^2 = 1$.

The *angle* θ between two nonzero vectors **u** and **v** in V_3 is defined precisely as it was in V_2. Thus if we let **u** and **v** have the same initial point, θ is the angle of least nonnegative measure having **u** and **v** as its sides (Figure 17.6), $0 \leq \theta \leq \pi$.

By the same argument that was used in Chapter 16, we can show that if α is the angle between the nonzero vectors **u** and **v**, then

17.4 $$\mathbf{u}\cdot\mathbf{v} = |\mathbf{u}||\mathbf{v}| \cos \theta.$$

Hence **u** and **v** are perpendicular if and only if $\mathbf{u}\cdot\mathbf{v} = 0$.

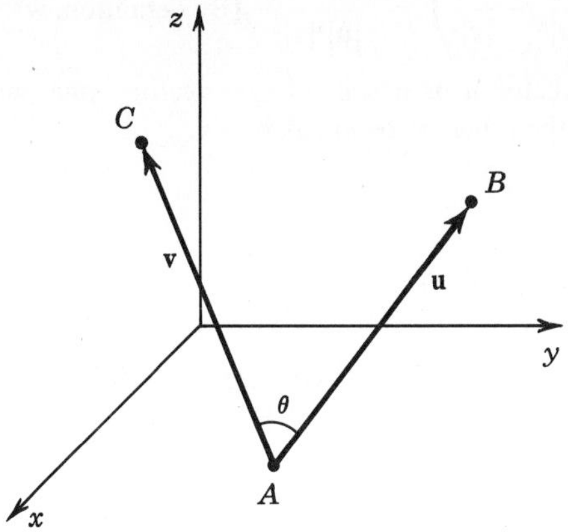

FIGURE 17.6

Each vector $\mathbf{v} = \langle r,s,t \rangle$ may be expressed as a linear combination of the basic vectors **i**, **j**, and **k**,

$$\mathbf{v} = r\mathbf{i} + s\mathbf{j} + t\mathbf{k}.$$

For example,

$$\langle 2,-7,3 \rangle = 2\mathbf{i} - 7\mathbf{j} + 3\mathbf{k}.$$

This fact will be used in subsequent sections of this chapter.

EXERCISES

1. List all the properties of addition, scalar multiplication, and the inner product for V_3.

2. Prove the Cauchy inequality for V_3.

2. Prove the triangle inequality for V_3.

4. If $\mathbf{u} = \mathbf{i} + \mathbf{j} + \mathbf{k}$, $\mathbf{v} = 2\mathbf{i} - 3\mathbf{j} + 4\mathbf{k}$, and $\mathbf{w} = \mathbf{j} - 2\mathbf{k}$, then find:
   a. $|\mathbf{u}|, |\mathbf{v}|, |\mathbf{w}|$.
   b. $\mathbf{u}\cdot\mathbf{v}, \mathbf{u}\cdot(\mathbf{u} + \mathbf{v} + \mathbf{w})$.
   c. $\mathbf{u} + \mathbf{v}, \mathbf{u} - \mathbf{v} + \mathbf{w}$.
   d. $|\mathbf{u} + \mathbf{v} + 2\mathbf{w}|$.

5. If $\mathbf{u}$ and $\mathbf{v}$ are unit vectors and α is the angle between them, then express $|\mathbf{u} - \mathbf{v}|$ in terms of α.

6. Find a unit vector perpendicular to both of the nonzero vectors $\langle a_1,b_1,c_1\rangle$ and $\langle a_2,b_2,c_2\rangle$.

7. Show that $\left(\frac{\mathbf{u}}{|\mathbf{u}|^2} - \frac{\mathbf{v}}{|\mathbf{v}|^2}\right)^2 = \frac{(\mathbf{u} - \mathbf{v})^2}{|\mathbf{u}|^2|\mathbf{v}|^2}$. (By definition, $\mathbf{w}^2 = \mathbf{w}\cdot\mathbf{w}$ for every $\mathbf{w}$ in V_3.)

8. Express the vector $\mathbf{u}$ as a sum of two vectors, one parallel to a given nonzero vector $\mathbf{v}$ and the other perpendicular to $\mathbf{v}$.

3 LINES IN SPACE

Vectors in V_3 can be considered to be *translations* of R^3, just as vectors in V_2 were considered to be translations of R^2. Thus, each vector $\mathbf{v} = \langle h,k,l\rangle$ translates the point $P = (a,b,c)$ into the point $Q = (a + h, b + k, c + l)$. As in Chapter 16, we write

$$P + \mathbf{v} = Q$$

to signify that $\mathbf{v}$ translates P into Q. For example, $\mathbf{v} = \langle 3,-5,2\rangle$ translates $P = (1,2,-3)$ into $Q = (4,-3,-1)$:

$$(1,2,-3) + \langle 3,-5,2\rangle = (4,-3,-1).$$

As was the case in R^2, the set L of all translations of a point P by scalar multiples of a nonzero vector $\mathbf{v}$ is a *line in space:*

$$L = \{P + t\mathbf{v} \mid t \text{ in } \mathsf{R}\}.$$

If $P = (a,b,c)$ and $\mathbf{v} = \langle h,k,l\rangle$, then

$$L = \{(a + th, b + tk, c + tl) \mid t \text{ in } \mathsf{R}\}.$$

In other words, L has *parametric equations* (with parameter t)

17.5 $$x = a + th, \quad y = b + tk, \quad z = c + tl.$$

To show that $L = \{P + t\mathbf{v} \mid t \text{ in } \mathsf{R}\}$ satisfies our intuitive notion of a line, observe that the angle θ between the vectors $s\mathbf{v}$ and $t\mathbf{v}$ is either 0 or π, since by **17.4**

$$\cos\theta = \frac{(s\mathbf{v})\cdot(t\mathbf{v})}{|s\mathbf{v}||t\mathbf{v}|} = \frac{st(\mathbf{v}\cdot\mathbf{v})}{|s||t||\mathbf{v}|^2} = \pm 1.$$

Thus $\cos\theta = 1$ and $\theta = 0$ if s and t have the same sign; and $\cos\theta = -1$ and $\theta = \pi$ if s and t have opposite signs (as illustrated in Figure 17.7).

For example, the line L passing through the point $P = (-1,4,3)$ and its translations by scalar multiples of the vector $\mathbf{v} = \langle 5,-3,7\rangle$ has the form

$$L = \{(-1 + 5t, 4 - 3t, 3 + 7t) \mid t \text{ in } \mathsf{R}\}.$$

Thus

$$x = -1 + 5t, \quad y = 4 - 3t, \quad z = 3 + 7t$$

are parametric equations of L.

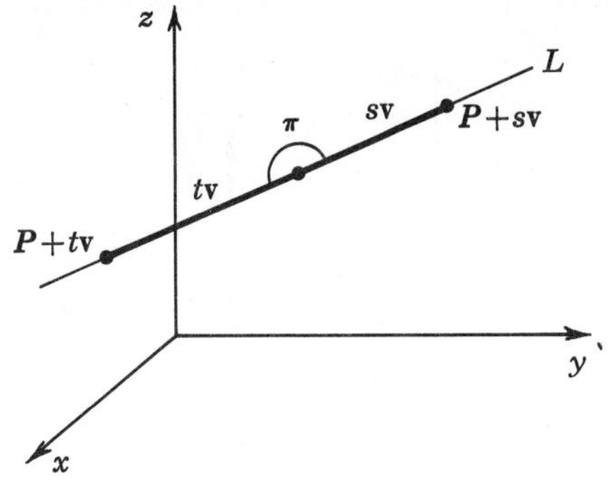

FIGURE 17.7

When a line L is given in the form $L = \{P + t\mathbf{v} \mid t \text{ in } \mathsf{R}\}$, $(\mathbf{v} \neq \mathbf{0})$, then there is a natural direction assigned to L, namely the direction of $\mathbf{v}$. Thus

$$L_1 = \{P + t\mathbf{v} \mid t > 0\}$$

is called the *positive half* of L and

$$L_2 = \{P + t\mathbf{v} \mid t < 0\}$$

is called the *negative half* of L. For example, if O is the origin, then $\{O + t\mathbf{i} \mid t > 0\}$ is the positive x axis and $\{O + t\mathbf{i} \mid t < 0\}$ is the negative x axis.

It is clear that for each point P, vector $\mathbf{v} \neq \mathbf{0}$ and scalar $c \neq 0$, the lines $L = \{P + t\mathbf{v} \mid t \text{ in } \mathsf{R}\}$ and $L' = \{P + s\mathbf{v}' \mid s \text{ in } \mathsf{R}\}$, where $\mathbf{v}' = c\mathbf{v}$, are the same, since $s\mathbf{v}' = t\mathbf{v}$ if $t = sc$. If $c > 0$, then the lines L and L' have the same direction; if $c < 0$, they have opposite directions. In particular, each line L may be considered to have the form

$$L = \{P + t\mathbf{u} \mid t \text{ in } \mathsf{R}\}, \qquad (\mathbf{u} \text{ a unit vector}).$$

Let $L = \{P + t\mathbf{u} \mid t \text{ in } \mathsf{R}\}$ be a line, where $\mathbf{u} = \langle l,m,n \rangle$ is a unit vector. If $A = P + \mathbf{i}$, $B = P + \mathbf{j}$, and $C = P + \mathbf{k}$, as indicated in Figure 17.8, then the angles α, β, and γ between $\mathbf{u}$ and the vectors $\mathbf{i}$, $\mathbf{j}$, and $\mathbf{k}$, respectively, are called the *direction angles* of the directed line L. Since $\mathbf{u}\cdot\mathbf{i} = l$, $\mathbf{u}\cdot\mathbf{j} = m$, and $\mathbf{u}\cdot\mathbf{k} = n$, and also $|\mathbf{u}| = |\mathbf{i}| = |\mathbf{j}| = |\mathbf{k}| = 1$, we have, by **17.4**, that

$$\cos\alpha = l, \quad \cos\beta = m, \quad \cos\gamma = n.$$

For this reason the coordinates l, m, and n of the unit vector $\mathbf{u}$ are called the *direction cosines* of the directed line L. Note that

$$\cos^2\alpha + \cos^2\beta + \cos^2\gamma = l^2 + m^2 + n^2 = |\mathbf{u}|^2 = 1.$$

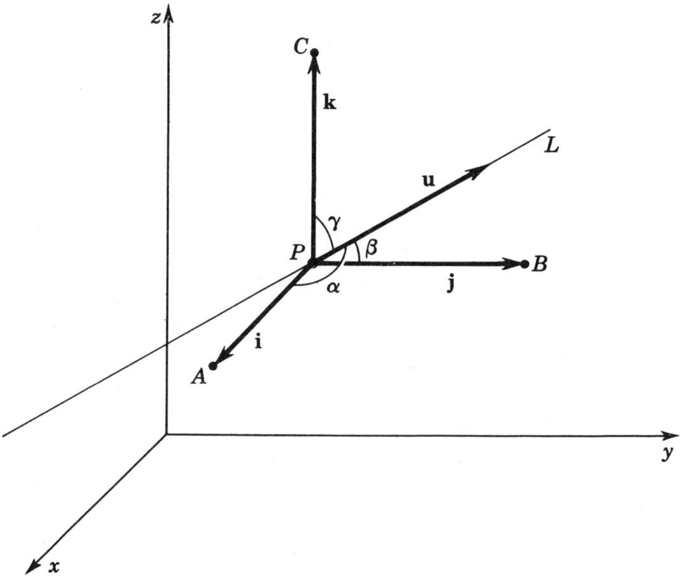

FIGURE 17.8

17.6 THEOREM. If l, m, and n are direction cosines of a directed line, then

$$l^2 + m^2 + n^2 = 1.$$

Conversely, if l, m, and n are numbers, such that $l^2 + m^2 + n^2 = 1$, then there exists a directed line having l, m, and n as its direction cosines.

We have already proved the first half of **17.6**. If l, m, and n are numbers such that $l^2 + m^2 + n_2 = 1$, then let $\mathbf{u} = \langle l,m,n \rangle$ and P be any point in R^3.

The line $L = \{P + t\mathbf{u} \mid t \text{ in } \mathsf{R}\}$ with direction $\mathbf{u}$ has direction cosines l, m, and n. This proves **17.6**.

For example, the directed line L of Figure 17.9 has direction cosines $-\frac{1}{2}$, $\frac{1}{2}$, $\sqrt{2}/2$ and direction angles 120°, 60°, and 45°.

Given two points on a line and a direction from one point toward the other point, we can easily express the line in the form given above. For example, if line L contains the points $P = (-1,2,3)$ and $Q = (2,0,1)$ and has the direction from P toward Q, then $L = \{P + t\mathbf{u} \mid t \text{ in } \mathsf{R}\}$ for some unit vector $\mathbf{u} = \langle l,m,n \rangle$. Now Q is on the positive half of L, so $P + t\mathbf{u} = Q$ for some positive number t. Hence $t\mathbf{u} = \langle tl,tm,tn \rangle$ and

$$P + t\mathbf{u} = (-1 + tl,\, 2 + tm,\, 3 + tn) = (2,0,1)$$

for some $t > 0$. Thus

$$\begin{aligned} -1 + tl &= 2 \\ 2 + tm &= 0 \\ 3 + tn &= 1 \end{aligned}$$

and $l = 3/t$, $m = -2/t$, $n = -2/t$. Since $\mathbf{u}$ is a unit vector, $l^2 + m^2 + n^2 = 1$. Therefore

$$\left(\frac{3}{t}\right)^2 + \left(-\frac{2}{t}\right)^2 + \left(-\frac{2}{t}\right)^2 = 1, \quad t^2 = 17, \quad t = \sqrt{17}.$$

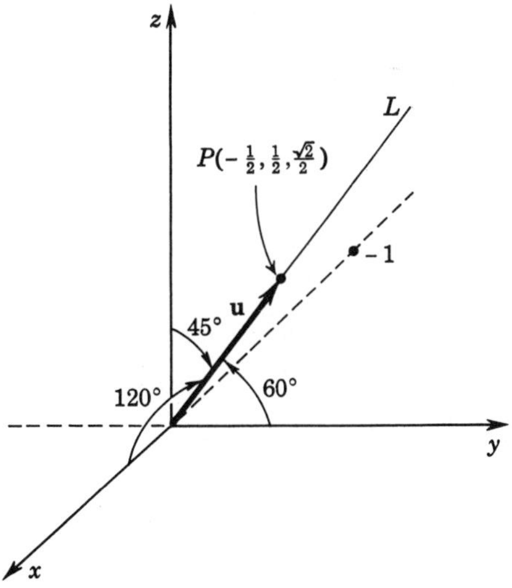

FIGURE 17.9

This gives

$$\mathbf{u} = \left\langle \frac{3}{\sqrt{17}}, -\frac{2}{\sqrt{17}}, -\frac{2}{\sqrt{17}} \right\rangle.$$

Just as slopes may be used to determine when two lines in a plane are parallel, so may direction cosines be used to determine when two lines are parallel in space. Thus lines $L = \{P + t\mathbf{u} \mid t \text{ in } \mathsf{R}\}$ and $L' = \{Q + t\mathbf{u}' \mid t \text{ in } \mathsf{R}\}$ with unit vectors $\mathbf{u}$ and $\mathbf{u}'$ are parallel and have the same direction if and only if $\mathbf{u}' = \mathbf{u}$; they are parallel and have the opposite direction if and only if $\mathbf{u}' = -\mathbf{u}$.

As we saw in Section 2, the lines $L = \{P + t\mathbf{v} \mid t \text{ in } \mathsf{R}\}$ and $L' = \{P + t\mathbf{v}' \mid t \text{ in } \mathsf{R}\}$ intersecting in point P are perpendicular if and only if $\mathbf{v} \cdot \mathbf{v} = 0$.

EXERCISES

I

1. Find parametric equations of the line passing through the point (2,3,1) and parallel to the vector $3\mathbf{i} - 7\mathbf{k} + 4\mathbf{j}$.

2. Find a unit vector parallel to the line $x = 3t + 1$, $y = 4t - 2$, $z = 9$.

In each of Exercises 3–5 find the direction cosines and direction angles of the half-line emanating from the origin and passing through the given point.

3. $(1,1,\sqrt{2})$. 4. (2,2,2). 5. $(-3\sqrt{2},-3,-3)$.

6. Find the direction cosines and direction angles of the positive coordinate axes and of the negative coordinate axes.

7. Under what conditions are l, m, and n direction cosines of a line parallel to a coordinate plane?

8. If $\pi/3$ and $3\pi/4$ are two of the direction angles of a half-line, find the third direction angle.

9. Prove that only one of the direction angles of a half-line can be less than 45°.

In Exercises 10 and 11, express the line passing through the given pair of points in the form $L = \{P + t\mathbf{v} \mid t \text{ in } \mathsf{R}\}$.

10. (5,1,2) and (7,2,4). 11. (2,−2,−2) and (0,0,1).

In each of Exercises 12–14 determine whether or not the given pair of lines intersect.

12. $x = 2 - t$, $y = -1 + 3t$, $z = t$; $x = -1 + 7s$, $y = 8 - 3s$, $z = 3 + s$.

13. $x = -3 + 3t$, $y = -2t$, $z = 7 + 6t$; $x = -6 + s$, $y = -5 - 3s$, $z = 1 + 2s$.

14. $x = 2 + t$, $y = 1 - 3t$, $z = t - 1$; $x = s + 1$, $y = -s$, $z = 5 - 3s$.

II

1. If lines L_1 and L_2 are respectively parallel to the two vectors $\langle 1,0,1\rangle$ and $\langle -1,1,2\rangle$, then find parametric equations of the line on the point (2,3,0) that is perpendicular to both L_1 and L_2.

2. Given lines L_1 and L_2 with respective parametric equations $x = 1 + 2t$, $y = 3 + t$, $z = -2 + t$ and $x = 1 + s$, $y = -2 - 4s$, $z = 9 + 2s$, find equations of the unique line L intersecting both L_1 and L_2 at right angles.

3. Prove algebraically that there is a unique line intersecting each of two skew (do not lie in one plane) lines in a right angle.

4. Find the distance from point $P = (h,k,l)$ to the line L with parametric equations $x = x_0 + at$, $y = y_0 + bt$, $z = z_0 + ct$ by: (a) finding a point Q on L such that PQ is perpendicular to L; (b) drawing a sphere around the point P and determining the radius so that there is only one point of intersection with L.

4 PLANES IN SPACE

Given a line

$$L = \{P + t\mathbf{u} \mid t \text{ in } \mathsf{R}\}$$

passing through the point P in the direction of vector $\mathbf{u}$, we have a unique plane p perpendicular to L at P (Figure 17.10). If we think of each point Q in

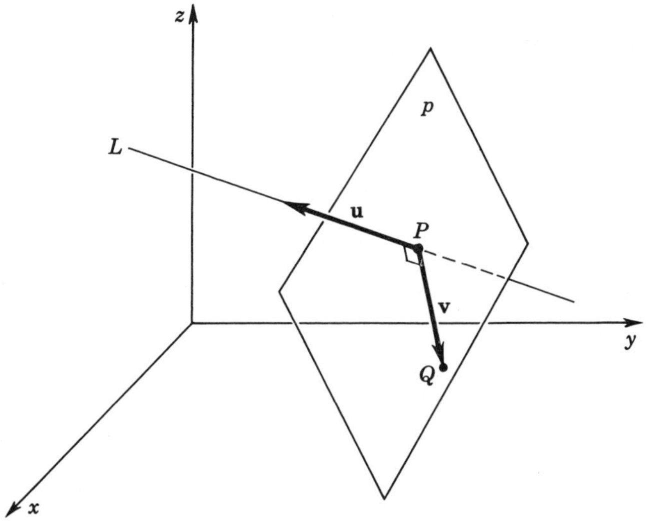

FIGURE 17.10

R^3 as a translate of P, say $Q = P + \mathbf{v}$, then Q is in plane p if and only if vector $\mathbf{v}$ is perpendicular to vector $\mathbf{u}$, i.e., if and only if $\mathbf{u}\cdot\mathbf{v} = 0$. Therefore

$$p = \{P + \mathbf{v} \mid \mathbf{v} \text{ in } V_3,\ \mathbf{u}\cdot\mathbf{v} = 0\}.$$

If

$$P = (x_0,y_0,z_0), \quad \mathbf{u} = \langle a,b,c\rangle, \quad Q = (x,y,z),$$

then

$$Q = P + \mathbf{v} \quad \text{for} \quad \mathbf{v} = \langle x - x_0, y - y_0, z - z_0\rangle.$$

By our remarks above, Q is in p if and only if $\mathbf{u}\cdot\mathbf{v} = 0$; i.e.,

17.7 $$a(x - x_0) + b(y - y_0) + c(z - z_0) = 0.$$

This is an *equation of the plane through the point* (x_0,y_0,z_0) and *perpendicular to the vector* $\langle a,b,c\rangle$. The nonzero vector $\langle a,b,c\rangle$ perpendicular to p is called a *normal vector* of plane p.

Actually, the graph in R^3 of every linear equation of the form

17.8 $$ax + by + cz + d = 0$$

is a plane. We assume, of course, that a, b, and c are not all zero. To see that **17.8** is an equation of a plane, we need only select any point (x_0,y_0,z_0) such that

$$ax_0 + by_0 + cz_0 + d = 0.$$

Then $d = -(ax_0 + by_0 + cz_0)$ and **17.8** can be put in the form

$$a(x - x_0) + b(y - y_0) + c(z - z_0) = 0.$$

It follows from **17.7** that **17.8** is an equation of a plane having $\langle a,b,c\rangle$ as a normal vector.

EXAMPLE 1. Find an equation of the plane passing through the point $(-2,1,3)$ and having normal vector $\langle 3,1,5\rangle$.

Solution: By **17.7**,

$$3(x + 2) + (y - 1) + 5(z - 3) = 0$$

or

$$3x + y + 5z - 10 = 0$$

is an equation of the plane.

EXAMPLE 2. Describe the plane with equation

$$3x + y + z - 6 = 0.$$

Solution: Points in the plane p may be found by giving arbitrary values to two of the variables in the equation and solving for the third variable. If we let $y = 0$ and $z = 0$, we get $x = 2$; thus the point $(2,0,0)$ is in the plane. The other intercepts are found to be (0,6,0) and (0,0,6). These three intercepts completely determine p, as sketched in Figure 17.11. Other points in p are (1,1,2), (0,3,3), and (2,1,−1).

The points (2,0,0) and (0,6,0) determine a line in the xy plane called the *trace* of the plane p in the xy plane. Thus the trace of p in the xy plane consists of those points in p for which $z = 0$. Substituting $z = 0$ into the equation of p, we get

$$3x + y - 6 = 0$$

as an equation of the trace of p in the xy plane. Similarly, an equation of the trace of p in the yz plane is

$$y + z - 6 = 0,$$

found by substituting $x = 0$ in the equation of p; and an equation of the trace of p in the xz plane is

$$3x + z - 6 = 0,$$

found by letting $y = 0$ in the equation of p.

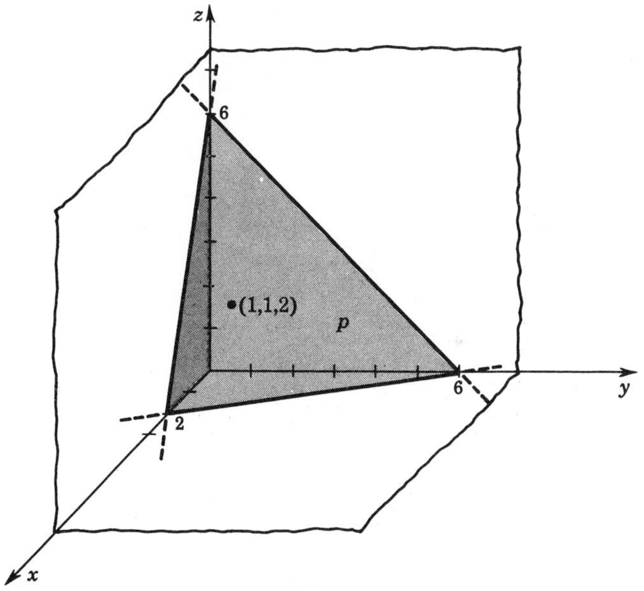

FIGURE 17.11

The xy plane has equation $z = 0$, since the point $P(x,y,z)$ is in the xy plane if and only if $z = 0$. Each plane parallel to the xy plane has an equation of the form $z = k$. Similarly, the xz and yz planes have equations $y = 0$ and $x = 0$, respectively, and planes parallel to the xz and yz planes have equations of the form $y = k$ and $x = k$.

The use of determinants makes it simple to find an equation of the plane passing through three noncollinear points (x_1,y_1,z_1), (x_2,y_2,z_2), and (x_3,y_3,z_3). Such an equation is

17.9
$$\begin{vmatrix} x & y & z & 1 \\ x_1 & y_1 & z_1 & 1 \\ x_2 & y_2 & z_2 & 1 \\ x_3 & y_3 & z_3 & 1 \end{vmatrix} = 0.$$

It is evident that 17.9 is a linear equation. If in 17.9 we replace (x,y,z) by (x_i,y_i,z_i), $(i = 1, 2, 3)$, then two rows of the matrix are equal and therefore its determinant is zero. Thus each of the given points is on the graph of 17.9.

EXAMPLE 3. Find an equation of the plane passing through the three points $(-1,1,2)$, $(2,0,-3)$, and $(5,1,-2)$.

Solution: By 17.9,

$$\begin{vmatrix} x & y & z & 1 \\ -1 & 1 & 2 & 1 \\ 2 & 0 & -3 & 1 \\ 5 & 1 & -2 & 1 \end{vmatrix} = 0$$

is such an equation. Expanding by minors of the first row, we have

$$\begin{vmatrix} 1 & 2 & 1 \\ 0 & -3 & 1 \\ 1 & -2 & 1 \end{vmatrix} x - \begin{vmatrix} -1 & 2 & 1 \\ 2 & -3 & 1 \\ 5 & -2 & 1 \end{vmatrix} y + \begin{vmatrix} -1 & 1 & 1 \\ 2 & 0 & 1 \\ 5 & 1 & 1 \end{vmatrix} z - \begin{vmatrix} -1 & 1 & 2 \\ 2 & 0 & -3 \\ 5 & 1 & -2 \end{vmatrix} = 0.$$

Evaluating each determinant, we obtain

$$4x - 18y + 6z + 10 = 0$$

or

$$2x - 9y + 3z + 5 = 0$$

as an equation of the plane.

Two planes with equations

$$a_1x + b_1y + c_1z + d_1 = 0$$
$$a_2x + b_2y + c_2z + d_2 = 0$$

are parallel if and only if their normal vectors have the same or opposite direction. Taking $\mathbf{v}_1 = \langle a_1,b_1,c_1\rangle$ and $\mathbf{v}_2 = \langle a_2,b_2,c_2\rangle$ as normal vectors, the planes are parallel if and only if

$$\mathbf{v}_2 = r\mathbf{v}_1 \quad \text{for some } r \text{ in } \mathsf{R},$$

i.e., if and only if $a_2 = ra_1$, $b_2 = rb_1$, $c_2 = rc_1$ for some r in R.

The two planes with equations as above are perpendicular if and only if their normal vectors are perpendicular, i.e., if and only if $\mathbf{v}_1 \cdot \mathbf{v}_2 = 0$ or

$$a_1a_2 + b_1b_2 + c_1c_2 = 0.$$

For example, the plane with equation

$$ax + by + d = 0$$

is perpendicular to the xy plane with equation $z = 0$, since $0 \cdot a + 0 \cdot b + 1 \cdot 0 = 0$. In other words, the plane having an equation with no z term is parallel to the z axis. Analogously, the plane with equation

$$ax + cz + d = 0$$

is parallel to the y axis, and so on.

Two nonparallel planes intersect in a line that can be easily determined, as illustrated in the following example.

EXAMPLE 4. Determine the line of intersection L of the two planes

$$2x - y + z - 4 = 0, \qquad x + 3y - z - 2 = 0.$$

Solution: Solving the two given equations simultaneously, we find one point such as $P = (0,3,7)$ on L. Hence $L = \{P + t\mathbf{u} \mid t \text{ in } \mathsf{R}\}$ for some vector $\mathbf{u}$ perpendicular to both normal vectors $\mathbf{v}_1 = \langle 2,-1,1\rangle$ and $\mathbf{v}_2 = \langle 1,3,-1\rangle$ of the given planes. Thus, if $\mathbf{u} = \langle l,m,n\rangle$, we have

$$2l - m + n = 0, \qquad l + 3m - n = 0.$$

One solution of this system of equations is seen to be $l = -2$, $m = 3$, $n = 7$. Therefore one possible choice of vector $\mathbf{u}$ is

$$\mathbf{u} = \langle -2,3,7\rangle.$$

Hence each point (x,y,z) on L has the form $(x,y,z) = P + t\mathbf{u} = (-2t, 3 + 3t, 7 + 7t)$. That is,

$$x = -2t, \quad y = 3 + 3t, \quad z = 7 + 7t$$

is a set of parametric equations of L.

EXERCISES

I

In each of Exercises 1–4, find an equation of the plane passing through the given point and perpendicular to the given vector.

1. $(3,1,3)$, $\langle 1,1,-1\rangle$.
2. $(0,2,-2)$, $\langle -1,2,-3\rangle$.

3. (a,b,c), $\langle 1,1,0\rangle$.

4. $(1,2,3)$, $\langle 0,5,0\rangle$.

In each of Exercises 5–8, find the traces in the coordinate planes of the given plane and sketch.

5. $2x + y + z = 4$.

6. $3x + 4y + 6z = 12$.

7. $4x + y = 6$.

8. $2y - 3z = 4$.

In each of Exercises 9–12, find an equation of the plane passing through the three given points.

9. $(0,0,0)$, $(1,1,1)$, $(-1,1,0)$.

10. $(2,1,3)$, $(5,2,-1)$, $(3,0,1)$.

11. $(2,1,-1)$, $(-1,3,1)$, $(4,0,1)$.

12. $(a,0,0)$, $(0,b,0)$, $(0,0,c)$.

13. Find an equation of the plane that passes through the points $(1,0,-1)$ and $(2,1,3)$ and is perpendicular to the plane $x + y - z + 2 = 0$.

14. Find an equation of the plane that passes through the point $(1,-1,4)$ and is perpendicular to each of the planes $2x + y - z + 2 = 0$ and $x - y + 3z - 1 = 0$.

In Exercises 15 and 16, find parametric equations for the line of intersection of the given pair of planes.

15. $x + 2y - z = 7$, $x - 2y + z = 3$.

16. $x + z = 5$, $y - z = 2$.

17. Find an equation of the plane containing the two lines in Exercise I-12, Section 3.

II

1. Find an equation of the plane containing the line $x = x_0 + at$, $y = y_0 + bt$, $z = z_0 + ct$ and the point (h,k,l).

2. Find an equation of the plane which contains the line $x = x_1 + a_1t$, $y = y_1 + b_1t$, $z = z_1 + c_1t$ and is parallel to the line $x = x_2 + a_2t$, $y = y_2 + b_2t$, $z = z_2 + c_2t$. Assume that the lines are skew.

3. Find an equation of the plane containing the point (h,k,l) and the line of intersection of the two planes $a_rx + b_ry + c_rz = d_r$, $(r = 1, 2)$.

4. Find the angle of intersection of the two planes in Exercise 3 (i.e., the angle between two normals).

5. Find the angle between the line of intersection of the planes $a_rx + b_ry + c_rz = 0$, $(r = 1, 2)$, and the line of intersection of the planes $a_r'x + b_r'y + c_r'z = 0$, $(r = 1, 2)$.

6. Find the condition under which the three planes $a_rx + b_ry + c_rz = d_r$, $(r = 1, 2, 3)$: (a) intersect in a line; (b) intersect in a point; (c) do not intersect either in a line or in a point.

7. Prove that the distance D between the point (h,k,l) and the plane $ax + by + cz + d = 0$ is given by

$$D = \frac{|ah + bk + cl + d|}{\sqrt{a^2 + b^2 + c^2}}.$$

8. Find the shortest distance between the two planes $a_r x + b_r y + c_r z + d_r = 0$, $(r = 1, 2)$. Consider all cases.

9. Prove that the sum of the lengths of the perpendiculars to the faces of a regular tetrahedron from a point within it is constant.

10. If a line makes equal angles with each of three given nonparallel lines in a plane, show that the line is perpendicular to the plane.

5 THE CROSS PRODUCT IN V_3

Given vectors

$$\mathbf{u} = \langle l_1, m_1, n_1 \rangle \qquad \text{and} \qquad \mathbf{v} = \langle l_2, m_2, n_2 \rangle$$

in V_3, we find that the associated linear equation

$$\begin{vmatrix} x & y & z \\ l_1 & m_1 & n_1 \\ l_2 & m_2 & n_2 \end{vmatrix} = 0 \tag{1}$$

has $x = l_1$, $y = m_1$, $z = n_1$ as a solution, since the determinant of a matrix with two equal rows is zero. Similarly, $x = l_2$, $y = m_2$, $z = n_2$ is also a solution. If we expand (1) by minors of the first row, we obtain the equivalent equation

$$\begin{vmatrix} m_1 & n_1 \\ m_2 & n_2 \end{vmatrix} x - \begin{vmatrix} l_1 & n_1 \\ l_2 & n_2 \end{vmatrix} y + \begin{vmatrix} l_1 & m_1 \\ l_2 & m_2 \end{vmatrix} z = 0 \tag{2}$$

or

$$\begin{vmatrix} m_1 & n_1 \\ m_2 & n_2 \end{vmatrix} x + \begin{vmatrix} n_1 & l_1 \\ n_2 & l_2 \end{vmatrix} y + \begin{vmatrix} l_1 & m_1 \\ l_2 & m_2 \end{vmatrix} z = 0. \tag{3}$$

Now if we define the vector $\mathbf{w}$ to be

$$\mathbf{w} = \left< \begin{vmatrix} m_1 & n_1 \\ m_2 & n_2 \end{vmatrix}, \begin{vmatrix} n_1 & l_1 \\ n_2 & l_2 \end{vmatrix}, \begin{vmatrix} l_1 & m_1 \\ l_2 & m_2 \end{vmatrix} \right>,$$

then $\mathbf{w} \cdot \langle x,y,z \rangle = 0$ for every solution x, y, z of (3). Hence, by our remarks above, $\mathbf{w} \cdot \mathbf{u} = 0$ and $\mathbf{w} \cdot \mathbf{v} = 0$. Thus $\mathbf{w}$ is a vector perpendicular to both $\mathbf{u}$ and $\mathbf{v}$.

Let us define the vector **w** above to be the product of **u** and **v**. Thus the *cross product* of vectors $\mathbf{u} = \langle l_1,m_1,n_1\rangle$ and $\mathbf{v} = \langle l_2,m_2,n_2\rangle$ is designated by $\mathbf{u} \times \mathbf{v}$ and is defined as follows:

17.10 $$\mathbf{u} \times \mathbf{v} = \langle m_1n_2 - m_2n_1,\ n_1l_2 - n_2l_1,\ l_1m_2 - l_2m_1\rangle.$$

In particular, the cross products of the unit vectors **i**, **j**, and **k** are given by

$$\mathbf{i} \times \mathbf{j} = \mathbf{k}, \qquad \mathbf{j} \times \mathbf{k} = \mathbf{i}, \qquad \mathbf{k} \times \mathbf{i} = \mathbf{j},$$
$$\mathbf{j} \times \mathbf{i} = -\mathbf{k}, \qquad \mathbf{k} \times \mathbf{j} = -\mathbf{i}, \qquad \mathbf{i} \times \mathbf{k} = -\mathbf{j}.$$

Since $\mathbf{i} \times \mathbf{j} = -\mathbf{j} \times \mathbf{i}$, evidently the cross product is a noncommutative operation. This operation is also nonassociative, as we shall soon see. The important properties of the cross product are listed below. They hold for all vectors **u**, **v**, and **w** and for each scalar c.

(P1) $\mathbf{u} \times \mathbf{v} = -\mathbf{v} \times \mathbf{u}$ (anticommutative law).

(P2) $(c\mathbf{u}) \times \mathbf{v} = \mathbf{u} \times (c\mathbf{v}) = c(\mathbf{u} \times \mathbf{v})$.

(P3) $(\mathbf{u} + \mathbf{v}) \times \mathbf{w} = \mathbf{u} \times \mathbf{w} + \mathbf{v} \times \mathbf{w}$,
$\mathbf{u} \times (\mathbf{v} + \mathbf{w}) = \mathbf{u} \times \mathbf{v} + \mathbf{u} \times \mathbf{w}$ (distributive laws).

(P4) $\mathbf{v} \times \mathbf{0} = \mathbf{0} \times \mathbf{v} = \mathbf{0}$.

(P5) $\mathbf{u}\cdot(\mathbf{v} \times \mathbf{w}) = (\mathbf{u} \times \mathbf{v})\cdot\mathbf{w}$.

(P6) $\mathbf{u} \times (\mathbf{v} \times \mathbf{w}) = (\mathbf{u}\cdot\mathbf{w})\mathbf{v} - (\mathbf{u}\cdot\mathbf{v})\mathbf{w}$.

(P7) $|\mathbf{u} \times \mathbf{v}| = \sqrt{|\mathbf{u}|^2|\mathbf{v}|^2 - (\mathbf{u}\cdot\mathbf{v})^2} = |\mathbf{u}||\mathbf{v}| \sin\theta$, ($\theta$ the angle between **u** and **v**).

These properties may be proved by using 17.10 and the definitions of the other operations in V_3. We shall prove some of them below and leave the rest as exercises. Let

$$\mathbf{u} = \langle l_1,m_1,n_1\rangle, \quad \mathbf{v} = \langle l_2,m_2,n_2\rangle, \quad \mathbf{w} = \langle l_3,m_3,n_3\rangle.$$

Proof of (P1): $\mathbf{u} \times \mathbf{v}$ is given by 17.10. We may obtain $\mathbf{v} \times \mathbf{u}$ from 17.10 by interchanging subscripts 1 and 2. Thus

$$\mathbf{v} \times \mathbf{u} = \langle m_2n_1 - m_1n_2,\ n_2l_1 - n_1l_2,\ l_2m_1 - l_1m_2\rangle.$$

Clearly, $\mathbf{v} \times \mathbf{u} = -\mathbf{u} \times \mathbf{v}$.

Proof of (P5): Evidently,

$$\mathbf{u}\cdot(\mathbf{v} \times \mathbf{w}) = l_1(m_2n_3 - m_3n_2) + m_1(n_2l_3 - n_3l_2) + n_1(l_2m_3 - l_3m_2),$$
$$(\mathbf{u} \times \mathbf{v})\cdot\mathbf{w} = (m_1n_2 - m_2n_1)l_3 + (n_1l_2 - n_2l_1)m_3 + (l_1m_2 - l_2m_1)n_3.$$

It is easily verified that these two numbers are equal.

Proof of (P6): Since $\mathbf{v} \times \mathbf{w} = \langle m_2n_3 - m_3n_2, n_2l_3 - n_3l_2, l_2m_3 - l_3m_2\rangle$, we have

$$\begin{aligned}\mathbf{u} \times (\mathbf{v} \times \mathbf{w}) &= \langle m_1(l_2m_3 - l_3m_2) - (n_2l_3 - n_3l_2)n_1, n_1(m_2n_3 - m_3n_2) \\ &\qquad - (l_2m_3 - l_3m_2)l_1, l_1(n_2l_3 - n_3l_2) - (m_2n_3 - m_3n_2)m_1\rangle \\ &= \langle(\mathbf{u}\cdot\mathbf{w})l_2 - (\mathbf{u}\cdot\mathbf{v})l_3, (\mathbf{u}\cdot\mathbf{w})m_2 - (\mathbf{u}\cdot\mathbf{v})m_3, (\mathbf{u}\cdot\mathbf{w})n_2 - (\mathbf{u}\cdot\mathbf{w})n_3\rangle \\ &= (\mathbf{u}\cdot\mathbf{w})\langle l_2,m_2,n_2\rangle - (\mathbf{u}\cdot\mathbf{v})\langle l_3,m_3,n_3\rangle.\end{aligned}$$

This proves (P6).

Proof of (P7): A straightforward calculation shows that

$$\begin{aligned}(l_1^2 + m_1^2 + n_1^2)(l_2^2 + m_2^2 + n_2^2) &= (l_1l_2 + m_1m_2 + n_1n_2)^2 \\ &\quad + (m_1n_2 - m_2n_1)^2 + (n_1l_2 - n_2l_1)^2 + (l_1m_2 - l_2m_1)^2,\end{aligned}$$

and therefore that $|\mathbf{u} \times \mathbf{v}|^2 = |\mathbf{u}|^2|\mathbf{v}|^2 - (\mathbf{u}\cdot\mathbf{v})^2$. We recall from **17.4** that $\mathbf{u}\cdot\mathbf{v} = |\mathbf{u}||\mathbf{v}| \cos\theta$. Hence

$$|\mathbf{u} \times \mathbf{v}|^2 = |\mathbf{u}|^2|\mathbf{v}|^2(1 - \cos^2\theta) = |\mathbf{u}|^2|\mathbf{v}|^2 \sin^2\theta.$$

Since $\sin\theta \geq 0$ for θ in $[0,\pi]$, we may take square roots of the quantities above to obtain (P7).

Geometrically, $|\mathbf{u} \times \mathbf{v}|$ is the area of the parallelogram $PABC$ determined by vectors $\mathbf{u}$ and $\mathbf{v}$ at any point P in R^3 (Figure 17.12). This fact follows directly from (P7), $|\mathbf{u} \times \mathbf{v}| = |\mathbf{u}||\mathbf{v}| \sin\theta$. If $\mathbf{u}$ and $\mathbf{v}$ are nonzero vectors, then $\mathbf{u} \times \mathbf{v} = \mathbf{0}$ if and only if the points P, A, B, and C of Figure 17.12 are collinear, i.e., if and only if $\mathbf{u} = c\mathbf{v}$ for some scalar c. We state this result in the following theorem.

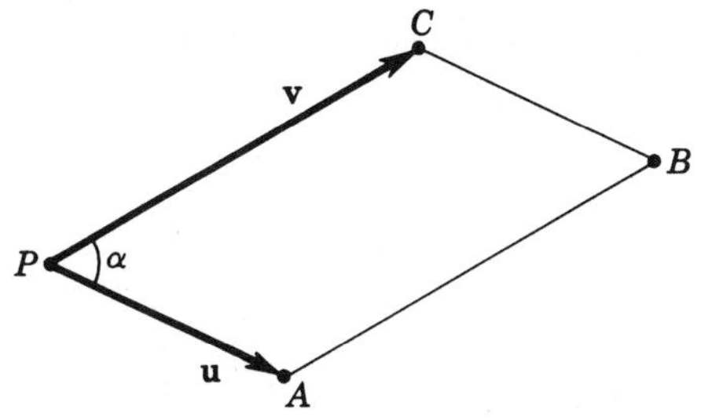

FIGURE 17.12

17.11 THEOREM. If $\mathbf{u}$ and $\mathbf{v}$ are nonzero vectors in V_3, then

$$\mathbf{u} \times \mathbf{v} = \mathbf{0} \text{ if and only if } \mathbf{u} = c\mathbf{v}$$

for some scalar c.

That cross product is a nonassociative operation is seen by the following example:

$$\mathbf{i} \times (\mathbf{i} \times \mathbf{j}) = \mathbf{i} \times \mathbf{k} = -\mathbf{j},\ (\mathbf{i} \times \mathbf{i}) \times \mathbf{j} = \mathbf{0} \times \mathbf{j} = \mathbf{0}.$$

Therefore $\mathbf{i} \times (\mathbf{i} \times \mathbf{j}) \neq (\mathbf{i} \times \mathbf{i}) \times \mathbf{j}$.

We call vectors **u** and **v** *independent* if neither is a scalar multiple of the other. By **17.11**, **u** and **v** are independent if and only if $\mathbf{u} \times \mathbf{v} \neq \mathbf{0}$.

If **u** and **v** are independent vectors and P is a point, then the three points P, $P + \mathbf{u}$, and $P + \mathbf{v}$ determine a unique plane p. A point Q of R^3 is in plane p if and only if $Q = P + (r\mathbf{u} + s\mathbf{v})$ for some scalars r and s, as indicated in Figure 17.13. Thus

$$p = \{P + (r\mathbf{u} + s\mathbf{v}) \mid r, s \text{ in } \mathsf{R}\}.$$

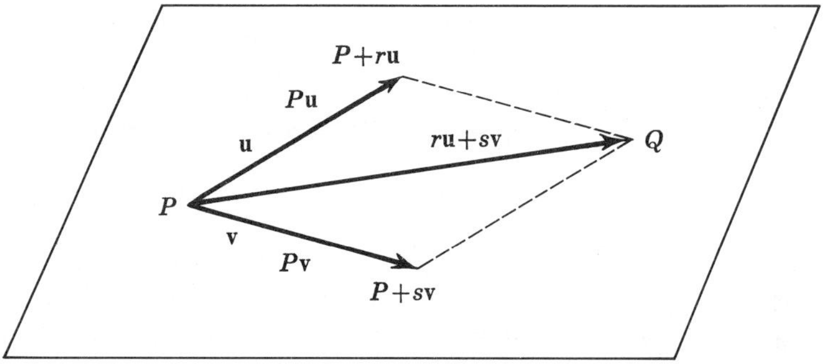

FIGURE 17.13

Since vector $\mathbf{u} \times \mathbf{v}$ is perpendicular to both **u** and **v**, and hence to plane p, evidently $\mathbf{u} \times \mathbf{v}$ is a normal vector of p. Thus we can also describe p as follows:

$$p = \{P + \mathbf{w} \mid \mathbf{w} \text{ in } V_3,\ (\mathbf{u} \times \mathbf{v}) \cdot \mathbf{w} = 0\}.$$

EXERCISES

I

In Exercises 1-6, evaluate the given expressions if $\mathbf{u} = \mathbf{i} + 2\mathbf{j} - 4\mathbf{k}$, $\mathbf{v} = 2\mathbf{j} - 3\mathbf{k}$, and $\mathbf{w} = -\mathbf{i} + 2\mathbf{k}$, then find each of Exercises 1–6.

1. $\mathbf{u} \cdot \mathbf{v}$, $\mathbf{w} \cdot \mathbf{u}$.
2. $\mathbf{u} \times \mathbf{v}$, $\mathbf{v} \times \mathbf{u}$.
3. $\mathbf{u} \times \mathbf{u} + \mathbf{v} \times \mathbf{v}$.
4. $\mathbf{u} \cdot \mathbf{v} \times \mathbf{w}$, $\mathbf{u} \times \mathbf{v} \cdot \mathbf{w}$.

5. $\mathbf{u} \times (\mathbf{v} \times \mathbf{w})$, $(\mathbf{u} \times \mathbf{v}) \times \mathbf{w}$.

6. $(\mathbf{u} \times \mathbf{v}) \cdot (\mathbf{u} \times \mathbf{w})$.

7. Show that if $\mathbf{u} = \langle a_1,a_2,a_3 \rangle$ and $\mathbf{v} = \langle b_1,b_2,b_3 \rangle$ then

$$\mathbf{u} \times \mathbf{v} = \begin{vmatrix} \mathbf{i} & \mathbf{j} & \mathbf{k} \\ a_1 & a_2 & a_3 \\ b_1 & b_2 & b_3 \end{vmatrix},$$

where the determinant is defined as usual (although it contains vectors).

8. Prove that $(\mathbf{u} + \mathbf{v}) \times (\mathbf{u} - \mathbf{v}) = 2\mathbf{v} \times \mathbf{u}$.

9. If $\mathbf{u} + \mathbf{v} + \mathbf{w} = 0$, show that $\mathbf{u} \times \mathbf{v} = \mathbf{v} \times \mathbf{w} = \mathbf{w} \times \mathbf{u}$.

10. If $\mathbf{u} = \langle a_1,a_2,a_3 \rangle$, $\mathbf{v} = \langle b_1,b_2,b_3 \rangle$, and $\mathbf{w} = \langle c_1,c_2,c_3 \rangle$, then show that

$$\mathbf{u} \cdot (\mathbf{v} \times \mathbf{w}) = (\mathbf{u} \times \mathbf{v}) \cdot \mathbf{w} = \begin{vmatrix} a_1 & a_2 & a_3 \\ b_1 & b_2 & b_3 \\ c_1 & c_2 & c_3 \end{vmatrix}.$$

Give a geometric interpretation of this number.

6 CYLINDERS AND SURFACES OF REVOLUTION

The graph in space of an equation in x, y, and z is called a *surface*. Two examples of surfaces have been studied thus far in this chapter, namely the sphere **(17.2)** and the plane **(17.7)**.

Although it is easy to visualize a plane or a sphere, and even easy to sketch these surfaces on a plane, the general problem of visualizing and sketching a surface is much more difficult than the corresponding problem of sketching a curve in the plane. Of course, this is due to the fact that a surface in space can be sketched in perspectivity only on a piece of paper. Three-dimensional models of the common surfaces are available and are of great help in visualizing these surfaces.

One of the easiest surfaces to visualize is a cylinder. A *cylinder* is a surface that may be thought of as being generated by a line (called the *generator*) moving along a given curve in such a way as always to remain parallel to its original position. The curve along which the generating line moves is called a *directrix** of the cylinder. Each of the lines on the cylinder parallel to the generator is called a *ruling* of the cylinder.

If the directrix is a straight line, the cylinder is simply a plane. Other than a plane, the most common cylinder is the right circular cylinder, generated by a

* A directrix of a cylinder is in no way related to the directrix of a parabola.

line moving along a circle so as always to be perpendicular to the plane of the circle.

The right circular cylinder sketched in Figure 17.14 has as its directrix a circle of radius r in the xy plane with its center at the origin. A point $P(x,y,z)$ is on this cylinder if and only if the projection $Q(x,y,0)$ of P on the xy plane is on the directrix of the cylinder. Thus $P(x,y,z)$ is a point on the cylinder if and only if

$$x^2 + y^2 = r^2,$$

and we conclude that this equation of the cylinder is just an equation of its directrix in the xy plane.

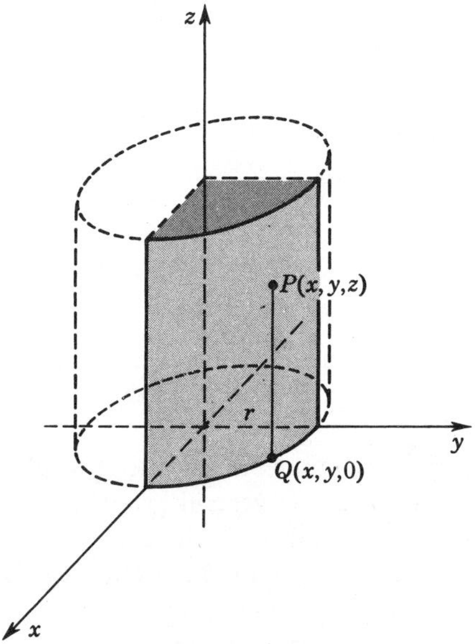

FIGURE 17.14

It is clear from the preceding example that an equation in x and y has as its graph in space a cylinder with generator parallel to the z axis. Similarly, an equation in x and z has as its graph in space a cylinder with generator parallel to the y axis, and so on. In each case the directrix is the graph in a coordinate plane of the given equation in two variables.

EXAMPLE 1. Discuss and sketch the graph of the equation

$$z = 4 - x^2.$$

Solution: The graph of this equation in the xz plane is a parabola symmetric to the z axis with vertex at (0,0,4). The graph in space is a parabolic cylinder with directrix the parabola in the xz plane and generator parallel to the y axis. It is sketched in Figure 17.15.

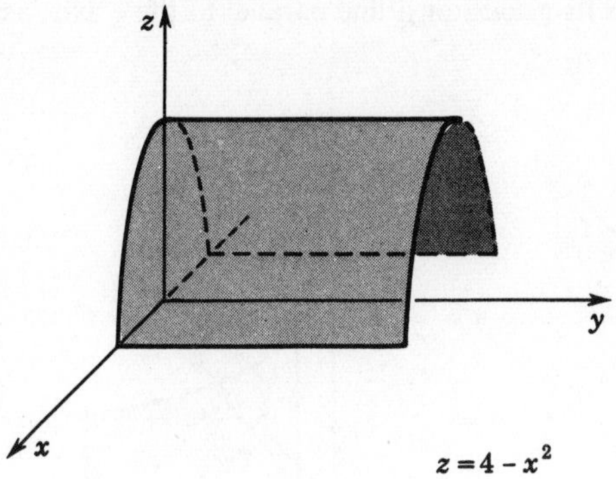

FIGURE 17.15

EXAMPLE 2. Discuss and sketch the graph of the equation

$$z = |y|.$$

Solution: The graph of this equation in the yz plane consists of two half-lines emanating from the origin. Thus its graph in space is a cylinder with generator parallel to the x axis and directrix the two half-lines. It looks like a trough made up of two half-planes meeting on the x axis at an angle of 90°, as sketched in Figure 17.16.

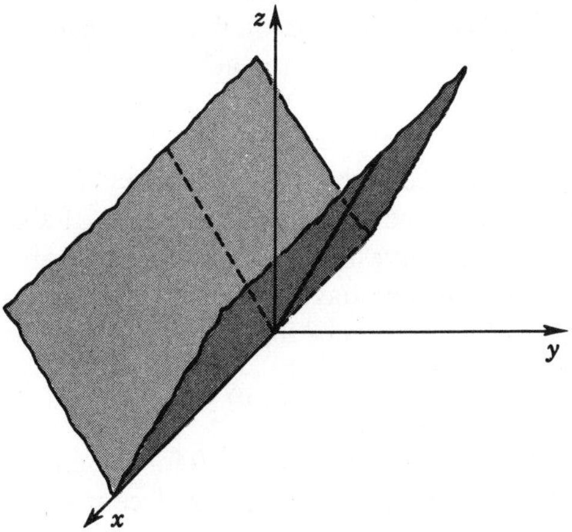

FIGURE 17.16

EXAMPLE 3. Discuss and sketch the graph of the equation

$$y = e^x.$$

Solution: The cylinder has as its directrix the exponential curve $y = e^x$ in the xy plane and as its generator a line parallel to the z axis, as sketched in Figure 17.17.

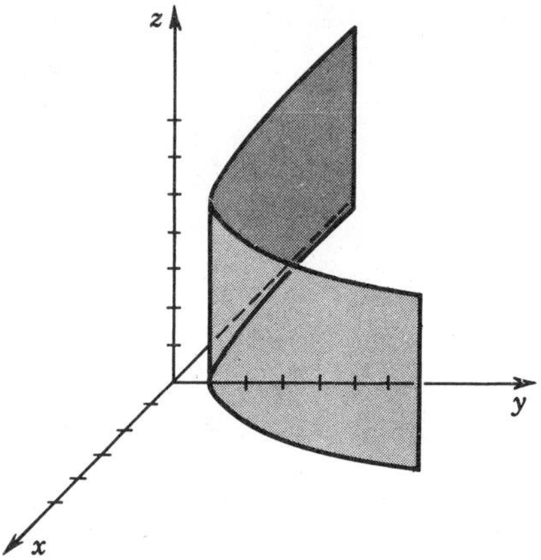

FIGURE 17.17

A fact that makes the sketching of a cylinder comparatively easy is that the cross section of the cylinder in each plane parallel to the plane of the directrix is the same as the directrix. By the *cross section* of a surface in a plane, we mean the set of all points of the surface that are on the given plane. For example, the cross section of a right circular cylinder in each plane parallel to the plane of the directrix is a circle.

Another surface that is easy to visualize is the surface of revolution discussed in previous chapters. We recall that a surface of revolution is generated by rotating a plane curve about some fixed axis in its plane. If a surface of revolution is generated by rotating a curve in a coordinate plane about a coordinate axis, then an equation of the surface may be easily found, as we shall now show.

Let the surface of revolution be formed by rotating the graph of an equation

$$f(x,y) = 0$$

about the x axis. We shall assume that $y \geq 0$ for each point (x,y) on the generating curve. A point $P(x,y,z)$ will be on this surface if and only if $Q(x,y_0,0)$ is on the generating curve, where

$$y_0 = |PA| = \sqrt{y^2 + z^2},$$

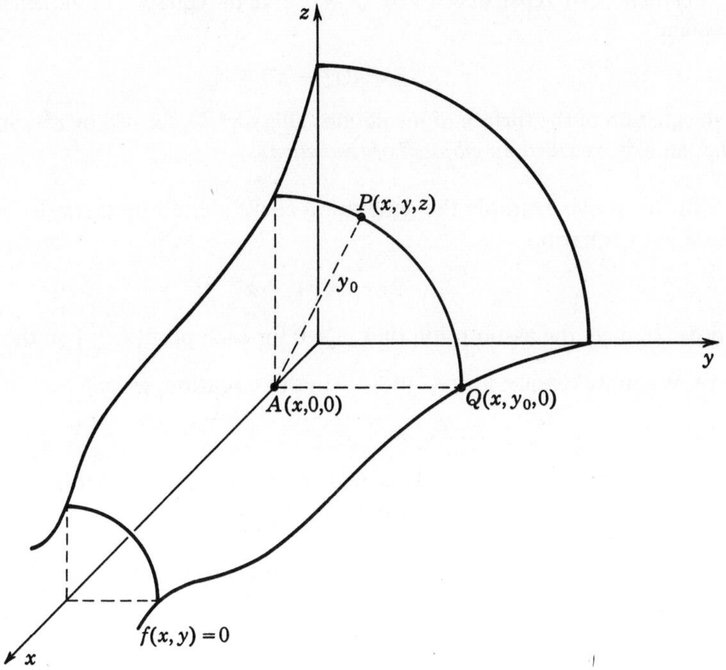

FIGURE 17.18

as indicated in Figure 17.18. Since $Q(x,y_0,0)$ is on the generating curve if and only if $f(x,y_0) = 0$, the point $P(x,y,z)$ is on the surface of revolution if and only if

$$f(x, \sqrt{y^2 + z^2}) = 0.$$

Hence this equation in x, y, and z is an equation of the surface of revolution.

It is clear that similar remarks can be made if the generating curve is in any one of the coordinate planes and the axis of revolution is a coordinate axis in that plane. If, for example, the surface is generated by rotating a curve in the yz plane about the y axis, then the equation of the surface is obtained by replacing each z by $\sqrt{x^2 + z^2}$ in an equation of the generating curve.

We might summarize our remarks above by saying that the graph of an equation in x, y, and z is a surface of revolution if and only if two of the variables occur together in the form $x^2 + y^2$, $x^2 + z^2$, or $y^2 + z^2$.

EXAMPLE 4. Find an equation of the surface generated by rotating the curve

$$x^2 + 4y^2 = 4$$

in the xy plane about the x axis.

Solution: We replace each y by $\sqrt{y^2 + z^2}$ in the equation of the generating curve to obtain

$$x^2 + 4(y^2 + z^2) = 4$$

as an equation of the surface of revolution. This surface, formed by rotating an ellipse about an axis, is called an *ellipsoid of revolution.*

In the above example the generating curve should be taken to be the semi-ellipse with equation

$$2y = \sqrt{4 - x^2}$$

in order to meet the assumption that $y \geq 0$ for each point (x,y) on the generating curve. When we replace y by $\sqrt{y^2 + z^2}$ in this equation, we get

$$2\sqrt{y^2 + z^2} = \sqrt{4 - x^2}$$

as an equation of the surface. It is evident that the graph of this equation is the same as that of the equation obtained in Example 4.

EXAMPLE 5. Find an equation of the surface generated by rotating the curve

$$x^2 = 4z$$

in the xz plane about the z axis.

Solution: We replace each x^2 by $x^2 + y^2$ to obtain

$$x^2 + y^2 = 4z$$

as an equation of this surface. Since the surface is formed by rotating a parabola about its axis, it is called a *paraboloid of revolution.*

EXAMPLE 6. Describe the graph of the equation

$$x^2 - 9y^2 + z^2 = 36.$$

Solution: Since this equation has the form

$$(x^2 + z^2) - 9y^2 = 36,$$

its graph is a surface of revolution obtained by rotating the curve

(1) $$x^2 - 9y^2 = 36$$

in the xy plane about the y axis. This surface, obtained by rotating the hyperbola (1) about an axis, is called a *hyperboloid of revolution.* Incidentally, the surface may also be generated by rotating the hyperbola

$$z^2 - 9y^2 = 36$$

in the yz plane about the y axis.

EXERCISES

I

In each of Exercises 1–16, discuss and sketch the graph in space of the equation.

1. $x^2 + y^2 = 9$.
2. $y^2 + z^2 = 4$.
3. $x^2 = 8z$.
4. $x^2 - y^2 = 1$.
5. $x^2 + y^2 + 9z^2 = 9$.
6. $y^2 + z^2 = \sin x$.
7. $y^2 = x^2 + z^2$.
8. $xz = 1$.
9. $x^2 = y^2$.
10. $x^2 + y^2 = 4z$.
11. $x^2(y^2 + z^2) = 1$.
12. $4x^2 + y^2 + 4z^2 = 16$.
13. $y^2 + z^2 = e^x$.
14. $y = 9 - x^2$.
15. $y^2 = 4 + z^2$.
16. $x^2 - y^2 - z^2 = 1$.
17. Find an equation of the ellipsoid of revolution obtained by rotating the ellipse $x^2/a^2 + y^2/b^2 = 1$ in the xy plane about (a) the x axis, (b) the y axis. Sketch.
18. Find an equation of the hyperboloid of revolution obtained by rotating the hyperbola $x^2/a^2 - y^2/b^2 = 1$ in the xy plane about (a) the x axis, (b) the y axis. Sketch.
19. Find an equation of the paraboloid of revolution obtained by rotating the parabola $y^2 = 4px$ in the xy plane about the x axis. Sketch.
20. Find an equation of the cone obtained by rotating the curve $|y| = mx$ in the xy plane about the y axis. Sketch.

II

1. Find an equation of and describe the surface generated by revolving the circle $(x - h)^2 + z^2 = r^2$ in the xz plane about the z axis (assume $h > r$).
2. Find an equation of the graph of a moving point which is equidistant from a given plane and a given line parallel to the plane. Describe the graph.
3. Find an equation of the graph of a moving point which is equidistant from a given point and a given plane. Describe the graph.
4. Show that an equation of a surface of revolution whose axis is the line with parametric equations $x = x_0 + at$, $y = y_0 + bt$, $z = z_0 + ct$ has the form $(x - x_0)^2 + (y - y_0)^2 + (z - z_0)^2 = F(ax + by + cz)$ for some function F of one variable. Show that when the axis is one of the coordinate axes, the form reduces to that given in the text (page 000).
5. Show that if a bounded surface is a surface of revolution about two different axes then it must be spherical.

7 QUADRIC SURFACES

The graph of a second-degree equation in x, y, and z is called a *quadric surface.* We shall give some standard forms of equations of quadric surfaces in this section.

The graph of an equation of the form

17.12 $$\frac{x^2}{a^2} + \frac{y^2}{b^2} + \frac{z^2}{c^2} = 1$$

is called an *ellipsoid.* If $a^2 = b^2 = c^2$, **17.12** is an equation of a sphere. If $a^2 = b^2$ (or $b^2 = c^2$, or $a^2 = c^2$), **17.12** is an equation of an ellipsoid of revolution, as discussed in the previous section.

If we let $z = 0$ in **17.12**, we get

$$\frac{x^2}{a^2} + \frac{y^2}{b^2} = 1$$

as the equation of the cross section of the ellipsoid in the xy plane. Clearly, this cross section is an ellipse. The cross sections of **17.12** in the other coordinate planes are easily seen to be ellipses also.

Letting $z = k$ in **17.12**, we get the equation

$$\frac{x^2}{a^2} + \frac{y^2}{b^2} = 1 - \frac{k^2}{c^2}$$

of the cross section of the ellipsoid in the plane $z = k$, a plane parallel to the xy plane. This cross section again is an ellipse if $k^2 < c^2$. Similar statements may be made for cross sections in planes parallel to the other coordinate planes. The graph of **17.12** is sketched in Figure 17.19.

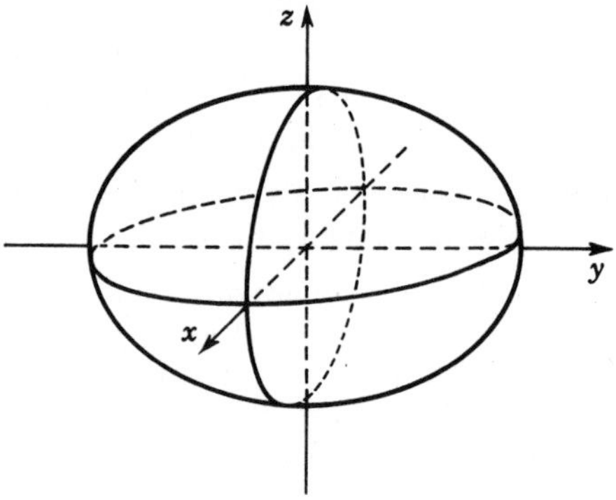

FIGURE 17.19

The graph of an equation of the form

17.13
$$\frac{x^2}{a^2} + \frac{y^2}{b^2} = cz$$

is called an *elliptic paraboloid*, so named because each cross section of the surface in a plane $z = k$ is an ellipse (if $ck > 0$) whereas each cross section in a plane $x = k$ or $y = k$ is a parabola. If $a^2 = b^2$, **17.13** is an equation of a paraboloid of revolution with the z axis as axis of revolution. If $c > 0$, the graph of **17.13** is as shown in Figure 17.20.

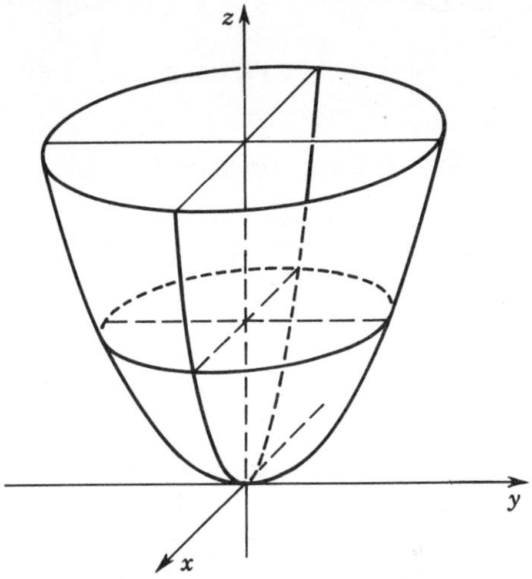

FIGURE 17.20

The quadric surface with equation of the form

17.14
$$\frac{y^2}{b^2} - \frac{x^2}{a^2} = cz$$

is called a *hyperbolic paraboloid*. If $c > 0$, it is the saddle-shaped surface shown in Figure 17.21. We note that if $z = 0$, the cross section consists of the lines

$$\frac{x}{a} = \pm \frac{y}{b},$$

whereas if $z = k$, ($k \neq 0$) the cross section is a hyperbola. The cross sections in planes parallel to the xz and yz planes are parabolas.

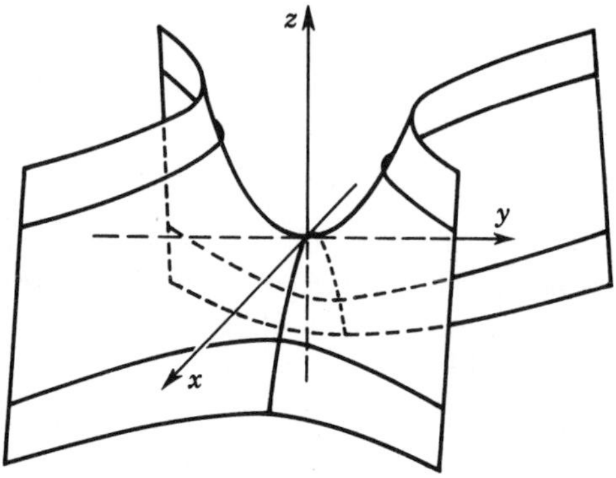

FIGURE 17.21

Quadric surfaces with equations of the form

17.15 $$\frac{x^2}{a^2} + \frac{y^2}{b^2} - \frac{z^2}{c^2} = 1,$$

or

17.16 $$\frac{x^2}{a^2} + \frac{y^2}{b^2} - \frac{z^2}{c^2} = -1$$

are called *hyperboloids*. For each surface the cross section in a plane $z = k$ is an ellipse, and the cross sections in the planes $x = k$ and $y = k$ are hyperbolas. If $a^2 = b^2$, these surfaces are hyperboloids of revolution. The graph of **17.15**, shown in Figure 17.22, is called a *hyperboloid of one sheet*. The graph of **17.16**, shown in Figure 17.23, is called a *hyperboloid of two sheets*.

Closely related to the hyperboloids is the quadric surface with equation

17.17 $$\frac{x^2}{a^2} + \frac{y^2}{b^2} - \frac{z^2}{c^2} = 0.$$

This surface is related to each of the hyperboloids as the asymptotes are to a hyperbola. It is an *elliptic cone*, frequently called the asymptotic cone of each of the hyperboloids **17.15** and **17.16**. For $z = k$ the cross section of **17.17** is an ellipse; for $x = k$ or $y = k$ the cross section is a hyperbola if $k \neq 0$ and a pair of lines intersecting at the origin if $k = 0$.

A cone may be thought of as a surface generated by a line moving along a given plane curve and passing through a fixed point, called the *vertex* of the cone. Thus, if V is the vertex of a cone and P is any point on the cone, every point on the line through V and P is also on the cone. The most common cone is the right circular cone generated by a line moving along a circle (**17.17** if $a^2 = b^2$).

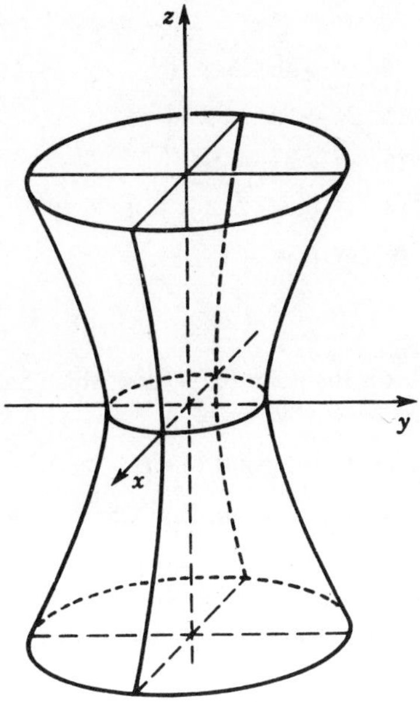

FIGURE 17.22

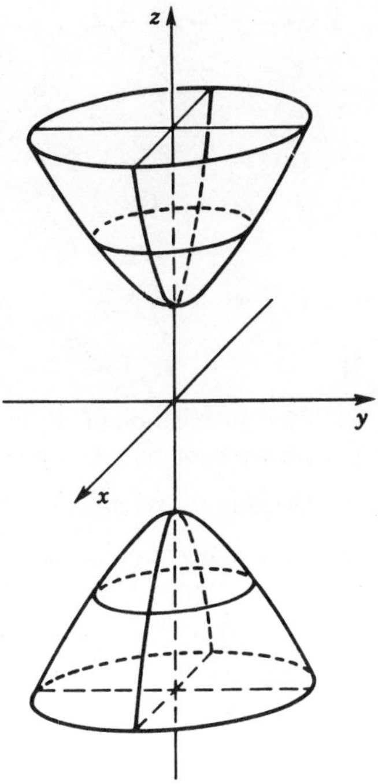

FIGURE 17.23

We may prove that 17.17 is a cone as follows. If $P(x_0,y_0,z_0)$ is any point on the graph of 17.17 other than the origin O, then the line L on P and O has parametric equations

$$x = x_0t, \quad y = y_0t, \quad z = z_0t.$$

Each point on L is also on the graph of 17.17, since

$$\frac{(x_0t)^2}{a^2} + \frac{(y_0t)^2}{b^2} - \frac{(z_0t)^2}{c^2} = t^2\left(\frac{x_0^2}{a^2} + \frac{y_0^2}{b^2} - \frac{z_0^2}{c^2}\right) = 0.$$

Thus the graph of 17.17 is a cone.

EXERCISES

I

Name and sketch the graph of each of the following equations. (It is sometimes helpful to relabel the axes.)

1. $x^2 + 4y^2 + 9z^2 = 36.$

2. $x^2 + 4y^2 = 4z.$

3. $x^2 - y^2 + 4z^2 = 4.$
4. $x^2 - y^2 - 4z^2 = 4.$
5. $x^2 = z^2 + 4y.$
6. $16x^2 + y^2 = 64 - 4z^2.$
7. $4x^2 + 8y + z^2 = 0.$
8. $x^2 + 9y^2 = z^2.$
9. $16x^2 - 9y^2 - z^2 - 144 = 0.$
10. $36 + 4y^2 = x^2 + 9z^2.$
11. $x^2 + 25z^2 = 9y^2.$
12. $y^2 = 4x + 4z^2.$
13. $x^2 + 25y^2 - 50z = 0.$
14. $x^2 + 4y^2 = 4z^2 - 4z + 1.$
15. $x^2 + y^2 = 4x.$
16. $x^2 + y^2 = 1 + z.$

II

1. Find an equation of the cone whose vertex is the point $(0,0,l)$ and which has as its cross section in the xy plane the ellipse $x^2/a^2 + y^2/b^2 = 1$.
2. Generalize Exercise 1 by changing the vertex to the point (h,k,l).
3. Find an equation of the sphere circumscribing the tetrahedron whose vertices are (x_r,y_r,z_r), $(r = 1, 2, 3, 4)$.
4. Show that if a rectangular parallelepiped is inscribed in an ellipsoid $x^2/a^2 + y^2/b^2 + z^2/c^2 = 1$ (with a, b, and c all different positive numbers) then its faces must be parallel to the coordinate planes.

8 SPACE CURVES

Just as a mapping of an interval into R^2 is called a plane curve, so is a mapping λ of an interval I into R^3 called a *space curve*. When we speak of a *curve* in this chapter, it is understood to be a space curve. (Of course, a plane curve may be regarded as a special type of a space curve.)

Our remarks on plane curves in Chapter 16 carry over almost verbatim to space curves. For example, the range of a space curve λ is called the *trace* of λ. A curve λ with domain I has *direction* determined by the order in I; if $t_1 < t_2$ in I, then we say that $\lambda(t_1)$ precedes $\lambda(t_2)$. One-to-one curves and simple closed curves are defined just as they were in Chapter 16. Also, λ is *continuous* at c in I if for each open ball $B(\lambda(c),\epsilon)$ there exists a neighborhood N of c such that

$$\lambda(t) \text{ is in } B(\lambda(c),\epsilon) \text{ for every } t \text{ in } N \cap I.$$

Each curve λ with domain I may be given in the form

17.18 $$\lambda(t) = (x(t), y(t), z(t)),$$

where x, y, and z are ordinary functions. Note that λ is a plane curve lying in the xy plane if $z(t) = 0$ for each t in I. By the obvious extension of **16.3** to space, λ is continuous at c if and only if the functions x, y, and z are continuous at c.

We recall that

$$\lim_{t\to c} \lambda(t) = P$$

if the curve λ can be made continuous at c by defining (or redefining) $\lambda(c) = P$. If λ is given in the form **17.18**, then clearly

$$\lim_{t\to c} \lambda(t) = (\lim_{t\to c} x(t), \lim_{t\to c} y(t), \lim_{t\to c} z(t)).$$

If λ is a curve with domain I and if t, c are in I, then the vector $\mathbf{s}(t)$, which translates point $\lambda(t)$ into point $\lambda(c)$ is called a *secant vector* of λ. The vector $\boldsymbol{\lambda}'(c)$ defined by

$$\boldsymbol{\lambda}'(c) = \lim_{t\to c} \frac{1}{t - c}\,\mathbf{s}(t)$$

is called the *tangent vector* of λ at c as in Chapter 16. If λ is given by **17.18**, $\lambda(t) = (x(t), y(t), z(t))$, then

17.19 $$\boldsymbol{\lambda}'(t) = \langle x'(t), y'(t), z'(t)\rangle.$$

We call λ a *differentiable curve* if λ and $\boldsymbol{\lambda}'$ have the same domain, and a *smooth curve* if, in addition, $\boldsymbol{\lambda}'$ is continuous in its domain.

The higher derivatives of a curve λ can be defined in the usual way. Thus, if $\lambda(t) = (x(t), y(t), z(t))$, the nth derivative of λ is denoted by $\boldsymbol{\lambda}^{[n]}$ and defined by

17.20 $$\boldsymbol{\lambda}^{[n]}(t) = \langle x^{[n]}(t), y^{[n]}(t), z^{[n]}(t)\rangle.$$

We call λ an *n-smooth* curve if $\boldsymbol{\lambda}^{[n]}$ has the same domain I as λ and if $\boldsymbol{\lambda}^{[n]}$ is continuous in I.

Given a differentiable curve $\boldsymbol{\lambda}$ with domain I and a number c in I such that $\boldsymbol{\lambda}'(c) \neq \mathbf{0}$, then the line

$$L(\lambda,c) = \{\lambda(c) + t\boldsymbol{\lambda}'(c) \mid t \text{ in } \mathsf{R}\}$$

is called the *tangent line* to λ at c. The tangent line $L(\lambda,c)$ is close to curve λ at c in the sense that

$$\lim_{t\to 0} \frac{d(\lambda(t + c), \lambda(c) + t\boldsymbol{\lambda}'(c))}{|t|} = 0$$

(see **16.9**).

The screw thread on a bolt or the wire holding together a spiral notebook are interesting examples of a curve. This curve, called a circular helix, lies on a circular cylinder

$$x^2 + y^2 = r^2.$$

The cross section of this cylinder in the xy plane is a circle which may be described as the trace of the curve δ defined by

$$\delta(t) = (r \cos t, r \sin t, 0).$$

Now imagine a curve λ starting from the point $(r,0,0)$ when $t = 0$ and winding about the given cylinder in such a way that each point (x,y,z) on the curve has z coordinate proportional to t when $x = r \cos t$ and $y = r \sin t$. In other words, the curve λ is defined by

17.21 $$\lambda(t) = (r \cos t, r \sin t, at)$$

for some constant $a \neq 0$ (Figure 17.24). We call λ a *circular helix*. Evidently, λ is an n-smooth curve for every positive integer n. Its tangent vector is given by

$$\boldsymbol{\lambda}'(t) = \langle -r \sin t, r \cos t, a\rangle$$

at each number t. It is interesting to note that the length of the tangent vector is constant,

$$|\boldsymbol{\lambda}'(t)| = \sqrt{(-r \sin t)^2 + (r \cos t)^2 + a^2} = \sqrt{r^2 + a^2}.$$

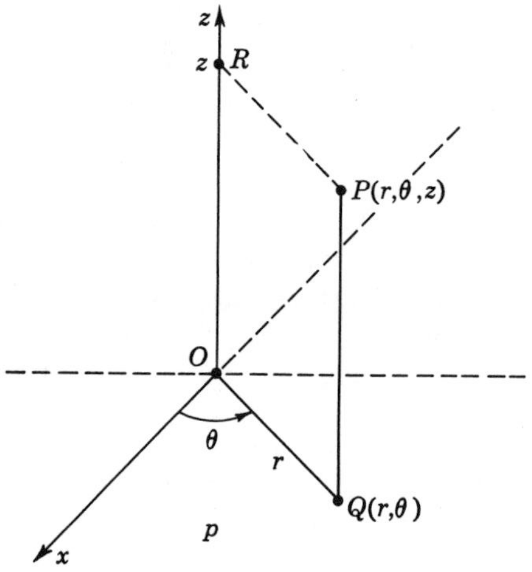

FIGURE 17.24

If λ is a differentiable curve with domain I and c is a number in I such that $\boldsymbol{\lambda}'(c) \neq \mathbf{0}$, then the plane $p(\lambda,c)$ passing through the point $\lambda(c)$ and perpendicular to the tangent vector $\boldsymbol{\lambda}'(t)$ is called the *normal plane* to λ at c. Thus, if $\lambda(t) = (x(t), y(t), z(t))$, then $\boldsymbol{\lambda}'(t) = \langle x'(t), y'(t), z'(t)\rangle$, and a point (X,Y,Z) is in $p(\lambda,c)$

if and only if the vector $\langle X - x(c),\ Y - y(c),\ Z - z(c)\rangle$ is perpendicular to $\lambda'(c)$, i.e.,

$$\langle X - x(c), Y - y(c), Z - z(c)\rangle \cdot \lambda'(c) = 0,$$

that is,

17.22 $$x'(c)(X - x(c)) + y'(c)(Y - y(c)) + z'(c)(Z - z(c)) = 0.$$

Hence **17.22** is an equation of the normal plane to λ at c. Note that we have used capital letters X, Y, and Z for coordinates of points in the plane in order to distinguish them from the coordinates $x(t)$, $y(t)$, and $z(t)$ of points in the trace of λ.

EXAMPLE 1. Describe the normal plane to the helix **17.21** at any point on it.

Solution: We have $\lambda(t) = (r \cos t, r \sin t, at)$ and $\lambda'(t) = \langle -r \sin t, r \cos t, a\rangle$. By **17.22**,

$$-r \sin t(X - r \cos t) + r \cos t(Y - r \sin t) + a(Z - at) = 0$$

or

$$(-r \sin t)X + (r \cos t)Y + aZ = a^2 t$$

is an equation of the normal plane to λ at the point $\lambda(t)$. If, for example, $t = 0$, then we obtain

$$rY + aZ = 0$$

as an equation of the tangent plane at the point $(r,0,0)$ of the helix.

A smooth plane curve λ with domain $[a,b]$ has length $L_a^b(\lambda)$ given by **16.20**. The arguments used there carry over to space curves to yield the following result.

17.23 THEOREM. If λ is a smooth curve with domain $[a,b]$, then the length of the curve λ exists and is given by

$$L_a^b(\lambda) = \int_a^b |\lambda'(t)|\, dt.$$

EXAMPLE 2. Find the length of the helix **17.21** between $t = 0$ and $t = k$, (k a positive number).

Solution: We saw previously that $|\lambda'(t)| = \sqrt{r^2 + a^2}$ for every number t. Hence

$$L_0^k(\lambda) = \int_0^k \sqrt{r^2 + a^2}\, dt = k\sqrt{r^2 + a^2}.$$

Thus, as might be anticipated, the length of a circular helix is a constant $\sqrt{r^2 + a^2}$ times the central angle k swept out in tracing the curve. For example, in one revolution around the cylinder the helix has length $2\pi\sqrt{r^2 + a^2}$.

EXERCISES

I

In each of Exercises 1–3, find equations of the tangent line and normal plane to the given space curve at the indicated point.

1. $\lambda(t) = (t - 3, t^2 + 1, t^2)$, $t = 3$.
2. $\lambda(t) = (t^2, t^{-1}, \sin \pi t)$, $t = 1$.
3. $\lambda(t) = (a \sin kt, b \cos kt, ct^2)$, $t = t_0$.
4. Express in parametric form the curve of intersection of the two surfaces $x^2 + y^2 = 25z$ and $y^2 + z^2 = 17$. Find an equation of the normal plane to this curve at the point (3,4,1).
5. Show that the two curves defined by $\lambda_1(t) = (t, 2t^2, -t^{-1})$ and $\lambda_2(s) = (1 - s, 2 \cos s, \sin s - 1)$ intersect at right angles.
6. a. Find all points of intersection of the two curves defined by $\lambda_1(t) = (t, t^2 - t, 1 - t/2)$ and $\lambda_2(s) = (2 \sin s, 2 \sin s, \cos s)$.
   b. Find the angle of intersection of λ_1 and λ_2 at each of their points of intersection.
7. Find the length of the space curve defined by $\lambda(t) = (t^2 + 1, t^2 - 1, 8t)$, domain $\lambda = [1,3]$.
8. Find the length of the space curve defined by $\lambda(t) = (t \cos t, t \sin t, t^2)$, domain $\lambda = [0,a]$.

II

1. It was remarked on page 598 that the space curve $\lambda(t) = (x(t), y(t), z(t))$ reduces to a plane curve if $z(t) = 0$ for each t. Show that if λ is a plane curve then necessarily $\boldsymbol{\lambda}'(t) \cdot \boldsymbol{\lambda}''(t) \times \boldsymbol{\lambda}'''(t) = 0$ for each t. A more difficult problem is to show, conversely, that if the above equation holds then λ is a plane curve.
2. Prove that all the normal planes to the space curve $\lambda(t) = (a \sin^2 t, a \sin t \cos t, a \cos t)$ pass through a fixed point. What other interesting property does λ have?
3. If all the tangent lines to a space curve λ pass through a fixed point, show that λ is a straight line.
4. If all the tangent lines to a space curve λ are parallel to a given straight line, show that λ is a straight line.
5. Find the space curve of shortest length between the two points $(a,0,0)$ and $(a \cos t, a \sin t, h)$ and lying on the cylinder $x^2 + y^2 = a^2$. [*Hint:* Cut the cylinder along a generator and lay it out flat.]

9 CURVATURE

If λ is a smooth curve with domain $[a,b]$ such that $\lambda'(t) \neq 0$ for every t in $[a,b]$, then the arc-length function h defined by

$$h(t) = \int_a^t |\lambda'(p)| \, dp, \qquad \text{domain } h = [a,b],$$

is a smooth function for which $h'(t) = |\lambda'(t)| > 0$, t in $[a,b]$. Since $h'(t) > 0$, the function h is strictly increasing in $[a,b]$. Therefore h has an inverse function h^{-1} with domain $[0,h(b)]$. The curve δ defined by

$$\delta(s) = \lambda(h^{-1}(s)), \qquad \text{domain } \delta = [0,h(b)],$$

evidently is smooth and has the same trace as λ. By definition, $\delta(s)$ is the point on curve λ that is s units from $\lambda(a)$ measured along the curve (Figure 17.25). That is, if $s = h(t)$, then $t = h^{-1}(s)$ and $\lambda(t) = \lambda(h^{-1}(s)) = \delta(s)$. We call curve δ the *reparametrization of* λ *by arc length.*

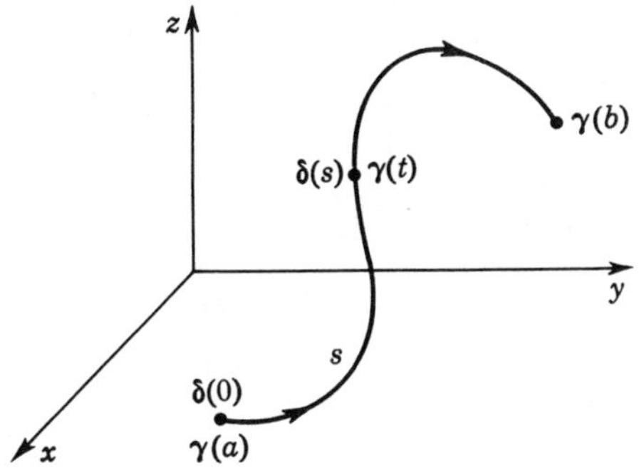

FIGURE 17.25

The reparametrization by arc length of the helix λ of 17.21 is very simple. If we restrict the domain of λ to be $[0,b]$ for some positive number b, then clearly $\lambda'(t) \neq 0$ in $[0,b]$ By Example 2, page 601,

$$h(t) = \int_0^t |\lambda'(p)| \, dp = ct,$$

where $c = \sqrt{r^2 + a^2}$. Hence $h^{-1}(s) = s/c$ and $\delta(s) = \lambda(h^{-1}(s))$ is given by

17.24 $$\delta(s) = \left(r \cos\frac{s}{c}, r \sin\frac{s}{c}, \frac{as}{c}\right), \qquad c = \sqrt{r^2 + a^2}.$$

Curve δ of **17.24** is still a helix. However, δ has the nice property that point $\delta(s)$ is s units from the point $\delta(0) = (r,0,0)$ if distance is measured along the curve.

In what follows, let us assume that λ is a 2-smooth curve with domain $[a,b]$ such that $\boldsymbol{\lambda}'(t) \neq \mathbf{0}$ in $[a,b]$, let the arc-length function h be as defined above, and let δ be the reparametrization of λ by arc length. Thus

$$\delta(s) = \lambda(t) \text{ if } s = h(t), \qquad \text{domain } \delta = [0,h(b)].$$

Since $d\delta/ds = (d\lambda/dt)/(ds/dt)$ by the chain rule and **11.36**, we have

17.25
$$\boldsymbol{\delta}'(s) = \frac{1}{|\boldsymbol{\lambda}'(t)|}\boldsymbol{\lambda}'(t) \quad \text{if } s = h(t).$$

Hence $\boldsymbol{\delta}'(s)$ is the *unit tangent vector* of curve λ at $t = h^{-1}(s)$.

Since $\boldsymbol{\delta}'(s)\cdot\boldsymbol{\delta}'(s) = 1$, we have by differentiation that

$$\boldsymbol{\delta}'(s)\cdot\boldsymbol{\delta}''(s) = 0, \qquad s \text{ in } [0,h(b)].$$

That is, vector $\boldsymbol{\delta}''(s)$ is perpendicular to $\boldsymbol{\delta}'(s)$. We call $\boldsymbol{\delta}''(s)$ the *principal normal* to curve λ at $t = h^{-1}(s)$. The length of $\boldsymbol{\delta}''(s)$ is called the *curvature* of λ at t and is designated by $k(t)$,

17.26
$$k(t) = |\boldsymbol{\delta}''(s)| \quad \text{if } s = h(t).$$

The curvature is a measure of the concavity of λ. Clearly, $k = 0$ if λ is a straight line. If $k(t) \neq 0$, then its reciprocal is called the *radius of curvature* and is designated by $\rho(t)$,

17.27
$$\rho(t) = \frac{1}{k(t)}.$$

EXAMPLE 1. Find k and ρ for a circle of radius r.

Solution: The curve λ defined by

$$\lambda(t) = (r\cos t, r\sin t, 0), \qquad \text{domain } \lambda = [0,2\pi],$$

is a circle of radius r in the xy plane. Clearly, $\boldsymbol{\lambda}'(t) = \langle -r\sin t, r\cos t, 0\rangle$ and $|\boldsymbol{\lambda}'(t)| = r$. Hence $h(t) = rt$ and the reparametrization of λ by arc length is given by

$$\delta(s) = \left(r\cos\frac{s}{r}, r\sin\frac{s}{r}, 0\right), \qquad \text{domain } \delta = [0,2\pi r].$$

Therefore

$$\boldsymbol{\delta}'(s) = \left\langle -\sin\frac{s}{r}, \cos\frac{s}{r}, 0\right\rangle$$

and

$$\boldsymbol{\delta}''(s) = \left\langle -\frac{1}{r}\cos\frac{s}{r}, -\frac{1}{r}\sin\frac{s}{r}, 0\right\rangle.$$

Hence

$$k(t) = |\delta''(s)| = \frac{1}{r} \quad \text{and} \quad \rho(t) = r$$

for every t. Thus a circle has a constant curvature equal to the reciprocal of its radius.

It should be clear from the above example that the circle actually was the curve in mind when $|\delta''(s)|$ was chosen as a measure of concavity. Then the concavity of any curve at a point P is measured by approximating the curve at P by a circle.

We do not have to find the reparametrization of λ by arc length in order to find the curvature k. For $\delta''(s) = d\delta'/ds = (d\delta'/dt)/(ds/dt)$; i.e.,

$$\delta''(s) = \frac{1}{|\lambda'(t)|}\frac{d}{dt}\left[\frac{1}{|\lambda'(t)|}\lambda'(t)\right] \quad \text{if } s = h(t).$$

Then the curvature can be obtained by finding the length of this vector.

EXAMPLE 2. Find the curvature of the helix **17.21**.

Solution: We have $\lambda(t) = (r \cos t, r \sin t, at)$, $\lambda'(t) = \langle -r \sin t, r \cos t, a\rangle$, and $|\lambda'(t)| = \sqrt{r^2 + a^2}$. Hence

$$\delta''(s) = \frac{1}{r^2 + a^2}\lambda''(t) = \frac{1}{r^2 + a^2}\langle -r \cos t, -r \sin t, 0\rangle,$$

by the equation above, and

$$k(t) = |\delta''(s)| = \frac{r}{r^2 + a^2}.$$

Just as for the circle, the curvature of the helix is constant.

If δ is the reparametrization of curve λ by arc length as above, then the vector

$$\mathbf{v}(t) = \rho(t)\delta''(s), \qquad s = h(t),$$

clearly is a unit vector in the direction of the principal normal. We call $\mathbf{v}(t)$ the *unit normal vector* to curve λ at t. In turn, the vector

$$\beta(t) = \lambda'(s) \times \mathbf{v}(t)$$

is called the *binormal* to λ at t. It is a unit vector perpendicular to both the tangent vector $\lambda'(s)$ and the normal vector $\mathbf{v}(t)$.

The point $C(t)$ which is $\rho(t)$ units from the point $\lambda(t)$ along the unit normal is called the *center of curvature* of λ at t. Thus

$$C(t) = \lambda(t) + \rho(t)\mathbf{v}(t).$$

In turn, the plane

$$p(C(t), \beta(t))$$

passing through $C(t)$ and with normal line $\beta(t)$ is called the *osculating plane* of λ at t. The circle in plane $p(C(t), \beta(t))$ with center $C(t)$ and radius $\rho(t)$ is called the *osculating circle* of λ at t. It is easily seen that the point $\lambda(t)$ lies on this circle.

EXAMPLE 3. The curve λ defined by

$$\lambda(t) = (t^2,t,t^3)$$

is called a *twisted cubic*. Find the center and radius of curvature of λ at 1.

Solution: We have $\boldsymbol{\lambda}'(t) = \langle 2t,1,3t^2\rangle$ and $|\boldsymbol{\lambda}'(t)| = \sqrt{1 + 4t^2 + 9t^4}$. Hence

$$\boldsymbol{\delta}'(s) = (1 + 4t^2 + 9t^4)^{-1/2}\langle 2t,1,3t^2\rangle$$

and

$$\boldsymbol{\delta}''(s) = \frac{1}{\sqrt{1 + 4t^2 + 9t^4}}[-(4t + 18t^3)(1 + 4t^2 + 9t^4)^{-3/2}\langle 2t,1,3t^2\rangle + (1 + 4t^2 + 9t^4)^{-1/2}\langle 2,0,6t\rangle].$$

At $t = 1$ we compute

$$\boldsymbol{\delta}''(s) = \tfrac{1}{98}\langle -8,-11,9\rangle$$

and

$$k(1) = |\boldsymbol{\delta}''(s)| = \frac{\sqrt{266}}{98}, \qquad \rho(1) = \frac{98}{\sqrt{266}}.$$

The unit normal is given by

$$\boldsymbol{\nu}(1) = \frac{1}{\sqrt{266}}\langle -8,-11,9\rangle.$$

Hence the center of curvature $C(1)$ is given by

$$C(1) = (1,1,1) + \left(\frac{98}{\sqrt{266}}\frac{1}{\sqrt{266}}\langle -8,-11,9\rangle\right)$$

$$= (1,1,1) + \left\langle -\frac{56}{19}, -\frac{77}{19}, \frac{63}{19}\right\rangle = \left(-\frac{37}{19}, -\frac{58}{19}, \frac{82}{19}\right).$$

EXERCISES

I

1. Reparametrize by arc length the curve λ defined by $\lambda(t) = \left(t \sin t, t \cos t, \frac{2\sqrt{2}}{2} t^{3/2}\right)$.

2. Show that the curvature k of the plane curve $\lambda(t) = (x(t), y(t))$ is given by $k(t) = |x'(t)y''(t) - x''(t)y'(t)|/[x'^2(t) + y'^2(t)]^{3/2}$.

3. Use Exercise 2 to obtain a formula for the curvature of the graph of the equation $y = f(x)$.

In each of Exercises 4–6 find the curvature of the given curve at the indicated points.

4. $\lambda(t) = (t, \sin t)$, $t = 0$, $t = \pi/2$.

5. $\lambda(t) = (\sin t, \cos 2t)$, $t = \pi/6$.

6. $\lambda(t) = (t, \ln t)$, $t = 1$, $t = e$.

7. If $r = f(\theta)$ is the equation of a curve in polar coordinates, show that its curvature is given by $k = |2f'^2 - ff'' + f^2|/(f'^2 + f^2)^{3/2}$.

In each of Exercises 8–11 find the curvature of the graph of the given equation at the indicated points.

8. $r = a\theta$, $\theta = \theta_0$.

9. $r = ae^{b\theta}$, $\theta = \theta_0$.

10. $r = 2 + \sin\theta$, $\theta = 0$, $\theta = \pi/2$.

11. $r(2\sin\theta + 3\cos\theta) = 1$, $\theta = \theta_0$.

In Exercises 12 and 13, find the maximum and minimum radii of curvature for the given curve. Locate these points on a sketch of the trace of the curve.

12. $\lambda(t) = (t, t^2)$.

13. $\lambda(t) = (a\cos t, b\sin t)$.

14. Find the radius of curvature ρ of the curve in Exercise 1.

II

1. Show that the curvature of a curve λ is unchanged if the parameter t is replaced by another parameter r, where $t = h(r)$ and $h'(r) > 0$.

2. Let $s = s(t)$ be the length of arc of the curve λ from a fixed point A to the point P, and let $\theta(s)$ be the inclination of the tangent line to λ at P (see the accompanying figure). Show that the instantaneous rate of change of θ with respect to s is also a measure of the curvature of λ at P; i.e., $k(t) = |d\theta/ds|$.

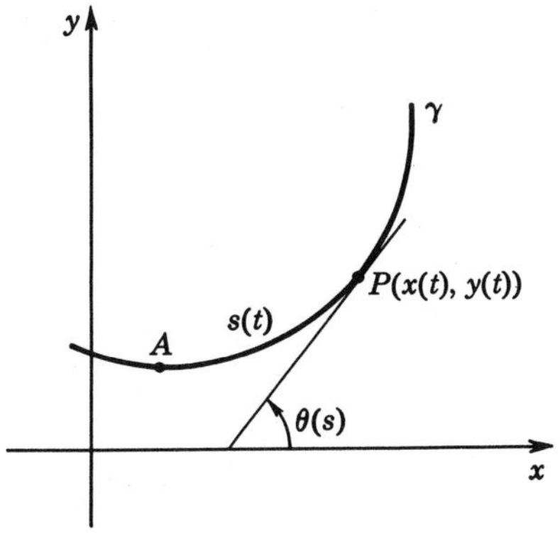

3. Show that the radius of curvature of the curve $\lambda(t) = (x(t), y(t), z(t))$ is given by the absolute value of

$$\frac{(x'^2 + y'^2 + z'^2)^{3/2}}{\left(\begin{vmatrix} y' & z' \\ y'' & z'' \end{vmatrix}^2 + \begin{vmatrix} z' & x' \\ z'' & x'' \end{vmatrix}^2 + \begin{vmatrix} x' & y' \\ x'' & y'' \end{vmatrix}^2\right)^{1/2}}.$$

4. Show that the unit normal vector $\mathbf{v}$ of the curve λ expressed in terms of the parameter t only is given by

$$\mathbf{v}(t) = \frac{\rho(t)}{|\lambda'(t)|^4}(\lambda'(t) \times [\lambda''(t) \times \lambda'(t)]).$$

5. Show that the binormal vector β of the curve λ expressed in terms of the parameter t only is given by $\beta(t) = \dfrac{\rho(t)}{|\lambda'(t)|^3}\lambda'(t) \times \lambda''(t)$.

10 CYLINDRICAL AND SPHERICAL COORDINATE SYSTEMS

There are two common generalizations in space of the polar coordinate system in a plane.

The basis of a *cylindrical coordinate system* is a plane p with a polar coordinate system on it and a z axis perpendicular to p with the origin of the z axis at the pole of p. Each point P in space then has coordinates (r,θ,z), where (r,θ) are the polar coordinates of the projection Q of P on p, and z is the coordinate of the projection R of P on the z axis (Figure 17.26).

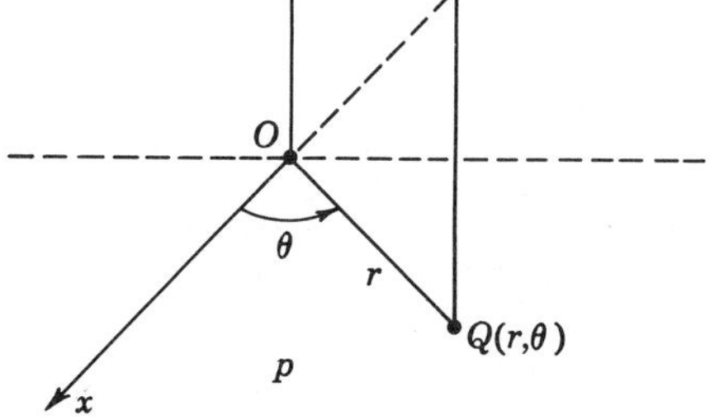

FIGURE 17.26

The graph of an equation of the form

$$r = c, \qquad (c > 0),$$

is a right circular cylinder of radius c having the z axis as its axis. This is the reason for the name "cylindrical" coordinate system. The graph of

$$\theta = c$$

is a half-plane emanating from the z axis; the graph of

$$z = c$$

is a plane parallel to the given polar coordinate plane p.

If a rectangular coordinate system and a cylindrical coordinate system are placed in space as in Figure 17.27, with the cylindrical coordinate system having

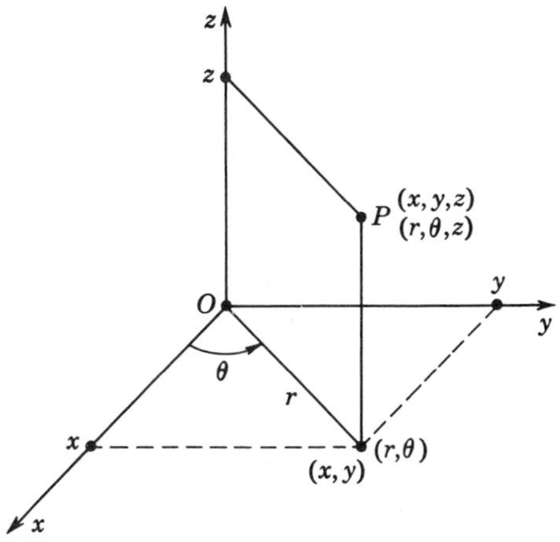

FIGURE 17.27

the xy plane as its polar plane and the positive x axis as its polar axis, then each point P has two sets of coordinates, (x,y,z) and (r,θ,z), related by the equations

17.28 $$x = r\cos\theta, \quad y = r\sin\theta, \quad z = z.$$

This is evident from **16.12**.

For a *spherical coordinate system*, we start off with a plane p having a polar coordinate system on it and a z axis perpendicular to p with the origin of the z axis meeting the plane p at the pole. Each point P in space has coordinates (ρ,θ,ϕ), where

$$\rho = |OP|,$$

θ is the polar angle associated with the projection Q of P on plane p, and ϕ is the direction angle of the half-line from the pole through P relative to the z axis (Figure 17.28). The origin has coordinates $(0,\theta,\phi)$ for any θ and ϕ. If $P(\rho,\theta,\phi)$ is a point different from the origin, then necessarily $\rho > 0$ and $0 \leq \phi \leq \pi$, with

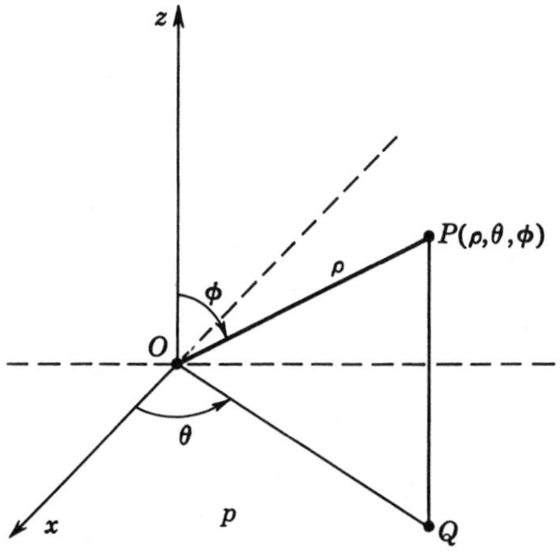

FIGURE 17.28

$\phi = 0$ if P is on the positive z axis and $\phi = \pi$ if P is on the negative z axis. There are no restrictions on the angle θ.

The graph of

$$\rho = c, \qquad (c > 0),$$

is a sphere of radius c with center at the pole; hence the name "spherical" coordinate system. The graph of

$$\theta = c$$

is a half-plane emanating from the z axis, and the graph of

$$\phi = c, \qquad (0 < c < \pi),$$

is a right circular cone having the z axis as its axis and the pole as its vertex.

If we place a rectangular coordinate system and a spherical coordinate system together, as indicated in Figure 17.29, then each point P in space has two sets of coordinates, (x,y,z) and (ρ,θ,ϕ). By **17.28**, with $r = |OQ|$, we have

$$x = |OQ| \cos \theta, \qquad y = |OQ| \sin \theta.$$

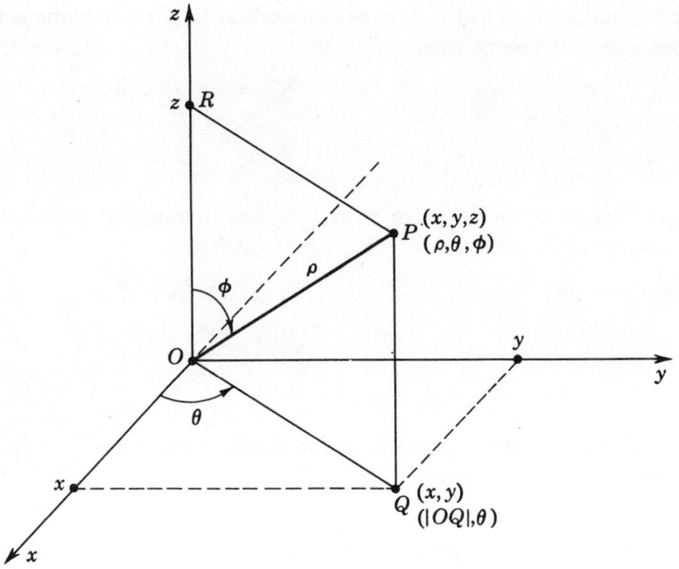

FIGURE 17.29

Since $|OQ| = |PR| = \rho \sin \phi$ and $z = \rho \cos \phi$, we obtain

17.29 $$x = \rho \sin \phi \cos \theta, \qquad y = \rho \sin \phi \sin \theta, \qquad z = \rho \cos \phi$$

as the equations relating x, y, and z to ρ, θ, and ϕ.

EXERCISES

I

1. Find spherical coordinates for the following points given in rectangular coordinates:

   a. $(4,2,-4)$. b. $(1,-\sqrt{3},4)$.

2. Find cylindrical coordinates for the points in Exercise 1.

3. Find rectangular coordinates for the following points given in cylindrical coordinates:

   a. $(2, \arccos \frac{3}{5}, 6)$ b. $(10,-\frac{1}{2}\pi,4)$.

4. Find rectangular coordinates for the following points given in spherical coordinates:

   a. $(2,\frac{1}{4}\pi,\frac{1}{3}\pi)$. b. $(3,\frac{1}{3}\pi,-\frac{1}{6}\pi)$.

5. Find equations in cylindrical coordinates of the graphs of the following equations given in rectangular coordinates:

a. $(x + y)^2 = z - 5.$

b. $x^2z^2 = 25 - y^2z^2.$

c. $\dfrac{x^2}{a^2} + \dfrac{y^2}{b^2} = 1.$

d. $ax + by + cz = x^2 + y^2 + z^2.$

6. The following surfaces are given in spherical coordinates. Find their equations in rectangular coordinates and describe the surfaces:

a. $\cot \phi = \sin \theta + \cos \theta.$

b. $\rho^2 \cos 2\phi = a^2.$

c. $\rho = a \sin \phi \sin \theta.$

d. $\rho^2 \sin^2 \phi \sin 2\theta = a^2.$

II

1. Give a complete set of transformation equations between a cylindrical and a spherical coordinate system.

2. Discuss symmetry conditions for a surface whose equation is given in: (a) cylindrical coordinates; (b) spherical coordinates.

REVIEW

Oral Exercises

1. What are the conditions for symmetry of a surface whose equation is given in rectangular coordinates with respect to the coordinate axes? To the coordinate planes?

2. What is a vector?

3. What is the inner product of two vectors?

4. What algebraic laws are satisfied by the operations of addition, scalar multiplication, and inner product of vectors?

5. Give a geometric or physical interpretation of the inner product. What is implied if the inner product of two vectors is zero?

6. What is the cross product of two vectors? Give its geometric meaning.

7. What is the Cauchy inequality? Give a geometric interpretation.

8. What are direction angles? Direction cosines?

9. Give a general equation for: (a) a line; (b) a plane; (c) a sphere.

Define or explain each of the following:

10. Unit tangent vector of a curve.

11. Normal plane of a curve.

12. Principal normal of a curve.

13. Binormal of a curve.

14. Curvature of a curve.

15. Center of curvature of a curve.

16. Length of a curve.

17. Define: (a) a cylinder; (b) a surface of revolution; (c) a cone; (d) a quadric surface.

18. Describe: (a) a cylindrical coordinate system; (b) a spherical coordinate system.

I

1. Find the sides and angles of the triangles having the following vertices: (a) (0,0,3), (4,0,0), (0,8,0); (b) (3,−3,−3), (4,2,7), (−1,−2,−5).

2. Given the distinct points $P_1 = (x_1,y_1,z_1)$ and $P_2 = (x_2,y_2,z_2)$, find the point P on the segment P_1P_2 such that $|P_1P|/|PP_2| = r$.

3. What special properties has the tetrahedron with vertices (6,−6,0), (3,−4,4), (2,−9,2), and (−1,−7,6)?

4. Show that the six planes $2x - y + z = -3$, $4x - 2y + 2z = 5$, $x - y + 4z = 0$, $9x + 3y - 6z = 7$, $3x + y - 2z = -8$, and $-7x - 7y + 28z = 6$ bound a parallelepiped. Find the volume of this parallelepiped.

5. Show that the lines

$$\begin{cases} 3x + y - z = 1 \\ 2x - z = 2, \end{cases} \qquad \begin{cases} 2x - y + 2z = 4 \\ x - y + 2z = 3 \end{cases}$$

intersect and are perpendicular.

6. Discuss the graphs of the equations:

a. $x^2 + y^2 + z^2 + 2x - 4y - 6z = 2.$

b. $x^2 + 4y^2 + 9z^2 + 2x - 4y - 6z = -4.$

7. Find parametric equations of the line passing through the point (1,3,−5) and parallel to the vector ⟨2,3,−4⟩.

8. Find an equation of a plane passing through the given point and perpendicular to the given vector.

a. (1,2,−2), ⟨2,−1,−3⟩.

b. (2,−1,−3), ⟨1,2,−2⟩.

9. Determine which set of four points, if any, are coplanar.

   a. (1,2,3), (3,−1,−1), (4,1,−2), (0,0,4).
   b. (1,2,3), (3,1,1), (4,−1,2), (1,5,3).

10. Under what conditions on the numbers a, b, c, and d does the graph of the equation $x^2 + y^2 + z^2 + ax + by + cz + d = 0$ consist of a single point?

In each of Exercises 11–13, find an equation of the given sphere.

11. The sphere has its center on the z axis and passes through the points (0,2,2) and (4,0,0).

12. The sphere passes through the points $(a,a,0)$, $(0,a,a)$, and $(a,0,a)$ and has radius r.

13. The sphere has the two points (x_1,y_1,z_1) and (x_2,y_2,z_2) as ends of a diameter.

14. Find an equation of the path of a point which moves in such a way that it is always m times as far from the point (a,b,c) as it is from the point (r,s,t). What does the graph reduce to for the special case $m = 1$?

15. Discuss and sketch the graph in space of each of the following equations.

   a. $xy = 0$.
   b. $xy = 1$.
   c. $x^2 + y^2 - z^2 = 1$.
   d. $x^2 - y^2 - z^2 = 1$.

16. Find an equation of the surface obtained by rotating the hyperbola $xy = a^2$ in the xy plane about the x axis; about the y axis. Sketch.

17. If $\mathbf{u} = \mathbf{i} + \mathbf{j}$, $\mathbf{v} = \mathbf{j} + \mathbf{k}$, $\mathbf{w} = \mathbf{k} + \mathbf{i}$, $\mathbf{y} = \mathbf{i} - \mathbf{j} + 2\mathbf{k}$, then find:

   a. $\mathbf{u}^2, \mathbf{v}^2, \mathbf{w}^2, \mathbf{y}^2$.
   b. $\mathbf{u}\cdot\mathbf{v}, \mathbf{v}\cdot\mathbf{w}, \mathbf{w}\cdot\mathbf{u}, \mathbf{u}\cdot\mathbf{y}$.
   c. $\mathbf{u}\times\mathbf{v}, \mathbf{v}\times\mathbf{w}, \mathbf{w}\times\mathbf{u}, \mathbf{u}\times\mathbf{y}$.
   d. $\mathbf{u}\cdot\mathbf{v}\times\mathbf{w}$.
   e. $\mathbf{u}\times(\mathbf{v}\times\mathbf{w}) - (\mathbf{u}\times\mathbf{v})\times\mathbf{w}$.

18. Given the vectors $\mathbf{u} = \langle 2,1,-1\rangle$, $\mathbf{v} = \langle 1,2,-1\rangle$, and $\mathbf{w} = \langle 1,1,3\rangle$, determine a unit vector which is a linear combination of $\mathbf{v}$ and $\mathbf{w}$ and is perpendicular to $\mathbf{u}$.

19. Show vectorially that every angle inscribed in a semicircle is a right angle.

20. Prove the Jacobi identity: $\mathbf{u}\times(\mathbf{v}\times\mathbf{w}) + \mathbf{v}\times(\mathbf{w}\times\mathbf{u}) + \mathbf{w}\times(\mathbf{u}\times\mathbf{v}) = \mathbf{0}$.

21. If $\mathbf{u}$, $\mathbf{v}$, and $\mathbf{w}$ are vector functions of one variable, then prove that:

   a. $D(\mathbf{u}\times\mathbf{v}) = (D\mathbf{u})\times\mathbf{v} + \mathbf{u}\times(D\mathbf{v})$.
   b. $D(\mathbf{u}\cdot\mathbf{v}\times\mathbf{w}) = (D\mathbf{u})\cdot\mathbf{v}\times\mathbf{w} + \mathbf{u}\cdot(D\mathbf{v})\times\mathbf{w} + \mathbf{u}\cdot\mathbf{v}\times(D\mathbf{w})$.

22. Show that the volume of a parallelepiped which has three coterminal edges given by the vectors $\mathbf{A} = \langle a_1,a_2,a_3\rangle$, $\mathbf{B} = \langle b_1,b_2,b_3\rangle$, $\mathbf{C} = \langle c_1,c_2,c_3\rangle$, is given by

$$V = \mathbf{A}\cdot\mathbf{B}\times\mathbf{C} = \begin{vmatrix} a_1 & a_2 & a_3 \\ b_1 & b_2 & b_3 \\ c_1 & c_2 & c_3 \end{vmatrix}.$$

[*Hint:* $|\mathbf{B}\times\mathbf{C}|$ is the area of one of the faces.]

23. Using the preceding exercise, show that the volume of a tetrahedron whose vertices are $(0,0,0)$, (a_1,a_2,a_3), (b_1,b_2,b_3), (c_1,c_2,c_3) is given by

$$V = \frac{1}{6}\mathbf{A}\cdot\mathbf{B}\times\mathbf{C}.$$

24. Determine the volume of a tetrahedron whose vertices are $(1,1,1)$, $(1,2,3)$, $(3,3,3)$, $(5,6,8)$. [*Hint:* Translate the coordinate system so that one of the vertices is at the origin.]

25. For each of the following space curves, find equations of the tangent line and normal plane at the indicated point.

a. $\lambda(t) = (t^2 + 1, t^2 - 1, t)$, $t = 1$.

b. $\lambda(t) = (2 \sin t, 3 \cos t, t^3)$, $t = \pi/2$.

26. Find the length of the curve λ defined by $\lambda(t) = (t, \ln \sec t, 0)$, domain $[0,\pi/4]$.

27. Find the length of the curve λ defined by $\lambda(t) = (t^2,2t, \ln t)$, domain $[1,3]$.

28. Find the curvature of each of the following curves at the indicated points:

a. $\lambda(t) = (\sin 2t, \cos t)$, $t = \pi$ (Use Exercise I-2, Section 9).

b. $r = 2 + 3 \sin \theta$, $\theta = 0$ (Use Exercise I-7, Section 9).

c. $\lambda(t) = (a \sin kt, a \cos kt, bt)$, $t = 0$ (Use Exercise II-3, Section 9), check answer for $b = 0$.

II

1. Find an equation of the plane determined by the point (h,k,l) and the line of intersection of the two planes $a_r x + b_r y + c_r z = d_r$, $r = 1, 2$.

2. Find an equation of the plane containing the two points (x_r,y_r,z_r), $r = 1, 2$, which is parallel to the line $x = x_0 + at$, $y = y_0 + bt$, $z = z_0 + ct$.

3. Find an equation of the plane which contains the line of intersection of the two planes $a_r x + b_r y + c_r y = d_r$, $r = 1, 2$, and is perpendicular to the plane $ax + by + cz = d$.

4. Given two points $P_r = (x_r,y_r,z_r)$, $r = 1, 2$, and the vector $\mathbf{v} = \langle a,b,c \rangle$ find an equation of the plane determined by the two parallel lines $L_r = \{P_r + t\mathbf{v} \mid t \text{ in } \mathsf{R}\}$, $r = 1, 2$.

5. If the graph of the equation $F(x,y,z) = 0$ is symmetric with respect to each of two planes, must the planes intersect?

6. Prove algebraically that the lines of intersection of any two parallel planes with a third plane are parallel.

7. If (x_r,y_r,z_r), $r = 1, 2, 3$, denotes the coordinates of three vertices of a regular tetrahedron, find the coordinates of the fourth vertex.

8. Find the area of a triangle whose vertices are (x_r,y_r,z_r), $r = 1, 2, 3$.

9. Show that $x^2 + y^2 + z^2 - (ax + by + cz)^2 = r^2$ is an equation of the right circular cylinder of radius r whose axis is the line with parametric equations $x = at$, $y = bt$, $z = ct$, where $a^2 + b^2 + c^2 = 1$.

10. A circle with radius r and center (h,k,l) lies in the plane $ax + by + cz = d$. Find an equation of the cylinder whose axis is parallel to the z axis and which contains the given circle.

11. For any given function f, show that the graph of the equation $x/a - z/c = f(y/b - z/c)$ is a cylinder with generator parallel to the vector $\langle a,b,c \rangle$.

12. Find an equation of the sphere of radius r which passes through the circle of intersection of the two spheres $x^2 + y^2 + z^2 + a_r x + b_r y + c_r z + d_r = 0$, $(r = 1, 2)$.

13. Find the length of a tangent from the point (h,k,l) to the sphere $x^2 + y^2 + z^2 + 2ax + 2by + 2cz = d$.

14. Find an equation of the surface generated by the one-parameter family of straight lines

$$\begin{cases} ax + by = tz \\ ax - by = t^{-1}z \end{cases},$$

where t is the parameter. (This is an example of a ruled surface, i.e., one generated by a moving straight line.)

15. Find an equation of the cone whose vertex is at the center of the ellipsoid $x^2/a^2 + y^2/b^2 + z^2/c^2 = 1$ and which passes through the cross section of the ellipsoid by the plane $lx + my + nz = 1$.

16. Prove the following:

a. $\mathbf{a}\cdot\mathbf{b} \times (\mathbf{c} \times \mathbf{d}) = \mathbf{a} \times \mathbf{b}\cdot\mathbf{c} \times \mathbf{d}$. b. $(\mathbf{a} \times \mathbf{b})\cdot(\mathbf{c} \times \mathbf{d}) = \begin{vmatrix} \mathbf{a}\cdot\mathbf{c} & \mathbf{a}\cdot\mathbf{d} \\ \mathbf{b}\cdot\mathbf{c} & \mathbf{b}\cdot\mathbf{d} \end{vmatrix}$.

17. Simplify $(\mathbf{a} \times \mathbf{b}) \times (\mathbf{c} \times \mathbf{d})$.

18. Find the distance between the two skew lines $x = at$, $y = bt$, $z = ct$, where $a^2 + b^2 + c^2 = 1$, and $x = x_0 + ls$, $y = y_0 + ms$, $z = z_0 + ns$, where $l^2 + m^2 + n^2 = 1$, by each of the following methods:

a. Passing a plane through one line parallel to the other line.
b. Using Exercise 9 above.
c. Vectorially, by first showing that if A, B, C, D are four noncoplanar points, then

$$\frac{|\overrightarrow{AB} \times \overrightarrow{CD}\cdot\overrightarrow{AC}|}{|\overrightarrow{AB} \times \overrightarrow{CD}|}$$

is the distance between the line on A and B and the line on C and D.

19. If all the normal planes to a curve pass through a fixed line, then prove that the curve is a circle.

20. If all the normal planes to a curve pass through a fixed point, then prove that the curve lies on the surface of a sphere.

18

DIFFERENTIAL CALCULUS OF FUNCTIONS OF SEVERAL VARIABLES

LIMITS AND DERIVATIVES of functions of two or more variables are discussed in this chapter. The results obtained are applied to problems of finding tangent planes to surfaces and extrema of functions of several variables.

1 CONTINUITY

A mapping f having its domain in R^2 and its range in R is called a (real-valued) *function of two variables*. Similarly, a mapping g having its domain in R^3 and its range in R is called a (real-valued) *function of three variables*. If f is a function of two variables, then we shall denote its value at each point $P = (x,y)$ in its domain either by $f(P)$ or by $f(x,y)$, whichever is more convenient. A similar remark holds for functions of three variables.

For the most part we shall confine our remarks in this section to functions of two variables, leaving it to the reader to check that they also apply to functions of three (or more) variables.

An example of a function f of two variables is

$$f(x,y) = \sqrt{4 - x^2 - y^2}.$$

The domain S of f is taken to be $\{(x,y) \mid 4 - x^2 - y^2 \geq 0\}$; i.e.,

$$S = \{(x,y) \mid x^2 + y^2 \leq 4\},$$

the closed disc $B[O,2]$.

A function f of two variables with domain S has a graph in space defined by

$$\text{Graph } f = \{(x,y,f(x,y)) \mid (x,y) \text{ in } S\}.$$

For example, the graph of the function f above is the graph of the equation

$$z = \sqrt{4 - x^2 - y^2}.$$

This is the hemisphere on and above the xy plane with radius 2 and center the origin.

If

$$g(x,y) = x^2 + y^2,$$

then the graph of g is the graph of the equation

$$z = x^2 + y^2,$$

a paraboloid of revolution about the z axis.

The concept of continuity of a function of several variables is closely related to that of a function of one variable, as the following definition shows.

18.1 **DEFINITION.** A function f of two variables is said to be *continuous* at a point P if for every neighborhood N of $f(P)$ in R there exists an open disc $B(P,\delta)$ in the domain of f such that $f(Q)$ is in N for every Q in $B(P,\delta)$.

If a function f of two variables has an open set S as its domain and if f is continuous at each point in S, then f is called a *continuous function.* Consider the following simple example of a continuous function.

EXAMPLE 1. If $f(x,y) = x$, with R^2 the domain of f, prove that f is a continuous function.

Solution: We wish to prove that for every point $P = (a,b)$ and every neighborhood $(a - \epsilon\ a + \epsilon)$ of $f(P) = a$ there exists an open disc $B(P,\delta)$ such that $f(Q)$ is in $(a - \epsilon, a + \epsilon)$ for every Q in $B(P,\delta)$. If we observe that $f(P)$ is the projection of P on the x axis, then $f(Q)$ clearly is in $(a - \epsilon, a + \epsilon)$ for every Q in the open disc $B(P,\epsilon)$ (Figure 18.1). This proves that f is continuous.

Similarly, it may be shown that the function g defined by $g(x,y) = y$ is continuous. Trivially, every constant function is continuous.

Corresponding to the limit theorems for functions of one variable **(4.8-4.10)** is the following theorem for functions of two variables.

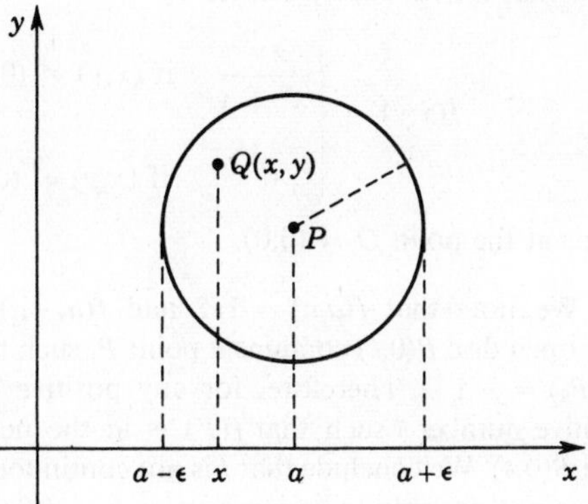

FIGURE 18.1

18.2 THEOREM. If functions f and g are continuous at point P in R^2, then

(1) $f + g$ is continuous at P,
(2) fg is continuous at P,
(3) f/g is continuous at P provided $g(P) \neq 0$.

The proof of **18.2** is analogous to that of the corresponding theorem for functions of one variable, and hence it is omitted.

A function f having domain R^2 is called a *polynomial function* of two variables if $f(x,y)$ consists of a sum of terms of the form $ax^m y^n$, where a is in R and m and n are nonnegative integers. For example, f defined by

$$f(x,y) = x^2 - 3xy + y^2 + 7$$

is a polynomial function. A function h such that $h = g/f$, where g and f are polynomial functions, is called a *rational function* of two variables.

Since every polynomial function can be represented as a sum of products of the simple functions

$$f(x,y) = x, \quad g(x,y) = y, \quad h(x,y) = c, \quad (c \text{ a constant}),$$

and these three functions are continuous, every polynomial function is continuous by **18.2**. In turn, each rational function is continuous since it is a quotient of continuous functions.

It might be instructive to give an example of a function that is not continuous at some point in its domain.

EXAMPLE 2. Show that the function f defined by

$$f(x,y) = \begin{cases} \dfrac{xy}{x^2 + y^2} & \text{if } (x,y) \neq (0,0), \\ 0 & \text{if } (x,y) = (0,0) \end{cases}$$

is not continuous at the point $O = (0,0)$.

Solution: We note that $f(a,a) = 1/2$ and $f(a,-a) = -1/2$ for every $a \neq 0$. Therefore every open disc $B(0,\delta)$ contains a point P_1 such that $f(P_1) = 1/2$ and a point P_2 such that $f(P_2) = -1/2$. Therefore, for any positive number $\epsilon < 1/2$ there does not exist a positive number δ such that $f(P)$ is in the neighborhood $(-\epsilon,\epsilon)$ of 0 for every point P in $B(0,\delta)$. We conclude that f is not continuous at 0.

Actually it is not possible to assign a value b to $f(0,0)$ so that f is continuous at $(0,0)$. This is true because no interval $(b - \epsilon, b + \epsilon)$ can contain both $1/2$ and $-1/2$ if $\epsilon < 1/2$.

Let f be a function of two variables, P a point in the domain of f, and L a line in R^2 passing through P. If we consider R^2 as the xy plane in R^3, then we can construct a plane p in R^3 passing through line L and perpendicular to the xy plane. Plane p will intersect the graph of f in a curve C, called the cross section of the graph of f in p (Figure 18.2).

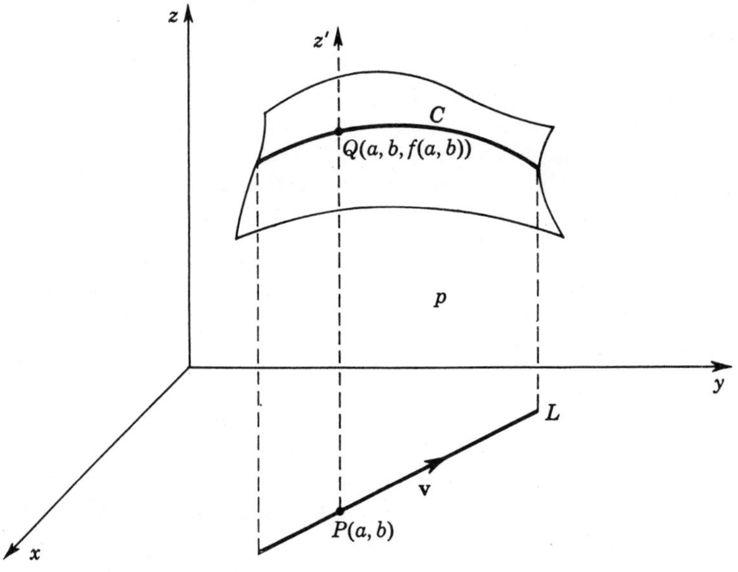

FIGURE 18.2

If

$$L = \{P + t\mathbf{v} \mid t \text{ in } \mathsf{R}\}, \qquad \mathbf{v} \text{ a unit vector in } V_2,$$

then we can define a function g of one variable by

$$g(t) = f(P + t\mathbf{v}).$$

It is clear from Figure 18.2 that C is the graph of g in plane p if we let L be one coordinate axis, P be the origin, and the other axis have the same direction as the z axis. Since $\mathbf{v}$ is a unit vector, the unit of length is the same in plane p as it is in the underlying coordinate system.

In case the function f of two variables is continuous at P, the function g of one variable defined above is continuous at 0; i.e.,

(1) $$\operatorname*{limit}_{t \to 0} g(t) = g(0) = f(P).$$

To prove (1), we know that for every neighborhood N of $f(P)$ there exists an open disc $B(P,\delta)$ such that $f(Q)$ is in N for every Q in $B(P,\delta)$. Since $d(P,P + t\mathbf{v}) = |t\mathbf{v}| = |t|$, $P + t\mathbf{v}$ is in N if t is in $(-\delta,\delta)$. Thus for every neighborhood N of $f(P)$ there exists a neighborhood $(-\delta,\delta)$ of 0 such that $g(t)$ is in N if t is in $(-\delta,\delta)$. This proves (1).

We state this result in the following form.

18.3 THEOREM. If the function f is continuous at P, then for each line $L = \{P + t\mathbf{v} \mid t \text{ in } \mathsf{R}\}$ passing through P,

$$\operatorname*{limit}_{t \to 0} f(P + t\mathbf{v}) = f(P).$$

It may be shown by example that the converse of **18.3** does not hold. That is, knowing that $\operatorname*{limit}_{t \to 0} f(P + t\mathbf{v}) = f(P)$ for every vector $\mathbf{v}$ in V_2 is not enough to assert that f is continuous at P. (See Exercise 7-II, at end of section.)

Once we know what it means for a function f to be continuous at a point in R^2, we can easily define the limit of f at a point of R^2 as follows.

18.4 DEFINITION. Let f be a function of two variables and P a point in R^2 such that f is defined at every point in some open disc $B(P,r)$ except possibly at P. Then $\operatorname*{limit}_{Q \to P} f(Q)$ exists provided we can find a number c such that f is continuous at P if we define (or redefine) $f(P) = c$. In this case we write

$$\operatorname*{limit}_{Q \to P} f(Q) = c.$$

If $P = (a,b)$, then the above limit is often written in the form

$$\operatorname*{limit}_{(x,y) \to (a,b)} f(x,y) = c.$$

We can form the composite $h \circ f$ of a function h of one variable and a function f of two variables, thereby obtaining a function $h \circ f$ of two variables.

For example, if

$$h(t) = \sqrt{t} \quad \text{and} \quad f(x,y) = 4 - x^2 - y^2,$$

then

$$(h \circ f)(x,y) = h(f(x,y)) = h(4 - x^2 - y^2) = \sqrt{4 - x^2 - y^2}.$$

As another example, if

$$F(t) = \sin t \quad \text{and} \quad G(x,y) = xy - y^2,$$

then

$$(F \circ G)(x,y) = F(xy - y^2) = \sin(xy - y^2).$$

In view of the following theorem, both functions $h \circ f$ and $F \circ G$ in the examples above are continuous.

18.5 **THEOREM.** If h is a function of one variable and f a function of two variables such that f is continuous at point P and h is continuous at $f(P)$, then $h \circ f$ is also continuous at P.

We shall not prove this theorem, but shall instead refer the reader to the proof of a similar theorem (**4.26**) for functions of one variable.

EXERCISES

I

In each of Exercises 1–8 discuss the continuity of the given function.

1. $F(x,y) = ax + by.$

2. $G(x,y) = \dfrac{x + y}{1 + x^2}.$

3. $f(x,y) = \sin(x^2 + y).$

4. $g(x,y) = \ln(1 + x^2 + y^4) + \sin xy.$

5. $H(x,y) = \dfrac{x^2y}{1 + x}$ if $x \neq -1$, $H(-1,y) = y.$

6. $F(x,y) = \dfrac{x^2y}{x^3 + y^3}$ if $(x,y) \neq (0,0)$; $F(0,0) = 0.$

7. $G(x,y) = \dfrac{x^3 + y^3}{x^2 + y^2}$ if $(x,y) \neq (0,0)$; $G(0,0) = 0.$

8. $h(x,y) = \dfrac{x^3 + y^2}{x^2 + y}$ if $(x,y) \neq (0,0)$; $h(0,0) = 0$.

II

In each of Exercises 1–4, can the given function be appropriately defined at (0,0) in order to be continuous there? Explain each answer.

1. $g(x,y) = \sin x/y$.
2. $G(x,y) = \dfrac{x^2y^2}{x^4 + y^4}$.
3. $F(x,y) = \dfrac{x^5 + y^5}{x^4 + y^4}$.
4. $H(x,y) = x^2 \ln (x^2 + y^2)$.
5. Show that the function

$$F(x,y,z) = \frac{xyz}{x^2 + y^2 + z^2} \quad \text{if } (x,y,z) \neq (0,0,0);\ F(0,0,0) = 0,$$

is continuous at (0,0,0).

6. Is a function f of two variables necessarily continuous at (0,0) if, for each value of y, f is a continuous function of x at $x = 0$, and for each value of x, f is a continuous function of y at $y = 0$? Prove your answer.
7. Use the example

$$f(x,y) = \frac{xy^2}{x^2 + y^4} \quad \text{if } (x,y) \neq (0,0),\ f(0,0) = 0$$

to show that the converse of **18.3** does not hold.

2 DIRECTIONAL DERIVATIVES

Given a function f of two variables, a point P in its domain, and a nonzero vector $\mathbf{v}$ in V_2, we can consider values of f along the line $L = \{P + t\mathbf{v} \mid t \text{ in } \mathsf{R}\}$ which passes through P in the direction $\mathbf{v}$. If we consider $f(P + t\mathbf{v})$ as a function of t, then the derivative of f at $t = 0$ is denoted by $D_{\mathbf{v}}f(P)$. Thus,

18.6 $$D_{\mathbf{v}}f(P) = \lim_{t \to 0} \frac{f(P + t\mathbf{v}) - f(P)}{t}.$$

We call $D_{\mathbf{v}}f(P)$ the *derivative of f at P in the direction* $\mathbf{v}$. If $g(t) = f(P + t\mathbf{v})$, then $D_{\mathbf{v}}f(P)$ is simply $g'(0)$.

EXAMPLE 1. If $f(x,y) = x^2 - xy + 5y$, find the derivative of f at $P = (-1,2)$ in the direction $\mathbf{v} = \langle 3,-4\rangle$.

Solution: If we let $g(t) = f(P + t\mathbf{v})$ as above, then $P + t\mathbf{v} = (-1,2) + \langle 3t,-4t\rangle = (-1 + 3t, 2 - 4t)$ and

$$g(t) = f(-1 + 3t, 2 - 4t) = (-1 + 3t)^2 - (-1 + 3t)(2 - 4t) + 5(2 - 4t)$$

or

$$g(t) = 13 - 36t + 21t^2.$$

Hence, $g'(t) = -36 + 42t$ and

$$D_{\mathbf{v}}f(P) = g'(0) = -36.$$

If $g(t) = f(P + t\mathbf{v})$ as above and $h(t) = g(ct) = f(P + tc\mathbf{v})$ for some number c, then $h'(t) = cg'(ct)$ by the chain rule. Letting $t = 0$, this proves that

18.7 $$D_{c\mathbf{v}}f(P) = cD_{\mathbf{v}}f(P).$$

It is customary to call $D_{\mathbf{v}}f(P)$ the *directional derivative of f at P in the direction* **v** if **v** is a unit vector. In this case, $D_{\mathbf{v}}f(P)$ is the slope of the tangent line to a cross section of the graph of f as indicated in Figure 18.3. For if $P = (a,b)$ and $\mathbf{v} = \langle r,s\rangle$, then the vector

$$\mathbf{w} = \langle r,s,D_{\mathbf{v}}f(P)\rangle$$

in V_3 translates the point $Q = (a,b,f(a,b))$ of R^3 into the point $Q + \mathbf{w} = (a + r, b + s, f(P) + D_{\mathbf{v}}f(P))$ along the tangent line T. This is clear once we realize that $Q + \mathbf{w}$ is directly above (or below) the point $P + \mathbf{v} = (a + r, b + s)$ and that the vertical distance to T from the point $P + t\mathbf{v}$ is $g(0) + tg'(0)$. In particular, the vertical distance is $f(P) + D_{\mathbf{v}}f(P)$ if $t = 1$. We call **w** the *tangent vector to the graph of f in the direction* **v**.

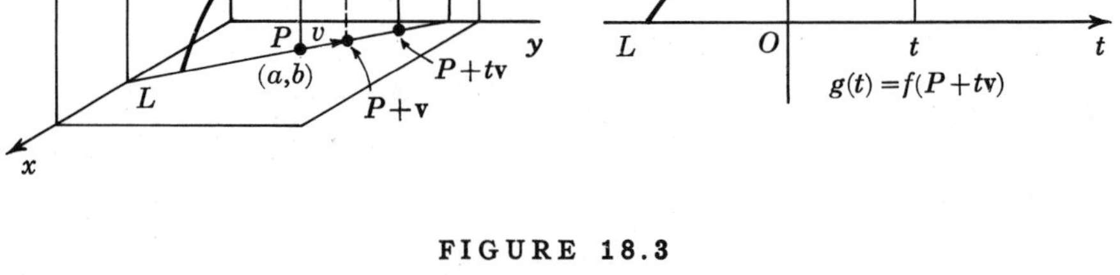

FIGURE 18.3

EXAMPLE 2. If $f(x,y) = (x + y)/(x - y)$, find the directional derivative of f at $P = (1,-1)$ in the direction $\mathbf{v} = \langle 1/2, \sqrt{3}/2 \rangle$.

Solution: First, we find $f(P) = f(1,-1) = 0$ and

$$f(P + t\mathbf{v}) = f(1 + t/2, -1 + \sqrt{3}t/2).$$

Hence, by definition,

$$D_{\mathbf{v}}f(P) = \operatorname*{limit}_{t\to 0} \frac{f(P + t\mathbf{v}) - f(P)}{t}$$

$$= \operatorname*{limit}_{t\to 0} \frac{1}{t} \frac{1 + \dfrac{t}{2} - 1 + \dfrac{\sqrt{3}t}{2}}{1 + \dfrac{t}{2} + 1 - \dfrac{\sqrt{3}t}{2}}$$

$$= \operatorname*{limit}_{t\to 0} \frac{1 + \sqrt{3}}{4 + (1 - \sqrt{3})t} = \frac{1 + \sqrt{3}}{4}.$$

Directional derivatives of functions of three or more variables are defined in exactly the same way as they are for functions of two variables. We illustrate with the following example.

EXAMPLE 3. If $F(x,y,z) = x + xy - yz$, find $D_{\mathbf{v}}F(P)$ for $P = (-1,1,2)$ and $\mathbf{v} = \langle 3,1,1 \rangle$.

Solution: We have $P + t\mathbf{v} = (-1,1,2) + t\langle 3,1,1 \rangle = (-1 + 3t, 1 + t, 2 + t)$. Hence

$$D_{\mathbf{v}}F(P) = \operatorname*{limit}_{t\to 0} \frac{F(P + t\mathbf{v}) - F(P)}{t}$$

$$= \operatorname*{limit}_{t\to 0} \frac{(-1 + 3t) + (-1 + 3t)(1 + t) - (1 + t)(2 + t) - (-4)}{t}$$

$$= \operatorname*{limit}_{t\to 0} \frac{2t + 2t^2}{t} = 2.$$

EXERCISES

I

In each of Exercises 1–4, find the directional derivative of the given function at the indicated point and in the indicated direction.

1. $f(x,y) = ax^2 + 2bxy + cy^2$; $P = (1,1)$; $\mathbf{v} = \langle \frac{4}{5}, -\frac{3}{5} \rangle$.

2. $g(x,y) = x^2 - y^2$; $P = (4,4)$; $\mathbf{v} = \langle \frac{5}{13}, -\frac{12}{13} \rangle$.

3. $F(x,y,z) = x^2 + y^2 + xyz$; $P = (1,1,1)$; $\mathbf{v} = \langle \frac{1}{3}, \frac{2}{3}, \frac{2}{3} \rangle$.

4. $G(x,y,z) = x + y + z$; $P = (a,b,c)$; $\mathbf{v} = \langle -\frac{2}{3}, -\frac{2}{3}, \frac{1}{3} \rangle$.

5. For which directions does the directional derivative of the function f at point (a,b) vanish if $f(x,y) = x^2 + y^2$?

6. Find the maximum and minimum directional derivatives of the function f defined by: (a) $f(x,y) = x^2 + 2xy + y^2$ at point (a,b); (b) $f(x,y) = x^2 + y^2 + x - y + 1$ at point $(1,-1)$.

II

1. What is the maximum directional derivative of the function f defined by $f(x,y,z) = x^2 + y^2 + z^2$ at point (a,b,c)?

2. Let the function f be defined by $f(x,y) = x^2 + y^2$. Starting from the point $P = (a,b)$, draw a line segment in the direction $\mathbf{v}$ and of length $D_{\mathbf{v}}f(P)$, drawing the segment backward if the derivative is negative. Show that the ends of these segments lie on a circle which is tangent to the graph of the equation $f(x,y) = a^2 + b^2$.

3 PARTIAL DERIVATIVES

Two directional derivatives of f of particular importance are those in the directions of the coordinate axes, $D_{\mathbf{i}}f(P)$ and $D_{\mathbf{j}}f(P)$. If $P = (x,y)$, then $P + t\mathbf{i} = P + \langle t,0 \rangle = (x + t,y)$ and

$$D_{\mathbf{i}}f(x,y) = \operatorname*{limit}_{t \to 0} \frac{f(x + t, y) - f(x,y)}{t}.$$

Similarly,

$$D_{\mathbf{j}}f(x,y) = \operatorname*{limit}_{t \to 0} \frac{f(x, y + t) - f(x,y)}{t}.$$

Thus $D_{\mathbf{i}}f(x,y)$ is the ordinary derivative of f if f is considered a function of one variable x (i.e., if y is considered a constant); and $D_{\mathbf{j}}f(x,y)$ is the ordinary derivative of f if f is considered a function of one variable y.

We shall usually use the notation $D_1f(x,y)$ in place of $D_{\mathbf{i}}f(x,y)$ and $D_2f(x,y)$ in place of $D_{\mathbf{j}}f(x,y)$. Actually, D_1f and D_2f are functions of two variables, called the *first partial derivatives* of f. Other common notations for the first partial derivatives of f are

$$D_{\mathbf{i}}f = D_1f = f_1 = \frac{\partial f}{\partial x},$$

$$D_{\mathbf{j}}f = D_2f = f_2 = \frac{\partial f}{\partial y}.$$

EXAMPLE 1. Find the first partial derivatives of the function f defined by

$$f(x,y) = x^3 - 3x^2y + y^2 + x - 7.$$

Solution: We have

$$D_1f(x,y) = \frac{\partial f}{\partial x} = 3x^2 - 6xy + 1,$$

$$D_2f(x,y) = \frac{\partial f}{\partial y} = -3x^2 + 2y.$$

Partial derivatives for functions of three or more variables may be defined in precisely the same way that they were above for functions of two variables.

The three first partial derivatives of a function f of three variables are commonly designated by D_1f, D_2f, and D_3f rather than by D_if, D_jf, and D_kf.

EXAMPLE 2. Find the first partial derivatives of the function f defined by

$$f(x,y,z) = \ln (x + y^2 + z^3).$$

Solution: We have

$$D_1f(x,y,z) = \frac{\partial f}{\partial x} = 1/(x + y^2 + z^3),$$

$$D_2f(x,y,z) = \frac{\partial f}{\partial y} = 2y/(x + y^2 + z^3),$$

$$D_3f(x,y,z) = \frac{\partial f}{\partial z} = 3z^2/(x + y^2 + z^3).$$

If f is a function of two variables, then D_1f and D_2f are also functions of two variables. As such, D_1f and D_2f have first partial derivatives $D_1(D_1f)$, $D_2(D_1f)$, $D_1(D_2f)$, and $D_2(D_2f)$. These four functions are called the *second partial derivatives* of f. Common notations for the second partial derivatives of f are

$$f_{11} = D_{11}f = D_1(D_1f) = \frac{\partial^2 f}{\partial x^2},$$

$$f_{12} = D_{12}f = D_2(D_1f) = \frac{\partial^2 f}{\partial y\, \partial x},$$

$$f_{21} = D_{21}f = D_1(D_2f) = \frac{\partial^2 f}{\partial x\, \partial y},$$

$$f_{22} = D_{22}f = D_2(D_2f) = \frac{\partial^2 f}{\partial y^2}.$$

A function of three variables has nine possible second partial derivatives (of which usually only six are distinct).

Higher partial derivatives of a function of several variables are defined in the obvious way. For example, if f is a function of two variables, then

$$f_{122} = D_{122}f = D_2(D_2(D_1 f)) = \frac{\partial^3 f}{\partial y\, \partial y\, \partial x},$$

$$f_{2122} = D_{2122}f = D_2(D_2(D_1(D_2 f))) = \frac{\partial^4 f}{\partial y\, \partial y\, \partial x\, \partial y}.$$

EXAMPLE 3. If $f(x,y,z) = xe^{yz} + yze^{x}$, find f_{213} and $\partial^3 f/\partial x^2\, \partial y$.

Solution: We have

$$f_2(x,y,z) = \frac{\partial y}{\partial f} = xze^{yz} + ze^{x},$$

$$f_{21}(x,y,z) = \frac{\partial^2 f}{\partial x\, \partial y} = \frac{\partial f_2}{\partial x} = ze^{yz} + ze^{x},$$

$$f_{213}(x,y,z) = \frac{\partial^2 f}{\partial z\, \partial x\, \partial y} = \frac{\partial f_{21}}{\partial z} = e^{yz} + zye^{yz} + e^{x},$$

$$\frac{\partial^3 f}{\partial x^2\, \partial y} = \frac{\partial f_{21}}{\partial x} = ze^{x}.$$

EXERCISES

I

In each of Exercises 1–4 find the indicated partial derivatives of the given function.

1. F_{12} and F_{22} where $F(x,y) = \ln(x + y)$.
2. G_{123} and G_{312} where $G(x,y,z) = x^3 + 3yz + \sin xyz$.
3. F_{1223} and F_{1222} where $F(x,y,z) = x^4 + y^4 - 2z^4 + 2x^2yz$.
4. $\dfrac{\partial^2 F}{\partial x^2}$ and $\dfrac{\partial^2 F}{\partial y^2}$ where $F(x,y) = \ln(x^2 + y^2)$.
5. Show that the directional derivative of $F(x,y,z)$ at the point $P = (x_0,y_0,z_0)$ in the direction $\mathbf{v} = \langle v_1,v_2,v_3\rangle$ $(\mathbf{v}\cdot\mathbf{v} = 1)$ is given by

$$D_{\mathbf{v}}F(P) = \frac{\partial F}{\partial x}v_1 + \frac{\partial F}{\partial y}v_2 + \frac{\partial F}{\partial z}v_3$$

evaluated at the point $P = (x_0,y_0,z_0)$.

II

1. A function $F(x,y,z)$ possessing continuous partial derivatives of second order in a domain G and satisfying

$$\frac{\partial^2 F}{\partial x^2} + \frac{\partial^2 F}{\partial y^2} + \frac{\partial^2 F}{\partial z^2} = 0 \quad \text{(Laplace's equation)}$$

at all points of G is said to be "harmonic" there. Show that each of the following functions is harmonic:
   a. $\ln \sqrt{x^2 + y^2}$ (in a region excluding (0,0)).
   b. $(x^2 + y^2 + z^2)^{-1/2}$ (in a region excluding (0,0,0)).

2. a. How many nth order derivatives are there for a function of two variables? Of three variables? (Consider F_{122}, F_{212}, F_{221}, and so on, to be different.)
   b. Same as in a, except that all derivatives are assumed to be independent of the order in which they are taken (e.g., $F_{122} = F_{212} = F_{221}$, and so on).

4 DIFFERENTIALS

If f is a function of two variables and P is a point in R^2 at which $D_1f(P)$ and $D_2f(P)$ exist, then the *gradient* of f at P is denoted by $\nabla f(P)$ (read "del-f of P") and defined by

$$\nabla f(P) = \langle D_1f(P), D_2f(P)\rangle.$$

For example, if

$$f(x,y) = x^2 - 3xy + y^3$$

then

$$D_1f(x,y) = 2x - 3y, \qquad D_2f(x,y) = -3x + 3y^2$$

and

$$\nabla f(x,y) = \langle 2x - 3y, -3x + 3y^2\rangle.$$

We recall that the differential dg of a function g of one variable is given by

$$dg = g'(x)\,dx.$$

Thus dg is a function of two variables x and dx.

The differential df of a function f of two variables is intuitively defined by

$$df = \frac{\partial f}{\partial x}\,dx + \frac{\partial f}{\partial y}\,dy.$$

Thus df is a function of four variables x, y, dx, and dy. If we observe that df as defined above is the inner product of $\nabla f(x,y) = \left\langle \frac{\partial f}{\partial x}, \frac{\partial f}{\partial y} \right\rangle$ and the vector $\mathbf{v} = \langle dx,dy \rangle$, then the following definition should seem natural.

The *differential* df of a function f of two variables is defined by

18.8 $$df(P,\mathbf{v}) = \nabla f(P)\cdot\mathbf{v}, \qquad P \text{ in } \mathsf{R}^2, \ \mathbf{v} \text{ in } V_2.$$

Thus, the differential df is a function of two variables P in R^2 and $\mathbf{v}$ in V_2. (Of course, P in turn is a function of x and y and $\mathbf{v} = \langle h,k \rangle$ is a function of h and k.) The domain of df is the set of all pairs $(P,\mathbf{v})$ for which the gradient $\nabla f(P)$ exists.

A function f of two variables is said to be *differentiable at point P* provided an open set containing P is contained in the domain of f and

18.9 $$\operatorname*{limit}_{P+\mathbf{v}\to P} \frac{f(P+\mathbf{v}) - f(P) - df(P,\mathbf{v})}{|\mathbf{v}|} = 0.$$

The differential of a function of two variables has properties similar to the differential of a function of one variable, as we shall now show. Let P be a point at which f is differentiable, and let function g be defined by

$$g(\mathbf{v}) = f(P) + df(P,\mathbf{v}).$$

Then, by **18.9**,

$$\operatorname*{limit}_{P+\mathbf{v}\to P} \frac{f(P+\mathbf{v}) - g(\mathbf{v})}{|\mathbf{v}|} = 0.$$

Hence for every $\epsilon > 0$ there exists a disc $B(P,\epsilon)$ such that

$$|f(P+\mathbf{v}) - g(\mathbf{v})| < \epsilon|\mathbf{v}| \qquad \text{for every } P+\mathbf{v} \text{ in } B(P,\epsilon).$$

Thus $g(\mathbf{v}) = f(P) + df(P,\mathbf{v})$ is a good approximation of $f(P+\mathbf{v})$ when $P+\mathbf{v}$ is close to P, i.e., when $|\mathbf{v}|$ is close to 0. This corresponds to the statement for functions of one variable that $g(x) + dg$ is a good approximation of $g(x+dx)$ when dx is small.

EXAMPLE 1. An isosceles triangle T has dimensions as shown in Figure 18.4. Approximately what change occurs in the area of T if the lengths of the equal sides are increased by 1 inch and the vertex angle is increased by .04 radian?

Solution: An isosceles triangle with equal sides of length x and vertex angle α has area

$$m(x,\alpha) = \tfrac{1}{2}x^2 \sin \alpha.$$

Thus the given triangle has area

$$m\left(3, \frac{\pi}{6}\right) = \frac{9}{4}.$$

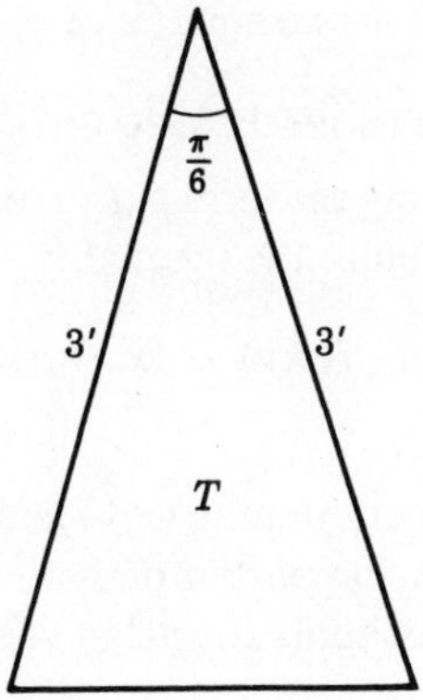

FIGURE 18.4

Assuming that the function m of two variables is differentiable (which is true by **18.10** below), we have

$$D_1m(x,\alpha) = x \sin \alpha, \quad D_2m(x,\alpha) = \tfrac{1}{2}x^2 \cos \alpha,$$
$$\nabla m(x,\alpha) = \langle x \sin \alpha, \tfrac{1}{2}x^2 \cos \alpha \rangle,$$

and
$$dm((x,\alpha),\mathbf{v}) = \nabla m(x,\alpha) \cdot \mathbf{v}$$

for every $\mathbf{v}$ in V_2. In particular, if we let $P = (3,\pi/6)$ and $\mathbf{v} = \langle \frac{1}{12},.04 \rangle$ then

$$D_1m\left(3,\frac{\pi}{6}\right) = \frac{3}{2}, \quad D_2m\left(3,\frac{\pi}{6}\right) = \frac{9\sqrt{3}}{4}, \quad \nabla m(P) = \left\langle \frac{3}{2}, \frac{9\sqrt{3}}{4} \right\rangle.$$

The change in the area of T is $m(P + V) - m(P)$, and this is approximately equal to $df(P,\mathbf{v})$. Thus

$$m(P + \mathbf{v}) - m(P) \doteq df(P,\mathbf{v}) = \left\langle \frac{3}{2}, \frac{9\sqrt{3}}{4} \right\rangle \cdot \left\langle \frac{1}{12},.04 \right\rangle$$
$$\doteq \frac{1}{8} + .09\sqrt{3} \doteq .28,$$

and the area of the triangle is increased by approximately .28 ft².

Examples may be given to show that the existence of $\nabla f(P)$ is not enough to make f differentiable at P. Although we shall not give such examples, the following theorem gives conditions which insure the differentiability of a function of two variables.

18.10 THEOREM. If D_1f and D_2f exist in an open disc $B(P,r)$ and are continuous at point P, then the function f of two variables is differentiable at P.

Proof: Let $P = (a,b)$ and g be the function defined by

$$g(\mathbf{v}) = f(P + \mathbf{v}) - f(P) - df(P,\mathbf{v}), \qquad \text{domain } g = \{\mathbf{v} \text{ in } V_2 \mid |\mathbf{v}| < r\}.$$

Letting $\mathbf{v} = \langle x - a, y - b \rangle$ we have $(x,y) = P + \mathbf{v}$ and

$$g(\mathbf{v}) = f(x,y) - f(a,b) - D_1f(a,b)(x - a) - D_2f(a,b)(y - b).$$

By adding and subtracting the term $f(a,y)$ to and from the right side of the equation above, we easily obtain the inequality

$$(1) \qquad |g(\mathbf{v})| \leq |f(x,y) - f(a,y) - (x - a)D_1f(a,b)| + |f(a,y) - f(a,b) - (y - b)D_2f(a,b)|.$$

Since both the line segment joining (x,y) and (a,y) and the segment joining (a,y) and (a,b) are in $B(P,r)$, the partial derivatives of f exist at each point on these segments. Hence we may apply the mean value theorem to obtain

$$f(x,y) - f(a,y) = (x - a)D_1f(x_1,y) \quad \text{for some } x_1 \text{ between } x \text{ and } a,$$
$$f(a,y) - f(a,b) = (y - b)D_2f(a,y_1) \quad \text{for some } y_1 \text{ between } y \text{ and } b.$$

Inserting these in (1), we get

$$(2) \quad |g(\mathbf{v})| \leq |x - a||D_1f(x_1,y) - D_1f(a,b)| + |y - b||D_2f(a,y_1) - D_2f(a,b)|.$$

Since D_1f and D_2f are continuous at P, for every number $\epsilon > 0$ there exists an open disc $B(P,\delta)$ such that $|D_1f(Q) - D_1f(P)| < \epsilon/2$ and $|D_2f(Q) - D_2f(P)| < \epsilon/2$ for every Q in $B(P,\delta)$. Clearly, (x_1,y) and (a,y_1) are also in $B(P,\delta)$ if $Q = (x,y)$ is. Hence $|D_1f(x_1,y) - D_1f(a,b)| < \epsilon/2$ and $|D_2f(a,y_1) - D_2f(a,b)| < \epsilon/2$ if Q is in $B(P,\delta)$. Therefore, by (2),

$$(3) \qquad |g(\mathbf{v})| < \frac{\epsilon}{2}(|x - a| + |y - b|) \quad \text{for every } P + \mathbf{v} \text{ in } B(P,\delta).$$

Since $|\mathbf{v}| = \sqrt{(x - a)^2 + (y - b)^2} \geq |x - a|$ and, similarly, $|\mathbf{v}| \geq |y - b|$ evidently $|x - a| + |y - b| \leq 2|\mathbf{v}|$ and

$$(4) \qquad |g(\mathbf{v})| < \epsilon|\mathbf{v}| \quad \text{for every } P + \mathbf{v} \text{ in } B(P,\delta).$$

We have proved that for every $\epsilon > 0$ there exists a $B(P,\delta)$ such that $g(\mathbf{v})/|\mathbf{v}| < \epsilon$ for every $P + \mathbf{v}$ in $B(P,\delta)$. This proves that

$$\operatorname*{limit}_{P+\mathbf{v}\to P} \frac{f(P + \mathbf{v}) - f(P) - \nabla f(P)\cdot\mathbf{v}}{|\mathbf{v}|} = 0,$$

and hence proves the theorem.

The differential of f at P and the derivative of f at P in a given direction are the same in certain circumstances, according to the following result.

18.11 **THEOREM.** If the function f is differentiable at P, then $D_{\mathbf{v}}f(P)$ exists for each nonzero $\mathbf{v}$ in V_2 and, furthermore, $D_{\mathbf{v}}f(P) = df(P,\mathbf{v})$.

Rather than giving a formal proof of **18.11**, let us show informally why it is true. We see that

$$\left|\frac{f(P+t\mathbf{v})-f(P)}{t}-df(P,\mathbf{v})\right| = |\mathbf{v}|\,\frac{|f(P+t\mathbf{v})-f(P)-df(P,t\mathbf{v})|}{|t\mathbf{v}|}.$$

Since f is differentiable at P, the right side of the above equation approaches 0 as $P+t\mathbf{v}$ approaches P. Hence

$$\operatorname*{limit}_{t\to 0}\frac{f(P+t\mathbf{v})-f(P)}{t} = df(P,\mathbf{v}),$$

as desired.

By the basic properties of the inner product,

$$\nabla f(P)\cdot(a\mathbf{u}+b\mathbf{v}) = a\,\nabla f(P)\cdot\mathbf{u} + b\,\nabla f(P)\cdot\mathbf{v}.$$

In particular, if $\mathbf{v} = a\mathbf{i}+b\mathbf{j}$, then $\nabla f(P)\cdot\mathbf{v} = a\,\nabla f(P)\cdot\mathbf{i} + b\,\nabla f(P)\cdot\mathbf{j}$. Therefore, if f is a differentiable function at P, we have, by **18.11**, that

18.12 if $\mathbf{v} = \langle a,b\rangle$, then $D_{\mathbf{v}}f(P) = aD_1f(P) + bD_2f(P)$.

This gives us an easy way to compute derivatives in any direction.

If a function f of two variables is differentiable at point P in R^2, then the question might arise as to the unit vector $\mathbf{v}$ in V_2 at which $D_{\mathbf{v}}f(P)$ is maximum. If $\nabla f(P) = \mathbf{0}$, then $D_{\mathbf{v}}f(P) = 0$ for every $\mathbf{v}$ in V_2 and 0 is the maximum (and minimum) value of $D_{\mathbf{v}}f(P)$. If $\nabla f(P) \neq \mathbf{0}$, then, by the Cauchy inequality,

$$|D_{\mathbf{v}}f(P)| = |\nabla f(P)\cdot\mathbf{v}| \leq |\nabla f(P)||\mathbf{v}| = |\nabla f(P)|,$$

since $\mathbf{v}$ is a unit vector. Actually, $D_{\mathbf{u}}f(P)$ has the value $|\nabla f(P)|$ if $\mathbf{u} = c\nabla f(P)$ where $c = |\nabla f(P)|^{-1}$. For then

$$\begin{aligned} D_{\mathbf{u}}f(P) &= \nabla f(P)\cdot c\nabla f(P) \\ &= c(\nabla f(P)\cdot\nabla f(P)) = c|\nabla f(P)|^2 = |\nabla f(P)|. \end{aligned}$$

This proves the following result.

18.13 THEOREM. If function f is differentiable at point P, then $|\nabla f(P)|$ is the maximum value of the directional derivative $D_{\mathbf{v}}f(P)$. Furthermore, if $\nabla f(P) \neq \mathbf{0}$, the maximum value of $D_{\mathbf{v}}f(P)$ occurs when

$$\mathbf{v} = |\nabla f(P)|^{-1}\,\nabla f(P).$$

EXAMPLE 2. If $f(x,y) = x^2 + xy$ and $P = (1,-1)$, find the maximum value of any directional derivative $D_{\mathbf{v}}f(P)$.

Solution: Since $D_1f(x,y) = 2x + y$ and $D_2f(x,y) = x$, we have

$$\nabla f(P) = \langle D_1f(P), D_2f(P)\rangle = \langle 1,1\rangle.$$

Since $|\nabla f(P)| = \sqrt{2}$, the maximum value of $D_{\mathbf{v}}f(P)$ is $\sqrt{2}$ by **18.13**. It occurs in the direction $\mathbf{v} = \langle 1/\sqrt{2}, 1/\sqrt{2}\rangle$.

A function f of two variables that is differentiable at a point P is also continuous at P. For if f is differentiable at P, then

$$\operatorname*{limit}_{P+\mathbf{v}\to P} g(P+\mathbf{v}) = 0, \quad \text{where} \quad g(P+\mathbf{v}) = \frac{f(P+\mathbf{v}) - f(P) - df(P,\mathbf{v})}{|\mathbf{v}|}.$$

Hence for every neighborhood $(-\epsilon,\epsilon)$ of 0 there exists an open disc $B(P,\delta)$ contained in the domain of f such that $g(P+\mathbf{v})$ is in $(-\epsilon,\epsilon)$ for every $P+\mathbf{v} \neq P$ in $B(P,\delta)$. If, in particular, we let $\epsilon = 1$, then we obtain

$$|f(P+\mathbf{v}) - f(P) - \nabla f(P)\cdot\mathbf{v}| < |\mathbf{v}|$$

for every $P+\mathbf{v}$ in some $B(P,\delta)$. In turn, we have

$$|f(P+\mathbf{v}) - f(P)| - |\nabla f(P)\cdot\mathbf{v}| < |\mathbf{v}|$$

and

$$|f(P+\mathbf{v}) - f(P)| < |\nabla f(P)\cdot\mathbf{v}| + |\mathbf{v}|$$

for every $P+\mathbf{v}$ in $B(P,\delta)$. Using the Cauchy inequality, we finally get

$$|f(P+\mathbf{v}) - f(P)| < |\nabla f(P)||\mathbf{v}| + |\mathbf{v}|$$

or

$$|f(P+\mathbf{v}) - f(P)| < (1 + |\nabla f(P)|)|\mathbf{v}|$$

for every $P+\mathbf{v}$ in $B(P,\delta)$. It follows readily from this inequality that

$$\operatorname*{limit}_{P+\mathbf{v}\to P} f(P+\mathbf{v}) = f(P).$$

This proves the following theorem.

18.14 THEOREM. If a function f of two variables is differentiable at a point P, then f is continuous at P.

The work of this section holds for functions of three or more variables just as well as it does for functions of two variables. For example, if F is a function of three variables, then the gradient of F at a point P in R^3 is given by

$$\nabla F(P) = \langle D_1F(P), D_2F(P), D_3F(P)\rangle.$$

The definition of the differential dF of F is the same,

$$dF(P,\mathbf{v}) = \nabla F(P)\cdot\mathbf{v}$$

for P in R^3 and $\mathbf{v}$ in V_3. Also, F is differentiable if **18.9** holds (with f replaced by F).

Whenever the need arises in the sequel, we shall use the results of this section for functions of two or more variables.

EXERCISES

I

In each of Exercises 1–3 find the differential of the given function at the indicated point and the vector $\mathbf{v} = \langle a,b,c \rangle$.

1. $f(x,y,z) = \ln \sqrt{x^2 + y^2 + z^2}, \quad P = (1,1,1).$

2. $g(x,y,z) = \sin (x + y) \sin (y + z), \quad P = (h,k,l).$

3. $F(x,y,z) = \sqrt{e^{x^2} + e^{y^2}} + \sin (x + y + z), \quad P = (0,0,0).$

In each of Exercises 4–8, approximate the given number by means of differentials. (See Example 1, Section 4.)

4. $\sqrt{299^2 + 399^2}$. (Note that $\sqrt{300^2 + 400^2} = 500$.)

5. $\sqrt{100^2 + 199^2 + 201^2}$.

6. $\sqrt{102^2 + 99^2 + 2503}$.

7. $\sin 44° \cos 31°$.

8. $\sin 28° \cos 29° \tan 44°$.

9. The length, width, and height of a rectangular box are measured to be 10.2 in., 20.4 in., and 9.9 in., respectively. The volume is then found to be $10.2 \times 20.4 \times 9.9$, or 2059.992 in.^{3}. Are we justified in rounding off the volume to 2060.0 in.^{3}? (When we say that $L = 10.2$, we mean that $10.15 \leq L \leq 10.25$, etc.)

Use Theorem **18.13** to work each of the following exercises.

10. Exercise I-6a, Section 2.

11. Exercise I-6b, Section 2.

12. Exercise II-1, Section 2.

II

1. If the function F is defined by $F(x,y) = (y^3 - x^3)/(y^2 + x^2)$ when $(x,y) \neq (0,0)$, $F(0,0) = 0$, then show that $F_1(0,0) = -F_2(0,0) = -1$, but that F is not differentiable at the origin.

2. Show that although the function G defined by $G(x,y) = (x^3 + y^3)/(x - y)$ when $x \neq y$, $G(x,y) = 0$ if $x = y$, is discontinuous at the origin, $G_{11}(0,0)$ exists.

3. Establish the result of Exercise II-2, section 2, for a general differentiable function f.

4. Generalize the result of Exercise 3 for functions of three variables.

5. If $P = x_1 \cdot x_2 \cdot \cdots \cdot x_n$ and each x_r has an error within $\pm\Delta x_r$, show that the relative error in P is approximately equal to

$$\frac{\Delta P}{P} \doteq \frac{\Delta x_1}{x_1} + \frac{\Delta x_2}{x_2} + \cdots + \frac{\Delta x_n}{x_n}$$

and hence

$$\frac{\Delta P}{P} \leq \sum_{i=1}^{n} \left|\frac{\Delta x_i}{x_i}\right|.$$

6. One practice in rounding off answers in a calculation, say of $F(x,y,z)$, is never to carry any more decimal places in the answer than the number in the least accurately given variable. Is this practice justifiable?

5 TANGENT PLANES

We recall that each function f of two variables having domain S has $\{(x,y,f(x,y)) \mid (x,y) \text{ in } S\}$ as its graph in R^3. If $P = (a,b)$ is a point in S at which f is differentiable, then for each vector $\mathbf{v} = \langle r,s \rangle$ in V_2

$$\langle r,s,D_{\mathbf{v}}f(P)\rangle$$

is a tangent vector to the graph of f at P in the direction $\mathbf{v}$. In particular,

$$\mathbf{w}_1 = \langle 1,0,D_1f(P)\rangle \quad \text{and} \quad \mathbf{w}_2 = \langle 0,1,D_2f(P)\rangle$$

are tangent vectors in the directions i and j, respectively.

If $\mathbf{v} = \langle r,s \rangle$ is nonzero, then by **18.12**, $D_{\mathbf{v}}f(P) = rD_1f(P) + sD_2f(P)$. Hence

$$\langle r,s,D_{\mathbf{v}}f(P)\rangle = r\langle 1,0,D_1f(P)\rangle + s\langle 0,1,D_2f(P)\rangle = r\mathbf{w}_1 + s\mathbf{w}_2;$$

i.e., every tangent vector to the graph of f at $P = (a,b)$ is a linear combination of $\mathbf{w}_1$ and $\mathbf{w}_2$. In other words, every tangent vector lies in the plane (see p. 586)

$$p = \{Q + (r\mathbf{w}_1 + s\mathbf{w}_2) \mid r,s \text{ in } \mathsf{R}\},$$

where $Q = (a,b,f(P))$. We call p the *tangent plane* to the graph of f at P (Figure 18.5).

We can obtain an equation of plane p by finding a normal vector of p. An obvious choice of a normal vector is either $\mathbf{w}_1 \times \mathbf{w}_2$ or $\mathbf{w}_2 \times \mathbf{w}_1$. We easily compute $\mathbf{w}_2 \times \mathbf{w}_1$ to be

$$\mathbf{w}_2 \times \mathbf{w}_1 = \langle D_1f(P),D_2f(P),-1\rangle.$$

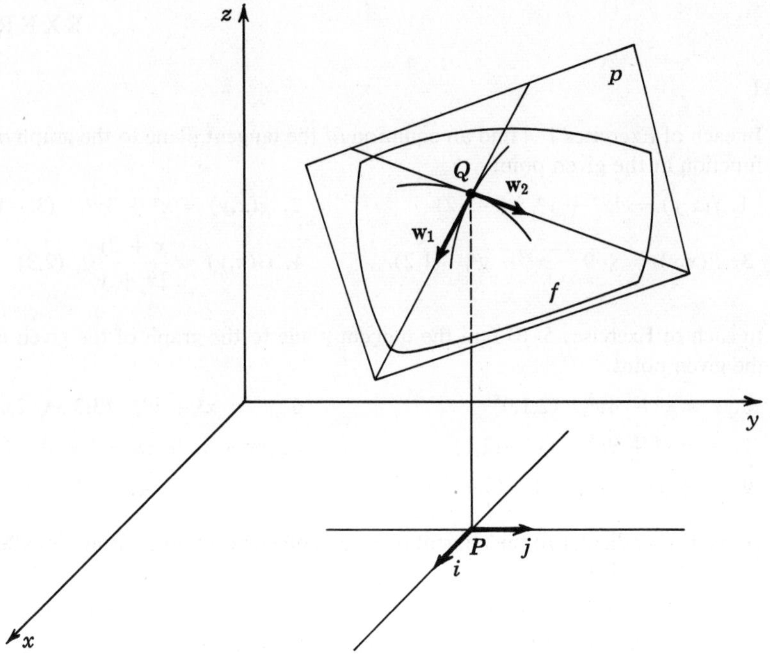

FIGURE 18.5

Therefore, if $P = (x_0,y_0)$,

18.15 $$D_1f(P)(x - x_0) + D_2f(P)(y - y_0) - (z - f(x_0,y_0)) = 0$$

is an equation of the tangent plane to the graph of f at point P, according to **17.7.**

EXAMPLE. Find an equation of the tangent plane to the graph of the equation $z = x^2 + 4y^2$ at the point $(-2,1,8)$.

Solution: If we let

$$f(x,y) = x^2 + 4y^2,$$

then we wish to find an equation of the tangent plane to the graph of f at the point $P = (-2,1)$ in R^2. Since

$$D_1f(x,y) = 2x, \qquad D_2f(x,y) = 8y,$$

evidently $D_1f(P) = -4$ and $D_2f(P) = 8$. Hence, by **18.15,**

$$-4(x + 2) + 8(y - 1) - (z - 8) = 0$$

or

$$4x - 8y + z + 8 = 0$$

is an equation of the tangent plane.

EXERCISES

I

In each of Exercises 1–4 find an equation of the tangent plane to the graph of the given function at the given point.

1. $f(x,y) = 4x^2 + y^2$, $(-1,2)$.
2. $g(x,y) = x^2 + 3y^2$, $(3,-1)$.
3. $F(x,y) = \sqrt{9 - x^2 - y^2}$, $(1,2)$.
4. $G(x,y) = \dfrac{x + 2y}{2x + y}$, $(2,3)$.

In each of Exercises 5–10 find the tangent plane to the graph of the given equation at the given point.

5. $z = x^2 - 4y^2$, $(2,1,0)$.
6. $z^2 = x^2 + y^2$, $(3,3,3\sqrt{2})$.
7. $x = y^2 + 9z^2$, $(13,-2,1)$.
8. $xy + yz + zx + 1 = 0$, $(-1,1,-1)$
9. $x^2 + y^2 - 4z^2 = 4$, $(2,-2,1)$.
10. $9x^2 - y^2 - 4z^2 = 1$, $(1,-2,1)$.

A line perpendicular to the tangent plane at a given point on a surface is called a *normal line* of the surface.

11. If f is a differentiable function of two variables at the point $P = (a,b)$, then prove that the normal line to the graph of f at P has parametric equations $x = a + tf_1(a,b)$, $y = b + tf_2(a,b)$, $z = f(a,b) - t$.
12. Prove that every normal line of a sphere passes through the center of the sphere.

II

1. If $F(x,y) = 2xy/\sqrt{x^2 + y^2}$ for $(x,y) \neq (0,0)$, $F(0,0) = 0$, then show that $F_1(0,0) = 0$, $F_2(0,0) = 0$, and also that the graph of F has no tangent plane at $(0,0)$.
2. Prove a converse of Exercise I-12 above; i.e., if every normal line to a surface passes through a fixed point, then the surface is spherical.
3. Prove that every normal line to a surface of revolution intersects the axis of revolution.
4. Prove a converse of Exercise 3; i.e., if every normal line to a surface intersects a fixed line, then the surface is a surface of revolution about the fixed line.

6 THE CHAIN RULE AND OTHER TOPICS

The mean value theorem for functions of one variable (6.5) has the following analogue for functions of two or more variables.

18.16 **MEAN VALUE THEOREM.** Let f be a differentiable function of two variables in an open set S of R^2, P a point in S, and $\mathbf{v}$ a vector in V_2 such that the line segment $\{P + t\mathbf{v} \mid t \text{ in } [0,1]\}$ is contained in S. Then there exists a number s in $(0,1)$ such that

$$f(P + \mathbf{v}) - f(P) = D_{\mathbf{v}}f(P + s\mathbf{v}).$$

Proof: If we let

$$g(t) = f(P + t\mathbf{v}), \qquad \text{domain } g = [0,1],$$

then it is easily shown that $g'(t) = D_{\mathbf{v}}f(P + t\mathbf{v})$. Hence, by **6.5**, $g(1) - g(0) = g'(s)$ for some s in $(0,1)$. This proves **18.16**.

If f is a polynomial function, say, for example,

$$f(x,y) = x^3 - 2x^2y + xy^2 + 4y^3,$$

then

$$D_1f(x,y) = 3x^2 - 4xy + y^2,\ D_2f(x,y) = -2x^2 + 2xy + 12y^2$$

and

$$D_{12}f(x,y) = D_2(D_1f)(x,y) = -4x + 2y,$$
$$D_{21}f(x,y) = D_1(D_2f)(x,y) = -4x + 2y.$$

Thus the *mixed* second partial derivatives $D_{12}f$ and $D_{21}f$ are equal. That this is always true for well-behaved functions is a consequence of the following theorem.

18.17 **THEOREM.** If f is a function of two variables for which $D_{12}f$ and $D_{21}f$ are continuous functions in some open set S of R^2, then

$$D_{12}f(P) = D_{21}f(P)$$

for every P in S.

We shall sketch a proof of **18.17**. Let $P = (x,y)$ and $\mathbf{v} = \langle a,b \rangle$ be a nonzero vector in V_2 such that all the points used below are in S. If

$$H(\mathbf{v}) = f(P + \mathbf{v}) - f(P + a\mathbf{i}) - f(P + b\mathbf{j}) + f(P)$$

and $F(t) = f(x + a,t) - f(x,t)$, then

$$H(\mathbf{v}) = F(y + b) - F(y).$$

Hence, by the mean value theorem (**6.5**),

$$H(\mathbf{v}) = bF'(y_1) = b[f_2(x + a,y_1) - f_2(x,y_1)]$$

for some number y_1 between y and $y + b$. By another application of **6.5**,

$$f_2(x + a,y_1) - f_2(x,y_1) = af_{21}(x_1,y_1)$$

for some number x_1 between x and $x + a$. Therefore

$$(1) \qquad H(\mathbf{v}) = abf_{21}(x_1,y_1).$$

On the other hand, if we had started with $G(t) = f(t, y + b) - f(t,y)$ instead of F, then $H(\mathbf{v}) = G(x + a) - G(x)$ and, by the same line of reasoning as above, we would obtain

$$H(\mathbf{v}) = abf_{12}(x_2,y_2) \tag{2}$$

for some number x_2 between x and $x + a$, and y_2 between y and $y + b$. On comparing (1) and (2), we see that $f_{21}(x_1,y_1) = f_{12}(x_2,y_2)$. Since f_{12} and f_{21} are continuous in S, we can take limits as $P + \mathbf{v}$ approaches P, obtaining $f_{21}(P) = f_{12}(P)$ as desired.

A consequence of **18.17** is that the order of differentiation may be interchanged for a function of several variables. For example, if f is a function of two variables having continuous partial derivatives in some open set of R_2, then

$$f_{211} = f_{121} = f_{112}, \qquad f_{2211} = f_{2121} = f_{1221},$$

and so on.

A function f of one or more variables is called *smooth* if the function and its first derivatives are continuous. In turn, f is called *2-smooth* if f and its first and second derivatives are continuous. More generally, f is called *n-smooth* if f and all its derivatives up to and including the nth are continuous.

We recall that for functions of one variable the chain rule gives us a method of differentiating the composite of two functions,

$$D(f \circ g)(x) = f'(g(x))g'(x).$$

Let us extend this rule to functions of several variables.

18.18 CHAIN RULE. Let F be a smooth function of two variables in an open set S. Also, let f and g be smooth functions of one variable in an interval I such that the point $P(t) = (f(t),g(t))$ is in S for every t in I. If

$$G(t) = F(P(t)), \qquad t \text{ in } I,$$

then

$$G'(t) = F_1(P(t))f'(t) + F_2(P(t))g'(t).$$

Proof: By definition,

$$G'(t) = \lim_{h\to 0} \frac{F(P(t + h)) - F(P(t))}{h},$$

if this limit exists. By the mean value theorem **(6.5)**,

$$f(t + h) = f(t) + hf'(t_1) \quad \text{for some } t_1 \text{ between } t \text{ and } t + h,$$
$$g(t + h) = g(t) + hg'(t_2) \quad \text{for some } t_2 \text{ between } t \text{ and } t + h.$$

If $\mathbf{v} = \langle f'(t_1), g'(t_2)\rangle$, then $P(t + h) = P(t) + h\mathbf{v}$ and

$$F(P(t + h)) - F(P(t)) = D_{h\mathbf{v}}F(P(t) + sh\mathbf{v})$$

for some s in (0,1), by the mean value theorem (**18.16**). Hence

$$\frac{F(P(t + h)) - F(P(t))}{h} = \nabla F(P(t) + sh\mathbf{v})\cdot\mathbf{v}.$$

Therefore

$$G'(t) = \lim_{h\to 0} \nabla F(P(t) + sh\mathbf{v})\cdot\mathbf{v} = \nabla F(P(t))\cdot\langle f'(t), g'(t)\rangle$$

by the continuity of the functions D_1F, D_2F, f', and g'. Thus

$$\begin{aligned} G'(t) &= \langle F_1(P(t)), F_2(P(t))\rangle\cdot\langle f'(t), g'(t)\rangle \\ &= F_1(P(t))f'(t) + F_2(P(t))g'(t), \end{aligned}$$

and the proof of **18.18** is complete.

If the ∂-notation is used, we have proved that if $G(t) = F(f(t), g(t))$ then

$$G'(t) = \frac{\partial F}{\partial x}\frac{\partial x}{\partial t} + \frac{\partial F}{\partial y}\frac{\partial y}{\partial t},$$

where it is understood that $x = f(t)$ and $y = g(t)$.

EXAMPLE 1. If $F(x,y) = xy^2 + x^3 + y$ and

$$f(t) = t^2 - 1, \quad g(t) = 2t - t^3, \quad G(t) = F(f(t), g(t)),$$

find $G'(t)$.

Solution: We have

$$F_1(x,y) = y^2 + 3x^2, \quad F_2(x,y) = 2xy + 1, \quad f'(t) = 2t, \quad g'(t) = 2 - 3t^2.$$

If we let $P(t) = (f(t), g(t)) = (t^2 - 1, 2t - t^3)$, then, by the chain rule,

$$\begin{aligned} G'(t) &= F_1(P(t))f'(t) + F_2(P(t))g'(t) \\ &= [(2t - t^3)^2 + 3(t^2 - 1)^2]2t + [2(t^2 - 1)(2t - t^3) + 1](2 - 3t^2). \end{aligned}$$

Similar to **18.18**, there are chain rules for functions of three or more variables. For example, if F is a function of three variables and $x = x(s,t)$, $y = y(s,t)$, $z = z(s,t)$, and

$$G(s,t) = F(x(s,t), y(s,t), z(s,t)),$$

then

$$\frac{\partial G}{\partial s} = \frac{\partial F}{\partial x}\frac{\partial x}{\partial s} + \frac{\partial F}{\partial y}\frac{\partial y}{\partial s} + \frac{\partial F}{\partial z}\frac{\partial z}{\partial s}$$

$$\frac{\partial G}{\partial t} = \frac{\partial F}{\partial x}\frac{\partial x}{\partial t} + \frac{\partial F}{\partial y}\frac{\partial y}{\partial t} + \frac{\partial F}{\partial z}\frac{\partial z}{\partial t},$$

assuming all derivatives exist and are continuous in the proper sets. The proof that $\partial G/\partial s$ is as given above is exactly the same as the proof of **18.18**, except that three variables are involved, and similarly for $\partial G/\partial t$.

More generally, if F is a function of n variables and $x_1, x_2, \cdots, x_n$ are functions of m variables, and if $G(t_1,t_2, \cdots, t_m) = F(x_1(t_1, \cdots, t_m), x_2(t_1, \cdots, t_m), \cdots, x_n(t_1, \cdots, t_m))$, then

18.19
$$\frac{\partial G}{\partial t_j} = \sum_{i=1}^{n} \frac{\partial G}{\partial x_i}\frac{\partial x_i}{\partial t_j}, \qquad j = 1, 2, \cdots, m.$$

Thus **18.19** is a set of m equations, one for each variable t_j, and each equation is a sum of n terms, one for each variable x_i. We are assuming, of course, that the functions involved and their first derivatives are continuous in the proper domains.

EXAMPLE 2. The area of a rectangle is given by the formula

$$A = xy,$$

where x and y are the lengths of its sides. If u and θ are as indicated in Figure 18.6, then

$$x = u \cos \theta, \qquad y = u \sin \theta,$$

and A can be expressed in terms of u and θ. Find $\partial A/\partial u$ and $\partial A/\partial \theta$.

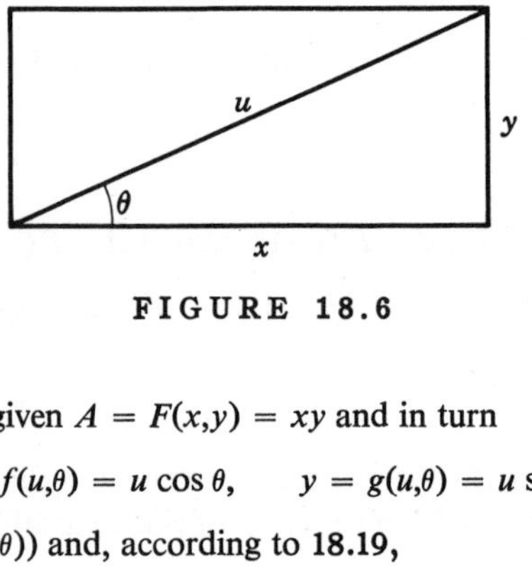

FIGURE 18.6

Solution: We are given $A = F(x,y) = xy$ and in turn

$$x = f(u,\theta) = u \cos \theta, \qquad y = g(u,\theta) = u \sin \theta.$$

Hence $A = F(f(u,\theta),g(u,\theta))$ and, according to **18.19**,

$$\frac{\partial A}{\partial u} = F_1(u \cos \theta, u \sin \theta)f_1(u,\theta) + F_2(u \cos \theta, u \sin \theta)g_1(u,\theta).$$

Since $F_1(x,y) = y$ and $F_2(x,y) = x$, and $f_1(u,\theta) = \cos \theta$ and $g_1(u,\theta) = \sin \theta$, we have

$$\frac{\partial A}{\partial u} = (u \sin \theta) \cos \theta + (u \cos \theta) \sin \theta$$

$$= 2u \sin \theta \cos \theta = u \sin 2\theta.$$

Similarly,

$$\frac{\partial A}{\partial \theta} = F_1(u\cos\theta, u\sin\theta)f_2(u,\theta) + F_2(u\cos\theta, u\sin\theta)g_2(u,\theta)$$

$$= (u\sin\theta)(-u\sin\theta) + (u\cos\theta)(u\cos\theta)$$

$$= u^2(\cos^2\theta - \sin^2\theta) = u^2\cos 2\theta.$$

In this example, of course, we could have expressed A in the form

$$A = (u\cos\theta)(u\sin\theta) = \tfrac{1}{2}u^2\sin 2\theta,$$

and then found $\partial A/\partial u$ and $\partial A/\partial\theta$ directly.

EXERCISES

I

In each of Exercises 1–4 find dw/dt.

1. $w = x^2 + y^2,\ x = \dfrac{t-1}{t},\ y = \dfrac{t}{t+1}.$

2. $w = x\sin y + y\sin z,\ x = t^2,\ y = e^{2t},\ z = \dfrac{1}{t}.$

3. $w = t\sin xy,\ x = \ln t,\ y = t^3.$

4. $w = x\tan y + y\tan x,\ x = te^t,\ y = te^{-t}.$

In each of Exercises 5–10 find $\partial z/\partial u$ and $\partial z/\partial v$.

5. $z = x^2 + y^2,\ x = u\cos v,\ y = u\sin v.$

6. $z = xe^y + ye^x,\ x = u\ln v,\ y = v\ln u.$

7. $z = \sin^{-1} xy,\ x = u + v,\ y = u - v.$

8. $z = \sqrt{x^2 + y^2},\ x = u\cos v,\ y = u\sin v.$

9. $z = e^{x/y},\ x = 2u - v,\ y = u + 2v.$

10. $z = \tan^{-1}\dfrac{y}{x},\ x = u + \sin v,\ y = u - \cos v.$

In Exercises 11 and 12, find $\partial w/\partial r$, $\partial w/\partial s$, and $\partial w/\partial t$.

11. $w = \dfrac{x+y}{z},\ x = r - 2s + t,\ y = 2r + s - 3t,\ z = r^2 + s^2 + t^2.$

12. $w = xy + yz + zx$, $x = r\cos s$, $y = r\sin t$, $z = st$.

In Exercises 13 and 14 find $\partial w/\partial u$ and $\partial w/\partial v$.

13. $w = \sqrt{x^2 + y^2 + z^2}$, $x = u\sin v$, $y = u\cos v$, $z = uv$.

14. $w = \dfrac{x^2 + y^2}{y^2 + z^2}$, $x = ue^v$, $y = ve^u$, $z = \dfrac{1}{u}\cdot$

15. If $z = F(x,y)$, $x = f(u,v)$, and $y = g(u,v)$, show that

$$\frac{\partial^2 z}{\partial u^2} = \frac{\partial^2 z}{\partial x^2}\left(\frac{\partial x}{\partial u}\right)^2 + 2\frac{\partial^2 z}{\partial x\,\partial y}\frac{\partial x}{\partial u}\frac{\partial y}{\partial u} + \frac{\partial^2 z}{\partial y^2}\left(\frac{\partial y}{\partial u}\right)^2 + \frac{\partial z}{\partial x}\frac{\partial^2 x}{\partial u^2} + \frac{\partial z}{\partial y}\frac{\partial^2 y}{\partial u^2}\cdot$$

16. If $z = F(x,y)$, $x = f(u,v)$, and $y = g(u,v)$, find a formula for $\partial^2 z/\partial v\,\partial u$ analogous to that of Exercise 15.

17. If $z = x + f(u)$ and $u = xy$, show that

$$x\frac{\partial z}{\partial x} - y\frac{\partial z}{\partial y} = x.$$

18. If $z = f(u/v)/v$, show that $v\dfrac{\partial z}{\partial v} + u\dfrac{\partial z}{\partial u} + z = 0$. [*Hint:* Let $x = u/v$ and $y = 1/v$, so that $z = yf(x)$.]

19. If $z = f(u^2 + v^2)$, show that $u\dfrac{\partial z}{\partial v} - v\dfrac{\partial z}{\partial u} = 0$. (*Hint:* Let $x = u^2 + v^2$.)

20. If $z = f(x,y)$, $x = r\cos\theta$, and $y = r\sin\theta$, show that

$$\left(\frac{\partial z}{\partial r}\right)^2 + \frac{1}{r^2}\left(\frac{\partial z}{\partial \theta}\right)^2 = \left(\frac{\partial z}{\partial x}\right)^2 + \left(\frac{\partial z}{\partial y}\right)^2\cdot$$

21. If $F(x,y) = f(y + ax) + g(y - ax)$, show that

$$\frac{\partial^2 F}{\partial x^2} = a^2\frac{\partial^2 F}{\partial y^2}\cdot$$

22. If $z = F(u,v)$ and $u = g(x,v)$, find $\left(\dfrac{\partial z}{\partial x}\right)_v$ and $\left(\dfrac{\partial z}{\partial v}\right)_x\cdot$ [*Note:* $\left(\dfrac{\partial z}{\partial x}\right)_v$ means v is kept fixed.]

23. If $H = E + PV$ and $E = g(P,V)$, find $\left(\dfrac{\partial H}{\partial V}\right)_P\cdot$

24. If $E = G(V,T)$ and $PV = k$, where k is a constant, find

$$\left(\frac{\partial E}{\partial P}\right)_T \quad\text{and}\quad \left(\frac{\partial E}{\partial T}\right)_P\cdot$$

II

1. A function f of two variables is said to be *homogeneous of degree n* if $f(tx,ty) = t^n f(x,y)$ for all x, y, and t such that (x,y) and (tx,ty) are in the domain of f. Show that for each 2-smooth homogeneous function f of degree n: (a) $xf_1(x,y) + yf_2(x,y) = nf(x,y)$, and (b) $x^2f_{11}(x,y) + 2xyf_{12}(x,y) + y^2f_{22}(x,y) = n(n-1)f(x,y)$ (Euler). (*Hint:* Differentiate with respect to t).

2. If $F(x,y) = \sqrt{x^2 - y^2}\sin^{-1}y/x$, find $xF_1(x,y) + yF_2(x,y)$.

3. If $g(x,y) = x \ln y/x$, show that $x^2g_{11}(x,y) + 2xyg_{12}(x,y) + y^2g_{22}(x,y) = 0$.

4. Referring to Exercise I-20, show that

$$\frac{\partial^2 z}{\partial r^2} + \frac{1}{r}\frac{\partial z}{\partial r} + \frac{1}{r^2}\frac{\partial^2 z}{\partial r^2} = \frac{\partial^2 z}{\partial x^2} + \frac{\partial^2 z}{\partial y^2}.$$

Show that the following functions satisfy Laplace's equation (see Exercise II-1, section 3).

5. $F(x,y) = \arctan\dfrac{y}{x}$.

6. $F(x_1,x_2,\cdots,x_n) = (x_1^2 + x_2^2 + \cdots + x_n^2)^{1-n/2}$

(Here Laplace's equation is $F_{11} + F_{22} + \cdots + F_{nn} = 0$).

7. If the function $F(x,y)$ satisfies Laplace's equation, show also that the function $G(x,y)$ has the same property where

$$G(x,y) = F\left(\frac{ax}{x^2+y^2}, \frac{ay}{x^2+y^2}\right) \qquad \text{(Kelvin's theorem)}.$$

7 IMPLICIT DIFFERENTIATION

The method of implicit differentiation was used in Chapter 5 to find the derivative of a function defined implicitly by an equation. We shall see in this section how the derivative of an implicitly defined function may be found through the use of partial derivatives.

Let F be a smooth function of two variables and f be a differentiable function of one variable such that

$$F(x,f(x)) = 0$$

for every x in the domain of f. We may use the chain rule **18.19** (with $x_1 = x$, $x_2 = y$, $u_1 = x$) to obtain

$$0 = DF(x,f(x)) = \frac{\partial F}{\partial x}\frac{dx}{dx} + \frac{\partial F}{\partial y}\frac{dy}{dx}.$$

Solving this equation for dy/dx, we get

18.20 $$\frac{dy}{dx} = -\frac{\partial F/\partial x}{\partial F/\partial y}$$

at every x in the domain of f for which $F_2(x,f(x)) \neq 0$.

EXAMPLE 1. If f is a differentiable function such that $y = f(x)$ satisfies the equation

$$x^3 + x^2y^2 - x - 2y + 1 = 0,$$

find dy/dx.

Solution: If $F(x,y) = x^3 + x^2y^2 - x - 2y + 1$, then

$$\frac{\partial F}{\partial x} = 3x^2 + 2xy^2 - 1, \qquad \frac{\partial F}{\partial y} = 2x^2y - 2,$$

and, by **18.20**,

$$\frac{dy}{dx} = -\frac{3x^2 + 2xy^2 - 1}{2x^2y - 2}.$$

A function of several variables might be defined implicitly by an equation or a set of equations. For example, an equation

$$F(x,y,z) = 0$$

might be satisfied by

$$z = f(x,y),$$

where F and f are smooth functions. Since $F(x,y,f(x,y)) = 0$, we have, by **18.19** (with $x_1 = x$, $x_2 = y$, $x_3 = z$, $t_1 = x$, $t_2 = y$),

$$0 = \frac{\partial}{\partial x} F(x,y,f(x,y)) = \frac{\partial F}{\partial x}\frac{\partial x}{\partial x} + \frac{\partial F}{\partial y}\frac{\partial y}{\partial x} + \frac{\partial F}{\partial z}\frac{\partial z}{\partial x}.$$

Remembering that $\partial x/\partial x = 1$ and $\partial y/\partial x = 0$, we may solve this equation for $\partial z/\partial x$ to yield

$$\frac{\partial z}{\partial x} = -\frac{\partial F/\partial x}{\partial F/\partial z}.$$

Similarly, we find

$$\frac{\partial z}{\partial y} = -\frac{\partial F/\partial y}{\partial F/\partial z}.$$

Note the similarity of these equations to **18.20**.

EXAMPLE 2. Find $\partial z/\partial x$ and $\partial z/\partial y$ if $z = f(x,y)$ satisfies the equation

$$xy^2 + yz^2 + z^3 + x^3 - 4 = 0.$$

Solution: If $F(x,y,z) = xy^2 + yz^2 + z^3 + x^3 - 4$, then

$$\frac{\partial F}{\partial x} = y^2 + 3x^2, \quad \frac{\partial F}{\partial y} = 2xy + z^2, \quad \frac{\partial F}{\partial z} = 2yz + 3z^2,$$

and

$$\frac{\partial z}{\partial x} = -\frac{y^2 + 3x^2}{2yz + 3z^2}, \quad \frac{\partial z}{\partial y} = -\frac{2xy + z^2}{2yz + 3z^2}.$$

EXERCISES

I

In each of Exercises 1–6 find the derivative of each differentiable function f such that $y = f(x)$ satisfies the equation.

1. $x + y^2 + \sin xy = 0.$
2. $x \ln x - ye^y + 3 = 0.$
3. $\tan^{-1} \frac{x}{y} + y^3 - 1 = 0.$
4. $x \sec y + y \sec x - 2 = 0.$
5. $x^3 - 2x^2y^2 + y^3 - 3xy + 1 = 0.$
6. $x^2 \ln y - y^3 + e^x = 0.$

In each of Exercises 7–10, f is a function of two variables having continuous first partial derivatives such that $z = f(x,y)$ satisfies the equation. Find $\partial z/\partial x$ and $\partial z/\partial y$.

7. $x^2z + yz^2 + xy^2 - z^3 = 0.$
8. $xe^{yz} + ye^{xz} - y^2 + 3 = 0.$
9. $x^3 + y^3 + z^2(x + y) = 2z^3.$
10. $\tan^{-1} x + \tan^{-1} y + \tan^{-1} z - 3 = 0.$
11. The equations

$$xu + yv + x^2u^2 + y^2v^2 - 3 = 0,$$
$$xu^2 + x^2u - yv^2 - y^2v - 2 = 0$$

can be solved simultaneously to yield $x = f(u,v)$ and $y = g(u,v)$. Find $\partial x/\partial u$, $\partial x/\partial v$, $\partial y/\partial u$, and $\partial y/\partial v$ without actually solving the equations, by use of implicit differentiation.

12. If the equations for changing from spherical coordinates to rectangular coordinates

$$x = \rho \sin \phi \cos \theta, \quad y = \rho \sin \phi \sin \theta, \quad z = \rho \cos \phi,$$

were solved for ρ, ϕ, and θ in terms of x, y, and z, then the first-order partial derivatives of ρ, ϕ, and θ with respect to x, y, and z could be found directly. Show how to find these partial derivatives without actually solving the above equations.

II

1. If F is a function of two variables and f is a function of one variable such that $F(x,f(x)) = 0$, express $f''(x)$ in terms of partial derivatives of F.

2. If F and G are functions of three variables and f and g are functions of one variable such that

$$F(x,f(x),g(x)) = 0, \qquad G(x,f(x),g(x)) = 0,$$

express $f'(x)$ and $g'(x)$ in terms of partial derivatives of F and G.

3. If F and G are functions of four variables and f and g are functions of two variables such that

$$F(x,y,f(x,y),g(x,y)) = 0, \qquad G(x,y,f(x,y),g(x,y)) = 0,$$

express the first-order partial derivatives of f and g in terms of partial derivatives of F and G.

8 EXTREMA OF A FUNCTION OF TWO VARIABLES

The concept of an extremum of a function of one variable easily extends to a function of several variables, as we shall indicate in this section for functions of two variables.

If f is a function of two variables and S is a subset of the domain of f, and if P is a point of S such that $f(P) \geq f(Q)$ for every point Q in S, then $f(P)$ is called the *maximum value* of f in S. We call $f(P)$ a *relative maximum value* of f if there exists a disc $B(P,r)$ such that $f(P) > f(Q)$ for every Q in $B(P,r)$, $Q \neq P$. Relative minimum values of a function are similarly defined. If $f(P)$ is either a relative maximum or a relative minimum value of f, then $f(P)$ is called a *relative extremum* of the function f.

If a function f of two variables is continuous in a closed region of the plane, such as a rectangle or a disc, then it actually has a maximum value and a minimum value in that region. We shall not attempt to prove this result here, but rather state that its proof is analogous to that of **18.3** for functions of one variable.

The relative extrema of a function f of two variables occur at the "mountain peaks" and "valley bottoms" of the graph of f. Let us now show how the relative extrema of a function of two variables are found. Henceforth, in discussing relative extrema of a function, we shall usually omit the word *relative*, it being implicitly understood that *extrema* means *relative* extrema.

In the first place, if $f(a,b)$ is a maximum value of f, then $(a,b,f(a,b))$ must be a maximum point on the cross section of the graph of f in each of the planes $x = a$ and $y = b$, and similarly for minimum values of f. Thus, if $f(a,b)$ is a relative extremum of f and if f has first partial derivatives at (a,b), then necessarily

$$f_1(a,b) = 0, \qquad f_2(a,b) = 0.$$

Hence, as is intuitively evident, the tangent plane at a relative extremum is parallel to the xy plane. The procedure to be followed in finding the extrema of a function f of two variables is clear from our remarks above. We find the simultaneous solutions of the equations

$$f_1(x,y) = 0, \qquad f_2(x,y) = 0,$$

and then test each of these solutions to see if the function has a maximum or minimum value there. An extremum might occur at a point (a,b) at which the partial derivatives do not exist, but we shall not consider such a possibility here.

EXAMPLE 1. If $f(x,y) = 4 - x^2 - y^2$, find the extrema of f.

Solution: We have $f_1(x,y) = -2x$ and $f_2(x,y) = -2y$. The only solution of the equations

$$-2x = 0, \qquad -2y = 0$$

is $x = 0$ and $y = 0$. Thus $f(0,0)$ is the only possible extremum of f. Since $4 - x^2 - y^2 < 4$ if $(x,y) \neq (0,0)$, $f(0,0) = 4$ is a maximum value of f.

EXAMPLE 2. If $g(x,y) = 4 + x^2 - y^2$, find the extrema of g.

Solution: We have $g_1(x,y) = 2x$, $g_2(x,y) = -2y$, so that again $g(0,0)$ is the only possible extremum of g. The cross section

$$z = 4 + x^2$$

of the surface $z = 4 + x^2 - y^2$ in the xz plane has a minimum point at (0,0,4), whereas the cross section

$$z = 4 - y^2$$

of this surface in the yz plane has a maximum point at (0,0,4). Therefore it is evident that $g(0,0) = 4$ is neither a maximum nor a minimum value of g. The point (0,0,4) is called a *saddle point* of the surface, and it resembles the origin on the surface in Figure 17.21. The function g has no extrema.

For a more complicated example than those given above, it might be very difficult to decide whether or not a given point at which the first partial derivatives of f are zero leads to an extremum of f. Therefore we shall give a test, corresponding to the second derivative test for functions of one variable, for extrema of a function of two variables.

If $f_1(a,b) = 0$ and $f_2(a,b) = 0$, and if the second partial derivatives $f_{11}(a,b)$ and $f_{22}(a,b)$ exist and are nonzero, then the cross sections of the graph of f in the planes $x = a$ and $y = b$ must be concave downward and we must have

$$f_{11}(a,b) < 0, \qquad f_{22}(a,b) < 0,$$

if $f(a,b)$ is a maximum value of f. Similarly, if $f(a,b)$ is a minimum value of f,

$$f_{11}(a,b) > 0, \qquad f_{22}(a,b) > 0.$$

If $f_{11}(a,b)$ and $f_{22}(a,b)$ differ in sign, then $f(a,b)$ cannot be an extremum of f.

18.21 **TEST FOR EXTREMA.** Let f be a 2-smooth function of two variables in an open set S of R^2 and let function F be defined by

$$F(Q) = f_{11}(Q)f_{22}(Q) - f_{12}^2(Q), \qquad \text{domain } F = S.$$

If P is a point in S such that

$$f_1(P) = 0 \qquad \text{and} \qquad f_2(P) = 0,$$

then

(1) $f(P)$ is a maximum value of f if $F(P) > 0$ and $f_{11}(P) < 0$.
(2) $f(P)$ is a minimum value of f if $F(P) > 0$ and $f_{11}(P) > 0$.
(3) $f(P)$ is not an extremum of f if $F(P) < 0$.

If $F(P) > 0$, then evidently the first term of $F(P)$ is positive, $f_{11}(P)f_{22}(P) > 0$. Hence $f_{11}(P)$ and $f_{22}(P)$ must agree in sign, and $f_{11}(P)$ can be replaced by $f_{22}(P)$ in either part (1) or part (2) of the test.

The theorem gives no information about $f(P)$ if $F(P) = 0$. In such a case a direct analysis (as in Examples 1 and 2) may be made to determine if $f(P)$ is an extremum of f.

EXAMPLE 3. Find the extrema of the function f defined by

$$f(x,y) = x^3 - 12xy + 8y^3.$$

Solution: Evidently,

$$f_1(x,y) = 3x^2 - 12y, \qquad f_2(x,y) = -12x + 24y^2.$$

The two equations

$$3x^2 - 12y = 0, \qquad -12x + 24y^2 = 0$$

have as their simultaneous solutions (0,0) and (2,1). The second partial derivatives of f are

$$f_{11}(x,y) = 6x, \quad f_{12}(x,y) = -12, \quad f_{22}(x,y) = 48y.$$

We easily compute

$$F(0,0) = -144, \qquad F(2,1) = 432.$$

Since $F(0,0) < 0, f(0,0)$ is not an extremum of f, by **18.21**(3). And since $F(2,1) > 0$ and $f_{11}(2,1) > 0, f(2,1) = -8$ is a minimum value of f, by **18.21**(2). This is the only extremum of f.

Proof of 18.21(1): By assumption, $f_{11}(P) < 0$, $F(P) > 0$, and the second partial derivatives of f are continuous in S. It follows immediately that $f_{11}(Q) < 0$ and $F(Q) > 0$ for every point Q in some disc $B(P,\epsilon)$. We shall prove the theorem by showing that $D_{\mathbf{v}}^2 f(Q) < 0$ for every Q in $B(P,\epsilon)$ and every nonzero $\mathbf{v}$ in V_2. This will mean that $D_{\mathbf{v}}f$ is a strictly decreasing function in $B(P,\epsilon)$ along every vector $\mathbf{v}$, which in turn will mean that $f(P)$ is the maximum value of f in $B(P,\epsilon)$ along every $\mathbf{v}$. It will follow that $f(P)$ is the maximum value of f in $B(P,\epsilon)$, and hence that $f(P)$ is a relative maximum value of f.

If $\mathbf{v} = \langle h,k \rangle$, then $D_{\mathbf{v}}f(Q) = \nabla f(Q)\cdot\mathbf{v} = hf_1(Q) + kf_2(Q)$ and

$$\begin{aligned} D_{\mathbf{v}}^2 f(Q) &= D_{\mathbf{v}}(D_{\mathbf{v}}f)(Q) = \nabla D_{\mathbf{v}}f(Q)\cdot\mathbf{v} \\ &= \langle hf_{11} + kf_{21}, hf_{12} + kf_{22}\rangle\cdot\mathbf{v}, \end{aligned}$$

where each second partial derivative of f is evaluated at Q. Since $f_{12} = f_{21}$, we have

$$D_{\mathbf{v}}^2 f(Q) = h^2 f_{11} + 2hkf_{12} + k^2 f_{22}.$$

It is a simple exercise in algebra to change this into the form

$$D_{\mathbf{v}}^2 f(Q) = f_{11}\left[h + \frac{f_{12}}{f_{11}}k\right]^2 + \frac{k^2}{f_{11}}F(Q).$$

Since $f_{11}(Q) < 0$ and $F(Q) > 0$, and h and k are not both zero, evidently $D_{\mathbf{v}}^2 f(Q) < 0$ for every Q in $B(P,\epsilon)$. This proves **18.21**(1).

The proof of **18.21**(2) is similar to that for **18.21**(1) and hence is omitted. We shall leave the proof of **18.21**(3) as an exercise for the reader.

EXAMPLE 4. A rectangular box without a top is to have a given volume. How should the box be made so as to use the least amount of material?

Solution: Let k designate the volume of the box. Hence, if the base of the box is x by y units and the altitude is z units, then

$$k = xyz.$$

The surface area S of the box is given by

$$S = xy + 2xz + 2yz.$$

Since $z = k/xy$, we may express S in the form

$$S = xy + \frac{2k}{y} + \frac{2k}{x}.$$

The problem is to find the minimum value of S. Hence we solve simultaneously the equations

$$S_1 = y - \frac{2k}{x^2} = 0, \qquad S_2 = x - \frac{2k}{y^2} = 0.$$

Since $x^2y = 2k$ and $xy^2 = 2k$, clearly $x = y$ and $x^3 = y^3 = 2k$. It is easily established that $F(\sqrt[3]{2k},\sqrt[3]{2k}) > 0$ and $S_{11} > 0$, so that $(\sqrt[3]{2k},\sqrt[3]{2k})$ gives a minimum value for S.

We have

$$z = \frac{k}{xy} = \frac{kx}{x^3} = \frac{x}{2},$$

and therefore we conclude that the box should have a square base and an altitude half the length of the base.

EXERCISES

I

In each of Exercises 1–10, find the extrema of the function.

1. $f(x,y) = x^2 + xy + y^2$.
2. $g(x,y) = x^2 - xy + y^2 + 6x$.
3. $F(x,y) = x^3 - 12x + y^2$.
4. $G(x,y) = x^3 + x^2 - y^3 + y^2$.
5. $g(x,y) = x^2 - 2xy + y^2 - y^3$.
6. $f(x,y) = (2x - y)^2 - x^3$.
7. $f(x,y) = \frac{1}{x} + xy - \frac{8}{y}$.
8. $F(x,y) = xy(4 - x - y)$.
9. $F(x,y) = x^2 + \frac{2}{xy^2} + y^2$.
10. $g(x,y) = \sin x + \sin y + \sin (x + y)$.
11. Find the minimum distance between the point $(1,-1,2)$ and the plane $3x + y - 2z = 4$. [*Hint:* Express in terms of x and y the distance between the point $(1,-1,2)$ and the point (x,y,z) on the plane.]
12. Find the minimum distance between the point $(0,-2,-4)$ and the plane $x + y - 4z = 5$.
13. Show that the volume of the largest rectangular parallelepiped that can be inscribed in the ellipsoid

$$\frac{x^2}{a^2} + \frac{y^2}{b^2} + \frac{z^2}{c^2} = 1$$

is $8abc/3\sqrt{3}$. (Use Exercise II-4, Section 7, Chapter 16).

14. Find the minimum distance between the lines with parametric equations $x = t$, $y = 3 - 2t$, $z = 1 + 2t$ and $x = -1 - s$, $y = s$, $z = 4 - 3s$.
15. A rectangular box without top has a surface area of S ft². Determine the dimensions of the box if the volume is to be a maximum. (*Note:* This is the dual of Example 4, Section 8).

16. A rectangular parallelepiped has three of its faces in the coordinate planes and its vertex opposite the origin in the first octant and on the plane $2x + y + 3z = 6$. Find the maximum volume this box can have.

17. Indicate the changes that must be made in the proof of **18.21**(1) to give the proof of **18.2**(2).

18. Prove **18.21**(3).

II

1. Show that the minimum (or maximum) distance from a given point to a given simple smooth closed surface is along a normal line from the point to the surface.

2. Determine which point of the sphere $x^2 + y^2 + z^2 = 25/2$ is at the greatest distance from the point (3,4,5) (using methods of this section). Check your answer by redoing the problem using synthetic geometry.

3. Determine the extrema of $x^n + y^n + z^n$ (n integer > 1) subject to the constraints $x + y + z = S$ (constant), $x,y,z \geq 0$ (using the methods of this section).

4. Show how to obtain the maximum value in the preceding exercise in a more elementary way by using mathematical induction.

5. Solve Example 4, Section 8, by using the theorem of the arithmetic-geometric mean.

6. (a) Solve Exercise I-16 above by using the theorem of the arithmetic-geometric mean.
   (b) What other exercises of Part I could be solved in this manner?

7. Determine the values of a and b such that the ellipse $x^2/a^2 + y^2/b^2 = 1$ has least area and contains the circle $(x - 1)^2 + y^2 = 1$.

9 LINE INTEGRALS

The theory of integration of real-valued functions of one variable can be extended to the integration of functions of two or three variables over curves. We shall restrict our remarks to the integration of functions of three variables over space curves, leaving it for the reader to observe that they also apply to functions of two variables over plane curves.

Let f be a continuous function of three variables in some open set S of R^3 and let λ be a smooth curve with domain $[a,b]$ and trace contained in S. Then we denote the *integral of f over λ* by $\int_\lambda f$ and define it as follows:

18.22
$$\int_\lambda f = \int_a^b f(\lambda(t))|\lambda'(t)|\, dt.$$

The integral above always exists. In fact, it is clear that the integral exists as long as f is defined and continuous in the trace of λ.

This integral is often written in the form

$$\int_\lambda f\, ds,$$

it being understood that s is the arc-length function defined in Chapter 16 by

$$s(t) = \int_a^t |\lambda'(p)|\, dp,$$

so that $ds = |\lambda'(t)|\, dt$.

A possible physical interpretation of **18.22** is the following. Let λ be a 1–1 or a simple closed curve with domain $[a,b]$, and think of the trace of λ as a thin wire in R^3. Now imagine a continuous function ρ of three variables defined in some open set of R^3 containing the wire such that $\rho(\lambda(t))$ is the density of the wire at point $\lambda(t)$. Then, intuitively,

$$W = \int_\lambda \rho = \int_a^b \rho(\lambda(t))|\lambda'(t)|\, dt$$

is the mass of the wire. Furthermore, if $\lambda(t) = (x(t), y(t), z(t))$, then

$$M_{yz} = \int_\lambda x\rho = \int_a^b x(t)\rho(\lambda(t))|\lambda'(t)|\, dt$$

is the moment of the wire with respect to the yz plane. Defining M_{xz} and M_{xy} analogously, we see intuitively that the point

$$\left(\frac{M_{yz}}{W}, \frac{M_{xz}}{W}, \frac{M_{xy}}{W}\right)$$

is the center of mass of the wire.

EXAMPLE 1. Find the center of mass of a piece of wire of constant density ρ bent in the shape of the helix

$$\lambda(t) = (4\cos t, 4\sin t, 3t), \qquad (t \text{ in } [0,\pi]).$$

Solution: By Example 2, page 601, the mass of the wire is $5\pi\rho$. Also,

$$M_{yz} = 5\rho \int_0^\pi 4\cos t\, dt = 20\rho \sin t\Big|_0^\pi = 0,$$

$$M_{xz} = 5\rho \int_0^\pi 4\sin t\, dt = -20\rho\cos t\Big|_0^\pi = 40\rho,$$

$$M_{xy} = 5\rho \int_0^\pi 3t\, dt = \frac{15}{2}\pi^2\rho.$$

Hence $(0,8/\pi,3\pi/2)$ is the center of mass of the wire.

We turn now to another kind of integration that can be defined on curves. Let λ be a curve with domain $[a,b]$ and let f be a smooth function of three variables in some open set S of R^3 containing the trace of λ. We recall that the differential of f is given by

$$df(P,\mathbf{v}) = \nabla f(P)\cdot\mathbf{v}, \qquad P \text{ in } S, \mathbf{v} \text{ in } V_3.$$

Then let us denote the integral of df over λ by $\int_\lambda df$ and define it as follows:

$$\int_\lambda df = \int_a^b df(\lambda(t), \lambda'(t))\, dt.$$

If we let $\lambda(t) = (x(t), y(t), z(t))$, then the integral above has the form

$$\int_\lambda df = \int_a^b [D_1f(\lambda(t))x'(t) + D_2f(\lambda(t))y'(t) + D_3f(\lambda(t))z'(t)]\, dt.$$

By the chain rule, the integrand above is $Df(\lambda(t))$; hence

18.23 $$\int_\lambda df = \int_a^b Df(\lambda(t))\, dt = f(\lambda(b)) - f(\lambda(a))$$

by the fundamental theorem of the calculus.

We can consider ∇f as a function with domain S and range a subset of V_3; thus

$$\nabla f(P) = \langle D_1f(P), D_2f(P), D_3f(P)\rangle, \qquad P \text{ in } S.$$

Then the differential of f is given by

$$df(P,\mathbf{v}) = \nabla f(P)\cdot\mathbf{v}, \qquad P \text{ in } S \text{ and } \mathbf{v} \text{ in } V_3.$$

A possible way to generalize the differential is to consider any function $\mathbf{F}$ with domain an open set S of R^3 and range a subset of V_3. Then define the function w by

18.24 $$w(P,\mathbf{v}) = \mathbf{F}(P)\cdot\mathbf{v}, \qquad P \text{ in } S \text{ and } \mathbf{v} \text{ in } V_3.$$

We call the function w a 1-*form* in S, and say that w is continuous, differentiable, or smooth according to whether the function $\mathbf{F}$ is.

If w is the continuous 1-form defined by **18.24** and λ is a smooth curve with domain $[a,b]$ and trace in S, then the *line integral* of w over λ is denoted by $\int_\lambda w$ and is defined as follows:

18.25 $$\int_\lambda w = \int_a^b w(\lambda(t), \lambda'(t))\, dt.$$

Thus, if $w(P,\mathbf{v}) = \mathbf{F}(P)\cdot\mathbf{v}$, then

$$\int_\lambda w = \int_a^b \mathbf{F}(\lambda(t))\cdot\lambda'(t)\, dt.$$

The common form in which the line integral is written may be obtained as follows. Since **F** maps S into V_3, the function **F** has the form

$$\mathbf{F}(P) = \langle A(P), B(P), C(P)\rangle, \qquad P \text{ in } S,$$

where A, B, and C are real-valued functions of three variables. If we let $\lambda(t) = (x(t), y(t), z(t))$ as usual, then

$$\mathbf{F}(\lambda(t))\cdot\boldsymbol{\lambda}'(t) = A(\lambda(t))x'(t) + B(\lambda(t))y'(t) + C(\lambda(t))z'(t).$$

Using differentials $dx = x'(t)\,dt$, $dy = y'(t)\,dt$, and $dz = z'(t)\,dt$, **18.25** may be expressed in the form

$$\int_\lambda w = \int_\lambda (A\,dx + B\,dy + C\,dz).$$

The right-hand integral is evaluated as stated above:

$$\int_\lambda (A\,dx + B\,dy + C\,dz) = \int_a^b [A(\lambda(t))x'(t) + B(\lambda(t))y'(t) + C(\lambda(t))z'(t)]\,dt.$$

If w is a 1-form in an open set S of R^2, say $w(P,\mathbf{v}) = \mathbf{F}(P)\cdot\mathbf{v}$ for P in S and $\mathbf{v}$ in V_2, and λ is a smooth curve in R^2, then the line integral of w over λ is still defined as in **18.25.** The common form in which this integral is written is

$$\int_\lambda w = \int_\lambda (A\,dx + B\,dy),$$

where $\mathbf{F}(P) = \langle A(P),B(P)\rangle$ for P in S.

A physical example of a line integral is afforded by a force field in R^3. Abstractly, a *force field* is a function **F** with domain in R^3 and range in V_3. For each point P in R^3 we interpret the vector $\mathbf{F}(P)$ as a force acting on a particle at P. We say that **F** acts on a moving particle of mass m if the particle moves along a curve λ in such a way that Newton's law holds. That is, if $\lambda(t)$ is the position of the particle at time t, then

$$\mathbf{F}(\lambda(t)) = \frac{d}{dt}\,[m\boldsymbol{\lambda}'(t)].$$

The vector $m\boldsymbol{\lambda}'(t)$ is called the *momentum* of the particle at time t. If we assume that the mass m is a constant, then Newton's law takes on the familiar form that the force is the product of the mass and the acceleration of the particle,

18.26 $$\mathbf{F}(\lambda(t)) = m\boldsymbol{\lambda}''(t).$$

Given a force field, one problem that arises is that of finding a curve λ for which **18.26** holds. As we can see, this involves solving a vector differential equation. We shall not try to solve this equation, but rather shall assume that we have a curve λ for which **18.26** holds.

If a particle moves along a curve λ with domain $[a,b]$, then the work done in moving the particle from time $t = a$ to time $t = b$ can be approximated as follows. Select a partition $\{t_0, t_1, \cdots, t_n\}$ of $[a,b]$. Then the work done in the time interval $[t_{i-1},t_i]$ is approximately equal to $\mathbf{F}(\lambda(t_i))\cdot[\lambda(t_i) - \lambda(t_{i-1})]$. Hence the work done in the interval $[a,b]$ is approximately equal to

$$\sum_{i=1}^{n} \mathbf{F}(\lambda(t_i)) \cdot \left[\frac{1}{\Delta t_i}(\lambda(t_i) - \lambda(t_{i-1}))\right] \Delta t_i.$$

If we consider a sequence of partitions of $[a,b]$ whose norms approach zero, the corresponding sequences of sums of the type above will approach the integral

$$\int_a^b \mathbf{F}(\lambda(t))\cdot\boldsymbol{\lambda}'(t)\, dt.$$

Since this is simply the line integral of w over λ, where $w(P,\mathbf{v}) = \mathbf{F}(P)\cdot\mathbf{v}$, the following definition of the *work* W done in moving the particle along curve λ should seem reasonable:

18.27 $$W = \int_\lambda w, \quad \text{where } w(P,\mathbf{v}) = \mathbf{F}(P)\cdot\mathbf{v}.$$

EXAMPLE 2. If a particle of unit mass is located at the origin of our coordinate system, then the gravitational field $\mathbf{F}$ of this particle may be shown to be given by

18.28 $$\mathbf{F}(x,y,z) = \frac{-k}{(x^2 + y^2 + z^2)^{3/2}} \langle x,y,z\rangle$$

for a positive constant k. Find the work done by another particle moving in this force field from point $P = (\lambda(1),0,0)$ to point $Q = (\lambda(8),0,0)$ along the curve λ defined by

$$\lambda(t) = (at^{2/3},0,0), \text{ where } a^3 = 9k/2.$$

Solution: We may readily check that **18.26** is satisfied by λ if we properly choose the positive number a. Hence, by **18.27**,

$$W = \int_1^8 \mathbf{F}(\lambda(t))\cdot\boldsymbol{\lambda}'(t)\, dt = -\frac{2k}{3a}\int_1^8 t^{-5/3}\, dt$$

$$= \frac{k}{a} t^{-2/3}\Big|_1^8 = -\frac{3k}{4a}.$$

EXERCISES

I

1. Find the center of mass of a piece of thin wire of constant density which is bent into the shape of the curve $\lambda(t) = (a\cos t, a\sin t, ct)$, domain $\lambda = [0,2\pi]$.

2. Find the center of mass of a piece of thin wire of density $\rho(t) = k \sin 2t$ which is bent into the shape of the elliptical helix $\lambda(t) = (a \cos t, b \sin t, ct)$, domain $\lambda = [0,\pi/2]$.

3. Set up the integrals for the moments of inertia I_x, I_y, and I_z of the wire in Exercise 2.

4. Find the work done by a particle moving along the helix $\lambda(t) = (a \cos t, a \sin t, bt)$ from $t = 0$ to $t = 2\pi$ if it is subject to the force field of **18.28**.

5. What would be the result of Exercise 4 if the helix were replaced by an arbitrary curve λ with domain $[0,t_0]$?

6. Evaluate the line integral $\int x\,dy - y\,dx$ around: (a) the circle $(x - h)^2 + (y - k)^2 = a^2$; (b) the ellipse $\lambda(t) = (a \cos t, b \sin t)$, domain $\lambda = [0,2\pi]$.

7. Evaluate the line integral $\int \frac{x\,dy - y\,dx}{x^2 + y^2}$ around: (a) the circle $(x - 2a)^2 + (y - 2a)^2 = a^2$; (b) the circle $x^2 + y^2 = a^2$.

8. Evaluate the line integral $\int y^2\,dx + 2xy\,dy$ around the two curves in Exercise 6.

9. Evaluate the line integral $\int_\lambda (A\,dx + B\,dy + C\,dz)$ for: (a) $\lambda(t) = (a \cos t, b \sin t, t^2)$, domain $\lambda = [0,2\pi]$, $A = x + y$, $B = y + z$, $C = z + x$; (b) $\lambda(t) = (at,bt^2,ct^3)$ domain $\lambda = [0,1]$, $A = x + y + z$, $B = xyz$, $C = x^2y^2z^2$.

II

1. At each point of a thin stiff wire bent into the shape of a closed plane curve, a force of constant magnitude acts inwardly along the normal. Show that the wire is in equilibrium (ignore the weight of the wire).

REVIEW

Oral Exercises

Define or explain each of the following.

1. Continuity of a function of several variables.
2. Directional derivative.
3. Partial derivative.
4. Gradient.
5. Differential of a function of several variables.

6. Tangent plane and normal line to a surface.
7. The chain rule.
8. Implicit differentiation.
9. Extrema of a function of several variables.
10. Saddle point of a surface.
11. Line integral.
12. Force field.
13. Work.

I

In each of Exercises 1–4 determine the domain of the given function.

1. $z = \sqrt{x + y} + \sqrt{x - y}$.

2. $z = \dfrac{1}{\sqrt{x + y}} + \dfrac{1}{\sqrt{x - y}}$.

3. $z = (a^2 - x^2 - y^2)^{-1}$.

4. $z = c\sqrt{1 - \dfrac{x^2}{a^2} - \dfrac{y^2}{b^2}}$.

5. Find the maximum directional derivative of the function $F(x,y) = 100 - 2x^2 - y^2$ at the point (5,5).

6. If the shape of a mountain is given by the graph of $z = 100 - 2x^2 - y^2$, give a physical interpretation of the result of the previous exercise. (*Hint:* Consider the level lines of the mountain, i.e., the cross sections given by the family of curves $100 - 2x^2 - y^2 = \text{const.}$)

In each of Exercises 7–9 verify that $F_{12} = F_{21}$, $F_{112} = F_{211}$, $F_{221} = F_{122}$.

7. $F(x,y) = xe^{x+y}$.

8. $F(x,y) = \dfrac{x}{1 + y^2}$.

9. $F(x,y) = e^x \sin(x + y)$.

In each of Exercises 10–12, sketch the surface and the tangent plane to the surface at the given point.

10. $z = 10 - x^2 - y^2$, (1,3,0).

11. $z = \dfrac{9}{1 + x^2 + y^2}$, (2,2,1).

12. $y = \sqrt{x + z}$, (1,2,3).

If $z = x/(x + y)$, find dz/dt in each of Exercises 13–15.

13. $x = t$, $y = at$.

14. $x = \sin t$, $y = \cos t$.

15. $x = 2 + t$, $y = g(t)$.

16. Let C be the curve of intersection of the surface $z = x^2 + y^2$ and the cylinder whose parametric equations are $x = \cos t$, $y = \sin t$. Find dz/dt and hence find parametric equations for the tangent line to C at the point where $t = \pi/4$. Verify that this tangent line lies in the tangent plane to the surface $z = x^2 + y^2$ at the given point.

Find the extrema of the function in each of Exercises 17–20.

17. $f(x,y) = x^2e^{x+y}$.

18. $F(x,y) = 4xy - 2x^2 - y^4$.

19. $g(x,y) = (x - 1) \ln y - x^2$.

20. $z = x/\sqrt{x^2 + y^2 + 1}$.

In each of Exercises 21–22, approximate the given number by differentials.

21. 1.04^{202}.

22. $(99.99)(49.98)(9.97)$.

23. Find an equation of the tangent plane and of the normal line to the graph of

$$\frac{x^2}{a^2} + \frac{y^2}{b^2} + \frac{z^2}{c^2} = 1$$

at the point of the graph (h,k,l).

24. Show that

$$c = \frac{A}{\sqrt{t}} e^{-x^2/4kt} \qquad (A \text{ const.})$$

satisfies the partial differential equation (of one dimensional diffusion)

$$\frac{\partial c}{\partial t} = k \frac{\partial^2 c}{\partial x^2}.$$

25. A rectangular box without a top and bottom is to have a volume of V ft³. Determine the dimensions of the box if the surface area is to be a minimum.

26. Consider the dual of the previous exercise. The surface area is S ft² (given). Determine the dimensions of the box if the volume of the box is to be a maximum.

In each of Exercises 27–29 evaluate the line integrals.

27. $\int xy\, ds$ around the square whose vertices are $(\pm a, \pm a)$.

28. $\int xy\, ds$ around the ellipse $x = a \cos t$, $y = b \sin t$.

29. $\int x^2\, dy + y^2\, dz + z^2\, dx$ along the curve $\lambda(t) = (t^2, t + 1, t - 1)$, domain $\lambda = [0,1]$.

II

1. If $F(x,y) = \dfrac{xy(x^2 - y^2)}{x^2 + y^2}$, $(x,y) \neq (0,0)$, $F(0,0) = 0$, show that $F_{xy}(0,0) \neq F_{yx}(0,0)$.

2. Extend Euler's result on homogeneous functions (Exercise II-1, Section 6) to a function of three variables.

3. Assuming differentiability, show that if $F(x,y,z) = 0$, then

$$\left(\frac{\partial x}{\partial y}\right)_z \left(\frac{\partial y}{\partial z}\right)_x \left(\frac{\partial z}{\partial x}\right)_y = -1$$

where, as in Exercise I-22, Section 6, $\left(\frac{\partial x}{\partial y}\right)_z$ means the partial derivative of x with respect to y keeping z fixed.

4. Given functions f and g of two variables, we can imagine solving the system of equations

$$\begin{cases} u = f(x,y) \\ v = g(x,y) \end{cases}$$

for x and y in terms of u and v, thereby obtaining the system

$$\begin{cases} x = F(u,v) \\ y = G(u,v). \end{cases}$$

Assuming this is possible and that all functions are differentiable, prove that

$$\begin{vmatrix} f_1 & f_2 \\ g_1 & g_2 \end{vmatrix} \cdot \begin{vmatrix} F_1 & F_2 \\ G_1 & G_2 \end{vmatrix} = 1,$$

where the functions f and g are evaluated at x and y and F and G are evaluated at $(f(x,y),g(x,y))$. (*Note:* These determinants are called *Jacobians.*)

5. If $f_1(x,y) = f_2(x,y) = 0$ for every point (x,y) in an open disc S, show that $f(x,y)$ is a constant in S.

6. If $f_1(x,y) = g_1(x,y)$, $f_2(x,y) = g_2(x,y)$ for every point (x,y) in an open disc, show that f and g differ by a constant.

7. Let ∇^2 denote the harmonic operator $\frac{\partial^2}{\partial x^2} + \frac{\partial^2}{\partial y^2} + \frac{\partial^2}{\partial z^2}$. Thus $\nabla^2 F = 0$ if F is a harmonic function. Prove that if F and G are harmonic functions, then

a. $\nabla^2(FG) = 2\nabla F \cdot \nabla G$.
b. $\nabla^2\nabla^2[F + (x^2 + y^2 + z^2)G] = 0$.

(*Note:* A function H having continuous fourth derivatives such that $\nabla^2\nabla^2 H = 0$ is called a biharmonic function. See also Exercise II-1, Section 3.)

8. If $x = F(u,v)$, $y = G(u,v)$ where

$$\frac{\partial F}{\partial u} = \frac{\partial G}{\partial v}, \quad \frac{\partial F}{\partial v} = -\frac{\partial G}{\partial u},$$

show that

$$\frac{\partial^2 H}{\partial u^2} + \frac{\partial^2 H}{\partial v^2} = \left(\frac{\partial^2 H}{\partial x^2} + \frac{\partial^2 H}{\partial y^2}\right)\left[\left(\frac{\partial F}{\partial u}\right)^2 + \left(\frac{\partial F}{\partial v}\right)^2\right].$$

9. If A and B are fixed points and $\phi(x,y,z)$ is the angle at point $P = (x,y,z)$ subtended by the segment AB, then show that the vector $\nabla\phi(x,y,z)$ is normal to the circle passing through the three points A, B, and P.

10. If $f_1(x,y)$ and $f_2(x,y)$ are the distances from the point $P = (x,y)$ to the foci of an ellipse, then prove that $\mathbf{v}\cdot\nabla(f_1 + f_2)(P) = 0$ for every point P on the ellipse and unit vector $\mathbf{v}$ tangent to the ellipse at P. Give a geometric interpretation of this equation.

11. Show that all plane cross sections of the graph of $z = (y - x^2)(y - 2x^2)$ which contain the z axis have a minimum at the origin.
Does the function $f(x,y) = (y - x^2)(y - 2x^2)$ have a minimum at $(0,0)$?

12. Find the extrema of $x + y + z$ subject to the constraint $x^{-1} + y^{-1} + z^{-1} = S$ (constant), $x,y,z, \geq 0$.

13. Find the point within a given triangle for which the sum of the squares of its perpendicular distances from the sides is least.

14. A wire of given length L may be cut into pieces to form a circle, a square, and an equilateral triangle.
a. Determine the minimum of the sum of the areas formed.
b. Determine the maximum of the sum of the areas formed.

15. Approximate $(2.01)^{1.99^{2.99}}$ by the method of differentials.

16. Show that all the planes which are tangent to a surface whose equation is of the form $z = xF(y/x)$ are concurrent.

17. Show that every tangent plane to the surface whose equation is

$$\sqrt{x} + \sqrt{y} + \sqrt{z} = \sqrt{k},$$

cuts off segments on the coordinate axes whose sum is constant.

18. Prove that

$$\left|\int_\lambda A\,dx + B\,dy + C\,dz\right| \leq LM$$

where L is the length of λ and M is an upper bound of $\sqrt{A^2 + B^2 + C^2}$ on λ.

19. For what differentiable functions f, g, and h is the equation

$$f(x + y) = g(x) + h(y) \tag{1}$$

true for all real numbers x and y? We call equation (1) a *functional equation*.
(*Hint:* Compare f_1 and f_2).

Solve each of the following functional equations, assuming appropriate differentiability conditions.

20. $F(xy) = G(x) + H(y)$.

21. $F(x,y) = G(x^2 + y^2) = M(x)N(y)$.

22. $f(x + y) + f(x - y) = 2f(x)f(y)$.

19

MULTIPLE INTEGRATION

THE CONCEPT of an integral of a function of one variable, given in Chapters 7, 8, and 9, may be extended to a function of several variables, as we shall demonstrate in the present chapter. For a function of two or three variables, analogous geometrical and physical applications will be shown to hold for the multiple integral.

1 REPEATED INTEGRALS

Two points $A = (a_1,a_2)$ and $B = (b_1,b_2)$, with $a_1 \leq b_1$ and $a_2 \leq b_2$, determine a rectangle with edges parallel to the coordinate axes, as shown in Figure 19.1. The four points A, (b_1,a_2), B, and (a_1,b_2) are called the *vertices* of this rectangle and the segments joining consecutive vertices are called the *edges*. Let us call the set of all points inside this rectangle an *open rectangle* and denote it by (A,B). Thus

$$(A,B) = \{(x,y) \text{ in } \mathsf{R}^2 \mid a_1 < x < b_1,\ a_2 < y < b_2\}.$$

The set of all points in (A,B) together with the points on the edges of this rectangle is called a *closed rectangle* and is denoted by $[A,B]$. Thus

$$[A,B] = \{(x,y) \text{ in } \mathsf{R}^2 \mid a_1 \leq x \leq b_1,\ a_2 \leq y \leq b_2\}.$$

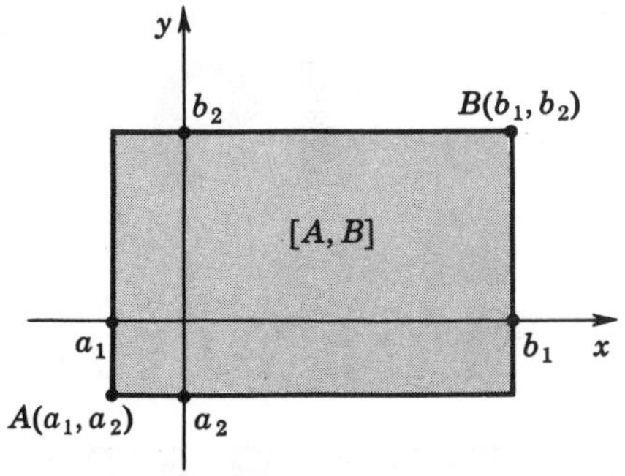

FIGURE 19.1

If f is a continuous function of two variables in a closed rectangle $[A,B]$, where $A = (a_1,a_2)$ and $B = (b_1,b_2)$, then for each number x in the closed interval $[a_1,b_1]$ there is defined a continuous function g of one variable,

$$g(y) = f(x,y), \qquad (y \text{ in } [a_2,b_2]).$$

Hence the integral

$$\int_{a_2}^{b_2} f(x,t)\,dt$$

exists for each x in $[a_1,b_1]$. A basic property of this integral is given below.

19.1 THEOREM. If the function f of two variables is continuous in $[A,B]$, then the function G defined by

$$G(x) = \int_{a_2}^{b_2} f(x,t)\,dt, \qquad \text{domain of } G = [a_1,b_1],$$

is continuous.

Before proving this theorem, we remark that just as a continuous function of one variable in a closed interval is uniformly continuous **(8.19)**, so is a continuous function of two variables in a closed rectangle *uniformly continuous.* That is, if f is continuous in a closed rectangle $[A,B]$, then for every number $\epsilon > 0$ there exists some number $\delta > 0$ such that $|f(P) - f(Q)| < \epsilon$ for all P, Q in $[A,B]$ satisfying $d(P,Q) < \delta$. We shall not prove the uniform continuity of f since the proof is similar to that for functions of one variable.

The proof of **19.1** is as follows. If $a_2 = b_2$, $G(x) = 0$ for each x and G is obviously continuous. So let us assume that $a_2 \neq b_2$. For all x and c in $[a_1,b_1]$, we have

$$|G(x) - G(c)| = \left|\int_{a_2}^{b_2} [f(x,t) - f(c,t)]\,dt\right| \leq (b_2 - a_2)M,$$

where M is the maximum value of $|f(x,t) - f(c,t)|$ for t in $[a_2,b_2]$. By the uniform continuity of f, for each number $\epsilon > 0$ there exists a number $\delta > 0$ such that

$$|f(P) - f(Q)| < \frac{\epsilon}{b_2 - a_2} \quad \text{if } d(P,Q) < \delta, \quad P \text{ and } Q \text{ in } [A,B].$$

If we select x and c so that $|x - c| < \delta$, then $d((x,t), (c,t)) < \delta$ for every t in $[a_2,b_2]$ and hence $|f(x,t) - f(c,t)| < \epsilon/(b_2 - a_2)$. Therefore

$$|G(x) - G(c)| < (b_2 - a_2) \cdot \frac{\epsilon}{b_2 - a_2} = \epsilon \quad \text{if } |x - c| < \delta.$$

This proves that G is continuous at c. Thus **19.1** is proved.

If

$$H(y) = \int_{a_1}^{b_1} f(t,y)\, dt, \qquad \text{domain of } H = [a_2,b_2],$$

then H is continuous by a similar proof.

Since functions G and H defined above are continuous, their integrals exist. We write

$$\int_{a_1}^{b_1} \left(\int_{a_2}^{b_2} f(x,y)\, dy \right) dx \qquad \text{or} \qquad \int_{a_1}^{b_1} dx \int_{a_2}^{b_2} f(x,y)\, dy$$

for $\int_{a_1}^{b_1} G(x)\, dx$ and

$$\int_{a_2}^{b_2} \left(\int_{a_1}^{b_1} f(x,y)\, dx \right) dy \qquad \text{or} \qquad \int_{a_2}^{b_2} dy \int_{a_1}^{b_1} f(x,y)\, dx$$

for $\int_{a_2}^{b_2} H(y)\, dy$. Each of the integrals above is called a *repeated* (or *iterated*) *integral* of f over $[A,B]$. As we shall presently show, these two repeated integrals of f over $[A,B]$ are equal.

EXAMPLE 1. If $f(x,y) = x^2 - 2xy$, find $\int_{-1}^{2} dx \int_{1}^{4} f(x,y)\, dy$.

Solution: In evaluating $\int_1^4 (x^2 - 2xy)\, dy$, we are to assume that x is a constant.

Hence

$$\int_1^4 (x^2 - 2xy)\, dy = (x^2y - xy^2)\Big|_1^4 = (4x^2 - 16x) - (x^2 - x)$$
$$= 3x^2 - 15x,$$

and

$$\int_{-1}^{2} dx \int_1^4 (x^2 - 2xy)\, dy = \int_{-1}^{2} (3x^2 - 15x)\, dx = x^3 - \frac{15}{2}x^2 \Big|_{-1}^{2} = \frac{27}{2}.$$

Before proving the equality of the two repeated integrals, let us generalize **19.1**.

19.2 THEOREM. If the function f of two variables is continuous in $[A,B]$, then the function G of two variables defined by

$$G(x,y) = \int_{a_2}^{y} f(x,t)\,dt$$

is also continuous in $[A,B]$. Similarly, the function H defined by

$$H(x,y) = \int_{a_1}^{x} f(t,y)\,dt$$

is continuous in $[A,B]$.

As in the proof of **19.1**, we might as well assume that $a_2 \neq b_2$. Let M be the maximum value of $|f|$ in $[A,B]$. For every number $\epsilon > 0$ there exists a number δ, with $0 < \delta < \epsilon/2(M+1)$, such that

$$|f(Q) - f(P)| < \frac{\epsilon}{2(b_2 - a_2)} \quad \text{if } d(P,Q) < \delta,\ P \text{ and } Q \text{ in } [A,B].$$

If we think of P as the fixed point (x_0,y_0) and $Q = (x,y)$ as any point in $[A,B]$ such that $d(P,Q) < \delta$, then $d((x,t),(x_0,t)) < \delta$ for every t in $[a_2,b_2]$ and $|y - y_0| < \delta$ so that

$$\begin{aligned}
|G(Q) - G(P)| &= \left|\int_{a_2}^{y} f(x,t)\,dt - \int_{a_2}^{y_0} f(x_0,t)\,dt\right| \\
&\le \left|\int_{a_2}^{y_0} [f(x,t) - f(x_0,t)]\,dt\right| + \left|\int_{y_0}^{y} f(x,t)\,dt\right| \\
&< (y_0 - a_2)\cdot\frac{\epsilon}{2(b_2 - a_2)} + |y - y_0|\cdot M \\
&< \frac{\epsilon}{2} + \delta M < \frac{\epsilon}{2} + \frac{\epsilon}{2} = \epsilon.
\end{aligned}$$

Therefore $|G(Q) - G(P)| < \epsilon$ for every Q in the open disc $B(P,\delta)$. This proves that G is continuous at P. Thus **19.2** is proved.

The question sometimes arises as to how a function defined by an integral such as G in **19.1** should be differentiated. The answer is the expected one given below.

19.3 THEOREM. If f is a function of two variables such that f and $D_1 f$ are continuous in a rectangle $[(a_1,a_2),(b_1,b_2)]$, then

$$D\int_{a_2}^{b_2} f(x,t)\,dt = \int_{a_2}^{b_2} D_1 f(x,t)\,dt.$$

By definition,

$$D\int_{a_2}^{b_2} f(x,t)\,dt = \lim_{h\to 0}\frac{1}{h}\int_{a_2}^{b_2} [f(x+h,t) - f(x,t)]\,dt.$$

Hence, by the mean value theorem (6.5),

$$D \int_{a_2}^{b_2} f(x,t)\, dt = \lim_{h \to 0} \int_{a_2}^{b_2} D_1 f(x + z,t)\, dt,$$

where z is a number between x and $x + h$ which depends on h and t. Since by 19.1 $\int_{a_2}^{b_2} D_1 f(x,t)\, dt$ is a continuous function in x, it is intuitively clear that

$$\lim_{h \to 0} \int_{a_2}^{b_2} D_1 f(x + z,t)\, dt = \int_{a_2}^{b_2} D_1 f(x,t)\, dt.$$

This outlines a proof of **19.3**.

Evidently, a similar result holds for $\int_{a_1}^{b_1} f(t,y)\, dt$.

We are now ready to prove the equality of the repeated integrals.

19.4 THEOREM. If f is a continuous function of two variables in the rectangle $[(a_1,a_2), (b_1,b_2)]$, then

$$\int_{a_1}^{b_1} dx \int_{a_2}^{b_2} f(x,y)\, dy = \int_{a_2}^{b_2} dy \int_{a_1}^{b_1} f(x,y)\, dx.$$

If we let

$$G(t,y) = \int_{a_1}^{t} f(x,y)\, dx \qquad \text{and} \qquad F(t) = \int_{a_2}^{b_2} G(t,y)\, dy,$$

then $F(a_1) = 0$ and

$$F(b_1) = \int_{a_2}^{b_2} dy \int_{a_1}^{b_1} f(x,y)\, dx.$$

By the fundamental theorem of the calculus (**7.19**),

$$D_1 G(t,y) = f(t,y)$$

and, by **19.3**,

$$F'(t) = \int_{a_2}^{b_2} D_1 G(t,y)\, dy = \int_{a_2}^{b_2} f(t,y)\, dy.$$

Hence we have

$$F(b_1) = F(b_1) - F(a_1) = \int_{a_1}^{b_1} F'(x)\, dx = \int_{a_1}^{b_1} dx \int_{a_2}^{b_2} f(x,y)\, dy.$$

This proves **19.4**.

EXERCISES

I

In Exercises 1–2 verify Theorem **19.4** by direct integration of each side of the equation.

1. $\int_{a}^{b} dx \int_{0}^{1} (3x^2 + xy + y^2)\, dy = \int_{0}^{1} dy \int_{a}^{b} (3x^2 + xy + y^2)\, dx.$

2. $\int_1^3 dx \int_1^2 \ln(x+2y)\,dy = \int_1^2 dy \int_1^3 \ln(x+2y)\,dx.$

3. Show that

$$\int_a^b dx \int_c^d [F(x,y) + G(x,y)]\,dy = \int_a^b dx \int_c^d F(x,y)\,dy + \int_a^b dx \int_c^d G(x,y)\,dy.$$

4. Starting with integration formulas for $\int \sin ax\,dx$ and $\int \cos ax\,dx$, use Theorem 19.3 to obtain formulas for $\int x^2 \sin ax\,dx$ and $\int x^2 \cos ax\,dx$.

5. Evaluate $\int e^{ax} \sin bx\,dx$ by assuming that the answer has the form

$$e^{ax}[A \sin bx + B \cos bx] + k$$

and determining the unknown constants A and B.

6. Using Theorem 19.3 and Exercise 5, determine $\int x\,e^{ax} \sin bx\,dx$ and $\int x\,e^{ax} \cos bx\,dx$.

7. Apply Theorem 19.3 to each of the following integration formulas to obtain a new formula. Check your answer by use of the fundamental theorem of the calculus.

a. $\int \frac{1}{t^2 + x^2}\,dt = \frac{1}{x} \tan^{-1} \frac{t}{x}.$

b. $\int (x^2 - t^2)^{-1/2}\,dt = \sin^{-1} \frac{t}{x}.$

c. $\int \frac{1}{t\sqrt{t^2 - x^2}}\,dt = \frac{1}{x} \sec^{-1} \frac{t}{x}.$

d. $\int t^x\,dt = \frac{t^{x+1}}{x+1}.$

8. Starting from $\int e^{xt}\,dt = \frac{e^{xt}}{x} + c$, use Theorem 19.3 to obtain $\int t^n e^{xt}\,dt$ (n integer > 0).

II

1. Show that $\int_0^1 dx \int_0^1 f(x,y)\,dy = -\int_0^1 dy \int_0^1 f(x,y)\,dx = \frac{1}{2}$ (Hardy), where $f(x,y) = (x - y)/(x + y)^3$. Why doesn't Theorem 19.4 apply here?

2 DOUBLE INTEGRALS

Another possible way of considering the integral of a function f of two variables is by the methods of Chapter 7 for functions of one variable. This will lead to the double integral of a function of two variables.

We start by defining what is meant by a partition of a rectangle $[A,B]$. Let us assume in the following that $A = (a_1,a_2)$, $B = (b_1,b_2)$, and $a_1 < b_1$, $a_2 < b_2$. If $\{x_0,x_1, \cdots, x_r\}$ is a partition of $[a_1,b_1]$ and $\{y_0,y_1, \cdots, y_s\}$ is a partition of $[a_2,b_2]$, and if Q_{ij} is the closed rectangle

$$Q_{ij} = [(x_{i-1},y_{j-1}), (x_i,y_j)],$$

then

$$p = \{Q_{ij} \mid i = 1, \cdots, r, j = 1, \cdots, s\}$$

is called a *partition* of rectangle $[A,B]$. Evidently, p consists of rs subrectangles of $[A,B]$, as shown in Figure 19.2, if $r = 4$ and $s = 3$. If we let

$$\Delta x_i = x_i - x_{i-1}, \qquad (i = 1, \cdots, r),$$
$$\Delta y_j = y_j - y_{j-1}, \qquad (j = 1, \cdots, s),$$

then evidently $\Delta x_i \Delta y_j = A(Q_{ij})$, the area of the rectangle Q_{ij}. The length of the longest diagonal of any Q_{ij} of partition p is called the *norm* of p and is denoted by $\|p\|$. Thus $\|p\|$ is the largest of the numbers

$$\sqrt{\Delta x_i^2 + \Delta y_j^2}, \qquad (i = 1, \cdots, r, j = 1, \cdots, s).$$

Clearly, no two points of any subrectangle Q_{ij} of $[A,B]$ are farther apart than $\|p\|$. The norm of a partition of a rectangle will play the same role here as did the norm of a partition of an interval in Chapter 8.

Let f be a continuous function of two variables and $Q = [A,B]$ a rectangle contained in the domain of f. For each partition $p = \{Q_{ij} \mid i = 1, \cdots, r, j = 1, \cdots, s\}$, let us select points T_{ij} and V_{ij} in each Q_{ij} such that $f(T_{ij})$ is the minimum value and $f(V_{ij})$ the maximum value of f in Q_{ij}. Then

$$l(p) = \sum_{i=1}^{r} \sum_{j=1}^{s} f(T_{ij})A(Q_{ij})$$

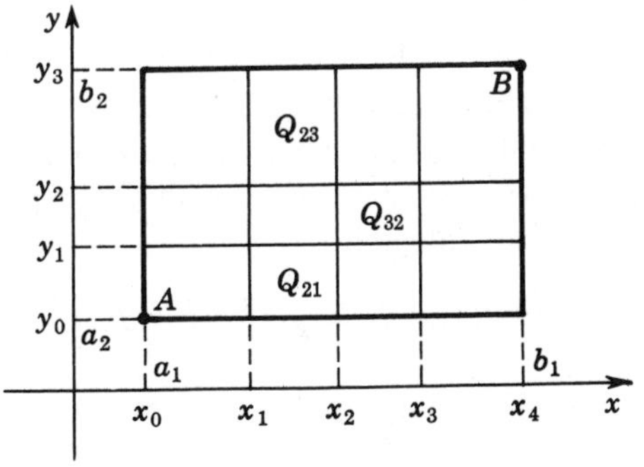

FIGURE 19.2

is called a *lower sum* and

$$u(p) = \sum_{i=1}^{r} \sum_{j=1}^{s} f(V_{ij})A(Q_{ij})$$

is called an *upper sum* of f over Q. If K is the maximum value of f in Q, then each $f(T_{ij}) \leq K$ and

$$l(p) \leq \sum_{i=1}^{r} \sum_{j=1}^{s} KA(Q_{ij}) = KA(Q).$$

Similarly, if k is the minimum value of f in Q, the $u(p) \geq kA(Q)$. Therefore, the set L of all lower sums of f over Q has an upper bound $KA(Q)$ and the set U of all upper sums of f over Q has a lower bound $kA(Q)$. Thus the lower integral $\underline{\int_Q} f$ and the upper integral $\overline{\int_Q} f$ of f over Q can be defined as in **7.10** for functions of one variable:

$$\underline{\int_Q} f = \text{l.u.b. } L, \qquad \overline{\int_Q} f = \text{g.l.b. } U.$$

If the lower integral and the upper integral of f over Q are equal, then their common value is called the *double integral of f over Q* and is denoted by

$$\int_Q f.$$

That the integral of a continuous function exists is given by the following theorem.

19.5 THEOREM. If the function f of two variables is continuous in a closed rectangle $Q = [(a_1,a_2), (b_1,b_2)]$, then $\int_Q f$ exists and

$$\int_Q f = \int_{a_1}^{b_1} dx \int_{a_2}^{b_2} f(x,y)\, dy.$$

The proof of **19.5** is briefly as follows. In the first place, the existence of the double integral $\int_Q f$ follows from uniform continuity in the same way as for functions of one variable (**8.20**). To show that the double integral equals either one of the repeated integrals (which exist by **19.1**), let $p = \{Q_{ij} \mid i = 1, 2, \cdots, r, j = 1, 2, \cdots, s\}$ be a partition of Q, with $Q_{ij} = [(x_{i-1}, y_{j-1}), (x_i,y_j)]$. By the additivity of the ordinary integral,

$$\int_{a_1}^{b_1} dx \int_{a_2}^{b_2} f(x,y)\, dy = \sum_{i=1}^{r} \sum_{j=1}^{s} \int_{x_{i-1}}^{x_i} dx \int_{y_{j-1}}^{y_j} f(x,y)\, dy.$$

Since f is continuous in each Q_{ij}, f assumes a minimum value $f(T_{ij})$ and a maximum value $f(V_{ij})$ in each Q_{ij} (T_{ij} and V_{ij} in Q_{ij}), so that

$$f(T_{ij})\, \Delta x_i\, \Delta y_j \leq \int_{x_{i-1}}^{x_i} dx \int_{y_{j-1}}^{y_j} f(x,y)\, dy \leq f(V_{ij})\, \Delta x_i\, \Delta y_j.$$

Summing on i and j, we get

$$l(p) \leq \int_{a_1}^{b_1} dx \int_{a_2}^{b_2} f(x,y)\, dy \leq u(p)$$

for every partition p of Q. However, $\int_Q f$ is the only number between $l(p)$ and $u(p)$ for every partition p of Q. Therefore, the double integral and the repeated integrals are equal. This proves **19.5**.

It might be pointed out that **19.4** follows from **19.5**, since each repeated integral is equal to $\int_Q f$ by **19.5** and hence the repeated integrals are equal to each other.

Just as an integral of a function of one variable may be given as a limit of a sequence of Riemann sums (**8.16**), so can a double integral of a function of two variables be represented as a limit of a sequence of double sums. Thus, if $p = \{Q_{ij} \mid i = 1, 2, \cdots, r, j = 1, 2, \cdots, s\}$ is a partition of a rectangle Q, then a sum of the form

$$s = \sum_{i=1}^{r} \sum_{j=1}^{s} f(x_i', y_j') A(Q_{ij}),$$

where (x_i', y_j') is any point in Q_{ij}, is called a *Riemann sum* of the function f over Q. For a continuous function f of two variables over a closed rectangle Q, the double integral analogue of **8.16** states that

$$\operatorname*{limit}_{n \to \infty} s_n = \int_Q f,$$

where $s_1, s_2, \cdots, s_n, \cdots$ is a sequence of Riemann sums of f over Q relative to a sequence $p_1, p_2, \cdots, p_n, \cdots$ of partitions of Q for which

$$\operatorname*{limit}_{n \to \infty} \|p_n\| = 0.$$

EXERCISES

I

In each of Exercises 1–4, Q is the rectangle $[(0,0), (4,2)]$ and p_n is the partition of Q into n^2 equivalent rectangles. The numbers l_n and u_n are the lower and upper sums, respectively, of f relative to p_n.

1. If $f(x,y) = 2x + y$, find l_2, l_4, u_2, and u_4. Also find l_n in terms of n, and then find $\int_Q f$.

2. If $f(x,y) = 4 - x - y$, find l_3 and u_3. Also, find u_n in terms of n, and then find $\int_Q f$.

3. If $f(x,y) = x^2 + y$, find l_4 and u_4. Also, find l_n in terms of n, and then find $\int_Q f$.

4. If $f(x,y) = xy$, find l_3 and u_3. Also, find u_n in terms of n, and then find $\int_Q f$.

II

1. If $Q = [(0,0), (1,1)]$ and $f(x,y) = (x - y)/(x + y)^3$ if $(x,y) \neq (0,0)$, with $f(0,0) = 0$, does $\int_Q f$ exist?

3 VOLUME

If the function f of two variables is continuous and nonnegative in a closed rectangle $Q = [(a_1,a_2), (b_1,b_2)]$, then the graph of f and the planes $z = 0$, $x = a_1$, $x = b_1$, $y = a_2$, and $y = b_2$ bound a solid (Figure 19.3):

$$S(f,Q) = \{(x,y,z) \mid (x,y) \text{ in } Q, 0 \leq z \leq f(x,y)\}.$$

The volume of this solid can be found by integration, as we shall show below.

A parallelepiped P in R^3 having its edges parallel to the coordinate axes has volume equal to the product abc of the lengths of the three edges meeting at each vertex (Figure 19.4). In turn, the volume of a solid made up of nonoverlapping parallelepipeds is the sum of the volumes of the individual parallelepipeds.

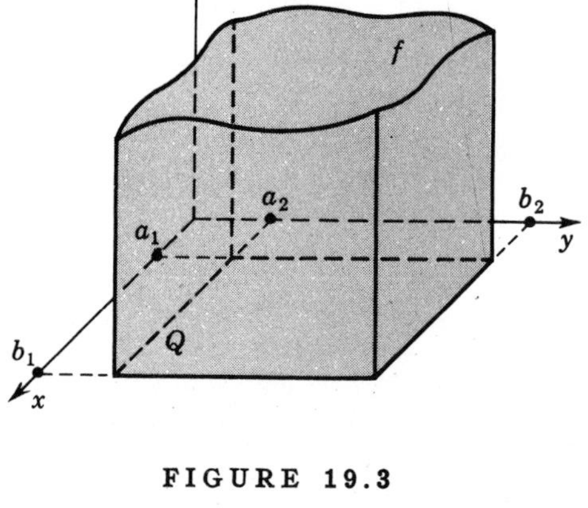

FIGURE 19.3

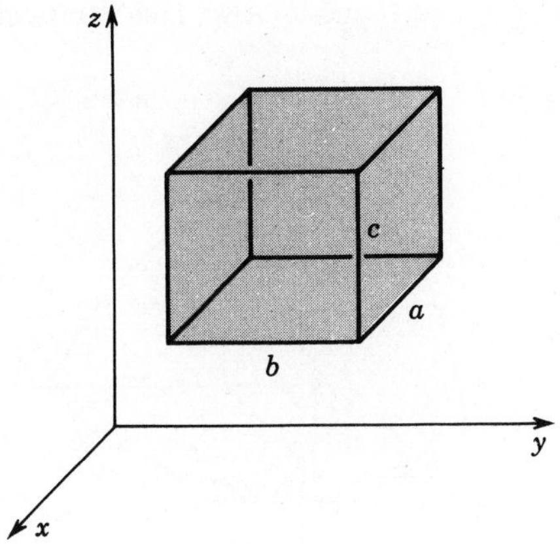

FIGURE 19.4

Each lower sum

$$l = \sum_{i=1}^{r} \sum_{j=1}^{s} f(T_{ij})A(Q_{ij})$$

of f over Q is the volume of a solid made up of rs parallelepipeds and inscribed in $S(f,Q)$ and, similarly, each upper sum u of f over Q is the volume of a solid circumscribing $S(f,Q)$. The volume of solid $S(f,Q)$ is defined to be the l.u.b. of the set L of all lower sums of f over Q, or, equivalently, the g.l.b. of the set U of all upper sums of f over Q. Hence, the solid $S = S(f,Q)$ has volume $V(S)$ defined by

19.6 $$V(S) = \int_Q f.$$

In actually computing the volume of a solid, we use the fact that the double integral equals a repeated integral (**19.5**), as shown in the following example.

EXAMPLE. If $f(x,y) = 4 - \frac{1}{100}(25x^2 + 16y^2)$ and $Q = [(0,0),(2,3)]$, find the volume of solid $S = S(f,Q)$ (Figure 19.5).

Solution: We have

$$V(S) = \int_Q f = \int_0^2 dx \int_0^3 \left[4 - \frac{1}{100}(25x^2 + 16y^2)\right] dy$$

$$= \int_0^2 \left[4y - \frac{1}{4}x^2y - \frac{4}{75}y^3\right]\Bigg|_{y=0}^{y=3} dx$$

$$= \int_0^2 \left(\frac{264}{25} - \frac{3}{4}x^2\right) dx = 19.12.$$

Hence the volume of S is 19.12 cubic units.

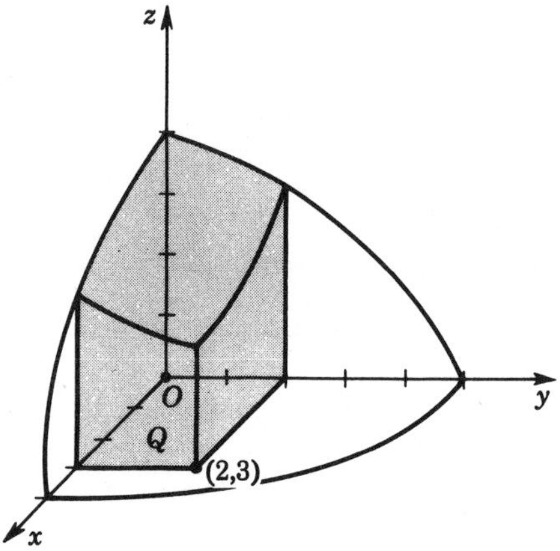

FIGURE 19.5

4 INTEGRALS OVER NONRECTANGULAR REGIONS

If a region T of the plane is bounded by line segments and graphs of smooth functions g_1 and g_2 [assuming $g_1(t) \leq g_2(t)$], as shown in Figures 19.6 or 19.7, then the double integral of each continuous function f over T,

$$\int_T f,$$

may be shown to exist. To evaluate this double integral, we go to repeated integrals as before.

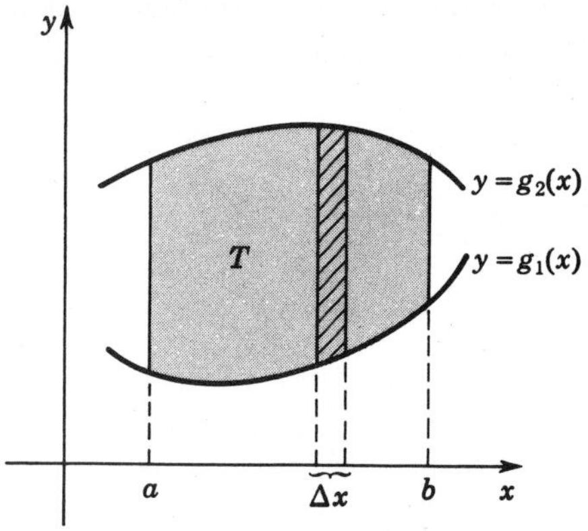

FIGURE 19.6

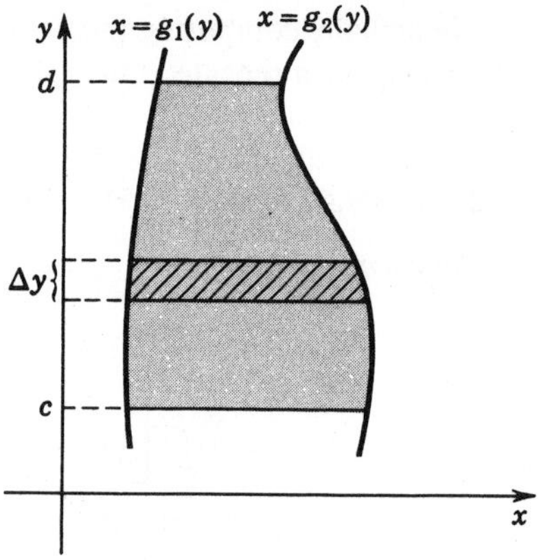

FIGURE 19.7

We may imagine the region T of Figure 19.6 cut into strips parallel to the y axis. A representative strip is shown in the figure. The double integral of f over this strip is approximately equal to

$$\Delta x \int_{g_1(x)}^{g_2(x)} f(x,y)\,dy.$$

The limit (as Δx approaches 0) of the sum of these double integrals for the strips of T between $x = a$ and $x = b$ should give the double integral of f over T; hence it seems reasonable that

19.7 $$\int_T f = \int_a^b dx \int_{g_1(x)}^{g_2(x)} f(x,y)\,dy.$$

If the region T is bounded by the curves $x = g_1(y)$ and $x = g_2(y)$ and by the lines $y = c$ and $y = d$ (Figure 19.7), then a similar intuitive argument leads us to believe that

19.8 $$\int_T f = \int_c^d dy \int_{g_1(y)}^{g_2(y)} f(x,y)\,dx.$$

The informal arguments above for the equality of a double integral and a repeated integral can be made mathematically rigorous, but we shall not attempt to do so at this time. We do mention, however, that the existence of each repeated integral above is assured by the work of Section 1.

EXAMPLE 1. If

$$f(x,y) = \frac{2y - 1}{x + 1},$$

and if the region T is bounded by $x = 0$, $y = 0$, and $2x - y - 4 = 0$, find the double integral of f over T.

Solution: The region T (Figure 19.8) may be thought of as being bounded by the curves $y = 0$ and $y = 2x - 4$ between $x = 0$ and $x = 2$. Hence by **19.7**,

$$\int_T f = \int_0^2 dx \int_{2x-4}^{0} \frac{2y - 1}{x + 1}\,dy = \int_0^2 \frac{y^2 - y}{x + 1}\Bigg|_{y=2x-4}^{y=0} dx$$

$$= -\int_0^2 \frac{4x^2 - 16x + 16 - 2x + 4}{x + 1}\,dx$$

$$= -2\int_0^2 \left(2x - 11 + \frac{21}{x + 1}\right) dx$$

$$= -2(x^2 - 11x + 21 \ln (x + 1))\Big|_0^2 = -6(7 \ln 3 - 6).$$

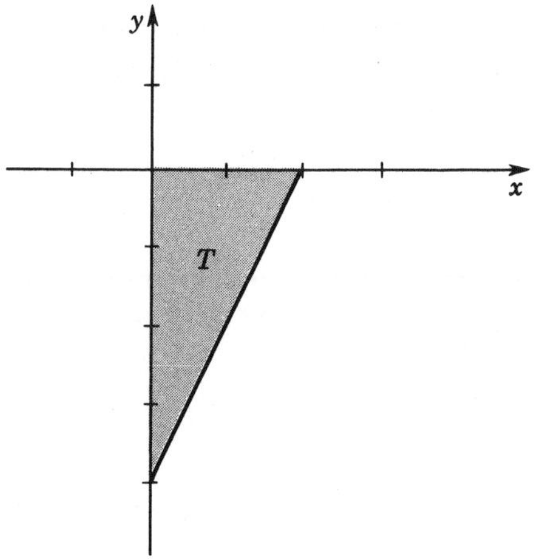

FIGURE 19.8

We could think of the region T as being bounded by the curves $x = 0$ and $x = (y + 4)/2$ between $y = -4$ and $y = 0$, in which case (by **19.8**)

$$\int_T f = \int_{-4}^{0} dy \int_0^{(y+4)/2} \frac{2y-1}{x+1}\,dx$$

$$= \int_{-4}^{0} (2y-1)\ln(x+1)\Big|_{x=0}^{x=(y+4)/2} dy$$

$$= \int_{-4}^{0} (2y-1)\ln\frac{y+6}{2}\,dy,$$

and so on. It is clear that the integration is easier in the first case.

If the continuous function f is nonnegative in a region T, then the double integral $\int_T f$ can be interpreted as the volume of a cylindrical solid S having region T as its base, generators parallel to the z axis, and the graph of f as its top just as before when T was a rectangle. In the particular case that $f(x,y) = 1$ for all x and y, $\int_T f$ is the area of region T. Some examples are given below.

EXAMPLE 2. Find the area of the region T bounded by the parabolas $y = x^2$ and $y = 4 - x^2$ (Figure 19.9).

Solution: Using **19.7**, we have the area given by

$$\int_T 1 = \int_{-\sqrt{2}}^{\sqrt{2}} dx \int_{x^2}^{4-x^2} dy = \int_{-\sqrt{2}}^{\sqrt{2}} (4 - x^2 - x^2)\,dx = \frac{16}{3}\sqrt{2}.$$

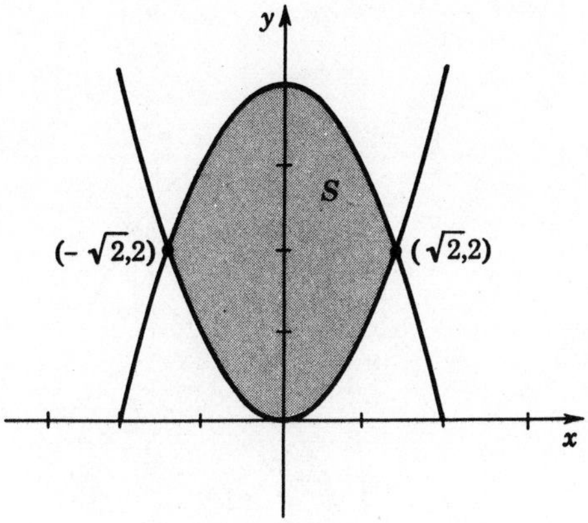

FIGURE 19.9

EXAMPLE 3. Find the volume of the solid S under the surface

$$z = 4 - x^2 - 4y^2$$

and above the region T of the xy plane bounded by $x = 0$, $y = 0$, and $x + 2y - 2 = 0$ (Figure 19.10).

Solution: The volume $V(S)$ of this solid is given by

$$V(S) = \int_T z.$$

Using **19.8**, we evaluate this double integral by a repeated integral

$$V(S) = \int_0^1 dy \int_0^{2-2y} (4 - x^2 - 4y^2)\, dx.$$

For a given y the inner integral

$$\int_0^{2-2y} (4 - x^2 - 4y^2)\, dx = 8(1 - y) - \frac{8}{3}(1 - y)^3 - 8y^2 + 8y^3$$

is the area of a section of the solid S parallel to the xz plane, as indicated in Figure 19.10. Then the volume can be interpreted as the sum of the volumes of all slices between $y = 0$ and $y = 1$. Continuing the integration, we obtain

$$V(S) = \int_0^1 \left[8(1 - y) - \frac{8}{3}(1 - y)^3 - 8y^2 + 8y^3 \right] dy = \frac{8}{3}.$$

EXAMPLE 4. Find the volume of the solid S under the plane $z = x + 2y$ and over the quarter-circle of radius 2 in the first quadrant of the xy plane (Figure 19.11).

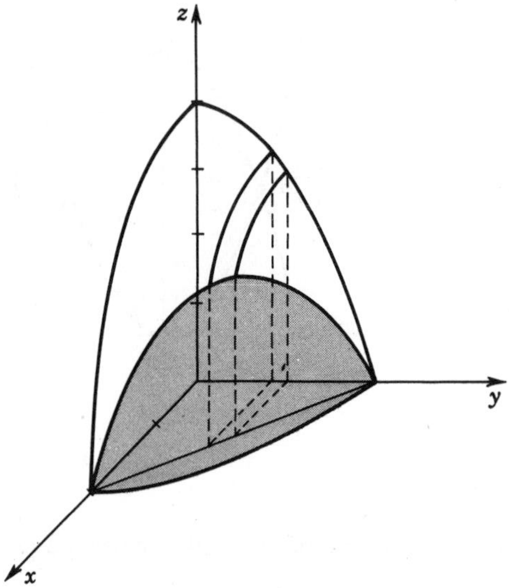

FIGURE 19.10

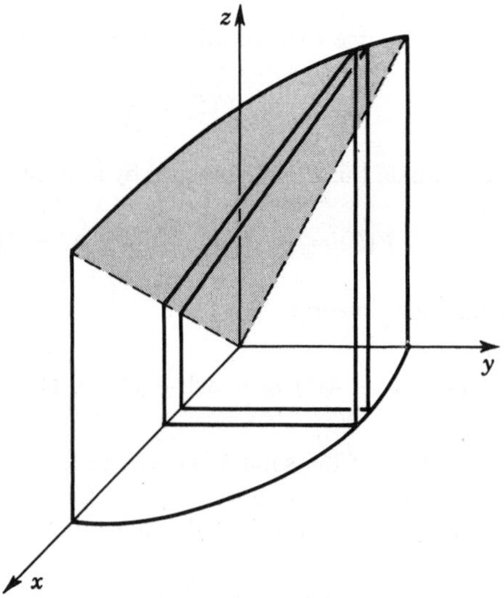

FIGURE 19.11

Solution: The quarter-circle may be described as the region T bounded by the curves $y = 0$ and $y = \sqrt{4 - x^2}$ between $x = 0$ and $x = 2$. Hence the volume of solid S under the plane $z = x + 2y$ and above T is given by **19.7**,

$$V(S) = \int_0^2 dx \int_0^{\sqrt{4-x^2}} (x + 2y)\, dy$$

$$= \int_0^2 (x\sqrt{4 - x^2} + 4 - x^2)\, dx = \left[-\frac{1}{3}(4 - x^2)^{3/2} + 4x - \frac{1}{3}x^3 \right]\Bigg|_0^2 = 8.$$

Again the inner integral is the area of a section of S, this time parallel to the yz plane, as indicated in Figure 19.11, and the outer integral sums up the volumes of the slices from $x = 0$ to $x = 2$.

EXERCISES

I

In each of Exercises 1–10, by the use of repeated integrals, find the double integral of the function over the given region S of the plane, and sketch the region S.

1. $f(x,y) = 2x - y + 4$; S bounded by $x = 1$, $x = 4$, $y = -1$, $y = 2$.
2. $g(x,y) = 3x - y + 2xy$; S bounded by $x = -2$, $x = 0$, $y = 0$, $y = 3$.
3. $F(x,y) = y \sin x - xe^y$; S bounded by $x = \frac{\pi}{2}$, $x = 0$, $y = -1$, $y = 1$.
4. $G(x,y) = \dfrac{y^2}{1 + x^2}$; S bounded by $x = -1$, $x = 1$, $y = 0$, $y = 2$.
5. $g(x,y) = 3x - y + 1$; S bounded by $x = 0$, $y = 0$, $x + 3y - 3 = 0$.
6. $f(x,y) = 2x + 2y - 1$; S bounded by $x = y$, $x + y - 4 = 0$, $x = 0$.
7. $G(x,y) = xy - x^2 + 1$; S bounded by $x - 2y + 2 = 0$, $x + 3y - 3 = 0$, $y = 0$.
8. $F(x,y) = 2x^2y - x + 3$; S bounded by $3y = x$, $x + y - 4 = 0$, $y = -1$.
9. $f(x,y) = \dfrac{2y - 1}{x^2 + 1}$; S bounded by $y = 4 - x^2$, $y = 0$.
10. $g(x,y) = 2xy - 3x^2$; S bounded by $y = \ln |x|$, $y = 0$, $y = -2$.

In each of Exercises 11–16, by the use of repeated integrals find the area of the region bounded by the given curves.

11. $x = y^2$, $x - y - 2 = 0$.
12. $y = x^3 - x$, $x = -1$, $2x + y - 2 = 0$.

13. $y = \sin \pi x$, $y = x^2 - x$.

14. $y = \ln x$, $2x + y - 2 = 0$, $y = 2$.

15. $y = |x|$, $4y = 4x^2 + 1$.

16. $x^2 + 4y^2 = 16$, $x^2 = 12y$ (smaller region).

17. Find the volume of the solid under the plane $z = 2x + y + 1$ and above the region bounded by $x = 0$, $y = 0$, and $x + 3y - 3 = 0$. Sketch the solid, and describe an alternate way of finding its volume.

18. Find the volume of the solid under the plane $x - z + y + 2 = 0$ and above the region bounded by $y = x$, $x + 2y = 2$, and $y = 1$. Sketch.

19. Find the volume of the solid under the plane $z = 3x + y$ and above the part of the ellipse $4x^2 + 9y^2 = 36$ in the first quadrant. Sketch.

20. Find the volume of the solid under the plane $z = 2x + y + 10$ and above the circle $x^2 + y^2 = 16$. Sketch.

21. Find the volume of the solid under the plane $z = 2y$ and above the region bounded by $y = x^2$, $y = 0$, and $x = 2$. Sketch.

22. Find the volume of the solid in the first octant bounded by the cylinder $y^2 + z^2 = 4$, the plane $y = x$, and the xy plane. Sketch.

23. Find the volume of the solid in the first octant bounded by the paraboloid $z = 16 - x^2 - 4y^2$. Sketch.

24. Find the volume of the solid in the first octant bounded by the cylinder $z = x^2$ and the planes $x = 2y$ and $x = 2$. Sketch.

25. Find the volume of the solid in the first octant bounded by the cylinder $x^2 + y^2 = 9$ and the planes $y = 0$, $z = 0$, $z = x$. Sketch.

26. Find the volume of the solid in the first octant bound by the two cylinders $z = 4 - x^2$ and $y = 4 - x^2$. Sketch.

In each of Exercises 27–32 describe and sketch the solid whose volume is given by the repeated integral, and find each volume.

27. $\int_0^2 dx \int_0^3 x\, dy$.

28. $\int_1^3 dy \int_1^4 (2 + x + y)\, dx$.

29. $\int_0^r dy \int_0^y \sqrt{r^2 - y^2}\, dx$.

30. $\int_0^1 dx \int_{-3x}^{\sqrt{1-x^2}} (3x + y)\, dy$.

31. $\int_0^2 dx \int_0^{\sqrt{4-x^2}} (x^2 + 4y^2)\, dy$.

32. $\int_0^2 dy \int_{2-y}^{2y+2} (x^2 + 4y^2)\, dx$.

II

1. Set up a repeated integral for the volume of the ellipsoid $x^2/a^2 + y^2/b^2 + z^2/c^2 = 1$.

2. Show that the volume V of the solid bounded by the graph of the equation $\sqrt{x/a} + \sqrt{y/b} + \sqrt{z/c} = 1$ and the coordinate planes is given by $V = abc/90$.

3. Show that the volume V of the solid bounded by the graph of the equation $x^{2/3} + y^{2/3} + z^{2/3} = a^{2/3}$ is given by $V = \pi a^3/35$.

4. Use repeated integrals to find the volume of the solid common to two right circular cylinders of radius r whose axes intersect orthogonally. (*Note:* This has been done by a single integration in Example 3, page 258.)

5. Use repeated integrals to find the volume of the solid common to three right circular cylinders of radius r whose axes are mutually orthogonal and concurrent.

6. Prove that

$$\int_0^a dx \int_0^x F(x,y)\,dy = \int_0^a dy \int_y^a F(x,y)\,dx,$$

assuming that F is continuous.

7. Using Exercise 6, show that

$$\int_0^a dx \int_0^x G(y)\,dy = \int_0^a (a-y)G(y)\,dy,$$

and, generally,

$$\int_0^a dx_1 \int_0^{x_1} dx_2 \cdots \int_0^{x_{n-1}} dx_n \int_0^{x_n} G(y)\,dy = \frac{1}{n!}\int_0^a (a-y)^n G(y)\,dy \qquad \text{(Dirichlet).}$$

5 POLAR COORDINATES

Let us show in this section how a double integral over a region of a polar coordinate plane can be defined and represented as a repeated integral.

Let S be the region on a polar coordinate plane bounded by the lines $\theta = \alpha$ and $\theta = \beta$ and by the circles $r = a$ and $r = b$. The region S may be divided into mn subregions by a partition

$$p = \{S_{ij} \mid i = 1, 2, \cdots, n, j = 1, 2, \cdots, m\},$$

where the i,jth subregion S_{ij} of p is bounded by the lines $\theta = \theta_{i-1}$ and $\theta = \theta_i$ and by the circles $r = r_{j-1}$ and $r = r_j$ (Figure 19.12). The area $A(S_{ij})$ of S_{ij} is given by

$$A(S_{ij}) = \tfrac{1}{2}\,\Delta\theta_i(r_j^2 - r_{j-1}^2) = \bar{r}_j\,\Delta r_j\,\Delta\theta_i,$$

where $\Delta\theta_i = \theta_i - \theta_{i-1}$, $\Delta r_j = r_j - r_{j-1}$, and $\bar{r}_j = (r_{j-1} + r_j)/2$.

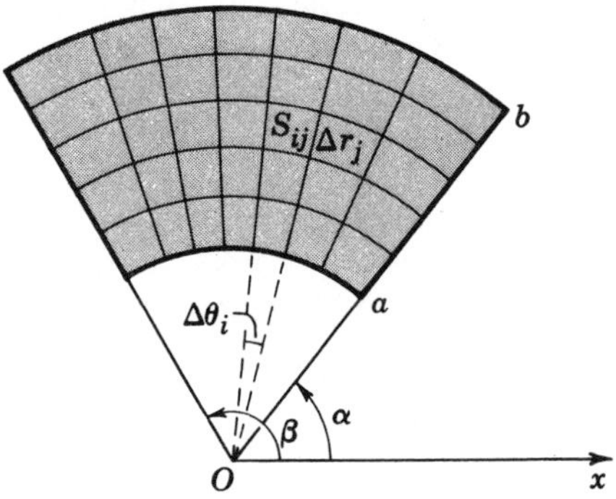

FIGURE 19.12

If f is a continuous function of two variables in S, then relative to a partition p of S we can define a Riemann sum s_p of f as follows:

$$s_p = \sum_{i=1}^{n}\sum_{j=1}^{m} f(r_j',\theta_i')\bar{r}_j\,\Delta r_j\,\Delta\theta_i,$$

where (r_j',θ_i') is any point of S_{ij}. By taking a sequence of partitions of S with norms approaching 0, the limit of the corresponding sequence of Riemann sums of f will be the double integral of f over S, just as for a rectangular coordinate plane. In turn, this double integral of f over S may be shown to equal a repeated integral having one of two possible forms:

19.9 $$\int_S f = \int_\alpha^\beta d\theta \int_a^b f(r,\theta)r\,dr = \int_a^b dr \int_\alpha^\beta f(r,\theta)r\,d\theta.$$

Note that the integrand in each repeated integral is not just $f(r,\theta)$, but r times $f(r,\theta)$.

The double integral of a continuous function f of two variables can be defined over regions of the polar coordinate plane other than the ones described above. If, for example, the region S is bounded by the graphs of the smooth curves $r = g_1(\theta)$ and $r = g_2(\theta)$ and by the lines $\theta = \alpha$ and $\theta = \beta$ (Figure 19.13), where $g_1(\theta) \leq g_2(\theta)$ in $[\alpha,\beta]$, then it may be shown that the double integral of f over S exists and equals a repeated integral as follows:

19.10 $$\int_S f = \int_\alpha^\beta d\theta \int_{g_1(\theta)}^{g_2(\theta)} f(r,\theta)r\,dr.$$

If the region S is bounded by the smooth curves $\theta = h_1(r)$ and $\theta = h_2(r)$ and by the circles $r = a$ and $r = b$, as in Figure 19.14, where $h_1(r) \leq h_2(r)$ in $[a,b]$, then

19.11 $$\int_S f = \int_a^b dr \int_{h_1(r)}^{h_2(r)} f(r,\theta)r\,d\theta.$$

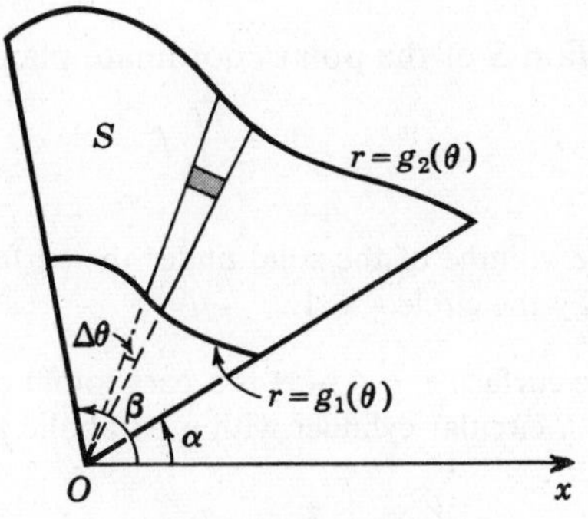

FIGURE 19.13

We may figure out which of the above evaluations of a double integral of f over a region S to use by a device similar to that used for a rectangular coordinate plane. Thus, if we can cut S into strips by lines drawn through the pole, then

$$\Delta\theta \int_{g_1(\theta)}^{g_2(\theta)} f(r,\theta)r\,dr$$

is approximately equal to the double integral of f over the strip at θ (shown in Figure 19.13), where $g_1(\theta)$ and $g_2(\theta)$ are the values of r at each end of the strip. On summing up the double integrals over all the strips and taking a limit, we obtain **19.10**.

If the region S can be cut into strips by circles with centers at the pole, as in Figure 19.14, then the double integral of f over S will be evaluated by **19.11**. In many examples either **19.10** or **19.11** may be used.

The double integral of a function f over a region S of a polar coordinate plane may be interpreted as a volume of a solid in a cylindrical coordinate space. Thus it may be shown that the volume of the solid under the surface

$$z = f(r,\theta)$$

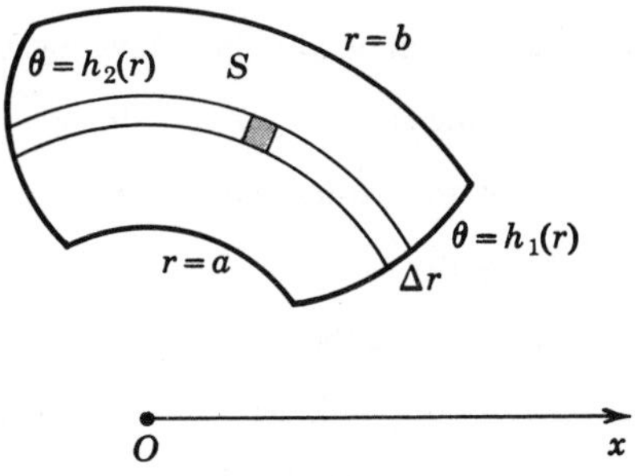

FIGURE 19.14

and above the region S of the polar coordinate plane is given by

$$V = \int_S f.$$

EXAMPLE 1. Find the volume of the solid under the surface $z = 4 - r^2$ and above the region S bounded by the circle $r = 1$.

Solution: The surface $z = 4 - r^2$ is a paraboloid of revolution about the z axis, so that the solid is a circular cylinder with a parabolic top. Its volume is given by

$$\begin{aligned} V &= \int_S z \\ &= \int_0^1 dr \int_0^{2\pi} (4 - r^2)r\, d\theta \\ &= 2\pi \int_0^1 (4r - r^3)\, dr = \frac{7}{2}\pi. \end{aligned}$$

EXAMPLE 2. Find the volume of the solid bounded by the cylinder $r = 2\cos\theta$, the cone $z = r$, $(r \geq 0)$, and the plane $z = 0$.

Solution: The solid in question is under the surface $z = r$, $(r \geq 0)$, and above the circular region S bounded by $r = 2\cos\theta$. If we imagine the region S cut into strips by lines through the pole, then we may evaluate the volume of this solid as follows:

$$V = \int_S z = \int_{-\pi/2}^{\pi/2} d\theta \int_0^{2\cos\theta} r^2\, dr = \frac{8}{3}\int_{-\pi/2}^{\pi/2} \cos^3\theta\, d\theta = \frac{32}{9}.$$

EXERCISES

I

Find the volume of the solid bounded by the following surfaces.

1. The cylinder $r = 2$ and the sphere $z^2 + r^2 = 9$.
2. The cylinder $r = 2\sin\theta$, the paraboloid $z = 4 - r^2$, and the plane $z = 0$.
3. The ellipsoid $z^2 + 4r^2 = 4$.
4. The ellipsoid $z^2 + 4r^2 = 4$ and the cylinder $r = \cos\theta$.
5. The cone $z = 2r$, $(r \geq 0)$, the cylinder $r = 1 - \cos\theta$, and the plane $z = 0$.
6. The cylinder $r = 1 + \cos\theta$, and the planes $z = r\cos\theta$ and $z = 0$, in the first octant.

II

1. Find the volume of the solid drilled out of a sphere of radius R by a bit of radius a if the axis of the bit passes through the center of the sphere.

2. If $I = \int_0^x e^{-t^2}\,dt$, show that

$$\tfrac{1}{4}\pi(1 - e^{-x^2}) < I^2 < \tfrac{1}{4}\pi(1 - e^{-2x^2})$$

by expressing I^2 as a double integral. Then show that

$$\int_0^\infty e^{-t^2}\,dt = \frac{\sqrt{\pi}}{2}.$$

3. Using the results and ideas of Exercise 2, show that

$$\frac{d}{da}\int_0^\infty e^{-a^2t^2}\,dt = \int_0^\infty \frac{\partial}{\partial a} e^{-a^2t^2}\,dt = -2a\int_0^\infty t^2\,e^{-a^2t^2}\,dt = \frac{d}{da}\frac{\sqrt{\pi}}{2a}.$$

6 CENTER OF MASS OF A LAMINA

Single integrals were used in Chapter 13 to find the center of mass of a homogeneous lamina. We shall now employ double integrals to find the center of mass of any lamina, whether or not it is homogeneous.

Let a given lamina have the shape of region S in a rectangular coordinate plane, and let ρ be the density function of the lamina. Thus ρ is a continuous function of two variables in S, and the mass of any piece of the lamina of area ΔS lies between $\rho_m\,\Delta S$ and $\rho_M\,\Delta S$, where ρ_m is the minimum value and ρ_M is the maximum value of ρ in the piece. It is clear by the usual arguments that the mass W of the lamina is given by

$$W = \int_S \rho.$$

The moment of a piece of the lamina about the x axis is between $y_m\rho_m\,\Delta S$ and $y_M\rho_M\,\Delta S$, where y_m is the minimum and y_M the maximum y coordinate of any point in the piece, and ρ and ΔS are as described above. Hence the moment about the x axis of the whole lamina is given by

$$M_x = \int_S y\rho,$$

and, similarly, its moment about the y axis is

$$M_y = \int_S x\rho.$$

The center of mass of the lamina is the point $(\bar{x},\bar{y})$, where

$$\bar{x} = \frac{M_y}{W}, \qquad \bar{y} = \frac{M_x}{W}.$$

Each of the double integrals above may be evaluated by a repeated integral. We illustrate the method in the following examples.

EXAMPLE 1. Find the center of mass of a homogeneous lamina (of constant density ρ) having the shape of the region bounded by the parabola $y = 2 - 3x^2$ and the line $3x + 2y - 1 = 0$ (Figure 19.15).

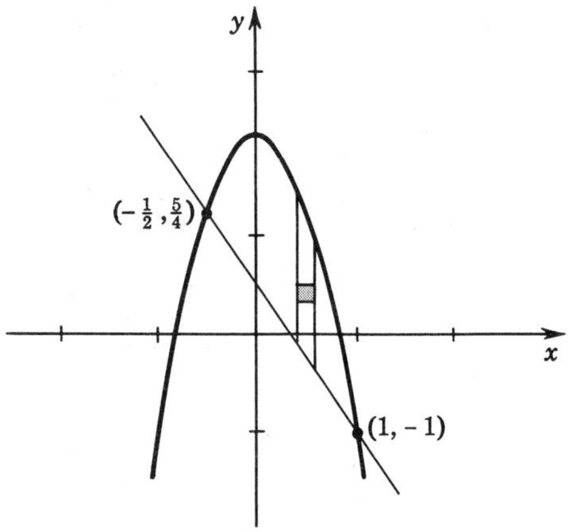

FIGURE 19.15

Solution: It is easily verified that the parabola and the line meet at the points $(-\frac{1}{2},\frac{5}{4})$ and $(1,-1)$. Integrating first with respect to y, we have

$$W = \int_{-1/2}^{1} dx \int_{(1-3x)/2}^{2-3x^2} \rho\, dy = \rho \int_{-1/2}^{1} \left[2 - 3x^2 - \frac{1}{2}(1 - 3x)\right] dx = \frac{27}{16}\rho,$$

$$M_x = \int_{-1/2}^{1} dx \int_{(1-3x)/2}^{2-3x^2} \rho y\, dy = \frac{\rho}{2} \int_{-1/2}^{1} \left[(2 - 3x^2)^2 - \frac{1}{4}(1 - 3x)^2\right] dx = \frac{27}{20}\rho,$$

$$M_y = \int_{-1/2}^{1} dx \int_{(1-3x)/2}^{2-3x^2} \rho x\, dy = \rho \int_{-1/2}^{1} \left[2x - 3x^3 - \frac{1}{2}(x - 3x^2)\right] dx = \frac{27}{64}\rho.$$

Hence $\bar{x} = M_y/W = \frac{1}{4}$, $\bar{y} = M_x/W = \frac{4}{5}$, and the center of mass of the lamina is the point $(\frac{1}{4},\frac{4}{5})$.

EXAMPLE 2. Find the center of mass of a rectangular lamina $ABCD$ if the density of the lamina at any point P is the product of the distances of P from AB and BC.

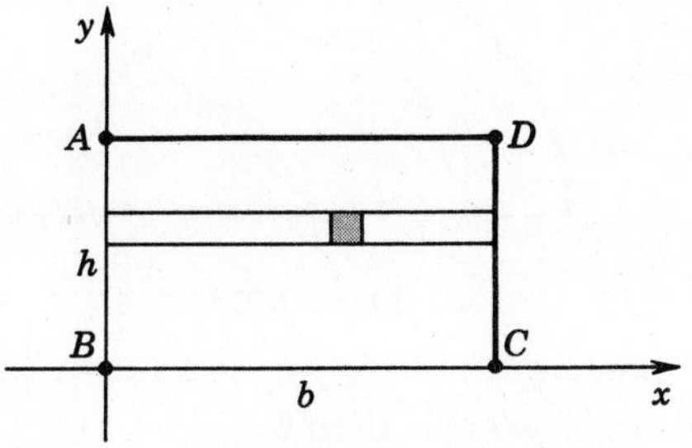

FIGURE 19.16

Solution: Let us choose coordinate axes as in Figure 19.16. By assumption, the density $\rho(x,y)$ at point (x,y) is given by

$$\rho(x,y) = xy.$$

Hence

$$W = \int_0^h dy \int_0^b xy\,dx = \frac{b^2}{2}\int_0^h y\,dy = \frac{b^2h^2}{4},$$

$$M_x = \int_0^h dy \int_0^b xy^2\,dx = \frac{b^2}{2}\int_0^h y^2\,dy = \frac{b^2h^3}{6},$$

$$M_y = \int_0^h dy \int_0^b x^2y\,dx = \frac{b^3}{3}\int_0^h y\,dy = \frac{b^3h^2}{6}.$$

Hence $(\bar{x},\bar{y}) = (\frac{2}{3}b,\frac{2}{3}h)$ is the center of mass.

The formulas for W, M_x, and M_y hold for a polar coordinate system, M_x being the moment of the lamina about the polar axis and M_y being the moment of the lamina about the line perpendicular to the polar axis at the pole. Thus, for a lamina having the shape of a region S of the polar coordinate plane and density function ρ,

$$W = \int_S \rho, \qquad M_x = \int_S \rho\, r \sin\theta, \qquad M_y = \int_S \rho\, r\cos\theta.$$

These integrals are equal to certain repeated integrals, as shown in the previous section.

EXAMPLE 3. Find the center of mass of a semicircular lamina if the density of the lamina at any point P is proportional to the distance between P and the center of the circle.

Solution: Let us choose a polar coordinate system as in Figure 19.17, with the semicircle having equation

$$r = a, \qquad (0 \le \theta \le \pi).$$

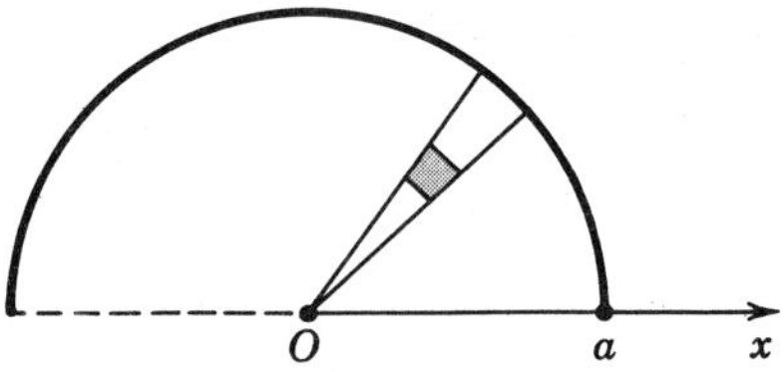

FIGURE 19.17

The density $\rho(r,\theta)$ at point (r,θ) is given by

$$\rho(r,\theta) = kr$$

for some constant k. Hence (by **19.10**)

$$W = \int_0^\pi d\theta \int_0^a (kr)r\,dr = \frac{ka^3}{3}\int_0^\pi d\theta = \frac{\pi ka^3}{3},$$

$$M_x = \int_0^\pi d\theta \int_0^a (kr)(r\sin\theta)r\,dr = \frac{ka^4}{4}\int_0^\pi \sin\theta\,d\theta = \frac{ka^4}{2},$$

$$M_y = \int_0^\pi d\theta \int_0^a (kr)(r\cos\theta)r\,dr = \frac{ka^4}{4}\int_0^\pi \cos\theta\,d\theta = 0.$$

and $(0,3a/2\pi)$ in rectangular coordinates, or $(3a/2\pi,\pi/2)$ in polar coordinates, is the center of mass.

EXERCISES

I

In each of Exercises 1–10, find the center of mass of a lamina having density function ρ and the shape of a region bounded by the given curves. Sketch each region.

1. $y = \sqrt{x}$, $y = 0$, $x = 4$; ρ a positive constant.
2. $y = \sqrt{x}$, $y = 0$, $x = 4$; $\rho(x,y) = x + y$.
3. $y = 0$, $y = h$, $x = 0$, $x = b$; $\rho(x,y) = kx$, h, b, k, positive constants.
4. $y = \ln x$, $y = 0$, $x = e$; $\rho(x,y) = y$.
5. $r = a$, $\theta = 0$, $\theta = \frac{1}{2}\pi$; $\rho(r,\theta) = \theta$, a a positive constant.
6. $r = 1 + \cos\theta$, $\theta = 0$, $\theta = \frac{1}{2}\pi$; $\rho(r,\theta) = r\sin\theta$.
7. $x^2 - y^2 = 1$, $x = 3$; $\rho(x,y) = x$.
8. $y = \sin x$, $y = 0$, $x = 0$, $x = \pi$; $\rho(x,y) = ky$, k a positive constant.

9. $r = \cos 2\theta$, $\theta = -\frac{1}{4}\pi$, $\theta = \frac{1}{4}\pi$; $\rho(r,\theta) = r$.

10. $r = \cos 2\theta$, $\theta = 0$, $\theta = \frac{1}{4}\pi$; $\rho(r,\theta) = r\theta$.

11. The density at a point P of a triangular lamina with base of length b and altitude h is proportional to the distance of P from the base. Find the distance from the base to the center of mass of the lamina.

12. A lamina has the shape of the region cut off from a parabola by its latus rectum. If the density at point P of the lamina is proportional to the distance of P from the latus rectum, find the center of mass of the lamina.

13. The density of a semicircular lamina at any point P is proportional to the square of the distance of P from the center of the circle. Find the center of mass of the lamina.

14. The density of a lamina in the shape of a quarter of an ellipse (bounded by the semimajor and semiminor axes) at any point P equals the sum of its distances from the axes. Find the center of mass of the lamina.

II

In Exercises 1 and 2, find the center of mass of a lamina having density function ρ and the shape of a region bounded by the given curves. Sketch each region.

1. $\sqrt{x} + \sqrt{y} = \sqrt{a}$, $x = 0$, $y = 0$; $\rho(x,y) = xy$.

2. $x^{2/3} + y^{2/3} = a^{2/3}$, $x = 0$, $y = 0$; $\rho(x,y) = x^2y^2$.

3. Describe a lamina whose moment about the polar axis is given by

$$M_x = \int_\alpha^\beta d\theta \int_c^{(a^4\cos^4\theta + b^4\sin^4\theta)^{-1/4}} \sin 2\theta\, dr.$$

4. Evaluate the double integrals

a. $\int_S x^2$, b. $\int_S x^4y^3$, c. $\int_S x^2y^2$, d. $\int_S x^4$,

over the closed disc $S = \{(x,y) \mid x^2 + y^2 \leq a^2\}$ by using the symmetry properties of the circle. $\left(Hint\text{: } \int_S x^2 = \int_S y^2.\right)$

7 MOMENTS OF INERTIA

If a particle of mass m is d units from a line L (Figure 19.18), then the number md^2 is called the *moment of inertia* of the particle about L. The moment of a particle studied in Section 6 is frequently called the *first moment*, and the moment of inertia the *second moment*, of the particle about L.

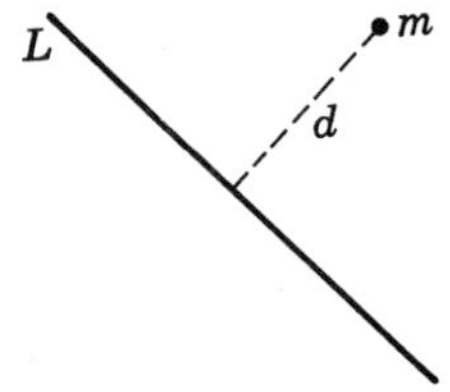

FIGURE 19.18

A system of n particles of masses $m_1, m_2, \cdots, m_n$ and at distances $d_1, d_2, \cdots, d_n$ units, respectively, from a line L has a moment of inertia I defined as the sum of the moments of the individual particles:

$$I = \sum_{i=1}^{n} m_i d_i^2.$$

It is clear that by our usual limiting process the moment of inertia of a lamina having the shape of a plane region S and density function ρ can be found about any line L. In particular, it is clear that the moments of inertia I_x and I_y of the lamina about the x and y axes, respectively, are given by

$$I_x = \int_S \rho y^2, \qquad I_y = \int_S \rho x^2.$$

EXAMPLE 1. Find I_x and I_y for the homogeneous lamina having the shape of the region S bounded by the curve $y = \sqrt{x}$ and by the lines $y = 0$ and $x = 4$ (Figure 19.19).

Solution: Since ρ is a constant by assumption, we have

$$I_x = \int_S \rho y^2 = \int_0^4 dx \int_0^{\sqrt{x}} \rho y^2\, dy = \frac{\rho}{3} \int_0^4 x^{3/2}\, dx = \frac{64}{15} \rho,$$

$$I_y = \int_S \rho x^2 = \int_0^4 dx \int_0^{\sqrt{x}} \rho x^2\, dy = \rho \int_0^4 x^{5/2}\, dx = \frac{256}{7} \rho.$$

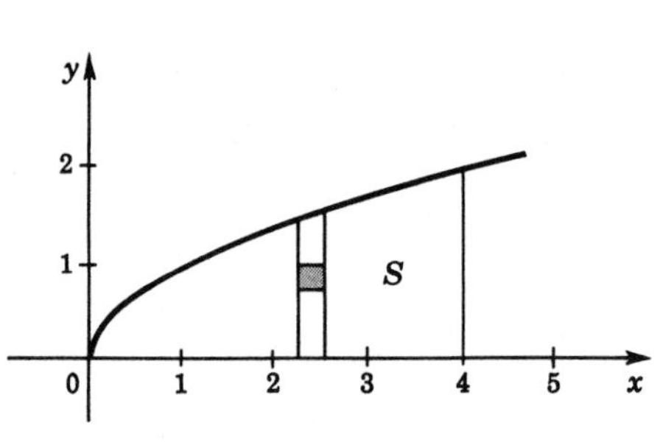

FIGURE 19.19

The physical meaning of the moment of inertia is to be found in the study of the *kinetic energy* of a moving particle. A particle of mass m moving at a speed v has kinetic energy

$$K = \tfrac{1}{2}mv^2.$$

If a particle of mass m at a distance of d units from a line L is rotating about L with an angular velocity of ω radians per unit of time, then $|\omega d|$ is the speed of the particle and

$$K = \tfrac{1}{2}m(\omega d)^2 = \tfrac{1}{2}I\omega^2$$

is its kinetic energy, where I is the moment of inertia of the particle. Noting the similarity between $\frac{1}{2}I\omega^2$ and $\frac{1}{2}mv^2$, we can say that I is the "rotation mass" of the particle. Similarly, if I is the moment of inertia of a system of particles about L, then $\frac{1}{2}I\omega^2$ is again the kinetic energy of the system when rotated about L with an angular velocity of ω.

A lamina (or system of particles) of total mass m and moment of inertia I about a line L has *radius of gyration d* defined by the equation

$$I = md^2.$$

Accordingly, a particle of mass m located d units from L has the same moment of inertia as the given lamina; i.e., in computing the moment of inertia of the lamina, the mass of the lamina may be considered to be concentrated at a point d units from L.

EXAMPLE 2. Find the radius of gyration of a semicircular lamina about its diameter, if the density of the lamina at a point is proportional to the distance of the point from the diameter.

Solution: If we select the coordinate axes as in Figure 19.20, the density of the lamina at point (x,y) is given by $\rho(x,y) = ky$, (k a positive constant). Evidently,

$$I_x = \int_S \rho y^2 = \int_{-a}^{a} dx \int_0^{\sqrt{a^2-x^2}} ky^3\,dy = \frac{k}{4}\int_{-a}^{a} (a^2 - x^2)^2\,dx = \frac{4}{15}ka^5.$$

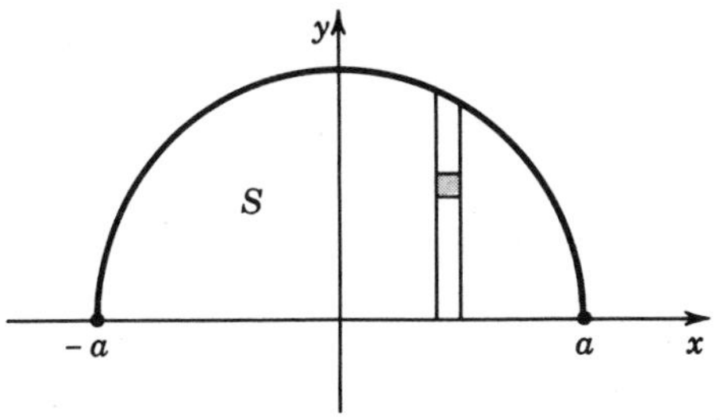

FIGURE 19.20

The mass m of the lamina is given by

$$m = \int_S \rho = \int_{-a}^{a} dx \int_0^{\sqrt{a^2-x^2}} ky\, dy = \frac{k}{2}\int_{-a}^{a} (a^2 - x^2)\, dx = \frac{2}{3} ka^3.$$

Hence the radius of gyration d of the lamina satisfies the equation

$$\tfrac{4}{15}ka^5 = (\tfrac{2}{3}ka^3)\, d^2,$$

from which we conclude that $d = (\sqrt{10}/5)a \doteq .63a$.

If a lamina has the shape of a region S of the polar coordinate plane, then its moment of inertia about the polar axis is given by

$$I_x = \int_S \rho r^2 \sin^2 \theta,$$

where ρ is the density function of the lamina, and its moment of inertia about the axis perpendicular to the polar axis at the pole (the "y axis") is given by

$$I_y = \int_S \rho r^2 \cos^2 \theta.$$

Since the distance of a point (x,y) in the xy plane from the z axis is $\sqrt{x^2 + y^2}$, the moment of inertia of a particle of mass m at (x,y) about the z axis is $m(x^2 + y^2)$. Similarly, a lamina having the shape of a region S of the xy plane and density function ρ will have

$$I_z = \int_S \rho(x^2 + y^2)$$

as its moment of inertia about the z axis. Clearly,

$$I_z = I_x + I_y.$$

If the region S is in the polar coordinate plane of a cylindrical coordinate system, then

$$I_z = \int_S \rho r^2.$$

EXAMPLE 3. Find I_z for the lamina of Example 2.

Solution: We are assuming that the z axis is perpendicular to the plane of the semicircle at the origin. In polar coordinates the semicircle has equation $r = a$, $(0 \leq \theta \leq \pi)$, and $\rho = kr \sin \theta$. Hence

$$I_z = \int_S \rho r^2 = k \int_0^{\pi} d\theta \int_0^{a} r^4 \sin \theta\, dr = \frac{2}{5} ka^5.$$

EXAMPLE 4. Find the radius of gyration d of a homogeneous lamina in the shape of a right triangle about an axis perpendicular to the plane of the triangle at the vertex of the right angle.

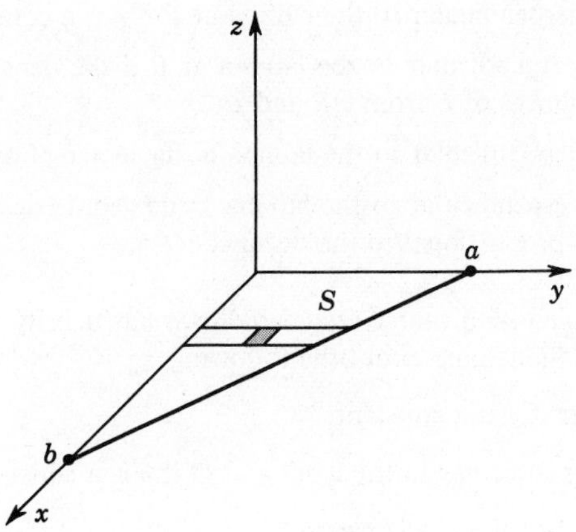

FIGURE 19.21

Solution: If the coordinate axes are chosen as in Figure 19.21, the hypotenuse has equation

$$y = -\frac{a}{b}x + a$$

in the xy plane. Hence (with ρ the constant density)

$$I_z = \int_S \rho(x^2 + y^2) = \rho \int_0^b dx \int_0^{-ax/b+a} (x^2 + y^2)\, dy$$

$$= \rho \int_0^b \left[x^2\left(-\frac{a}{b}x + a\right) + \frac{1}{3}\left(-\frac{a}{b}x + a\right)^3\right] dx = \frac{1}{12}\rho ab(a^2 + b^2).$$

The mass of the lamina is $\rho ab/2$, and therefore

$$\tfrac{1}{12}\rho ab(a^2 + b^2) = \tfrac{1}{2}\rho ab\, d^2,$$

and $d = \sqrt{a^2 + b^2}/\sqrt{6}$.

EXERCISES

I

A rectangular lamina $ABCD$ has density function ρ. Find the radius of gyration of the lamina about the following.

1. AB if ρ is a constant.
2. AB if the density at a point P is the sum of the distances of P from AB and BC.

3. The line perpendicular to the lamina at B if ρ is a constant.
4. The line perpendicular to the lamina at B if the density at a point P is the sum of the distances of P from AB and BC.
5. The line perpendicular to the lamina at its center of mass if ρ is a constant.
6. The line perpendicular to the lamina at its geometric center O if the density at a point P is proportional to the distance $|OP|$.

A circular lamina with center O and radius a has density function ρ. Find the radius of gyration of the lamina about the following.

7. A diameter if ρ is a constant.
8. A line perpendicular to the lamina at O if ρ is a constant.
9. A tangent line if ρ is a constant.
10. A diameter if the density at P is proportional to the distance of point P from the diameter.
11. A line perpendicular to the lamina at O if the density at P is proportional to the distance of point P from O.
12. A tangent line if the density at P is proportional to the distance of P from the point of tangency.
13. A lamina has the shape of a triangle with sides of lengths a, b, and c. Assuming ρ is a constant, find the moment of inertia of the lamina about the side of length c.
14. Find the moment of inertia in Exercise 13 when the density at point P is proportional to the distance of P from the side of length c.
15. A homogeneous lamina is bounded by one loop of the curve $r^2 = \cos 2\theta$ in the polar plane. Find its radius of gyration about an axis perpendicular to the polar plane at the pole.
16. A homogeneous lamina is bounded by the curve $r = 1 + \cos\theta$ in the polar plane. Find the radius of gyration of the lamina about an axis perpendicular to the polar plane at the pole.

II

1. Show that the moment of inertia of any plane lamina about an axis in its plane is equal to its moment of inertia about a parallel axis passing through the center of mass plus the product of the mass times the square of the distance between the two axes (theorem of parallel axes). This shows that of all parallel axes the moment of inertia about the one passing through the center of mass is the least.
2. Show that, for any plane lamina, $I_\theta = I_x \cos^2\theta - I_{xy}\sin 2\theta + I_y \sin^2\theta$, where I_θ is the moment of inertia of the lamina about the line $y = x\tan\theta$ and $I_{xy} = \iint xy\,dx\,dy$ (product of inertia), integrated over the lamina.

3. When rectangular coordinate axes are so chosen at a point of a lamina that the product of inertia $I_{xy} = 0$, these axes are called *principal axes* at the point. In this case I_x and I_y are called *principal moments* of inertia of the lamina.
   a. Prove that at every point of the lamina there exists a pair of principal axes.
   b. If the coordinate axes are principal axes, show that $\max I_\theta = \max \{I_x,I_y\}$, $\min I_\theta = \min \{I_x,I_y\}$.

4. If there are three lines such that $I_{\theta_1} = I_{\theta_2} = I_{\theta_3}$ in Exercise 2, then show that I_θ is the same for all directions.

8 TRIPLE INTEGRALS

A region S of R^3 of the form

$$S = \{(x,y,z) \text{ in } \mathsf{R}^3 \mid a_1 \le x \le b_1,\ a_2 \le y \le b_2,\ a_3 \le z \le b_3\}$$

is a rectangular parallelepiped with edges parallel to the coordinate axes. If f is a continuous function of three variables in S, then we may show by the methods of Section 1 that the repeated integral of f over S exists and has the same value for all six possible choices of the order of integration. One such ordering is

$$\int_{a_1}^{b_1} dx \int_{a_2}^{b_2} dy \int_{a_3}^{b_3} f(x,y,z)\, dz,$$

where we integrate f first with respect to z (holding x and y constant), then with respect to y (holding x constant), and finally with respect to x.

As with functions of two variables, we can also consider the integral of a continuous function f of three variables by the method of Chapter 7. Thus, we partition the parallelepiped S above into a set $p = \{S_{ijk} \mid i = 1, \cdots, r,\ j = 1, \cdots, s,\ k = 1, \cdots, t\}$ of smaller disjoint parallelepipeds, and then select points T_{ijk} and P_{ijk} in each S_{ijk} such that $f(T_{ijk})$ is the minimum value and $f(P_{ijk})$ is the maximum value of f in S_{ijk}. Then

$$l(p) = \sum_{i=1}^{r}\sum_{j=1}^{s}\sum_{k=1}^{t} f(T_{ijk})V(S_{ijk})$$

is called a *lower sum* and

$$u(p) = \sum_{i=1}^{r}\sum_{j=1}^{s}\sum_{k=1}^{t} f(P_{ijk})V(S_{ijk})$$

is called an *upper sum* of f over S, where $V(S_{ijk})$ denotes the volume of S_{ijk}.

The l.u.b. of the set L of all lower sums of f over S is called the *lower integral* of f over S, and the g.l.b. of the *set* U of all upper sums of f over S is called the *upper integral* of f over S. Actually, since f is continuous, the upper integral and the lower integral are equal. Their common value is called the *triple integral* of f over S and is designated by

$$\int_S f.$$

By arguments similar to those employed in the proof of **19.5**, it may be shown that if f is continuous in the parallelepiped S then the triple integral of f over S does exist and is equal to each of the repeated integrals described above,

$$\int_S f = \int_{a_1}^{b_1} dx \int_{a_2}^{b_2} dy \int_{a_3}^{b_3} f(x,y,z)\, dz.$$

EXAMPLE 1. If $f(x,y,z) = 3(x^2y + y^2z)$, find the triple integral of f over the rectangular parallelepiped S bounded by the planes $x = 1, x = 3, y = -1, y = 1, z = 2$, and $z = 4$.

Solution: We have

$$\begin{aligned}\int_S f &= \int_2^4 dz \int_{-1}^1 dy \int_1^3 3(x^2y + y^2z)\, dx\\ &= \int_2^4 dz \int_{-1}^1 (x^3y + 3xy^2z)\Big|_{x=1}^{x=3} dy\\ &= \int_2^4 dz \int_{-1}^1 (26y + 6y^2z)\, dy = \int_2^4 (13y^2 + 2y^3z)\Big|_{y=-1}^{y=1} dz\\ &= \int_2^4 4z\, dz = 24.\end{aligned}$$

We could equally well have started with

$$\int_S f = \int_{-1}^1 dy \int_2^4 dz \int_1^3 3(x^2y + y^2z)\, dx,$$

or any other one of the six possible threefold repeated integrals.

The triple integral of a continuous function f of three variables can be defined over a region of space other than a rectangular parallelepiped. For example, it can be defined over the region S of Figure 19.22, a region bounded below by the surface $z = h_1(x,y)$, above by $z = h_2(x,y)$, and laterally by the cylinders $y = g_1(x)$ and $y = g_2(x)$ and by the planes $x = a_1$ and $x = a_2$, where the functions involved are smooth. It may be shown that

$$\int_S f = \int_{a_1}^{a_2} dx \int_{g_1(x)}^{g_2(x)} dy \int_{h_1(x,y)}^{h_2(x,y)} f(x,y,z)\, dz.$$

The region S might be oriented differently with respect to the axes, in which case the repeated integral might have to be taken in a different order. If $f(x,y,z) = 1$ throughout the region S, then the triple integral of f over S is simply the volume V of the region S:

$$V = \int_S 1.$$

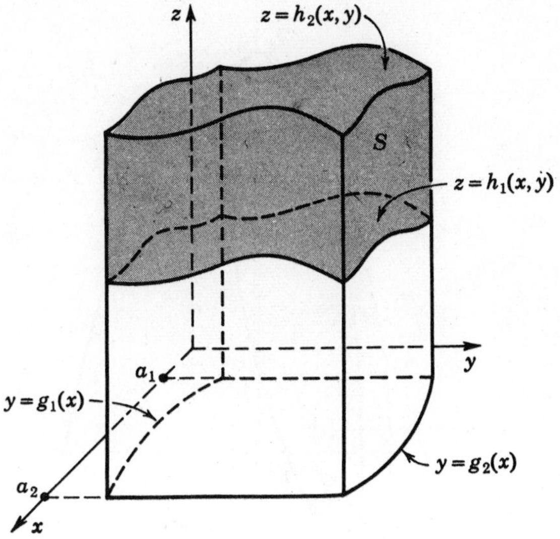

FIGURE 19.22

EXAMPLE 2. Find the volume of the solid bounded above by the paraboloid $z = 4 - x^2 - y^2$ and below by the plane $z = 4 - 2x$.

Solution: The solid is sketched in Figure 19.23. If we eliminate z between the two given equations, we obtain $4 - 2x = 4 - x^2 - y^2$, or

$$y^2 = 2x - x^2,$$

as the equation of a cylinder containing the curve of intersection of the given paraboloid and plane. Thus $y = -\sqrt{2x - x^2}$ and $y = \sqrt{2x - x^2}$ are the y limits of integration, and the volume of the solid is given by

$$\begin{aligned} V &= \int_0^2 dx \int_{-\sqrt{2x-x^2}}^{\sqrt{2x-x^2}} dy \int_{4-2x}^{4-x^2-y^2} dz \\ &= \int_0^2 dx \int_{-\sqrt{2x-x^2}}^{\sqrt{2x-x^2}} [(4 - x^2 - y^2) - (4 - 2x)]\, dy \\ &= \int_0^2 \left(-x^2y - \frac{1}{3}y^3 + 2xy\right)\Bigg|_{y=-\sqrt{2x-x^2}}^{y=\sqrt{2x-x^2}} dx \\ &= \frac{4}{3}\int_0^2 (2x - x^2)^{3/2}\, dx = \frac{\pi}{2}. \end{aligned}$$

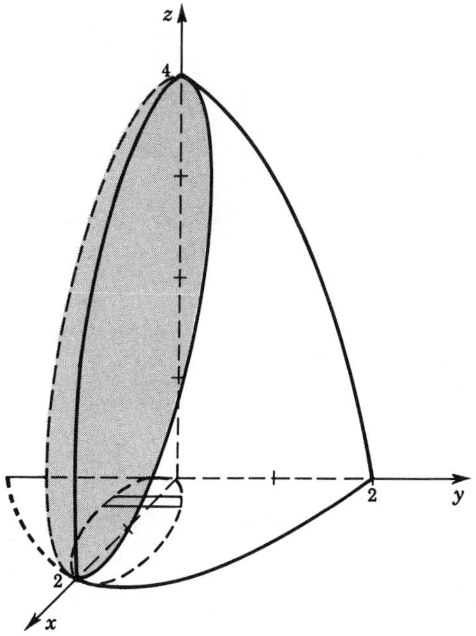

FIGURE 19.23

EXERCISES

I

Find the volume of each of the following regions of space, and also find the value of the triple integral of the given function f over each region. Sketch each region.

1. Region S bounded by the planes $x = -1$, $x = 2$, $y = 0$, $y = 3$, $z = 1$, and $z = 4$; $f(x,y,z) = x - 2y + z$.
2. Region S bounded by the planes $x = 0$, $x = 1$, $y = -1$, $y = 2$, $z = 0$, and $z = 5$; $f(x,y,z) = 3xyz$.
3. Region S bounded by the cylinder $x^2 + y^2 = 16$ and the planes $z = 0$ and $z = 3$; $f(x,y,z) = xz + yz$.
4. Region S bounded by the cylinder $y^2 + z^2 = 9$ and the planes $x = 0$ and $x + z = 3$; $f(x,y,z) = 3y + yz$.
5. Region S bounded by the cylinders $x^2 = z$ and $x^2 = 4 - z$, and the planes $y = 0$ and $z + 2y = 4$; $f(x,y,z) = 2x - z$.

6. Region S bounded by the cylinder $x = \sqrt{4 + y^2}$ and the planes $z = 0$ and $x + 2z = 4$; $f(x,y,z) = xy$.

7. Region S bounded by the surface $z = y/(1 + x^2)$ and the planes $x = 0$, $y = 0$, $z = 0$, and $x + y = 1$; $f(x,y,z) = y + x^2y$.

8. Region S bounded by the surface $y^2 + z^2 = 2x$ and the plane $x + y = 1$; $f(x,y,z) = 3z$.

9. Region S in the first octant bounded by the cylinders $x^2 + y^2 = a^2$ and $y^2 + z^2 = a^2$; $f(x,y,z) = xyz$.

10. Region S bounded by the ellipsoid $x^2/a^2 + y^2/b^2 + z^2/c^2 = 1$; $f(x,y,z) = xz$.

II

Follow the same directions as in Part I.

1. Region S bounded by the graphs of the equations $x = 0$, $y = 0$, $z = 0$, and $\sqrt{x/a} + \sqrt{y/b} + \sqrt{z/c} = 1$; $f(x,y,z) = xyz$.

2. Region S bounded by the graphs of the equation $(x/a)^{2/3} + (y/b)^{2/3} + (z/c)^{2/3} = 1$; $f(x,y,z) = x^2 + y^2 + z^2$.

9 PHYSICAL APPLICATIONS OF TRIPLE INTEGRALS

If a material object has the shape of a region S of space and has a constant density ρ, then the mass W of the object is given by

$$W = \int_S \rho.$$

It could be argued that W is the mass of the object even if ρ is variable, but we shall not consider such a possibility here.

A particle of mass m located at the point (x,y,z) has moments mx, my, and mz with respect to the yz, xz, and xy planes, respectively. Using familiar arguments, we find that the moments with respect to the coordinate planes of a homogeneous material object of density ρ and having the shape of a region S of space are given by

$$M_{xy} = \int_S \rho z, \quad M_{xz} = \int_S \rho y, \quad M_{yz} = \int_S \rho x.$$

The center of mass of the object is the point $(\bar{x},\bar{y},\bar{z})$, where

$$\bar{x} = \frac{M_{yz}}{W}, \quad \bar{y} = \frac{M_{xz}}{W}, \quad \bar{z} = \frac{M_{xy}}{W}.$$

EXAMPLE 1. Find the center of mass of a homogeneous material object bounded by the coordinate planes, the plane $x + y = 1$, and the paraboloid

$$z = 4 - x^2 - 4y^2.$$

Solution: The object is sketched in Figure 19.24. Evidently, its mass is given by

$$W = \int_0^1 dx \int_0^{1-x} dy \int_0^{4-x^2-4y^2} \rho \, dz,$$

and we easily show that

$$W = \frac{19}{12}\rho.$$

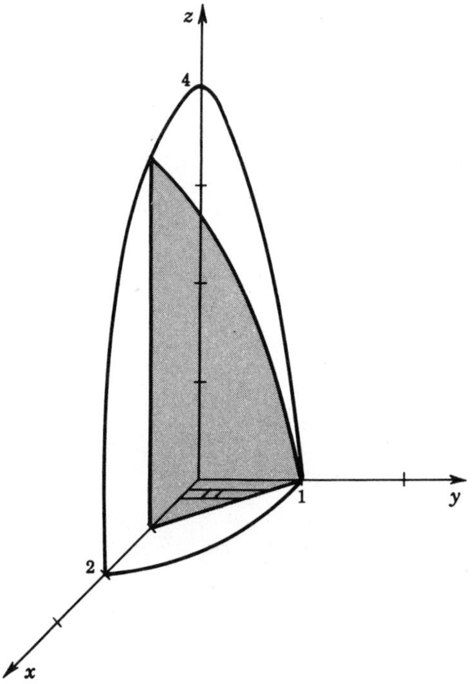

FIGURE 19.24

Also,

$$M_{xy} = \int_0^1 dx \int_0^{1-x} dy \int_0^{4-x^2-4y^2} \rho z \, dz,$$

which may be evaluated to yield

$$M_{xy} = \frac{95}{36}\rho.$$

Similarly,

$$M_{xz} = \int_0^1 dx \int_0^{1-x} dy \int_0^{4-x^2-4y^2} \rho y \, dz = \frac{9}{20}\rho,$$

$$M_{yz} = \int_0^1 dx \int_0^{1-x} dy \int_0^{4-x^2-4y^2} \rho x \, dz = \frac{11}{20}\rho.$$

Thus $(\frac{33}{95}, \frac{27}{95}, \frac{5}{3})$ is the center of mass of the object.

We may use triple integrals to find the moment of inertia of a material object about some line. Since a particle of mass m located at the point (x,y,z) in space has $m(y^2 + z^2)$ as its moment of inertia about the x axis, it seems reasonable that the moment of inertia about the x axis of a material object of constant density ρ having the shape of region S of space is given by

$$I_x = \int_S \rho(y^2 + z^2).$$

Similarly,

$$I_y = \int_S \rho(x^2 + z^2), \qquad I_z = \int_S \rho(x^2 + y^2).$$

EXAMPLE 2. Find the moment of inertia and radius of gyration about the z axis of the homogeneous solid of density ρ bounded by the coordinate planes and the plane

$$\frac{x}{a} + \frac{y}{b} + \frac{z}{c} = 1, \qquad (a, b, c \text{ positive}).$$

Solution: The solid is the tetrahedron shown in Figure 19.25. Since the trace of the given plane in the xy plane has equation

$$y = b - \frac{b}{a}x,$$

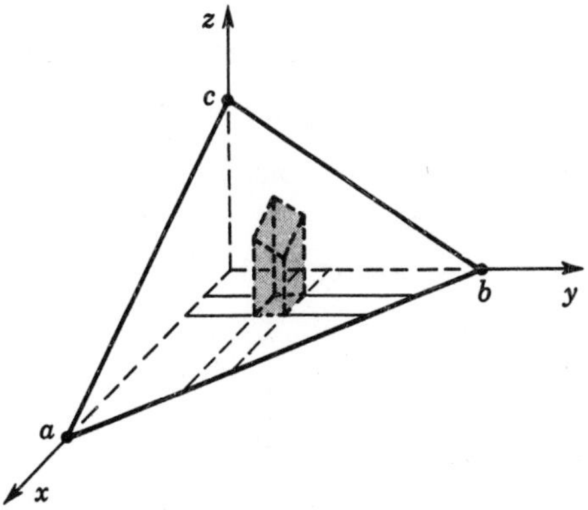

FIGURE 19.25

we have

$$I_z = \int_0^a dx \int_0^{b-bx/a} dy \int_0^{c-cx/a-cy/b} \rho(x^2 + y^2)\, dz$$

$$= \rho c \int_0^a dx \int_0^{b-bx/a} (x^2 + y^2)\left(1 - \frac{1}{a}x - \frac{1}{b}y\right) dy$$

$$= \rho bc \int_0^a \left[\frac{1}{2}x^2 - \frac{1}{a}x^3 + \frac{1}{2a^2}x^4 + \frac{b^2}{12}\left(1 - \frac{1}{a}x\right)^4\right] dx$$

$$= \frac{\rho abc}{60}(a^2 + b^2).$$

The volume of the given solid is $abc/6$, and its mass is therefore $\rho abc/6$. Hence the radius r of gyration is given by

$$\frac{\rho abc}{60}(a^2 + b^2) = \frac{\rho abc}{6} r^2$$

and $r = \sqrt{a^2 + b^2}/\sqrt{10}$.

EXERCISES

I

In each of Exercises 1–10, find the center of mass of the homogeneous solid having the given shape.

1. The tetrahedron with vertices (0,0,0), $(a,0,0)$, $(0,b,0)$, $(0,0,c)$.
2. The first octant of the sphere $x^2 + y^2 + z^2 = a^2$. [*Hint:* $\bar{x} = \bar{y} = \bar{z}$ by symmetry.)
3. The region bounded by the xy plane and the paraboloid $z = 1 - x^2/a^2 - y^2/b^2$.
4. The region in the first octant bounded by the cylinder $x = y^2$ and the planes $x = 4$, $z = 0$, and $z = 2$.
5. Region S of Exercise 4, Section 8, I.
6. Region S of Exercise 5, Section 8, I.
7. Region S of Exercise 6, Section 8, I.
8. Region S of Exercise 8, Section 8, I.
9. Region S of Exercise 9, Section 8, I.
10. An octant of the ellipsoid $x^2/a^2 + y^2/b^2 + z^2/c^2 = 1$.

Set up an integral for I_z for each of the following homogeneous solids of density ρ.

11. A hemisphere, z the axis of symmetry.

12. The solid bounded by the plane $z = h$ and the paraboloid $z = x^2/a^2 + y^2/b^2$.

13. The solid bounded by the plane $z = h$ and the paraboloid $z = x^2 + y^2$.

14. A right circular cylinder of radius r and altitude h, z the axis of symmetry.

15. The solid having the shape of region S in Exercise 7.

16. The solid having the shape of region S in Exercise 9.

17. A rectangular parallelepiped of length a, width b, and height c, the z axis along an edge of length c. (Compute.)

18. The rectangular parallelepiped of Exercise 17, the z axis along a diagonal.

II

1. State and prove the parallel axis theorem for a solid (see Exercise II-1, page 694).

2. Show that, for any solid S with density function ρ,

$$I_L = a^2I_x + b^2I_y + c^2I_z - 2bcP_x - 2acP_y - 2abP_z,$$

where I_L is the moment of inertia of S about a line L through the origin with direction $\langle a,b,c\rangle$, and where $P_x = \int_S \rho yz$, $P_y = \int_S \rho xz$, $P_z = \int_S \rho xy$ are the products of inertia. (See Exercise II-2, Section 7, for the plane version.)

3. When rectangular coordinate axes are so chosen at a point of a solid that the products of inertia, P_x, P_y, and P_z, are zero, these axes are then called *principal axes* at the point. In this case I_x, I_y, and I_z are called the *principal moments* of inertia. It can be shown that at any point of a solid there exists a set of principal axes. Show that the maximum and minimum values of I_L (defined in Exercise 2) are two of the principal moments of inertia I_x, I_y, and I_z.

4. Show that for any solid S, $I_x + I_y + I_z$ evaluated at any fixed point O of S is independent of the set of coordinate axes chosen.

5. Find the moment of inertia of a cube of edge e about: (a) a body diagonal; (b) a face diagonal.

10 CYLINDRICAL AND SPHERICAL COORDINATES

Triple integrals may be defined for continuous functions of three variables over regions of a cylindrical or spherical coordinate space much as they are over regions of a rectangular coordinate space. We shall indicate in this section how such triple integrals may be evaluated by repeated integrals.

A region S of cylindrical coordinate space bounded by the curves $r = a_1$, $r = a_2$, $\theta = b_1$, $\theta = b_2$, $z = c_1$, and $z = c_2$ may be partitioned into subregions of the same type. One such subregion is shown in Figure 19.26. This subregion is a

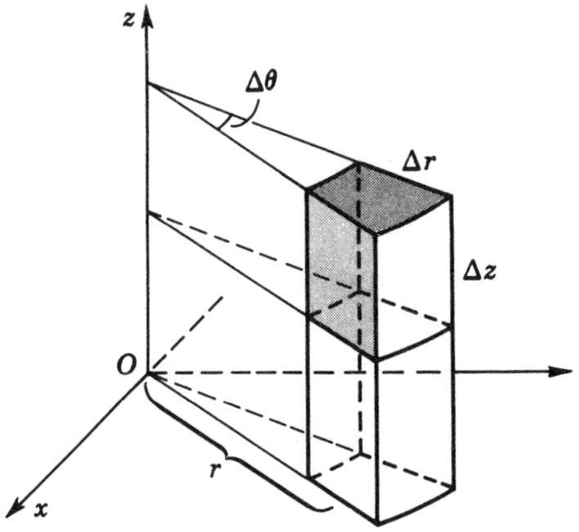

FIGURE 19.26

cylinder having its generator parallel to the z axis. Hence its volume, $V(S)$, is the product of the area of its base, $r\,\Delta r\,\Delta\theta$, and its altitude Δz,

$$V(S) = r\,\Delta r\,\Delta\theta\,\Delta z,$$

where r is the average radius of its base.

If f is a continuous function of three variables over S, then the triple integral of f over S may be defined as usual in terms of the l.u.b. of the set of all lower sums of f over partitions of S. Then it may be shown that the triple integral of f over S can be expressed in the form

$$\int_S f = \int_{a_1}^{a_2} dr \int_{b_1}^{b_2} d\theta \int_{c_1}^{c_2} f(r,\theta,z)r\,dz.$$

Again there are six possible permutations of the single integrals on the right side of the above equation.

The usual modifications of the limits of integration must be made if the triple integral of f is taken over a region S of space not bounded by coordinate surfaces like the region described above. Centers of mass and moments of inertia of an object may be found if the formulas of Section 9 are modified in the obvious way.

EXAMPLE 1. Find the center of mass and moment of inertia about the z axis of the homogeneous solid bounded by the cylinder $r = a$, the cone $z = r$, and the plane $z = 0$.

Solution: This solid S is a right circular cylinder with a cone hollowed out of it, as shown in Figure 19.27. If ρ designates its constant density, then its mass is given by

$$W = \rho(\pi a^3 - \tfrac{1}{3}\pi a^3) = \tfrac{2}{3}\rho\pi a^3.$$

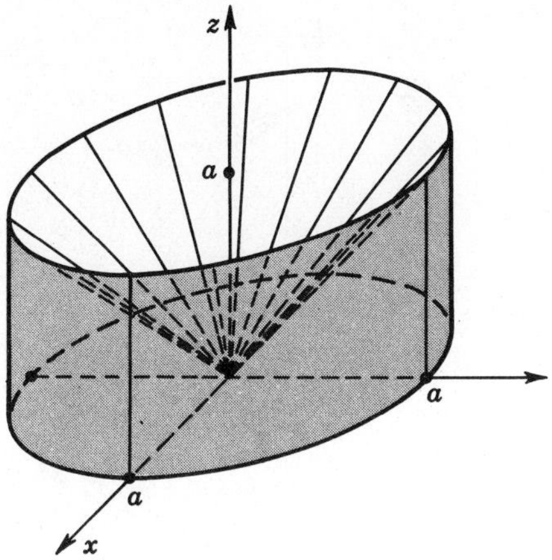

FIGURE 19.27

It is clear by symmetry that the center of mass of the solid is on the z axis. The moment M_p of the solid with respect to the polar coordinate plane p is given by

$$M_p = \int_S \rho z = \int_0^{2\pi} d\theta \int_0^a dr \int_0^r zr\,dz$$
$$= \frac{\rho}{2}\int_0^{2\pi} d\theta \int_0^a r^3\,dr = \frac{\rho}{8}\int_0^{2\pi} a^4\,d\theta = \frac{\rho}{4}\pi a^4.$$

Hence $\bar{z} = M_p/W = 3a/8$, and the point $(0,0,3a/8)$ is the center of mass of the solid.

A particle of mass m located at the point (r,θ,z) is r units from the z axis. Hence mr^2 is its moment of inertia about the z axis. Therefore it is clear that the moment of inertia about the z axis of the solid of Figure 19.27 is given by

$$I_z = \int_S \rho r^2 = \rho \int_0^{2\pi} d\theta \int_0^a dr \int_0^r r^3\,dz$$
$$= \rho\int_0^{2\pi} d\theta \int_0^a r^4\,dr = \frac{\rho}{5}\int_0^{2\pi} a^5\,d\theta = \frac{2}{5}\rho\pi a^5.$$

The basic region of spherical coordinate space is the region S bounded by the spheres $\rho = a_1$ and $\rho = a_2$, the planes $\theta = b_1$ and $\theta = b_2$, and the cones $\phi = c_1$ and $\phi = c_2$. If such a region is partitioned into subregions in the usual way, then one such subregion is shown in Figure 19.28. The volume $V(S)$ of this subregion may be shown by geometry to be approximately equal to

$$V(S) = \rho^2 \sin\phi \, \Delta\rho \, \Delta\theta \, \Delta\phi.$$

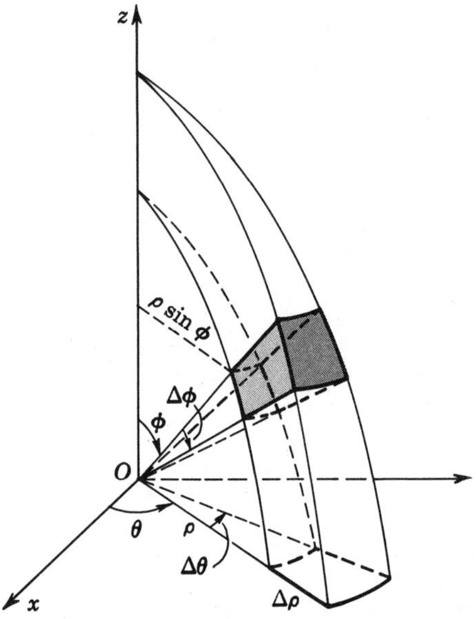

FIGURE 19.28

Although we shall not prove it, we can imagine that the triple integral of a continuous function f over S is given by

$$\int_S f = \int_{a_1}^{a_2} d\rho \int_{b_1}^{b_2} d\theta \int_{c_1}^{c_2} f(\rho,\theta,\phi)\rho^2 \sin\phi \, d\phi.$$

There are six possible permutations of the single integrals in the above repeated integral.

An application of spherical coordinates to the problem of finding the center of gravity and moment of inertia of a solid is indicated in the following example.

EXAMPLE 2. Find the volume, center of mass, and moment of inertia about the axis of symmetry of the solid (of constant density 1) bounded above by the sphere $\rho = a$ and below by the cone $\phi = k$.

Solution: The solid is a cone with a spherical top; a quarter of it is shown in Figure 19.29. The volume of the solid is given by

$$V = \int_0^{2\pi} d\theta \int_0^k d\phi \int_0^a \rho^2 \sin\phi \, d\rho = \frac{2}{3}\pi a^3(1 - \cos k),$$

and its moment about the polar coordinate plane p (recalling that $z = \rho \cos \phi$) by

$$M_p = \int_0^{2\pi} d\theta \int_0^k d\phi \int_0^a (\rho\cos\phi)\rho^2 \sin\phi \, d\rho$$

$$= \frac{a^4}{4}\int_0^{2\pi} d\theta \int_0^k \sin\phi\cos\phi \, d\phi$$

$$= \frac{a^4}{8}\sin^2 k \int_0^{2\pi} d\theta = \frac{1}{4}\pi a^4 \sin^2 k.$$

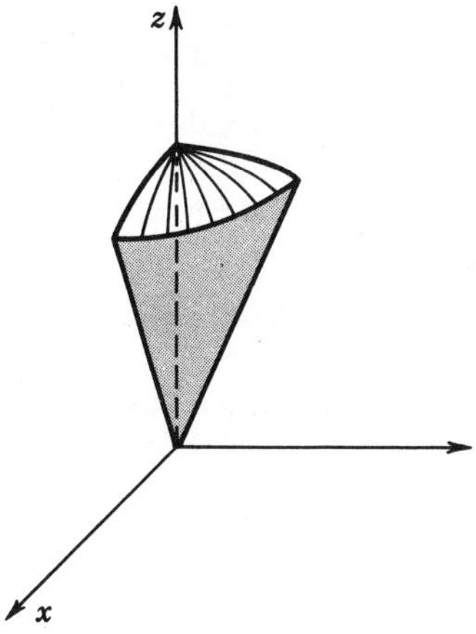

FIGURE 19.29

By symmetry, the center of mass is on the vertical z axis above the pole at the distance of

$$\bar{z} = \frac{M_p}{V} = \frac{3}{8}a(1 + \cos k).$$

Thus $(\frac{3}{8}a(1 + \cos k),0,0)$ is the center of mass of the solid. Note that if $k = \pi/2$ we obtain $(\frac{3}{8}a,0,0)$ as the center of mass of a hemisphere.

The distance r of a point (ρ,θ,ϕ) from the vertical z axis is given by $r = \rho \sin \phi$. Hence the moment of inertia about the z axis of a particle of mass m located at the point (ρ,θ,ϕ) is $m\rho^2 \sin^2 \phi$. With this in mind, we find that evidently the moment of inertia about the z axis of the given solid (assuming a constant density of 1) is

$$I_z = \int_0^{2\pi} d\theta \int_0^k d\phi \int_0^a (\rho^2 \sin^2 \phi)\rho^2 \sin \phi \, d\rho$$

$$= \frac{a^5}{5} \int_0^{2\pi} d\theta \int_0^k \sin^3 \phi \, d\phi$$

$$= \frac{2}{15} \pi a^5(\cos^3 k - 3 \cos k + 2).$$

EXERCISES

I

1. Given a right circular cone having radius of base a and altitude h, find:
   a. its center of mass;
   b. its moment of inertia about the axis of symmetry;
   c. its moment of inertia about a diameter of the base.

2. Given a right circular cylinder of diameter a and altitude h, find:
   a. its moment of inertia about the axis of symmetry;
   b. its moment of inertia about a generator;
   c. its moment of inertia about a diameter of the base.

3. Given a hemispherical shell having inner radius a and outer radius b, find:
   a. its center of mass;
   b. its moment of inertia about the axis of symmetry;
   c. its moment of inertia about a diameter of the base.

4. Given the cone $\phi = k$ (spherical coordinates) cut out of the solid hemisphere $\rho = a$, $(0 \leq \phi \leq \pi/2)$, find:
   a. the center of mass of the solid remaining;
   b. its moment of inertia about the axis of symmetry;
   c. its moment of inertia about a diameter of the base.

5. Given a solid bounded by the cylinder $r = a \cos \theta$, the paraboloid $z = br^2$, and the plane $z = 0$ (cylindrical coordinates), find:
   a. its volume;
   b. its center of mass.

II

In each of Exercises 1–4 evaluate the integral over the solid ball $S = B[0,a]$ by using symmetry conditions, e.g., $\int_S x^2 = \int_S y^2$.

1. $\int_S x^2$. 2. $\int_S x^4$. 3. $\int_S x^4y^3$. 4. $\int_S x^2y^2$.

REVIEW

Oral Exercises

In each of Exercises 1–7 define the concept.

1. Repeated or iterated integral.
2. Uniform continuity of a function of two variables.
3. Double integral.
4. Triple integral.
5. Center of mass.
6. Moment of inertia.
7. Parallel axes theorem.
8. List at least five applications of multiple integrals.
9. What are the differences and similarities of double integrals in rectangular and polar coordinates?
10. What are the fundamental volume elements for triple integrals in rectangular, cylindrical, and spherical coordinates?

I

In each of Exercises 1–6, compute the integral.

1. $\int_0^1 dx \int_0^2 (x + y)\, dy.$
2. $\int_0^2 dx \int_0^1 (x + y)\, dy.$
3. $\int_{-1}^0 dx \int_1^2 dz \int_0^3 (x^2 - y + z)\, dy.$
4. $\int_1^2 dz \int_0^3 dy \int_{-1}^0 (x^2 - y + z)\, dx.$
5. $\int_0^2 dx \int_0^x (x^2 + y^2)\, dy.$
6. $\int_1^2 dy \int_0^{y^2} (x + 2y)\, dx.$
7. Interpret each of the integrals in Exercises 1, 2, 5, and 6 as the volume of a solid.
8. Prove that
$$\int_a^b dx \int_c^d f(x)g(y)\, dy = \left\{\int_a^b f(x)\, dx\right\} \cdot \left\{\int_c^d g(y)\, dy\right\}.$$

In each of Exercises 9–12, evaluate the double integral, using the theorem given in Exercise 8.

9. $\int_0^1 dx \int_0^1 xy\, dy.$
10. $\int_0^{\pi/2} d\theta \int_0^1 r^2\theta\, dr.$
11. $\int_{-\pi}^{\pi} d\theta \int_0^1 r \sin\theta\, dr.$
12. $\int_0^1 dx \int_0^1 e^{x+y}\, dy.$
13. State and prove a theorem analogous to that of Exercise 8 for triple integrals.

In each of Exercises 14–18 set up integrals for the volume and the center of mass of the solid with the given boundaries.

14. $x + y + z = 2, \quad (x = 0, y = 0, z = 0).$

15. $z = \dfrac{1}{x^2 + y^2}$, $(z = 0;\ x^2 + y^2 = 1)$.

16. $z = \cos(x^2 + y^2)$, $\left(z = 0;\ x^2 + y^2 \le \dfrac{\pi}{2}\right)$.

17. $z = \cos(x^2 + y^2)$, $\left(z = 0;\ \dfrac{3\pi}{2} \le x^2 + y^2 \le \dfrac{5\pi}{2}\right)$.

18. $\dfrac{x^2}{a^2} + \dfrac{y^2}{b^2} + \dfrac{z^2}{c^2} = 1$.

In Exercises 19 and 20 set up the triple integral for the moment of inertia of the given uniform solid about the indicated axis.

19. $\dfrac{x^2}{a^2} + \dfrac{y^2}{b^2} + \dfrac{z^2}{c^2} = 1$; z axis.

20. $x^2 + y^2 + z^2 \le a^2$, $z \ge x^2 + y^2$; y axis.

II

1. Show by evaluating the repeated integrals that

$$\int_0^1 dx \int_0^1 \frac{x^2 - y^2}{(x^2 + y^2)^2}\,dy \ne \int_0^1 dy \int_0^1 \frac{x^2 - y^2}{(x^2 + y^2)^2}\,dx.$$

2. Starting with

$$\frac{d}{dx} G(\alpha(x), \beta(x), \lambda(x)) = \alpha'(x)G_1 + \beta'(x)G_2 + \lambda'(x)G_3,$$

show that

$$\frac{d}{dx}\int_{\alpha(x)}^{\beta(x)} F(x,t)\,dt = \beta'(x)F(x,\beta(x)) - \alpha'(x)F(x,\alpha(x)) + \int_{\alpha(x)}^{\beta(x)} F_1(x,t)\,dt.$$

3. Express the area A of the region bounded by the parabola $y = 4ax^2$ and its latus rectum by means of a definite integral. Now find dA/da (a) by first integrating to find A and then differentiating with respect to a, (b) by differentiating the integral with respect to a, using Exercise 2.

4. Starting with the formula $\int_0^\pi 1/(a + b\cos t)\,dt = \pi/\sqrt{a^2 - b^2}$, $(a > b > 0)$, and using Exercise 2, derive the formula

$$\int_0^\pi \frac{\cos t}{(a + b\cos t)^3}\,dt = -\frac{3\pi}{2}\frac{ab}{(a^2 - b^2)^{5/2}}.$$

5. Prove that $\dfrac{d^n}{dt^n}\displaystyle\int_{-t}^{t} f(x + t)\,dx = 2^n f^{[n-1]}(2t), n \ge 1$.

6. If a function f is periodic of period a, show by two different methods that $\int_0^a f(x + y)\,dx$ is independent of y.

7. Establish Routh's mnemonic rule for moments of inertia of a rectangular, circular or elliptical lamina, and of a spherical or ellipsoidal solid; i.e., the moment of inertia about an axis of symmetry is

$$\text{mass} \times \frac{\text{sum of squares of perpendicular semiaxes}}{3,\ 4,\ \text{or}\ 5},$$

according to whether the body is rectangular, elliptical, or ellipsoidal.

8. In a large number of physical applications of multiple integration, it is necessary to evaluate double and triple integrals of the form

$$I_2 = \int_{S_2} x^{m-1}y^{n-1} \quad \text{and} \quad I_3 = \int_{S_3} x^{m-1}y^{n-1}z^{p-1},$$

where S_2 is the region in the first quadrant bounded by the graph of an equation $(x/a)^r + (y/b)^s = 1$, and S_3 is the region in the first octant bounded by the graph of an equation $(x/a)^r + (y/b)^s + (z/c)^t = 1$. These integrals can be evaluated in terms of the *gamma function* Γ defined by $\Gamma(n) = \int_0^\infty e^{-x}x^{n-1}\,dx$, $(n > 0)$.

Prove the following: **a.** The existence of the improper integral by showing $\int_0^t e^{-x}x^{n-1}\,dx$ is monotonic in x and bounded for $t \geq 0$. **b.** $\Gamma(n+1) = n\Gamma(n)$. **c.** $\Gamma(n+1) = n!$ if n is an integer. It can also be shown that $\Gamma(x)\Gamma(1-x) = \pi/\sin \pi x$ and $\Gamma(\frac{1}{2}) = \sqrt{\pi}$. Furthermore, if the *beta function* B is defined by $B(m,n) = \int_0^1 x^{m-1}(1-x)^{n-1}\,dx$, ($m$ and n positive), then it can be shown that $B(m,n) = \Gamma(m)\Gamma(n)/\Gamma(m+n)$.

9. Using the results stated in Exercise 8, show that:

a. $I_2 = \dfrac{a^m b^n}{rs}\,\dfrac{\Gamma(m/r)\Gamma(n/s)}{\Gamma(m/r + n/s + 1)}$.

b. $I_3 = \dfrac{a^m b^n c^p}{rst}\,\dfrac{\Gamma(m/r)\Gamma(n/s)\Gamma(p/t)}{\Gamma(m/r + n/s + p/t + 1)}$ Dirichlet.

In each of Exercises 10–14, solve the given previous exercise by using the results of Exercise 9.

10. Exercise II-2, Section 4.

11. Exercise II-3, Section 4.

12. Exercise II-2, Section 6.

13. Exercise II-2, Section 8.

14. Exercise II-1, Section 10.

15. Show how to find I_x for the ellipsoid $(x/a)^2 + (y/b)^2 + (z/c)^2 = 1$ from I_x for the sphere $x^2 + y^2 + z^2 = 1$. [*Hint:* Use the affine transformation $x' = x/a$, $y' = y/b$, $z' = z/c$.)

20

LINEAR ALGEBRA

In the last four chapters, vectors have been used to aid in the development of certain topics in the calculus. The present chapter studies vectors in a more general setting. Included in this study are matrices and linear transformations.

1 VECTOR SPACES

We have used two particular vector spaces in preceding chapters, $V_2 = \{\langle h,k \rangle \mid h,k \text{ in } \mathsf{R}\}$ in Chapter 16 and $V_3 = \{\langle h,k,l \rangle \mid h,k,l \text{ in } \mathsf{R}\}$ in Chapter 17. These geometric examples illustrate the following definition.

20.1 **DEFINITION.** A vector space consists of a set V, an operation of addition in V, and an operation of scalar multiplication of V by R. Addition in V has the following properties:

(1) $\mathbf{x} + \mathbf{y} = \mathbf{y} + \mathbf{x}$ for all $\mathbf{x}, \mathbf{y}$ in V. (Commutative law)

(2) $\mathbf{x} + (\mathbf{y} + \mathbf{z}) = (\mathbf{x} + \mathbf{y}) + \mathbf{z}$ for all $\mathbf{x},\mathbf{y},\mathbf{z}$ in V. (Associative law)

(3) There exists an element $\mathbf{0}$ in V such that

$$\mathbf{0} + \mathbf{x} = \mathbf{x} + \mathbf{0} = \mathbf{x} \quad \text{for all } \mathbf{x} \text{ in } V. \quad \text{(Identity element)}$$

(4) For each $\mathbf{x}$ in V there exists $-\mathbf{x}$ in V such that

$$\mathbf{x} + (-\mathbf{x}) = (-\mathbf{x}) + \mathbf{x} = \mathbf{0} \quad \text{for all } \mathbf{x} \text{ in } V. \quad \text{(Inverse elements)}$$

For each $\mathbf{x}$ in V and a in R, the scalar product of $\mathbf{x}$ by a is a unique element of V denoted by $a\mathbf{x}$. Scalar multiplication has the following properties:

(5) $a(\mathbf{x} + \mathbf{y}) = a\mathbf{x} + a\mathbf{y}$ for all a in R, $\mathbf{x},\mathbf{y}$ in V. (Distributive law)
(6) $(a + b)\mathbf{x} = a\mathbf{x} + b\mathbf{x}$ for all a,b in R, $\mathbf{x}$ in V. (Distributive law)
(7) $(ab)\mathbf{x} = a(b\mathbf{x})$ for all a,b in R, $\mathbf{x}$ in V. (Associative law)
(8) $1\mathbf{x} = \mathbf{x}$ for all $\mathbf{x}$ in V. (Identity element)

We shall call elements of V *vectors* and real numbers *scalars*. Vectors are denoted by boldface letters $\mathbf{u},\mathbf{v},\mathbf{w},\mathbf{x}, \ldots$ and scalars by letters $a, b, c, d, \ldots$.

Additional properties of a vector space V may be derived from the eight defining ones, such as the following three:

20.2 THEOREM. If $\mathbf{x} + \mathbf{z} = \mathbf{y} + \mathbf{z}$, then $\mathbf{x} = \mathbf{y}$. (Cancellation law)

20.3 THEOREM. $a\mathbf{x} = \mathbf{0}$ if and only if either $a = 0$ or $\mathbf{x} = \mathbf{0}$.

20.4 THEOREM. $-(a\mathbf{x}) = (-a)\mathbf{x} = a(-\mathbf{x})$.

Proof of 20.2: If $\mathbf{x} + \mathbf{z} = \mathbf{y} + \mathbf{z}$ then

$$(\mathbf{x} + \mathbf{z}) + (-\mathbf{z}) = (\mathbf{y} + \mathbf{z}) + (-\mathbf{z})$$
$$\mathbf{x} + [\mathbf{z} + (-\mathbf{z})] = \mathbf{y} + [\mathbf{z} + (-\mathbf{z})] \qquad \text{(Assoc. law)}$$
$$\mathbf{x} + \mathbf{0} = \mathbf{y} + \mathbf{0} \qquad \text{(Inverse el.)}$$
$$\mathbf{x} = \mathbf{y} \qquad \text{(Identity el.)}$$

The proofs of 20.3 and 20.4 are left as exercises for the reader.

An operation of *subtraction* in V is defined as follows:

$$\mathbf{x} - \mathbf{y} = \mathbf{x} + (-\mathbf{y}) \quad \text{for all } \mathbf{x},\mathbf{y} \text{ in } V.$$

Subtraction has the usual properties, including the ones listed below.

$$a(\mathbf{x} - \mathbf{y}) = a\mathbf{x} - a\mathbf{y} \quad \text{for all } a \text{ in R, } \mathbf{x},\mathbf{y} \text{ in } V.$$
$$-(\mathbf{x} - \mathbf{y}) = (-\mathbf{x}) + \mathbf{y} \quad \text{for all } \mathbf{x},\mathbf{y} \text{ in } V.$$

If V is a vector space and S is a nonempty subset of V which is closed under addition and scalar multiplication (i.e., $\mathbf{x} + \mathbf{y}$ and $a\mathbf{x}$ are in S for all $\mathbf{x},\mathbf{y}$ in S and a in R), then S is also a vector space. We call S a *subspace* of V.

Given two subspaces S_1 and S_2, their *intersection* $S_1 \cap S_2$ is easily proved to be a subspace. Their *sum* $S_1 + S_2$ defined by

$$S_1 + S_2 = \{\mathbf{x}_1 + \mathbf{x}_2 \mid \mathbf{x}_1 \text{ in } S_1, \mathbf{x}_2 \text{ in } S_2\}$$

is also a subspace. For if $\mathbf{x}_1,\mathbf{y}_1$ are in S_1 and $\mathbf{x}_2,\mathbf{y}_2$ are in S_2, then the sum of $\mathbf{x}_1 + \mathbf{x}_2$

and $\mathbf{y}_1 + \mathbf{y}_2$ equals $(\mathbf{x}_1 + \mathbf{y}_1) + (\mathbf{x}_2 + \mathbf{y}_2)$, an element of $S_1 + S_2$, and the scalar product $a(\mathbf{x}_1 + \mathbf{x}_2)$ equals $a\mathbf{x}_1 + a\mathbf{x}_2$, an element of $S_1 + S_2$.

Another way of forming a subspace of a vector space V is to start with a set of vectors $\{\mathbf{x}_1,\mathbf{x}_2,\cdots,\mathbf{x}_n\}$ and form the set

$$S = \{a_1\mathbf{x}_1 + a_2\mathbf{x}_2 + \cdots + a_n\mathbf{x}_n \mid a_1,a_2,\cdots,a_n \text{ in } \mathsf{R}\}$$

Using the sigma notation, each vector $\mathbf{x}$ in S has the form

$$\mathbf{x} = \sum_{i=1}^{n} a_i\mathbf{x}_i.$$

If $\mathbf{y} = \sum_{i=1}^{n} b_i\mathbf{x}_i$ is another vector of S, then

$$\mathbf{x} + \mathbf{y} = \sum_{i=1}^{n} a_i\mathbf{x}_i + \sum_{i=1}^{n} b_i\mathbf{x}_i = \sum_{i=1}^{n} (a_i + b_i)\mathbf{x}_i$$

and

$$c\mathbf{x} = c\sum_{i=1}^{n} a_i\mathbf{x}_i = \sum_{i=1}^{n} (ca_i)\mathbf{x}_i$$

Thus $\mathbf{x} + \mathbf{y}$ and $c\mathbf{x}$ are in S for all $\mathbf{x},\mathbf{y}$ in S and c in R, and S is a subspace of V. We call S the vector space *spanned* by the vectors $\mathbf{x}_1,\mathbf{x}_2,\cdots,\mathbf{x}_n$. Each $\mathbf{x}$ in S is said to be a *linear combination* of the vectors $\mathbf{x}_1,\mathbf{x}_2,\cdots,\mathbf{x}_n$.

For example, the vectors $\mathbf{i} = \langle 1,0,0\rangle$ and $\mathbf{j} = \langle 0,1,0\rangle$ in V_3 span the subspace $S = \{\langle h,k,0\rangle \mid h,k \text{ in } \mathsf{R}\}$, since

$$h\mathbf{i} + k\mathbf{j} = \langle h,0,0\rangle + \langle 0,k,0\rangle = \langle h,k,0\rangle$$

for all h,k in R.

The vectors $\mathbf{x}_1,\mathbf{x}_2,\cdots,\mathbf{x}_n$ of a vector space V are called *linearly dependent* if and only if some one of the $\mathbf{x}_i$ is a linear combination of the remaining $\mathbf{x}_j$. If no $\mathbf{x}_i$ is a linear combination of the remaining $\mathbf{x}_j$, then the vectors $\mathbf{x}_1,\mathbf{x}_2,\cdots,\mathbf{x}_n$ are called *linearly independent*.

For example, the vectors $\mathbf{i} = \langle 1,0,0\rangle$, $\mathbf{j} = \langle 0,1,0\rangle$, $\mathbf{k} = \langle 0,0,1\rangle$ are linearly independent, since $\mathbf{i}$ is not a linear combination of $\mathbf{j}$ and $\mathbf{k}$ (i.e., $\mathbf{i} \neq a\mathbf{j} + b\mathbf{k}$ for all a,b in R), $\mathbf{j}$ is not a linear combination of $\mathbf{i}$ and $\mathbf{k}$, and $\mathbf{k}$ is not a linear combination of $\mathbf{i}$ and $\mathbf{j}$. On the other hand, the vectors $\mathbf{i} - \mathbf{k}$, $4\mathbf{i} + 2\mathbf{j}$, $\mathbf{j} + 2\mathbf{k}$ are linearly dependent, since

$$4\mathbf{i} + 2\mathbf{j} = 4(\mathbf{i} - \mathbf{k}) + 2(\mathbf{j} + 2\mathbf{k}).$$

A useful way of deciding whether or not a set of vectors is linearly independent is given below.

20.5 THEOREM. The vectors $\mathbf{x}_1,\mathbf{x}_2, \cdots, \mathbf{x}_n$ of a vector space V are linearly independent if and only if the only scalars $a_1,a_2, \cdots, a_n$ such that

$$\sum_{i=1}^{n} a_i\mathbf{x}_i = \mathbf{0}$$

are $a_1 = 0, a_2 = 0, \cdots, a_n = 0$.

Proof: If $\mathbf{x}_1,\mathbf{x}_2, \cdots, \mathbf{x}_n$ are linearly dependent, then some $\mathbf{x}_i$ is a linear combination of the remaining $\mathbf{x}_j$, say, for simplicity of notation, that $\mathbf{x}_1$ is a linear combination of $\mathbf{x}_2,\mathbf{x}_3, \cdots, \mathbf{x}_n$:

$$\mathbf{x}_1 = a_2\mathbf{x}_2 + a_3\mathbf{x}_3 + \cdots + a_n\mathbf{x}_n \qquad \text{for some } a_i \text{ in R.}$$

Then

$$(-1)\mathbf{x}_1 + a_2\mathbf{x}_2 + a_3\mathbf{x}_3 + \cdots + a_n\mathbf{x}_n = \mathbf{0}$$

and $\Sigma a_i\mathbf{x}_i = \mathbf{0}$ with not all $a_i = 0$, since $a_1 = -1$. Thus if the only scalars a_i such that $\Sigma a_i\mathbf{x}_i = \mathbf{0}$ are $a_1 = 0, a_2 = 0, \cdots, a_n = 0$, then the vectors $\mathbf{x}_1,\mathbf{x}_2, \cdots, \mathbf{x}_n$ are linearly independent.

Conversely, if $\Sigma a_i\mathbf{x}_i = \mathbf{0}$ with not all $a_i = 0$, say $a_1 \neq 0$, then

$$a_1\mathbf{x}_1 = -a_2\mathbf{x}_2 - \cdots - a_n\mathbf{x}_n$$

and

$$\mathbf{x}_1 = -\frac{a_2}{a_1}\mathbf{x}_2 - \cdots - \frac{a_n}{a_1}\mathbf{x}_n$$

Thus $\mathbf{x}_1$ is a linear combination of $\mathbf{x}_2, \cdots, \mathbf{x}_n$ and the vectors $\mathbf{x}_1,\mathbf{x}_2, \cdots, \mathbf{x}_n$ are linearly dependent. This proves that if the vectors $\mathbf{x}_1,\mathbf{x}_2, \cdots, \mathbf{x}_n$ are linearly independent then the only scalars a_i such that $\Sigma a_i\mathbf{x}_i = \mathbf{0}$ are $a_1 = 0, a_2 = 0, \cdots, a_n = 0$. Thus, **20.5** is proved.

EXAMPLE 1. Are the vectors $\mathbf{x}_1 = \langle 1,-2,0\rangle$, $\mathbf{x}_2 = \langle 2,0,3\rangle$, $\mathbf{x}_3 = \langle 1,-1,4\rangle$ of V_3 linearly independent?

Solution: We use **20.5** as follows. If $a\mathbf{x}_1 + b\mathbf{x}_2 + c\mathbf{x}_3 = \mathbf{0}$, that is,

$$a\langle 1,-2,0\rangle + b\langle 2,0,3\rangle + c\langle 1,-1,4\rangle = \langle 0,0,0\rangle,$$

then

$$\langle a,-2a,0\rangle + \langle 2b,0,3b\rangle + \langle c,-c,4c\rangle = \langle 0,0,0\rangle$$

or

$$\langle a + 2b + c, -2a - c, 3b + 4c\rangle = \langle 0,0,0\rangle.$$

Hence

$$\begin{aligned} a + 2b + c &= 0 \\ -2a - c &= 0 \\ 3b + 4c &= 0. \end{aligned}$$

We solve this system of three linear equations in three unknowns a,b,c in the usual manner. If we multiply the first equation by 2 and add it to the second equation, we obtain $4b + c = 0$. Thus $c = -4b$ and

$$3b + 4(-4b) = -13b = 0$$

from the third equation. Hence $b = 0$, $4 \cdot 0 + c = 0$ and $c = 0$, and $a + 2 \cdot 0 + 0 = 0$ and $a = 0$. Since the only scalars a,b,c such that $a\mathbf{x}_1 + b\mathbf{x}_2 + c\mathbf{x}_3 = \mathbf{0}$ are $a = 0$, $b = 0$, $c = 0$, the vectors $\mathbf{x}_1,\mathbf{x}_2,\mathbf{x}_3$ are linearly independent according to **20.5**.

EXAMPLE 2. Are the vectors $\mathbf{y}_1 = \langle -3,5,2\rangle$, $\mathbf{y}_2 = \langle 4,1,-3\rangle$, $\mathbf{y}_3 = \langle -1,17,0\rangle$ of V_3 linearly independent?

Solution: Proceeding as above, if

$$a\langle -3,5,2\rangle + b\langle 4,1,-3\rangle + c\langle -1,17,0\rangle = \langle 0,0,0\rangle$$

then

$$\begin{aligned} -3a + 4b - c &= 0 \\ 5a + b + 17c &= 0 \\ 2a - 3b &= 0. \end{aligned}$$

We easily show that $a = 3$, $b = 2$, $c = -1$ is a solution of this system. Hence the vectors $\mathbf{y}_1,\mathbf{y}_2,\mathbf{y}_3$ are dependent by **20.5**. Actually,

$$\mathbf{y}_3 = 3\mathbf{y}_1 + 2\mathbf{y}_2.$$

The vectors $\mathbf{i},\mathbf{j},\mathbf{k}$ of V_3 are linearly independent and span V_3. These vectors form a basis of V_3 according to the following definition.

20.6 DEFINITION. A set $\{\mathbf{u}_1,\mathbf{u}_2, \cdots, \mathbf{u}_n\}$ of vectors of a vector space V is called a *basis* of V if and only if the vectors $\mathbf{u}_1,\mathbf{u}_2, \cdots, \mathbf{u}_n$ are linearly independent and span V.

If $\{\mathbf{u}_1,\mathbf{u}_2, \cdots, \mathbf{u}_n\}$ is a basis of V and $\mathbf{x}$ is any vector of V, then

$$\mathbf{x} = \sum_{i=1}^{n} c_i\mathbf{u}_i$$

for some scalars $c_1,c_2, \cdots, c_n$. The scalars $c_1,c_2, \cdots, c_n$ are unique. For if $\mathbf{x}$ is also given by

$$\mathbf{x} = \sum_{i=1}^{n} d_i\mathbf{u}_i,$$

then $\Sigma\, c_i\mathbf{u}_i = \Sigma\, d_i\mathbf{u}_i$ and

$$\sum_{i=1}^{n} (c_i - d_i)\mathbf{u}_i = \mathbf{0}.$$

Since $\mathbf{u}_1,\mathbf{u}_2, \cdots, \mathbf{u}_n$ are linearly independent, $c_1 - d_1 = 0$, $c_2 - d_2 = 0, \cdots,$ $c_n - d_n = 0$ by **20.5**. Hence, $d_1 = c_1, d_2 = c_2, \cdots, d_n = c_n$ and the scalars $c_1,c_2, \cdots, c_n$ are indeed unique. We state this result below.

20.7 THEOREM. If $\{\mathbf{u}_1,\mathbf{u}_2, \cdots, \mathbf{u}_n\}$ is a basis of the vector space V, then each vector $\mathbf{x}$ of V is uniquely expressible as a linear combination of the basis vectors.

An important property of a vector space is that any two bases have the same number of elements. We shall not prove this property in general, but indicate why it is so in V_3.

One basis of V_3 is $\{\mathbf{i},\mathbf{j},\mathbf{k}\}$. If $\mathbf{u}_1$ is any nonzero vector of V_3, then

$$\mathbf{u}_1 = a_1\mathbf{i} + a_2\mathbf{j} + a_3\mathbf{k} \tag{1}$$

for some unique scalars a_1,a_2,a_3. Since $\mathbf{u}_1 \neq \mathbf{0}$, at least one of a_1,a_2,a_3 is nonzero. Assume $a_1 \neq 0$. Then we claim that

$$\{\mathbf{u}_1,\mathbf{j},\mathbf{k}\}$$

is also a basis of V_3. To prove this, we first observe that by (1)

$$a_1\mathbf{i} = \mathbf{u}_1 - a_2\mathbf{j} - a_3\mathbf{k}$$

and therefore

$$\mathbf{i} = b_1\mathbf{u}_1 + b_2\mathbf{j} + b_3\mathbf{k} \tag{2}$$

where $b_1 = 1/a_1$, $b_2 = -a_2/a_1$, $b_3 = -a_3/a_1$. If $\mathbf{x} = c_1\mathbf{i} + c_2\mathbf{j} + c_3\mathbf{k}$ is any element of V_3, then from (2), $\mathbf{x} = c_1(b_1\mathbf{u}_1 + b_2\mathbf{j} + b_3\mathbf{k}) + c_2\mathbf{j} + c_3\mathbf{k} = (c_1b_1)\mathbf{u}_1 + (c_1b_2 + c_2)\mathbf{j} + (c_1b_3 + c_3)\mathbf{k}$. Since each vector of V_3 is a linear combination of $\mathbf{u}_1,\mathbf{j},\mathbf{k}$, V_3 is spanned by $\mathbf{u}_1,\mathbf{j},\mathbf{k}$. To prove that $\mathbf{u}_1,\mathbf{j},\mathbf{k}$ are linearly independent, assume that $d_1\mathbf{u}_1 + d_2\mathbf{j} + d_3\mathbf{k} = \mathbf{0}$. Then by (1), $d_1(a_1\mathbf{i} + a_2\mathbf{j} + a_3\mathbf{k}) + d_2\mathbf{j} + d_3\mathbf{k} = \mathbf{0}$ and

$$(d_1a_1)\mathbf{i} + (d_1a_2 + d_2)\mathbf{j} + (d_1a_3 + d_3)\mathbf{k} = \mathbf{0}.$$

Since $\mathbf{i},\mathbf{j},\mathbf{k}$ are linearly independent, necessarily $d_1a_1 = 0$, $d_1a_2 + d_2 = 0$, $d_1a_3 + d_3 = 0$. By assumption, $a_1 \neq 0$, and therefore $d_1 = 0$, $d_2 = 0$, $d_3 = 0$. Since the only scalars d_1,d_2,d_3 such that $d_1\mathbf{u}_1 + d_2\mathbf{j} + d_3\mathbf{k} = \mathbf{0}$ are $d_1 = 0$, $d_2 = 0$, $d_3 = 0$, the vectors $\mathbf{u}_1,\mathbf{j},\mathbf{k}$ are linearly independent. This proves that $\{\mathbf{u}_1,\mathbf{j},\mathbf{k}\}$ is a basis of V_3.

If $\mathbf{u}_1$ and $\mathbf{u}_2$ are linearly independent vectors of V_3, then $\mathbf{u}_2 = a_1\mathbf{u}_1 + a_2\mathbf{j} + a_3\mathbf{k}$ for some scalars a_1,a_2,a_3. We cannot have both $a_2 = 0$ and $a_3 = 0$, for then we would have $\mathbf{u}_2 = a_1\mathbf{u}_1$ and $\mathbf{u}_1,\mathbf{u}_2$ would be linearly dependent. If $a_2 \neq 0$, then by the same argument as above,

$$\{\mathbf{u}_1,\mathbf{u}_2,\mathbf{k}\}$$

may be shown to be a basis of V_3.

Finally, if $\mathbf{u}_1,\mathbf{u}_2,\mathbf{u}_3$ are linearly independent vectors of V_3, then

$$\mathbf{u}_3 = a_1\mathbf{u}_1 + a_2\mathbf{u}_2 + a_3\mathbf{k}$$

for some scalars a_1,a_2,a_3. We must have $a_3 \neq 0$, for otherwise $\mathbf{u}_1,\mathbf{u}_2,\mathbf{u}_3$ would be linearly dependent. Then the same argument as before shows that

$$\{\mathbf{u}_1,\mathbf{u}_2,\mathbf{u}_3\}$$

is a basis of V_3. That is, *any three linearly independent vectors of V_3 form a basis.*

There cannot be four linearly independent vectors of V_3. For our statement above shows that any three of them form a basis, and hence the fourth vector is a linear combination of the other three. Naturally, there also cannot be more than four linearly independent vectors of V_3.

20.8 DEFINITION. The number of elements in a basis of a vector space V is called the *dimension* of V.

According to this definition, V_2 has dimension 2 since a basis $\{\mathbf{i},\mathbf{j}\}$ has two elements and V_3 has dimension 3 since a basis $\{\mathbf{i},\mathbf{j},\mathbf{k}\}$ has three elements. By Example 1 and our remarks above,

$$\{\langle 1,-2,0\rangle, \langle 2,0,3\rangle, \langle 1,-1,4\rangle\}$$

is another basis of V_3.

In general, for any positive integer n we can form the set

$$V_n = \{\langle a_1,a_2, \cdots, a_n\rangle \mid a_i \text{ in } \mathsf{R}\}$$

of all ordered n-tuples of real numbers. Addition and scalar multiplication are defined in V_n coordinatewise as they are in V_2 and V_3. Thus

$$\langle a_1,a_2, \cdots, a_n\rangle + \langle b_1,b_2, \cdots, b_n\rangle = \langle a_1 + b_1,a_2 + b_2, \cdots, a_n + b_n\rangle$$
$$c\langle a_1,a_2, \cdots, a_n\rangle = \langle ca_1,ca_2, \cdots, ca_n\rangle.$$

The eight properties of a vector space listed in **20.1** are easily shown to hold for V_n. If $\mathbf{u}_i$ is the vector with 1 in the ith coordinate and 0's elsewhere, then for any scalars a_i in R,

$$\sum_{i=1}^{n} a_i\mathbf{u}_i = \langle a_1,a_2, \cdots, a_n\rangle.$$

Evidently $\{\mathbf{u}_1,\mathbf{u}_2, \cdots, \mathbf{u}_n\}$ is a basis of V_n. Hence vector space V_n has dimension n.

EXAMPLE 3. Are the vectors $\mathbf{x}_1 = \langle 1,0,-1,0\rangle$, $\mathbf{x}_2 = \langle 1,1,0,-1\rangle$, $\mathbf{x}_3 = \langle 0,1,-1,0\rangle$ of V_4 linearly independent? If so, find a vector $\mathbf{x}_4$ such that $\{\mathbf{x}_1,\mathbf{x}_2,\mathbf{x}_3,\mathbf{x}_4\}$ is a basis of V_4.

Solution: If $a\mathbf{x}_1 + b\mathbf{x}_2 + c\mathbf{x}_3 = \mathbf{0}$, that is, if

$$\langle a,0,-a,0\rangle + \langle b,b,0,-b\rangle + \langle 0,c,-c,0\rangle = \langle 0,0,0,0\rangle,$$

then

$$\begin{aligned} a + b &= 0 \\ b + c &= 0 \\ -a - c &= 0 \\ -b &= 0. \end{aligned}$$

From these equations we easily see that $b = 0$, $a = 0$, $c = 0$. Hence $\mathbf{x}_1$, $\mathbf{x}_2$, $\mathbf{x}_3$ are linearly independent by **20.5**.

The vectors $\mathbf{x}_1,\mathbf{x}_2,\mathbf{x}_3$ along with some one of the $\mathbf{u}_i$ defined above will be a basis of V_4. Since $a\mathbf{x}_1 + b\mathbf{x}_2 + c\mathbf{x}_3 \neq \mathbf{u}_1$ for all choices of the scalars a, b, c, the vectors $\mathbf{x}_1$, $\mathbf{x}_2$, $\mathbf{x}_3$, $\mathbf{u}_1$ are linearly independent. Any four linearly independent vectors of V_4 span V_4; and hence $\{\mathbf{x}_1,\mathbf{x}_2,\mathbf{x}_3,\mathbf{u}_1\}$ is a basis of V_4.

EXERCISES

1. Prove **20.3**. [*Hint:* If $a = 0$, then $a + a = a$, $a\mathbf{x} = (a + a)\mathbf{x} = a\mathbf{x} + a\mathbf{x}$, $a\mathbf{x} + \mathbf{0} = a\mathbf{x} + a\mathbf{x}$, etc. If $\mathbf{x} = \mathbf{0}$, argue similarly. Conversely, if $a\mathbf{x} = \mathbf{0}$, then consider the two possible cases $a = 0$ and $a \neq 0$.]

2. Prove **20.4**. [*Hint:* $a\mathbf{x} + [-(a\mathbf{x})] = \mathbf{0}$ by **20.1** (4). Also, $a\mathbf{x} + (-a)\mathbf{x} = [a + (-a)]\,\mathbf{x} = \mathbf{0}$ by **20.1**(6) and **20.3**. Hence $a\mathbf{x} + [-(a\mathbf{x})] = a\mathbf{x} + (-a)\mathbf{x}$, etc.]

3. Prove the following properties of subtraction: (1) $a(\mathbf{x} - \mathbf{y}) = a\mathbf{x} - a\mathbf{y}$. (2) $-(\mathbf{x} - \mathbf{y}) = (-\mathbf{x}) + \mathbf{y}$.

4. Prove that the intersection of two subspaces of a vector space V is also a subspace of V.

In each of Exercises 5–10, tell whether or not the set of vectors is a basis of the given vector space.

5. $\{2\mathbf{i} - \mathbf{j}, \mathbf{i} + 3\mathbf{j}\}$ in V_2.

6. $\{\mathbf{i} - \mathbf{j},\ \mathbf{i} + \mathbf{j},\ 3\mathbf{i} + 2\mathbf{j}\}$ in V_2.

7. $\{\mathbf{i} - 3\mathbf{j},\ 2\mathbf{i} + \mathbf{k}, \mathbf{i} + 9\mathbf{j} + 2\mathbf{k}\}$ in V_3.

8. $\{\langle 1,0,-1,0\rangle, \langle 0,1,0,1\rangle, \langle 1,1,0,0\rangle, \langle 0,0,1,1\rangle\}$ in V_4.

9. $\{\langle 1,0,-1,0\rangle, \langle 0,1,0,1\rangle, \langle 1,1,0,0\rangle, \langle 0,0,1,-1\rangle\}$ in V_4.

10. $\{\mathbf{u}_1, \mathbf{u}_1 + \mathbf{u}_2, \mathbf{u}_1 + \mathbf{u}_2 + \mathbf{u}_3, \cdots, \mathbf{u}_1 + \mathbf{u}_2 + \cdots + \mathbf{u}_n\}$ in V_n.

In each of Exercises 11–16, show that the vectors are linearly independent and find a basis of the given vector space containing the given vectors.

11. $\{2\mathbf{i} - \mathbf{j}, \mathbf{i} + \mathbf{k}\}$ in V_3.

12. $\{\langle 1,0,1,0\rangle, \langle -2,1,1,1\rangle, \langle 3,1,2,1\rangle\}$ in V_4.

13. $\{\langle 1,1,0,0,0\rangle, \langle 1,1,1,0,0\rangle, \langle 1,1,1,1,0\rangle\}$ in V_5.

14. $\{\mathbf{i} + \mathbf{j}, \mathbf{k}\}$ in V_3.

15. $\{\langle 1,0,1\rangle, \langle 0,1,0\rangle, \langle -1,1,1\rangle\}$ in V_3.

16. $\{\langle 1,-1,0,0\rangle\}$ in V_4.

2 MATRICES

A rectangular array of numbers such as

$$A = \begin{bmatrix} a_{11} & a_{12} & \cdots & a_{1n} \\ a_{21} & a_{22} & \cdots & a_{2n} \\ & \cdots\cdots & & \\ & \cdots\cdots & & \\ a_{m1} & a_{m2} & \cdots & a_{mn} \end{bmatrix}$$

is called an $m \times n$ *matrix.* It consists of m row vectors $A_1, A_2, \cdots, A_m$, where for each i:

$$A_i = (a_{i1}, a_{i2}, \cdots, a_{in}),$$

and n column vectors $A^1, A^2, \cdots, A^n$, where for each j:

$$A^j = \begin{bmatrix} a_{1j} \\ a_{2j} \\ \cdot \\ \cdot \\ \cdot \\ a_{mj} \end{bmatrix}.$$

We shall often describe A as the $m \times n$ matrix (a_{ij}). If $m = n$, then A is called a *square matrix.*

The row vectors of the $m \times n$ matrix $A = (a_{ij})$ are n-tuples which belong to the vector space V_n. Hence they generate a subspace S of V_n consisting of all linear combinations of the vectors $A_1, A_2, \cdots, A_m$:

$$S = \{\sum_{i=1}^{m} r_i A_i \mid r_i \text{ in } \mathsf{R}\}.$$

We call S the *row space* of matrix A, and the dimension of S the *row rank* of A:

$$\text{rr}(A) = \dim S.$$

Similarly, the columns of an $m \times n$ matrix $A = (a_{ij})$ generate a subspace T of the vector space V_m. We call T the *column space* of A, and the dimension of T the column rank of A:

$$\text{cr}(A) = \dim T.$$

Since the row space S of the $m \times n$ matrix A is generated by m vectors, $\dim S \leq m$; and since S is a subspace of the n-dimensional space V_n, $\dim S \leq n$. Thus

$$\text{rr}(A) \leq \min(m,n),$$

and similarly

$$\text{cr}(A) \leq \min(m,n).$$

There are three *elementary row operations* on an $m \times n$ matrix A which might change A but do not change rr(A):

(1) Multiply a row of A by any nonzero number r.

(2) Interchange two rows of A.

(3) Replace a row A_j of A by $A_j + rA_i$ for any number r and any row A_i with $i \neq j$.

If for example

$$A = \begin{bmatrix} 1 & 2 & -1 \\ 3 & 0 & 2 \end{bmatrix},$$

then A has two rows $A_1 = (1,2,-1)$ and $A_2 = (3,0,2)$. The matrix

$$B = \begin{bmatrix} -4 & -8 & 4 \\ 3 & 0 & 2 \end{bmatrix}$$

has rows $-4A_1$ and A_2, and hence is obtained from A by elementary row operation (1). If we interchange the rows of A, we obtain matrix

$$C = \begin{bmatrix} 3 & 0 & 2 \\ 1 & 2 & -1 \end{bmatrix}.$$

This illustrates elementary row operation (2). Finally, the matrix

$$D = \begin{bmatrix} 1 & 2 & -1 \\ 6 & 6 & -1 \end{bmatrix},$$

which has rows A_1 and $A_2 + 3A_1$, is obtained from A by elementary row operation (3).

The elementary row operations on an $m \times n$ matrix A do not change the row rank of A for the simple reason that they do not change the row space of A. This is evident for operations (1) and (2). If the row vectors of A are $A_1, A_2, \cdots, A_m$ and of B are $A_1 + rA_2, A_2, \cdots, A_n$, then the row space S_2 of B is clearly contained in the row space S_1 of A. On the other hand, $A_1 = (A_1 + rA_2) + (-r)A_2$, and therefore each of the rows of A is a linear combination of the rows of B. Hence, $S_1 = S_2$. This illustrates why operation (3) does not change the row space of a matrix.

Similarly, there are three elementary column operations on a matrix A which do not change the column rank of A. We shall not do so, but it can be shown that the elementary column operations on A also do not change the row rank of A. Once this has been observed, it is possible to prove that

$$\mathrm{cr}(A) = \mathrm{rr}(A)$$

for every matrix A. We omit the proof of this fact in this book. Since the column and row ranks are the same, we can define the *rank of a matrix A*, denoted by $r(A)$, to be this common value,

$$r(A) = \mathrm{cr}(A) = \mathrm{rr}(A).$$

By definition, the rank of a matrix A is the largest integer k such that some k of the row (or column) vectors of A are linearly independent. Having found k independent row (or column) vectors, every other row (or column) vector is a linear combination of these k vectors.

A practical way of finding the rank of a matrix is to change it into *echelon form* by use of elementary row (or column) operations. A matrix A is said to be in echelon form if successive row (or column) vectors of A start with more and more zeros. For example, the 3×4 matrix

$$A = \begin{bmatrix} 1 & 2 & -1 & 0 \\ 0 & 5 & 4 & 2 \\ 0 & 0 & 0 & 7 \end{bmatrix}$$

is in echelon form, since its successive row vectors start with more and more zeros: its first row starts with 0 zeros, its second row starts with 1 zero, and its third row starts with 3 zeros. The rank of A is obviously three, since

$$a(1,2,-1,0) + b(0,5,4,2) + c(0,0,0,7) = (0,0,0,0)$$

if and only if $a = 0$, $b = 0$, and $c = 0$. Thus the three row vectors of A are linearly independent and $r(A) = \mathrm{rr}(A) = 3$.

More generally, if a matrix is in (row) echelon form, *the rank of A is the number of nonzero row vectors of A*. A similar result holds if A is in column echelon form.

EXAMPLE 1. Find the rank of the matrix

$$A = \begin{bmatrix} -3 & 2 & 4 \\ 1 & -5 & -3 \\ -9 & -7 & 7 \end{bmatrix}.$$

Solution: If we interchange, the first two rows of A, which is an elementary row operation, we obtain the matrix

$$B = \begin{bmatrix} 1 & -5 & -3 \\ -3 & 2 & 4 \\ -9 & -7 & 7 \end{bmatrix} \begin{matrix} (B_1) \\ (B_2) \\ (B_3) \end{matrix}$$

having the same rank as A. In turn, the matrix

$$C = \begin{bmatrix} 1 & -5 & -3 \\ 0 & -13 & -5 \\ 0 & -52 & -20 \end{bmatrix} \begin{matrix} (C_1 = B_1) \\ (C_2 = B_2 + 3B_1) \\ (C_3 = B_3 + 9B_1) \end{matrix}$$

whose row vectors are obtained from those of B by elementary row operations as indicated, has the same rank as B. Finally, the matrix

$$D = \begin{bmatrix} 1 & -5 & -3 \\ 0 & -13 & -5 \\ 0 & 0 & 0 \end{bmatrix} \begin{matrix} (D_1 = C_1) \\ (D_2 = C_2) \\ (D_3 = C_3 - 4C_2) \end{matrix}$$

whose row vectors are obtained from those of C by elementary row operations as indicated, has the same rank as C. The matrix D is in (row) echelon form, and has rank 2. Hence $r(C) = r(B) = r(A) = 2$.

EXAMPLE 2. Find the rank of the matrix

$$A = \begin{bmatrix} 2 & 1 & 0 \\ 1 & -1 & 1 \\ 4 & 1 & 2 \\ 2 & -3 & 3 \end{bmatrix}.$$

Solution: We have $r(A) = cr(A) \leq 3$. If A has column vectors A^1, A^2, A^3, then

$$B = \begin{bmatrix} 1 & 0 & 0 \\ -1 & 1 & 3 \\ 1 & 2 & 2 \\ -3 & 3 & 8 \end{bmatrix}$$

has column vectors A^2, A^3, $A^1 - 2A^2$. Hence $r(B) = r(A)$. In turn,

$$C = \begin{bmatrix} 1 & 0 & 0 \\ -1 & 1 & 0 \\ 1 & 2 & -4 \\ -3 & 3 & -1 \end{bmatrix}$$

has column vectors B^1, B^2, $B^3 - 3B^2$, and hence $r(C) = r(B) = r(A)$. Now C is in column echelon form, and evidently has rank 3. Hence $r(A) = 3$.

EXERCISES

Find the rank of each of the following matrices.

1. $\begin{bmatrix} 0 & 1 & 1 & -1 \\ 0 & 0 & 2 & 1 \end{bmatrix}$.

2. $\begin{bmatrix} -1 & 3 \\ 2 & -6 \end{bmatrix}$.

3. $\begin{bmatrix} 1 & 2 & 4 \\ -1 & 1 & 5 \\ 0 & 1 & 3 \\ 1 & 0 & -2 \end{bmatrix}$.

4. $\begin{bmatrix} 2 & -2 & 2 \\ 1 & 0 & -1 \\ 0 & 1 & 1 \end{bmatrix}$.

5. $\begin{bmatrix} 2 & 0 & 2 & 0 \\ 1 & 1 & 0 & 1 \\ 1 & -3 & 4 & -3 \end{bmatrix}$.

6. $\begin{bmatrix} 2 & -1 \\ 1 & 3 \\ 5 & 7 \end{bmatrix}$.

7. $\begin{bmatrix} 1 & 1 & 1 & 1 \\ -1 & 1 & 1 & -1 \\ 1 & 0 & 1 & 1 \\ 1 & 1 & 0 & 1 \end{bmatrix}$.

8. $\begin{bmatrix} 1 & -1 & 1 & -1 \\ 1 & 1 & -1 & -1 \\ 1 & 0 & -1 & 1 \\ 1 & -1 & 0 & 1 \end{bmatrix}$.

3 SYSTEMS OF LINEAR EQUATIONS

All of us are familiar with systems of linear equations, such as

$$\begin{aligned} x - 2y &= 3 \\ 3x + y &= -5 \end{aligned} \tag{1}$$

and

$$\begin{aligned} x + 3y - z &= 1 \\ -2x + y + 2z &= 5 \\ 3x - 2y - z &= 0. \end{aligned} \tag{2}$$

Associated with system (1) are the two matrices

$$\begin{bmatrix} 1 & -2 \\ 3 & 1 \end{bmatrix} \text{ and } \begin{bmatrix} 1 & -2 & 3 \\ 3 & 1 & -5 \end{bmatrix},$$

called the *matrix of coefficients of the unknowns* and the *augmented matrix*, respectively. The matrix of coefficients of the unknowns and the augmented matrix of system (2) are respectively

$$\begin{bmatrix} 1 & 3 & -1 \\ -2 & 1 & 2 \\ 3 & -2 & -1 \end{bmatrix} \text{ and } \begin{bmatrix} 1 & 3 & -1 & 1 \\ -2 & 1 & 2 & 5 \\ 3 & -2 & -1 & 0 \end{bmatrix},$$

We can solve a system of linear equations simply by reducing its augmented matrix to echelon form by use of elementary row operations. In terms of the given system of linear equations, these operations in order: (1) multiply one equation by any nonzero number r, (2) interchange two equations, and (3) replace an equation E_j by $E_j + rE_i$ for any number r and any equation E_i with $i \neq j$. Such operations on a system of linear equations transform the system into an *equivalent system*, i.e., a system with the same solutions. We illustrate with the examples above.

The augmented matrix of system (1)

$$\begin{bmatrix} 1 & -2 & 3 \\ 3 & 1 & -5 \end{bmatrix} \begin{matrix} E_1 \\ E_2 \end{matrix}$$

can be transformed into echelon form

$$\begin{bmatrix} 1 & -2 & 3 \\ 0 & 7 & -14 \end{bmatrix} \begin{matrix} E_1 \\ E_2 - 3E_1. \end{matrix}$$

Hence system (1) has the same solutions as the system having the augmented matrix above:

$$(1') \qquad \begin{aligned} x - 2y &= 3 \\ 7y &= -14. \end{aligned}$$

From the second equation, $y = -2$, and substituting $y = -2$ in the first equation, $x = -1$. Thus the unique solution of system (1′), and hence also of (1), is

$$x = -1, y = -2.$$

The augmented matrix of system (2)

$$\begin{bmatrix} 1 & 3 & -1 & 1 \\ -2 & 1 & 2 & 5 \\ 3 & -2 & -1 & 0 \end{bmatrix} \begin{matrix} E_1 \\ E_2 \\ E_3 \end{matrix}$$

can be reduced to echelon form as follows:

$$\begin{bmatrix} 1 & 3 & -1 & 1 \\ 0 & 7 & 0 & 7 \\ 0 & -11 & 2 & -3 \end{bmatrix} \quad \begin{matrix} E_1 & = F_1 \\ E_2 + 2E_1 & = F_2 \\ E_3 - 3E_1 & = F_3 \end{matrix}$$

$$\begin{bmatrix} 1 & 3 & -1 & 1 \\ 0 & 7 & 0 & 7 \\ 0 & 0 & 2 & 8 \end{bmatrix} \quad \begin{matrix} F_1 \\ F_2 \\ F_3 + \frac{11}{7}F_2. \end{matrix}$$

Therefore system (2) has the same solution as the system having the augmented matrix above:

$$(2') \qquad \begin{aligned} x + 3y - z &= 1 \\ 7y &= 7 \\ 2z &= 8. \end{aligned}$$

From the last equation of (2′), $z = 4$; from the second equation, $y = 1$; letting $y = 1$ and $z = 4$ in the first equation, $x = 2$. Thus the unique solution of system (2′), and hence also of (2), is

$$x = 2,\ y = 1,\ z = 4.$$

Not every system of linear equations need have a solution, as the following example shows.

EXAMPLE 1. Solve the system

$$\begin{aligned} 2x - 3y + z &= 6 \\ 3x + y + 2z &= 7 \\ x - 18y - z &= 4. \end{aligned}$$

Solution: This system has augmented matrix

$$\begin{bmatrix} 2 & -3 & 1 & 6 \\ 3 & 1 & 2 & 7 \\ 1 & -18 & -1 & 4 \end{bmatrix} \quad \begin{matrix} E_1 \\ E_2. \\ E_3 \end{matrix}$$

For simpler arithmetic, let us interchange E_1 and E_3:

$$\begin{bmatrix} 1 & -18 & -1 & 4 \\ 3 & 1 & 2 & 7 \\ 2 & -3 & 1 & 6 \end{bmatrix} \quad \begin{matrix} E_3 \\ E_2. \\ E_1 \end{matrix}$$

Then we put this matrix in echelon form as follows:

$$\begin{bmatrix} 1 & -18 & -1 & 4 \\ 0 & 55 & 5 & -5 \\ 0 & 33 & 3 & -2 \end{bmatrix} \begin{matrix} E_3 = F_1 \\ E_2 - 3E_3 = F_2 \\ E_1 - 2E_3 = F_3 \end{matrix}$$

$$\begin{bmatrix} 1 & -18 & -1 & 4 \\ 0 & 55 & 5 & -5 \\ 0 & 0 & 0 & 1 \end{bmatrix} \begin{matrix} F_1 \\ F_2 \\ F_3 - \frac{3}{5}F_2. \end{matrix}$$

Hence, the given system has the same solution as the system having the augmented matrix above:

$$\begin{aligned} x - 18y - z &= 4 \\ 55y + 5z &= -5 \\ 0 &= 1. \end{aligned}$$

Since the last equation has no solution (the last equation is false!), the system has no solution. Therefore the given system has no solution.

A system of linear equations can have more than one solution, as the following example shows.

EXAMPLE 2. Solve the system

$$\begin{aligned} x + 2y - 3z &= -4 \\ -2x + y - 4z &= 3 \\ -x + 8y - 17z &= -6. \end{aligned}$$

Solution: This system has augmented matrix

$$\begin{bmatrix} 1 & 2 & -3 & -4 \\ -2 & 1 & -4 & 3 \\ -1 & 8 & -17 & -6 \end{bmatrix} \begin{matrix} E_1 \\ E_2 \\ E_3 \end{matrix}$$

It can be put in echelon form as follows:

$$\begin{bmatrix} 1 & 2 & -3 & -4 \\ 0 & 5 & -10 & -5 \\ 0 & 10 & -20 & -10 \end{bmatrix} \begin{matrix} E_1 = F_1 \\ E_2 + 2E_1 = F_2 \\ E_3 + E_1 = F_3 \end{matrix}$$

$$\begin{bmatrix} 1 & 2 & -3 & -4 \\ 0 & 5 & -10 & -5 \\ 0 & 0 & 0 & 0 \end{bmatrix} \begin{matrix} F_1 \\ F_2 \\ F_3 - 2F_2. \end{matrix}$$

Therefore the given system has the same solutions as the following system with augmented matrix above.

$$\begin{aligned} x + 2y - 3z &= -4 \\ 5y - 10z &= -5 \\ 0 &= 0. \end{aligned}$$

The third equation above has all values of x, y, and z as solutions. We solve the second equation for y in terms of z, $y = 2z - 1$, and substitute this in the first equation, obtaining $x = -z - 2$. Hence

$$x = -z - 2, \quad y = 2z - 1$$

is a solution of the given system for all values of z. For example,

$$x = -2, y = -1, z = 0 \quad \text{and} \quad x = -3, y = 1, z = 1$$

are solutions.

EXERCISES

Solve each of the following systems of equations.

1. $2x + y = 1$
   $x - 2y = 8.$

2. $3x - y = 1$
   $-6x + 2y = -2$
   $5x - 3y = -3.$

3. $x + y - z = -2$
   $2x + y + 2z = 7$
   $3x - 2y - 7z = 1.$

4. $2x + 3y - z = 5$
   $3x - 2y + 2z = 3$
   $7x + 4y = 5.$

5. $x + 3y = -7$
   $3x + 5y + 4z = -9$
   $2x - y + 7z = 7.$

6. $2x + 2y - z = 13$
   $x - 3y + 2z = -21$
   $-25x + 3y + 4z = 3.$

7. $x + y + z + w = 1$
   $-x + z + 2w = 1$
   $3x + 2y - w = 1$
   $x + y + 2z + 2w = 1.$

8. $2x + 3y + z + 2w = 3$
   $x - y - z + w = 0$
   $3x + 2y + 2z + w = -1$
   $5y - 2z + w = 1.$

9. $2x - y = 3$
   $y + 2z = 5$
   $3x + w = -1$
   $3z - w = 2.$

10. $2x + y - 8z + w = 0$
    $x - 3y + 3z + 4w = -7$
    $x + y - 5z = 1$
    $-x + 2y + z - 3w = 5.$

4 DETERMINANTS

If we cross out the rth row and sth column of an $m \times n$ matrix $A = (a_{ij})$, we obtain an $(m - 1) \times (n - 1)$ matrix, which we call a *submatrix* of A and denote by A_{rs}. For example, if A is the 3×3 matrix,

$$A = \begin{bmatrix} a_{11} & a_{12} & a_{13} \\ a_{21} & a_{22} & a_{23} \\ a_{31} & a_{32} & a_{33} \end{bmatrix}$$

then

$$A_{12} = \begin{bmatrix} a_{21} & a_{23} \\ a_{31} & a_{33} \end{bmatrix}$$

is the 2 × 2 submatrix of A obtained by crossing out the 1st row and 2nd column of A. Similarly,

$$A_{11} = \begin{bmatrix} a_{22} & a_{23} \\ a_{32} & a_{33} \end{bmatrix}, \qquad A_{23} = \begin{bmatrix} a_{11} & a_{12} \\ a_{31} & a_{32} \end{bmatrix}.$$

Associated with each square matrix $A = (a_{ij})$ is a number called the *determinant* of A and designated by $|A|$ or det A. The determinant can be defined inductively as follows:

(1) If $A = (a_{11})$, a 1 × 1 matrix, then $|A| = a_{11}$.

Having defined the determinant of every $(n - 1) \times (n - 1)$ matrix, we define $|A|$ for each $n \times n$ matrix $A = (a_{ij})$ by

(2) $$|A| = a_{11}|A_{11}| - a_{12}|A_{12}| + a_{13}|A_{13}| - \cdots + (-1)^{1+n}a_{1n}|A_{1n}|.$$

In this way the determinant of every square matrix is defined.

For example, if $A = (a_{ij})$ is a 2 × 2 matrix, then $A_{11} = (a_{22})$, $A_{12} = (a_{21})$, and by (2) and (1)

(3) $$\begin{vmatrix} a_{11} & a_{12} \\ a_{21} & a_{22} \end{vmatrix} = a_{11}|A_{11}| - a_{12}|A_{12}| = a_{11}a_{22} - a_{12}a_{21}.$$

If $A = (a_{ij})$ is a 3 × 3 matrix, then by (3),

$$|A_{11}| = \begin{vmatrix} a_{22} & a_{23} \\ a_{32} & a_{33} \end{vmatrix} = a_{22}a_{33} - a_{23}a_{32}$$

$$|A_{12}| = \begin{vmatrix} a_{21} & a_{23} \\ a_{31} & a_{33} \end{vmatrix} = a_{21}a_{33} - a_{23}a_{31}$$

$$|A_{13}| = \begin{vmatrix} a_{21} & a_{22} \\ a_{31} & a_{32} \end{vmatrix} = a_{21}a_{32} - a_{22}a_{31}.$$

Hence, by (2),

(4) $$\begin{vmatrix} a_{11} & a_{12} & a_{13} \\ a_{21} & a_{22} & a_{23} \\ a_{31} & a_{32} & a_{33} \end{vmatrix} = a_{11}|A_{11}| - a_{12}|A_{12}| + a_{13}|A_{13}|$$

$$= a_{11}(a_{22}a_{33} - a_{23}a_{32}) - a_{12}(a_{21}a_{33} - a_{23}a_{31}) + a_{13}(a_{21}a_{32} - a_{22}a_{31}).$$

The following facts about determinants are stated without proof. Proofs may be found in almost any modern algebra text. For any square matrix A:

20.9 **THEOREM.** If B is the matrix obtained from A by multiplying a row or column of A by k, then $|B| = k|A|$.

20.10 THEOREM. If B is the matrix obtained from A by interchanging two rows or columns of A, then $|B| = -|A|$.

If A has a row or column of zeros, then that row or column is unchanged when we multiply it by 0. Hence, $|A| = 0\,|A| = 0$, by **20.9.** If two rows or columns of A are the same, then $|A| = -|A|$ when we interchange these equal rows or columns by **20.10.** Hence $2\,|A| = 0$ and $|A| = 0$ in this case. We state these cases below.

20.11 THEOREM. If A has a row or column of zeros, then $|A| = 0$.

20.12 THEOREM. If two rows or columns of A are equal, then $|A| = 0$.

Equation (2) of the definition of $|A|$ is called *the expansion of the determinant of the $n \times n$ matrix $A = (a_{ij})$ by minors of the first row.* It can be proved that $|A|$ can be expanded by minors of any row (or column). Thus *the expansion of $|A|$ by minors of the* ith *row* is as follows:

20.13 $$|A| = (-1)^{i+1}a_{i1}|A_{i1}| + (-1)^{i+2}a_{i2}|A_{i2}| + \cdots + (-1)^{i+n}a_{in}|A_{in}|.$$

EXAMPLE 1. If

$$A = \begin{bmatrix} 3 & -4 & 2 \\ -2 & 0 & 5 \\ 1 & -1 & 3 \end{bmatrix},$$

find $|A|$ by expanding $|A|$ by minors of the 2nd row.

Solution: We have

$$\begin{aligned} |A| &= (-1)^3(-2)\begin{vmatrix} -4 & 2 \\ -1 & 3 \end{vmatrix} + (-1)^4(0)\begin{vmatrix} 3 & 2 \\ 1 & 3 \end{vmatrix} + (-1)^5 5\begin{vmatrix} 3 & -4 \\ 1 & -1 \end{vmatrix} \\ &= 2(-12+2) + 0 - 5(-3+4) = -25. \end{aligned}$$

A square matrix $A = (a_{ij})$ for which $a_{ij} = 0$ if $i \neq j$ is called a *diagonal matrix.* A-3 $\times$ 3 diagonal matrix has the form

$$A = \begin{bmatrix} a_{11} & 0 & 0 \\ 0 & a_{22} & 0 \\ 0 & 0 & a_{33} \end{bmatrix}.$$

It is easy to check that for this diagonal matrix,

$$|A| = a_{11}a_{22}a_{33}.$$

In general, if $A = (a_{ij})$ is an $n \times n$ diagonal matrix, then

$$|A| = a_{11}a_{22} \cdots a_{nn}.$$

EXERCISES

Find the determinant of each of the following matrices.

1. $\begin{bmatrix} 2 & -3 \\ 1 & 2 \end{bmatrix}$.

2. $\begin{bmatrix} 1 & -1 & 0 \\ 2 & 0 & 1 \\ 0 & -1 & 1 \end{bmatrix}$.

3. $\begin{bmatrix} 4 & 1 & 2 \\ -1 & -3 & 1 \\ 0 & 5 & 1 \end{bmatrix}$.

4. $\begin{bmatrix} 2 & -1 & 1 & 3 \\ 0 & 0 & 2 & -2 \\ 1 & -1 & 1 & 4 \\ 0 & 1 & -3 & 5 \end{bmatrix}$.

5. $\begin{bmatrix} 5 & 0 & 0 & 0 \\ 1 & 2 & 0 & 0 \\ -1 & 0 & 1 & 0 \\ 2 & 1 & 0 & 3 \end{bmatrix}$.

6. $\begin{bmatrix} 1 & 0 & 1 & 0 \\ 0 & 1 & 0 & 1 \\ 0 & 0 & 1 & 1 \\ 1 & 1 & 0 & 0 \end{bmatrix}$.

7. $\begin{bmatrix} 1 & 0 & 0 \\ 0 & 0 & 1 \\ 0 & 1 & 0 \end{bmatrix}$.

8. $\begin{bmatrix} 0 & 3 & 4 \\ 0 & -1 & 2 \\ 1 & 1 & 1 \end{bmatrix}$.

9. $\begin{bmatrix} 0 & 1 & 0 & 1 & 0 \\ 1 & 0 & -1 & 0 & 0 \\ 1 & 1 & 0 & 0 & 0 \\ 0 & 0 & 0 & 1 & -1 \\ 0 & 0 & -1 & 1 & 0 \end{bmatrix}$.

10. $\begin{bmatrix} 1 & -1 & 0 & 0 & 0 \\ 1 & -1 & 1 & 0 & 0 \\ 0 & -1 & 1 & -1 & 0 \\ 0 & 0 & 1 & -1 & 1 \\ 0 & 0 & 0 & -1 & 1 \end{bmatrix}$.

5 ALGEBRA OF MATRICES

It is possible to add $m \times n$ matrices coordinatewise. Thus, if $A = (a_{ij})$ and $B = (b_{ij})$ are $m \times n$ matrices, their sum $A + B$ is the $m \times n$ matrix having $a_{ij} + b_{ij}$ as its element in the ith row and jth column:

$$(a_{ij}) + (b_{ij}) = (a_{ij} + b_{ij}).$$

For example,

$$\begin{bmatrix} a_{11} & a_{12} \\ a_{21} & a_{22} \end{bmatrix} + \begin{bmatrix} b_{11} & b_{12} \\ b_{21} & b_{22} \end{bmatrix} = \begin{bmatrix} a_{11} + b_{11} & a_{12} + b_{12} \\ a_{21} + b_{21} & a_{22} + b_{22} \end{bmatrix}.$$

We can also multiply an $m \times n$ matrix $A = (a_{ij})$ by a real number k, obtaining the $m \times n$ matrix $kA = (ka_{ij})$:

$$k(a_{ij}) = (ka_{ij}).$$

As with vectors, we call this operation *scalar multiplication*. For 2×2 matrices we have

$$k\begin{bmatrix} a_{11} & a_{12} \\ a_{21} & a_{22} \end{bmatrix} = \begin{bmatrix} ka_{11} & ka_{12} \\ ka_{21} & ka_{22} \end{bmatrix}.$$

Each $m \times n$ matrix can be thought of as a $m \times n$-tuple. It is then clear that the set $M_{m\times n}$ of all $m \times n$ matrices over R is a vector space if addition and scalar multiplication are as defined above. The additive identity element is (a_{ij}) where all $a_{ij} = 0$. For example,

$$\begin{bmatrix} 0 & 0 \\ 0 & 0 \end{bmatrix}$$

is the additive identity element of $M_{2\times 2}$. We call this matrix the *zero matrix* and denote it by 0. The *additive inverse* of the $m \times n$ matrix $A = (a_{ij})$ is $-A = (-a_{ij})$. For example, in $M_{2\times 2}$

$$-\begin{bmatrix} a_{11} & a_{12} \\ a_{21} & a_{22} \end{bmatrix} = \begin{bmatrix} -a_{11} & -a_{12} \\ -a_{21} & -a_{22} \end{bmatrix}.$$

All the rules for a vector space [**20.1**, (1)-(8)] hold for $M_{m\times n}$.

Matrices can be multiplied in a meaningful way if they have the proper number of rows and columns. Thus, if $A = (a_{ij})$ is an $m \times n$ matrix and $B = (b_{ij})$ is an $n \times p$ matrix, AB is the $m \times p$ matrix defined below.

$$AB = (c_{ij}),$$

where

$$c_{ij} = \sum_{k=1}^{n} a_{ik}b_{kj}, \qquad i = 1, \cdots, m, j = 1, \cdots, p.$$

The simplest example of matrix multiplication is that of a $1 \times n$ matrix (a_{1j}) by an $n \times 1$ matrix (b_{i1}). The result is a 1×1 matrix, or number, as follows.

$$(a_{11}\, a_{12} \cdots a_{1n})\begin{bmatrix} b_{11} \\ b_{21} \\ \cdot \\ \cdot \\ \cdot \\ b_{n1} \end{bmatrix} = a_{11}b_{11} + a_{12}b_{21} + \cdots + a_{1n}b_{n1}.$$

For example,

$$(2\ 1\ 3)\begin{pmatrix}-1\\3\\4\end{pmatrix} = (-2+3+12) = 13.$$

The product of an $m \times n$ matrix A and an $n \times p$ matrix B can be easily remembered if we consider it made up of products of row vectors of A ($1 \times n$ matrices) by column vectors of B ($n \times 1$ matrices). Thus if $A_1, A_2, \cdots, A_m$ are the row vectors of A and $B^1, B^2, \cdots, B^p$ are the column vectors of B, the (i,j)th element of AB is A_iB^j:

$$AB = (A_iB^j).$$

For

$$A_i = (a_{i1}, a_{i2}, \cdots, a_{in}),$$

$$B^j = \begin{bmatrix} b_{1j} \\ b_{2j} \\ \cdot \\ \cdot \\ \cdot \\ b_{nj} \end{bmatrix}$$

and

$$A_iB^j = \sum_{k=1}^{n} a_{ik}b_{kj}.$$

We shall not give the details, but it may be shown that matrix multiplication is associative:

$$A(BC) = (AB)C.$$

Of course we are assuming that the number of columns of A equals the number of rows of B, and the number of columns of B equals the number of rows of C. Also, the usual distributive laws hold: if A_1, A_2 are $m \times n$ matrices and B_1, B_2 are $n \times p$ matrices, then

$$(A_1 + A_2)B_1 = A_1B_1 + A_2B_1,\ A_1(B_1 + B_2) = A_1B_1 + A_1B_2.$$

Of special interest is the multiplication of $n \times n$ square matrices. The set $M_{n\times n}$ of all $n \times n$ square matrices over R is closed under addition, scalar multiplication, and matrix multiplication. Matrix multiplication is not commutative. For example, in $M_{2\times 2}$

$$\begin{bmatrix}1 & 0\\0 & 0\end{bmatrix}\begin{bmatrix}0 & 1\\0 & 0\end{bmatrix} = \begin{bmatrix}0 & 1\\0 & 0\end{bmatrix},\quad \begin{bmatrix}0 & 1\\0 & 0\end{bmatrix}\begin{bmatrix}1 & 0\\0 & 0\end{bmatrix} = \begin{bmatrix}0 & 0\\0 & 0\end{bmatrix}.$$

There is a multiplicative identity element in $M_{n\times n}$, namely the diagonal matrix

$$I = \begin{bmatrix} 1 & 0 & 0 & \cdots & 0 \\ 0 & 1 & 0 & \cdots & 0 \\ \cdot & & & & \cdot \\ \cdot & & & & \cdot \\ \cdot & & & & \cdot \\ \cdot & & & & 0 \\ 0 & 0 & 0 & \cdot\cdot 0 & 1 \end{bmatrix}.$$

For example, the 2×2 identity matrix is

$$\begin{bmatrix} 1 & 0 \\ 0 & 1 \end{bmatrix}.$$

It has the property

$$\begin{bmatrix} a_{11} & a_{12} \\ a_{21} & a_{22} \end{bmatrix}\begin{bmatrix} 1 & 0 \\ 0 & 1 \end{bmatrix} = \begin{bmatrix} 1 & 0 \\ 0 & 1 \end{bmatrix}\begin{bmatrix} a_{11} & a_{12} \\ a_{21} & a_{22} \end{bmatrix} = \begin{bmatrix} a_{11} & a_{12} \\ a_{21} & a_{22} \end{bmatrix}.$$

Scalar multiplication and matrix multiplication are related as follows:

$$k(AB) = (kA)B = A(kB)$$

for all k in R and A,B in $M_{n\times n}$.

Some nonzero matrices A in $M_{n\times n}$ have multiplicative inverses and some do not. In fact, it can be shown that A has an inverse if and only if $|A| \neq 0$. Why this is so is indicated below.

We recall by **20.13** that

(1) $$|A| = \sum_{k=1}^{n} (-1)^{j+k} a_{jk} |A_{jk}|, \quad j = 1, \cdots, n.$$

If we replace the jth row of A by its ith row, $i \neq j$, then the determinant of the resulting matrix is zero by **20.12**. Hence, by **20.13** again

(2) $$0 = \sum_{k=1}^{n} (-1)^{j+k} a_{ik} |A_{jk}|, \quad i \neq j, \quad i,j = 1, \cdots, n.$$

The element

$$a'_{kj} = (-1)^{j+k} |A_{jk}|$$

is called the *cofactor* of a_{jk}. By (1) and (2),

(3) $$\sum_{k=1}^{n} a_{ik} a'_{kj} = \begin{cases} |A| & \text{if } i = j \\ 0 & \text{if } i \neq j. \end{cases}$$

Thus if we define the *adjoint* of matrix A by

$$\operatorname{adj} A = (a'_{ij}),$$

then (3) shows that

$$A \cdot \operatorname{adj} A = \begin{bmatrix} |A| & 0 & 0 & \cdots & 0 \\ 0 & |A| & 0 & \cdots & 0 \\ \cdot & & & & \cdot \\ \cdot & & & & \cdot \\ \cdot & & & & \cdot \\ \cdot & & & & 0 \\ 0 & 0 & \cdots & 0 & |A| \end{bmatrix} = |A|\, I$$

i.e., $A \cdot \operatorname{adj} A$ is a diagonal matrix with the number $|A|$ along the diagonal. It can also be shown that $\operatorname{adj} A \cdot A = |A|I$. Thus, if $|A| \neq 0$,

$$A \cdot \frac{1}{|A|} \operatorname{adj} A = \frac{1}{|A|} \operatorname{adj} A \cdot A = I$$

and A has multiplicative inverse A^{-1} given by

20.14 $$A^{-1} = \frac{1}{|A|} \operatorname{adj} A.$$

EXAMPLE 1. Find A^{-1}, if it exists, for

$$A = \begin{bmatrix} 3 & 1 \\ 4 & 2 \end{bmatrix}.$$

Solution: By definition, $A_{11} = (2)$, $A_{12} = (4)$, $A_{21} = (1)$, $A_{22} = (3)$. Therefore, $a_{11} = (-1)^{1+i}|A_{11}| = 2$, $a_{12} = (-1)^{1+2}|A_{21}| = -1$, $a_{21} = (-1)^{2+1}|A_{12}| = -4$, $a_{22} = (-1)^{2+2}|A_{22}| = 3$, and

$$\operatorname{adj} A = \begin{bmatrix} 2 & -1 \\ -4 & 3 \end{bmatrix}.$$

We easily check that $|A| = 2$ and that

$$A \cdot \operatorname{adj} A = \operatorname{adj} A \cdot A = \begin{bmatrix} 2 & 0 \\ 0 & 2 \end{bmatrix}.$$

Thus

$$A^{-1} = \tfrac{1}{2} \operatorname{adj} A = \begin{bmatrix} 1 & -\frac{1}{2} \\ -2 & \frac{3}{2} \end{bmatrix}.$$

EXAMPLE 2. Find A^{-1}, if it exists, for

$$A = \begin{bmatrix} 1 & 0 & -1 \\ 2 & 1 & 0 \\ 0 & 1 & 1 \end{bmatrix}.$$

Solution: We first compute the $|A_{ij}|$ as follows:

$$|A_{11}| = \begin{vmatrix} 1 & 0 \\ 1 & 1 \end{vmatrix} = 1,\ |A_{12}| = \begin{vmatrix} 2 & 0 \\ 0 & 1 \end{vmatrix} = 2,\ |A_{13}| = \begin{vmatrix} 2 & 1 \\ 0 & 1 \end{vmatrix} = 2,$$

$$|A_{21}| = \begin{vmatrix} 0 & -1 \\ 1 & 1 \end{vmatrix} = 1,\ |A_{22}| = \begin{vmatrix} 1 & -1 \\ 0 & 1 \end{vmatrix} = 1,\ |A_{23}| = \begin{vmatrix} 1 & 0 \\ 0 & 1 \end{vmatrix} = 1,$$

$$|A_{31}| = \begin{vmatrix} 0 & -1 \\ 1 & 0 \end{vmatrix} = 1,\ |A_{32}| = \begin{vmatrix} 1 & -1 \\ 2 & 0 \end{vmatrix} = 2,\ |A_{33}| = \begin{vmatrix} 1 & 0 \\ 2 & 1 \end{vmatrix} = 1.$$

Hence $a'_{11} = 1$, $a'_{12} = -1$, $a'_{13} = 1$, $a'_{21} = -2$, $a'_{22} = 1$, $a'_{23} = -2$, $a'_{31} = 2$, $a'_{32} = -1$, $a'_{33} = 1$, and

$$\text{adj } A = \begin{bmatrix} 1 & -1 & 1 \\ -2 & 1 & -2 \\ 2 & -1 & 1 \end{bmatrix}.$$

We now check that

$$A \cdot \text{adj } A = \text{adj } A \cdot A = \begin{bmatrix} -1 & 0 & 0 \\ 0 & -1 & 0 \\ 0 & 0 & -1 \end{bmatrix}.$$

Therefore, $|A| = -1$ and

$$A^{-1} = \frac{1}{-1} \text{adj } A = \begin{bmatrix} -1 & 1 & -1 \\ 2 & -1 & 2 \\ -2 & 1 & -1 \end{bmatrix}.$$

EXERCISES

Find the inverse, if it exists, of each of the following matrices.

1. $\begin{bmatrix} 2 & 1 \\ 1 & 1 \end{bmatrix}$.

2. $\begin{bmatrix} -3 & 4 \\ 2 & -3 \end{bmatrix}$.

3. $\begin{bmatrix} 5 & -3 \\ -2 & 2 \end{bmatrix}$.

4. $\begin{bmatrix} 0 & 3 \\ 2 & 1 \end{bmatrix}$.

5. $\begin{bmatrix} 1 & 0 & 0 \\ 0 & 0 & 1 \\ 0 & 1 & 0 \end{bmatrix}$.

6. $\begin{bmatrix} 1 & 0 & 1 \\ 0 & 1 & -1 \\ 1 & -1 & 0 \end{bmatrix}$.

7. $\begin{bmatrix} 2 & -1 & 2 \\ 1 & 3 & -1 \\ 4 & -9 & 8 \end{bmatrix}$.

8. $\begin{bmatrix} 3 & 0 & 4 \\ 1 & 2 & 0 \\ -2 & 0 & 1 \end{bmatrix}$.

9. $\begin{bmatrix} 2 & -1 & 2 \\ -1 & 2 & -1 \\ 0 & 3 & 1 \end{bmatrix}$.

10. $\begin{bmatrix} 2 & 1 & 0 & 0 \\ -1 & 2 & 0 & 0 \\ 0 & 0 & 1 & 3 \\ 0 & 0 & -1 & 2 \end{bmatrix}$.

6 LINEAR TRANSFORMATIONS

Certain mappings of a vector space V into itself have important geometrical and physical applications. Before defining these so-called linear transformations, let us describe our notation for mappings. If f denotes a mapping of V into V, then for each $\mathbf{x}$ in V the corresponding element of V will be denoted by $\mathbf{x}f$, rather than the usual $f(\mathbf{x})$. There are advantages to the notation $\mathbf{x}f$ which will become evident later on.

20.15 **DEFINITION.** A mapping f of a vector space V into itself is called a *linear transformation* (l.t.) if and only if

(1) $$(\mathbf{x} + \mathbf{y})f = \mathbf{x}f + \mathbf{y}f$$

and

(2) $$(k\mathbf{x})f = k(\mathbf{x}f)$$

for all $\mathbf{x},\mathbf{y}$ in V and k in R.

In words, a linear transformation preserves addition, as stated in (1), and scalar multiplication, as stated in (2).

If we let $k = 0$ in 20.15(2), and use the fact that $0x = \mathbf{0}$, then we obtain $0f = 0(xf) = \mathbf{0}$; that is, every l.t. f maps $\mathbf{0}$ into $\mathbf{0}$. By letting $k = -1$ in 20.15(2), we see that

$$(-\mathbf{x})f = -(\mathbf{x}f) \qquad \text{for every } \mathbf{x} \text{ in } V.$$

If f is an l.t., then

$$(k_1\mathbf{x}_1 + k_2\mathbf{x}_2)f = (k_1\mathbf{x}_1)f + (k_2\mathbf{x}_2)f = k_1(\mathbf{x}_1f) + k_2(\mathbf{x}_2f).$$

Continuing, we see that

20.16 $$\left(\sum_{i=1}^{n} k_i\mathbf{x}_i\right)f = \sum_{i=1}^{n} k_i(\mathbf{x}_if) \quad \text{for all } k_i \text{ in } \mathsf{R},\ \mathbf{x}_i \text{ in } V.$$

Let vector space V have ordered basis $(\mathbf{x}_1,\mathbf{x}_2, \cdots, \mathbf{x}_n)$. If $(\mathbf{y}_1,\mathbf{y}_2, \cdots, \mathbf{y}_n)$ is any ordered set of n elements of V, then there exists a unique l.t. f such that $\mathbf{x}_if = \mathbf{y}_i$, $i = 1, \cdots, n$. Thus since $(\mathbf{x}_1, \cdots, \mathbf{x}_n)$ is a basis, each vector of V is uniquely expressible in the form $\sum_{i=1}^{n} k_i\mathbf{x}_i$ for some k_i in R. If we define the mapping f of V into V by

$$\left(\sum_{i=1}^{n} k_i\mathbf{x}_i\right)f = \sum_{i=1}^{n} k_i\mathbf{y}_i,$$

then clearly $\mathbf{x}_i f = \mathbf{y}_i$ (as we see by letting $k_i = 1$ and $k_j = 0$ if $i \neq j$). Also, if $\sum_{i=1}^{n} k_i\mathbf{x}_i$ and $\sum_{i=1}^{n} l_i\mathbf{x}_i$ are any two elements of V, then

$$\left(\sum_{i=1}^{n} k_i\mathbf{x}_i + \sum_{i=1}^{n} l_i\mathbf{x}_i\right)f = \left(\sum_{i=1}^{n} (k_i + l_i)\mathbf{x}_i\right)f$$

$$= \sum_{i=1}^{n} (k_i + l_i)\mathbf{y}_i$$

$$= \sum_{i=1}^{n} k_i\mathbf{y}_i + \sum_{i=1}^{n} l_i\mathbf{y}_i$$

$$= \left(\sum_{i=1}^{n} k_i\mathbf{x}_i\right)f + \left(\sum_{i=1}^{n} l_i\mathbf{x}_i\right)f.$$

Thus **20.15**(1) is satisfied by f. The reader can easily show **20.15**(2) also holds. Hence f is an l.t. Clearly it is unique; i.e., there is only one l.t. f such that $\mathbf{x}_i f = \mathbf{y}_i$, $i = 1, \cdots, n$.

It is true, conversely, that every l.t. of V is uniquely determined by what it does to a basis of V. Thus if we know that $(\mathbf{x}_1,\mathbf{x}_2, \cdots, \mathbf{x}_n)$ is an ordered basis of V and f is an l.t. of V, then f is completely known once we know $\mathbf{x}_1 f, \mathbf{x}_2 f, \cdots, \mathbf{x}_n f$. For if $\mathbf{x}$ is any vector of V, then $\mathbf{x} = \sum_{i=1}^{n} k_i\mathbf{x}_i$ for some k_i in R and $xf = \sum_{i=1}^{n} k_i(\mathbf{x}_i f)$ by **20.16**.

If $(\mathbf{x}_1,\mathbf{x}_2, \ldots, \mathbf{x}_n)$ is an ordered basis of a vector space V and f is an l.t. of V, then there exist a_{ij} in R such that

20.17
$$\mathbf{x}_i f = \sum_{j=1}^{n} a_{ij}\mathbf{x}_j, \qquad i = 1,2, \cdots, n.$$

Thus corresponding to each l.t. f is an $n \times n$ matrix (a_{ij}) given by **20.17**. Conversely, corresponding to each $n \times n$ matrix (a_{ij}) is a l.t. f defined by **20.17**.

For example, V_3 has ordered basis $(\mathbf{i},\mathbf{j},\mathbf{k})$. Let the l.t. f be defined by

$$\mathbf{i}f = \langle 3,-5,4\rangle = 3\mathbf{i} - 5\mathbf{j} + 4\mathbf{k}$$

$$\mathbf{j}f = \langle -7,0,6\rangle = -7\mathbf{i} + 0\mathbf{j} + 6\mathbf{k}$$

$$\mathbf{k}f = \langle 2,2,-1\rangle = 2\mathbf{i} + 2\mathbf{j} - \mathbf{k}.$$

Then the 3×3 matrix A corresponding to f is the matrix of coefficients of $\mathbf{i},\mathbf{j},\mathbf{k}$ in the three equations above:

$$A = \begin{bmatrix} 3 & -5 & 4 \\ -7 & 0 & 6 \\ 2 & 2 & -1 \end{bmatrix}.$$

On the other hand, given the 3 × 3 matrix

$$B = \begin{bmatrix} 0 & 1 & 0 \\ 2 & -3 & 7 \\ 1 & 5 & -2 \end{bmatrix},$$

there is defined a unique l.t. g whose corresponding matrix is B:

$$\begin{aligned} \mathbf{i}g &= 0\mathbf{i} + 1\mathbf{j} + 0\mathbf{k} = \langle 0,1,0 \rangle \\ \mathbf{j}g &= 2\mathbf{i} - 3\mathbf{j} + 7\mathbf{k} = \langle 2,-3,7 \rangle \\ \mathbf{k}g &= 1\mathbf{i} + 5\mathbf{j} - 2\mathbf{k} = \langle 1,5,-2 \rangle. \end{aligned}$$

To find what $\mathbf{x}g$ is for any $\mathbf{x}$ in V_3, we simply use the equations above and **20.16**. For example,

$$\begin{aligned} \langle 3,1,2 \rangle g &= (3\mathbf{i} + \mathbf{j} + 2\mathbf{k})g \\ &= 3(\mathbf{i}g) + \mathbf{j}g + 2(\mathbf{k}g) \\ &= 3\,\langle 0,1,0 \rangle + \langle 2,-3,7 \rangle + 2\langle 1,5,-2 \rangle \\ &= \langle 4,10,3 \rangle. \end{aligned}$$

7 EUCLIDEAN SPACES

In Chapters 16 and 17 an inner product was defined in V_2 and V_3. We easily extend this operation to V_n as follows.

20.18
$$\langle a_1,a_2, \cdots, a_n \rangle \cdot \langle b_1,b_2, \cdots, b_n \rangle = \sum_{i=1}^{n} a_i b_i.$$

Thus for any $\mathbf{x},\mathbf{y}$ in V_n, $\mathbf{x}\cdot\mathbf{y}$ is in R. This operation in V_n has the following properties. For all $\mathbf{x},\mathbf{y},\mathbf{z}$ in V_n and a in R:

(1) $\mathbf{x}\cdot\mathbf{y} = \mathbf{y}\cdot\mathbf{x}$ (2) $\mathbf{x}\cdot(\mathbf{y} + \mathbf{z}) = \mathbf{x}\cdot\mathbf{y} + \mathbf{x}\cdot\mathbf{z}$

(3) $(a\mathbf{x})\cdot\mathbf{y} = a(\mathbf{x}\cdot\mathbf{y})$ (4) $\mathbf{x}\cdot\mathbf{x} \geq 0$, with $\mathbf{x}\cdot\mathbf{x} = 0$ if and only if $\mathbf{x} = \mathbf{0}$.

These properties can be proved by straightforward calculations. If, for example, $\mathbf{x} = \langle a_1,a_2, \cdots, a_n \rangle$ then

$$\mathbf{x}\cdot\mathbf{x} = a_1^2 + a_2^2 + \cdots + a_n^2.$$

Since $a_i^2 \geq 0$ for each i, $\mathbf{x}\cdot\mathbf{x} \geq 0$; and $\mathbf{x}\cdot\mathbf{x} = 0$ if and only if all $a_i = 0$.

A vector space V having an operation $(\cdot)$ such that $\mathbf{x}\cdot\mathbf{y}$ is in R for all $\mathbf{x},\mathbf{y}$ in V is called a *Euclidean space* if the operation has properties (1)–(4) stated above.

Thus, V_2, V_3, and in general V_n are Euclidean spaces. It is easy to show that

20.19
$$\left(\sum_{i=1}^{n} a_i\mathbf{x}_i\right)\cdot\left(\sum_{j=1}^{m} b_j\mathbf{y}_j\right) = \sum_{i=1}^{n}\sum_{j=1}^{m} a_ib_j\,(\mathbf{x}_i\cdot\mathbf{y}_j)$$

in any Euclidean space V.

We recall that in V_2 and V_3, each vector $\mathbf{x}$ has a length $|\mathbf{x}|$ given by $|\mathbf{x}| = \sqrt{\mathbf{x}\cdot\mathbf{x}}$. This leads us to *define* the length of a vector $\mathbf{x}$ in a Euclidean space V by

20.20
$$|\mathbf{x}| = \sqrt{\mathbf{x}\cdot\mathbf{x}}.$$

Thus in V_n we have

$$|\langle a_1,a_2,\cdots,a_n\rangle| = \sqrt{a_1^2 + a_2^2 + \cdots + a_n^2}.$$

As in Chapter 16, we can show that for all $\mathbf{x},\mathbf{y}$ in a Euclidean space V and all a in R,

$$|a\mathbf{x}| = |a||\mathbf{x}|$$
$$|\mathbf{x}\cdot\mathbf{y}| \leq |\mathbf{x}||\mathbf{y}| \qquad \text{(Cauchy's inequality).}$$

A vector of length 1 is called a *unit vector.*

If $\mathbf{x}$ and $\mathbf{y}$ are nonzero vectors of V_2 or V_3 and θ is the least angle between $\mathbf{x}$ and $\mathbf{y}$, then by **16.4** or **17.4**,

$$\mathbf{x}\cdot\mathbf{y} = |\mathbf{x}||\mathbf{y}|\cos\theta.$$

With this fact in mind, we *define* the angle θ between two nonzero vectors $\mathbf{x}$ and $\mathbf{y}$ of a Euclidean space V to be the least positive angle θ such that

20.21
$$\cos\theta = \frac{\mathbf{x}\cdot\mathbf{y}}{|\mathbf{x}||\mathbf{y}|}.$$

For example, if

$$\mathbf{x} = \langle 1,-1,2,2\rangle, \quad \mathbf{y} = \langle 2,1,-1,-2\rangle$$

in V_4, then $\mathbf{x}\cdot\mathbf{y} = -5$, $|\mathbf{x}| = |\mathbf{y}| = \sqrt{10}$,

$$\cos\theta = -\tfrac{1}{2}, \quad \theta = 2\pi/3.$$

Two nonzero vectors $\mathbf{x}$ and $\mathbf{y}$ of a Euclidean space V are called *orthogonal* (or, *perpendicular*), and we write $\mathbf{x} \perp \mathbf{y}$, if and only if the angle between them is a right angle. Since $\cos \pi/2 = 0$, we have by **20.21** that (see **16.5**)

$$\mathbf{x} \perp \mathbf{y} \qquad \text{if and only if} \quad \mathbf{x}\cdot\mathbf{y} = 0.$$

A basis $\{\mathbf{x}_1,\mathbf{x}_2,\cdots,\mathbf{x}_n\}$ of V is called an *orthonormal basis* if and only if $|\mathbf{x}_i| = 1$ and $\mathbf{x}_i \perp \mathbf{x}_j$ if $i \neq j$, $i,j = 1,2,\cdots,n$. It may be shown that every Euclidean space has an orthonormal basis.

For example, $\{\mathbf{i},\mathbf{j}\}$ is an orthonormal basis of V_2 since $|\mathbf{i}| = |\mathbf{j}| = 1$ and $\mathbf{i} \perp \mathbf{j}$; and $\{\mathbf{i},\mathbf{j},\mathbf{k}\}$ is an orthonormal basis of V_3.

More generally, if we let

$$\mathbf{u}_1 = \langle 1,0,0, \cdots, 0\rangle, \ \mathbf{u}_2 = \langle 0,1,0, \cdots, 0\rangle, \ \cdots, \ \mathbf{u}_n = \langle 0,0, \cdots, 0,1\rangle$$

in V_n, then $\{\mathbf{u}_1,\mathbf{u}_2, \cdots, \mathbf{u}_n\}$ is an orthonormal basis of V_n. This is true because $|\mathbf{u}_i| = 1$ for each i and $\mathbf{u}_i \cdot \mathbf{u}_j = 0$ whenever $i \neq j$.

If a linear transformation f of V_n is represented by the matrix (a_{ij}) relative to the basis $(\mathbf{u}_1,\mathbf{u}_2, \cdots, \mathbf{u}_n)$, so that

$$\mathbf{u}_i f = \sum_{j=1}^{n} a_{ij}\mathbf{u}_j, \qquad i = 1,2, \cdots, n,$$

then it is easy to compute the effect of f on any vector of V_n by use of matrix multiplication. Thus if we consider $\mathbf{x} = \langle b_1,b_2, \cdots, b_n\rangle$ as a $1 \times n$ matrix, then $\mathbf{x} \cdot A$ is a $1 \times n$ matrix which we can consider to be in V_n. We claim that

$$\mathbf{x}f = \mathbf{x} \cdot A \qquad \text{for all } \mathbf{x} \text{ in } V_n.$$

To prove this, we have

$$\begin{aligned} \mathbf{x}f = \left(\sum_{i=1}^{n} b_i\mathbf{u}_i\right)f &= \sum_{i=1}^{n} b_i(\mathbf{u}_i f) \\ &= \sum_{i=1}^{n}\sum_{j=1}^{n} b_i a_{ij}\mathbf{u}_j \\ &= \langle \mathbf{x} \cdot A^1, \mathbf{x} \cdot A^2, \cdots, \mathbf{x} \cdot A^n\rangle, \end{aligned}$$

where $A^1,A^2, \cdots, A^n$ are the column vectors of A.

For example, let f be an l.t. of V_3 with matrix

$$A = \begin{bmatrix} -1 & 4 & 2 \\ 1 & -1 & 3 \\ 2 & 0 & -4 \end{bmatrix}$$

relative to the basis $(\mathbf{i},\mathbf{j},\mathbf{k})$. Then

$$\begin{aligned} \langle 3,2,-5\rangle f &= \langle 3,2,-5\rangle \cdot A \\ &= \langle 3\cdot(-1) + 2\cdot 1 + (-5)\cdot 2, 3\cdot 4 + 2\cdot(-1), 3\cdot 2 + 2\cdot 3 + (-5)\cdot(-4)\rangle \\ &= \langle -11,10,32\rangle. \end{aligned}$$

A linear transformation f of a Euclidean space V is called an *isometry* if and only if f preserves the length of each vector of V, i.e.,

$$|\mathbf{x}f| = |\mathbf{x}| \qquad \text{for all } \mathbf{x} \text{ in } V.$$

Evidently this statement is the same as the following:

$$\mathbf{x}f \cdot \mathbf{x}f = \mathbf{x} \cdot \mathbf{x} \qquad \text{for all } \mathbf{x} \text{ in } V.$$

If f is an isometry of V and $\mathbf{x},\mathbf{y}$ are in V, then $(\mathbf{x} + \mathbf{y})f \cdot (\mathbf{x} + \mathbf{y})f = (\mathbf{x} + \mathbf{y}) \cdot (\mathbf{x} + \mathbf{y})$. Thus $(\mathbf{x}f + \mathbf{y}f) \cdot (\mathbf{x}f + \mathbf{y}f) = (\mathbf{x} + \mathbf{y}) \cdot (\mathbf{x} + \mathbf{y})$ and expanding both sides,

$$\mathbf{x}f \cdot \mathbf{x}f + 2(\mathbf{x}f \cdot \mathbf{y}f) + \mathbf{x}f \cdot \mathbf{y}f = \mathbf{x} \cdot \mathbf{x} + 2(\mathbf{x} \cdot \mathbf{y}) + \mathbf{y} \cdot \mathbf{y}.$$

Since $\mathbf{x}f \cdot \mathbf{x}f = \mathbf{x} \cdot \mathbf{x}$ and $\mathbf{y}f \cdot \mathbf{y}f = \mathbf{y} \cdot \mathbf{y}$, clearly $\mathbf{x}f \cdot \mathbf{y}f = \mathbf{x} \cdot \mathbf{y}$ by the above equation; that is, if f is an isometry of V then

20.22 $$\mathbf{x}f \cdot \mathbf{y}f = \mathbf{x} \cdot \mathbf{y} \quad \text{for all } \mathbf{x},\mathbf{y} \text{ in } V.$$

By looking at the definition of an angle (20.21) and at 20.22, we see that an *isometry preserves not only the length of a vector but also the angle between any two vectors.*

A geometric example of an isometry of V_2 is the l.t. f which rotates the vectors $\mathbf{i}$ and $\mathbf{j}$ through an angle θ (Figure 20.1). Thus by the figure,

$$\mathbf{i}f = (\cos\theta)\mathbf{i} + (\sin\theta)\mathbf{j}$$
$$\mathbf{j}f = (-\sin\theta)\mathbf{i} + (\cos\theta)\mathbf{j}.$$

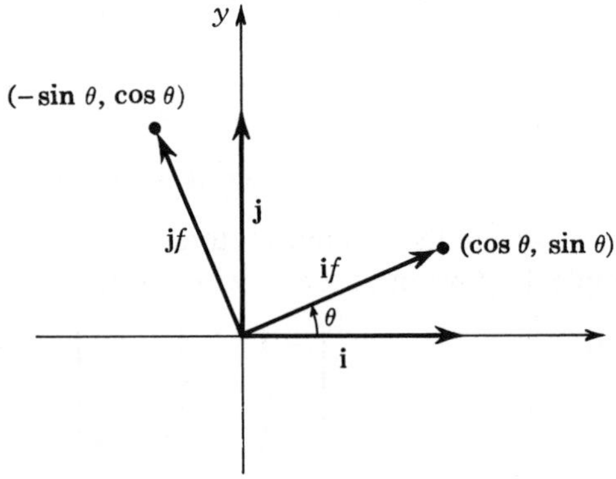

FIGURE 20.1

Evidently f is represented by the matrix

$$A = \begin{bmatrix} \cos\theta & \sin\theta \\ -\sin\theta & \cos\theta \end{bmatrix}.$$

If $\mathbf{v} = a\mathbf{i} + b\mathbf{j} = \langle a,b \rangle$ is any vector of V_2, then

$$\mathbf{v}f = \mathbf{v} \cdot A = \langle a\cos\theta - b\sin\theta, \quad a\sin\theta + b\cos\theta \rangle.$$

It is easily checked that $|\mathbf{v}f| = |\mathbf{v}| = \sqrt{a^2 + b^2}$, and hence f is an isometry of V_2.

EXERCISES

1. Let V_n have orthonormal basis $(\mathbf{u}_1,\mathbf{u}_2, \cdots, \mathbf{u}_n)$ as above. Prove that if f is an l.t. of V_n such that $(\mathbf{u}_1f,\mathbf{u}_2f, \cdots, \mathbf{u}_nf)$ is an orthonormal basis of V_n, then f is an isometry.

   [*Hint:* Each $\mathbf{x}$ in V_n has the form $\mathbf{x} = \sum_{i=1}^{n} a_i\mathbf{v}_i$ for some a_i in R. Use **20.19** to show that $|\mathbf{x}f|^2 = |\mathbf{x}|^2$.]

2. Prove that V_n is a Euclidean space if the inner product is defined by **20.18**.

Find an orthonormal basis of V_3 containing each of the following vectors.

3. $\langle 1/3,-2/3,2/3\rangle$.
4. $\langle 1/\sqrt{2},0,1/\sqrt{2}\rangle$.
5. $\langle 1/\sqrt{3},-1/\sqrt{3},1/\sqrt{3}\rangle$.
6. $\langle 0,3/5,4/5\rangle$.

Tell whether or not each of the following l.t. f of V_3 is an isometry.

7. $\mathbf{i}f = \mathbf{j},\ \mathbf{j}f = \mathbf{k},\ \mathbf{k}f = -\mathbf{i}$.
8. $\mathbf{i}f = \mathbf{i} + \mathbf{j},\ \mathbf{j}f = \mathbf{k},\ \mathbf{k}f = \mathbf{i} - \mathbf{j}$.
9. $\mathbf{i}f = \frac{1}{5}(3\mathbf{j} - 4\mathbf{k}),\ \mathbf{j}f = \mathbf{j},\ \mathbf{k}f = \frac{1}{5}(4\mathbf{j} + 3\mathbf{k})$.
10. $\mathbf{i}f = \dfrac{1}{\sqrt{5}}(2\mathbf{i} + \mathbf{k}),\ \mathbf{j}f = \dfrac{1}{\sqrt{5}}(\mathbf{i} - 2\mathbf{k}),\ \mathbf{k}f = \mathbf{j}$.

8 CHARACTERISTIC VALUES

In this section, let us restrict our attention to the Euclidean space V_n and its orthonormal basis $(\mathbf{u}_1,\mathbf{u}_2, \cdots, \mathbf{u}_n)$ described previously. If f is an l.t. of V_n, then a nonzero vector $\mathbf{x}$ in V_n is called a *characteristic vector* (or, *eigenvector*) of f if and only if

$$\mathbf{x}f = c\mathbf{x}$$

for some scalar c. We call c the *characteristic value* (or, *eigenvalue*) of f belonging to $\mathbf{x}$.

The actual computation of characteristic vectors and values can be carried out by going to the matrix representation of an l.t. If the l.t. f is represented by matrix $A = (a_{ij})$ relative to the basis $(\mathbf{u}_1,\mathbf{u}_2, \cdots, \mathbf{u}_n)$ and $\mathbf{x}$ is a characteristic vector of f with characteristic value c, so that $\mathbf{x}f = c\mathbf{x}$, then

$$\mathbf{x}f = \mathbf{x}\cdot A = c\mathbf{x} = \mathbf{x}\cdot(cI),$$

where I is the $n \times n$ identity matrix. Thus it is clear that the nonzero vector $\mathbf{x}$ is a characteristic vector of f if and only if

$$\mathbf{x}\cdot(A - cI) = \mathbf{0}$$

for some scalar c. From this equation, the determinant of the $n \times n$ matrix $A - cI$ must be 0. For otherwise, $A - cI$ would have an inverse $(A - cI)^{-1}$, and $\mathbf{x} = \mathbf{x}\cdot I = \mathbf{x}\cdot(A - cI)(A - cI)^{-1} = \mathbf{0}\cdot(A - cI)^{-1} = \mathbf{0}$ contrary to the assumption that $\mathbf{x} \neq \mathbf{0}$. It can be shown conversely that if $|A - cI| = 0$ for some c in R, then c is a characteristic value of f; i.e., there exists a nonzero vector $\mathbf{x}$ such that $\mathbf{x}\cdot A = c\mathbf{x}$. It is customary to call $\mathbf{x}$ a *characteristic vector* and c a *characteristic value* of the matrix A as well as of f.

If A is an $n \times n$ matrix and λ is an unknown, then $|A - \lambda I|$ is a polynomial in λ of degree n. For example, if $A = (a_{ij})$ is a 3×3 matrix, then

$$A - \lambda I = \begin{bmatrix} a_{11} - \lambda & a_{12} & a_{13} \\ a_{21} & a_{22} - \lambda & a_{23} \\ a_{31} & a_{32} & a_{33} - \lambda \end{bmatrix}$$

and

$$|A - \lambda I| = -\lambda^3 + (a_{11} + a_{22} + a_{33})\lambda^2 - (a_{11}a_{22} + a_{11}a_{33} + a_{22}a_{33} - a_{23}a_{32} - a_{12}a_{21} - a_{13}a_{31})\lambda + |A|.$$

Therefore, the $n \times n$ matrix A can have at most n distinct characteristic values, namely the real roots of the polynomial equation

$$|A - \lambda I| = 0$$

of degree n.

For example, if

$$A = \begin{bmatrix} 1 & 0 & -1 \\ 2 & 1 & 0 \\ 0 & -1 & -2 \end{bmatrix}$$

then

$$|A - \lambda I| = \begin{vmatrix} 1 - \lambda & 0 & -1 \\ 2 & 1 - \lambda & 0 \\ 0 & -1 & -2 - \lambda \end{vmatrix} = -\lambda^3 + 3\lambda = -\lambda(\lambda - \sqrt{3})(\lambda + \sqrt{3})$$

and the characteristic values of A are 0, $\sqrt{3}$, and $-\sqrt{3}$. Characteristic vectors associated with these values can be found as follows. If $\mathbf{x} = \langle a,b,c\rangle$ is a characteristic vector associated with 0, then $\mathbf{x}\cdot(A - 0I) = \mathbf{0}$, i.e.,

$$\langle a,b,c\rangle\cdot\begin{bmatrix} 1 & 0 & -1 \\ 2 & 1 & 0 \\ 0 & -1 & -2 \end{bmatrix} = \langle 0,0,0\rangle.$$

We easily check that $a = 2$, $b = -1$, $c = -1$ satisfy this equation. Hence, $\mathbf{x} = \langle 2,-1,-1\rangle$ is a characteristic vector of A having characteristic value 0. Of course, $k\mathbf{x}$ is also a characteristic vector having characteristic value 0 for any nonzero scalar k. To find a characteristic vector for $\sqrt{3}$, we solve the equation

$$\langle a,b,c\rangle \cdot \begin{bmatrix} 1-\sqrt{3} & 0 & -1 \\ 2 & 1-\sqrt{3} & 0 \\ 0 & -1 & -2-\sqrt{3} \end{bmatrix} = \langle 0,0,0\rangle$$

for a, b, and c (not all zero). This is equivalent to solving the system of linear equations

$$\begin{aligned} (1-\sqrt{3})a + 2b &= 0 \\ (1-\sqrt{3})b - c &= 0 \\ -a - (2+\sqrt{3})c &= 0. \end{aligned}$$

If we let $b = 1$, then $c = 1 - \sqrt{3}$ and $a = 1 + \sqrt{3}$. Thus $\langle 1+\sqrt{3}, 1, 1-\sqrt{3}\rangle$ is a characteristic vector of A having associated characteristic value $\sqrt{3}$. A similar calculation will find a characteristic vector associated with $-\sqrt{3}$.

Associated with an $m \times n$ matrix $A = (a_{ij})$ is an $n \times m$ matrix A^T, the *transpose* of A, having the column vectors of A as its row vectors and the row vectors of A as its column vectors. For example, if

$$A = \begin{bmatrix} a_{11} & a_{12} & a_{13} \\ a_{21} & a_{22} & a_{23} \end{bmatrix}, \quad \text{then} \quad A^T = \begin{bmatrix} a_{11} & a_{21} \\ a_{12} & a_{22} \\ a_{13} & a_{23} \end{bmatrix}.$$

We leave the calculations to the reader to show that for any $m \times n$ matrices A and B,

$$(A + B)^T = A^T + B^T$$

and for any $m \times n$ matrix A and $n \times p$ matrix B,

$$(AB)^T = B^T A^T.$$

Also, for any square matrix A,

$$|A| = |A^T|.$$

For example, if $A = (a_{ij})$ is a 2×2 matrix,

$$|A^T| = \begin{vmatrix} a_{11} & a_{21} \\ a_{12} & a_{22} \end{vmatrix} = a_{11}a_{22} - a_{12}a_{21} = |A|.$$

The transpose of a matrix plays a fundamental role in the consideration of an isometry f of V_n. Let A be the matrix of f relative to the orthonormal basis $(\mathbf{u}_1,\mathbf{u}_2,\cdots,\mathbf{u}_n)$. Then

$$\mathbf{u}_i f\cdot\mathbf{u}_j f = \mathbf{u}_i\cdot\mathbf{u}_j = \begin{cases}1 & \text{if } i=j\\ 0 & \text{if } i\neq j\end{cases}$$

by **20.22**. Thus the set $(\mathbf{u}_1 f,\mathbf{u}_2 f,\cdots,\mathbf{u}_n f)$ is also an orthonormal basis of V_n. That is, an *isometry of V_n maps an orthonormal basis into an orthonormal basis*. Also, we have

$$\begin{aligned}\mathbf{u}_i f\cdot\mathbf{u}_j f &= \left(\sum_{k=1}^{n} a_{ik}\mathbf{u}_k\right)\cdot\left(\sum_{l=1}^{n} a_{jl}\mathbf{u}_l\right)\\ &= \sum_{k=1}^{n}\sum_{l=1}^{n} a_{ik}a_{jl}(\mathbf{u}_k\cdot\mathbf{u}_l)\\ &= \sum_{k=1}^{n} a_{ik}a_{jk}.\end{aligned}$$

Hence

$$\sum_{k=1}^{n} a_{ik}a_{jk} = \begin{cases}1 & \text{if } i=j\\ 0 & \text{if } i\neq j.\end{cases}$$

In matrix form, this equation is

$$AA^T = I.$$

That is, the *transpose of A is also the inverse of A*. Such a matrix is called an *orthogonal matrix*. We summarize our results above as follows.

20.23 THEOREM. An isometry of V_n is represented by an orthogonal matrix relative to an orthonormal basis.

We saw in Section 7 that a rotation of V_2 about the origin through an angle θ is represented by the matrix

$$A = \begin{bmatrix}\cos\theta & \sin\theta\\ -\sin\theta & \cos\theta\end{bmatrix}.$$

We easily check that

$$A^T = \begin{bmatrix}\cos\theta & -\sin\theta\\ \sin\theta & \cos\theta\end{bmatrix}$$

and that $AA^T = I$. Thus A is an orthogonal matrix, as it must be since it represents an isometry.

If $\mathbf{x}$ is a characteristic vector of an isometry f of V_n, so that $\mathbf{x}f = c\mathbf{x}$ for some scalar c, then $|\mathbf{x}f| = |\mathbf{x}| = |c\mathbf{x}| = |c||\mathbf{x}|$ and necessarily $|c| = 1$. Hence, the only possible characteristic values of f are 1 and -1.

For example, the l.t. f of V_2 defined by

$$(a\mathbf{i} + b\mathbf{j})f = a\mathbf{i} - b\mathbf{j}$$

clearly is an isometry. Geometrically, f is the reflection of the plane in the x-axis. Since

$$\mathbf{i}f = \mathbf{i} \quad \text{and} \quad \mathbf{j}f = -\mathbf{j}$$

$\mathbf{i}$ and $\mathbf{j}$ are characteristic vectors of f. The characteristic value of f belonging to $\mathbf{i}$ is 1; belonging to $\mathbf{j}$ is -1.

EXERCISES

Find the characteristic values and corresponding characteristic vectors for each of the following matrices.

1. $\begin{bmatrix} 2 & 1 \\ -4 & -3 \end{bmatrix}$.
2. $\begin{bmatrix} -1 & 3 \\ 2 & 0 \end{bmatrix}$.
3. $\begin{bmatrix} 5 & 1 \\ 8 & -2 \end{bmatrix}$.
4. $\begin{bmatrix} 2 & 1 \\ -4 & -2 \end{bmatrix}$.
5. $\begin{bmatrix} 0 & 1 & 0 \\ 2 & 0 & 1 \\ 0 & 2 & 0 \end{bmatrix}$.
6. $\begin{bmatrix} -1 & -1 & -1 \\ 3 & 3 & 1 \\ -3 & -4 & -2 \end{bmatrix}$.
7. $\frac{1}{3}\begin{bmatrix} 2 & 1 & -2 \\ 1 & 2 & 2 \\ 2 & -2 & 1 \end{bmatrix}$.
8. $\frac{1}{5}\begin{bmatrix} 0 & 3 & -4 \\ 0 & 5 & 0 \\ 0 & 4 & 3 \end{bmatrix}$.

9 SYMMETRIC MATRICES

A linear transformation f of the Euclidean space V_n is called *symmetric* if and only if

$$\mathbf{x}f\cdot\mathbf{y} = \mathbf{x}\cdot f\mathbf{y} \quad \text{for all } \mathbf{x},\mathbf{y} \text{ in } V_n.$$

On the other hand, an $n \times n$ matrix $A = (a_{ij})$ is called *symmetric* if and only if $A^T = A$; i.e.,

$$a_{ij} = a_{ji} \quad \text{for all } i \text{ and } j.$$

For example, the 3×3 matrix

$$\begin{bmatrix} 2 & -3 & 5 \\ -3 & 1 & 0 \\ 5 & 0 & -2 \end{bmatrix}$$

is symmetric. The connection between symmetric l.t. and matrices is given below.

20.24 THEOREM. A linear transformation f of V_n is symmetric if and only if the matrix A representing f relative to the orthonormal basis $(\mathbf{u}_1, \mathbf{u}_2, \cdots, \mathbf{u}_n)$ of V_n is symmetric.

Proof: If f is an l.t. of V_n represented by the matrix $A = (a_{ij})$, then

$$\mathbf{u}_i f \cdot \mathbf{u}_j = \left(\sum_{k=1}^{n} a_{ik}\mathbf{u}_k\right) \cdot \mathbf{u}_j = \sum_{k=1}^{n} a_{ik}(\mathbf{u}_k \cdot \mathbf{u}_j) = a_{ij},$$

whereas it is similarly shown that

$$\mathbf{u}_i \cdot \mathbf{u}_j f = a_{ji}.$$

Since $\mathbf{x}f \cdot \mathbf{y} = \mathbf{x} \cdot \mathbf{y}f$ for all $\mathbf{x},\mathbf{y}$ in V_n if and only if $\mathbf{u}_i f \cdot \mathbf{u}_j = \mathbf{u}_i \cdot \mathbf{u}_j f$ for all i and j, evidently f is symmetric if and only if A is symmetric.

An important property of a symmetric l.t. is given below.

20.25 THEOREM. If f is a symmetric linear transformation of V_n, then there exists an orthonormal basis $(\mathbf{x}_1, \mathbf{x}_2, \cdots, \mathbf{x}_n)$ of V_n made up of characteristic vectors of f.

We shall not give a proof of this theorem in general, but rather refer the reader to any textbook on linear algebra. We shall give a proof in case $n = 2$.

To this end, let f be a symmetric l.t. represented by

$$A = \begin{bmatrix} a & c \\ c & b \end{bmatrix}$$

relative to the basis $(\mathbf{i},\mathbf{j})$ of V_2. If $c = 0$, then $\mathbf{i}$ and $\mathbf{j}$ are characteristic vectors of f and 20.25 is proved. So let us assume $c \neq 0$. The discriminant D of the quadratic polynomial

$$|A - \lambda I| = \begin{vmatrix} a - \lambda & c \\ c & b - \lambda \end{vmatrix} = \lambda^2 - (a + b)\lambda + (ab - c^2)$$

is given by

$$D = (a + b)^2 - 4(ab - c^2) = (a - b)^2 + 4c^2.$$

Hence $D > 0$ and A has two distinct real characteristic values k_1 and k_2. Let $\mathbf{x}_1$ and $\mathbf{x}_2$ be unit characteristic vectors of f associated with k_1 and k_2 respectively. Then $\mathbf{x}_1 f = k_1\mathbf{x}_1$, $\mathbf{x}_2 f = k_2\mathbf{x}_2$, and

$$k_1(\mathbf{x}_1\cdot\mathbf{x}_2) = (k\mathbf{x}_1)\cdot\mathbf{x}_2 = (\mathbf{x}_1 f)\cdot\mathbf{x}_2 = \mathbf{x}_1\cdot(\mathbf{x}_2 f) = \mathbf{x}_1\cdot(k_2\mathbf{x}_2) = k_2(\mathbf{x}_1\cdot\mathbf{x}_2).$$

Since $k_1 \neq k_2$, necessarily $\mathbf{x}_1\cdot\mathbf{x}_2 = 0$. Therefore $(\mathbf{x}_1,\mathbf{x}_2)$ is an orthonormal basis of V_2. This proves **20.25** in case $n = 2$.

For example, let us find characteristic vectors of the symmetric matrix

$$A = \begin{bmatrix} 1 & 2 \\ 2 & -2 \end{bmatrix}.$$

Evidently

$$|A - \lambda I| = \begin{vmatrix} 1-\lambda & 2 \\ 2 & -2-\lambda \end{vmatrix} = \lambda^2 + \lambda - 6 = (\lambda + 3)(\lambda - 2)$$

and the characteristic values of A are $2, -3$. In order that

$$\langle a,b\rangle\cdot A = 2\langle a,b\rangle, \qquad \langle a,b\rangle\cdot\langle a,b\rangle = 1$$

we have

$$a + 2b = 2a$$
$$2a - 2b = 2b$$
$$a^2 + b^2 = 1.$$

A solution of this system of equations is $a = 2/\sqrt{5}$, $b = 1/\sqrt{5}$. Thus, $\mathbf{x}_1 = \langle 2/\sqrt{5}, 1/\sqrt{5}\rangle$ is a unit characteristic vector of A having characteristic value 2. In a similar way, we find that $\mathbf{x}_2 = \langle 1/\sqrt{5}, -2/\sqrt{5}\rangle$ is a unit characteristic vector of A having characteristic value -3. We verify that $\mathbf{x}_1$ and $\mathbf{x}_2$ are orthogonal vectors, i.e., $\mathbf{x}_1\cdot\mathbf{x}_2 = 0$. Thus, $(\mathbf{x}_1,\mathbf{x}_2)$ is an orthonormal basis of V_2 consisting of characteristic vectors of A.

EXERCISES

For each of the following symmetric matrices, find the characteristic values and the corresponding orthonormal characteristic vectors.

1. $\begin{bmatrix} 3 & -1 \\ -1 & 3 \end{bmatrix}$.

2. $\begin{bmatrix} -1 & 8 \\ 8 & 11 \end{bmatrix}$.

3. $\begin{bmatrix} 4 & -2 \\ -2 & 1 \end{bmatrix}$.

4. $\begin{bmatrix} 0 & 1 \\ 1 & 0 \end{bmatrix}$.

5. $\begin{bmatrix} 0 & 1 & 1 \\ 1 & -1 & 0 \\ 1 & 0 & 1 \end{bmatrix}$.

6. $\frac{1}{9}\begin{bmatrix} -7 & 2 & 10 \\ 2 & 2 & -8 \\ 10 & -8 & -4 \end{bmatrix}$.

7. $\frac{1}{3}\begin{bmatrix} 1 & -2 & -4 \\ -2 & -2 & 2 \\ -4 & 2 & 1 \end{bmatrix}$.   8. $\begin{bmatrix} 0 & -2 & 0 \\ -2 & 0 & 0 \\ 0 & 0 & 0 \end{bmatrix}$.

10 QUADRATIC EQUATIONS

A quadratic equation of the form

$$ax^2 + 2cxy + by^2 = d$$

can be expressed in matrix form

$$XAX^T = d,$$

where X is a 1×2 matrix and A is a symmetric 2×2 matrix as follows:

$$X = (x\,y), \quad A = \begin{bmatrix} a & c \\ c & b \end{bmatrix}.$$

For example, the quadratic equation

$$x^2 + 4xy - 2y^2 = 6$$

can be expressed as

$$XAX^T = 6$$

where $X = (x\,y)$ and

$$A = \begin{bmatrix} 1 & 2 \\ 2 & -2 \end{bmatrix}.$$

Thus,

$$XA = (x\,y)\begin{bmatrix} 1 & 2 \\ 2 & -2 \end{bmatrix} = (x + 2y, 2x - 2y)$$

and

$$\begin{aligned} XAX^T &= (x + 2y, 2x - 2y)\begin{pmatrix} x \\ y \end{pmatrix} \\ &= (x + 2y)x + (2x - 2y)y \\ &= x^2 + 4xy - 2y^2 = 6. \end{aligned}$$

The graph of the quadratic equation $ax^2 + 2cxy + by^2 = d$ in a rectangular coordinate plane is the set of all points $X = (x,y)$ such that $XAX^T = d$. If $c = 0$, then we know that the graph is a conic section if $a > 0, b > 0, d > 0$ or if $a > 0$, $b < 0$, and $d \neq 0$. Even if $c \neq 0$, the graph is usually a conic section, as we shall show below.

If in a plane we have two sets of rectangular coordinate axes, as shown in Fig. 20.2, then each point P has two sets of coordinates, (x,y) and (x',y'). These are related by equations of the form

$$x = p_{11}x' + p_{12}y'$$
$$y = p_{21}x' + p_{22}y'.$$

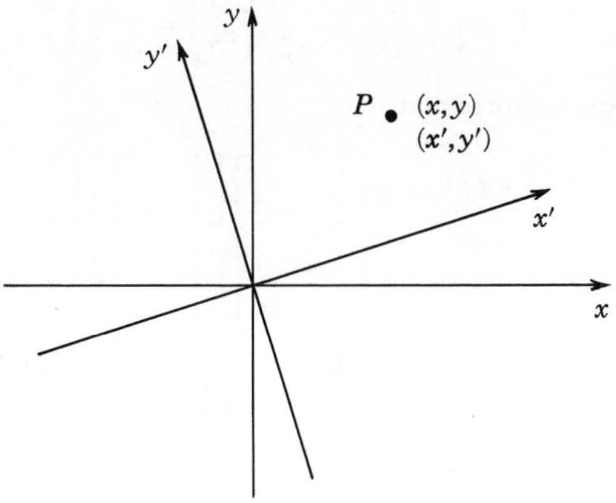

FIGURE 20.2

In matrix form,

$$(x\ y) = (x'\ y')P, \quad \text{where} \quad P = \begin{bmatrix} p_{11} & p_{12} \\ p_{21} & p_{22} \end{bmatrix}.$$

The condition that the two sets of axes be rectangular is equivalent to the condition that the matrix P be orthogonal. This fact may be proved by the methods of Section 7.

If a 2×2 symmetric matrix A has characteristic values e and f and respective orthonormal characteristic vectors $\mathbf{u}$ and $\mathbf{v}$ (see 20.25), then $\mathbf{u}\cdot A = e\mathbf{u}$, $\mathbf{v}\cdot A = f\mathbf{v}$, and if we let P be the 2×2 matrix whose row vectors are $\mathbf{u}$ and $\mathbf{v}$,

$$P = \begin{bmatrix} \mathbf{u} \\ \mathbf{v} \end{bmatrix}$$

then P is an orthogonal matrix and

$$PAP^T = \begin{bmatrix} e\mathbf{u} \\ f\mathbf{v} \end{bmatrix} (\mathbf{u}^T\ \mathbf{v}^T) = \begin{pmatrix} e\mathbf{u}\cdot\mathbf{u} & e\mathbf{u}\cdot\mathbf{v} \\ f\mathbf{v}\cdot\mathbf{u} & f\mathbf{v}\cdot\mathbf{v} \end{pmatrix} = \begin{pmatrix} e & 0 \\ 0 & f \end{pmatrix}.$$

For example, we saw in the preceding section that the symmetric matrix

$$A = \begin{bmatrix} 1 & 2 \\ 2 & -2 \end{bmatrix}$$

has characteristic values 2 and -3, and corresponding orthonormal characteristic vectors $\mathbf{u} = \langle 2/\sqrt{5}, 1/\sqrt{5} \rangle$ and $\mathbf{v} = \langle 1/\sqrt{5}, -2/\sqrt{5} \rangle$. Thus

$$P = \begin{bmatrix} 2/\sqrt{5} & 1/\sqrt{5} \\ 1/\sqrt{5} & -2/\sqrt{5} \end{bmatrix} = \frac{1}{\sqrt{5}} \begin{bmatrix} 2 & 1 \\ 1 & -2 \end{bmatrix}$$

is an orthogonal matrix and

$$\begin{aligned} PAP^T &= \tfrac{1}{5} \begin{bmatrix} 2 & 1 \\ 1 & -2 \end{bmatrix} \begin{bmatrix} 1 & 2 \\ 2 & -2 \end{bmatrix} \begin{bmatrix} 2 & 1 \\ 1 & -2 \end{bmatrix} \\ &= \tfrac{1}{5} \begin{bmatrix} 4 & 2 \\ -3 & 6 \end{bmatrix} \begin{bmatrix} 2 & 1 \\ 1 & -2 \end{bmatrix} \\ &= \tfrac{1}{5} \begin{bmatrix} 10 & 0 \\ 0 & -15 \end{bmatrix} = \begin{bmatrix} 2 & 0 \\ 0 & -3 \end{bmatrix}. \end{aligned}$$

We can use the remarks above to identify graphs of quadratic equations of the form

(1) $$ax^2 + 2cxy + by^2 = d \quad \text{or} \quad XAX^T = d$$

considered earlier. Let P be the orthogonal matrix such that PAP^T has diagonal form D, say

$$PAP^T = D = \begin{bmatrix} e & 0 \\ 0 & f \end{bmatrix},$$

and also let

$$(x' \; y') = X' = XP^T \qquad \text{(or, equivalently, } X = X'P).$$

Then

$$d = XAX^T = X'PAP^TX'^T = X'DX'^T.$$

On multiplying the matrices in $X'DX'^T$, we obtain the equation

(2) $$ex'^2 + fy'^2 = d.$$

If we let $\mathbf{u}, \mathbf{v}$ be the row vectors of P, and then select new rectangular coordinate axes along these orthonormal vectors, then the graph of equation (1) relative to the given axes (along $\mathbf{i}$ and $\mathbf{j}$) is the same as the graph of equation (2) relative to the new axes. Since the graph of (2) is easily recognized, the graph of (1) is also evident.

EXAMPLE 1. Describe the graph of the equation $x^2 + 4xy - 2y^2 = 6$.

Solution: This equation has matrix form

$$(x\ y)\begin{bmatrix} 1 & 2 \\ 2 & -2 \end{bmatrix}\begin{bmatrix} x \\ y \end{bmatrix} = 6.$$

By previous work,

$$PAP^T = \begin{bmatrix} 2 & 0 \\ 0 & -3 \end{bmatrix}, \quad \text{where} \quad P = \frac{1}{\sqrt{5}}\begin{bmatrix} 2 & 1 \\ 1 & -2 \end{bmatrix}, \quad A = \begin{bmatrix} 1 & 2 \\ 2 & -2 \end{bmatrix}.$$

If we select the x' axis along the vector $\mathbf{u} = \langle 2/\sqrt{5}, 1/\sqrt{5} \rangle$ and the y'-axis along $\mathbf{v} = \langle 1/\sqrt{5}, -2/\sqrt{5} \rangle$, then the graph of the given equation is the same as the graph of the equation

$$2x'^2 - 3y'^2 = 6.$$

When put in the normal form

$$\frac{x'^2}{(\sqrt{3})^2} - \frac{y'^2}{(\sqrt{2})^2} = 1$$

we recognize the graph to be a hyperbola with transverse axis along the x'-axis, as sketched in Figure 20.3.

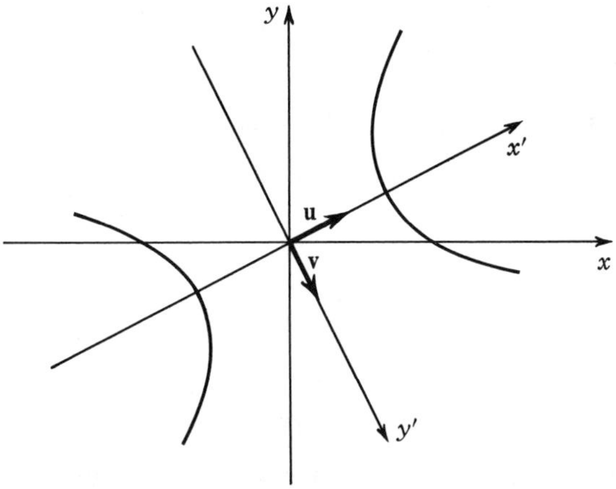

FIGURE 20.3

The more general quadratic equation

$$ax^2 + 2cxy + by^2 + dx + ey = f$$

can be studied in much the same way as the ones above. In the first place, it can be put in matrix form

$$XAX^T + BX^T = f,$$

where

$$X = (x\,y), \quad A = \begin{bmatrix} a & c \\ c & b \end{bmatrix}, \quad B = (d\,e).$$

Now if P is an orthogonal matrix such that

$$PAP^T = D = \begin{bmatrix} g & 0 \\ 0 & h \end{bmatrix}$$

and if

$$X' = (x'\,y') = XP^T,$$

then

$$X'PAP^TX'^T + BP^TX'^T = f.$$

This yields an equation of the form

$$gx'^2 + hy'^2 + kx' + my' = f,$$

whose graph relative to a new set of axes is the same as the given equation relative to the old axes. Since this new equation has no xy term, its graph is easily determined by the methods of Chapter 13.

EXAMPLE 2. Describe the graph of the equation

$$x^2 - 4xy + 4y^2 + 2\sqrt{5}x - \sqrt{5}y = 0.$$

Solution: If we let

$$X = (x\,y), A = \begin{bmatrix} 1 & -2 \\ -2 & 4 \end{bmatrix}, \quad B = (2\sqrt{5} \; -\sqrt{5}),$$

then the equation has the matrix form

$$XAX^T + BX^T = 0.$$

We find the characteristic values of A to be 0 and 5, and the corresponding orthonormal characteristic vectors to be $\langle 2/\sqrt{5}, 1/\sqrt{5}\rangle$ and $\langle -1/\sqrt{5}, 2/\sqrt{5}\rangle$. Hence

$$P = \frac{1}{\sqrt{5}}\begin{bmatrix} 2 & 1 \\ -1 & 2 \end{bmatrix}$$

and

$$X' = (x'\,y') = XP^T.$$

Therefore

$$PAP^T = \begin{bmatrix} 0 & 0 \\ 0 & 5 \end{bmatrix}, \quad BP^T = (3 \ \ -4)$$

and the new equation is

$$5y'^2 + 3x' - 4y' = 0.$$

We recognize this to be an equation of a parabola.

With almost no changes being made, the work of this section can be extended to quadratic surfaces. We illustrate this fact with the following simple example.

EXAMPLE 3. Describe the graph in space of the equation

$$2xy - z^2 = 1.$$

Solution: This equation has matrix form

$$XAX^T = 1, \quad \text{where } X = (x\,y\,z), \quad A = \begin{bmatrix} 0 & 1 & 0 \\ 1 & 0 & 0 \\ 0 & 0 & -1 \end{bmatrix}.$$

The equation

$$|A - \lambda I| = \begin{vmatrix} -\lambda & 1 & 0 \\ 1 & -\lambda & 0 \\ 0 & 0 & -1-\lambda \end{vmatrix} = 0$$

has roots 1 and -1. By solving the equations $\mathbf{v}\cdot A = \mathbf{v}$ and $\mathbf{v}\cdot A = -\mathbf{v}$ for $\mathbf{v}$, we find orthonormal characteristic vectors

$$\langle 2/3,-2/3,1/3\rangle,\ \langle 1/3\sqrt{2},-1/3\sqrt{2},-4/3\sqrt{2}\rangle,\ \langle 1/\sqrt{2},1/\sqrt{2},0\rangle$$

with respective characteristic values -1, -1, and 1. Thus, if

$$P = \frac{1}{3\sqrt{2}}\begin{bmatrix} 2\sqrt{2} & -2\sqrt{2} & \sqrt{2} \\ 1 & -1 & -4 \\ 3 & 3 & 0 \end{bmatrix}, \quad X' = XP^T,$$

we have

$$PAP^T = \begin{bmatrix} -1 & 0 & 0 \\ 0 & -1 & 0 \\ 0 & 0 & 1 \end{bmatrix}.$$

Hence the given equation has the same graph as the equation $X'PAP^TX'^T = 1$, or

$$-x'^2 - y'^2 + z'^2 = 1.$$

By **17.16**, the graph is a hyperboloid of two sheets.

EXERCISES

Describe the graph of each of the following equations.

1. $2x^2 + 6xy + 10y^2 = 1$.
2. $xy = 1$.
3. $8x^2 + 6xy = 1$.
4. $x^2 - 4xy + y^2 = 4$.
5. $29x^2 - 24xy + 36y^2 + 118x - 24y = 55$.
6. $13x^2 + 8xy + 4xz + 13y^2 + 4yz + 10z^2 = 36$.

REVIEW

Oral Exercises

Define:

1. Vector space.
2. The space V_n.
3. Basis of a vector space.
4. Dimension of a vector space.
5. Rank of a matrix.
6. Elementary row operations on a matrix.
7. Echelon form of a matrix.
8. Determinant of a matrix.
9. Adjoint of a matrix.
10. Inverse of a matrix.
11. Linear transformation.
12. Euclidean space.
13. Orthonormal basis.
14. Isometry.
15. Characteristic value and characteristic vector.
16. Orthogonal matrix.

17. Symmetric matrix.

18. Symmetric linear transformation.

I

In each of Exercises 1–4 tell whether or not the set of vectors is a basis of the given vector space.

1. $\{\mathbf{i} + 7\mathbf{j}, 2\mathbf{i} - \mathbf{j}\}$ in V_2.
2. $\{\mathbf{i} - 3\mathbf{j} + \mathbf{k}, 2\mathbf{i} - 4\mathbf{j} + 3\mathbf{k}, \mathbf{i} + \mathbf{j} + 3\mathbf{k}\}$ in V_3.
3. $\{2\mathbf{i} - 5\mathbf{j}, 3\mathbf{i} + 7\mathbf{k}, 15\mathbf{j} + 14\mathbf{k}\}$ in V_3.
4. $\{\langle 1,1,0,3\rangle, \langle 0,1,2,-1\rangle, \langle 1,-1,1,0\rangle, \langle -2,0,1,-1\rangle\}$ in V_4.

In each of Exercises 5–8 find the rank of the matrix:

5. $\begin{bmatrix} 1 & -1 \\ 1 & 1 \end{bmatrix}$.

6. $\begin{bmatrix} 2 & -1 & 3 \\ 1 & 4 & -7 \\ 4 & -11 & 23 \end{bmatrix}$.

7. $\begin{bmatrix} 2 & 0 & 1 & 4 \\ 3 & 1 & -1 & 1 \\ 1 & 4 & 1 & 4 \end{bmatrix}$.

8. $\begin{bmatrix} 4 & 7 & -5 \\ -1 & -2 & 2 \\ 2 & 3 & -1 \\ 3 & 5 & -3 \end{bmatrix}$.

In each of Exercises 9–12 solve the system of linear equations.

9. $\begin{aligned} 3x + y + 2z &= 1 \\ -x - y + 4z &= -15 \\ 2x - 5y + z &= -4. \end{aligned}$

10. $\begin{aligned} 3x + y - z &= 14 \\ 2x + 3y + 4z &= 14 \\ -x + 2y + 5z &= 0. \end{aligned}$

11. $\begin{aligned} x + y - 5w &= 1 \\ 2x - 3y - 5z &= -13 \\ x - y - 2z - w &= -5. \end{aligned}$

12. $\begin{aligned} x + y - z + w &= 10 \\ x - y + z + w &= 0 \\ x + y + z - w &= 2 \\ 2x - 3y + z + w &= -6. \end{aligned}$

In each of Exercises 13–16 find the inverse, if possible, of the matrix.

13. $\begin{bmatrix} -5 & 4 \\ 4 & -3 \end{bmatrix}$.

14. $\begin{bmatrix} 0 & -2 \\ 5 & -3 \end{bmatrix}$.

15. $\begin{bmatrix} -1 & 1 & 0 \\ 0 & 2 & 3 \\ 1 & 0 & 4 \end{bmatrix}$.

16. $\begin{bmatrix} 0 & 1 & 5 \\ 2 & 0 & -2 \\ 1 & -3 & 0 \end{bmatrix}$.

In each of Exercises 17–20 tell whether or not the given l.t. is an isometry.

17. $\mathbf{i}f = \frac{1}{2}(-\sqrt{3}\mathbf{i} + \mathbf{j})$, $\mathbf{j}f = \frac{1}{2}(\mathbf{i} + \sqrt{3}\mathbf{j})$ of V_2.

18. $\mathbf{i}f = \frac{1}{5}(3\mathbf{i} + 4\mathbf{j})$, $\mathbf{j}f = \frac{1}{5}(3\mathbf{i} - 4\mathbf{j})$ of V_2.

19. $\mathbf{i}f = \mathbf{j}$, $\mathbf{j}f = \mathbf{k}$, $\mathbf{k}f = \mathbf{j}$ of V_3.

20. $\mathbf{i}f = \frac{1}{3}(2\mathbf{i} - \mathbf{j} + 2\mathbf{k})$, $\mathbf{j}f = \dfrac{1}{\sqrt{5}}(\mathbf{i} + 2\mathbf{j})$, $\mathbf{k}f = \dfrac{1}{3\sqrt{5}}(-4\mathbf{i} + 2\mathbf{j} + 5\mathbf{k})$ of V_3.

In each of Exercises 21–24 describe the graph of the quadratic equation.

21. $-x^2 + 16xy + 11y^2 = 5$.

22. $4x^2 - 4x + y^2 = 9$.

23. $3x^2 + 4xy = 4$.

24. $\frac{1}{3}(7x^2 - 4xz + 5y^2 + 4yz + 6z^2) = 1$.

21

DIFFERENTIAL EQUATIONS

THE THEORY OF differential equations is a large part of mathematics, and the application of the results of this theory constitutes a strong tool of science. Parts of the brief treatment of the subject in this chapter suggest the character of the general theory. A surprising number of applications may be made of the limited set of topics covered.

1 INTRODUCTION

If G is a function of $n + 2$ variables, the equation

$$G(x,y,y',y'',\cdots,y^{[n]}) = 0,$$

where $y', y'', \cdots, y^{[n]}$ formally designate the first, second, $\cdots$, nth derivative of y at x, is called an *ordinary differential equation of order n*. A function f is a *solution* of this equation if

$$G(x,f(x),f'(x),f''(x),\cdots,f^{[n]}(x)) = 0$$

for every x in the domain of f.

The separable differential equation

21.1 $$M(x) + N(y)y' = 0$$

studied in Chapter 12 is an example of an ordinary differential equation of order 1.

The equation

$$y'' - 4y = 0$$

is an example of an ordinary differential equation of order 2. It is easily verified that the function f defined by $f(x) = e^{2x}$ is a solution of this equation.

In contrast to ordinary differential equations, an equation such as

$$\frac{\partial^2 z}{\partial x^2} = \frac{\partial^2 z}{\partial y^2}$$

is called a *partial differential equation.* A function f of two variables is a solution of this equation if

$$\frac{\partial^2 f}{\partial x^2} = \frac{\partial^2 f}{\partial y^2}.$$

We shall focus our attention in this chapter on ordinary differential equations of the more elementary types and of order 1 or 2.

If M and N are continuous functions, then it was shown in **12.7** that the separable differential equation **21.1** has solution

21.2 $$\int M(x)\,dx + \int N(y)\,dy = C.$$

That is, every solution f (with continuous derivative) of **21.1** satisfies **21.2** for some constant C, and vice versa.

For example, the differential equation

(1) $$3x^2 + 1 + e^y y' = 0$$

has solution

(2) $$x^3 + x + e^y = C,$$

by **21.2**. Thus each differentiable function f that is a solution of (1) satisfies (2) [with $y = f(x)$] for some constant C, and vice versa. Equation (2) is called an *implicit solution* of (1). We may solve (2) for y, thereby obtaining an explicit solution

$$y = \ln (C - x^3 - x)$$

of (1). The function f defined by $f(x) = \ln (C - x^3 - x)$ is a solution of (1) for every constant C.

Equation (2) is typical of the solution of a differential equation of order 1 in that it contains one arbitrary parameter C. Such a description of the solution of a differential equation in terms of one or more parameters is called the *general solution* of the equation.

For example, the differential equation

$$y'' - 4y = 0 \tag{3}$$

may be shown to have the general solution

$$y = C_1 e^{2x} + C_2 e^{-2x}. \tag{4}$$

We note in this example that the differential equation is of order 2 and the general solution has two parameters C_1 and C_2.

On the other hand, the second-order partial differential equation

$$\frac{\partial^2 z}{\partial x^2} = \frac{\partial^2 z}{\partial y^2}$$

has solutions described in terms of two arbitrary *functions* f and g:

$$z = f(x - y) + g(x + y).$$

EXAMPLE 1. Verify that, for any constants C_1 and C_2, Equation (4) above is a solution of (3).

Solution: If y is as given in (4), then

$$y' = 2C_1 e^{2x} - 2C_2 e^{-2x}, \qquad y'' = 4C_1 e^{2x} + 4C_2 e^{-2x},$$

and $y'' = 4y$. Thus (4) is a solution of (3) for any constants C_1 and C_2.

In this example the solution of the differential equation is given explicitly, so that we might verify it by direct computation of y' and y'' and subsequent substitution of these functions into the given differential equation. If the solution of a differential equation is given implicitly, then the solution may be verified by implicit differentiation, as illustrated in the following example.

EXAMPLE 2. Show that, for every constant C,

$$x^2 - 2xy + y^4 = C$$

is a solution of the differential equation

$$x - y + (2y^3 - x)y' = 0.$$

Solution: If f is a differentiable function such that $y = f(x)$ satisfies

$$x^2 - 2xy + y^4 = C$$

for some constant C, then we have by implicit differentiation that

$$2x - 2y + (-2x + 4y^3)y' = 0$$

or $\quad x - y + (2y^3 - x)y' = 0.$

EXAMPLE 3. Find the general solution of the differential equation

$$\frac{1}{x} + \frac{y'}{y} = 0.$$

Solution: This separable differential equation has the general solution

$$\int \frac{1}{x}\,dx + \int \frac{1}{y}\,dy = C_1,$$

or

(1) $$\ln|x| + \ln|y| = C_1,$$

where C_1 is a parameter. That is, a function f is a solution of the given differential equation if and only if $y = f(x)$ is a solution of (1) for some constant C_1. It is evident that the solution (1) may be put in the form $\ln|xy| = C_1$, or

(2) $$|xy| = e^{C_1} = C_2.$$

We can show, moreover, that

(3) $$xy = C$$

(where $C = \pm C_2$) is also a solution for each nonzero C. Thus

$$y = \frac{C}{x}$$

is an explicit solution of the given equation.

That (2) implies (3) is a consequence of the following remarks. If the function G is continuous in an interval $[a,b]$ and if $G(x) \neq 0$ in this interval, then either $G(x) > 0$ or $G(x) < 0$ in $[a,b]$. Hence either $|G(x)| = G(x)$ or $|G(x)| = -G(x)$ in $[a,b]$.

EXERCISES

I

In each of Exercises 1–7 verify that if C, C_1, C_2 are any constants then the given relation between x and y satisfies the corresponding differential equation.

1. $y = Ce^{2x}$; $y' = 2y$.
2. $y = Ce^{x^2}$; $y' = 2xy$.
3. $y = C_1 + C_2x$; $y'' = 0$.
4. $y = C_1 \sin x + C_2 \cos x$; $y'' + y = 0$.
5. $xy + \cos x = C$; $xy' + y = \sin x$.
6. $y = \dfrac{C + x}{x^2 + 1}$; $y' = \dfrac{1 - 2xy}{x^2 + 1}$.
7. $y = C_1(x^2 + C_2)$; $y' = y''x$.

8. Show that if f and g are any functions possessing second derivatives and if $z = f(x - y) + g(x + y)$, then $\dfrac{\partial^2 z}{\partial x^2} = \dfrac{\partial^2 z}{\partial y^2}$.

Find the general solution of the following differential equations.

9. $x - yy' = 0$.

10. $\sin x - (\sin y)y' = 0$.

11. $dy/dx = y/x$.

12. $x + y(1 + x^2)\,Dy = 0$.

13. $xy' = 2y$.

14. $y' = x^{-2}$.

15. $y'' = x^{-1}$.

16. $y''' = x$.

II

1. a. If C_1 and C_2 are any constants, then show that the equation $y = C_1F(x) + C_2G(x)$ is a solution of the differential equation

$$\begin{vmatrix} y & F(x) & G(x) \\ y' & F'(x) & G'(x) \\ y'' & F''(x) & G''(x) \end{vmatrix} = 0.$$

b. Show that part a includes Exercises I-3, I-4, and I-7 as special cases.

c. Under what condition does part a reduce to a first-order differential equation?

2. If f is a differentiable function and $z = x^n f(y/x)$, then show that

$$x\frac{\partial z}{\partial x} + y\frac{\partial z}{\partial y} = nz.$$

3. If functions F and G have second derivatives and $z = F(x + G(y))$, then show that

$$\frac{\partial z}{\partial x}\frac{\partial^2 z}{\partial x \partial y} = \frac{\partial z}{\partial y}\frac{\partial^2 z}{\partial x^2}.$$

4. If two polynomials $P(x)$ and $Q(x)$ satisfying the equation

$$\sqrt{1 - P^2(x)} = Q(x)\sqrt{1 - x^2},$$

show that $dP/\sqrt{1 - P^2(x)} = n\,dx/\sqrt{1 - x^2}$ for some integer n.

2 FAMILIES OF CURVES

The differential equation

$$y' = 2$$

has the general solution

$$y = 2x + C.$$

We may interpret this solution as the set, or *family*, of all straight lines in the plane having slope 2 (Figure 21.1).

Similarly, the equation

$$xy' + y = 0$$

has the general solution

$$xy = C,$$

which may be interpreted as the family of all hyperbolas in the plane, each having the coordinate axes as asymptotes. Note that in these examples the parameter C of the general solution of a differential equation is the parameter of the family of curves.

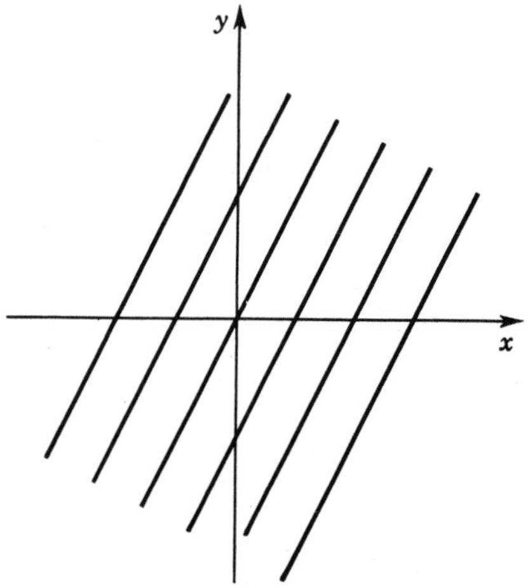

FIGURE 21.1

It is true, conversely, that a family of curves described with one parameter may often be shown to be the general solution of a first-order differential equation.

For example, the equation

$$y = Cx^2 \tag{1}$$

describes the family of parabolas, each of which has its vertex at the origin and axis along the y axis (Figure 21.2). If we differentiate (1), we obtain

$$y' = 2Cx. \tag{2}$$

We may eliminate C between (1) and (2), thereby getting the differential equation

$$xy' = 2y. \tag{3}$$

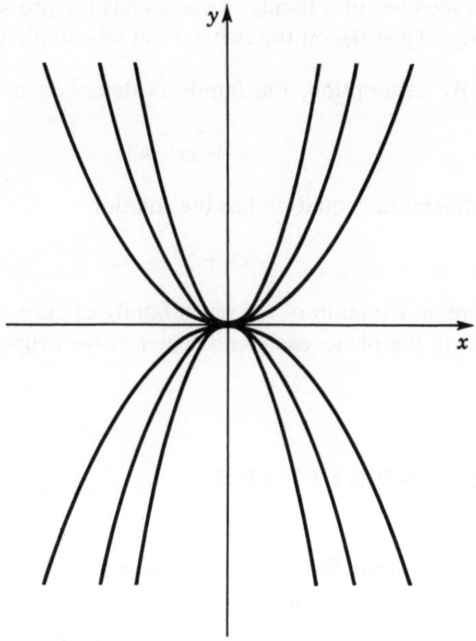

FIGURE 21.2

It is easily shown that (1) is the general solution of (3), so that (3) is completely descriptive of the given family of parabolas.

According to (3), $y' = 2y/x$; i.e., at each point (x,y) (other than the origin) on each of the parabolas of the given family, the slope of the tangent line to that parabola is $2y/x$. Therefore this is a property of every member of the family. Equation (2), on the other hand, expresses a property of a particular member of the family.

EXAMPLE 1. Find a differential equation describing the family of hyperbolas

(1) $$xy = Cx - 1.$$

Solution: We may differentiate (1), obtaining

(2) $$xy' + y = C.$$

On eliminating C between (1) and (2), we get

$$xy = (xy' + y)x - 1$$
$$\text{or} \quad x^2y' = 1$$

as the differential equation of the family of hyperbolas.

EXAMPLE 2. Each member of a family of curves has the property that its slope is $-x/y$ at each point (x,y), $(y \neq 0)$, on the curve. Find an equation describing this family.

Solution: By assumption, the family is described by the differential equation $y' = -x/y$, or

$$x + yy' = 0.$$

This separable differential equation has the solution

$$x^2 + y^2 = C,$$

which is therefore an equation of the given family of curves. Clearly, this family consists of all circles in the plane, each with center at the origin.

3 BOUNDARY CONDITIONS

It was shown above that the differential equation $x + yy' = 0$ has a family of circles $x^2 + y^2 = C$ as its general solution. There is one and only one circle of this family passing through a given point of the plane.

For example, to find the circle passing through the point (2,1), we must determine the value of C such that $2^2 + 1^2 = C$. Clearly, $C = 5$ and

$$x^2 + y^2 = 5$$

is the particular circle of the family passing through the point (2,1).

The equation $x^2 + y^2 = 5$ is called a *particular solution* of $x + yy' = 0$, as distinguished from the general solution $x^2 + y^2 = C$. It is the unique solution satisfying the condition $y = 1$ when $x = 2$. Such a condition is called a *boundary condition* of the given differential equation.

A differential equation of order 1 has one parameter in its general solution, and one boundary condition suffices to determine a particular solution. For a differential equation of order 2, two boundary conditions are needed to determine a particular solution (for example, $y = b$ and $y' = c$ when $x = a$). Similar remarks may be made for higher order equations.

EXAMPLE 1. Determine the member of the family of parabolas $y = Cx^2$ that passes through the point $(10,-3)$.

Solution: Substituting $x = 10$ and $y = -3$ in $y = Cx^2$, we get $-3 = 100C$ and hence $C = -.03$. Thus

$$y = -.03x^2$$

is the parabola desired.

EXAMPLE 2. Find the particular solution of the differential equation

$$(1 - \tan^2\theta) + 2r\tan\theta\,\frac{d\theta}{dr} = 0$$

satisfying the boundary condition $r = 1$ when $\theta = \pi/8$.

Solution: The given differential equation may be put in the form

$$\frac{1}{r} + \frac{2\tan\theta}{1 - \tan^2\theta}\frac{d\theta}{dr} = 0,$$

or

$$\frac{1}{r} + \tan 2\theta\,\frac{d\theta}{dr} = 0.$$

Its general solution is therefore

$$\ln|r| + \tfrac{1}{2}\ln|\sec 2\theta| = C_1,$$

or

$$r^2 = C\cos 2\theta.$$

If $\theta = \pi/8$ and $r = 1$, we find $C = \sqrt{2}$. Hence

$$r^2 = \sqrt{2}\cos 2\theta$$

is the desired particular solution.

EXAMPLE 3. Find a function f that is a solution of the differential equation

$$x + e^x + 3y^2y' = 0$$

and is such that $f(0) = 3$.

Solution: We are asked to find an explicit solution $y = f(x)$ of the equation satisfying the boundary condition $y = 3$ when $x = 0$. The given differential equation has the general solution

$$\tfrac{1}{2}x^2 + e^x + y^3 = C,$$

or

$$y = \sqrt[3]{C - \tfrac{1}{2}x^2 - e^x}.$$

If $y = 3$ when $x = 0$, then $C = 28$. Hence

$$f(x) = \sqrt[3]{28 - \tfrac{1}{2}x^2 - e^x}$$

defines the solution for which $f(0) = 3$.

EXERCISES

I

Sketch four different members of each of the following families of curves, and find a differential equation of the family.

1. $y = Cx$.
2. $y^2 = x - C$.

3. $y = x^2 + C$.

4. $\dfrac{x^2}{4} + \dfrac{y^2}{9} = C$.

5. $x^2 - y^2 = C$.

6. $x^2 + (y - C)^2 = 1$.

7. $(x - C)^2 + (y - C)^2 = C^2$.

8. $\dfrac{x^2}{C^2} + \dfrac{y^2}{9} = 1$.

Solve each of the following differential equations, and sketch that member of the family of solutions passing through the given point.

9. $y' = 2x$; $(-2,0)$.

10. $y' = -3$; $(1,-1)$.

11. $xy' + y = 0$; $(-1,3)$.

12. $y' = 2\sqrt{y}$; $(2,4)$.

13. $yy' + x - 2 = 0$; $(0,0)$.

14. $(y - 1)y' = x$; $(0,1)$.

In each of Exercises 15–18 find the particular solution of each of the following differential equations that satisfies the given boundary condition.

15. $r^2 \dfrac{dr}{d\theta} = \sin\theta$; $r = 1$ when $\theta = \dfrac{\pi}{4}$.

16. $\dfrac{dz}{du} = \ln u$; $z = 2$ when $u = e$.

17. $yy' = x + 1$; $y = 3$ when $x = 0$.

18. $e^{y-x}y' + x = 0$; $y = 2$ when $x = 2$.

19. Show that $y'' = 0$ is the differential equation of the family of curves $y = C_1x + C_2$. Interpret this result geometrically.

20. Show that the particular solution of the differential equation

$$M(x) + N(y)y' = 0$$

satisfying the boundary condition $y = y_0$ when $x = x_0$ is given by

$$\int_{x_0}^{x} M(x)\,dx + \int_{y_0}^{y} N(y)\,dy = 0.$$

Solve Exercises 17 and 18 by this method.

21. If one family of curves has the differential equation $y' = G(x,y)$ and another family of curves has the differential equation $y' = -1/G(x,y)$, then each member of the first family is *orthogonal* to each member of the second family (i.e., they meet at right angles). The second family is called the set of *orthogonal trajectories* of the first family, and vice versa. Show that the two families with equations $y^2 = Cx^3$ and $2x^2 + 3y^2 = K$ are orthogonal trajectories of each other.

In each of Exercises 22–25 find the orthogonal trajectories of the family of curves. [*Hint:* Find the differential equation of the family, replace y' by $-1/y'$, and then solve the resulting differential equation.]

22. $y = Cx$.

23. $xy = Cx - 1$.

24. $y^2 = x^2 + C$.

25. $y^2 = Cx$.

26. Show that the family of curves $y^2 = 4C(x + C)$ is self-orthogonal; i.e., each two members of the family that meet necessarily meet at right angles.

27. Show that the family of circles $(y - 1)^2 + (x - C)^2 = 1$ has the differential equation $y^2 - 2y + (y - 1)^2(y')^2 = 0$. Show that this differential equation also has the solutions $y = 0$ and $y = 2$. Explain this phenomenon geometrically.

II

In each of Exercises 1–7 find a differential equation for the given family of curves.

1. Circles of radius 1 which are tangent to the x axis.

2. Circles of radius 1 in the plane.

3. All circles in the plane.

4. Parabolas with axes parallel to the x axis.

5. Ellipses with centers at the origin.

6. $y = c_1f(x) + c_2g(x) + c_3h(x)$, ($c_1$, c_2, c_3 constants).

7. $y = a^2F(x) + abG(x) + b^2H(x)$, ($a$, b constants).

8. Find the equation into which $y' = H(x,y)$ transforms under the transformation $y = f(u,v)$, $x = g(u,v)$.

9. Solve the differential equation $y' = (x^2 + y^2)/2xy$ by means of the transformation $y = u - v$, $x = u + v$.

10. Find the orthogonal trajectories of the family of circles passing through the two points $(a,0)$ and $(-a,0)$.

11. Show how to find a family of curves $F(x,y) = C$ which is orthogonal to the family $F(y,x) = C_1$.

4 EXACT DIFFERENTIAL EQUATIONS

We shall study in this section methods of solving a large class of differential equations of the first order, among which are the separable differential equations.

21.3 DEFINITION. The differential equation

$$M(x,y) + N(x,y)y' = 0$$

is called *exact* if

$$\frac{\partial M}{\partial y} = \frac{\partial N}{\partial x}.$$

For example,

$$2x - y + (y^2 - x)y' = 0$$

is an exact differential equation, since

$$\frac{\partial}{\partial y}(2x - y) = -1 = \frac{\partial}{\partial x}(y^2 - x).$$

We shall always assume that the functions M and N of two variables have continuous first partial derivatives. If we let

$$F(x,y) = \int_a^x M(s,y)\,ds + \int_b^y N(a,t)\,dt$$

for some fixed a and b, then it is easy to show that if $\partial M/\partial y = \partial N/\partial x$, then

$$\frac{\partial F}{\partial x} = M, \quad \frac{\partial F}{\partial y} = N.$$

That is, there exists a function F such that $\nabla F = \langle M,N \rangle$. Let us prove the following result.

21.4 **THEOREM.** The exact differential equation

$$M(x,y) + N(x,y)y' = 0$$

has the general solution

$$F(x,y) = C$$

where F is any smooth function of two variables such that $\nabla F = \langle M,N \rangle$.

Proof: If f is a solution of the differential equation, then by the chain rule

$$\begin{aligned} DF(x,f(x)) &= D_1F(x,f(x)) + D_2F(x,f(x))f'(x) \\ &= M(x,f(x)) + N(x,f(x))f'(x) = 0. \end{aligned}$$

Hence $F(x,f(x)) = C$ for some constant C.

On the other hand, if $F(x,f(x)) = C$, then $DF(x,f(x)) = DC = 0$. Therefore, using the chain rule as above, we have

$$M(x,f(x)) + N(x,f(x))f'(x) = 0.$$

Hence f is a solution.

Possible methods of finding the function F of the above theorem are given in the following examples.

EXAMPLE 1. Solve the differential equation

$$2x - y + (y^2 - x)y' = 0.$$

Solution: We verified above that this equation is exact. Its solution will be $F(x,y) = C$, where F is a function such that

$$(1) \qquad D_1F(x,y) = 2x - y,$$
$$(2) \qquad D_2F(x,y) = y^2 - x.$$

By integration, it follows from (1) that

$$F(x,y) = x^2 - xy + g(y)$$

for some function g. Hence, by (2),

$$D_1F(x,y) = -x + g'(y) = y^2 - x,$$

so that $g'(y) = y^2$ and $g(y) = y^3/3$. Thus

$$F(x,y) = x^2 - xy + \tfrac{1}{3}y^3,$$

and the given differential equation has the general solution

$$x^2 - xy + \tfrac{1}{3}y^3 = C.$$

EXAMPLE 2. Solve the differential equation

$$\sin y + (x \cos y + y \cos y + \sin y)y' = 0.$$

Solution: We easily verify that

$$\frac{\partial}{\partial y} \sin y = \cos y = \frac{\partial}{\partial x}(x \cos y + y \cos y + \sin y),$$

and hence that the given equation is exact. We wish to find a function F such that

$$(1) \qquad D_1F(x,y) = \sin y,$$
$$(2) \qquad D_2F(x,y) = x \cos y + y \cos y + \sin y.$$

We have from (1) that

$$F(x,y) = x \sin y + g(y)$$

for some function g. Therefore, using (2),

$$D_2F(x,y) = x \cos y + g'(y) = x \cos y + y \cos y + \sin y,$$

and

$$g'(y) = y \cos y + \sin y.$$

Hence (using Formula 51 of the Table of Integrals)

$$g(y) = \int (y \cos y + \sin y)\, dy = y \sin y,$$

and $F(x,y) = x \sin y + y \sin y$. Thus the given differential equation has the general solution

$$x \sin y + y \sin y = C.$$

For the separable differential equation **21.1**,

$$M(x) + N(y)y' = 0,$$

we clearly have $D_2M(x) = D_1N(y) = 0$. Thus this equation is exact, and if

$$F(x,y) = \int M(x)\,dx + \int N(y)\,dy,$$

then evidently $D_1F = M$ and $D_2F = N$. Hence

$$\int M(x)\,dx + \int N(y)\,dy = C$$

is the general solution of **21.1**, and we have another proof of **12.7**.

5 THE DIFFERENTIAL NOTATION

The first-order differential equation

$$R(x,y) + S(x,y)\frac{dy}{dx} = 0$$

is equivalent to the equation

$$R(x,y)\,dx + S(x,y)\,dy = 0$$

if we use the differential notation. That is, letting $dy = y'\,dx$, $y = f(x)$ is a solution of the first equation above if and only if it is a solution of the second one when $dx \neq 0$. This second equation is called the *symmetric form* of the given differential equation.

EXAMPLE 1. Solve the equation $y' = \dfrac{2xy}{y^2 - x^2}$.

Solution: If we let $y' = dy/dx$, this equation has symmetric form

$$2xy\,dx + (x^2 - y^2)\,dy = 0.$$

We recognize the equation above as an exact differential equation. If

$$F(x,y) = x^2y - \tfrac{1}{3}y^3,$$

then $D_1F(x,y) = 2xy$ and $D_2F(x,y) = x^2 - y^2$. Hence

$$x^2y - \tfrac{1}{3}y^3 = C$$

is the general solution of the given equation.

EXAMPLE 2. Find the particular solution of the equation

$$(\sin y + y \sin x)\,dx + (x \cos y - \cos x)\,dy = 0$$

that satisfies the boundary condition $y = \pi/2$ when $x = \pi$.

Solution: The given equation is exact. If

$$F(x,y) = x \sin y - y \cos x,$$

then $D_1F(x,y) = \sin y + y \sin x$ and $D_2F(x,y) = x \cos y - \cos x$. Hence

$$x \sin y - y \cos x = C$$

is the general solution of the given differential equation. If $y = \pi/2$ when $x = \pi$, then $C = 3\pi/2$, and

$$x \sin y - y \cos x = \frac{3\pi}{2}$$

is the desired particular solution.

EXERCISES

I

Solve the following differential equations.

1. $(x + y)\,dx + (x + 2y)\,dy = 0.$
2. $1 + r \cos\theta + \sin\theta \dfrac{dr}{d\theta} = 0.$
3. $ye^x - x + (e^x + 1)y' = 0.$
4. $ye^x - y + (e^x + 1)y' = 0.$
5. $(x \sin y - y)y' = \cos y.$
6. $(x \sin y - x)y' = \cos y.$
7. $(ye^{xy} + 2xy)\,dx + (xe^{xy} + x^2)\,dy = 0.$
8. $(r + e^\theta)\,d\theta + (\theta + e^r)\,dr = 0.$
9. $y \sec^2 x\,dx + \tan x\,dy = 0.$
10. $y' = \dfrac{x(6xy + 2)}{3y - 2x^3}.$
11. $(e^x \sin y + y)y' = e^x \cos y.$
12. $\ln(y^2 + 1) + \dfrac{2xy}{y^2 + 1} y' = 0.$

In Exercises 13 and 14 find the particular solution satisfying the given boundary condition for each equation.

13. $(x - y)\,dx + (2y^3 - x)\,dy = 0;\ y = 1$ when $x = 2.$
14. $y \cos xy + (1 + x \cos xy)y' = 0;\ y = -1$ when $x = \pi/4.$

15. a. Show that if $M(x,y)\,dx + N(x,y)\,dy = 0$ is an exact differential equation then the solution which satisfies the boundary condition $x = x_0$, $y = y_0$ can be given in the form

$$\int_{x_0}^{x} M(s,y)\,ds + \int_{y_0}^{y} N(x_0,t)\,dt = 0.$$

b. Solve Exercises 13 and 14 by this method.

If $I(x,y)M(x,y)\,dx + I(x,y)N(x,y)\,dy = 0$ is an exact differential equation, then $I(x,y)$ is said to be an *integrating factor* for the equation

$$M(x,y)\,dx + N(x,y)\,dy = 0.$$

Show in each of the following exercises that $I(x,y)$ is an integrating factor, and solve the equation.

16. $y\,dx - x\,dy = 0$; $I(x,y) = y^{-2}$.

17. $y\,dx - x\,dy = 0$; $I(x,y) = x^{-2}$.

18. $y\,dx - x\,dy = 0$; $I(x,y) = \dfrac{1}{xy}$.

19. $x + y + y' = 0$; $I(x,y) = e^{x}$.

20. $xy' = x - 3y$; $I(x,y) = x^2$.

21. $(y + x)\,dx + (y - x)\,dy = 0$; $I(x,y) = (x^2 + y^2)^{-1}$.

II

1. Show that once one integrating factor has been found for the differential equation $M(x,y)\,dx + N(x,y)\,dy = 0$ then an indefinite number of them can be found. (See Exercise I-15.)

2. Show that $1/(x^2 + y^2)$ and $2/(x^2 - y^2)$ are also integrating factors for Exercises I-16, I-17, and I-18.

3. Using Exercise 2, solve:

a. $x\,dy - y\,dx = (x^2 - y^2)\,dx$.

b. $x\dfrac{dy}{dx} - y = x^3 + xy^2$.

4. If $I_1(x,y)$ and $I_2(x,y)$ are two (independent) integrating factors of the differential equation in Exercise 1, then show that $I_1/I_2 = C$, (C a constant), is a solution of the differential equation.

6 HOMOGENEOUS EQUATIONS

A function F of two variables is said to be *homogeneous of degree n* if

21.5 $$F(tx,ty) = t^{n}F(x,y)$$

for every number t and every number pair (x,y) such that both (x,y) and (tx,ty) are in the domain of F.

The polynomial functions defined by

$$f(x,y) = ax + by,$$
$$g(x,y) = ax^2 + bxy + cy^2,$$
$$h(x,y) = ax^3 + bx^2y + cxy^2 + dy^3,$$

and so on, are examples of homogeneous functions, f of degree 1, g of degree 2, h of degree 3, and so on. As another example, the function F defined by

$$F(x,y) = x^2 + \frac{x^3 + 2y^3}{y}$$

is homogeneous of degree 2, since

$$F(tx,ty) = (tx)^2 + \frac{(tx)^3 + 2(ty)^3}{ty} = t^2F(x,y).$$

Also, the function G defined by

$$G(x,y) = \frac{1}{x+y} \sin \frac{x-y}{x+y}$$

is homogeneous of degree -1, since

$$G(tx,ty) = \frac{1}{tx+ty} \sin \frac{tx-ty}{tx+ty} = t^{-1}G(x,y).$$

The equation

21.6 $$R(x,y) + S(x,y)y' = 0$$

is called a *homogeneous differential equation* if the functions R and S are homogeneous of the same degree. Let us show how such an equation may be solved.

We shall seek a solution of **21.6** of the form

$$y = xg(x), \qquad (x \neq 0),$$

for some differentiable function g. If we let $v = g(x)$, then

$$y = xv, \qquad y' = v + xv',$$

and **21.6** takes on the form

$$R(x,xv) + S(x,xv)(v + xv') = 0.$$

If R and S are homogeneous of degree n, then, by **21.5**,

$$R(x,xv) = x^nR(1,v), \qquad S(x,xv) = x^nS(1,v),$$

and the above differential equation becomes (on dividing out x^n)

$$R(1,v) + S(1,v)(v + xv') = 0,$$

or

21.7
$$\frac{1}{x} + \frac{S(1,v)}{R(1,v) + vS(1,v)} v' = 0.$$

Retracing our steps, we see that if $v = g(x)$ is a solution of **21.7**, then $y = xg(x)$ is a solution of **21.6**.

Thus we are always able to transform a homogeneous differential equation **21.6** into a separable differential equation **21.7**. The transformation $y = xv$, ($v = g(x)$), is said to *reduce* **21.6** to the simpler form **21.7**. Examples of reductions of other first- and second-order differential equations will be given in the exercises.

In the differential notation the substitution

$$y = xv, \qquad dy = x\,dv + v\,dx$$

transforms the homogeneous differential equation

$$R(x,y)\,dx + S(x,y)\,dy = 0$$

into the separable differential equation

$$\frac{1}{x}\,dx + \frac{S(1,v)}{R(1,v) + vS(1,v)}\,dv = 0.$$

EXAMPLE 1. Solve the differential equation

$$(y - 4x)\,dx + (y + 2x)\,dy = 0.$$

Solution: In this example

$$R(x,y) = y - 4x, \qquad S(x,y) = y + 2x,$$

and R and S are homogeneous of degree 1. The substitution

$$y = xv, \qquad dy = x\,dv + v\,dx$$

changes the given equation into the form

$$(xv - 4x)\,dx + (xv + 2x)(x\,dv + v\,dx) = 0,$$

or, on dividing by $x \neq 0$,

$$(v - 4)\,dx + (v + 2)(x\,dv + v\,dx) = 0.$$

A separation of variables yields the equation

$$\frac{1}{x}\,dx + \frac{v + 2}{v^2 + 3v - 4}\,dv = 0,$$

whose solution is

$$\ln|x| + \tfrac{2}{5}\ln|v+4| + \tfrac{3}{5}\ln|v-1| = C_1.$$

This may be put into the form

$$\ln|x^5(v+4)(v-1)^3| = 5C_1,$$

$$x^5(v+4)^2(v-1)^3 = C,$$

or

$$(xv+4x)^2(xv-x)^3 = C.$$

Since $xv = y$, we have

$$(y+4x)^2(y-x)^3 = C$$

as the general solution of the given differential equation.

EXAMPLE 2. Solve the differential equation

$$\left(x - y\tan\frac{y}{x}\right)dx + x\tan\frac{y}{x}\,dy = 0.$$

Solution: This equation again is homogeneous of degree 1. Substituting

$$y = xv, \qquad dy = x\,dv + v\,dx$$

in this equation, we get the separable differential equation

$$\frac{1}{x}\,dx + \tan v\,dv = 0,$$

whose solution is

$$\ln|x| + \ln|\sec v| = C_1,$$

or

$$x\sec v = C.$$

Hence the original equation has solution

$$x\sec\frac{y}{x} = C.$$

EXERCISES

I

Solve each of the following equations.

1. $(x - 2y)\,dx + x\,dy = 0.$

2. $y' = \dfrac{x^2 + y^2}{x^2}.$

3. $(2ye^{y/x} - x)\,dy + (2x + y)\,dx = 0.$

4. $(y^2 - x^2 + 2xy)\,dx + (y^2 - x^2 - 2xy)\,dy = 0.$

Show that each of the equations in Exercises 5 and 6 is both homogeneous and exact, and solve it by each of the corresponding methods.

5. $(x^2 + y^2)\,dx + 2xy\,dy = 0.$

6. $(2x + y)\,dx + (x + 3y)\,dy = 0.$

7. Let the point (h,k) be the point of intersection of the lines

$$4x + 3y + 1 = 0,$$
$$x + y + 1 = 0.$$

Show that the transformation

$$X = x - h, \qquad dX = dx,$$
$$Y = y - k, \qquad dY = dy,$$

reduces the equation

$$(4x + 3y + 1)\,dx + (x + y + 1)\,dy = 0$$

to a homogeneous equation, and solve the equation.

8. Show that the transformation

$$z = 2x + y, \qquad dz = 2\,dx + dy$$

reduces the equation

$$(2x + y)\,dx + (1 - 4x - 2y)\,dy = 0$$

to a separable equation, and solve the equation. Why does this problem require a solution different from that of Exercise 7?

Solve each of the following equations.

9. $(x + 2y + 1)\,dx + (x + y)\,dy = 0.$

10. $(2x + y + 1)\,dx + (2x + y)\,dy = 0.$

A second-order differential equation of the form $F(x,y',y'') = 0$ in which y is missing may be reduced to one of the first order by the transformation $p = y'$, $p' = y''$. Solve each of the following equations.

11. $y'' = y'.$

12. $y'' = -2y'.$

13. $y'' = \sin x.$

14. $xy'' = y' + 1.$

15. $y'' = \sqrt{(y')^2 + 1}.$

16. $y'' - e^x y' = 0.$

II

1. Solve the differential equation $dy/dx = (a_1x + b_1y + c_1)/(a_2x + b_2y + c_2)$. Consider all possible cases. (See Exercise I-7.)

2. Show that a second-order differential equation of the form $F(y,y',y'') = 0$ in which x is missing can be reduced to the first order by the transformation $p = y'$, $p(dp/dy) = y''$.

3. Using Exercise 2, solve the following differential equations:

a. $2y'' = e^y.$

b. $(y'')^2 = (1 + y'^2)^3.$

4. Transform the differential equation $F(x,y,y',y'') = 0$ into a form in which y is the independent variable and x is the dependent variable.

5. Solve the differential equation $y'' = F(y)y'^3$ by the method of: (a) Exercise 2; (b) Exercise 4.

7 FIRST-ORDER LINEAR DIFFERENTIAL EQUATIONS

The equation

21.8
$$y' + P(x)y = Q(x),$$

where P and Q are continuous functions, is called a *linear differential equation of the first order*. We shall show below how this equation can be solved.

If the function Q is zero, the resulting equation $y' + P(x)y = 0$ may be put in the form

$$\frac{1}{y}y' + P(x) = 0.$$

This separable differential equation has solution

$$y = Ce^{-\int P(x)dx},$$

$$\text{or} \quad ye^{\int P(x)dx} = C.$$

To return to the solution of 21.8, we first note that

$$D_1 ye^{\int P(x)dx} = y'e^{\int P(x)dx} + yP(x)e^{\int P(x)dx}.$$

Hence, if we multiply each side of 21.8 by $I(x)$, where

$$I(x) = e^{\int P(x)dx},$$

the left side becomes $D_1 yI(x)$ and 21.8 has the form

$$D_1 yI(x) = Q(x)I(x).$$

Integrating, we get

$$yI(x) = \int Q(x)I(x)\,dx + C,$$

or

21.9
$$y = e^{-\int P(x)dx}\left(\int Q(x)e^{\int P(x)dx}\,dx + C\right)$$

as the general solution of 21.8. We call $I(x)$ an *integrating factor* for the equation 21.8.

EXAMPLE 1. Solve the differential equation

$$y' + y = x.$$

Solution: This equation has the form **21.8** with $P(x) = 1$ and $Q(x) = x$. If we multiply each side of the equation by the integrating factor

$$I(x) = e^{\int P(x)dx} = e^x,$$

we obtain the equation

$$e^x y' + e^x y = xe^x,$$

$$\text{or} \qquad D(ye^x) = xe^x.$$

Hence $ye^x = \int xe^x\,dx + C = (x - 1)e^x + C$, and

$$y = x - 1 + Ce^{-x}$$

is the general solution of the given equation.

The differential equation

21.10 $$y' + R(x)y = S(x)y^k, \qquad (k \neq 0,1),$$

is called a *Bernoulli equation.** Since k is neither 0 nor 1, this equation is not linear. However, it may be reduced to a linear equation by a suitable transformation, as we now show.

Assuming that $y \neq 0$, let us multiply each side of **21.10** by $(1 - k)y^{-k}$ to obtain

$$(1 - k)y^{-k}y' + (1 - k)R(x)y^{1-k} = (1 - k)S(x).$$

If $v = y^{1-k}$, then $v' = (1 - k)y^{-k}y'$, and the above equation may be put in the form

$$v' + (1 - k)R(x)v = (1 - k)S(x),$$

which is a linear differential equation with $P(x) = (1 - k)R(x)$ and $Q(x) = (1 - k)S(x)$ (in **21.8**). This equation may be solved, as in **21.9**, for v. Then $y^{1-k} = v$ is a solution of **21.10**.

EXAMPLE 2. Solve the differential equation

$$y' + \frac{1}{x}y = x^5y^4.$$

---

*Jacob Bernoulli (1654–1705) proposed this equation for solution in 1695. The solution given here is that of Leibnitz published in 1696. Jacob Bernoulli is credited with the first use of the word *integral*. He was a member of a very large and famous family of Swiss mathematicians.

Solution: This is a Bernoulli equation (21.10) with $k = 4$. If we let $v = y^{-3}$ as above, and multiply each side of the given equation by $-3y^{-4}$, we obtain the equation

$$-3y^{-4}y' - \frac{3}{x}y^{-3} = -3x^5,$$

or

(1) $$v' - \frac{3}{x}v = -3x^5, \qquad (v = y^{-3}).$$

This differential equation may be solved by multiplying each side by the integrating factor

$$\begin{aligned} I(x) &= e^{\int(-3/x)dx} \\ &= e^{-3\ln|x|} \\ &= |x|^{-3}. \end{aligned}$$

Thus $I(x) = x^{-3}$ if $x > 0$, whereas $I(x) = -x^{-3}$ if $x < 0$. In either case (1) becomes

$$x^{-3}v' - 3x^{-4}v = -3x^2,$$
$$D_1x^{-3}v = -3x^2,$$

and thus

$$x^{-3}v = -x^3 + C.$$

Hence

$$v = -x^6 + Cx^3$$

is the solution of (1), and

$$y^{-3} = -x^6 + Cx^3,$$

or

$$(-x^6 + Cx^3)y^3 = 1,$$

is the solution of the given equation.

EXERCISES

I

Solve each of the following differential equations.

1. $y' + xy = x$.
2. $y' - 2y = 3$.
3. $y' + by = c$, (b, c constants).
4. $y' - y/x = x \sin x$.
5. $y' + y \tan x = \sec x$.
6. $y' + y \tan x = \sin x$.
7. $y' = e^{2x} + 3y$.
8. $y' = e^{ax} + ay$, (a constant).
9. $(x^2 + 1)y' = 2x(x^2 + 1)^2 + 2xy$.
10. $y' \sin x + y \cos x = 1$.

11. $y' + xy = xy^2$.

12. $y' = y^3e^{2x} + 3y$.

13. $yy' - 2y^2 = e^x$.

14. $xy' + y = x^2e^xy^2$.

II

1. Show that the family of tangent lines to the family of solutions of the linear differential equation $y' + P(x)y = Q(x)$ at the points corresponding to $x = k$ (k any constant) are concurrent.

2. Prove a converse of Exercise 1; i.e., if the family of solutions of the differential equation $y' = F(x,y)$ has the preceding property, then the differential equation is linear.

3. By considering the derivative of the differential equation $dy/dx + P(x)y = Q(x)$, solve the differential equation $y'' + (P' - P^2)y = Q' - PQ$.

8 APPLICATIONS

The solutions of many physical problems are naturally described by differential equations. For example, it was shown in Chapter 10 that the amount of a radioactive substance left after a period of time is given by the differential equation

$$\frac{dy}{dt} = ky.$$

Other examples are given in this section.

EXAMPLE 1. A body of mass m falls from rest in a straight line toward the earth. Describe the motion of the body, assuming that the force due to air resistance on the body is proportional to its speed.

Solution: Let us choose an x axis directed downward, with its origin at the point from which the body is dropped. Let $x = x(t)$ be the position of the body at time t, and let us assume that $x = 0$ when $t = 0$. Then $v = x'(t)$ is the velocity of the body at time t. By assumption, $x = 0$ and $v = 0$ when $t = 0$.

The weight of the body is mg, where g is the acceleration due to gravity. Thus mg is the force due to gravity acting on the body in the direction of the positive x axis. The force due to air resistance on the body will be a vector directed upward (in direction opposite to that of the motion). By assumption, its magnitude is $-k_1v$ for some number $k_1 > 0$. Hence the sum of the forces acting on the body is $mg - k_1v$. By Newton's second law, this force equals ma where a is the acceleration of the body. Therefore

$$ma = mg - kv.$$

It is convenient to let $k_1 = mk$, in which case the equation above yields $a = g - kv$, or

(1) $$v' = g - kv,$$

as the differential equation of the motion.

Equation (1) is separable and has the solution

$$-\frac{1}{k} \ln |g - kv| = +C_1,$$

or $$g - kv = Ce^{-kt}.$$

Since $v = 0$ when $t = 0$, we have $C = g$ and

(2) $$v = \frac{g}{k}(1 - e^{-kt}).$$

We note in passing that the body has a limiting velocity given by

$$\lim_{t \to \infty} v = \lim_{t \to \infty} \frac{g}{k}(1 - e^{-kt}) = \frac{g}{k}.$$

Since $v(t) = x'(t)$, (2) is the differential equation

$$x' = \frac{g}{k}(1 - e^{-kt}).$$

This equation has the solution

$$x = \frac{g}{k}\left(t + \frac{1}{k}e^{-kt}\right) + C_2.$$

If we let $x = 0$ when $t = 0$, we get $C_2 = -g/k^2$. Hence

$$x = \frac{g}{k}t + \frac{g}{k^2}(e^{-kt} - 1)$$

is the equation of motion of the body.

It is interesting to note that $x'' = ge^{-kt}$, and that

$$\lim_{t \to \infty} x'' = 0.$$

That is, the forces of gravity and air resistance tend to balance each other, giving rise to the limiting velocity mentioned above.

EXAMPLE 2 (CATENARY PROBLEM). A flexible rope is suspended from two fixed points and hangs at rest under its own weight. Find the curve in which the rope hangs.

Partial solution: Let $Q(x_0,y_0)$ be any fixed point on the curve and let $P(x,y)$ be any other point on the curve (Figure 21.3). If H_0 and H are the horizontal components of the forces acting at Q and P, respectively, then

$$H_0 = H$$

since the rope is at rest. We interpret the term *flexible rope* to mean that y' is continuous. Hence the length L of the rope between P and Q is given by

$$L = \int_{x_0}^{x} \sqrt{1+y'^2}\,dx.$$

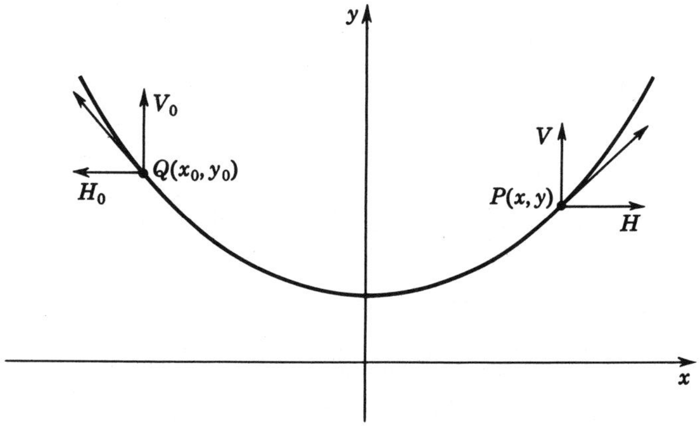

FIGURE 21.3

If w is the weight of a unit length of the rope, then wL is the weight of the rope between P and Q. The sum $V_0 + V$ of the vertical components of the forces acting at Q and P must be the weight of the rope between P and Q; i.e.,

$$(1) \qquad V_0 + V = w\int_{x_0}^{x} \sqrt{1+y'^2}\,dx.$$

The force vector at P lies along the tangent line to the curve, and therefore

$$y' = \frac{V}{H}.$$

Hence $V = Hy' = H_0y'$, and (1) becomes

$$(2) \qquad \frac{V_0}{H_0} + y' = k\int_{x_0}^{x} \sqrt{1+y'^2}\,dx,$$

where $k = w/H_0$. We may differentiate each side of (2), obtaining the differential equation

$$(3) \qquad y'' = k\sqrt{1+y'^2}.$$

One of the solutions of (3) has as its graph the curve in which the rope hangs.

We may start solving (3) by letting $p = y'$, thereby obtaining the equation

$$p' = k\sqrt{1 + p^2},$$

which may be solved for p. In turn, this solution is a first-order differential equation which may be solved for y. When $x = 0$, it is convenient to choose $y' = 0$ and $y = 1/k$ as boundary conditions.

EXAMPLE 3. A mirror has the shape of a surface of revolution. If there exists a point F on the axis of the mirror such that light emitted from this point will be reflected from the mirror in rays parallel to the axis, prove that the mirror is parabolic and that F is the focus of the generating parabola.

Partial solution 1: Let the surface be generated by rotating the curve $r = f(\theta)$ in a polar coordinate plane about the polar axis, and let F be at the pole. If L is a light ray reflected from the surface at the point (r,θ) so that $\alpha = \beta$ in Figure 21.4, then $\theta = \alpha + \beta = 2\alpha$ if L is parallel to the polar axis. By **16.16**, $r' = r\cot(\alpha - \theta) = -r\cot(\theta/2)$; i.e.,

$$\cot\frac{\theta}{2} = -\frac{r'}{r}.$$

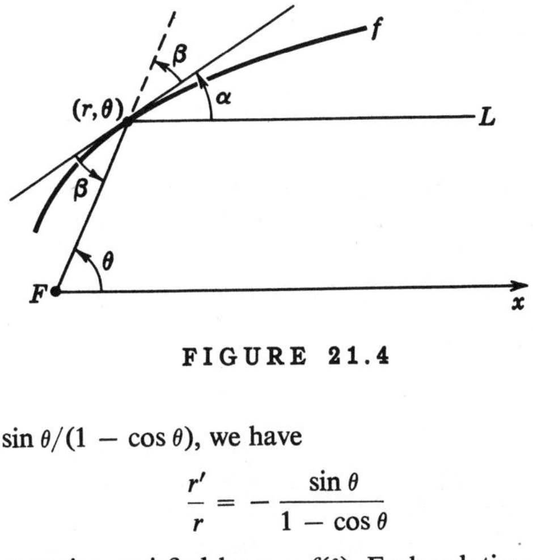

FIGURE 21.4

Since $\cot(\theta/2) = \sin\theta/(1 - \cos\theta)$, we have

$$\frac{r'}{r} = -\frac{\sin\theta}{1 - \cos\theta}$$

as the differential equation satisfied by $r = f(\theta)$. Each solution of this equation may be shown to be a parabola with focus at F.

Partial solution 2: Let the surface be generated by rotating the curve $y = g(x)$ in a rectangular coordinate plane about the x axis, and let F be at the origin (Figure 21.5). If L is a light ray reflected from the surface at the point (x,y) so that $\alpha = \beta$ in the figure, then $\theta = \alpha + \beta = 2\alpha$ if L is parallel to the x axis. Evidently,

$$\tan\theta = \frac{y}{x}$$

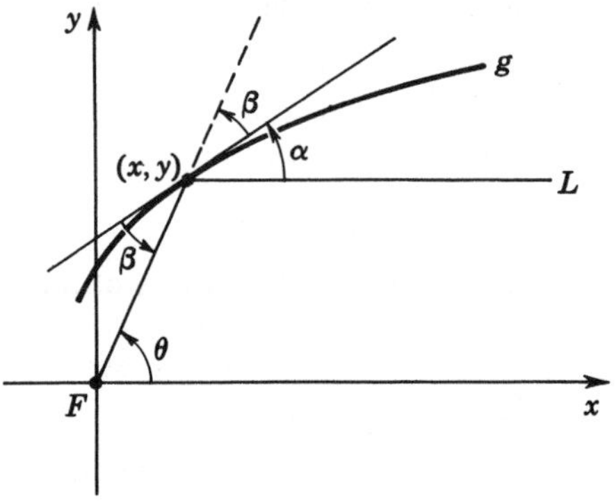

FIGURE 21.5

and $\tan \alpha = y'$. In solving the resulting differential equation satisfied by $y = g(x)$, it is reasonable to assume that $y' > 0$.

EXERCISES

I

1. An object falls from rest in a straight line toward the earth. Assume the drag due to air resistance is proportional to the square of the velocity. Show that the differential equation of motion is $a = g - k^2v^2$, and solve the equation. It is convenient to let $r^2 = gk^2$ and to give the result in terms of r.

2. Complete the solution of Example 2.

3. Complete both solutions of Example 3.

In the circuit of Figure 21.6, R is the resistance, L is the inductance, and E is an impressed emf. If $I = I(t)$ is the current in the circuit at the time t, then $I(t)R$ is the voltage drop across the resistor and $I'(t)L$ is the voltage drop across the inductor. The sum of the voltage drops in the circuit must equal the impressed emf, i.e.,

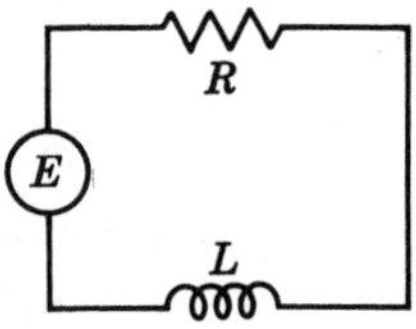

$$LI' + RI = E.$$

FIGURE 21.6

The numbers L and R are constants. If $I(0) = 0$, determine $I(t)$ in each of Exercises 4–6.

4. $L = 10$, $R = 5$, $E = 1$.

5. $L = 5, R = 20, E = 1$.

6. $L = 1, R = 2, E = \sin t$.

7. Solve the equation

$$LI' + RI = E(t).$$

Let A and B be chemical substances which combine to form a chemical substance C. If a and b are the amounts of A and B present at the time $t = 0$ and if $x = x(t)$ is the amount of C formed at the time t, then, under certain conditions, $a - x(t)$ and $b - x(t)$ will be the amounts of A and B, respectively, remaining at the time t. We assume $x(0) = 0$. If the rate of increase of $x(t)$ is proportional to the product of the amounts of A and B present at the time t, the chemical action is known as a *second-order process*, and the differential equation is

$$x' = k(a - x)(b - x).$$

Solve this equation in each of the cases given in Exercises 8–11.

8. $a = 10, b = 5$.

9. $a = b = 10$.

10. $a \neq b$.

11. $a = b$.

12. A radioactive substance A changes into a substance B, which in turn changes into a substance C. Let a be the amount of A present at the time $t = 0$. Let $x(t)$ be the amount of B which has been formed up to the time t, and let $y(t)$ be the amount of C which has been formed up to the time t. Then $x(t) - y(t)$ is the amount of B present at the time t. Assuming that the radioactivity is proportional to the amount present at a given time, we get the equations

$$x' = k_1(a - x), \qquad y' = k_2(x - y).$$

Solve for $x(t)$ and $y(t)$.

II

1. Determine a curve such that the part of the tangent line intercepted between the coordinate axes is bisected at the point of tangency.

2. Determine a curve such that the angle between the tangent and normal lines at each point of the curve is bisected by the radius vector at that point.

3. Integrate completely Exercise I-7 for the case $E(t) = E_0 \sin ct$ if $I(0) = 0$.

4. In a chemical reaction a substance A decomposes into two substances B and C. The rate at which each of the latter is formed is proportional to the amount of A at time t (the proportionality factors being different in general). If the reaction starts with an amount a of A, and at $t = 1$ hr the amount of B is $a/3$ and the amount of C is $a/6$, find the limiting amounts of B and C.

5. Show that if a liquid rotates about a vertical axis with a constant angular velocity then the surface of the liquid assumes the shape of a paraboloid of revolution.

6. It had started snowing before noon. At noon a snowplow set out to clear a road. If the plow covers the first mile in one hour and the second mile in two hours, what time did it start snowing? Assume that it continues to snow at a constant rate and that the snowplow removes snow at a constant rate.

9 SECOND-ORDER LINEAR DIFFERENTIAL EQUATIONS

A differential equation of the form

$$y^{[n]} + a_1(x)y^{[n-1]} + \cdots + a_{n-1}(x)y' + a_n(x)y = G(x)$$

is called a *linear differential equation of order n*. We shall not study the general linear equation above, but rather shall limit our remarks to the second-order linear differential equation

21.11 $$y'' + by' + cy = G(x)$$

with constant coefficients b and c.

Let us first solve the so-called *homogeneous* linear differential equation

21.12 $$y'' + by' + cy = 0.$$

The solutions of **21.12** will be used in finding the solutions of **21.11**.

21.13 THEOREM. If $y = u(x)$ and $y = v(x)$ are solutions of **21.12**, then so is $y = C_1u(x) + C_2v(x)$ for any numbers C_1 and C_2.

Proof: By assumption,

$$u''(x) + bu'(x) + cu(x) = 0,$$
$$v''(x) + bv'(x) + cv(x) = 0.$$

Hence

$$D_{11}[C_1u(x) + C_2v(x)] + bD_1[C_1u(x) + C_2v(x)] + c[C_1u(x) + C_2v(x)]$$
$$= C_1[u''(x) + bu'(x) + cu(x)] + C_2[v''(x) + bv'(x) + cv(x)] = 0,$$

and the theorem is proved.

This theorem will allow us to express the general solution of **21.12** in terms of two particular solutions.

We first inquire whether the exponential function defined by

$$y = e^{mx}$$

is a solution of 21.12. Since $D_1 e^{mx} = me^{mx}$ and $D_{11} e^{mx} = m^2 e^{mx}$, this function is a solution of 21.12 if and only if

$$m^2 e^{mx} + bme^{mx} + ce^{mx} = 0,$$

or, on dividing by the nonzero number e^{mx}, if and only if

21.14 $$m^2 + bm + c = 0.$$

Equation 21.14 is called either the *characteristic equation* or the *auxiliary equation* of 21.12.

The roots of 21.14 are given by

$$m = \frac{-b \pm \sqrt{b^2 - 4c}}{2}.$$

Let us consider three cases as follows.

Case 1. $b^2 - 4c > 0$. Then 21.14 has distinct real roots m_1 and m_2, and $y = e^{m_1 x}$ and $y = e^{m_2 x}$ are particular solutions of 21.12. The general solution is given by

21.15 $$y = C_1 e^{m_1 x} + C_2 e^{m_2 x}.$$

Case 2. $b^2 - 4c = 0$. Then 21.14 has a double root $m = -b/2$, and $y = e^{mx}$ is a particular solution of 21.12. It is easily verified that $y = xe^{mx}$ also is a solution:

$$\begin{aligned} D_{11} xe^{mx} + b\, D_1 xe^{mx} + cxe^{mx} &= (m^2 xe^{mx} + 2me^{mx}) + b(mxe^{mx} + e^{mx}) + cxe^{mx} \\ &= (m^2 + bm + c)xe^{mx} + (2m + b)e^{mx} = 0. \end{aligned}$$

Hence

21.16 $$y = C_1 e^{mx} + C_2 xe^{mx}$$

is the general solution of 21.12 in this case.

Case 3. $b^2 - 4c < 0$. Then 21.14 has distinct imaginary roots $\alpha + \beta i$ and $\alpha - \beta i$, where

$$\alpha = -\frac{b}{2}, \qquad \beta i = \frac{\sqrt{b^2 - 4c}}{2}.$$

We shall use the following argument to lead us to two particular solutions of 21.12.

The calculus can be extended to functions of complex variables, and

$$y = A_1 e^{(\alpha+\beta i)x} + A_2 e^{(\alpha-\beta i)x},$$

or

$$y = e^{\alpha x}(A_1 e^{\beta i x} + A_2 e^{-\beta i x}),$$

is a solution of 21.12 for any (complex) constants A_1 and A_2.

The theorems on real infinite series (Chapter 15) can be extended to complex series, and it can be shown that

$$e^{iz} = 1 + (iz) + \frac{(iz)^2}{2!} + \frac{(iz)^3}{3!} + \frac{(iz)^4}{4!} + \frac{(iz)^5}{5!} + \cdots$$

holds for every real number z. Since $i^2 = -1$, $i^3 = -i$, and so on, we may write the series above in the form

$$e^{iz} = \left(1 - \frac{z^2}{2!} + \frac{z^4}{4!} - \cdots\right) + i\left(z - \frac{z^3}{3!} + \frac{z^5}{5!} - \cdots\right).$$

Since the series in parentheses represent $\cos z$ and $\sin z$, respectively, we finally obtain what is known as *Euler's formula*

$$e^{iz} = \cos z + i \sin z.$$

With the aid of Euler's formula, we easily derive the formulas

$$\sin \beta x = \frac{e^{\beta ix} - e^{-\beta ix}}{2i}, \qquad \cos \beta x = \frac{e^{\beta ix} + e^{-\beta ix}}{2}.$$

Hence, by choosing $A_1 = A_2 = \frac{1}{2}$, we have that $y = e^{\alpha x} \cos \beta x$ is a particular solution of **21.12**; and by choosing $A_1 = \frac{1}{2}i$ and $A_2 = -\frac{1}{2}i$, we have that $y = e^{\alpha x} \sin \beta x$ also is a particular solution of **21.12**. Thus in Case 3 we expect that

21.17 $$y = e^{\alpha x}(C_1 \cos \beta x + C_2 \sin \beta x)$$

will be the general solution of **21.12**.

EXAMPLE 1. Solve the differential equation

$$y'' - y' - 6y = 0.$$

Solution: The characteristic equation

$$m^2 - m - 6 = 0$$

has roots $m_1 = 3$ and $m_2 = -2$. Hence the given equation has solution (**21.15**),

$$y = C_1e^{3x} + C_2e^{-2x}.$$

EXAMPLE 2. Solve the differential equation

$$y'' + 2\sqrt{3}\, y' + 3 = 0.$$

Solution: The characteristic equation

$$m^2 + 2\sqrt{3}\, m + 3 = 0$$

has a double root $m = -\sqrt{3}$. Therefore, by **21.16**,

$$y = (C_1 + C_2x)e^{-\sqrt{3}x}$$

is the solution of the given equation.

EXAMPLE 3. Solve the differential equation

$$y'' - 6y' + 13y = 0.$$

Solution: The characteristic equation

$$m^2 - 6m + 13 = 0$$

has imaginary roots $3 \pm 2i$. Thus $\alpha = 3$ and $\beta = 2$ in **21.17**, and

$$y = e^{3x}(C_1 \cos 2x + C_2 \sin 2x)$$

is the general solution of the given equation.

21.18 THEOREM. Let $y = u(x)$ and $y = v(x)$ be solutions of the differential equation

$$y'' + by' + cy = 0$$

such that

$$u(x)v'(x) - v(x)u'(x) \neq 0$$

for all x. Then for any given numbers x_0, y_0, and y_1 there exists a solution

$$f(x) = C_1u(x) + C_2v(x)$$

of the given equation such that

$$f(x_0) = y_0, \qquad f'(x_0) = y_1.$$

Proof: We wish to show that the constants C_1 and C_2 can be determined so that $f(x_0) = y_0$ and $f'(x_0) = y_1$, i.e., so that

$$y_0 = C_1u(x_0) + C_2v(x_0), \qquad y_1 = C_1u'(x_0) + C_2v'(x_0).$$

This pair of linear equations in C_1 and C_2 has the unique solution

$$C_1 = \frac{y_0v'(x_0) - y_1v(x_0)}{w}, \qquad C_2 = \frac{y_1u(x_0) - y_0u'(x_0)}{w}.$$

where, by assumption, $w = u(x_0)v'(x_0) - v(x_0)u'(x_0) \neq 0$. That $y = f(x)$ is a solution of the differential equation for this choice of C_1 and C_2 follows from **21.13**.

In each of the three cases considered above, we have chosen the two solutions u and v so that the hypotheses of **21.18** are satisfied. For example, in Case 1, $u(x) = e^{m_1x}$ and $v(x) = e^{m_2x}$ with $m_1 \neq m_2$. Hence

$$u(x)v'(x) - v(x)u'(x) = (m_2 - m_1)e^{(m_1+m_2)x} \neq 0.$$

That the hypotheses of **21.18** are satisfied in the other two cases will be left for the reader to verify.

We shall prove in a later section that if $y = f(x)$ and $y = g(x)$ are solutions of **21.12** such that

$$f(x_0) = g(x_0), \qquad f'(x_0) = g'(x_0)$$

for some number x_0, then $f(x) = g(x)$ for every x. Now if $y = g(x)$ is any solution of **21.12**, then, by **21.18**, there exists a solution of **21.12** of the form

$$f(x) = C_1u(x) + C_2v(x)$$

such that $f(x_0) = g(x_0), f'(x_0) = g'(x_0)$. Hence it will follow that $g(x) = C_1u(x)+ C_2v(x)$, i.e., that $C_1u(x) + C_2v(x)$ is the general solution of **21.12**, as we contended in each of the cases above.

EXERCISES

I

1. Prove that in each of the following cases $u(x)v'(x) - v(x)u'(x) \neq 0$.

   a. $u(x) = e^{mx}, \quad v(x) = xe^{mx}$.

   b. $u(x) = e^{ax} \cos \beta x, \quad v(x) = e^{ax} \sin \beta x, \quad (\beta \neq 0)$.

Solve each of the following differential equations.

2. $y'' + 9y = 0$.
3. $y'' - 9y = 0$.
4. $y'' + 2y' + y = 0$.
5. $y'' + 2y' - y = 0$.
6. $y'' - y' - 6y = 0$.
7. $y'' - 3y' - 10y = 0$.
8. $y'' + y' = 0$.
9. $y'' + y' + 3y = 0$.
10. $y'' - 4y' + 29y = 0$.
11. $y'' - 2y' + 3y = 0$.
12. $y'' + 2y' + 3y = 0$.
13. $y'' + \sqrt{2}y' + 7y = 0$.
14. $6y'' + y' - 2y = 0$.
15. $3y'' - 2y' + 5y = 0$.
16. $y'' - 2y' + (1 - \pi)y = 0$.
17. $y'' - 2\sqrt{3}y' + (3 + \pi^2)y = 0$.

In each of Exercises 18–22 find the particular solution of the equation satisfying the given boundary conditions.

18. $y'' + y = 0$; $y = 0$, $y' = 1$ when $x = 0$.
19. $y'' - 3y' + 5y = 0$; $y = 0$, $y' = 0$ when $x = 0$.

20. $y'' - 2y' - 8y = 0$; $y = 10$, $y' = 1$ when $x = 0$.

21. $y'' - 5y' + 6y = 0$; $y = 1$, $y' = 1$ when $x = 1$.

22. $y'' - 4y' + 4y = 0$; $y = 3$, $y' = 0$ when $x = 2$.

23. An object is suspended from a fixed standard by a spring. There is a point at which this system is in equilibrium. The resultant of the force of the spring and the weight of the object is proportional to the vertical displacement of the object from the point of equilibrium. Describe the motion of the object.

II

1. Show that the substitution $y = -u'/u$ transforms the second-order differential equation $u'' + P(x)u' + Q(x)u = 0$ into the nonlinear first-order differential equation

$$y' = y^2 - P(x)y + Q(x) \qquad \text{(Ricatti's equation).}$$

2. If $y = v(x)$ is one solution of the differential equation $y'' + P(x)y' + Q(x)y = 0$, find the general solution.

3. The differential equation $P_0(x)y'' + P_1(x)y' + P_2(x)y = 0$ is said to be exact if the left-hand side of the equation is the derivative of some function $F(x,y,y')$. Show that a necessary and sufficient condition for exactness is that $P_2(x) - P_1'(x) + P_0''(x) = 0$.

4. Generalize Exercise 3.

5. Solve the following differential equations:

a. $(x - x^2)y'' + 4y' + 2y = 0$.   b. $(x^2 + x)y'' + (3x + 2)y' + y = 4x$.

10 NONHOMOGENEOUS LINEAR EQUATIONS

We shall consider in this section the problem of solving the nonhomogeneous second-order linear differential equation

21.19 $$y'' + by' + cy = G(x),$$

where b and c are constants and G is a continuous function.

In discussing the solutions of **21.19**, it is convenient to introduce the notation $L(y)$ for the left side of **21.19**:

$$L(y) = y'' + by' + cy.$$

The "operator" L is linear in the sense that

$$L(y_1 \pm y_2) = L(y_1) \pm L(y_2).$$

Using the L notation, the function g is a solution of **21.19** if and only if $L(g(x)) = G(x)$.

Let g_p designate a particular solution of **21.19** and let g be any other solution. If $f(x) = g(x) - g_p(x)$, then

$$L(f(x)) = L(g(x)) - L(g_p(x)) = 0;$$

i.e., f is a solution of the *complementary equation*

21.20 $$y'' + by' + cy = 0.$$

Conversely, if g_p is a particular solution of **21.19** and f is any solution of **21.20**, then $g(x) = g_p(x) + f(x)$ also is a solution of **21.19**. Consequently, the general solution of **21.19** has the form

$$y = g_p(x) + f_c(x),$$

where g_p is a particular solution of **21.19** and f_c is the general solution of **21.20**. Since we can find the general solution of the homogeneous linear differential equation **21.20** by the methods of Section 9, we can find the general solution of **21.19** provided we can find a particular solution of it. Various ways of finding particular solutions of **21.19** are given in the remainder of this section.

EXAMPLE 1. Solve the differential equation

$$y'' + y = 2x.$$

Solution: We see by inspection that $y_p = 2x$ is a solution. The complementary equation $y'' + y = 0$ has general solution

$$y_c = C_1 \cos x + C_2 \sin x.$$

Hence

$$y = C_1 \cos x + C_2 \sin x + 2x$$

is the general solution of the given equation.

The following procedure, called the method of *variation of parameters*, will yield a particular solution of **21.19.** Let

$$y_c = C_1 u(x) + C_2 v(x)$$

be the general solution of **21.20**; $L(y_c) = 0$. We shall find functions u_1 and v_1 which, when put in place of C_1 and C_2 in y_c, will give a particular solution

$$y_p = u_1(x)u(x) + v_1(x)v(x)$$

of **21.19.**

We first establish the condition that

$$u_1'u + v_1'v = 0.$$

This condition simplifies subsequent computations. Now if $y = u_1u + v_1v$, then $y' = u_1u' + u_1'u + v_1'v + v_1v'$, and, using the condition above,

$$y' = u_1u' + v_1v'.$$

Hence

$$y'' = u_1u'' + v_1v'' + u_1'u' + v_1'v',$$

and

$$L(u_1u + v_1v) = u_1L(u) + v_1L(v) + u_1'u' + v_1'v' = u_1'u' + v_1'v'.$$

Therefore $L(u_1u + v_1v) = G(x)$ if and only if $u_1'u' + v_1'v' = G(x)$. Consequently, if the functions u_1 and v_1 are chosen so that

21.21 $$u_1'u + v_1'v = 0, \qquad u_1'u' + v_1'v' = G(x),$$

then $y_p = u_1u + v_1v$ is a particular solution of **21.19**.

Equations **21.21** are two linear equations in the unknowns u_1' and v_1'. Since $uv' - vu' \neq 0$ by results of the preceding section, these equations may be solved for u_1' and v_1', yielding

$$u_1' = -\frac{vG(x)}{uv' - vu'}, \qquad v_1' = \frac{uG(x)}{uv' - vu'}.$$

Hence

$$u_1 = -\int \frac{vG(x)}{uv' - vu'}\,dx, \qquad v_1 = \int \frac{uG(x)}{uv' - vu'}\,dx$$

always exist.

EXAMPLE 2. Solve the differential equation

$$y'' + y = \sec x.$$

Solution: The complementary equation $y'' + y = 0$ has general solution

$$y_c = C_1 \sin x + C_2 \cos x.$$

We wish to determine functions u_1 and v_1 such that

$$y_p = u_1(x) \sin x + v_1(x) \cos x$$

is a particular solution of the given equation. For this example $G(x) = \sec x$, $u = \sin x$, $v = \cos x$, $u' = \cos x$, $v' = -\sin x$, and **21.21** becomes

$$u_1' \sin x + v_1' \cos x = 0, \qquad u_1' \cos x - v_1' \sin x = \sec x.$$

Solving for u_1' and v_1', we obtain

$$u_1' = 1, \qquad v_1' = -\sin x \sec x = -\tan x.$$

Hence

$$u_1 = x, \qquad v_1 = \ln |\cos x|,$$

and
$$y_p = x \sin x + (\ln |\cos x|) \cos x$$
is a particular solution. The general solution of the given equation is therefore $y_p + y_c$, or
$$y = (x + C_1) \sin x + (\ln |\cos x| + C_2) \cos x.$$

Another technique for finding a particular solution of **21.19**, called the *method of undetermined coefficients*, is illustrated below.

EXAMPLE 3. Determine A_1 and A_2 so that
$$y_p = A_1 \sin x + A_2 \cos x$$
is a particular solution of the differential equation
$$y'' - y' - 6y = \sin x.$$

Solution: Evidently,
$$y_p' = A_1 \cos x - A_2 \sin x, \qquad y_p'' = -A_1 \sin x - A_2 \cos x,$$
so that
$$y_p'' - y_p' - 6y_p = (A_2 - 7A_1) \sin x + (-A_1 - 7A_2) \cos x.$$
Hence y_p is a solution if
$$(A_2 - 7A_1) \sin x + (-A_1 - 7A_2) \cos x = \sin x,$$
i.e., if
$$A_2 - 7A_1 = 1, \qquad -A_1 - 7A_2 = 0.$$
Solving these equations for A_1 and A_2, we obtain
$$A_1 = -\tfrac{7}{50}, \qquad A_2 = \tfrac{1}{50}.$$
Thus
$$y_p = -\tfrac{7}{50} \sin x + \tfrac{1}{50} \cos x$$
is a particular solution of the given equation. The general solution is
$$y = C_1 e^{3x} + C_2 e^{-2x} - \tfrac{7}{50} \sin x + \tfrac{1}{50} \cos x.$$

EXERCISES

I

1. If $L(y) = y'' - 3y'$, find $L(\sin x)$, $L(e^x)$, $L(e^{3x})$, $L(xe^{3x})$, $L(x)$.
2. If $L(y) = y'' + y$, find $L(e^x)$, $L(\sin x)$, $L(\cos x)$, $L(A_1x^2 + A_2x + A_3)$.

3. Determine A_1, A_2, A_3 so that

$$y_p = A_1x^2 + A_2x + A_3$$

is a solution of the equation

$$y'' - 2y' + 2y = x^2 - 1,$$

and find the general solution.

4. Find a particular solution $y_p = Ax + B$, and find the general solution of the equation

$$y'' - 2y' - 8y = x + 3.$$

5. If $L(y) = y'' + 2y' - 2y$, find $L(A \sin x + B \cos x)$ and hence solve the equation

$$y'' + 2y' - 2y = 2 \sin x - \cos x.$$

In each of Exercises 6–11 use the method of variation of parameters to solve the equation.

6. $y'' + y = \csc x$.

7. $y'' + y = \tan x$.

8. $y'' - 4y' + 4y = x^2e^{2x}$.

9. $y'' - y = e^x \sin x$.

10. $y'' - y = \cos x$.

11. $y'' + 2y' = xe^{-2x}$.

12. If $L(y) = y'' - 3y' + 2y$, find $L(e^x)$ and $L(xe^x)$. Hence solve the equation

$$y'' - 3y' + 2y = 3e^x.$$

13. If $L(y) = y'' + 4y$, find $L(x \sin 2x)$ and $L(x \cos 2x)$, and solve the equation

$$y'' + 4y = \cos 2x.$$

Solve by any method each of the following equations.

14. $y'' - 3y = x$.

15. $y'' - 2y = 5x$.

16. $y'' - y' = 3x$.

17. $y'' + y' = e^x$.

18. $y'' + y' + y = \sin x$.

19. $y'' - 3y' - y = e^x$.

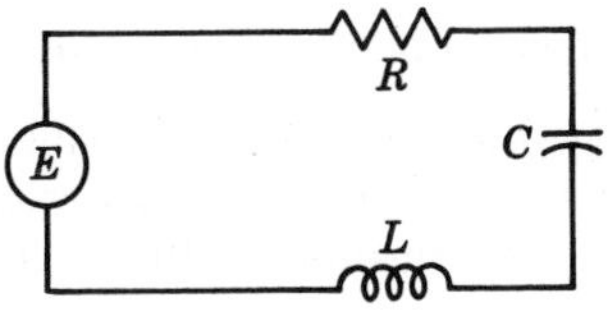

FIGURE 21.7

In the circuit of Figure 21.7 the current at the time t satisfies the equation

$$L\frac{dI}{dt} + RI + \frac{1}{C}\int I\,dt = E(t),$$

or

(1) $$L\frac{d^2I}{dt^2} + R\frac{dI}{dt} + \frac{1}{C}I = E'(t),$$

where $E(t)$ is the impressed emf, L, R, and C are the constants of inductance, resistance, and capacitance, respectively. Solve equation (1) in each of the following cases:

20. $R = 0$, $C = 1$, $L = 10$, $E = 5$.

21. $R = 10$, $C = \frac{1}{5}$, $L = 10$, $E = \sin t$.

22. $R = 1$, $C = 1$, $L = 1$, $E = 10 \sin 2t$.

23. Given that $m^3 - 6m^2 + 11m - 6 = (m - 1)(m - 2)(m - 3)$, solve the equation

$$y''' - 6y'' + 11y' - 6y = 0.$$

24. Solve the equation

$$y''' - 3y'' - y' + 3y = 0.$$

25. Solve the equation

$$y''' - 3y'' + y' - 3y = 0.$$

II

1. If $y = v(x)$ is a solution of the differential equation $[D^2 + P(x)D + Q(x)]y = 0$, find the general solution of the equation $[D^2 + P(x)D + Q(x)]y = R(x)$.

2. If $y = u_1(x)$ and $y = u_2(x)$ are two particular solutions of the differential equation $[D^2 + P(x)D + Q(x)]y = R(x)$, find the general solution.

3. If $L(D)$ is a linear operator in D, show that

$$e^{\int P\,dx} L(D)y = L(D - P)y\,e^{\int P\,dx}.$$

4. Using Exercise 3, solve the linear equation $(D + P)y = Q$.

5. Explain why the method of undetermined coefficients breaks down for the equation $(D - 1)^2y = e^x$. Using Exercise 3, show that a particular solution of this equation is $y = x^2e^x/2$.

6. Solve the differential equation $(D - 1)^n y = a\,e^x$.

7. Show that the general solution of the equation $L(D)y = F_1(x) + F_2(x)$ is $y = y_c + y_1 + y_2$, where y_c is the complementary solution (i.e., $L(D)y_c = 0$) and y_i is a particular solution of the equation $L(D)y = F_i(x)$, $(i = 1, 2)$.

8. Solve the differential equation

$$[D^4 - 8D^2 + 16]y = x^2e^{2x} + e^{-2x} + 2x^4 - 12x^2 + 3.$$

9. If a particular solution of the equation $L(D)y = F(x)$ can be found by the method of undetermined coefficients, what property must F have?

11 SOLUTIONS IN SERIES

The infinite series

$$f(x) = C_0 + C_1(x - x_0) + C_2(x - x_0)^2 + \cdots + C_n(x - x_0)^n + \cdots$$

defines a function f in the interval of convergence of the series. It is frequently possible to find solutions of differential equations in the form of infinite series, as is illustrated in the following example.

EXAMPLE. Find an infinite series solution of the differential equation

$$y'' + xy' + y = 0.$$

Solution: If

$$y = \sum_{k=0}^{\infty} C_k x^k$$

is a solution, then (by **15.24**),

$$y' = \sum_{k=1}^{\infty} kC_k x^{k-1}, \qquad y'' = \sum_{k=2}^{\infty} k(k-1)C_k x^{k-2} = \sum_{k=0}^{\infty} (k+2)(k+1)C_{k+2}x^k.$$

Hence

$$y'' + xy' + y = \sum_{k=0}^{\infty} [C_k + kC_k + (k+2)(k+1)C_{k+2}]x^k.$$

If y is to be a solution, the right side of the above equation must equal zero, and the coefficient of each power of x must be zero:

$$(1 + k)C_k + (k+2)(k+1)C_{k+2} = 0$$

or $C_k + (k+2)C_{k+2} = 0$. Thus

$$C_{k+2} = -\frac{1}{k+2}C_k, \qquad (k = 0, 1, 2, \cdots, n, \cdots).$$

In particular,

$$C_2 = -\frac{1}{2}C_0, \qquad C_3 = -\frac{1}{3}C_1,$$

$$C_4 = -\frac{1}{4}C_2 = \frac{1}{2\cdot 4}C_0, \qquad C_5 = -\frac{1}{5}C_3 = \frac{1}{3\cdot 5}C_1,$$

$$C_6 = -\frac{1}{6}C_4 = -\frac{1}{2\cdot 4\cdot 6}C_0, \qquad C_7 = -\frac{1}{7}C_5 = -\frac{1}{3\cdot 5\cdot 7}C_1,$$

and so on, with

$$C_{2n} = \frac{(-1)^n}{2\cdot 4\cdot \cdots \cdot 2n} C_0, \qquad C_{2n+1} = \frac{(-1)^n}{1\cdot 3\cdot \cdots \cdot (2n+1)} C_1.$$

Thus y may be expressed as a sum of two series, one containing the even powers of x and the other containing the odd powers:

$$y = C_0 \sum_{k=0}^{\infty} \frac{(-1)^k}{2\cdot 4\cdot \cdots \cdot 2k} x^{2k} + C_1 \sum_{k=0}^{\infty} \frac{(-1)^k}{1\cdot 3\cdot \cdots \cdot (2k+1)} x^{2k+1}.$$

The ratio test establishes that each of the series is convergent everywhere. This is the general solution of the given differential equation.

A function f which can be expressed as a power series in some interval is said to be *analytic* in that interval. Thus we are seeking analytic solutions of differential equations in this section.

The theory of Taylor's series (Chapter 15) gives us a criterion for determining whether or not a function is analytic. Let us use Taylor's theory to establish the following result.

21.22 THEOREM. If f is a solution of the differential equation

$$y'' = ky$$

in an interval $[x_1,x_2]$, then f is analytic in this interval.

Proof: Since f is a solution of $y'' = ky$, then f' and f'' exist in $[x_1,x_2]$. Furthermore, $f''(x) = kf(x), f'''(x) = kf'(x), f^{iv}(x) = kf''(x) = k^2f(x)$, and so on. That is, f possesses derivatives of every order in $[x_1,x_2]$.

By Taylor's formula (**14.10**).

$$f(x) = P_n(x) + R_n(x),$$

where

$$P_n(x) = \sum_{k=0}^{n} \frac{f^{[k]}(x_0)}{k!}(x - x_0)^k, \qquad R_n(x) = \frac{f^{[n+1]}(z_n)}{(n+1)!}(x - x_0)^{n+1},$$

for x_0 in $[x_1,x_2]$ and some z_n between x and x_0. If

$$\lim_{n\to\infty} R_n(x) = 0$$

for every x in $[x_1,x_2]$, then f is represented by its Taylor's series (i.e., f is analytic) in $[x_1,x_2]$,

$$f(x) = \sum_{k=0}^{\infty} \frac{f^{[k]}(x_0)}{k!}(x - x_0)^k,$$

according to **15.28**.

Since f and f' are continuous in $[x_1,x_2]$, there exists a number M such that

$$|f(x)| \leq M, \qquad |f'(x)| \leq M$$

in $[x_1,x_2]$. Let $m = |k|$ if $|k| > 1$ and $m = 1$ if $|k| \leq 1$. Then

$$|f''(x)| = |kf(x)| \leq Mm \leq Mm^2,$$
$$|f'''(x) = |kf'(x)| \leq Mm \leq Mm^3,$$
$$|f^{iv}(x)| = |kf''(x)| \leq m|f''(x)| \leq Mm^4,$$

and, in general,

$$|f^{[n]}(x)| \leq Mm^n$$

for every x in $[x_1,x_2]$. Hence

$$|R_n(x)| = \frac{|f^{[n+1]}(z_n)|}{(n+1)!}|x - x_0|^{n+1} \leq \frac{Mm^{n+1}}{(n+1)!}|x - x_0|^{n+1},$$

or $$|R_n(x)| \leq \frac{M}{(n+1)!}|m(x - x_0)|^{n+1}.$$

Now

$$\lim_{n\to\infty} \frac{M}{(n+1)!}|m(x - x_0)|^{n+1} = 0,$$

and therefore $\lim_{n\to\infty} R_n = 0$. This proves the theorem.

Let us consider the possibility that the equation

$$y'' = ky$$

has two solutions g_1 and g_2 in a given interval such that

$$g_1(x_0) = g_2(x_0), \qquad g_1'(x_0) = g_2'(x_0)$$

at some number x_0 in the interval. If we let

$$f(x) = g_1(x) - g_2(x),$$

then f is a solution of the given homogeneous linear differential equation such that

$$f(x_0) = 0, \qquad f'(x_0) = 0.$$

Since $f''(x_0) = kf(x_0)$, $f'''(x_0) = kf'(x_0)$, $f^{iv}(x_0) = k^2f(x_0)$, and so on, it is clear that

$$f^{[n]}(x_0) = 0$$

for every n.

By the proof of **21.22**, f is represented by its Taylor's series

$$f(x) = \sum_{k=0}^{\infty} \frac{f^{[k]}(x_0)}{k!}(x - x_0)^k$$

in the given interval. Since each coefficient of this power series is zero, evidently $f(x) = 0$. Hence

$$g_1(x) = g_2(x)$$

at every x in the interval. In other words, the boundary conditions

$$y = y_0, \qquad y' = y_1,$$

when $x = x_0$, determine a unique solution (see **21.18**) of the differential equation $y'' = ky$.

Since the differential equation

$$w'' + bw' + cw = 0$$

can be reduced to the equation

$$y'' = ky$$

by the transformation

$$y = we^{bx/2},$$

we have established the uniqueness of the solution of any second-order linear differential equation with constant coefficients.

EXERCISES

I

1. Prove that every solution of the equation $y''' = ky$ is analytic.

In each of Exercises 2–6 find series solutions for the equation, and determine the interval of convergence of the series.

2. $y' = y$.
3. $y' = xy$.
4. $y'' = xy$.
5. $y'' + x^2y' + xy = 0$.
6. $(1 - x^2)y'' + 2xy' + 4y = c$.
7. Solve the equation $y'' = y$ by infinite series to get the solution

$$y = A_1 \cosh x + A_2 \sinh x.$$

Show that this solution is equivalent to $y = C_1e^x + C_2e^{-x}$.

II

1. Show that the solution of the equation $y' = x + y^2$ is given by

$$y = a + a^2x + \left(\frac{1}{2} + a^3\right)x^2 + \left(\frac{a}{3} + a^4\right)x^3 + \cdots.$$

Also show that the series converges in the interval $(-1,1)$ if $|a| \leq \frac{1}{2}$.

2. Find the series solution of the equation $xy'' + y' + y = 0$. (Note that the complete solution is not obtained in this way; the other independent solution is singular at $x = 0$.)

3. Find the series solution of $(1 + x^2)y'' - 4xy' + 6y = 0$ and show that it converges for all x.

4. Find the series solution about the point $x = -3$ of the equation $y'' - 2(x + 3)y' - 3y = 0$. Show that the series is convergent for all x.

REVIEW

Oral Exercises

In each of Exercises 1–6 define the type of differential equation and indicate how to solve it if a general method exists.

1. Separable.
2. Exact.
3. Homogeneous.
4. First-order linear.
5. Bernoulli.
6. General linear.
7. What is an integrating factor?
8. Explain the method of undetermined coefficients.
9. Explain the method of variation of parameters.
10. Explain the method of solution by a Taylor series expansion.

I

In Exercises 1–8 solve the differential equation.

1. $\dfrac{dy}{dx} = \dfrac{xy}{1 + x^2}$.

2. $\dfrac{dy}{dx} + \dfrac{1 + y^2}{1 + x^2} = 0$ and $y = 1$ at $x = 0$.

3. $x\dfrac{dy}{dx} + y = 2\sqrt{xy}$.

4. $\dfrac{dy}{dx} = \dfrac{xe^{y/x} + y}{x}$.

5. $(x + y + 1)\,dx + (6x + 10y + 14)\,dy = 0$.

6. $(x + y + 4)\,dx - (2x + 2y - 1)\,dy = 0$.

7. $(x + 2y)\,dx + (2x - 3y)\,dy = 0$.

8. $(ax + by + c)\,dx + (bx + ay + c)\,dy = 0$.

9. Show that under the transformation $z = cx + ey$ the differential equation $dy/dx = g(cx + ey)$ becomes separable.

10. Solve the equation $y' = \cos(x + y)$ by the method of Exercise 9.

In each of Exercises 11–14 find integrating factors and solve.

11. $(1 - xy)\,dx + (xy - x^2)\,dy = 0$.

12. $(x^3 + y^4)\,dx + 8xy^3\,dy = 0$.

13. $xy' + y = 0$.

14. $y' + 2xy = x^3$.

In each of Exercises 15–18 solve the differential equation by two methods, one method being by series expansion. Compare the results.

15. $y' = 3x^2y$.

16. $y' = y(3x^2 + 2x)$.

17. $y'' + 2xy' = 2x$.

18. $x^2y'' - 6xy' + 10y = 0$. [*Hint:* Let $x = e^2$.]

Solve the following linear equations.

19. $y'' - 5y' - 6y = 0$.

20. $y'' - 5y' - 6y = e^{-x}$.

21. $y''' - 5y'' - 6y' = 0$.

22. $y''' - 5y'' - 6y' = \sin x$.

23. $y'' + 4y = x^2$.

24. $y''' + 4y' = x^2$.

25. $y''' - y'' + 4y' = \sin x$.

26. $y''' - y'' + 4y' - 4y = e^x$.

27. $y''' - 7y' + 6y = e^{-x}$.

28. Determine the curves such that the lengths of the tangent and normal at any point of the curve, intercepted by the coordinate axes, are equal.

29. A particle slides down a smooth plane making an angle θ with the horizontal plane. Assuming that air resistance is negligible and that the force of gravity is constant, find the velocity and distance at any time t. Assume particle starts from rest. [*Hint:* The acceleration is $g \sin\theta$, the component of g in the direction of motion.]

30. Using the results of the previous exercise, show that if a particle starts at rest from the highest point of a vertical circle, it will reach any other point of that circle

when sliding down the chord to that point in the same time that it takes to drop to the lowest point of the circle.

31. A motion is called *simple harmonic* if the acceleration is proportional to and opposite the displacement; i.e., $a = -k^2s$. Solve the equation if at $t = 0$, $s = s_0$, $v = v_0$. What is the period of the motion? What is the amplitude of the motion?

32. Show that the motion of a simple pendulum is simple harmonic for small oscillations. Determine its period and amplitude if its mass is m and length is l.

II

1. a. Show that the differential equation of the family of all parabolas in the plane is given by $D^2(D^2y)^{-2/3} = 0$.

   b. Show that the differential equation of the family of all conic sections in the plane is given by $D^3(D^2y)^{-2/3} = 0$ (Halphen).

2. For a given nonzero number a show that the family of curves $x^2/c + y^2/(c - a) = 1$ is self-orthogonal. Sketch a few members of the family.

3. Show that the family of curves whose differential equation is $F(x,y) = g(y') + g(-1/y')$ is self-orthogonal.

4. Using Exercise 3, find an explicit self-orthogonal family of curves different from that in Exercise 2.

5. Show how to solve the equation

$$\frac{dy}{dx} = \frac{a_1x + b_1y + c_1}{a_2x + b_2y + c_2}, \quad y = y_0 \text{ for } x = x_0,$$

in parametric form by considering the solution of the system of equations

$$\begin{cases} \dfrac{dy}{dt} = a_1x + b_1y + c_1 \\ \\ \dfrac{dx}{dt} = a_2x + b_2y + c_2. \end{cases}$$

[*Hint:* Obtain a linear equation in y by eliminating x and x' by differentiating with respect to t.]

6. Find the solution of the equation

$$\frac{dy}{dx} = \frac{x + y + 1}{x - y - 1}$$

passing through the point (x_0,y_0).

7. Find the solution of the system of equations

$$\begin{cases} \dfrac{dy}{dt} = a\,x \\ \\ \dfrac{dx}{dt} = -a\,y \end{cases}$$

passing through the point (0,1).

8. If $y = f(x)$ is a particular solution of the equation $y'' = a\,x^{n-2}y$, then show that $y = x\,f(1/x)$ is a solution of the equation $y'' = a\,x^{-n-2}y$.

9. Solve the equation $x^4y'' = a^2y$.

10. Show that the substitution $y = w\,e^{-\int P\,dx}$ transforms the equation

$$[D^2 + 2P(x)D + Q(x)]y = 0$$

into the form $[D^2 + Q(x) - P'(x) - P^2(x)]w = 0$.

11. Show that the two equations $[(1 - x^2)D^2 + (1 - 3x)D + k]z = 0$ and $[(1 - x^2)D^2 - (1 + x)D + k + 1]w = 0$ can be transformed into one another by means of Exercise 10.

12. Find the relationship between the functions P, Q, R, and S in order that the two equations $[D^2 + P(x)D + Q(x)]y = 0$ and $[D^2 + R(x)D + S(x)]y = 0$ have a non-zero common solution, and find the common solution.

13. If u and v are any two solutions of the equation $[D^2 + P(x)D + Q(x)]y = 0$, find a linear differential equation which has uv as a solution.

14. If $[D^2 + M(x)]u = 0$ and $[D^2 + N(x)]v = 0$, find a homogeneous linear differential equation which has uv as a solution.

15. A particle starts at rest and ends at rest after traversing one foot in one second along a straight line. Show that at some instant the acceleration of the particle is at least 4 ft/sec^2.

16. It had started snowing heavily before noon. Three snowplows set out to clear the same road at noon, 1 p.m., and 2 p.m., respectively. If subsequently the three plows meet simultaneously, determine at what time it had started snowing and at what time the plows meet. Assume that it continues to snow at a constant rate and that each plow removes snow at the same constant rate. (See Exercise II-6, Section 8.)

17. An electron which moves perpendicularly in a plane between two large parallel plates s units apart has equations of motion

$$m\,\frac{d^2y}{dt^2} = E\,e - \frac{H\,e}{c}\,\frac{dx}{dt}, \qquad m\,\frac{d^2x}{dt^2} = \frac{H\,e}{c}\,\frac{dy}{dt}$$

where m is the mass of the electron, e is the charge of the electron, H is the magnetic field in the z direction, E is the electric field in the y direction, c is the velocity of light, and x and y are the horizontal and vertical coordinates of the particle. Assume that the electron starts from rest at the origin. Show that the trajectory of the particle is a cycloid (assuming its velocity is small enough so that we can ignore the relativistic increase in its mass). Show that if $s > 2Emc^2/H^2e$ the electron fails to reach the upper plate.

18. Show that if a particle is dropped in a straight tunnel connecting any two points of the surface of a spherical planet of uniform density then the ensuing motion is simple harmonic (ignoring air resistance and rotational effects). Show also that the period is the same for every tunnel.

APPENDIX

FACTS AND FORMULAS FROM TRIGONOMETRY

IF ANGLE θ is placed in a rectangular coordinate plane as in Figure A.1, with its initial side on the positive x axis, then the coordinates of the point on the terminal side of θ one unit from the origin are $\cos\theta$ and $\sin\theta$. The other trigonometric functions are defined as follows:

$$\tan\theta = \frac{\sin\theta}{\cos\theta}, \qquad \cot\theta = \frac{\cos\theta}{\sin\theta},$$

$$\sec\theta = \frac{1}{\cos\theta}, \qquad \csc\theta = \frac{1}{\sin\theta}.$$

The basic trigonometric identities are as follows:

$$\sin^2\theta + \cos^2\theta = 1, \qquad \tan^2\theta + 1 = \sec^2\theta,$$

$$\sin(\theta \pm \phi) = \sin\theta\cos\phi \pm \cos\theta\sin\phi,$$

$$\cos(\theta \pm \phi) = \cos\theta\cos\phi \mp \sin\theta\sin\phi,$$

$$\tan(\theta \pm \phi)\,\frac{\tan\theta \pm \tan\phi}{1 \mp \tan\theta\tan\phi},$$

$$\sin\theta\sin\phi = -\tfrac{1}{2}[\cos(\theta+\phi) - \cos(\theta-\phi)],$$

$$\sin\theta\cos\phi = \tfrac{1}{2}[\sin(\theta+\phi) + \sin(\theta-\phi)],$$

$$\cos\theta\cos\phi = \tfrac{1}{2}[\cos(\theta+\phi) + \cos(\theta-\phi)],$$

$$\sin 2\theta = 2\sin\theta\cos\theta, \qquad \cos 2\theta = \cos^2\theta - \sin^2\theta,$$

$$\sin^2\frac{\theta}{2} = \frac{1-\cos\theta}{2}, \qquad \cos^2\frac{\theta}{2} = \frac{1+\cos\theta}{2}.$$

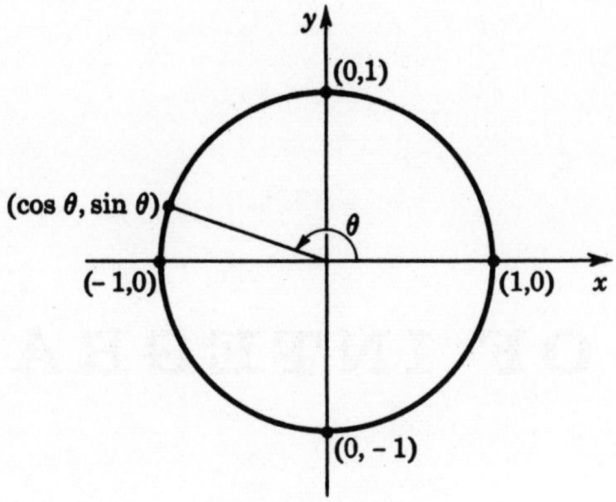

FIGURE A.1

If A, B, C are the angles of a triangle and a, b, c are the lengths of the respective opposite sides, then the following formulas hold:

Law of sines: $$\frac{\sin A}{a} = \frac{\sin B}{b}$$

Law of cosines: $$a^2 = b^2 + c^2 - 2bc \cos A.$$

TABLE OF INTEGRALS

1. $\int [f(x) \pm g(x)]\,dx = \int f(x)\,dx \pm \int g(x)\,dx.$

2. $\int cf(x)\,dx = c\int f(x)\,dx.$

3. $\int f(g(x))g'(x)\,dx = \int f(u)\,du\Big|_{u=g(x)}$

4. $\int x^n\,dx = \dfrac{1}{n+1}x^{n+1} + C, \ (n \neq -1).$

5. $\int \dfrac{1}{x}\,dx = \ln|x| + C.$

6. $\int \sin x\,dx = -\cos x + C.$

7. $\int \cos x\,dx = \sin x + C.$

8. $\int \sec^2 x\,dx = \tan x + C.$

9. $\int \csc^2 x\,dx = -\cot x + C.$

10. $\int \sec x \tan x\,dx = \sec x + C.$

11. $\int \csc x \cot x\,dx = -\csc x + C.$

12. $\int e^x\,dx = e^x + C.$

13. $\int \frac{1}{\sqrt{a^2 - x^2}}\,dx = \sin^{-1}\frac{x}{a} + C.$

14. $\int \frac{1}{a^2 + x^2}\,dx = \frac{1}{a}\tan^{-1}\frac{x}{a} + C.$

15. $\int \frac{1}{x\sqrt{x^2 - a^2}}\,dx = \frac{1}{a}\sec^{-1}\frac{x}{a} + C.$

16. $\int f(x)g'(x)\,dx = f(x)g(x) - \int g(x)f'(x)\,dx.$

17. $\int \frac{1}{x\sqrt{ax + b}}\,dx = \frac{1}{\sqrt{b}}\ln\left|\frac{\sqrt{ax + b} - \sqrt{b}}{\sqrt{ax + b} + \sqrt{b}}\right| + C, \ (b > 0).$

18. $\int \frac{1}{x\sqrt{ax + b}}\,dx = \frac{2}{\sqrt{-b}}\tan^{-1}\sqrt{\frac{ax + b}{-b}} + C, \ (b < 0).$

19. $\int \frac{1}{x^n\sqrt{ax + b}}\,dx = -\frac{1}{b(n - 1)}\frac{\sqrt{ax + b}}{x^{n-1}} - \frac{(2n - 3)a}{(2n - 2)b}\int \frac{1}{x^{n-1}\sqrt{ax + b}}\,dx, \ (n \neq 1).$

20. $\int \frac{\sqrt{ax + b}}{x}\,dx = 2\sqrt{ax + b} + b\int \frac{1}{x\sqrt{ax + b}}\,dx.$

21. $\int \frac{1}{x^2 - a^2}\,dx = \frac{1}{2a}\ln\left|\frac{x - a}{x + a}\right| + C.$

22. $\int \frac{1}{(ax + b)(cx + d)}\,dx = \frac{1}{bc - ad}\ln\left|\frac{cx + d}{ax + b}\right| + C, \ (bc - ad \neq 0).$

23. $\int \frac{x}{(ax + b)(cx + d)}\,dx = \frac{1}{bc - ad}\left\{\frac{b}{a}\ln|ax + b| - \frac{d}{c}\ln|cx + d|\right\} + C, \ (bc - ad \neq 0).$

24. $\int \frac{1}{(ax + b)^2(cx + d)}\,dx = \frac{1}{bc - ad}\left\{\frac{1}{ax + b} + \frac{c}{bc - ad}\ln\left|\frac{cx + d}{ax + b}\right|\right\} + C, \ (bc - ad \neq 0).$

25. $\int \frac{x}{(ax + b)^2(cx + d)}\,dx = -\frac{1}{bc - ad}\left\{\frac{b}{a(ax + b)} + \frac{d}{bc - ad}\ln\left|\frac{cx + d}{ax + b}\right|\right\} + C, \ (bc - ad \neq 0).$

26. $\int \sqrt{x^2 \pm a^2}\, dx = \frac{x}{2}\sqrt{x^2 \pm a^2} \pm \frac{a^2}{2} \ln |x + \sqrt{x^2 \pm a^2}| + C.$

27. $\int \frac{1}{\sqrt{x^2 \pm a^2}}\, dx = \ln |x + \sqrt{x^2 \pm a^2}| + C.$

28. $\int x^2 \sqrt{x^2 \pm a^2}\, dx = \frac{x}{8}(2x^2 \pm a^2)\sqrt{x^2 \pm a^2} - \frac{a^4}{8} \ln |x + \sqrt{x^2 \pm a^2}| + C.$

29. $\int \frac{x^2}{\sqrt{x^2 \pm a^2}}\, dx = \frac{x}{2}\sqrt{x^2 \pm a^2} \mp \frac{a^2}{2} \ln |x + \sqrt{x^2 \pm a^2}| + C.$

30. $\int (x^2 \pm a^2)^{3/2}\, dx = x(x^2 \pm a^2)^{3/2} - 3\int x^2 \sqrt{x^2 \pm a^2}\, dx.$

31. $\int \frac{1}{(x^2 \pm a^2)^{3/2}}\, dx = \frac{\pm x}{a^2 \sqrt{x^2 \pm a^2}} + C.$

32. $\int \frac{x^2}{(x^2 \pm a^2)^{3/2}}\, dx = \frac{-x}{\sqrt{x^2 \pm a^2}} + \ln |x + \sqrt{x^2 \pm a^2}| + C.$

33. $\int \frac{1}{x^2 \sqrt{x^2 \pm a^2}}\, dx = \mp \frac{\sqrt{x^2 \pm a^2}}{a^2 x} + C.$

34. $\int \frac{\sqrt{x^2 \pm a^2}}{x^2}\, dx = -\frac{\sqrt{x^2 \pm a^2}}{x} + \ln |x + \sqrt{x^2 \pm a^2}| + C.$

35. $\int \frac{\sqrt{x^2 \pm a^2}}{x}\, dx = \sqrt{x^2 \pm a^2} \pm a^2 \int \frac{1}{x\sqrt{x^2 \pm a^2}}\, dx.$

36. $\int \frac{1}{x\sqrt{x^2 + a^2}}\, dx = -\frac{1}{a} \ln \left| \frac{a + \sqrt{x^2 + a^2}}{x} \right| + C.$

37. $\int \sqrt{a^2 - x^2}\, dx = \frac{x}{2}\sqrt{a^2 - x^2} + \frac{a^2}{2} \sin^{-1} \frac{x}{a} + C.$

38. $\int x^2 \sqrt{a^2 - x^2}\, dx = -\frac{x}{4}(a^2 - x^2)^{3/2} + \frac{a^2}{4}\int \sqrt{a^2 - x^2}\, dx.$

39. $\int \frac{x^2}{\sqrt{a^2 - x^2}}\, dx = -\frac{x}{2}\sqrt{a^2 - x^2} + \frac{a^2}{2} \sin^{-1} \frac{x}{a} + C.$

40. $\int (a^2 - x^2)^{3/2}\, dx = \frac{x}{4}(a^2 - x^2)^{3/2} + \frac{3a^2}{4}\int \sqrt{a^2 - x^2}\, dx.$

41. $\int \frac{1}{(a^2 - x^2)^{3/2}}\,dx = \frac{x}{a^2\sqrt{a^2 - x^2}} + C.$

42. $\int \frac{x^2}{(a^2 - x^2)^{3/2}}\,dx = \frac{x}{\sqrt{a^2 - x^2}} - \sin^{-1}\frac{x}{a} + C.$

43. $\int \frac{1}{x\sqrt{a^2 - x^2}}\,dx = -\frac{1}{a}\ln\left|\frac{a + \sqrt{a^2 - x^2}}{x}\right| + C.$

44. $\int \frac{1}{x^2\sqrt{a^2 - x^2}}\,dx = -\frac{\sqrt{a^2 - x^2}}{a^2 x} + C.$

45. $\int \frac{\sqrt{a^2 - x^2}}{x}\,dx = \sqrt{a^2 - x^2} - a\ln\left|\frac{a + \sqrt{a^2 - x^2}}{x}\right| + C.$

46. $\int \frac{\sqrt{a^2 - x^2}}{x^2}\,dx = -\frac{\sqrt{a^2 - x^2}}{x} - \sin^{-1}\frac{x}{a} + C.$

47. $\int \frac{1}{(x^2 + a^2)^n}\,dx$

$$= \frac{1}{2(n-1)a^2}\left\{\frac{x}{(x^2 + a^2)^{n-1}} + (2n - 3)\int \frac{1}{(x^2 + a^2)^{n-1}}\,dx\right\}, \quad (n \neq 1).$$

48. $\int x \sin x\,dx = \sin x - x\cos x + C.$

49. $\int x^n \sin x\,dx = -x^n\cos x + nx^{n-1}\sin x - n(n-1)\int x^{n-2}\sin x\,dx.$

50. $\int x\cos x\,dx = \cos x + x\sin x + C.$

51. $\int x^n \cos x\,dx = x^n \sin x + nx^{n-1}\cos x - n(n-1)\int x^{n-2}\cos x\,dx.$

52. $\int \sin^m \cos^n x\,dx$

$$= \begin{cases} \dfrac{1}{m+n}\left[-\sin^{m-1} x\cos^{n+1} x + (m-1)\int \sin^{m-2} x\cos^n x\,dx\right] \\ \\ \dfrac{1}{m+n}\left[\sin^{m+1} x\cos^{n-1} x + (n-1)\int \sin^m x\cos^{n-2} x\,dx\right], \end{cases}$$

$(m + n \neq 0).$

53. $\int \sin^n x\,dx = -\frac{1}{n}\sin^{n-1} x\cos x + \frac{n-1}{n}\int \sin^{n-2} x\,dx, \; (n \geq 2).$

54. $\int \sin^2 x\, dx = -\frac{1}{2}\sin x \cos x + \frac{x}{2} + C.$

55. $\int \cos^n x\, dx = \frac{1}{n}\sin x \cos^{n-1} x + \frac{n-1}{n}\int \cos^{n-2} x\, dx, \ (n \geq 2).$

56. $\int \cos^2 x\, dx = \frac{1}{2}\sin x \cos x + \frac{x}{2} + C.$

57. $\int \sin^2 x \cos^2 x\, dx = -\frac{1}{4}\sin x \cos^3 x + \frac{1}{8}\sin x \cos x + \frac{x}{8} + C.$

58. $\int \tan x\, dx = \ln|\sec x| + C.$

59. $\int \tan^2 x\, dx = \tan x - x + C.$

60. $\int \tan^n x\, dx = \frac{1}{n-1}\tan^{n-1} x - \int \tan^{n-2} x\, dx, \ (n \geq 2).$

61. $\int \cot x\, dx = \ln|\sin x| + C.$

62. $\int \cot^2 x\, dx = -\cot x - x + C.$

63. $\int \cot^n x\, dx = -\frac{1}{n-1}\cot^{n-1} x - \int \cot^{n-2} x\, dx, \ (n \geq 2).$

64. $\int \sec x\, dx = \ln|\sec x + \tan x| + C.$

65. $\int \sec^n x\, dx = \frac{1}{n-1}\left\{\sec^{n-2} x \tan x + (n-2)\int \sec^{n-2} x\, dx\right\},$

$(n \geq 2).$

66. $\int \csc x\, dx = \ln|\csc x - \cot x| + C.$

67. $\int \csc^n x\, dx = \frac{1}{n-1}\left\{-\csc^{n-2} x \cot x + (n-2)\int \csc^{n-2} x\, dx\right\},$

$(n \leq 2).$

68. $\int x e^{ax}\, dx = \frac{1}{a^2}(ax - 1)e^{ax} + C.$

69. $\int x^n e^{ax}\,dx = \frac{x^n}{a}e^{ax} - \frac{n}{a}\int x^{n-1}e^{ax}\,dx.$

70. $\int e^{ax}\sin bx\,dx = \frac{1}{a^2+b^2}(a\sin bx - b\cos bx)e^{ax} + C.$

71. $\int e^{ax}\cos bx\,dx = \frac{1}{a^2+b^2}(a\cos bx + b\sin bx)e^{ax} + C.$

72. $\int \ln|x|\,dx = x\ln|x| - x + C.$

73. $\int x^m \ln^n|x|\,dx = \frac{1}{m+1}\left\{x^{m+1}\ln^n|x| - n\int x^m\ln^{n-1}|x|\,dx\right\},$

$(m \neq -1).$

74. $\int \ln^n|x|\,dx = x\ln^n|x| - n\int \ln^{n-1}|x|\,dx.$

75. $\int x^n\ln|x|\,dx = \frac{x^{n+1}}{n+1}\left(\ln|x| - \frac{1}{n+1}\right) + C, \ (n \neq -1).$

76. $\int \frac{\ln^n|x|}{x}\,dx = \frac{1}{n+1}\ln^{n+1}|x| + C, \ (n \neq -1).$

77. $\int \frac{1}{x\ln|x|}\,dx = \ln|\ln|x|| + C.$

78. $\int \sin^{-1}x\,dx = x\sin^{-1}x + \sqrt{1-x^2} + C.$

79. $\int x^n\sin^{-1}x\,dx = \frac{1}{n+1}\left\{x^{n+1}\sin^{-1}x - \int\frac{x^{n+1}}{\sqrt{1-x^2}}\,dx\right\}, \ (n \neq -1).$

80. $\int \tan^{-1}x\,dx = x\tan^{-1}x - \frac{1}{2}\ln(x^2+1) + C.$

81. $\int x^n\tan^{-1}x\,dx = \frac{1}{n+1}\left\{x^{n+1}\tan^{-1}x - \int\frac{x^{n+1}}{x^2+1}\,dx\right\}, \ (n \neq -1).$

82. $\int \sec^{-1}x\,dx = x\sec^{-1}x - \ln|x + \sqrt{x^2-1}| + C.$

NUMERICAL TABLES

I. *Logarithms to base* 10

II. *Logarithms to base e*

III. e^x *and* e^{-x}

IV. *Trigonometric functions*

TABLE I. Logarithms to Base 10

N	0	1	2	3	4	5	6	7	8	9
1.0	.0000	.0043	.0086	.0128	.0170	.0212	.0253	.0294	.0334	.0374
1.1	.0414	.0453	.0492	.0531	.0569	.0607	.0645	.0682	.0719	.0755
1.2	.0792	.0828	.0864	.0899	.0934	.0969	.1004	.1038	.1072	.1106
1.3	.1139	.1173	.1206	.1239	.1271	.1303	.1335	.1367	.1399	.1430
1.4	.1461	.1492	.1523	.1553	.1584	.1614	.1644	.1673	.1703	.1732
1.5	.1761	.1790	.1818	.1847	.1875	.1903	.1931	.1959	.1987	.2014
1.6	.2041	.2068	.2095	.2122	.2148	.2175	.2201	.2227	.2253	.2279
1.7	.2304	.2330	.2355	.2380	.2405	.2430	.2455	.2480	.2504	.2529
1.8	.2553	.2577	.2601	.2625	.2648	.2672	.2695	.2718	.2742	.2765
1.9	.2788	.2810	.2833	.2856	.2878	.2900	.2923	.2945	.2967	.2989
2.0	.3010	.3032	.3054	.3075	.3096	.3118	.3139	.3160	.3181	.3201
2.1	.3222	.3243	.3263	.3284	.3304	.3324	.3345	.3365	.3385	.3404
2.2	.3424	.3444	.3464	.3483	.3502	.3522	.3541	.3560	.3579	.3598
2.3	.3617	.3636	.3655	.3674	.3692	.3711	.3729	.3747	.3766	.3784
2.4	.3802	.3820	.3838	.3856	.3874	.3892	.3909	.3927	.3945	.3962
2.5	.3979	.3997	.4014	.4031	.4048	.4065	.4082	.4099	.4116	.4133
2.6	.4150	.4166	.4183	.4200	.4216	.4232	.4249	.4265	.4281	.4298
2.7	.4314	.4330	.4346	.4362	.4378	.4393	.4409	.4425	.4440	.4456
2.8	.4472	.4487	.4502	.4518	.4533	.4548	.4564	.4579	.4594	.4609
2.9	.4624	.4639	.4654	.4669	.4683	.4698	.4713	.4728	.4742	.4757
3.0	.4771	.4786	.4800	.4814	.4829	.4843	.4857	.4871	.4886	.4900
3.1	.4914	.4928	.4942	.4955	.4969	.4983	.4997	.5011	.5024	.5038
3.2	.5051	.5065	.5079	.5092	.5105	.5119	.5132	.5145	.5159	.5172
3.3	.5185	.5198	.5211	.5224	.5237	.5250	.5263	.5276	.5289	.5302
3.4	.5315	.5328	.5340	.5353	.5366	.5378	.5391	.5403	.5416	.5428
3.5	.5441	.5453	.5465	.5478	.5490	.5502	.5514	.5527	.5539	.5551
3.6	.5563	.5575	.5587	.5599	.5611	.5623	.5635	.5647	.5658	.5670
3.7	.5682	.5694	.5705	.5717	.5729	.5740	.5752	.5763	.5775	.5786
3.8	.5798	.5809	.5821	.5832	.5843	.5855	.5866	.5877	.5888	.5899
3.9	.5911	.5922	.5933	.5944	.5955	.5966	.5977	.5988	.5999	.6010
4.0	.6021	.6031	.6042	.6053	.6064	.6075	.6085	.6096	.6107	.6117
4.1	.6128	.6138	.6149	.6160	.6170	.6180	.6191	.6201	.6212	.6222
4.2	.6232	.6243	.6253	.6263	.6274	.6284	.6294	.6304	.6314	.6325
4.3	.6335	.6345	.6355	.6365	.6375	.6385	.6395	.6405	.6415	.6425
4.4	.6435	.6444	.6454	.6464	.6474	.6484	.6493	.6503	.6513	.6522
4.5	.6532	.6542	.6551	.6561	.6571	.6580	.6590	.6599	.6609	.6618
4.6	.6628	.6637	.6646	.6656	.6665	.6675	.6684	.6693	.6702	.6712
4.7	.6721	.6730	.6739	.6749	.6758	.6767	.6776	.6785	.6794	.6803
4.8	.6812	.6821	.6830	.6839	.6848	.6857	.6866	.6875	.6884	.6893
4.9	.6902	.6911	.6920	.6928	.6937	.6946	.6955	.6964	.6972	.6981
5.0	.6990	.6998	.7007	.7016	.7024	.7033	.7042	.7050	.7059	.7067
5.1	.7076	.7084	.7093	.7101	.7110	.7118	.7126	.7135	.7143	.7152
5.2	.7160	.7168	.7177	.7185	.7193	.7202	.7210	.7218	.7226	.7235
5.3	.7243	.7251	.7259	.7267	.7275	.7284	.7292	.7300	.7308	.7316
5.4	.7324	.7332	.7340	.7348	.7356	.7364	.7372	.7380	.7388	.7396
N	0	1	2	3	4	5	6	7	8	9

TABLE I. Logarithms to Base 10 (*continued*)

N	0	1	2	3	4	5	6	7	8	9
5.5	.7404	.7412	.7419	.7427	.7435	.7443	.7451	.7459	.7466	.7474
5.6	.7482	.7490	.7497	.7505	.7513	.7520	.7528	.7536	.7543	.7551
5.7	.7559	.7566	.7574	.7582	.7589	.7597	.7604	.7612	.7619	.7627
5.8	.7634	.7642	.7649	.7657	.7664	.7672	.7679	.7689	.7694	.7701
5.9	.7709	.7716	.7723	.7731	.7738	.7745	.7752	.7760	.7767	.7774
6.0	.7782	.7789	.7796	.7803	.7810	.7818	.7825	.7832	.7839	.7846
6.1	.7853	.7860	.7868	.7875	.7882	.7889	.7896	.7903	.7910	.7917
6.2	.7924	.7931	.7938	.7945	.7952	.7959	.7966	.7973	.7980	.7987
6.3	.7993	.8000	.8007	.8014	.8021	.8028	.8035	.8041	.8048	.8055
6.4	.8062	.8069	.8075	.8082	.8089	.8096	.8102	.8109	.8116	.8122
6.5	.8129	.8136	.8142	.8149	.8156	.8162	.8169	.8176	.8182	.8189
6.6	.8195	.8202	.8209	.8215	.8222	.8228	.8235	.8241	.8248	.8254
6.7	.8261	.8267	.8274	.8280	.8287	.8293	.8299	.8306	.8312	.8319
6.8	.8325	.8331	.8338	.8344	.8351	.8357	.8363	.8370	.8376	.8328
6.9	.8388	.8395	.8401	.8407	.8414	.8420	.8426	.8432	.8439	.8445
7.0	.8451	.8457	.8463	.8470	.8476	.8482	.8488	.8494	.8500	.8506
7.1	.8513	.8519	.8525	.8531	.8537	.8543	.8549	.8555	.8561	.8567
7.2	.8573	.8579	.8585	.8591	.8597	.8603	.8609	.8615	.8621	.8627
7.3	.8633	.8639	.8645	.8651	.8657	.8663	.8669	.8675	.8681	.8686
7.4	.8692	.8698	.8704	.8710	.8716	.8722	.8727	.8733	.8739	.8475
7.5	.8751	.8756	.8762	.8768	.8774	.8779	.8785	.8791	.8797	.8802
7.6	.8808	.8814	.8820	.8825	.8831	.8837	.8842	.8848	.8854	.8859
7.7	.8865	.8871	.8876	8882	.8887	.8893	.8899	.8904	.8910	.8915
7.8	.8921	.8927	.8932	.8938	.8943	.8949	.8954	.8960	.8965	.8971
7.9	.8976	.8982	.8987	.8993	.8998	.9004	.9009	.9015	.9020	.9025
8.0	.9031	.9036	.9042	.9047	.9053	.9058	.9063	.9069	.9074	.9079
8.1	.9085	.9090	.9096	.9101	.9106	.9112	.9117	.9122	.9128	.9133
8.2	.9138	.9143	.9149	.9154	.9159	.9165	.9170	.9175	.9180	.9186
8.3	.9191	.9196	.9201	.9206	.9212	.9217	.9222	.9227	.9232	.9238
8.4	.9243	.9248	.9253	.9258	.9263	.9269	.9274	.9279	.9284	.9289
8.5	.9294	.9299	.9304	.9309	.9315	.9320	.9325	.9330	.9335	.9340
8.6	.9345	.9350	.9355	.9360	.9365	.9370	.9375	.9380	.9385	.9390
8.7	.9395	.9400	.9405	.9410	.9415	.9420	.9425	.9430	.9435	.9440
8.8	.9445	.9450	.9455	.9460	.9465	.9469	.9474	.9479	.9484	.9489
8.9	.9494	.9499	.9504	.9509	.9513	.9518	.9523	.9528	.9533	.9538
9.0	.9542	.9547	.9552	.9557	.9562	.9566	.9571	.9576	.9581	.9586
9.1	.9590	.9595	.9600	.9605	.9609	.9614	.9619	.9624	.9628	.9633
9.2	.9638	.9643	.9647	.9652	.9657	.9661	.9666	.9671	.9765	.9680
9.3	.9685	.9689	.9694	.9699	.9703	.9708	.9713	.9717	.9722	.9727
9.4	.9731	.9736	.9741	.9745	.9750	.9754	.9759	.9763	.9768	.9773
9.5	.9777	.9782	.9786	.9791	.9795	.9800	.9805	.9809	.9814	.9818
9.6	.9823	.9827	.9832	.9836	.9841	.9845	.9850	.9854	.9859	.9863
9.7	.9868	.9872	.9877	.9881	.9886	.9890	.9894	.9899	.9903	.9908
9.8	.9912	.9917	.9921	.9926	.9930	.9934	.9939	.9943	.9948	.9952
9.9	.9956	.9961	.9965	.9969	.9974	.9978	.9983	.9987	.9991	.9996
N	**0**	**1**	**2**	**3**	**4**	**5**	**6**	**7**	**8**	**9**

TABLE II. Logarithms to Base e

N	.0	.1	.2	.3	.4	.5	.6	.7	.8	.9
1	0.000	0.095	0.182	0.262	0.336	0.405	0.470	0.531	0.588	0.642
2	0.693	0.742	0.788	0.833	0.875	0.916	0.956	0.993	1.030	1.065
3	1.099	1.131	1.163	1.194	1.224	1.253	1.281	1.308	1.335	1.361
4	1.386	1.411	1.435	1.459	1.482	1.504	1.526	1.548	1.569	1.589
5	1.609	1.629	1.649	1.668	1.686	1.705	1.723	1.740	1.758	1.775
6	1.792	1.808	1.825	1.841	1.856	1.872	1.887	1.902	1.917	1.932
7	1.946	1.960	1.974	1.988	2.001	2.015	2.028	2.041	2.054	2.067
8	2.079	2.092	2.104	2.116	2.128	2.140	2.152	2.163	2.175	2.186
9	2.197	2.208	2.219	2.230	2.241	2.251	2.262	2.272	2.282	2.293
10	2.303	2.313	2.322	2.332	2.342	2.351	2.361	2.370	2.380	2.389

TABLE III. e^x and e^{-x}

x	e^x	e^{-x}	x	e^x	e^{-x}
0.0	1.00	1.00	3.1	22.2	.045
0.1	1.11	.905	3.2	24.5	.041
0.2	1.22	.819	3.3	27.1	.037
0.3	1.35	.741	3.4	30.0	.033
0.4	1.49	.670	3.5	33.1	.030
0.5	1.65	.607	3.6	36.6	.027
0.6	1.82	.549	3.7	40.4	.025
0.7	2.01	.497	3.8	44.7	.022
0.8	2.23	.449	3.9	49.4	.020
0.9	2.46	.407	4.0	54.6	.018
1.0	2.72	.368	4.1	60.3	.017
1.1	3.00	.333	4.2	66.7	.015
1.2	3.32	.301	4.3	73.7	.014
1.3	3.67	.273	4.4	81.5	.012
1.4	4.06	.247	4.5	90.0	.011
1.5	4.48	.223	4.6	99.5	.010
1.6	4.95	.202	4.7	110	.0091
1.7	5.47	.183	4.8	122	.0082
1.8	6.05	.165	4.9	134	.0074
1.9	6.69	.150	5.0	148	.0067
2.0	7.39	.135	5.1	164	.0061
2.1	8.17	.122	5.2	181	.0055
2.2	9.02	.111	5.3	200	.0050
2.3	9.97	.100	5.4	221	.0045
2.4	11.0	.091	5.5	245	.0041
2.5	12.2	.082	5.6	270	.0037
2.6	13.5	.074	5.7	299	.0033
2.7	14.9	.067	5.8	330	.0030
2.8	16.4	.061	5.9	365	.0027
2.9	18.2	.055	6.0	403	.0025
3.0	20.1	.050			

TABLE IV. Trigonometric Functions

Degrees	*Radians*	*Sin*	*Tan*	*Cot*	*Cos*		*Degrees*
0°	.000	.000	.000		1.000	1.571	**90°**
1°	.017	.017	.017	57.29	1.000	1.553	89°
2°	.035	.035	.035	28.64	.999	1.536	88°
3°	.052	.052	.052	19.081	.999	1.518	87°
4°	.070	.070	.070	14.301	.998	1.501	86°
5°	.087	.087	.087	11.430	.996	1.484	**85°**
6°	.105	.105	.105	9.514	.995	1.466	84°
7°	.122	.122	.123	8.144	.993	1.449	83°
8°	.140	.139	.141	7.115	.990	1.431	82°
9°	.157	.156	.158	6.314	.988	1.414	81°
10°	.175	.174	.176	5.671	.985	1.396	**80°**
11°	.192	.191	.194	5.145	.982	1.379	79°
12°	.209	.208	.213	4.705	.978	1.361	78°
13°	.227	.225	.231	4.331	.974	1.344	77°
14°	.244	.242	.249	4.011	.970	1.326	76°
15°	.262	.259	.268	3.732	.966	1.309	**75°**
16°	.279	.276	.287	3.487	.961	1.292	74°
17°	.297	.292	.306	3.271	.956	1.274	73°
18°	.314	.309	.325	3.078	.951	1.257	72°
19°	.332	.326	.344	2.904	.946	1.239	71°
20°	.349	.342	.364	2.747	.940	1.222	**70°**
21°	.367	.358	.384	2.605	.934	1.204	69°
22°	.384	.375	.404	2.475	.927	1.187	68°
23°	.401	.391	.424	2.356	.921	1.169	67°
24°	.419	.407	.445	2.246	.914	1.152	66°
25°	.436	.423	.466	2.144	.906	1.134	**65°**
26°	.454	.438	.488	2.050	.899	1.117	64°
27°	.471	.454	.510	1.963	.891	1.100	63°
28°	.489	.469	.532	1.881	.883	1.082	62°
29°	.506	.485	.554	1.804	.875	1.065	61°
30°	.524	.500	.577	1.732	.866	1.047	**60°**
31°	.541	.515	.601	1.664	.857	1.030	59°
32°	.559	.530	.625	1.600	.848	1.012	58°
33°	.576	.545	.649	1.540	.839	.995	57°
34°	.593	.559	.675	1.483	.829	.977	56°
35°	.611	.574	.700	1.428	.819	.960	**55°**
36°	.628	.588	.727	1.376	.809	.942	54°
37°	.646	.602	.754	1.327	.799	.925	53°
38°	.663	.616	.781	1.280	.788	.908	52°
39°	.681	.629	.810	1.235	.777	.890	51°
40°	.698	.643	.839	1.192	.766	.873	**50°**
41°	.716	.656	.869	1.150	.755	.855	49°
42°	.733	.669	.900	1.111	.743	.838	48°
43°	.750	.682	.933	1.072	.731	.820	47°
44°	.768	.695	.966	1.036	.719	.803	46°
45°	.785	.707	1.000	1.000	.707	.785	**45°**
		Cos	*Cot*	*Tan*	*Sin*	*Radians*	*Degrees*

ANSWERS TO ODD-NUMBERED EXERCISES

CHAPTER 1

Section 2, Part I

1. $(-\infty,2)$. **3.** $(-\infty,\frac{3}{2})$. **5.** $(-\infty,\frac{5}{3}]$.
7. $(4.9,5.1)$. **9.** $[-1.575,-1.425]$. **11.** $[4,\infty)$.
13. $(-,b^2/4a]$ if $a > 0$. **15.** $(-1,3)$. **17.** $(-\infty,-3)$.
19. $\varnothing$. **21.** $[0,5]$, $[3,5]$, $[0,3)$, $(-\infty,\infty)$, B'.
23. $(-\infty,15]$, $(-\infty,7]$, $[7,15]$, $(-\infty,7) \cup (7,\infty)$, $(-\infty,7)\cup(15,\infty)$.
25. $[1,2]$, $(-\infty,1) \cup (1,\infty)$, $\{1\}$, $\varnothing$.

Section 2, Part II

1. Assume without loss of generality that $a > b$.
3. **a.** Use induction. **b.** Assume $a < b$ and obtain $a^n < b^n$ which is a contradiction.
5. Use Exercise II-4.
7. $\frac{81}{4}$; Use Exercise II-4.

Section 3, Part I

1. $(-2,4)$. **3.** $(.45,.55)$. **5.** $(-\frac{1}{3},3)$.
7. $[-1,0]$. **13.** $(-\infty,-2) \cup (2,\infty)$. **15.** $(-\infty,-7] \cup [3,\infty)$.

Section 3, Part II

5. $(-\infty,-13) \cup (-\frac{7}{3},\infty)$. (*Hint:* Consider separately $x \geq 3$, $3 > x > -5$, $-5 \geq x$.)
7. All x. (*Hint:* Consider separately $x \geq 1$, $1 > x > -3$, $-3 \geq x$.)

9. $(-\infty,-\sqrt{2}] \cup [-\sqrt{\frac{2}{5}},\sqrt{\frac{2}{5}}] \cup [\sqrt{2},\infty)$. (*Hint:* Let $x^2 - 1 = y$ and consider separately $y \geq 3$, $3 > y > 0$, $0 \geq y$.)

SECTION 4

1. $(-6,-1)$.
3. $[4,6]$.
5. $(0,\frac{1}{4}]$.
7. $(-1.505,-1.495)$.
9. $(-2.5,-2]$.
11. $[.009,.011]$.
13. $[-1,2)$.
15. $(0,.1)$.
19. $(-2-\epsilon/5,-2+\epsilon/5)$.
21. $(\sqrt{a^2-\epsilon}, \sqrt{a^2+\epsilon})$, $a^2 > \epsilon$.
23. $((\sqrt{a}-\epsilon)^2, (\sqrt{a}+\epsilon)^2)$, $a^2 > \epsilon$.

REVIEW, PART I

1. $(2,\infty)$.
3. $(-5,-2] \cup [2,5)$.
5. $\varnothing$.
7. Consider the arithmetic mean.
9. Assume without loss of generality that $x_1 \leq x_2$.

REVIEW, PART II

1. $(-\infty,\frac{13}{2}]$ (consider separately $x \geq 9$, $4 < x < 9$, $x \leq 4$).
3. $(-\infty,1] \cup [\frac{11}{3},\infty)$ (consider separately $x \geq 3$, $1 < x < 3$, $x \leq 1$).
5. $(-\infty,-\sqrt{\frac{13}{2}}] \cup [\sqrt{\frac{13}{2}},\infty)$ (let $x^2 - 9 = y$).
7. $(-\infty,\infty)$ (let $(x-1)^2 = y$).
9. $\alpha + \beta,\ \alpha + \beta,\ a\beta + b\alpha + \alpha\beta,\ \dfrac{a\beta + b\alpha}{b(b-\beta)}$.
11. 0.0000005 (multiply top and bottom by $\sqrt{1.0000020} + \sqrt{1.0000010}$).
13. $\left|\dfrac{r+2}{r+1} - \sqrt{2}\right| = \dfrac{\sqrt{2}-1}{r+1}\cdot|r-\sqrt{2}| < |r-\sqrt{2}|$.
15. Assume $b_1 < b_2 < b_3$ and consider the change in the function as x changes from b_r to $b_r + \Delta$ $(r = 1,2,3)$. For $r = 1$, the change is $\Delta(a_1 - a_2 - a_3)$. Thus if $a_1 > a_2 + a_3$, the change increases and the minimum is obtained at $x = b_1$. If $a_1 = a_2 + a_3$, the minimum is obtained for $b_1 \leq x \leq b_2$. If $a_1 < a_2 + a_3$, proceed to $x = b_2$ and repeat the above.
One geometric interpretation is obtained by assuming we have towns located at $x = b_r$ with a_r students. We are then looking for the "optimum" location of a school house, i.e., the one which will minimize the total number of student miles walked per day.

CHAPTER 2

SECTION 2, PART II

3. (*Hint:* $(x-y)^2 = 1$.)
5. Consider, separately, the four regions $(x \geq 0 \text{ or } x < 0) \cap (y \geq 0 \text{ or } y < 0)$.
11. The n-section points of the line segment between the points (x_1,y_1) and (x_2,y_2) are given by

$$\left(\frac{(n-r)x_1 + rx_2}{n}, \frac{(n-r)y_1 + ry_2}{n}\right), \qquad r = 1, 2, 3, \ldots, n-1.$$

SECTION 4, PART I

1. $x^2 + y^2 - 9x + y + 8 = 0$.
3. $x^2 + y^2 - 2x = 24$.
5. $x^2 + y^2 - 6y + 5 = 0$.
7. $x^2 + y^2 + 2x + 6y + 1 = 0$.

9. $x^2 + y^2 - 4x - 8y = 0.$
11. $x^2 + y^2 + 8x - 8y + 16 = 0.$
13. $(0,0)$, $r = 4.$
15. $(-3,5)$, $r = 3.$
17. $(0,-1)$, $r = \sqrt{3}/2.$
19. $(\frac{1}{3},-\frac{2}{3})$, $r = \frac{1}{3}.$
21. $x^2 + y^2 + 6x + 5 = 0.$

SECTION 4, PART II

1. $(8,0)$, $(\frac{8}{5},\frac{24}{5})$ (First subtract one equation from the other.)

3. Take the equation of the circle as $x^2 + y^2 = r^2$ and the endpoints of the diameter as $(\pm r,0)$. Now use the converse of the Pythagorean theorem.

5. The general equation of all circles passing through the 2 points of intersection of the two given circles is

$$x^2 + y^2 + a_1x + b_1y + c_1 = k(x^2 + y^2 + a_2x + b_2y + c_2),$$

where k is an arbitrary constant. k is determined by having the point (m,n) satisfy the equation.

SECTION 6, PART I

7. The area of a triangle whose vertices are (x_r,y_r), $r = 1,2,3$, is given by the determinant

$$A = \frac{1}{2}\begin{vmatrix} x_1 & y_1 & 1 \\ x_2 & y_2 & 1 \\ x_3 & y_3 & 1 \end{vmatrix}.$$

If $A = 0$, the points are collinear.

9. Choose the coordinates of the vertices as $(0,0)$, $(a,0)$, and (b,c). Now use the midpoint formula.

SECTION 6, PART II

1.

$$\theta = \alpha_2 - \alpha_1$$

$$\tan\theta = \tan(\alpha_2 - \alpha_1)$$

$$\tan\theta = \frac{\tan\alpha_2 - \tan\alpha_1}{1 + \tan\alpha_2\tan\alpha_1}$$

$$= \frac{m_2 - m_1}{1 + m_1m_2}$$

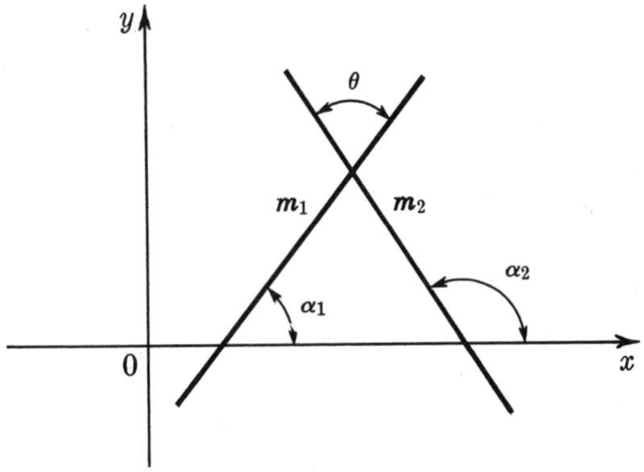

3. Either

$$(x_1 + y_1 - y_2, y_1 - x_1 + x_2),\ (x_2 + y_1 - y_2, y_2 + x_2 - x_1)$$

or

$$(x_1 - y_1 + y_2, y_1 + x_1 - x_2),\ (x_2 - y_1 + y_2, y_2 - x_2 + x_1).$$

Note that

$$CD = CB = y_1 - y_2$$

and

$$AB = DE = x_2 - x_1.$$

5. Let the coordinates of P and Q be (x_1,y_1) and (x_2,y_2), where $x_1^2 + y_1^2 = r_1^2 = x_2^2 + y_2^2$. Midpoint of PQ is $\left(\frac{x_1 + x_2}{2}, \frac{y_1 + y_2}{2}\right)$. Slope of line PQ is $\frac{y_2 - y_1}{x_2 - x_1}$, slope of other line is $\frac{y_1 + y_2}{x_2 + x_1}$.

$$\text{Product of slopes} = \frac{y_2^2 - y_1^2}{x_2^2 - x_1^2} = -1.$$

Equivalently, one can prove that the median and altitude to the base of an isosceles triangle are the same.

Section 7, Part I

1. $x - 3y = 2.$
3. $3x - y = 3.$
5. $y - 4x = 2.$
7. $y - 6x = 2.$
9. $y = 1.$
11. $mx - y = ma.$
13. $m = 2$, $a = -\frac{3}{2}$, $b = 3.$
15. $m = -\frac{1}{2}$, $a = -6$, $b = -3.$
17. No slope, $a = -\frac{5}{3}.$
19. $m = -5$, $a = -3$, $b = -15.$
21. $2x + y = 9$, $2y - x = 3.$
23. $3x - 2y = 8$, $2x + 3y = 1.$
25. $4x + 7y = 0$, $7x - 4y = 0.$
27. $(2,10).$
29. $(5,-4).$
31. $(4,2)$, $(-2,-6).$
33. $(2,4).$

Section 7, Part II

1. The family of all lines passing through the point of intersection of $a_rx + b_ry + c_r = 0$ $(r = 1,2)$ is given by

$$a_1x + b_1y + c_1 = \lambda(a_2x + b_2y + c_2).$$

Now determine λ by having the slope be m.

5. Consider, separately, the two regions $3x - 2y \geq 0$, $3x - 2y < 0$.

9. Take the two circles as

$$x^2 + y^2 = a^2 \quad \text{and} \quad (x-b)^2 + y^2 = c^2$$

and note that the y coordinates of the two points of intersection are mirror images with respect to the x axis.

Section 8, Part I

9. $y^2 = 16x.$
11. $(x+3)^2 = -12y.$
13. $(y-2)^2 = 8(x-2).$

Section 8, Part II

1. Consider, separately, the regions $x \geq y^2$, $x < y^2$.

3. Eliminating x^2, $y^2 + 2py = 2ay$. Thus, $a = p$.

5. Eliminating x from the two equations gives a fourth degree polynomial in y in which the y^3 term is missing. Thus the sum of the roots is zero.

REVIEW, PART I

1. $(a,-b)$.
3. (5,0), 5. (Either find the intersection of perpendicular bisectors of the sides or else use Ex. 4, p. 34.)
5. a. $x^2 = -20y$. **b.** $x^2 = -24y$. **c.** $(y-1)^2 = -16x$.
7. $(\pm s/\sqrt{2},0)$, $(0, \pm s/\sqrt{2})$; $(\pm s/2, \pm s/2)$.
9. 50. **13.** A circle.

REVIEW, PART II

1. a. (0,0), **c.** Any point on the line, **d.** $(-1,2)$, **e.** (0,0), **f.** $(0,-1)$.
3. The distance will be given by the radius r of the circle $(x-h)^2 + (y-k)^2 = r^2$ which is tangent to the line $ax + by + c = 0$. Now eliminate one of the variables to obtain a quadratic equation. The condition for a double root is that the discriminant vanishes or

$$r = \frac{ah + bk + c}{\sqrt{a^2 + b^2}}.$$

5. Use result of previous exercise.
7. $(h^2 + k^2 + ah + bk + c)^{1/2}$ (the square of the tangent plus the square of the radius = the square of the distance between (h,k) and the center).
9. $\{(h_2-h_1)^2 + (k_2-k_1)^2 - (r_2 \pm r_1)^2\}^{1/2}$.
For the common external tangent, consider the figure:

$$t = \sqrt{AB^2 - AC^2}.$$

For the common internal tangent, consider the figure:

$$t = \sqrt{AB^2 - BC^2}.$$

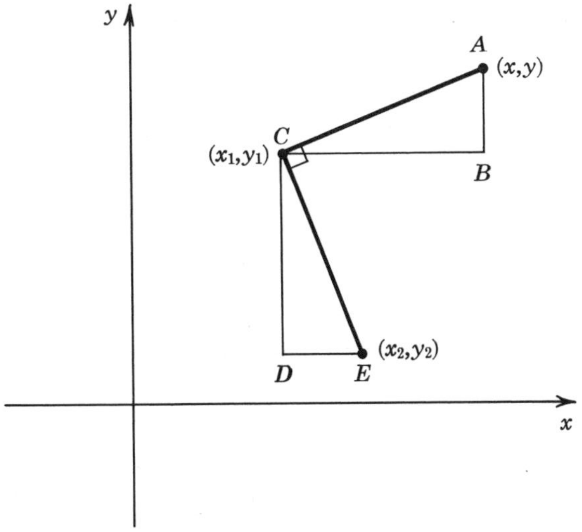

CHAPTER 3

Section 2, Part I

1. $1; 5; 4 + 3\sqrt{3}$.
3. $x + a - 3;\ 2x + h - 3$.
5. $1 - h^{-1};\ (x + y - 1)/(x + y + 1)$.
7. $0, 1; 0, 3/(a + 1),\ (a^2 \neq 1); x = \pm\sqrt{2}/2$.
9. πr^2.
11. $4A$.

Section 2, Part II

1. $81x^4 - 1;\ (x + 1)^3$.
3. $a_1 = a_{11} = (2 - x)/x,\ a_2 = a_{10} = x - 1$.
5. *Hint:* $a - b = \dfrac{a^3 - b^3}{a^2 + ab + b^2}$.
7. If x denotes a side of a rectangle of perimeter $2p$, the other side is $p - x$ and the area is $A = x(p - x)$. The graph of A versus x is a parabola whose vertex is at $x = p/2$. Thus, $M(p) = p^2/4$.

Section 4, Part I

1. $x^2 + 3x;\ x^2 - 3x - 2;\ 3x^3 + x^2 - 3x - 1;\ (x^2 - 1)/(3x + 1);\ 9x^2 + 6x;\ 3x^2 - 2$.
3. $(x^2 + 2x - 1)/(x^2 - 1);\ (x^2 + 1)/(1 - x^2);\ x/(x^2 - 1); (x - 1)/x(x + 1);$ $(x - 1)/(2x - 1);\ -1/x$.
5. $g(x) = \sqrt{x},\ x \geq 0;\ g(f(x)) = x$ if $x \geq 0$, $g(f(x)) = -x$ if $x < 0$.
7. $|x|$.

Section 4, Part II

1. $x;\ x^{-1}$.
3. $a + ab + b^2x;\ a + ab + ab^2 + b^3x$.
5. $\sqrt{1 + \sqrt{1 + x}};\ \sqrt{1 + \sqrt{1 + \sqrt{1 + x}}}$.
7. $a + ab + ab^2 + b^3x; a + ab + ab^2 + ab^3 + b^4x; \sqrt{1 + \sqrt{1 + \sqrt{1 + x}}}; a_4 = \sqrt{1 + a_3}$.
9. a. $p(x) = ax$; b. $p(x) = ax$ unless $h = 0$ and $p(0) = 0$; c. $p(x) = ax$.

Review, Oral

7. $F(x) = 0$.

Review, Part I

1. All $x \neq \pm 1;\ x \geq 2;\ x \geq 2;\ \sqrt{2} > x > 0$ and $x < -\sqrt{2};\ x \neq 0$.
5. Even; odd; even.
7. a. $(y - x)(y + x) = 0$. b. $(y - x^2)(y - x^2) = 0$.
   c. $(x^3 - y^3)(x^3 + y^3) = 0$, which has the same graph as $(x - y)(x + y) = 0$.
   d. $y = x,\ x \geq 0$.

Review, Part II

7. If the equations of the two circles are $x^2 + y^2 + a_rx + b_ry + c_r = 0$ $(r = 1,2)$, the family of circles passing through the two points of intersection is given by

$$x^2 + y^2 + a_1x + b_1y + c_1 + k(x^2 + y^2 + a_2x + b_2y + c_2) = 0.$$

Now determine k by having the given point satisfy the equation.

9. $\pi v\sqrt{3}/2$. (If the edge is e, the altitude is given by $e\sqrt{2/3}$ and the volume is $v = e^3\sqrt{2}/12$. Also, the center is $\frac{3}{4}$ the way down an altitude from the vertex.)

11. $\left[\frac{n}{5}\right] + \left[\frac{n}{5^2}\right] + \left[\frac{n}{5^3}\right] + \cdots$.

Here $[x]$ is the greatest integer $\leq x$. For every 5 factor in $n!$, there is also a 2 factor. $\left[\frac{n}{5}\right]$ counts the multiples of 5, $\left[\frac{n}{5^2}\right]$ counts those multiples of 5 in which there is an extra 5 factor, etc. $Z(1000) = 200 + 40 + 8 + 1 = 249$.

13. $R =$ constant.

15. $F(x) = \dfrac{F(x) + F(-x)}{2} + \dfrac{F(x) - F(-x)}{2}$.

17. $\left(\dfrac{\sqrt[5]{x} - b}{a}\right)^{1/3}$, x.

19. ax; $\tan x$; ax; a^x.

CHAPTER 4

Section 1, Part I.

1. -13. **3.** -6. **5.** -1. **7.** $\frac{1}{2}$. **9.** 0, 0.

11. $1/\sqrt{15}$.

13. $\frac{1}{4}$ $\left(\text{multiply by } \dfrac{\sqrt{x} + 2}{\sqrt{x} + 2}\right)$.

15. $1/2\sqrt{2}$ $\left(\text{multiply by } \dfrac{\sqrt{2 + h} + \sqrt{2}}{\sqrt{2 + h} + \sqrt{2}}\right)$.

Section 1, Part II

1. No limit.

3. $\frac{1}{4}$ $\left(\text{multiply by } \dfrac{\sqrt{4 + m + m^2} + 2}{\sqrt{4 + m + m^2} + 2}\right)$.

5. 3 (*Note:* $t^3 - 1 = (t - 1)(t^2 + t + 1)$).

7. Inner limits are to be evaluated first giving

$$\lim_{x\to 0} \left(\frac{a}{d}\right) - \lim_{y\to 0} \left(\frac{c}{f}\right) = \frac{a}{d} - \frac{c}{f}.$$

Section 2, Part I

11. $\left(\dfrac{x + 2}{x + 1} = 1 + \dfrac{1}{x + 1}\right)$.

13. $\left(\begin{aligned} |y| - y &= 0 \text{ for } y > 0 \\ &= -2y \text{ for } y < 0 \end{aligned}\right)$.

Section 2, Part II

1. $\left(\dfrac{x^2 + 4}{x - 2} = x + 2 + \dfrac{6}{x - 2}\right)$.

3. See illustrated Example 2.

7. $x^3 + 1 = (x + 1)(x^2 - x + 1)$.

9. Consider $x = 5 + \epsilon$ and $x = 5 - \epsilon$.

11. See text.

SECTION 3, PART I

3. $z - 4 = (\sqrt{z} - 2)(\sqrt{z} + 2)(z \geq 0)$.

9. $G(x) = 1 + \dfrac{2a}{x - a}\ (x \neq a)$.

11. $M(x) = x^2 - 1\ (x > 0)$
$= 1 - x^2 (x < 0)$.

SECTION 3, PART II

1. See Example 2 (p. 82).

3. Use definition of a limit.

SECTION 4, PART I

1. 1. **3.** -1. **5.** No limit $[x^3 - 27 = (x - 3)(x^2 + 3x + 9)]$.

SECTION 4, PART II

1. 1. **3.** 4. **5.** $2\left(\text{multiply by } \dfrac{\sqrt{1 + \sqrt{x}} + 1}{\sqrt{1 + \sqrt{x}} + 1}\right)$.

SECTION 5, PART I

1. ∞.

3. Let D_n and D_d denote the degrees of the numerator and denominator, respectively. Then the limit is ∞, 0, or the ratio of the coefficients of the highest power of t according as $D_n > D_d$, $D_n < D_d$, or $D_n = D_d$, respectively. In this example, if $ad \neq 0$ then limit $= a/d$.

5. ∞.

7. $x = 2$, vertical asymptote.

9. $x = 2$, vertical asymptote.

11.

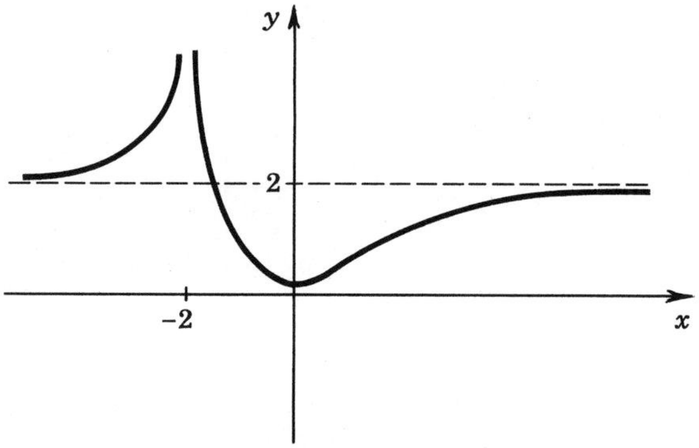

13.

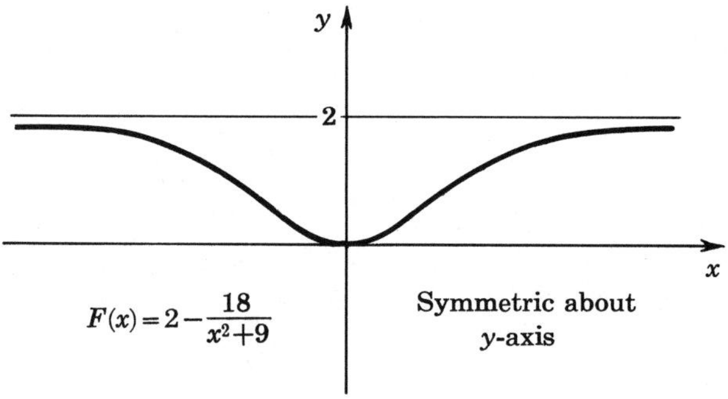

SECTION 5, PART II

1. ∞. **3.** 0.

5. $F(x) = \dfrac{(x-1)(x+1)}{(x-2)(x+2)}$ (Symmetric about y axis).

7. $F(x) = \dfrac{x^2+1}{(x-2)(x+2)}$ (Symmetric about y axis).

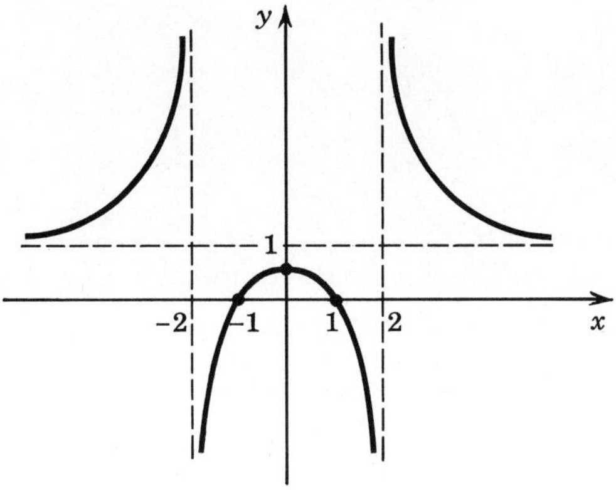

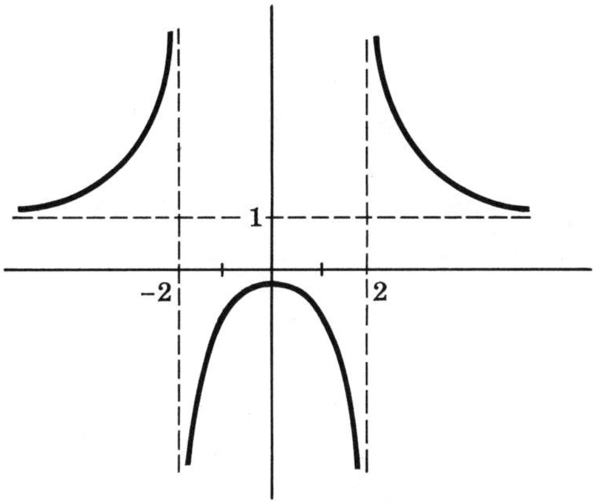

SECTION 6, PART I

1. $a^5 + 3a^2 + 2a + 1$. **3.** 0.

5. 3/2. **7.** -1. **9.** 0 **11.** 2.

SECTION 6, PART II

1. $4 \left(\text{multiply by } \dfrac{2+\sqrt{r^2+3}}{2+\sqrt{r^2+3}} \right)$.

3. $1 \left(\text{multiply by } \dfrac{\sqrt{4+m+m^2}+2}{\sqrt{4+m+m^2}+2} \cdot \dfrac{\sqrt{4+m-m^2}+2}{\sqrt{4+m-m^2}+2} \right)$.

SECTION 6, PART II

5. 0 $\left(\text{Multiply by } \dfrac{\sqrt{1+p}+\sqrt{p}}{\sqrt{1+p}+\sqrt{p}}\right)$.

REVIEW, ORAL

9. No. An example is the *everywhere* discontinuous function

$$F(x) = 1(x\text{-rational}),$$
$$F(x) = -1(x\text{-irrational}).$$

$\lim_{x\to a} |F(x)| = 1$ (all a), $\quad \lim_{x\to a} F(x)$ doesn't exist (all a).

REVIEW, PART I

1. -1. **3.** 4/7. **5.** continuous in $[a,\infty)$.
7. If $a < b$, continuous in $[a, b]$. **9.** Continuous in $(-\infty,\infty)$.
11. Redefine $G(a)$ to be b. This is an example of what is called a removable singularity. As a specific example, $G(x) = \dfrac{x-1}{x-1}$. This is not defined for $x = 1$. But if we define $G(1)$ to be 1, the function is continuous everywhere.

REVIEW, PART II

1. $2/3\sqrt[3]{t}$ $\left(\text{Use } a - b = \dfrac{a^3 - b^3}{a^2 + ab + b^2}\right)$.
3. -1 (Same hint as in Exercise 1).
5. $-1/3$ $\left(\dfrac{1-\sqrt[3]{1+t^3}}{t^3} + \dfrac{\sqrt[5]{1+t^5}-1}{t^3}\right.$; now use same hint as in Exercise 1 and also

$$\left. a - b = \frac{a^5 - b^5}{a^4 + a^3b + a^2b^2 + ab^3 + b^4}\right).$$

7. Note that $\lambda_1 = \sqrt{2+\sqrt{x}}$, $\lambda_2 = \sqrt{2+\sqrt{2+x}}, \ldots$, and that $\lim_{x\to4} \lambda_r = 2$ $(r = 0,1,2,\ldots)$. Let

$$L_r = \lim_{x\to4} \frac{\lambda_r - 2}{x-4} = \lim_{x\to4} \frac{\sqrt{2+\lambda_{r-1}} - 2}{x-4}$$

$$= \lim_{x\to4} \frac{\lambda_{r-1} - 2}{x-4} \cdot \frac{1}{\sqrt{2+\lambda_{r-1}}+2} = \frac{L_{r-1}}{4}.$$

$$L_0 = \lim_{x\to4} \frac{\sqrt{x}-2}{x-4} = \lim_{x\to4} \frac{1}{\sqrt{x}+2} = \frac{1}{4}.$$

Thus

$$L_1 = 4^{-2},\quad L_2 = 4^{-3},\quad L_3 = 4^{-4}, \ldots L_r = 4^{-r-1}.$$

9. Continuous in $(-\infty,\infty)$.
11. Consider the four ranges $x \leq -1$, $-1 < x < 1$, $x = 1$, $x > 1$. $H(x)$ is then, respectively, undefined (no limit), 0, 1, ∞.
13. G is defined, continuous, and increasing for all x.

CHAPTER 5

Section 2, Part I

1. $4x$. **3.** $9(3x+1)^2$. **5.** $5/2\sqrt{5x-6}$.
7. 12, 3, 0, 3, 12.
9. $y = 3(x-1)$, $-3y = x - 1$.
11. $x = -1$, $y = 1$.

Section 2, Part II

1.
$$\begin{aligned} DF(ax+b) &= \lim_{h\to 0} \frac{F(a(x+h)+b) - F(ax+b)}{h} \\ &= a \lim_{h\to 0} \frac{F(ax+b+ah) - F(ax+b)}{ah} \\ &= aG(ax+b). \end{aligned}$$

3. Tangent line at point (h,k) where $k = (h+1)^3$ is given by $y - k = 3(h+1)^2(x-h)$. To pass through the origin, $-k = 3(h+1)^2(-h) = -(h+1)^3$. Thus $h = -1$ and $h = 1/2$.

5. The tangent lines intersect on the directrix by symmetry and the two slopes are ± 1.

Section 5, Part I

1. $(x^2+3x-1)(2x-3) + (2x+3)(x^2-3x+1)$.
3. $z^3(6z-7) + 3z^2(3z^2-7z+5)$.
5. $2/(x+1)^2$.
7. $-\dfrac{2}{x^2}\left(2+\dfrac{1}{x}\right) - \dfrac{1}{x^2}\left(1+\dfrac{2}{x}\right)$.
9. $\dfrac{2x-x^2}{(x^2-2x+2)^2}$.
11. $3nx^{3n-1}$.

Section 5, Part II

1. $f'(x) = 2x$, $|x| > 2$,
$f'(x) = -2x$, $|x| < 2$.
3. 0 ($t > 1$ or $t < 0$),
$8t - 4$ ($0 < t < 1$).
5. 0 (x-nonintegral).
7. Use the product formula on $[F(x)G(x)]\cdot[H(x)]$.
9. $2ff'$, $3f^2f'$, $nf^{n-1}f'$ (Use the product formula).

Section 7, Part I

1. $(1-2x^2)/\sqrt{1-x^2}$.
3. $(3+3t)\sqrt{2t+t^2}$.
5. $(3t+1)^{-2/3}$.
7. $-1/x^2\sqrt{x^2+1}$.
9. $3/2\sqrt{2z}$.
11. $4(y-2) = x-3$; $2-y = 4(x-3)$.
13. $y = x$; $y = -x$.
15. $16(y-2) = x-4$, $2-y = 16(x-4)$.

Section 7, Part II

1. $\dfrac{1}{2\sqrt{x+\sqrt{x+\sqrt{x}}}}\left(1+\dfrac{1}{2\sqrt{x+\sqrt{x}}}\left(1+\dfrac{1}{2\sqrt{x}}\right)\right)$.
3. $\frac{2}{3}(2x)^{-2/3}$ if $x > 0$; 0 if $x < 0$.

SECTION 9, PART I

1. $-2;\ \frac{3}{2}$.
3. $-\frac{6}{5};\ -\frac{42}{125}$.
5. $(3y^2 - 2y)^{-1},\ (2 - 6y)/(3y^2 - 2y)^3$.
7. $4(x + 1)^{-2} - 8(x + 1)^{-3};\ -8(x + 1)^{-3} + 24(x + 1)^{-4}$.
9. $y + 2 = -(x + 2)$.
11. $y + 1 = -(x + 1)$.
13. Slope of tangent line at point (a, a) is -1 since curve is symmetric with respect to the line $x = y$.

SECTION 9, PART II

1. Differentiate implicitly three times and solve successively for y', y'', and y'''.
3. $n!a$.
5. $(-a)^n(ax + b)^{-n-1}$.

REVIEW, PART I

1. $\frac{2}{7}t^{-5/7} + \frac{21}{2}t^{-11/2}$.
3. $3\sqrt{t^3}(t^{-2} - 2t^{-1} + 1)^2(-2t^{-3} + 2t^{-2}) + \frac{3}{2}\sqrt{t}(t^{-2} - 2t^{-1} + 1)^3$.
5. $(2,8),\ (-2,-8)$.
7. $(1,0),\ (-1,-4)$.
9. Differentiate three times implicitly:

$$\begin{aligned} 1 &= 5y^4y' + y' \\ 0 &= 20y^3y'^2 + 5y^4y'' + y'' \\ 0 &= 60y^2y'^3 + 60y^3y'y'' + 5y^4y''' + y'''. \end{aligned}$$

Now solve for y' in first equation, then y'' in second equation, and then y''' in last equation.

11. $\sqrt[3]{1001} \doteq \sqrt[3]{1000} + \frac{1}{3}(1000)^{-2/3} \doteq 10.003333$.
$\sqrt[3]{1001} \doteq 10.003332$ (correct to 6 decimal places).
13. $\dfrac{dy}{dt} = \dfrac{dy}{dx} \cdot \dfrac{dx}{dz} \cdot \dfrac{dz}{dt} = F'(x)G'(z)H'(t)$.

REVIEW, PART II

1. Intuitively, 2, 1, 0, depending whether the point is outside, on, or inside the parabola, respectively. Analytically, let the parabola be $y^2 = 2ax$ and the given point be (h,k) and the corresponding tangent point be (x,y), then,

$$\frac{y - k}{x - h} = \text{slope of tangent} = \frac{a}{y} \quad \text{(by implicit differentiation)},$$

or

$$y(y - k) = \frac{y^2}{2} - ah.$$

Since this is a quadratic equation, there are at most two real roots.

3.
$$y^2 = 4ax$$
focus $(a, 0)$.

Point C is chosen such that

$$AB = BC \text{ (i.e., } (x + AB, y)).$$

Now show that the midpoint of AC lies on the normal line through B.

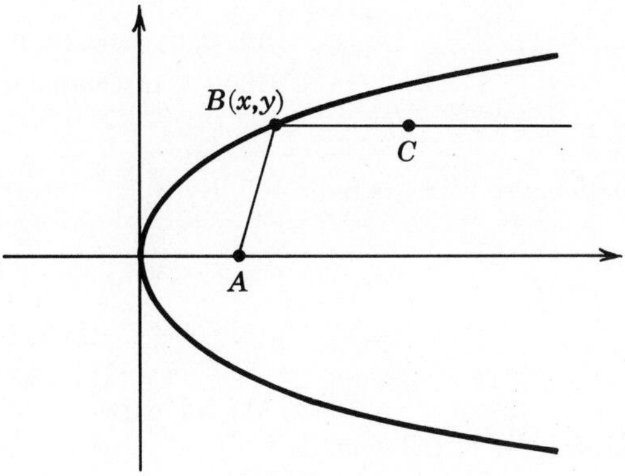

5. If the parabola be $y^2 = 4ax$, focus F is at $(a,0)$. Let A have coordinates (h,k) where $k^2 = 4ah$. Tangent line at A is $yk = 2a(x + h)$ which intercepts the y axis at point $B(0,k/2)$. Slope of $AB = 2a/k$, slope of $BF = -\dfrac{k}{2a}\cdot$ Product of slopes $= -1$.

7. In the result of Exercise 6, Section 9, change a^2 to $-a^2$. Or equivalently, note that $\dfrac{1}{x^2 + a^2} = \dfrac{1}{2ai}\left[\dfrac{1}{x - ai} - \dfrac{1}{x + ai}\right]$.

9. **a.** add the three equations.
   b. $D(F^3 + G^3 + H^3 - 3FGH) = 3[F^2F' + G^2G' + H^2H' - F'GH - FG'H - FGH']$
   $= 3[F^2G + G^2H + H^2F - G^2H - FH^2 - F^2G] = 0.$

11. Tangent line at $(x_0,F(x_0))$ is

$$y - F(x_0) = F'(x_0)(x - x_0)$$

and intercept with the x axis $(y = 0)$ is

$$x = x_0 - \frac{F(x_0)}{F'(x_0)}.$$

13.
$$x_1 = x_0 - \frac{F(x_0)}{F'(x_0)} = -x_0 \quad (\text{for } x_0 \geq 0).$$

$$x_2 = -x_0 - \frac{F(-x_0)}{F'(-x_0)} = x_0;$$

thus we get the periodic sequence $x_0, -x_0, x_0, -x_0, \ldots$.

CHAPTER 6

SECTION 1, PART I

1. $f(-2) = 6$, abs. max.; $f(4) = 0$, abs. min.
3. No max.; $F(2) = 0$, abs. min.
5. $F(-\frac{5}{2}) = \frac{37}{4}$, abs. max.; $F(0) = 3$, abs. min.
7. $f(-1) = -5$, abs. min.; $f(1) = -1$, abs. max.
9. $F(-2) = 0$, max.; $F(0) = -108$, min.; $F(4) = 36$, abs. max.; $F(-3) = -216$, abs. min.
11. $f(\pm\sqrt{2}) = 4$, abs. min.

13. $0, \pm\sqrt{3}; \pm 1$.

15. $0, a; 0, na/(n+1)$.

17. $c = \sqrt{3}$.

19. F is discontinuous.

Section 1, Part II

1. The original equation also vanishes for $x = 0$. By Rolle's theorem, the derivative must vanish in $(0,r)$.

Section 2, Part I

1. $[1,\infty); (-\infty,1]$.

3. $[(a+b)/2,\infty); (-\infty,(a+b)/2]$.

5. $[0,\infty)$.

7. $(-\infty,-1],[1,\infty); [-1,0), (0,1]$.

9. $F(0) = 6$, max.

11. No extrema.

13. $H(3) = 1/6$, max; $H(-1) = 1/2$, min.

Section 2, Part II

1. Parabola, vertex at $x = (a_1 + a_2 + \cdots + a_n)/n$. (Complete the square or find the minimum by differentiation).

3. Consider $a = 0$, $b = 2$; $F(x) = x$ for $0 \le x < 1$, $F(x) = x - 1$ for $1 \le x \le 2$.

Section 3, Part I

1. $f(2) = 0$, min.

3. $F(-\frac{5}{2}) = \frac{37}{4}$, max.

5. No extrema.

7. No extrema.

9. $g(-2) = 0$, max; $g(0) = -108$, min.

11. $f(\pm 2) = 0$, min; $f(0) = 16$, max.

13. $F(-2) = -16$ and $F(1) = 38$, max; $F(-1) = -38$ and $F(2) = 16$, min.

15. $f(1) = -4$, min; $f(-3) = 28$, max.

17. No extrema.

19. $g(0) = 0$, max.; $g(\pm 1) = -1$, min.

21. $f(0) = 0$, max.; $f(\frac{6}{5}) = -26{,}244/3{,}125$, min.

23. $g(0) = 0$, max.; $g(2) = -3\sqrt[3]{4}$, min.

25. $F(1) = -1$, min.

27. $f(\sqrt{3}) = \sqrt[3]{-6\sqrt{3}}$, min.; $f(-\sqrt{3}) = \sqrt[3]{6\sqrt{3}}$, max.

29. $G(\pm 1) = 2$, min.

Section 3, Part II

1. a. $F(1)$, min.; $f(-1)$, min.; $f((q-p)/(q+p))$, max.

b. $f(1)$, min.; $f((q-p)/(q+p))$, max.

c. $f(-1)$, max.; $f((q-p)/(q+p))$, min.

d. $f((q-p)/(q+p))$, min.

Section 5, Part I

1. $f(\frac{1}{5}) = \frac{4}{5}$, min.

3. $g(-3) = 37$, max.; $g(1) = 5$, min.

5. $F(2) = 3$, min.

7. $f(9) = \frac{2}{3}$, min.

9. $G(-1) = 4$, max.

11. $F(-\frac{1}{3}) = \frac{59}{27}$, max.; $F(1) = 1$, min.; $(\frac{1}{3},\frac{43}{27})$, pt. of infl.

13. $f(-1) = -2$, min.; $f(0) = 3$, max.; $f(2) = -29$, min.; pts. of infl. at $x = (1 \pm \sqrt{7})/3$.

15. $g(-\sqrt{5}) = 10\sqrt{5}$, max.; $g(\sqrt{5}) = -10\sqrt{5}$, min.

17. $G(\frac{5}{8}) = -15\sqrt[3]{25}/256$, min.

19. $F(-3) = 0$, max.; $F(-2) = -2$, min.

21. $f(0) = 0$, min.; $f(\frac{1}{2}) = 9\sqrt[3]{2}/8$, max.; $f(2) = 0$, min.

23. $g(1/a) = \frac{a}{|a|}\sqrt{a^2 + 1}$, max. if $a > 0$; min. if $a < 0$.

25. $(\pm 1,1/4)$.

27. $(1,5/6)$; $15x - 6y = 10$.

29. $a = 1$, $b = -5$, min.

SECTION 5, PART II

1. $a = 1$, $b = 1/4$; $(2,1)$ is a min. pt.

5. $F(1) = 13$, max.; $F(2) = -10$, min.

SECTION 6, PART I

1. 100×150.

3. $(6 - 2\sqrt{3}) \times 4\sqrt{3} \times (12 + 4\sqrt{3})$.

5. Radius = height.

7. Length = 2(width).

9. If (x,y) is to be the closest point, we must then minimize $(x - 11)^2 + (x^3 - 3x - 1)^2$.

11. $5\sqrt{5}$.

15. 3 miles from P.

17. 500.

SECTION 6, PART II

1. $(x_1 + x_2 + \cdots + x_n)/n$ (the arithmetic mean). (Also, see Exercise 1, Section 2, Part II).

3. Let the coordinates of the vertices be (x_r,y_r), $r = 1, 2, 3$ and that of P, (x,y). We then have to minimize

$$[(x - x_1)^2 + (x - x_2)^2 + (x - x_3)^2] + [(y - y_1)^2 + (y - y_2)^2 + (y - y_3)^2].$$

By Exercise 1, $x = (x_1 + x_2 + x_3)/3$, $y = (y_1 + y_2 + y_3)/3$ (P is the centroid of the triangle).

5.

$$a^2 = r^2 - (h - r)^2 = 2hr - h^2$$

$$V = \frac{\pi h a^2}{3} = \frac{\pi}{3}(2h^2 r - h^3)$$

$$\frac{dV}{dh} = 0 = 4hr - 3h^2$$

$$h = \frac{4}{3}r, \quad a = \frac{2r\sqrt{2}}{3}.$$

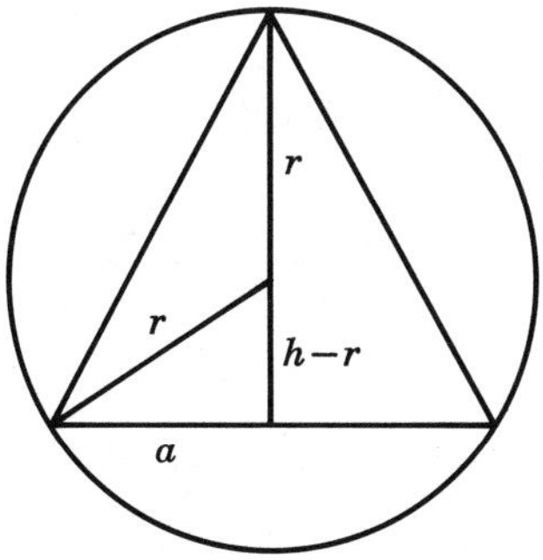

7. $\frac{d}{dx}(x^m(a - x)^n) = mx^{m-1}(a - x)^n - nx^m(a - x)^{n-1} = 0.$

$$x = \frac{ma}{m + n}, \qquad y = \frac{na}{m + n}.$$

$$\text{max. value} = \frac{m^m n^n a^{m+n}}{(m+n)^{m+n}}$$

9.
$$3w + 2l = 600$$
$$\text{Area} = lw.$$

By arithmetic-geometric mean inequality,

$$\frac{3w + 2l}{2} \geq \sqrt{6wl}$$

with equality if and only if $3w = 2l$. Thus $\sqrt{6wl}$ (and, consequently, wl) is a maximum when $3w = 2l = 300$; or

$$w = 100, \qquad l = 150.$$

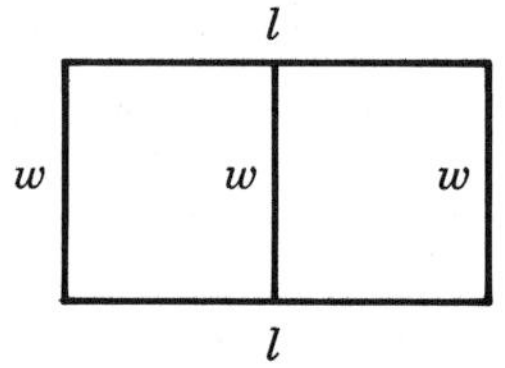

11. By similar triangles,

$$\frac{A - b}{A} = \frac{a}{B}$$

or

$$Aa + Bb = AB.$$
$$\text{Area} = ab.$$

Since

$$\frac{Aa + Bb}{2} \geq \sqrt{ABab},$$

the area is a maximum when $Aa = Bb = \frac{AB}{2}\cdot$ Thus

$$a = \frac{B}{2}, \qquad b = \frac{A}{2},$$

and area $\frac{AB}{4}$ is half the area of the triangle.

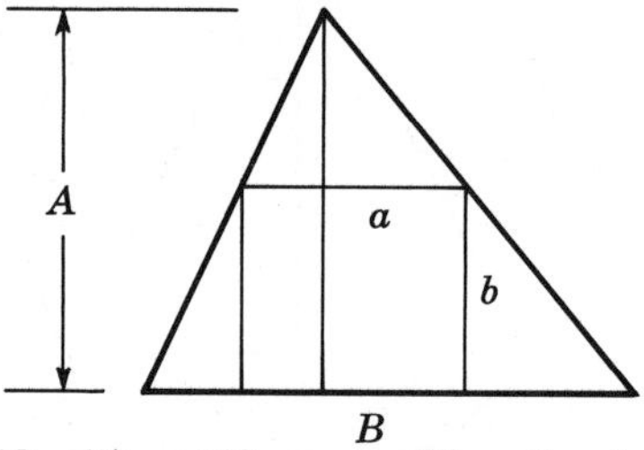

Section 7, Part I

1. $v = -32t + 80$, $a = -32$; $s(\frac{5}{2}) = 100$, max.; $s(0) = 0$, min.
3. $v = 2t - 8$, $a = 2$; $s(4) = -12$, min., $s(-2) = 24$, max.
5. $v = 3t^2 - 3$, $a = 6t$; $s(-1) = 2$, max., $s(1) = -2$, min.
7. $v = 1 - 2t - 3t^2$, $a = -2 - 6t$; $s(-1) = 1$, min., $s(\frac{1}{3}) = \frac{59}{27}$, max.
9. $v = 2t - 16t^{-2}$, $a = 2 + 32t^{-3}$; $s(2) = 12$, min.
11. $r' = (9\pi t^2)^{-1/3}$; .082 in./sec.

13. $d(t) = 4\sqrt{41t^2 - 120t + 225}$; closest at 11:28 A.M.

15. $h(t) = \sqrt{2}t/3$; $\frac{1}{6}$ ft/min.

SECTION 8, PART I

1. $x - 2x^2 + 3x^3$. **3.** $\frac{2}{5}x^{5/2} + \frac{2}{3}x^{3/2} - 5x$. **5.** $\frac{4}{5}(x+1)^{5/4}$.

7. $\frac{3}{4}(x+2)^4 - 12$. **9.** $4t^2 - 9t - 16$. **11.** 49 ft, 3.5 sec.

13. 40 ft/sec.

15. $s(t) = 4t^2$; $5\sqrt{2}$ sec; 34 ft/sec.

SECTION 8, PART II

1. $\dfrac{2(t_2s_1 - t_1s_2)}{t_1t_2(t_1 - t_2)}$; solve for a in

$$s_1 = vt_1 + at_1^2/2,$$
$$s_2 = vt_2 + at_2^2/2.$$

REVIEW, PART I

1. (0, −4), min.

3. $(\sqrt{3}/3, -2\sqrt{3}/9)$, min.; $(-\sqrt{3}/3, 2\sqrt{3}/9)$, max.; (0,0), pt. of infl.

5. (3,−756), min.; (−3,756), max.; (0,0), (−2,−494), (2,494), pts. of infl.

7. (0,0), min.; (0,0), min.; $(\frac{1}{4}m^2, -\frac{1}{4}m)$, max.

11. $\pm x + y\sqrt{6} = 2\sqrt{6}$, $x = 0$.

13. $\frac{3}{4}$.

15. **a.** 30 mph; **b.** 50 mph ($15\sqrt{14} >$ max. speed of 50 mph).

17.

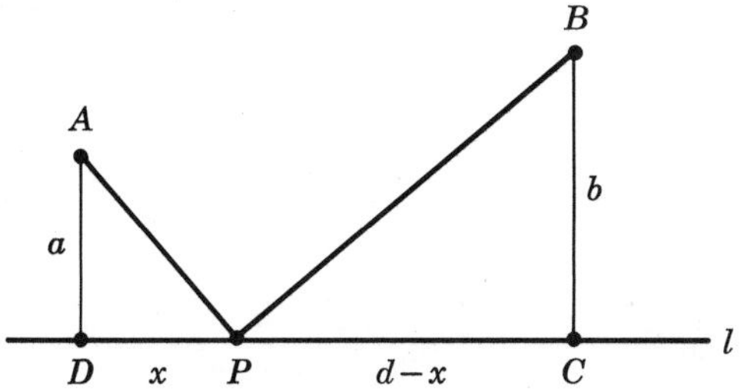

$$AP + BP = \sqrt{a^2 + x^2} + \sqrt{b^2 + (d-x)^2}$$

Differentiating,

$$\frac{x}{\sqrt{a^2 + x^2}} = \frac{d - x}{\sqrt{b^2 + (d-x)^2}},$$

Thus the two triangles are similar and $\angle APD = \angle BPC$.

19. 1, 3/5. **21.** min $(|a| + |b|)^2$, no max.

REVIEW, PART II

3. Note that F' doesn't change sign in the neighborhood of $x = \frac{1}{2}$ and $x = -\frac{5}{4}$ but that it does in the neighborhood of $x = -1$ and $x = -3$.

5. Note that

$$\frac{x^2 - 4x + 9}{x^2 + 4x + 9} = 1 - \frac{8}{x + \dfrac{9}{x} + 4}.$$

Now consider the max. and min. of right-hand side which occurs at ±3.

7. $\dfrac{x^2 + 4x + 3a}{x^2 + 2x + a} = 1 + \dfrac{2(x+a)}{x^2 + 2x + a}$. Thus $\dfrac{x + a}{x^2 + 2x + a}$ must also have $(-\infty, \infty)$ as its range. The roots of the denominator are $-1 \pm \sqrt{1-a}$, whence $a < 1$. For $0 < a < 1$, $-1 - \sqrt{1-a} < -a < -1 + \sqrt{1-a}$ and a sketch of the graph is given by

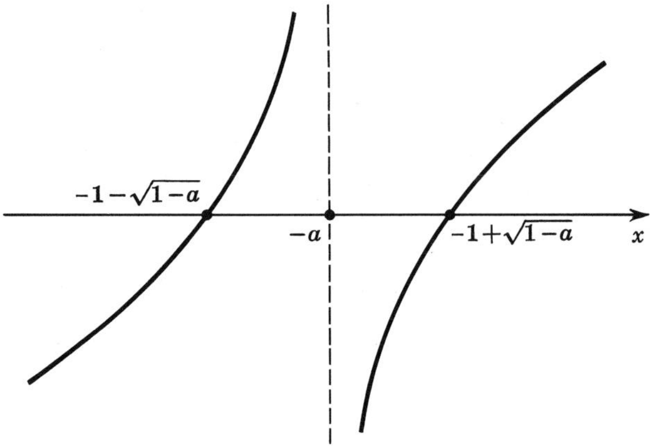

For $a < 0$, the graph is

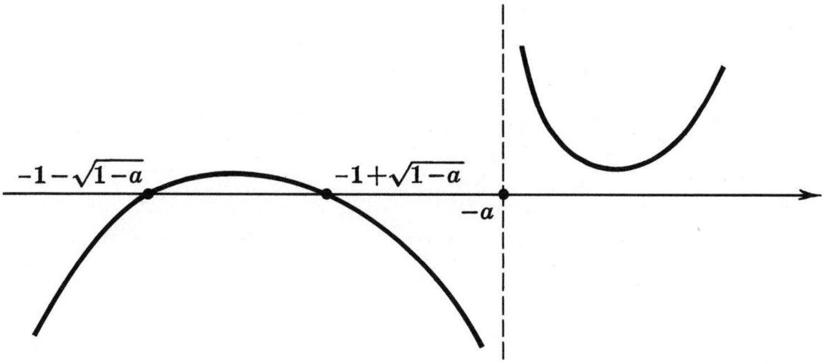

For this case, we would have to check to see if the minimum value can be $\leq$ the maximum value.

9. Locate a point P within a polygon $A_1A_2 \cdots A_n$ such that $A_1P^2 + A_2P^2 + \cdots + A_nP^2$ is a minimum. If coordinates of P are (x,y) and of A_r, (x_r,y_r), then

$$x = (x_1 + x_2 + \cdots + x_n)/n, \qquad y = (y_1 + y_2 + \cdots + y_n)/n.$$

11. Assume that G does not vanish between two consecutive zeros of F and obtain a contradiction. Note that $\frac{F}{G}$ and its derivative $D\frac{F}{G} = \frac{GF' - G'F}{G^2}$ are continuous in the interval. Then by Rolle's theorem, $GF' - G'F$ must vanish in the interval.

13.
$$a(x) = \frac{dv(x)}{dt} = \frac{dv(x)}{dx}\frac{dx}{dt} = \frac{dv(x)^2/2}{dx} = F(x).$$

Thus
$$\frac{v(x)^2}{2} = \text{an antiderivative of } F(x).$$

15.
$$ma = \frac{-mgR^2}{r^2},$$

or (using Exercise 13),
$$\frac{dv(r)^2}{dr} = \frac{-2gR^2}{r^2}.$$

Thus
$$v(r)^2 = \frac{2gR^2}{r} + \text{const.}$$

Since $v(R) = v_0$,
$$v_0^2 - v(r)^2 = 2gR - \frac{2gR^2}{r}.$$

At the maximum distance, $v(r) = 0$, whence
$$\frac{2gR^2}{r} = 2gR\left(1 - \frac{P}{100}\right) + r_{\max} = \frac{R}{1 - \frac{P}{100}}.$$

Note that $r_{\max} = \infty$ for $P = 100$. Thus escape velocity $= \sqrt{2gR}$. (This example includes Exercise 14 as a special case.)

CHAPTER 7

SECTION 1, PART I

3. Any finite set. $a_n = k^2(1 - 1/n)$. Any finite set. $a_n = k^2/n$.

5. $\text{l.u.b.}S = \max_n a_n$; $\text{g.l.b.}S = \min_n a_n$.

SECTION 1, PART II

1. a. $a_n = \sqrt{2\sqrt{2 \cdots \sqrt{2\sqrt{2}}}} < \sqrt{2\sqrt{2 \cdots \sqrt{2\sqrt{4}}}} = 2.$

   b. $a_n = 2^{2^{-1}+2^{-2}+\cdots+2^{-n}} = 2^{1-2^{-n}}$; thus $2 = \text{l.u.b.}S$.

3. a. $a_n = \sqrt{2+\sqrt{2+\cdots+\sqrt{2}}} < \sqrt{2+\sqrt{2+\cdots+\sqrt{4}}} = 2.$

b. $a^2_{n+1} - 4 = a_n - 2$ or $2 - a_{n+1} = \dfrac{2-a_n}{2+a_{n+1}} < \dfrac{2-a_n}{2}$. Thus

$$2 - a_{n+1} < \frac{2-a_1}{2^n} \quad \text{and} \quad 2 = \text{l.u.b.}S.$$

SECTION 2, PART I

1. a. $\dfrac{63}{4}, \dfrac{87}{4}$ b. $\dfrac{275}{16}, \dfrac{323}{16}$.

3. a. $\dfrac{7}{16}, \dfrac{15}{16}$ b. $\dfrac{175}{256}, \dfrac{207}{256}$.

5. a. $\dfrac{61}{144}, \dfrac{49}{36}$ b. .55, 1.02.

SECTION 2, PART II

1.

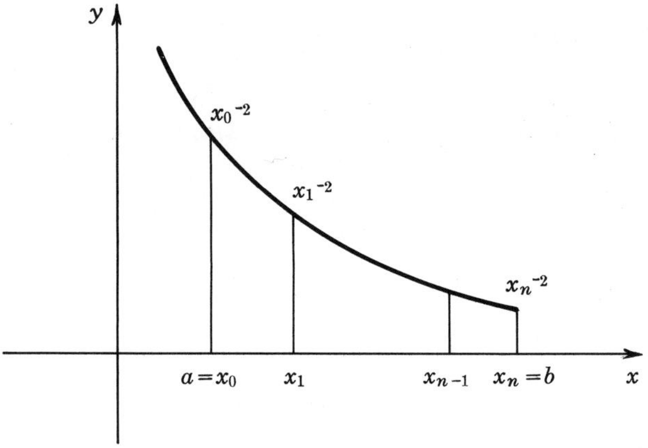

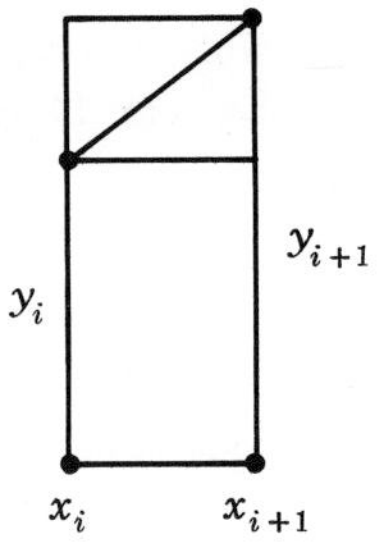

Consider the $(i + 1)^n$ interval $[x_i, x_{i+1}]$.

$$I_i = y_i(x_{i+1} - x_i),\ C_i = y_{i+1}(x_{i+1} - x_i).\ \text{Now}$$

$$x_i(x_{i+1} - x_i) < \frac{x_i + x_{i+1}}{2}(x_{i+1} - x_i) < x_{i+1}(x_{i+1} - x_i) \quad \text{or}$$

$$I_{i+1} < \frac{x_{i+1}^2 - x_i^2}{2} < C_{i+1}.$$

Letting $i = 0, 1, 2, \cdots$,

$$I_1 < \frac{x_1^2 - a^2}{2} < C_1,$$

$$I_2 < \frac{x_2^2 - x_1^2}{2} < C_2,$$

$$\vdots$$

$$I_n < \frac{b^2 - x^2_{n-1}}{2} < C_n.$$

Now adding up,

$$I(P) = I_1 + I_2 + \cdots + I_n < \frac{b^2 - a^2}{2} < C_1 + C_2 + \cdots + C_n = C(P).$$

3.

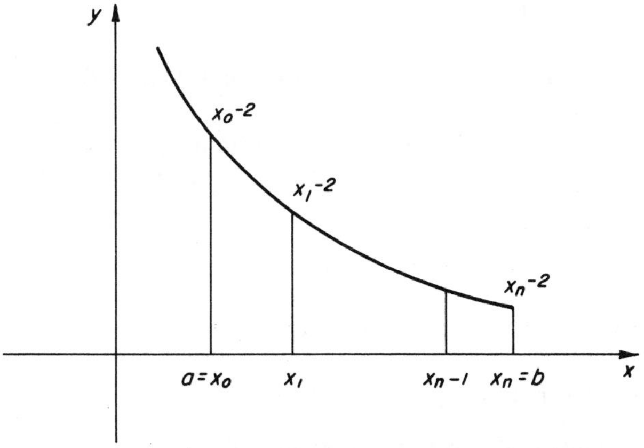

$$I(P) = \frac{b - a}{n}(x_1^{-2} + x_2^{-2} + \cdots + x_n^{-2}),$$

$$C(P) = \frac{b - a}{n}(x_0^{-2} + x_1^{-2} + \cdots + x_{n-1}^{-2}).$$

In the $(i + 1)$st interval,

$$I_{i+1} = \frac{x_{i+1} - x_i}{x^2_{i+1}} < \frac{x_{i+1} - x_i}{x_{i+1}x_i} < \frac{x_{i+1} - x_i}{x_i^2} = C_{i+1}.$$

Thus,

$$I_1 < \frac{1}{a} - \frac{1}{x_1} < C_1,$$

$$I_2 < \frac{1}{x_1} - \frac{1}{x_2} < C_2,$$

$$\vdots$$

$$I_n < \frac{1}{x_{n-1}} - \frac{1}{b} < C_n.$$

Now adding up

$$I(P) = I_1 + I_2 + \cdots + I_n < \frac{1}{a} - \frac{1}{b} < C_1 + C_2 + \cdots + C_n = C(P).$$

SECTION 3, PART I

1. $a^2n(n + 1)(2n + 1)/6 + abn(n + 1) + b^2n$

3. $n(n + 1)(n + 2)/3$

5. $[F(1) - F(0)] + [F(2) - F(1)] + \cdots + [F(n) - F(n - 1)] = F(n) - F(0).$

SECTION 3, PART II

1. $\sum_{i=1}^{n} i(i + 1)(i + 2) \cdots (i + r - 1) = n(n + 1)(n + 2) \cdots (n + r)/(r + 1).$

3. $n(n + 1)(n + 2)(n + 3)(n + 4)/5 + an(n + 1)(n + 2)(n + 3)/4$
$+ bn(n + 1)(n + 2)/3 + cn(n + 1)/2.$

SECTION 4, PART I

1. -1.75, .25.
3. .5, 2.5.
5. -5.56, -2.78.
7. -1.83, -1.08.
9. .55, 1.02.

SECTION 4, PART II

1. By definition of upper and lower integrals,

$$S(P) \leq \underline{\int_a^b} f \leq \frac{b^2 - a^2}{2} \leq \overline{\int_a^b} f \leq T(P).$$

Since by **7.14**, the upper integral equals the lower integral, they must both $=$ $(b^2 - a^2)/2$.

3. See (1) above.
5. 0, 1.

7. Since $S_f(P) \leq S_g(P)$, $\underline{\int_a^b} f \leq \underline{\int_a^b} g$ and similarly for the upper integral.

SECTION 5, PART I

3. Since $\int_a^b x^3\,dx = \dfrac{b^4 - a^4}{4}$, the area $= 20$.

SECTION 5, PART II

1. yes, continuous.

3. yes, continuous.

5. no, upper integral $= 1$, lower integral $= -1$.

SECTION 6, PART I

1. 21.

3. 8.

5. 582.

7. $-119/3$.

9. $14/3$.

11. 2

SECTION 6, PART II

1. $2\int_0^1 x\,dx = 1$.

3. 22; break up interval $[-2,4]$ to $[-2,-1] \cup [-1,1] \cup [1,4]$

SECTION 7, PART I

1. 2.

3. 15.

5. $136/3$.

7. 10.1.

9. $32/3$.

SECTION 7, PART II

1. $49/4$. $x^3 - x = x(x-1)(x+1)$;

$$\int_{-2}^{3} |x^3 - x|\,dx = \int_{-2}^{-1} (x - x^3)\,dx + \int_{-1}^{0} (x^3 - x)\,dx + \int_{0}^{1} (x - x^3)\,dx + \int_{1}^{3} (x^3 - x)\,dx.$$

3. $I(P) = [n](n + 1 - n) = n$. Using the partition $\{n, n + 1 - \epsilon, n + 1\}$, we see that

$$[n](n + 1 - \epsilon - n) + [n + 1](n + 1 - n - 1 + \epsilon) = n + \epsilon$$

is an upper sum $C(P)$ for every $\epsilon > 0$. Therefore

$$\int_n^{n+1} [x]\,dx = n.$$

SECTION 8, PART I

1. $14/3$.

3. 0 (by odd symmetry) or by integration.

5. -14.

7. $1/3$.

9. 0 (by odd symmetry) or by integration.

11. $16/3025$.

13. 0

15. $\frac{4}{3}(1 + \sqrt{x})^{3/2} + c$ (Let $y = \sqrt{x}$).

SECTION 8, PART II

1. $\frac{2}{3}\sqrt{x+1)^3} - 2\sqrt{x+1} + c$; either note that $\dfrac{x}{\sqrt{1+x}} = \dfrac{1+x}{\sqrt{1+x}} - \dfrac{1}{\sqrt{1+x}}$, or else let $1 + x = y$ or y^2.

3. $\dfrac{8 - 4\sqrt{2}}{3}$; let $x = y^2$ and then use Exercise 1.

5. $y = x^{5/2}$ is a multivalued function.

For $\quad -1 \leq y \leq 0, \quad y = -\sqrt{x^5}$,

for $\quad 0 \leq y \leq 1, \quad y = \sqrt{x^5}$.

Then

$$I = -\tfrac{5}{2}\int_1^0 x^{3/2}\,dx + \tfrac{5}{2}\int_0^1 x^{3/2}\,dx = 2.$$

SECTION 9, PART I

1.
$$\int_a^b x^n\,dx = (b-a)c^n = \frac{b^{n+1} - a^{n+1}}{n+1}.$$
$$c = \left\{\frac{b^{n+1} - a^{n+1}}{(n+1)(b-a)}\right\}^{1/n}.$$

3. Break up the interval $[a,b]$ in subintervals in which $F(x)$ has the same sign.

SECTION 9, PART II

1. Let m and M denote the smallest and largest values, respectively, of $f(x)$ in $[a,b]$. Then $mp(x) \leq f(x)p(x) \leq Mp(x)$ in $[a,b]$ and by Exercise I-2,
$$m\int_a^b p(x)\,dx \leq \int_a^b f(x)p(x)\,dx \leq M\int_a^b p(x)\,dx$$
Hence
$$m \leq \int_a^b f(x)p(x)\,dx \Big/ \int_a^b p(x)\,dx \leq M \text{ and } \int_a^b f(x)p(x)\,dx \Big/ \int_a^b p(x)\,dx = f(c)$$
for some c in $[a,b]$ by **7.25**.

REVIEW, PART I

7. $2 + 3/\sqrt{2}$.

9. $-4/5$, $-\frac{1}{5}[(1 + 5x - x^5)^5]_0^1$.

11. $2[(ad+b)^{3/2} - (ac+b)^{3/2}]/3a$

13. $(a^2 - 1)^{n+1}/2(n+1)$.

15. $\dfrac{2^{n-1} - 1}{(n-1)2^n a^{2n-2}}$.

17. $\dfrac{(a+1)^{2n+1} - (a-1)^{2n+1}}{2n+1}$ (integrand is $(x+a)^{2n}$).

19. 1. 21. No limit.

23. $f(a) = 0$:

$$D \int_a^x f(t)\,dt = f(x)$$

$$\int_a^x (Df)(t)dt = f(t)|_a^x = f(x) - f(a)$$

Review, Part II

1. a. $(x^3 - 1)/3$. b. $\dfrac{(x^2-a)^4 - (x-a)^4}{4}$.

c. $\frac{3}{4}(x^{8/3} - a^{4/3})$. d. $6x(6x^2 - 3)$.

e. $g'(x)f(g(x))$;

$$\frac{d}{dx} H(g(x)) = \frac{d}{dg(x)} H(g(x)) \frac{dg(x)}{dx} \text{ (chain rule).}$$

f. $\dfrac{3}{(3x)^4 + 1}$. g. $2x\sqrt{1 - x^4}$.

h. $\dfrac{3x^2}{1+x^9} - \dfrac{2x}{1+x^6}$;

$$\int_{x^2}^{x^3} \frac{1}{1+t^3}\,dt = \int_0^{x^3} \frac{1}{1+t^3}\,dt - \int_0^{x^2} \frac{1}{1+t^3}\,dt.$$

3. The graph of x *vs.* u consists of two sections with a discontinuity at $x = 0$. To make the change of variables properly, we first break up the interval of integration, i.e.,

$$I = \int_{-1}^{0} \frac{1}{1+x^2}\,dx + \int_0^1 \frac{1}{1+x^2}\,dx.$$

Now if we let

$$x = 1/u,$$

we obtain

$$I = \lim_{x\to 0-} \int_{-1}^{1/x} \frac{1}{1+u^2}\,du + \lim_{x\to 0+} \int_{1/x}^{1} \frac{1}{1+u^2}\,du.$$

The integrals

$$\int_{-1}^{-\infty} \frac{1}{1+u^2}\,du \quad \text{and} \quad \int_{\infty}^{1} \frac{1}{1+u^2}\,du$$

are called *improper integrals* and will be treated subsequently.

5. a. Consider $f = \begin{cases} 1 & \text{if } x \text{ rational} \\ -1 & \text{if } x \text{ irrational.} \end{cases}$

b. Since $-|f(x)| \leq f(x) \leq |f(x)|$, $-\int_a^b |f(x)|\,dx \leq \int_a^b f(x)\,dx \leq \int_a^b |f(x)|\,dx$ (See Exercise 7, Section 3, Part II).

7. $\int_0^{1/2} \frac{1}{\sqrt{1-x^n}}\,dx > \int_0^{1/2} dx = \frac{1}{2}$,

$$\int_0^{1/2} \frac{1}{\sqrt{1-x^n}}\,dx < \int_0^{1/2} \frac{1}{\sqrt{1-x}}\,dx = 2 - \sqrt{2} = 0.586.$$

9. Let

$$F(x) = ax^3 + bx^2 + cx + d,$$

then

$$F'(x) = 3ax^2 + 2bx + c$$

and

$$F(x) - F'(x) = ax^3 + x^2(b - 3a) + x(c - 2b) + d - c = -x^3.$$

Thus

$$a = -1, \quad b - 3a = 0, \quad c - 2b = 0, \quad d - c = 0$$

and

$$F(x) = -x^3 - 3x^2 - 6x - 6.$$

11. If

$$a\left(\frac{m}{n}\right)^2 + 2b\left(\frac{m}{n}\right) + c \geq 0.$$

for all m/n, then the discriminant of the quadratic equation

$$ax^2 + 2bx + c = 0$$

must be ≤ 0 (cannot have any real distinct roots). Thus

$$b^2 \leq ac.$$

Now let

$$a = \int_a^b F^2\,dx, \quad c = \int_a^b G^2\,dx, \quad b = \int_a^b F(x)G(x)\,dx.$$

13.

$$\int_0^1 \frac{1}{1+x^n}\,dx < \int_0^1 dx = 1.$$

$$\int_0^1 \frac{1}{1+x^n}\,dx \cdot \int_0^1 (1+x^n)\,dx \geq \left[\int_0^1 dx\right]^2 = 1$$

or

$$\int_0^1 \frac{1}{1+x^n}\,dx > \frac{1}{\int_0^1 (1+x^n)\,dx} = \frac{n+1}{n+2}.$$

CHAPTER 8

SECTION 1, PART I

1. $f(-3) = f(3) = 18$ max.; $f(0) = 9$ min.

3. $g(-1) = 7$ max.; $g(2) = -20$ min.

5. $F(3) = 3$ max.; $F(0) = 0$ min.

7. **a.** No. **b.** Yes; 1, 0. **c.** No.

9. $-1, 1$; No.

SECTION 1, PART II

1. Max. $= 0$ at $x = 0, 1, 2, 3$; lower bound $= -1$ which can be approached arbitrarily closely; points of discontinuity at $x = 1, 2, 3$.

3. By considering the area under the curve $y = f(x)$, the result is geometrically obvious. For an analytic proof, let mk denote the least integral multiple of $k \geq a$. Then

$$\int_a^{a+k} f(x)\,dx = \int_a^{mk} f(x)\,dx + \int_{mk}^{a+k} f(x)\,dx = \int_a^{mk} f(x)\,dx$$

$$+ \int_{(m-1)k}^{a} f(x)\,dx = \int_{(m-1)k}^{mk} f(x)\,dx = \int_0^k f(x)\,dx.$$

$$\int_0^k f(y+a)\,dy = \int_0^k f(y)\,dy.$$

5. If F took on another value a different from 1/2, then by **7.3** it would also have to take on all values between 1/2 and a which contradicts the hypothesis.

SECTION 2, PART I

1. $3, \frac{3}{2}, 1, \frac{3}{4}, \frac{3}{5}; 0.$

3. $\frac{1}{2}, \frac{4}{5}, 1, \frac{8}{7}, \frac{5}{4}; 2.$

5. $-1, \frac{1}{4}, -\frac{1}{9}, \frac{1}{16}, -\frac{1}{25}; 0.$

7. $-\frac{1}{3}, \frac{1}{3}, \frac{7}{11}, \frac{7}{9}, \frac{23}{27}; 1.$

9. $0, \frac{7}{12}, \frac{5}{6}, \frac{39}{40}, \frac{16}{15}; \frac{3}{2}.$

11. $\frac{4}{3}, -\frac{8}{3}, -\frac{108}{77}, -\frac{64}{63}, -\frac{500}{621}; 0.$

13. $1/\sqrt{2}, 1/\sqrt{5}, 1/\sqrt{10}, 1/\sqrt{17}, 1/\sqrt{26}; 0.$

SECTION 2, PART II

1. Just consider $a_n = (-1)^n$. Then $\lim_{n\to\infty} |a_n| = 1$, but $\lim_{n\to\infty} a_n$ doesn't exist.

3. limit $= 0$, if $|k| < 1$; limit $= 1$, if $k = 1$.

5. 0; multiply top and bottom by $\sqrt{n+2} + \sqrt{n+1}$.

7. 0; note that $a_{n+1} = a_n \left(\dfrac{10{,}000}{n+1}\right) < \dfrac{a_n}{2}$ for $n \geq 20{,}000$.

9. 0; note that $0 \leq a_n = \left(1 - \dfrac{1}{n}\right)\left(1 - \dfrac{2}{n}\right) \cdots \left(1 - \dfrac{n-2}{n}\right)\left(\dfrac{1}{n}\right) \leq \dfrac{1}{n}.$

Now use squeeze theorem **8.11.**

11. 0; note that $\dfrac{n}{(n+n)^2} \leq a_n \leq \dfrac{n}{(n+1)^2}.$

SECTION 3, PART I

1. 9.

3. $a^4/4 + a^3 + a^2.$

SECTION 3, PART II

1. i^p can be expressed in the form

$$i^p = a_1 i + a_2 i(i+1) + a_3 i(i+1)(i+2) + \cdots + a_p i(i+1)(i+2)\cdots(i+p-1)$$

where $a_p = 1$ by comparing coefficients of i^p. By letting $i = -1$, we can obtain a_1; by letting $i = -2$, we then get a_2; by letting $i = -3$, we then get a_3, etc. Since the left-hand side and the right-hand side are polynomials of the same degree p which takes on the same values for $-i = 0, 1, 2, \cdots, (p-1)$, they must then be identical. It now follows from Exercise II-1, Section 3, Chapter 7, that

$$\sum_{i=1}^{n} i^p = \frac{n(n+1)\cdots(n+p)}{p+1} + \frac{a_{p-1}n(n+1)\cdots(n+p-1)}{p} + \cdots.$$

Now divide by n^{p+1} and let $n \to \infty$ to obtain $\frac{1}{p+1}$. (All the terms but the first one on the right-hand side will have limit zero.)

3. a. $\lim_{n\to\infty} \sum_{i=0}^{n} \frac{1}{n+i} = \lim_{n\to\infty} \sum_{i=0}^{n} \frac{1}{1+i/n} \cdot \frac{1}{n} = \int_0^1 \frac{1}{1+x}\,dx.$

b. $\lim_{n\to\infty} \sum_{i=1}^{2n} \frac{n}{n^2+i^2} = \lim_{n\to\infty} \sum_{i=1}^{2n} \frac{1}{1+(i/n)^2} \cdot \frac{1}{n} = \int_0^2 \frac{1}{1+x^2}\,dx$

Section 4, Part I

1. $|2x^2 - 2y^2| = 2|x-y|\,|x+y| \le 12|x-y| < \epsilon$. Thus $|x-y| < \frac{\epsilon}{12}$ or $\delta(\epsilon) = \epsilon/12$.

3. $|ax^n - ay^n| = a|x-y|\,|x^{n-1} + x^{n-2}y + \cdots + xy^{n-2} + y^{n-1}| \le ak|x-y|$

where $k = n[\max(|c|,|d|)]^{n-1}$. Thus $\delta(\epsilon) = \frac{\epsilon}{ak}$.

5. $|\sqrt{x} - \sqrt{y}| = \frac{|x-y|}{|\sqrt{x}+\sqrt{y}|} < \frac{|x-y|}{2}$. Thus $\delta(\epsilon) = \frac{\epsilon}{2}$.

7. $\left|\frac{1}{x} - \frac{1}{y}\right| = \frac{|x-y|}{|xy|} < \epsilon$. Since x and y can be arbitrarily small, the value of $\delta(\epsilon)$ will depend on x and y.

9. Let $y = x - 1$. Then we consider the function $1 + 2/y$ in $0 < y < 1$. Now continue as in Exercise 7.

Section 4, Part II

1. $|\sqrt{x} - \sqrt{y}| = \frac{|x-y|}{\sqrt{x}+\sqrt{y}} \le \frac{|x-y|}{\sqrt{|x-y|}} = \sqrt{|x-y|}$, since $|\sqrt{x}+\sqrt{y}| \ge \sqrt{|x-y|}$ (just square out). For $\sqrt{|x-y|} < \epsilon$, we take $\delta(\epsilon) = \epsilon^2$.

3. $$|\sqrt{1-x^2} - \sqrt{1-y^2}| = \frac{|x+y|\,|x-y|}{\sqrt{1-x}\sqrt{1+x} + \sqrt{1-y}\sqrt{1+y}} \le \frac{2|x-y|}{\sqrt{1-x}+\sqrt{1-y}}$$
$$\le \frac{2|x-y|}{\sqrt{|x-y|}} = 2\sqrt{|x-y|}.$$

Note that $\sqrt{1-x} + \sqrt{1-y} \ge \sqrt{|(1-x)-(1-y)|}$.

Thus $\delta(\epsilon) = \frac{\epsilon^2}{4}$.

5. Since f is continuous, for any k in $[a,b]$, there exists a δ such that $|f(x) - f(k)| < \epsilon$ for all x satisfying $|x-k| < \delta$. Now consider the graph of $f(x)$. $g(x)$ will be the polygonal figure obtained by connecting the indicated points in turn by line segments. It follows from the construction that $g(x)$ has the desired property.

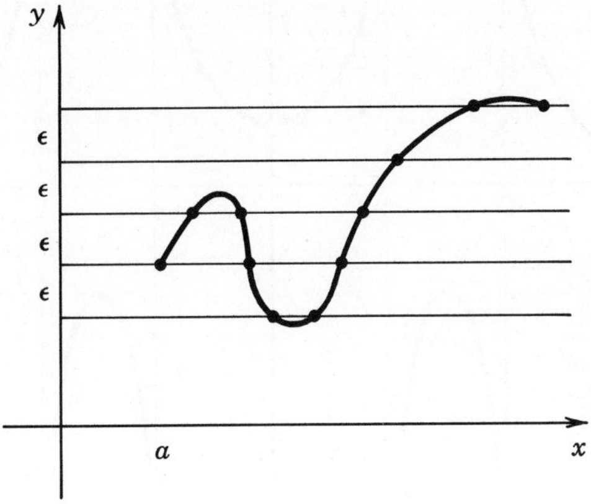

REVIEW, PART I

1. 1. **3.** 1. **5.** ∞.

7. **a.** $\frac{3}{5}, \frac{3}{5}, \frac{3}{5}$. **b.** Note that $u(n) \geq n$.

9. Dividing the intervale [0,1000] into [0,1], [1,2], [2,3], . . . , [999,1000], we get

$$S = \sum_{r=1}^{1000} r^{10} > \int_0^{1000} x^{10}\,dx > \sum_{r=0}^{999} r^{10} = S - 1000^{10}$$

or

$$1000^{10} + \frac{1000^{11}}{11} > S > \frac{1000^{11}}{11}.$$

11.
$$\int_0^{10} \frac{x\,dx}{x^3+16} = \int_0^1 \frac{x\,dx}{x^3+16} + \int_1^{10} \frac{x\,dx}{x^3+16}.$$

$$\int_0^1 \frac{x\,dx}{x^3+16} < \int_0^1 \frac{x\,dx}{16} = \frac{1}{32}; \qquad \int_1^{10} \frac{x\,dx}{x^3+16} < \int_1^{10} \frac{x\,dx}{x^3} = \frac{9}{10}.$$

Thus

$$\int_0^{10} \frac{x\,dx}{x^3+16} < \frac{1}{32} + \frac{9}{10} = \frac{149}{160}.$$

A smaller upper bound can be obtained by breaking the interval into $[0,a]$ and $[a,10]$, making the same approximation and then minimizing with respect to a.

13. That $\sqrt{x}$ is uniformly continuous in [1,10] follows from Exercise 5, Section 4. That $\sqrt[3]{x}$ is uniformly continuous follows from the previous exercise. Let $\delta_1(\epsilon)$ and $\delta_2(\epsilon)$ be appropriate δ functions for $\sqrt{x}$ and $\sqrt[3]{x}$, respectively. Then since

$$|\sqrt[3]{x} + \sqrt{x} - \sqrt[3]{x} - \sqrt{x}| \leq |\sqrt[3]{x} - \sqrt[3]{y}| + |\sqrt{x} - \sqrt{y}|,$$

an appropriate

$$\delta(\epsilon) = \min\left\{\delta_1\left(\frac{\epsilon}{2}\right), \delta_2\left(\frac{\epsilon}{2}\right)\right\}.$$

15.

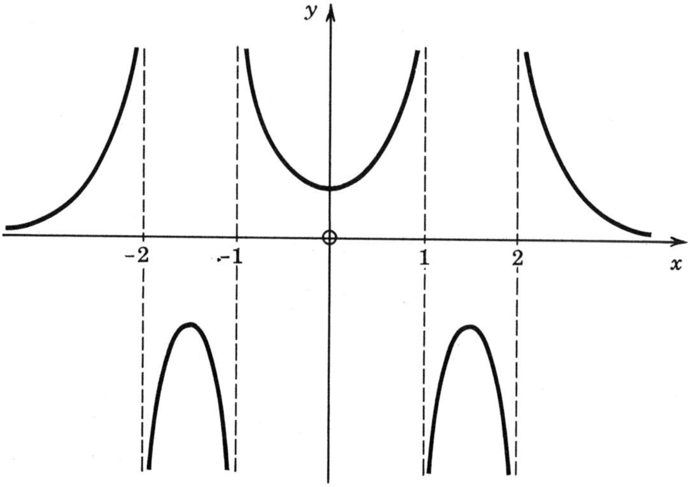

a. Continuous; $G(0) = \frac{1}{2}$, min; no max.
b. Discontinuous at $x = 1$; $G(0) = \frac{1}{2}$, min; no max.
c. Continuous; $G(0) = \frac{1}{2}$, min; $G(\pm\frac{1}{2}) = \frac{32}{45}$, max.
d. Discontinuous at $x = 1, 2$. $G(\sqrt{5/2}) = -8/9$, max.

REVIEW, PART II

1. If $\dfrac{a_1 + a_2 + \cdots + a_n}{n} \geq \dfrac{a_1 + a_2 + \cdots + a_{n+1}}{n+1}$,
then $a_1 + a_2 + \cdots + a_n \geq na_{n+1}$. This holds if $a_1 \geq a_2 \geq a_3 \cdots \geq a_{n+1}$. Similarly, if all the inequality signs are reversed.

3. $\displaystyle\sum_{n=1}^{k} \frac{1}{n(n+1)(n+2)} = \frac{1}{2}\sum_{n=1}^{k}\left\{\frac{1}{n(n+1)} - \frac{1}{(n+1)(n+2)}\right\} = \frac{1}{4} - \frac{1}{2(k+1)(k+2)}.$
(See also Chapter 7, Section 3, Exercise II-2.) Thus limit $= \frac{1}{4}$.

5. By the binomial theorem,

$$\left(1 + \frac{1}{n^2}\right)^n = 1 + \binom{n}{1}n^{-2} + \binom{n}{2}n^{-4} + \cdots + \binom{n}{n}n^{-2n}$$

$$= 1 + \frac{1}{n} + \frac{1 - \frac{1}{n}}{n^2 \cdot 2!} + \frac{\left(1 - \frac{1}{n}\right)\left(1 - \frac{2}{n}\right)}{n^3 \cdot 3!} + \cdots$$

$$+ \frac{\left(1 - \frac{1}{n}\right)\left(1 - \frac{2}{n}\right)\cdots\left(1 - \frac{n-1}{n}\right)}{n^n \cdot n!}.$$

Thus

$$1 \leq \left(1 + \frac{1}{n^2}\right)^n \leq 1 + \frac{1}{n} + \frac{1}{n^2} + \frac{1}{n^3} + \cdots + \frac{1}{n^n} + \cdots = \frac{1}{1 - \frac{1}{n}}.$$

Now let $n \to \infty$ to give limit $= 1$ (Theorem **8.11**).

7. Follows from

$$\begin{aligned}|F(x)G(x) - F(y)G(y)| &= |(F(x)G(x) - F(y)G(x)) + (F(y)G(x) - F(y)G(y))| \\ &\le |G(x)|\cdot|F(x) - F(y)| + |F(y)|\cdot|G(x) - G(y)| \\ &\le |F(x) - F(y)| \cdot \max|G(x)| + |G(x) - G(y)| \cdot \max|F(y)|.\end{aligned}$$

CHAPTER 9

Section 1, Part I

1. 20.
3. $\frac{32}{3}$.
5. $\frac{64}{3}$.
7. $\frac{4}{3}$.
9. $\frac{1}{2}$.
11. $\frac{8}{3}$.

Section 1, Part II

1. Tangent line at $(0,-3)$ is $y = 4x - 3$. By symmetry,
$$A = 2\int_0^2 [(4x - 3) - (-x^2 + 4x - 3)]\,dx = 16/3.$$

$$A = 4\int_0^a \sqrt{a^2x^6 - x^8}\,dx = 4\int_0^a x^3\sqrt{a^2 - x^2}\,dx$$
Let $a^2 - x^2 = y^2$, giving
$$A = \int_0^a 4y(a^2 - y^2)\,dy = a^4.$$

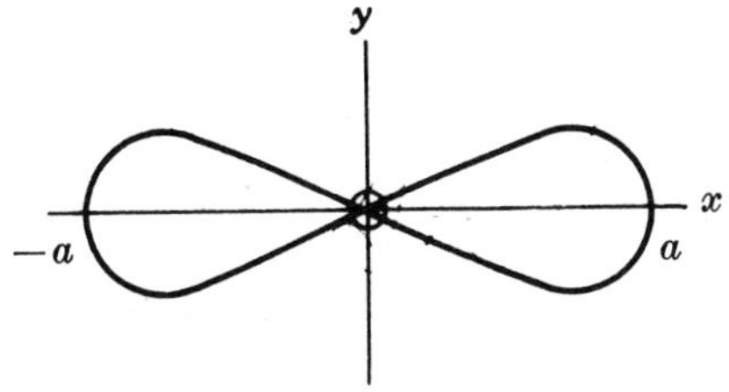

Symmetric with respect to both axis and tangent to x-axis at the origin.

Section 2, Part I

1. $32\pi/5$.
3. 8π.
5. $2\pi/3$.
7. $\pi/30$.
9. $31\pi/160$.
11. $\pi h(R^2 + Rr + r^2)/3$.
13. $32\pi p^3/15$.

Section 2, Part II

1. Note that volume $= \int_0^h A(x)\,dx$
3. Volume = volume of a sphere $\times$ the ratio of the area of a square to the area of its incircle
$$= \frac{4\pi r^3}{3}\cdot\frac{4r^2}{\pi r^2} = \frac{16}{3}r^3.$$
5. a. $A(h) = \pi(r^2 - h^2)$ for $-r \le h \le r$
$$V = \frac{2r}{6}(0 + 0 + 4\pi r^2) = \frac{4}{3}\pi r^3$$

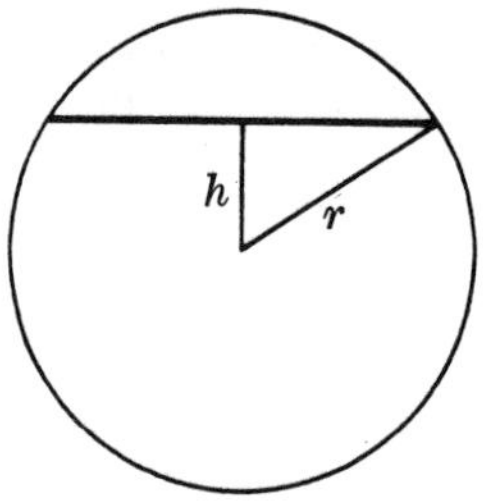

b. $V = \frac{r-h}{6}(0 + \pi(r^2 - h^2) + 4\pi(r^2 - (r+h)^2/4))$

$V = \pi(r-h)^2(2r+h)/3.$

c.

$$\frac{A(x)}{B_2} = \frac{(H-x)^2}{H^2}, \qquad \frac{B_1}{B_2} = \frac{(H-h)^2}{H^2}$$

$$V = \frac{h}{6}(B_1 + B_2 + 4A(h/2))$$

$$= \frac{h}{3}(B_1 + B_2 + \sqrt{B_1B_2})$$

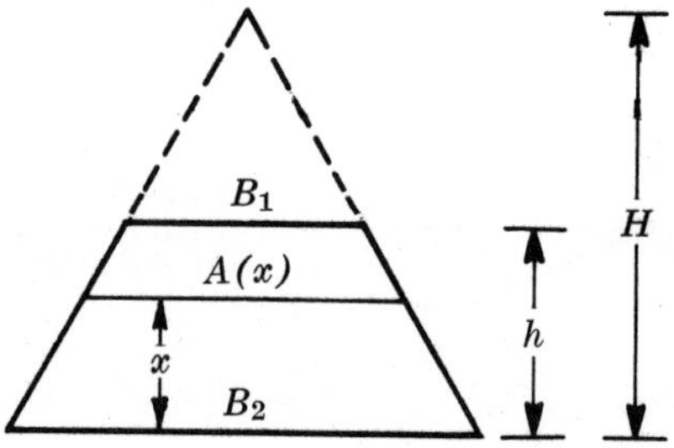

d. same as c (with $B_1 = 0$).

Section 3, Part I

1. 72 in/lbs.
3. 84,375 $\pi/4$ ft/lbs.
5. $29k/72$; 0.
7. $1{,}125\pi$ ft/lbs.
9. 37.5 ft³, 723,000 ft. lbs.

Section 4, Part I

1. $\frac{2}{27}(37^{3/2} - 1)$
3. 14/3
5. 134/27.

SECTION 4, PART II

1.
$$\begin{aligned} 3ay^2 &= x(x-a)^2 \\ 6ayy' &= (x-a)^2 + 2x(x-a) = (x-a)(3x-a) \\ (1+y'^2)^{1/2} &= \left\{\frac{36a^2y^2 + (x-a)^2(3x-a)^2}{36a^2y^2}\right\}^{1/2} \\ &= \frac{\sqrt{3}}{6\sqrt{a}}\left(3\sqrt{x} + \frac{a}{\sqrt{x}}\right) \end{aligned}$$

$$L = 2\int_0^a \sqrt{1+y'^2}\,dx = 4a/\sqrt{3}.$$

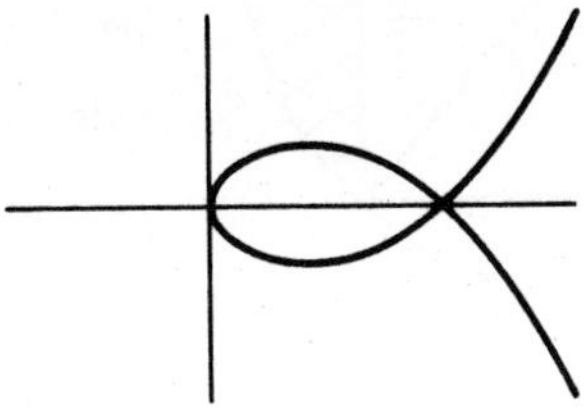

SECTION 5, PART I

1. 1.10. **3.** 3.00. **5.** 11.35.

SECTION 6, PART I

1. 1.10. **3.** 2.31. **5.** 3.15. **7.** 3.140. **9.** 1.20 a^2.

SECTION 6, PART II

1. Let $F(x) = A + 2Bx + 3Cx^2 + 4Dx^3$. It then follows that

$$\begin{aligned} \int_a^b F(x)\,dx &= (Ax + Bx^2 + Cx^3 + Dx^4)\Big]_a^b \\ &= (b-a)\,(A + B(b+a) + C(b^2 + ba + a^2) + D(b^3 + b^2a + ba^2 + a^3)) \\ &= \frac{b-a}{6}\left\{(A + 2Ba + 3Ca^2 + 4Da^3) + (A + 2Bb + 3Cb^2 + 4Db^3)\right. \\ &\qquad \left. + 4\left(A + 2B\left(\frac{a+b}{2}\right) + 3C\left(\frac{a+b}{2}\right)^2 + 4D\left(\frac{a+b}{2}\right)^3\right)\right\}. \end{aligned}$$

REVIEW, PART I

1. $\frac{125}{6}$. **3.** $4 - 2\sqrt{3}$. **5.** $16\pi\sqrt{pb^5}/5$.

7. $\pi a^5/80p^2$.

9. *Hint:* Show that the volume here is to the volume of Exercise 14 as the area of a regular pentagon is to the area of a square (of same length of edge).

11. $104\pi a^3/105$; same by symmetry.

13. 2.41. **15.** 91/27.

PART II

1. Eq. of circle: $(x - h)^2 + y^2 = h^2 - 200h + 6400 = (h - 40)(h - 160)$
Area of circular cross-section $= \pi(h^2 - 200h + 6400)$.
Vol. $= \int_0^{40} A(h)\, dh = \int_0^{40} \pi(h^2 - 200h + 6400)\, dh$.

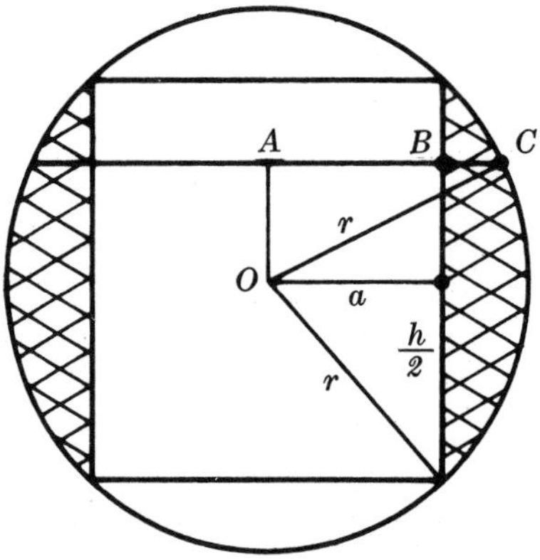

Cross-section through axis of cylinder.

Area of cross-section x above center
$= \pi AC^2 - \pi AB^2 = \pi(r^2 - x^2) - \pi a^2$
$= \pi(r^2 - x^2) - \pi\left(r^2 - \frac{h^2}{4}\right)$
$= \pi\left(\frac{h^2}{4} - x^2\right)$
$V = 2\int_0^{h/2} \pi\left(\frac{h^2}{4} - x^2\right) dx = \frac{\pi h^3}{6}$.
Thus V is independent of r; it only depends upon the height h. If $h = 2r$ (no hole), we get $V = \frac{4}{3}\pi r^3$; if $h = 0$ (all cut out), we get $V = 0$.

5. $\frac{2}{3}[(1 + a)^{3/2} - 1] = \int_0^a \sqrt{1 + F'(x)^2}\, dx$ where $y = F(x)$. Diff. both sides, yields $\sqrt{1 + a} = \sqrt{1 + F'(x)^2}$ or $F'(a) = \sqrt{a}$ (or $-\sqrt{a}$).
Thus, $F(a) = \frac{2}{3}a^{3/2} + C$ and $y = \frac{2}{3}x^{3/2} + C$.
7. If x feet of chain have been hauled up, the force necessary to pull up the next bit of chain is $(\rho(100 - x) + 500)$ lbs. Thus,
$$W = \int_0^{100} [\rho(100 - x) + 500]\, dx = (5000\,\rho + 50{,}000) \text{ ft lbs.}$$
9. $$\bar{d} = \frac{\int_0^a d^2\, dx}{a} = \frac{1}{a}\int_0^a [(h - x)^2 + k^2]\, dx.$$

CHAPTER 10

SECTION 2, PART I

1. $1, 2, 3, 4, -1, -2, -3, \frac{1}{2}, -\frac{1}{3}$.
3. $1, e, e^{-1}, e^{-3}, 2 + e^3, \pm\sqrt{5 - e^{-2}}$.
9. If $F(u) = \ln u + u$, then $F(1) > 0$, $F(1/e) < 0$. By continuity and monotonicity $(F'(u) > 0)$, there exists a unique root.
11. $\ln(-x)$.
13. Let $u = at$; $\int_a^{ax} \frac{1}{u}\, du = \ln(ax) - \ln a = \int_1^x \frac{1}{t}\, dt = \ln x$.

SECTION 2, PART II

1. Consider upper and lower sums for the integral $\int_1^m \frac{1}{x}\,dx$ obtained by dividing the interval $[1,m]$ into $m-1$ equal parts.
3. Differentiating yields: $\ln x = \ln x + 1 - 1$.
5. $\ln(m-1)! < \ln\left(\frac{m}{e}\right)^m e < \ln(m)!$, $\ln(m)! < \ln\left(\frac{m+1}{e}\right)^{m+1} e$,
$$\left(\frac{m+1}{e}\right)^{m+1} e > m! > \left(\frac{m}{e}\right)^m e$$
7. Integrating both sides between 0 and t yields
$$\ln(1+t) - \left(t - \frac{t^2}{2} + \cdots - \frac{t^{2n}}{2n}\right) = \int_0^t \frac{x^{2n}}{1+x}\,dx.$$
Now use
$$0 \le \int_0^t \frac{x^{2n}}{1+x}\,dx \le \int_0^t x^{2n}\,dx = \frac{t^{2n+1}}{2n+1}$$

SECTION 3, PART I

3. limit $= De^x]_{x=0} = e^0 = 1$.
5. $1 - e^{-2}$.
7. $F(-1) = -e^{-1}$, min; $F(-2) = -2e^{-2}$, pt. of infl.
9. $F(x) - F(0) = xF'(\theta)$, $0 < \theta < x$.
$e^x - 1 = xe^\theta \ge x$; similarly for $F = e^{-x}$.

SECTION 3, PART II

1. limit $= \int_0^1 e^{-ax}\,dx = \frac{1}{a}$.
3. $\frac{1}{1 - 1 + \frac{1}{2} - \frac{1}{6} + \frac{1}{24} - \frac{1}{120}} > e > 1 + 1 + \frac{1}{2} + \frac{1}{6} + \frac{1}{24} + \frac{1}{120}$.

SECTION 4, PART I

1. $2x^2e^{2x} + 2xe^{2x}$.
3. $-18xe^{-3x^2}(1 + e^{-3x^2})^2$.
5. $\ln|x^2 - 1| + \frac{2x}{x-1}$ $(x^2 \ne 1)$.
7. $\frac{2x}{\ln x} - \frac{x}{\ln^2 x}$.
9. $\frac{e^x}{e^x + 1}$.
11. $F(e^{-1}) = -e^{-1}$, min.
13. $F(0) = 1$, max, $F(\pm 1/a\sqrt{2}) = e^{-1/2}$, infl. pts.
15. $\frac{1 - e^{-10}}{5} \doteq \frac{1}{5}$.
17. $2e^{\sqrt{x}} + C$.
19. $\frac{x^3 + a^3 - a^3}{x + a} = x^2 - ax + a^2 - \frac{a^3}{x+a}$;
$$\int = \frac{x^3}{3} - \frac{ax^2}{2} + a^2x - a^3\ln(x+a) + C.$$
21. $\frac{\ln^2 x}{2}$.

SECTION 4, PART II

1. $e^x\exp(e^x)$, $(e^x + e^{2x})\exp(e^x)$.
3. $-e^x\exp(-e^x)$, $(e^{2x} - e^x)\exp(-e^x)$.

5. $\dfrac{1}{x\ln x}$.

7. $\ln f(x) = x\ln x; \dfrac{f'(x)}{f(x)} = \ln x + 1$ or $f'(x) = x^x(1 + \ln x)$.

9. $\ln f(x) = 4\ln(x^3 - 1) + 3\ln(\sqrt{x} + 1) + \frac{1}{2}\ln(e^{x^2} + 1) - \frac{1}{3}\ln(x^2 + 1)$.

$$\frac{f'(x)}{f(x)} = \frac{12x^2}{x^3 - 1} + \frac{3}{2\sqrt{x}(1 + \sqrt{x})} + \frac{xe^{x^2}}{e^{x^2} + 1} - \frac{2}{3}\frac{x}{x^2 + 1}.$$

11. $\ln\ln\ln x + C$.

13. $\int e^x e^{e^x} dx = e^{e^x} + C$.

Section 5, Part I

1. $\cosh x$, $\sinh x$.

3. $\operatorname{sech}^2 x$, $-2\operatorname{sech}^2 x\tanh x$.

5. $-\operatorname{csch} x \coth x$, $\dfrac{\cosh^2 x + 1}{\sinh^3 x}$ or $\operatorname{csch} x\coth^2 x + \operatorname{csch}^3 x$.

13. $-\operatorname{sech} x + C$.

15. $-(\operatorname{sech}^2 x)/2 + C$.

17. $\pi a^3(2 + \sinh 2)/4$.

Section 5, Part II

1. Let $x = y$ in **10.26.**

3. From Exercises 1 and 2, $\tanh 2x = \dfrac{\sinh 2x}{\cosh 2x} = \dfrac{2\sinh x\cosh x}{\cosh^2 x + \sinh^2 x} = \dfrac{2\tanh x}{1 + \tanh^2 x}$.

5. Set $y = 2x$ in **10.26** and then use Exercises 1 and 2.

7. Use Exercise 2. $\int \dfrac{\cosh 2x - 1}{2}\, dx = \dfrac{\sinh 2x}{4} - \dfrac{x}{2} + C$.

9. Use Exercise 4.

11. $\tanh x$ (use Exercise I-3).

Section 6, Part I

1. $\dfrac{-2\log_2 e}{5 - 2x}$.

3. $2x\log_{10}(3 + 2x^2) + \dfrac{4x^3\log_{10} e}{3 + 2x^2}$.

5. $\pi(\ln x + 1)^{\pi - 1}/x$.

7. $(1 + e)(1 + \sqrt{x})^e/2\sqrt{x}$.

9. $2^{2x}(2\ln 2)$.

11. $3/\ln 2$.

13. $990/\ln 10$.

15. Let $m = \log_a b$, $n = \log_b x$.
Then

$$b = a^m,\ x = b^n \text{ and } x = a^{mn}. \text{ Thus } mn = \log_a x = (\log_a b)(\log_b x).$$

Letting $x = a$, $1 = (\log_a b)(\log_b a)$.

Section 7, Part I

1. $50\sqrt{2}$, $\frac{25}{4}$; $1600(\ln .9)/\ln .5$.

3. $P = P_0 e^{kt}$, $625 \times 10^3/18$.

5. $(4\ln 20)/\ln 3$.

7. e^{-2x}.

9. $100 \cdot 2^{-x}$.

11. $25/8$.

Section 7, Part II

1. Since E = a constant, $DE = 0$
and

$$\int_{I_0}^{I} \frac{dI}{I} = -\int_0^t \frac{dt}{CR} \quad \text{or} \quad I = I_0 e^{-t/CR}.$$

Limiting value $= 0$.

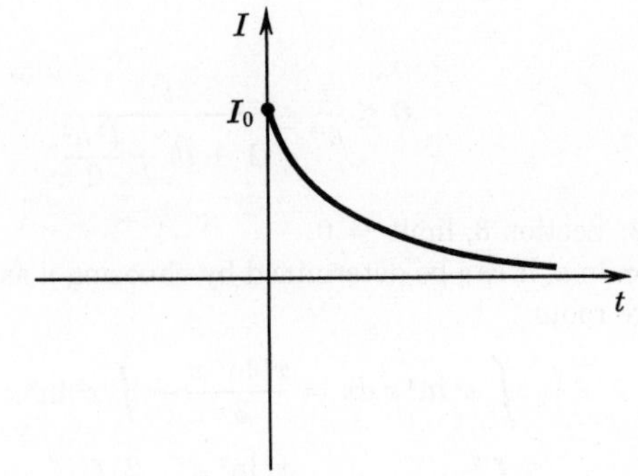

3. By Newton's laws,

$$ma = (F - um - kv)g = \frac{m\,dv}{dt}$$

or

$$\int_0^v \frac{1}{F - um - kv}\,dv = \int_0^t \frac{g}{m}\,dt$$

or

$$-\frac{1}{k}\ln\frac{F - um - kv}{F - um} = \frac{gt}{m}.$$

Thus

$$v = (F - um)(1 - e^{-gkt/m})/k$$

which shows that the velocity increases monotonically with time and approaches the terminal velocity $(F - um)/k$. Since $v = ds/dt$,

$$\int_0^s ds = \frac{F - um}{k}\int_0^t (1 - e^{-gkt/m})\,dt$$

or

$$s = \frac{F - um}{k}\left\{t - \frac{m}{gk}(1 - e^{-gkt/m})\right\}.$$

REVIEW, PART I

1. $x(1 + 2\ln x)$, $(2\ln x)/x$, $(1 + \ln\sqrt{x})/\sqrt{x}$.

3. $1/\sqrt{x^2 - 1}$. **5.** $-2xy/(1 - x^4)$. **7.** $-xy/(y + 2)$.

9. $(x)10^x\left\{\frac{10^x}{x} + 10^x(\ln x)(\ln 10)\right\} - (10)^{x^{10}}\{10x^9\ln 10\}$.

11. $2a^2\sinh 1$. **13.** $\pi a^2(e^{2bc} - 1)/2b$. **15.** $x - a\ln(x + a) + c$.

17. $x - \frac{2}{3}\ln(1 + e^{3x}) + c$. **19.** $(\ln 2)/4\ln 1.01$ yr.

21. Use **10.26**.

REVIEW, PART II

1. Let $x^2 = t$ giving $\frac{1}{2}\int\frac{\ln\ln t}{t\ln t}\,dt = \frac{1}{4}(\ln\ln t)^2 + c$.

3. Let $x = e^t$, then limit $= \lim\limits_{t\to\infty}\frac{t}{e^{th}}$.

Since

$$0 \leq \frac{t}{e^{th}} \leq \frac{t}{1 + th + \frac{t^2 h^2}{2}}$$

by Exercise II-2, Section 3, limit $= 0$.

5. Since the limit $= \ln a$, it can be determined by choosing n as a power of 2 and extracting successive square roots.

7.
$$\int x^2 \ln^3 x \, dx = \frac{x^3 \ln^3 x}{3} - \int x^2 \ln^2 x \, dx,$$
$$\int x^2 \ln^2 x \, dx = \frac{x^3 \ln^2 x}{3} - \frac{2}{3} \int x^2 \ln x \, dx,$$
$$\int x^2 \ln x \, dx = \frac{x^3 \ln x}{3} - \frac{1}{3} \int x^2 \, dx.$$

9. Assume $\int x^3 e^x \, dx = e^x(x^3 + ax^2 + bx + c) +$ constant. Differentiating,

$$x^2 e^x = e^x (x^3 + 3x^2 + 2ax + b + ax^2 + bx + c)$$
$$\text{or} \quad 3 + a = 0,\ 2a + b = 0,\ b + c = 0.$$

Thus, $a = -3$, $b = 6$, $c = -6$. More generally,

$$\int x^n e^{ax} \, dx = e^{ax} \left(\frac{x^n}{a^1} - \frac{nx^{n-1}}{a^2} + \frac{n(n-1)x^{n-2}}{a^3} - \frac{n(n-1)(n-2)x^{n-3}}{a^4} + \cdots \right) + \text{const.}$$

11. $\int_{T_0}^{T_1} \frac{dT}{T} = \int_0^\theta u d\theta$ or $\ln \frac{T_1}{T_0} = u\theta$. Thus

$$O = \frac{1}{.2} \ln \frac{10(2000)}{50} = 5 \ln 400 \text{ radians} = \frac{5}{2\pi} \ln 400 \text{ revolutions.}$$

13. For $b > a$,

$$(1 + \ln a) \int_a^b x^x \, dx < \int_a^b x^x(1 + \ln x) \, dx < (1 + \ln b) \int_a^b x^x \, dx.$$

Since

$$\int_a^b x^x(1 + \ln x) \, dx = b^b - a^a,$$

we obtain

$$\frac{b^b - a^a}{1 + \ln b} < \int_a^b x^x \, dx < \frac{b^b - a^a}{1 + \ln a} \int_a^b x^x \, dx.$$

An approximation within 10% is given by

$$\frac{100^{100} - 99^{99}}{1 + \ln 99}.$$

Note that $\int_{99}^{100} x^x \, dx$ is more than 98% of the entire integral.

CHAPTER 11

SECTION 3, PART I

1. $2 \cos 2x$.
3. $2/(1 + \cos 2x)$.
5. $(\frac{3}{2}) \tan^2 (x/2) \sec^2 (x/2)$.
7. $2 \sec^2 x \tan x(\tan^2 x + \sec^2 x)$.
9. $-2(\sin 2x + \cos 2x)$.
11. $\sec x$.
13. $2e^{2x}(\cos 2x - \sin 2x)$.
15. $x \cos x$.
17. $-2 \tan 2x \sec^2 2x/\sqrt{1 - \tan^2 2x}$.
19. $3x^2 \sec x^3 \tan x^3$.
21. $y'' = 12 \csc^3 2x(3 \cot^2 2x + \csc^2 2x)$.
23. $y'' = 4 \sec^2 x \tan x(3 \sec^2 x - 1)$.
25. $y'' = [2x^2 \sin (1/x) - 2x \cos (1/x) - \sin (1/x)]/x^2$.
27. $y'' = - 16 \cos 4x$.
29. $\sec y$.
31. $1/\sec y \tan y$.
33. $- [y \cos x + \sin (x + y)]/[\sin x + \sin (x + y)]$.
35. $f(\pi/4) = \sqrt{2}$ max.; $f(5\pi/4) = -\sqrt{2}$ min.
37. $F(0) = 1$ min.; $F(\pi/3) = \frac{5}{4}$ max.; $F(\pi) = - 1$ min.; $F(5\pi/3) = \frac{5}{4}$ max.
39. $g(\pi/6) = \sqrt{3}$ min.; $g(5\pi/6) = -\sqrt{3}$ max.
41. 1.
43. 1.
45. $-\frac{1}{2} \cos (2z + \pi/2) + c$.
47. $\ln \sin \theta + c$.
49. ln 2.
51. $-(4/\pi) \csc \pi\theta/4 + c$.
53. $- (\frac{1}{4}) \cos^3 x + c$.
55. $-(\frac{1}{2}) \csc^2 x + c$.
57. $[\cos (a^2 + 1) - \cos (b^2 + 1)]/2$.
61. ln 2.

SECTION 3; PART II

1. $\dfrac{\sin (x + y)}{\cos (x + y)} = \dfrac{\sin x \cos y + \cos x \sin y}{\cos x \cos y - \sin x \sin y} = \dfrac{\tan x + \tan y}{1 - \tan x \tan y}$.

3. $\cos 2x = \cos^2 x - \sin^2 x = 2 \cos^2 x - 1$.

5. $\cos 3x = \cos (x + 2x) = \cos x \cos 2x - \sin x \sin 2x$.
Now using Exercise 3,

$$\cos 3x = \cos x\,(2 \cos^2 x - 1) - \sin x\,(2 \sin x \cos x) = 4 \cos^3 x - 3 \cos x.$$

7. $(2ax^2 + \sin 2ax^2)/8a + c$; let $ax^2 = y$, then use Exercise 3.

9. $(9 \sin 2x^3 + \sin 6x^3)/72$; let $2x^3 = y$, then use Exercise 5.

11. $(12ax + 8 \sin 2ax + \sin 4ax)/32a$;

$$\cos^4 ax = \left(\frac{1 + \cos 2ax}{2}\right)^2 = \frac{1}{4} + \frac{1}{2} \cos 2ax + \frac{1}{4} \cos^2 2ax.$$

Now use Exercise 3 again.

13. $S(t) = \dfrac{v_0}{k} \sin kt$; $S(t) = S_0 \cos kt$; $S(t) = \dfrac{v_0}{k} \sin kt + S_0 \cos kt$.

15. From Exercise 14, $a \sin x + b \cos x = \sqrt{a^2 + b^2} \sin (x + \alpha)$ where $\cos \alpha = \dfrac{a}{\sqrt{a^2 + b^2}}$, $\sin \alpha = \dfrac{b}{\sqrt{a^2 + b^2}}$. Whence

$$\text{max displacement} = \sqrt{S_0^2 + (v_0/k)^2},$$
$$\text{max speed} = \sqrt{v_0^2 + k^2S_0^2}.$$

17. The graph of g oscillates infinitely often between the lines $y = \pm x$ and thus must have an infinite number of extrema. The extremum points satisfy the equation $g^1(x) = 0$ or $\tan\frac{\pi}{x} = \frac{\pi}{x}$. That the latter equation has an infinite number of roots can be seen by plotting $u = \tan v$ and $u = v$.

Since $-x \le g(x) \le x$, it follows that $\lim_{x\to 0} g(x) = 0$. Thus if we define $g(0)$ to be zero, $g(x)$ is continuous in $[0, 1]$

Since $D \sin \pi/x]_{x=0}$ does not exist, we cannot use the product rule to find $D^+g(0)$. We resort to the definition, i.e.,

$$D^+g(0) = \operatorname*{limit}_{h\to 0^+} \frac{g(h) - g(0)}{h} = \operatorname*{limit}_{h\to 0^+} \sin\frac{\pi}{h},$$

which does not exist.

SECTION 4, PART I

1. $\pi/6$. **3.** $\pi/4$. **5.** $-\pi/4$.
7. $1/\sqrt{2}$. **9.** -2.

SECTION 4, PART II

1.

If $\theta = \sin^{-1} x$, also

$$\theta = \tan^{-1}\frac{x}{\sqrt{1 - x^2}}. \text{ Thus } \tan(\sin^{-1} x) = \frac{x}{\sqrt{1 - x^2}}.$$

3. Since $\sin 3a = 3 \sin a - 4 \sin^3 a$ (Exercise II-4, Section 3), $\sin(3 \sin^{-1} x) = 3x - 4x^3$.

5. $\sin(A + B) = \sin A \cos B + \sin B \cos A$.
Now let $A = \sin^{-1} x$, $B = \sin^{-1} y$.

7. $\tan(A + B) = \dfrac{\tan A + \tan B}{1 - \tan A \tan B}$.
Now let $A = \tan^{-1} x$, $B = \tan^{-1} y$.

SECTION 5, PART I

1. $-1/\sqrt{1 - x^2}$.
5. $2/\sqrt{1 - 4x^2}$.
7. $1/x\sqrt{16x^2 - 1}$.
9. $6(1 + \arcsin 3x)/\sqrt{1 - 9x^2}$.
11. $2/(1 + e^{4x}) - (2 \arctan e^{2x})/e^{2x}$.
13. $\sin^{-1} x$.
15. $1/x\sqrt{x^2 - 1}$.
17. $1/2x\sqrt{x - 1}$.
19. $1/(1 + x^2) \arctan x$.
21. $2x^2/\sqrt{1 - x^2}$.
23. $6x^2 \tan^{-1} x$.
25. $c = -\pi/4$.
27. $\pi/3$.
29. $\pi/18$.
31. $\pi/12$.
33. $\arctan \sin x + c$.

SECTION 5, PART II

1. Differentiate implicitly.
3. Either find y' and y'' and substitute or else differentiate $\sin^{-1} y = a \sin^{-1} x$ twice and simplify.

5. $(2/a) \sec^{-1} \sqrt{x}/a$. Alternatively, let $x - a^2 = y^2$.

7. $(\tan^{-1} 2 - \pi/8)/3$; $\dfrac{1}{(x^2+1)(x^2+4)} = \dfrac{1}{3}\left(\dfrac{1}{x^2+1} - \dfrac{1}{x^2+4}\right)$.

9. $\frac{1}{3} \sin^{-1} x^3$; let $x^3 = y$.

SECTION 6, PART I

1. $f^{-1}(x) = x^3$; set of all real numbers.
3. $F^{-1}(x) = \tan^{-1} x$; set of all real numbers.
5. $f^{-1}(x) = x - 2$; set of all real numbers.
7. $g^{-1}(x) = x/2$; set of all real numbers.
9. $F^{-1}(x) = \log_a x$; set of all positive real numbers.
13. Note that $m + \dfrac{1}{m}$ is an increasing function for $m \geq 1$.

SECTION 6, PART II

1. Let $F^{-1}(x) = y$, then we have to show that $\int y\,dx = xy - G(y)$. Differentiating yields

$$y = xy' + y - G^1(y)y' \quad \text{or} \quad [x - G'(y)]y' = 0.$$

Since $F(x) = G'(x)$, $G'(y) = F(y) = x$.

3. $x \tan^{-1} 3x - \frac{1}{6} \ln (1 + ax^2) + c$.
5. $x \ln x - x + c$.

REVIEW, PART I

1. $\cot x$.

3. $(2/x) \sec^2 \ln x^2$.

5. $\dfrac{m \cos x}{\sqrt{1 - m^2 \sin^2 x}}$.

7. $\dfrac{x \arcsin x}{\sqrt{1 - x^2}}$.

9. O; note that $-|x| \leq x \sin \dfrac{1}{x} \leq |x|$, now use the squeeze theorem.

11. O; note that $\dfrac{\sin x^2}{x} = x \cdot \dfrac{\sin x^2}{x^2}$.

13. 4; use Exercise II-2, Section 3.

15. **a.** $2\pi/3$. **b.** 6π. **c.** Period of $\sin 2x$ is π, period of $2 \cos 4x$ is $\pi/2$; thus period of sum is π. **d.** Period of $2 \sin x/3$ is 6π, period of $\cos x/5$ is 10π; thus period of difference is 30π. **e.** Period of $\sin x/3$ is 6π, period of $-\cos x/6$ is 12π, period of $\tan x/9$ is 18π; thus period of sum is 36π. **f.** $2\pi/w$.

17. No extrema; $x = n\pi$ (n an integer), infl. pts.

19. $\frac{1}{2} \sec^{-1} x^2 + c$; let $y = x^2$.

21. $3 \tan \dfrac{x}{3} - x + c$; $\tan^2 y = \sec^2 y - 1$.

23. $(3x - \tan^{-1} 3x)/27 + c$; $\dfrac{x^2}{9x^2+1} = \dfrac{1}{9}\left(1 - \dfrac{1}{9x^2+1}\right)$.

25. 8; $y' = \dfrac{1 \mp x}{\sqrt{1 - x^2}}$.

$$L = \int_{-1}^{1} \sqrt{1 + \left(\frac{1-x}{\sqrt{1-x^2}}\right)^2}\, dx + \int_{-1}^{1} \sqrt{1 + \left(\frac{1+x}{\sqrt{1-x^2}}\right)^2}\, dx = 8.$$

27. $$V = \int_0^{\pi/a} \pi \sin^2 ax\, dx = \pi \int_0^{\pi/a} \frac{1 - \cos 2ax}{2}\, dx = \frac{\pi^2}{2a}.$$

REVIEW, PART II

1. Parts **a**, **b**, **d**, **e**, and **f** follow from the symmetry of the circle. For **c**, we must show that $OA = CF = DE$. This follows from congruent triangles. Also, these can all be obtained from the addition formula $\sin (x + y) = \sin x \cos y + \sin y \cos x$. Differentiating yields,

$$\cos (x + y) = \cos x \cos y - \sin y \sin x.$$

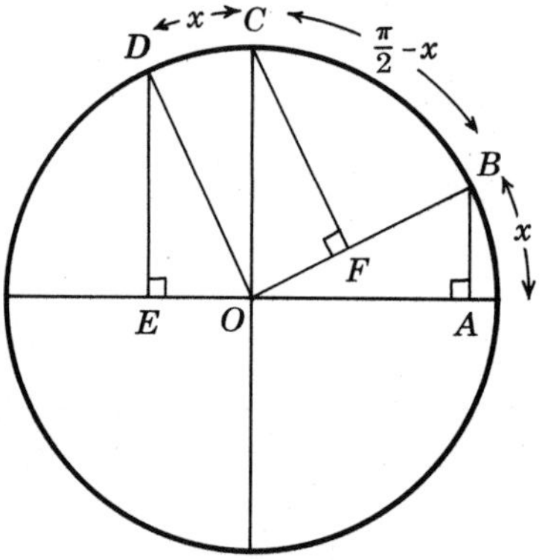

Now set $y = -x$, giving

$$0 = \sin x \cos (-x) + \sin (-x) \cos x$$
$$1 = \cos x \cos (-x) - \sin (-x) \sin x,$$

which on solving for $\cos (-x)$ and $\sin (-x)$ gives *a* and *b*. To obtain **e**, set $y = \pi$, and so on.

3. Let $x = 0$, then $\sin y = A(y) \cdot 0 + B(y) \cdot 1$, thus $B(y) = \sin y$, let $x = \pi/2$, then $\cos y = A(y) \cdot 1 + B(y) \cdot 0$, thus $A(y) = \cos y$

5. Case 1, $m = 1$: $\sin x + \cos x = \sqrt{2} \sin (x + \pi/4) = 1$. Thus $x = 0, \pi/2, 2\pi$.
Case 2, $m = 2$: Valid for all x.
Case 3, $m \geq 3$: Since $|\sin x|$ and $|\cos x| < 1$, both $\sin x$ and $\cos x$ must be positive. Also since $\sin^3 x \leq \sin^2 x$ and $\cos^3 x \leq \cos^2 x$, the only solutions occur when either $\sin x$ or $\cos x = 1$ or $x = 0, \pi/2, 2\pi$ (m odd) and $x = 0, \frac{\pi}{2}, \frac{3\pi}{2}, \pi, 2\pi$ (m even).

7.
$$D^{4n+1}\sin x = \cos x = \sin (x + (4n + 1)\pi/2) = \sin (x + \pi/2).$$
$$D^{4n+2}\sin x = -\sin x = \sin (x + (4n + 2)\pi/2) = \sin (x + \pi).$$
$$D^{4n+3}\sin x = -\cos x = \sin (x + (4n + 3)\pi/2) = \sin(x + 3\pi/2).$$
$$D^{4n+4}\sin x = \sin x = \sin (x + (4n + 4)\pi/2) = \sin(x + 2\pi).$$

9. **a.** $\sin 2\pi x/3$ (Period 3), $\sin \pi x - \sin 2\pi x/3$ (Period 6); Period of sum $= 2$.
b. $\sin \pi x$ (Period 2), $\sin 2\pi x/3$ (Period 3); Period of sum $= 6$.
Parts **c** and **d** are equivalent to parts **a** and **b**; just take e^f and e^g where f and g are as in **a** and **b**.

11. Yes; e.g., $F(x) = \sin^2 \pi x$, period 1,

$$G(x) = \begin{cases} 1, & 0 \leq x < 1 \\ -1, & 1 \leq x < 2 \end{cases} \quad \text{and} \quad G(x + 2) = G(x), \text{ period 2.}$$

$F \circ G(x) = 0$ for all x and $F \circ G$ has any period $p > 0$. ($G \circ F(x) = 1$ for all x).

13.
$$s = \cos vt$$
$$\frac{ds}{dt} = v \sin vt$$
$$\frac{d^2s}{dt^2} = -v^2 \cos vt = -v^2 s$$

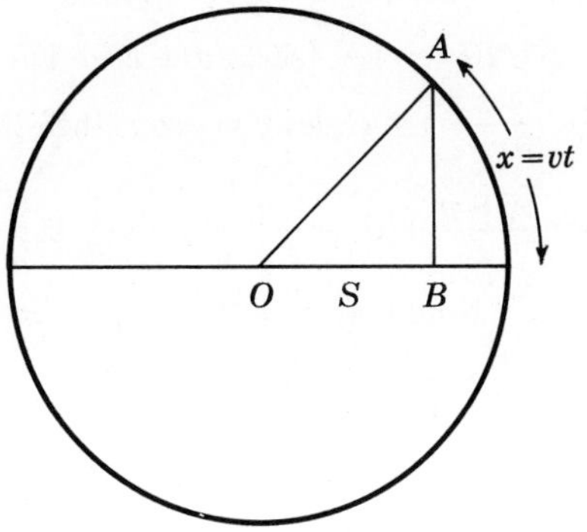

15. $F(P) = -\dfrac{km\,\frac{4}{3}\rho\pi r^3}{r^2} = -\frac{4}{3}km\pi\rho r.$

Here

k = universal gravitational constant
ρ = density of earth, assumed to be constant.

At surface of earth, $\dfrac{4}{3}km\pi\rho R = mg$. Thus $F(P) = -\dfrac{mgr}{R}$. By Newton's law, $F = ma$.

Whence
$$\frac{d^2r}{dt^2} = -\frac{gr}{R}$$

and motion is simple harmonic, with period $2\pi\sqrt{\dfrac{R}{g}}$. Half a period $= T = \pi\sqrt{\dfrac{R}{g}}$.

17. Just interchange F and x in the defining equation (in Exercise 16). This gives an equation of the same general form. Since e^x is transcendental, its inverse $\ln x$ must then also be transcendental.

CHAPTER 12

Section 1, Part I

1. $(\frac{2}{7})(x-2)^{7/2} + (\frac{4}{5})(x-2)^{5/2} + c.$
3. $(\cos^3 x - 3\cos x)/3 + c.$
5. $(2\cos x - \cos 2x)/4 + c.$
7. $(x-2)^2/2 + 4\ln(x+2) + c.$
9. $2x^{3/2}(60x^2 + 84x + 35)/105 + c.$
11. $(\frac{1}{3})\arctan(x-2)/3 + c.$

13. $\arcsin(x-1)+c.$

15. $\dfrac{1}{2\sqrt{2}}\arctan\dfrac{3x^2-1}{\sqrt{2}}.$

17. $(\frac{1}{2})\cos^2 x - \ln|\cos x| + c.$

19. $\sec x + \cos x + c.$

21. $-\ln(1+e^{-x})+c.$

23. Since $\cos 2x = 1 - 2\sin^2 x$, the difference is merely one of form.

Section 1, Part II

1. $-\int(1-\cos^2\theta)^2 d\cos\theta = -\cos\theta + \frac{2}{3}\cos^3\theta - \frac{1}{5}\cos^5\theta + C.$

3. $[\sin\{x(a-c)+b-d\}]/2(a-c) - [\sin\{x(a+c)+b+d\}]/2(a+c)+k.$

5. $2\sqrt{1+\cos x}\left(1-\dfrac{1+\cos x}{3}\right)+C$; let $y=\cos x$, then $t^2 = 1+y$.

7. $$\frac{1}{a}\arctan\frac{x+p}{a}+C,\ -\frac{1}{x+p}+C,\ \frac{1}{2b}\ln\left|\frac{x+p-b}{x+p+b}\right|+C$$

where $a^2 = -b^2 = q - p^2$. Note that $x^2+2px+q = (x+p)^2+q-p^2$.

9. $-\int\dfrac{1}{qy^2+2py+1}\,dy,\ -\int\dfrac{(a+by)}{y^2\sqrt{1+2py+qy^2}}\,dy.$

Section 2, Part I

1. $x^2(2\ln x - 1)/4 + c.$

3. $4(3\sqrt{2}\ln 2 - 2\sqrt{2}+1)/9.$

5. $[(x^2+1)\tan^{-1}x - x]/2 + c.$

7. $x\sin x + \cos x + c.$

9. $(\pi-2)/2.$

11. $e^x(x^2-2x+2)+c.$

13. $(x-1)\sqrt{2x+1}/3+c.$

15. $e^{2x}(2\sin 3x - 3\cos 3x)/13 + c.$

17. $2/15.$

19. $x\ln(x^2+1) - 2x + 2\tan^{-1}x + c.$

21. $x^{r+1}[(r+1)\ln x - 1]/(r+1)^2 + c.$

23. $x\sin^{-1}ax + \sqrt{1-a^2x^2}/a + c.$

25. $x\tan^{-1}ax - (1/2a)\ln(1+a^2x^2)+c.$

27. $[2ax + 2a^2x^2\tanh^{-1}ax + \ln|ax-1|/|ax+1|]/4a^2 + c.$

Section 2, Part II

1. Let $F^{-1}(x) = y$ to give $\int y\,dF(y) = yF(y) - \int F(y)\,dy.$

3. Let $x = 2a - y$, then $\int_0^{2a} xF(x)dx = \int_0^{2a}(2a-y)F(2a-y)dy$

$$= 2a\int_0^{2a}F(y)\,dy - \int_0^{2a} yF(y)dy.$$

5. $\int x^n\cos x\,dx = x^n\sin x + nx^{n-1}\cos x - n(n-1)\int x^{n-2}\cos x\,dx;$

integrate by parts twice; first let $u = x^n$, $\cos x\,dx = dv$.

7. Let $x = \pi/2 - y$.

Section 3, Part I

1. $[25\sin^{-1}x/5 + x\sqrt{25-x^2}]/2 + c.$

3. $\sin^{-1}x/5 + c.$

5. $(x/2)\sqrt{9x^2-4} - (\frac{2}{3})\ln|3x+\sqrt{9x^2-4}| + c.$

7. $-(\frac{1}{3})\ln|3+\sqrt{x^2+9}|/|x| + c.$

9. $-[4x/(x^2-4) + \ln|x-2|/|x+2|]/32 + c.$

11. $\sqrt{x^2 - a^2} - a \sec^{-1} x/a + c$.
13. $-\sqrt{a^2 - x^2}/x - \sin^{-1} x/a + c$.
15. $[x\sqrt{x^2 + a^2} + a^2 \ln (x + \sqrt{x^2 + a^2})]/2 + c$.
17. $[x\sqrt{x^2 - a^2} + a^2 \ln |x + \sqrt{x^2 - a^2}|]/2 + c$.
19. $-(1/a) \ln |a + \sqrt{a^2 - x^2}|/|x|$.
21. $[\tan^{-1} (x - 2) + (x - 2)/(x^2 - 4x + 5)]/2 + c$.

SECTION 3, PART II

1. Note that $x^2 + 2px + q = (x + p)^2 + q - p^2$. Now make an appropriate trigonometric or hyperbolic substitution.

3. $$\frac{x^2}{\sqrt{x^2 + 2px + q}} = \frac{x^2 + 2px + q}{\sqrt{x^2 + 2px + q}} - \frac{2px + q}{\sqrt{x^2 + 2px + q}}.$$

5. Let $x = 1/y$, $a = 1/b$.

SECTION 4, PART I

1. $\ln (x - 1)^2/|x| + c$.
3. $[2x^2 + 8x + 27 \ln |x - 3| + \ln |x + 1|]/4 + c$.
5. $[3 \ln |2x - 1| - (2x - 1)^{-1}]/4 + c$.
7. $[5 \ln |x + 2| + 4 \ln |x - 1| - 3 \ln |x|]/6 + c$.
9. $[\ln |x - 2|/|x + 2| + 2 \tan^{-1} x/2]/8 + c$.
11. $[8x - 2 \ln |x| + 9 \ln |x - 2| - 7 \ln |x + 2|]/8 + c$.
13. $[4(x - 2)^2 \ln |x - 2| - 8(x - 2) - 9]/2(x - 2)^2 + c$.
15. $[2 \ln (x^2 + 4) + \tan^{-1} x/2 + 3/(x^2 + 4)]/2 + c$.
17. $[\ln |x + 2|/|x - 2| - 14/(x - 2) + 10/(x + 2)]/32 + c$.
19. $[\ln |cx + d|/|ax + b|]/(bc - ad) + C$, $bc - ad \neq 0$,

$$\frac{1}{(ax + b)(cx + d)} = \frac{1}{bc - ad}\left(\frac{c}{cx + d} - \frac{a}{ax + b}\right).$$

21. See table of integrals at end of book,

$$\frac{x}{(ax + b)^2(cx + d)} = \frac{1}{a}\left(\frac{ax + b}{(ax + b)^2(cx + d)} - \frac{b}{(ax + b)^2(cx + d)}\right).$$

The 1st term on the right hand side corresponds to Exercise 19. To integrate the 2nd term, note that from Exercise 19 above,

$$\frac{1}{(ax + b)^2(cx + d)} = \frac{1}{bc - ad}\left\{\frac{c}{(ax + b)(cx + d)} - \frac{a}{(ax + b)^2}\right\}.$$

SECTION 4, PART II

1. $$\frac{x}{(x - a)^2(x - b)^2} = \frac{A}{x - a} + \frac{B}{(x - a)^2} + \frac{C}{x - b} + \frac{D}{(x - b)^2},$$

or

$$x = A(x - a)(x - b)^2 + B(x - b)^2 + C(x - a)^2(x - b) + D(x - a)^2.$$

Let

$$\begin{aligned} x &= a \quad \text{to give} \quad a = B(a - b)^2; \\ x &= b \quad \text{to give} \quad b = D(b - a)^2; \\ x &= 0 \quad \text{to give} \quad 0 = -Aab^2 - Cba^2 + Bb^2 + Da^2. \end{aligned}$$

Also,

$$0 = A + C.$$

Now solve for A and C and integrate.

3. $\dfrac{1}{(x-a)(x-b)(x-c)} = \dfrac{A}{x-a} + \dfrac{B}{x-b} + \dfrac{C}{x-c}$

or

$$1 = A(x-b)(x-c) + B(x-c)(x-a) + C(x-a)(x-b).$$

Now let $x = a, b, c$ successively to obtain A, B, and C. Finally, integrate termwise.

5. $\dfrac{x^4}{x^2-1} = \dfrac{x^4-1}{x^2-1} + \dfrac{1}{x^2-1} = x^2 + 1 + \dfrac{1}{2}\left(\dfrac{1}{x-1} - \dfrac{1}{x+1}\right)$; now integrate.

7. $\dfrac{x^7}{x^4+a^4} = x^3 - \dfrac{a^4x^3}{x^4+a^4}$; now integrate.

9. $\arctan x - \dfrac{1}{x} - \dfrac{1}{3x^3} + C$; let $x = \dfrac{1}{y}$ to give

$$-\int \frac{y^4}{y^2+1}\,dy = -\left\{\int (y^2+1)dy + \int \frac{1}{y^2+1}\,dy\right\}.$$

11. $\dfrac{1}{6}\ln\dfrac{(x+1)^2}{x^2-x+1} + \dfrac{1}{\sqrt{3}}\arctan\dfrac{2x-1}{3} + C$;

$$\frac{1}{x^3+1} = \frac{1}{(x+1)(x^2-x+1)} = \frac{a}{x+1} + \frac{bx+c}{x^2-x+1}.$$

Now determine a, b and c. Then note that

$$\frac{bx+c}{x^2-x+1} = \frac{b}{2}\left\{\frac{2x-1}{x^2-x+1} + \frac{2c/b+1}{(x-\frac{1}{2})^2+\frac{3}{4}}\right\}.$$

Section 5, Part I

1. $xy = c.$
3. $x^2 + 2/y = c.$
5. $y - x + \ln|y-1|/|x| = c.$
7. $e^{-x} + e^{-y} = c.$
9. $(\sec x + \tan x)\sec y = c.$
11. 58.9°; 4 min.

Section 5, Part II

1. By the chain rule,

$$\frac{dv}{dt} = \frac{dv}{dx}\frac{dx}{dt} = v\frac{dv}{dx}.$$

$$v\,dv + w^2x\,dx = 0$$
$$v^2 + w^2x^2 = c^2$$
$$v = \sqrt{c^2 - w^2x^2}$$

or

$$\frac{dx}{\sqrt{c^2-w^2x^2}} = dt$$

and

$$\frac{1}{w}\arcsin\frac{wx}{c} = t + c_1 \text{ or } x = \frac{c}{w}\sin w(t+c_1).$$

3. $A(h) = 25\pi$, $A_0 = \dfrac{\pi}{16}$.

Thus

$$25\pi \frac{dh}{dt} = -\frac{\pi^2}{16(\pi + 2)} \sqrt{2gh}$$

or

$$dt = -\frac{k\,dh}{\sqrt{h}},$$

where $k = \dfrac{400(\pi + 2)}{\pi\sqrt{2g}}$, $t = -2k\sqrt{h} + c$. Since $h = 20$ at $t = 0$, $t = 2k(\sqrt{20} - \sqrt{h})$.

When empty $h = 0$, and time $t = 2k\sqrt{20} = 800(\pi + 2)\sqrt{10}/\pi\sqrt{g}$ sec.

REVIEW, PART I

1. $x + 1 - 6 \ln |x + 1| - \dfrac{12}{x + 1} + \dfrac{4}{(x + 1)^2} + c$; $\left(\dfrac{x - 1}{x + 1}\right)^3 = \left(1 - \dfrac{2}{x + 1}\right)^3$, now expand.

3. $x(\ln^3 |x| - 3 \ln^2 |x| + 6 \ln |x| - 6) + c$.

5. $2e^{\sqrt{t}}(\sqrt{t} - 1) + c$.

7. $x \ln |x + \sqrt{x^2 - a^2}| - \sqrt{x^2 - a^2} + c$.

9. $\tan x + c$.

11. $(\arctan x)^3/3 + c$.

13. $-\cos e^x + c$.

15. $\dfrac{\sin 5x}{10} + \dfrac{\sin x}{2} + c$.

17. $\dfrac{5^x}{\ln^2 5} (x \ln 5 - 1) + c$.

19. $\dfrac{(x^3 + 1) \ln |1 + x|}{3} - \dfrac{x^3}{9} + \dfrac{x^2}{6} - \dfrac{x}{3} + c$.

21. $2e^{\sqrt{x}}(\sqrt{x} - 1) + c$.

REVIEW, PART II

1. Let $y^2 = 1 + e^{2x}$, then $dx = \dfrac{y}{y^2 - 1}\, dy$ giving $\displaystyle\int \frac{y^2}{y^2 - 1}\, dy$.

But

$$\frac{y^2}{y^2 - 1} = 1 + \frac{1}{2}\left\{\frac{1}{y - 1} - \frac{1}{y + 1}\right\}.$$

Now integrate termwise.

3. Let $x + 1 = y$ to give $\displaystyle\int \left(1 - \frac{2}{y}\right)^n dy$. But

$$\left(1 - \frac{2}{y}\right)^n = 1 - \binom{n}{1}\frac{2}{y} + \binom{n}{2}\left(\frac{2}{y}\right)^2 - \cdots + \binom{n}{n}\left(\frac{-2}{y}\right)^n$$

by the binomial theorem. Now integrate termwise.

5. $-e^{-x^2}(x^4 + 2x^2 + 2)/2 + c$; let $-x^2 = y$ and integrate by parts or else use Exercise II-4, Section 2.

7. $\theta = 2 \tan^{-1} z$ or $d\theta = \dfrac{2\,dz}{1 + z^2}$.

$$\sin\theta = 2 \sin\frac{\theta}{2} \cos\frac{\theta}{2} = \frac{2z}{\sqrt{1 + z^2}}\frac{1}{\sqrt{1 + z^2}} = \frac{2z}{1 + z^2}$$

$$\cos\theta = 2 \cos^2\frac{\theta}{2} - 1 = \frac{2z^2}{1 + z^2} - 1 = \frac{z^2 - 1}{z^2 + 1}$$

$$\int R\,(\sin\theta, \cos\theta)d\theta = \int R\left(\frac{2z}{1 + z^2}, \frac{1 - z^2}{1 + z^2}\right)\frac{2}{1 + z^2}\, dz.$$

Since the integrand is a rational function of z it can always be integrated by using the method of partial fractions.

9. Let $z = \tan \theta/2$, giving

$$\int_0^1 \frac{2}{b + a - (b - a)z^2}\, dz$$

or

$$\frac{1}{m(b - a)} \ln \frac{m + 1}{m - 1}$$

where $m^2 = \dfrac{b + a}{b - a}$.

11. $\displaystyle\int \frac{d \tan \theta}{a^2 \tan^2 \theta + b^2} = \frac{1}{ab} \arctan \frac{a \tan \theta}{b} + c.$

13. $\displaystyle\int x^n \ln^m x\, dx = \frac{x^{n+1}}{n + 1} \ln^m x - \frac{m}{n + 1} \int x^n \ln^{m-1} x\, dx;$

let $u = \ln^m x$, $x^n\, dx = dv$.

15. $\displaystyle\int \operatorname{sech}^n x\, dx = \left\{- \tanh x \operatorname{sech}^{n-2} x + (n - 2) \int \operatorname{sech}^{n-2} x\, dx\right\}/(n - 3);$

$$\int \operatorname{sech}^n x\, dx =$$

$$\int \operatorname{sech}^{n-2} x d \tanh x = \operatorname{sech}^{n-2} x \tanh x - (n - 2) \int \operatorname{sech}^{n-2} x\, (1 - \operatorname{sech}^2 x)\, dx.$$

17. $2 \sin^2 x = 1 - \cos 2x$; now use result of Exercise II-5, Section 2.

19. Here $A(h) = 40\sqrt{25 - h^2}$, where h is measured from the middle cross section. The height of this section above the bottom is $5 + h$ and h varies from 5 to -5; $A_0 = \pi/16$. The differential equation is then

$$40\sqrt{25 - h^2}\, \frac{dh}{dt} = \frac{-\pi^2}{16(\pi + 2)} \sqrt{2g(5 + h)}$$

or

$$dt = -k\sqrt{5 - h}\, dh,$$

where

$$k = \frac{640(\pi + 2)}{\pi^2\sqrt{2g}}$$

$$\text{time} = -k \int_5^{-5} \sqrt{5 - h}\, dh = 12{,}800\, (\pi + 2)\, \sqrt{5/g}/3\pi^2 \text{ sec.}$$

21. Since density $= \dfrac{dp}{dh}$, we have

$$\int_0^P \frac{1}{64(1 + 2 \times 10^{-8} P)}\, dP = \int_0^h dh,$$

or

$$64h = \frac{\ln (1 + 2 \times 10^{-8}P)}{2 \times 10^{-8}}$$

and

$$P = [e^{128h \cdot 10^{-8}} - 1]\, 10^8/2 \doteq 64h + 32h^2 \cdot 10^{-8} \quad \text{for small } 128h \cdot 10^{-8}.$$

CHAPTER 13

SECTION 1, PART I

1. Vertices $(\pm 2,0)$, foci $(\pm\sqrt{3},0)$.
3. Vertices $(0,\pm 5)$, foci $(0,\pm 4)$.
5. Vertices $(\pm\frac{3}{4},0)$, foci $(\pm\frac{9}{20},0)$.
7. Vertices $(0,\pm 1)$, foci $(0,\pm\sqrt{3}/2)$.
9. $9x^2 + 25y^2 = 25$.
11. $25x^2 + 4y^2 = 100$.
13. $9x^2 + 4y^2 = 36$.

SECTION 1, PART II

1. For any chord AB not containing the center O,

$$\overline{AB} < \overline{AO} + \overline{BO} \geq \max(\overline{AC},\overline{BD}).$$

Now use Exercise I-18.

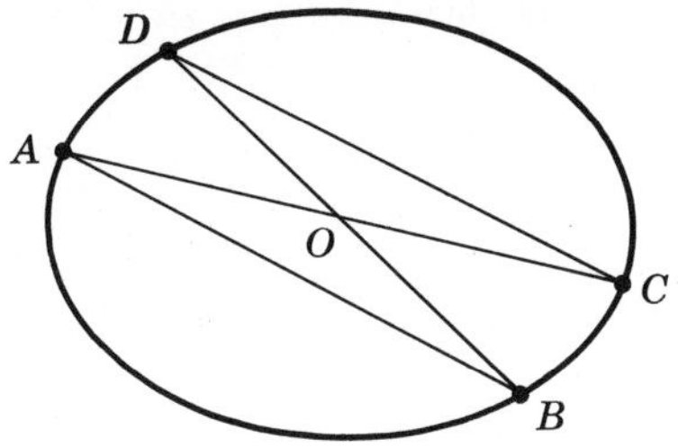

3. The only parallelograms which can be inscribed in a circle can easily be shown to be rectangles. If we orthogonally project a circle with an inscribed rectangle, we obtain

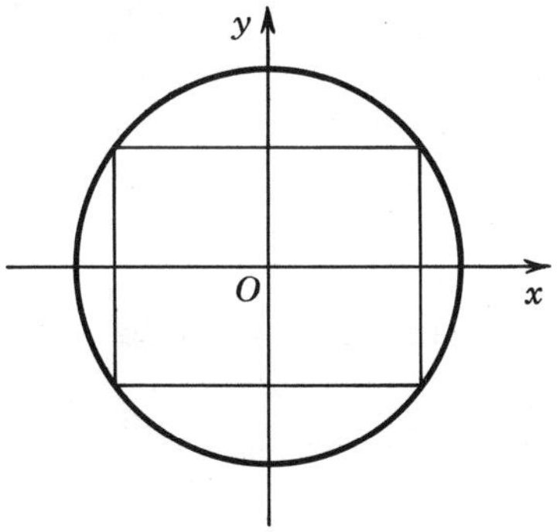

an ellipse with an inscribed parallelogram. In order for the parallelogram to be a rectangle, the original rectangle must have had its sides parallel to the axes as in the figure. Note that under the transformation **a**, angles are, in general, changed under the projection. However, right angles between lines parallel to the coordinate axes, project into right angles.

5. If the semiaxes of the ellipse are a and b with $a \geq b$, then by choosing $\cos\theta = b/a$, the ellipse can be orthogonally projected into a circle of radius b. By property (e) of Exercise 3, $A' = \pi b^2 = A\cos\theta$ and $A = \pi ab$.

In a similar manner, one could find centroids, moments, moments of inertia of elliptical regions from corresponding circular regions. These will appear in subsequent problems. There is also an analogous extension to three dimensions in which properties of ellipsoids can be obtained from corresponding properties of spheres. These will also appear in subsequent problems.

7. By Exercise 3, the coordinates of the square must have the form $(\pm m, \pm m)$. If the equation of the ellipse is

$$\frac{x^2}{a^2} + \frac{y^2}{b^2} = 1,$$

then

$$m^2\left(\frac{1}{a^2} + \frac{1}{b^2}\right) = 1$$

and

$$\text{Area} = 4m^2 = \frac{4a^2b^2}{a^2 + b^2}.$$

9. a. $L = 4\int_0^a \sqrt{1 + y'^2}\,dx$. Now choosing $x = a\cos\theta$, $y = b\sin\theta$ (which are parametric equations for the ellipse)

$$dx = -a\sin\theta\,d\theta, \qquad \frac{dy}{dx} = -\frac{b^2x}{a^2y} = -\frac{b^2\,a\cos\theta}{a^2\,b\sin\theta}.$$

Thus

$$L = 4a\int_0^{\pi/2}\sqrt{1 - e^2\cos^2\theta}\,d\theta = 4a\int_0^{\pi/2}\sqrt{1 - e^2\sin^2\theta}\,d\theta.$$

b. By the Schwarz-Buniakowsky inequality,

$$\int_0^{\pi/2} d\theta \cdot \int_0^{\pi/2} (1 - e^2\sin^2\theta)\,d\theta \geq \left\{\int_0^{\pi/2}\sqrt{1 - e^2\sin^2\theta}\,d\theta\right\}^2,$$

which gives the desired result on integrating the left-hand side.

c. By the trapezoidal rule ($n = 2$),

$$L > 4a\left(\frac{\pi}{8}\right)(1 + \sqrt{1 - e^2/2} + \sqrt{1 - e^2}) = \frac{\pi}{2}(a + b + \sqrt{(a^2 + b^2)/2}).$$

Section 2, Part I

1. Vertices $(\pm 2,0)$, foci $(\pm\sqrt{5},0)$, asymptotes $x = \pm 2y$.
3. Vertices $(0,\pm 3)$, foci $(0,\pm 5)$, asymptotes $3x = \pm 4y$.
5. Vertices $(\pm 2,0)$, foci $(\pm 2\sqrt{2},0)$, asymptotes $x = \pm y$.
7. Vertices $(0,\pm\frac{4}{3})$, foci $(0,\pm 2\sqrt{13}/3)$, asymptotes $2x = \pm 3y$.
9. $3x^2 - y^2 = 12$.
11. $16x^2 - 9y^2 = 576$.
13. $4x^2 - y^2 = 16$.

Section 2, Part II

1. Confocal ellipses and hyperbolas, foci $(\pm 4,0)$.

3. Hyperbola $\frac{x^2}{a^2} - \frac{y^2}{b^2} = 1$; asymptotes $\left(\frac{x}{a} - \frac{y}{b}\right)\left(\frac{x}{a} + \frac{y}{b}\right) = 0$, tangent line through (m,n) is $\frac{xm}{a^2} - \frac{yn}{b^2} = 1$. Intersection of latter line with $\frac{x}{a} - \frac{y}{b} = 0$ and $\frac{x}{a} + \frac{y}{b} = 0$ is

$$\left(\frac{a}{\frac{m}{a} - \frac{n}{b}}, \frac{b}{\frac{m}{a} - \frac{n}{b}}\right)$$

and

$$\left(\frac{a}{\frac{m}{a} + \frac{n}{b}}, \frac{b}{\frac{m}{a} + \frac{n}{b}}\right)$$

respectively.
Area of triangle through 3 points (x_i,y_i), $i = 1, 2, 3$, is

$$A = \frac{1}{2}\begin{vmatrix} x_1 & y_1 & 1 \\ x_2 & y_2 & 1 \\ x_3 & y_3 & 1 \end{vmatrix}.$$

$$A = \tfrac{1}{2}(x_1y_2 - x_2y_1) \quad \text{if} \quad x_3 = y_3 = 0.$$

Thus

$$A = \frac{1}{2}\frac{ab}{\frac{m^2}{a^2} - \frac{n^2}{b^2}} = \frac{ab}{2},$$

since $\dfrac{m^2}{a^2} - \dfrac{n^2}{b^2} = 1$.

5. a. $L = 2\displaystyle\int_a^{a \cosh k} \sqrt{1 + y'^2}\, dx$. Since $y' = \dfrac{b^2x}{a^2y}$, by letting $x = a \cosh \theta$, $y = b \sinh\theta$,

$$L = 2\int_0^k \sqrt{a^2 \sinh^2 \theta + b^2 \cosh^2 \theta}\, d\theta = 2a \int_0^k \sqrt{e^2 \cosh^2 \theta - 1}\, d\theta.$$

b. By the Schwarz-Buniakowsky inequality,

$$\int_0^k d\theta \cdot \int_0^k (e^2 \cosh^2 \theta - 1)\, d\theta \geq \left\{\int_0^k \sqrt{e^2 \cosh^2 \theta - 1}\, d\theta\right\}^2,$$

which gives the desired result on integrating the left-hand side.

7. The family of parallel lines $y = mx + n$ (m-fixed) intersects $\dfrac{x^2}{a^2} - \dfrac{y^2}{b^2} = 1$ in two points (x_1,y_1), (x_2,y_2) given by $b^2x^2 - a^2(mx + n)^2 = a^2b^2$ or $x^2(b^2 - a^2m^2) - 2a^2mnx - a^2(n^2 + b^2) = 0$. Thus

$$x = \frac{x_1 + x_2}{2} = \frac{a^2mn}{b^2 - a^2m^2}, \qquad y = \frac{y_1 + y_2}{2} = \frac{b^2n}{b^2 - a^2m^2}$$

and

$$\frac{y}{x} = \frac{b^2}{a^2m},$$

which is a straight line through the center for each m. The intersection of two such lines will then give the center.

SECTION 3, PART I

1. Parabola, vertex $(3,-2)$, focus $(3,-1)$.

3. Ellipse, center $(2,1)$, vertices $(-1,1)$, $(5,1)$, foci $(2 \pm 2\sqrt{2},1)$.

5. Ellipse, center $(1, -2)$, vertices $(1 \pm \sqrt{3},-2)$, foci $(0,-2)$, $(2,-2)$.

7. Hyperbola, center $(2,-2)$, vertices $(2,-1)$, $(2,-3)$, foci $(2,-2 \pm \sqrt{2})$, asymptotes $y + 2 = \pm(x - 2)$.
9. Parabola, vertex $(\frac{3}{4},0)$, focus $(-\frac{5}{4},0)$.
11. Hyperbola, center $(3,0)$, vertices $(1,0)$, $(5,0)$, foci $(3 \pm \sqrt{13},0)$, asymptotes $2y = \pm 3(x - 3)$.
13. $(y - k)^2 = 4p(x - h)$.
15. $(x - h)^2/a^2 + (y - k)^2/(a^2 - c^2) = 1$.
17. $(x - h)^2/a^2 - (y - k)^2/(c^2 - a^2) = 1$.
19. Since, equivalently, $y + \dfrac{b^2 - 4ac}{4a} = a\left(x + \dfrac{b}{2a}\right)^2$ (by completing the square), the vertex is at $\left(-\dfrac{b}{2a}, -\dfrac{b^2 - 4ac}{4a}\right)$.

SECTION 3, PART II

1. By completing the square, the equation of the graph is

$$\frac{(x + 2)^2}{4^2} - \frac{(y + 1)^2}{3^2} = 1.$$

Since the point $(-1,-1)$, is on the axis of the hyperbola, the closest point will be the vertex $(2,-1)$ and the shortest distance 3.

3. Subtracting one equation from the other, we get a linear equation which corresponds to the straight line containing the points of intersection. The latter line can only intersect an ellipse in at most two points. In general, two quadratic graphs will intersect in 4 points (real or complex).
5. One could give a proof directly from the definition of an ellipse. However, it is simpler to note that convexity is preserved under orthogonal projection since segments and interior points project to segments and interior points, respectively. Since a circle is convex and projects into an ellipse, ellipses also are convex.
7. Proceeding as in Exercise 3, we could find the two points of intersection and then verify that the midpoint of the segment joining them coincides with the midpoint of the segment joining the two centers. The algebra can be simplified by noting that one doesn't have to actually solve a quadratic $x^2 + rx + s = 0$ to find the average of the two roots $\dfrac{x_1 + x_2}{2}$, for this immediately $= -r$.

   A simpler way to do this problem is to note that the result holds for two congruent circles and then for the two congruent and parallel ellipses by orthogonal projection (property **d**).

SECTION 4, PART I

1. $(0,\frac{2}{7})$.
3. $(4,4)$.
5. The figure has a vertical axis of symmetry and its centroid must lie on it.

$$w = \rho(12 \times 12 - 2(2 \times 2) - 8 \times 4) = 104\rho.$$
$$w\bar{y} = \rho[(8 \times 6) \times 3 + 2(10 \times 2) \times 7 + (8 \times 2) \times 11]$$
$$\bar{y} = \frac{600}{104} = \frac{75}{13}.$$

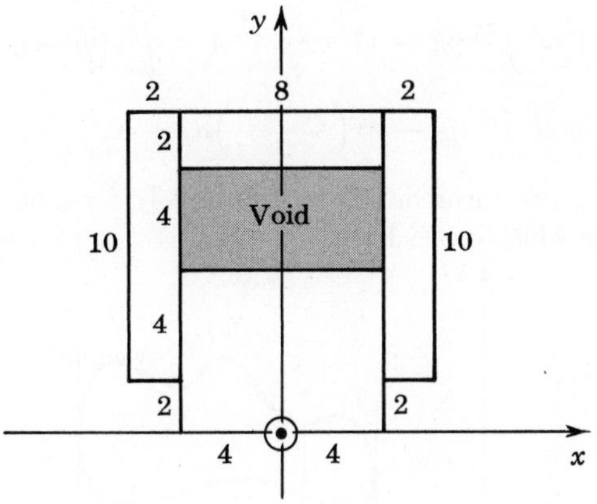

SECTION 4, PART II

1. We could divide the perforated circle into segments. But since we do not know the location of a centroid of a segment as yet, we use another method which is much simpler. We fill in the void and add its mass taken negatively at its centroid. This gives a mass of 100ρ acting at (0,0) and a mass of -48ρ acting at (4,3). Now taking moments

$$(100\rho - 48\rho)\bar{x} = 100\rho \times 0 - 48\rho \times 4; \quad \bar{x} = \tfrac{48}{13}.$$
$$(100\rho - 48\rho)\bar{y} = 100\rho \times 0 - 48\rho \times 3; \quad \bar{y} = \tfrac{36}{13}.$$

SECTION 5, PART I

1. $(\frac{12}{5},\frac{3}{4})$.
3. $(\frac{8}{5},\frac{16}{7})$.
5. $(\pi/2 - 1,\pi/8)$.
7. $((e^2 + 1)/4,e/2 - 1)$.
9. $\bar{x} = (\sqrt{2} - 1)/\ln(1 + \sqrt{2}),\ \bar{y} = \pi/8 \ln(1 + \sqrt{2})$.
11. $\bar{x} = 0,\ \bar{y} = 4a/3\pi$.
13. $\bar{x} = (a \cosh a - \sinh a)/(\cosh a - 1),\ \bar{y} = (\sinh 2a - 2a)/8(\cosh a - 1)$.

SECTION 5, PART II

1. $\bar{x} = \bar{y} = 4r/3\pi$.
3. $\bar{x} = 2r \sin\theta/3\theta,\ \bar{y} = 0$, where (0,0) is at the center of the circle and the x axis is the axis of symmetry; $\bar{x} = \dfrac{2r}{3},\ \bar{y} = 0$.

SECTION 6, PART I

1. $(\frac{8}{3},0)$.
3. $((\pi^2 + 4)/4\pi,0)$.
5. $(\ln 5/2 \tan^{-1} 2,0)$.
7. Three-fourths the way down the altitude from the vertex.
9. $\bar{y} = \dfrac{2p}{3}$ for parabola $y^2 = 4px$.

SECTION 6, PART II

1. For now, we consider simple type regions as shown:

$$V = \int_{x_1}^{x_2} (y_2^2 - y_1^2)\,dx, \qquad A = \int_{x_1}^{x_2} (y_2 - y_1)\,dx,$$

$$\bar{y} = \int_{x_1}^{x_2} (y_2 - y_1)\left(\frac{y_1 + y_2}{2}\right) dx \div A.$$

Thus, $2\pi\bar{y}A = V$. The theorem follows more easily for more complicated regions by double integration which comes later.

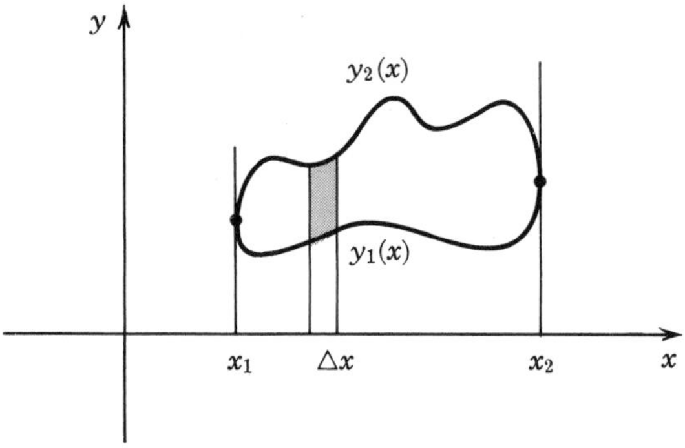

3. Since the volume of a sphere is $\frac{4}{3}\pi r^3$, we get $\frac{4}{3}\pi r^3 = 2\pi\bar{y}\left(\frac{\pi r^2}{2}\right)$. Thus $\bar{y} = \frac{4r}{3\pi}$ (above the base).

5. Rotating semiellipse about the x axis gives

$$V = 2\pi\bar{y}A = 2\pi\left(\frac{4b}{3\pi}\right)\frac{\pi ab}{2} = \frac{4}{3}\pi ab^2.$$

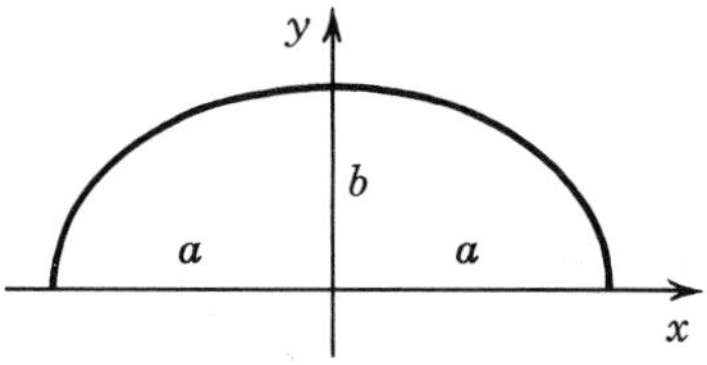

(For $\bar{y}$ see Exercise I-12, Section 5).

SECTION 7, PART I

1. 416,667 lb.

3. 9750 lb.

5. 3×10^6 lb.

7. 216.5 lb.

SECTION 7, PART II

1. a. For now, we consider simple types of regions as shown.

$$F = \int_{y_1}^{y_2} [x_2(y) - x_1(y)]\,\rho y\,dy$$

$$A = \int_{y_1}^{y_2} [x_2(y) - x_1(y)]\,dy$$

$$\bar{y} = \int_{y_1}^{y_2} [x_2(y) - x_1(y)]y\,dy \div A.$$

Thus $F = \rho\bar{y}A$.

b. $F = \rho\,12(6 \times 4) = 288\rho = 18{,}000$ lb.

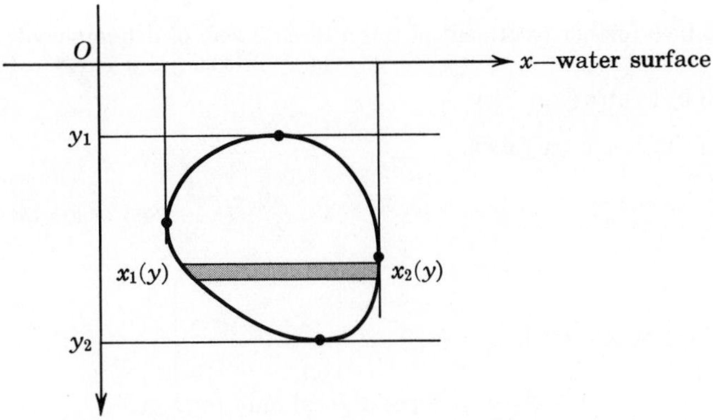

REVIEW, PART I

1. 2 lines from a point outside; one line from a point on the boundary; none from a point in the interior. This result is also valid for smooth convex regions. Additionally, there are at most two tangent lines from a point to the graph of the general quadratic equation $ax^2 + bxy + cy^2 + dx + ey + f = 0$. For let the point be (h,k) and the tangent line have slope m. Its equation is then $y - k = m(x - n)$. Eliminating y between the two equations, we obtain a quadratic equation in x. In order for the line to be tangent, we must have equal roots. Thus the discriminant must be zero which leads to at most two values of m.

3. Eliminating y^2 between the two equations, we obtain an equation of the form $y = rx^2 + sx + t$. Substituting back in the ellipse equation, we obtain a fourth-order equation in x. (Also see solution of Exercise II-3, Section 3).

5.
$$PQ = kPO \quad \text{or} \quad x + a = k\sqrt{x^2 + y^2}.$$

Squaring and simplifying,

$$(k^2 - 1)x^2 - 2xa + k^2y^2 = a^2.$$

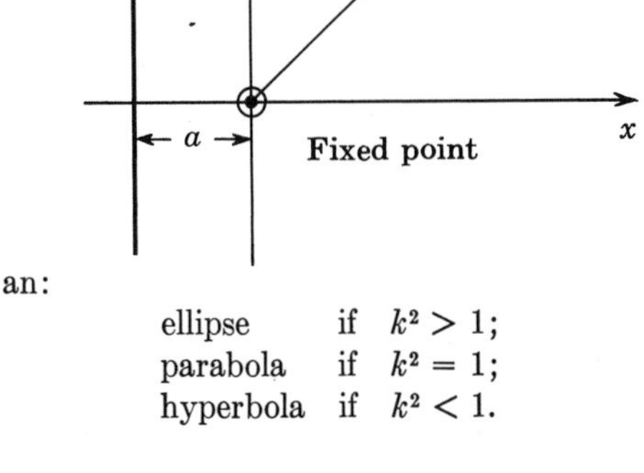

Thus, the graph is an:

ellipse if $k^2 > 1$;
parabola if $k^2 = 1$;
hyperbola if $k^2 < 1$.

There will be a further treatment of this alternate way of defining conics subsequently.

7. 3. **9.** 1. **11.** $\bar{x} = e - 2,\quad \bar{y} = (e^2 - 1)/8.$

13. $\bar{x} = \bar{y} = 0$ by centrosymmetry.

15. $\dfrac{e^2 + 3}{2(e^2 - 1)}$ from origin on x axis.

17. Origin.

19. $\dfrac{19 - 3e^2}{2(e^2 - 5)}$ from origin on x axis.

REVIEW, PART II

1. $-\dfrac{b^2x}{a^2y}$ = slope of tangent line at (x,y),

$$\frac{y}{x + ae} = \text{slopes of focal radii to } (x,y).$$

It suffices to show that the tangents of the angles between the tangent line and the focal radii are the same, i.e.,

$$\frac{\dfrac{y}{x + ae} + \dfrac{b^2x}{a^2y}}{1 - \dfrac{y}{x + ae}\dfrac{b^2x}{a^2y}} = -\frac{\dfrac{b^2x}{a^2y} + \dfrac{y}{x - ae}}{1 - \dfrac{y}{x - ae}\dfrac{b^2x}{a^2y}}.$$

This follows by simplifying and noting that

$$a^2y^2 + b^2x^2 = a^2b^2 \quad \text{and} \quad (ae)^2 = a^2 - b^2.$$

3. By considering the circumscribing rectangle whose sides are parallel to the axes, the circle will necessarily have the form $x^2 + y^2 = a^2 + b^2$.

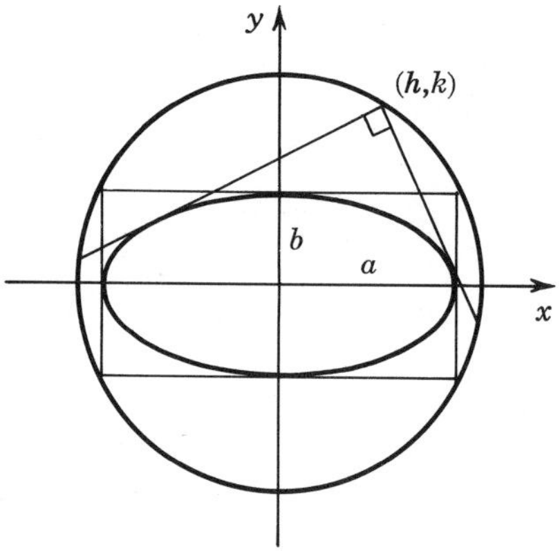

Here, $h = \sqrt{a^2 + b^2}\cos\theta,\ k = \sqrt{a^2 + b^2}\sin\theta$. Let $y - k = m(x - h)$ denote a tangent line from (h,k) to the ellipse. Eliminating y between the equations of the ellipse and the line, we get $b^2x^2 + a^2(mx - mh + k)^2 = a^2b^2$. The condition for the line to be tangent to the ellipse is that the discriminant be 0 or $m^2(h^2 - a^2) - 2mhk + k^2 - b^2 = 0$. Consequently, there are two possible values of m whose product is

$$\frac{k^2 - b^2}{h^2 - a^2} = \frac{(a^2 + b^2)\sin^2\theta - b^2}{(a^2 + b^2)\cos^2\theta - a^2} = -1.$$

5. If it could be done, then the circumscribing circle of the pentagon would intersect the ellipse in 5 points. This is impossible, because the maximum number is 4. (See solution of Exercise II-3, Section 3, and Exercise I-3, Review.)

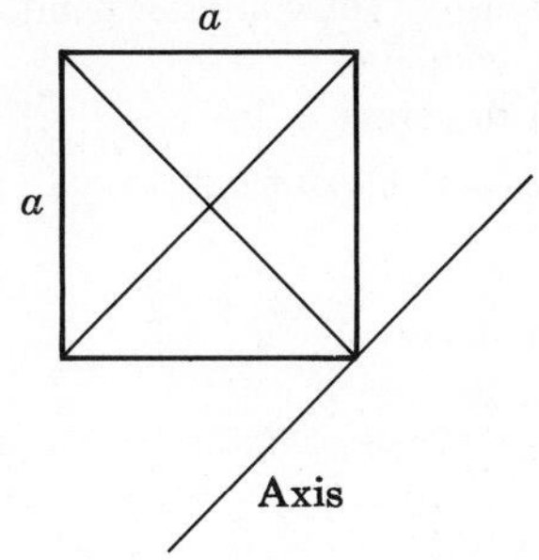

7. By Pappus' theorem, Exercise II-1, Section 5, the volume generated equals $2\pi\bar{y}A$. The maximum volume is obtained when $\bar{y} = \frac{1}{2}$ diagonal $= \dfrac{a}{\sqrt{2}}$ and $V_{\max} = \pi a^3\sqrt{2}$.

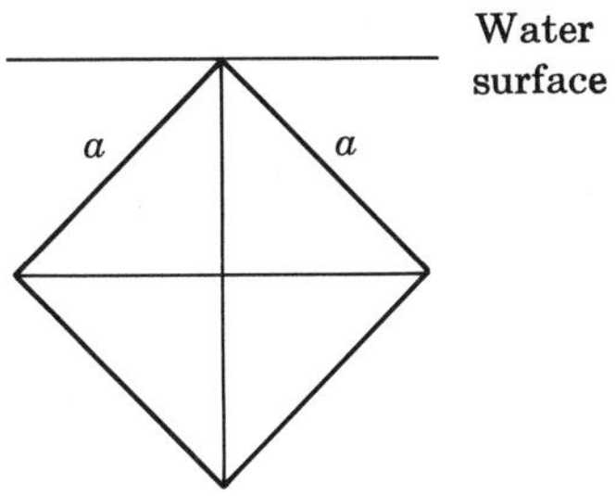

By Exercise II-1, Section 7,

$$F = \frac{\rho a}{\sqrt{2}} \cdot a^2.$$

CHAPTER 14

SECTION 1, PART I

5. $\dfrac{\sin x - x}{x^3} = \dfrac{\cos w - 1}{3w^2} = \dfrac{-\sin y}{6y}$

$$= -\frac{\cos z}{6} \qquad 0 < w < x, \quad 0 < y < w, \quad 0 < z < y.$$

7. By **6.5,** $e^x - e^0 = xe^z$ for some z in $(0,x)$. Thus,

$$e^x - 1 = xe^z.$$

Since e^x is increasing in $[0,\infty)$,

$$xe^x > e^x - 1 > x,$$

and

$$\frac{1}{1-x} > e^x > 1 + x.$$

SECTION 1, PART II

1. $F'(0)$ does not exist.

3. If there was more than one real root, then by Rolle's theorem, the derivative of $x^n - nx + a$ would have to vanish at some interior point of the interval. The derivative $nx^{n-1} - n$ only vanishes at an endpoint.

5. Let $H(x) = 1$ and expand out to obtain

$$F'(\lambda)[G(a) - G(b)] = G'(\lambda)[F(a) - F(b)].$$

SECTION 2, PART I

1. 1. **3.** 1. **5.** 1.
7. 0. **9.** 2. **11.** -1.
13. 0. **15.** $\frac{1}{6}$. **17.** $\frac{1}{9}$.
19. $\frac{2}{3}$. **21.** $\ln 10 - 1$.

SECTION 2, PART II

1. $\frac{1}{120}$, use l'Hospital's rule repeatedly.

3. $\frac{9}{20}$, use l'Hospital's rule repeatedly.

5. $n(n+1)/2$, use l'Hospital's rule repeatedly.

7. Using l'Hospital's rule,

$$\text{limit} = \operatorname*{limit}_{x\to 0} \sum_{k=1}^{n} k^x \ln k = \ln n!$$

9. Let $x = \lambda y$ to give

$$\operatorname*{limit}_{\lambda\to 0} \int_1^2 \frac{e^{-\lambda y}}{y}\, dy.$$

Intuitively, bringing in limit under the integral sign gives

$$\int_1^2 \frac{1}{y}\, dy = \ln 2.$$

To justify this:

$$\text{limit} = \operatorname*{limit}_{\lambda\to 0} \int_1^2 \frac{e^{-\lambda y} - 1}{y}\, dy + \int_1^2 \frac{1}{y}\, dy.$$

By the mean value theorem, $1 - e^{-\lambda y} < \lambda y$. Thus

$$0 \le \operatorname*{limit}_{\lambda\to 0} \int_1^2 \frac{1 - e^{-\lambda y}}{y}\, dy \le \operatorname*{limit}_{\lambda\to 0} \int_1^2 \frac{\lambda y}{y}\, dy = 0.$$

SECTION 3, PART I

1. 0. **3.** 0. **5.** 0.
7. $1/e$. **9.** 0. **11.** 1.
13. e^3. **15.** 1. **17.** e^a.

19. Follows from

$$\operatorname*{limit}_{x\to\infty} \frac{\ln x}{x^a} = 0 \quad \text{(by l'Hospital's rule)}$$

or else choose $N = e^{2/a^2}$. Then

$$\frac{2}{a^2} < e^{2/a} = 1 + \frac{2}{a} + \frac{2}{a^2} + \cdots.$$

SECTION 3, PART II

1. 1.

$$\lim_{x\to 0^+} (\sin x - x)\ln \sin x = \lim_{x\to 0^+}\left(\frac{\sin x - x}{x^3}\right)x^3\left(\ln x + \ln\frac{\sin x}{x}\right) = 0.$$

3. $1/e$. $\displaystyle\lim_{y\to 0}\frac{\ln(1-\sin y^2)}{\sin y^2} = -1.$

5.
$$\lim_{x\to 0}\frac{x-\sin^{-1}x}{x^2\sin^{-1}x} = \lim_{y\to 0}\frac{\sin y - y}{y\sin^2 y} = \lim_{y\to 0}\frac{\sin y - y}{y^3} = -\frac{1}{6}.$$

7. $\displaystyle\lim_{x\to\infty}\left(1+\frac{m}{x}\right)^x = \lim_{y\to\infty}\left[\left(1+\frac{1}{y}\right)^y\right]^m = e^m.$ Thus

$$\text{Inner limit} = \frac{e^{a\lambda}-e^{b\lambda}}{\lambda}; \qquad \text{outer limit} = a-b.$$

9. $$\lim_{x\to\infty} x\frac{\int_0^x e^{t^2}\,dt}{e^{x^2}} = \lim_{x\to\infty}\frac{\int_0^x e^{t^2}\,dt + xe^{x^2}}{2xe^{x^2}} = \frac{1}{2} + \lim_{x\to\infty}\frac{\int_0^x e^{t^2}\,dt}{2xe^{x^2}} = \frac{1}{2}.$$

SECTION 4, PART I

1. 2.
3. Doesn't exist.
5. 2.
7. 2.
9. $\frac{3}{2}$.
11. $\pi/4$.
13. Doesn't exist.
15. $1/2e$.
17. b. Let $f(x) = x^{2n-1}$, $n = 1, 2, 3, \cdots$.
19. $\pi/2$.
21. $3(1+\sqrt[3]{2})$.
25. 1; integrate by parts.
27. -1.

SECTION 4, PART II

1. $\displaystyle\int_0^1 x^a\,dx = \frac{x^{a+1}}{a+1}\Big]_0^1$; thus $a > -1$.

3. Consider two cases. (1) $b \geq 0$. For arbitrarily large x, the integrand behaves as x^{a-b} and thus for the integral to exist as far as the upper limit is concerned, $a - b + 1 < 0$. In the neighborhood of 0, the integrand behaves as x^a and thus for the integral to exist as far as the lower limit is concerned $a + 1 > 0$. Or, put together, $-1 < a < b - 1$, $b > 0$. (2) $b < 0$. At ∞, the integrand behaves as x^a, thus $a + 1 < 0$. At 0, the integrand behaves as x^{a-b}. Thus $a - b + 1 > 0$, or, put together,

$$-1 > a > b - 1, \qquad b < 0.$$

5. $n > -1$, $2/(n+1)^3$.
7. $n!/a^{n+1}$, $a < 0$.

SECTION 5, PART I

1. $\displaystyle f(x) = -\left(x-\frac{\pi}{2}\right) + \frac{1}{3!}\left(x-\frac{\pi}{2}\right)^3 - \frac{1}{5!}\left(x-\frac{\pi}{2}\right)^5 - \frac{1}{6!}\left(x-\frac{\pi}{2}\right)^6 \cos z$, z between $\frac{\pi}{2}$ and x.

3. $\displaystyle F(x) = \frac{\pi}{4} + \frac{1}{2}(x-1) - \frac{1}{4}(x-1)^2 + \frac{1}{12}(x-1)^3 - \frac{(x-1)^4 z(z^2-1)}{(z^2+1)^4}$, z between 1 and x.

5. $f(x) = \sqrt{2} + \sqrt{2}\left(x - \frac{\pi}{4}\right) + \frac{3\sqrt{2}}{2}\left(x - \frac{\pi}{4}\right)^2 + \frac{11\sqrt{2}}{6}\left(x - \frac{\pi}{4}\right)^3$
$+ \frac{1}{24}\left(x - \frac{\pi}{4}\right)^4 (24 \sec^5 z - 20 \sec^3 z + \sec z)$, z between $\frac{\pi}{4}$ and x.

7. $f(x) = x - \frac{x^3}{3!} + \frac{x^5}{5!} - \frac{x^7}{7!} \cos z$, z between 0 and x.

9. $g(x) = x - \frac{x^2}{2} + \frac{x^3}{3} - \frac{x^4}{4} + \frac{x^5}{5} - \frac{x^6}{6}(z+1)^{-6}$, z between 0 and x.

11. $F(x) = x + \frac{x^3}{3!} + \frac{3x^4}{4!}(1 - z^2)^{-7/2}(3z + 2z^3)$, z between 0 and x.

13. $f(x) = 1 + \frac{x}{2} + \frac{1\cdot 3}{2!2^2}x^2 + \frac{1\cdot 3\cdot 5}{3!2^3}x^3 + \frac{1\cdot 3\cdot 5\cdot 7}{4!2^4}x^4 + \frac{1\cdot 3\cdot 5\cdot 7\cdot 9}{5!2^4}x^5(1 - z)^{-11/2}$, z between 0 and x.

15. $g(x) = x + \frac{x^3}{3} + \frac{x^5}{15}(15 \sec^4 z - 15 \sec^2 z + 2) \sec^2 z$, z between 0 and x.

17. $F(x) = \frac{1}{2} - \frac{1}{4}x + \frac{1}{48}x^3 + \frac{x^4}{24}(e^{3z} - 11e^{2z} + 11e^z - 1)$, z between 0 and x.

Section 5, Part II

1. Maclaurin's formula becomes Taylor's formula if we let $f(x) = g(x + c)$.

3. $e^x - e^y y' = y + xy'$, hence $y'(0) = 1$.
$e^x - e^y y'^2 - e^y y'' = 2y' + xy''$, hence $y''(0) = -1$.
$e^x - e^y y'^3 - 2e^y y' y'' - e^y y''' = 3y'' + xy'''$, hence $y'''(0) = 2$.
$y(x) = x - x^2 + 2x^3 + \cdots$.

Section 6, Part I

1. $\sin x = x - (x^3/3!) + (x^5/5!) \pm .000002$; .479427.

3. $e^x = 1 + x/1! + x^2/2! + x^3/3! + x^4/4! + x^5/5! \pm .005$; 2.716.

5. Since $F^{[n+1]}(x) = 0$, $F(x)$ is the nth Taylor's polynomial of F at any number c.

Section 6, Part II

1. By Exercise I-6,

$$\ln(1 - y) = -y - \frac{y^2}{2} - \frac{y^3}{3} - \cdots, \qquad \ln(1 + y) = y - \frac{y^2}{2} + \frac{y^3}{3} - \cdots.$$

$$\ln\frac{1 - x^2}{1 + x^2} = \ln(1 - x^2) - \ln(1 + x^2) = -2\left\{\frac{x^4}{2} + \frac{x^8}{4} + \frac{x^{12}}{6} + \cdots\right\}.$$

3. $\cos^2 x = \frac{1 + \cos 2x}{2} = \frac{1}{2} + \frac{1}{2}\left[1 - \frac{(2x)^2}{2!} + \frac{(2x)^4}{4!} - \cdots\right]$.

5. Let a be an approximation to the desired root $\bar{a}$. By Taylor's formula, $F(x) = F(a) + (x - a)F'(a) + \frac{(x - a)^2}{2}F''(z)$. Since $F(\bar{a}) = 0$, and neglecting the last term which will be small if a is a sufficiently good first approximation, we get

$$0 \doteq F(a) + (\bar{a} - a)F'(a) \quad \text{or} \quad \bar{a} \doteq a - \frac{F(a)}{F'(a)}.$$

7. $\frac{a}{2c+b} = \frac{\sin A}{2+\cos A} = \frac{A}{3}\left(1 - \frac{A^4}{180} - \frac{A^6}{1512}\right)$ by Taylor's formula (A is in radians). For small A, the right-hand side $\doteq \frac{A}{3}$ giving $A \doteq \frac{3a}{2c+b}$. A better approximation is given by $\frac{a}{2c+b} \doteq \frac{A}{3}\left(1 - \frac{1}{180}\left(\frac{3a}{2c+b}\right)^4\right)$. In degrees, $A \doteq \frac{3\cdot 180}{\pi}\cdot\frac{a}{2c+b}$. Since $\frac{3\cdot 180}{\pi} \doteq 171.89$, we replace it by the simpler number 172.

True Value	Value by Formula
5°	5.0033°
15°	15.0094°
30°	30.0067°
45°	44.9270°

REVIEW, PART I

1. 1. **3.** 1. **5.** 0.

7. 0. **9.** $\frac{b}{a^2+b^2}$ (integrate by parts).

11. Does not exist. **13.** $\frac{\pi}{4}$ (let $y = e^x$).

15. $\frac{1}{2+x} = 1 - (x+1) + (x+1)^2 - (x+1)^3 + (x+1)^4 - \frac{(x+1)^5}{(2+z)^5}$.

17. 0.27633 (use the Maclaurin expansion for e^{-x^2}).

19. $F(b) - F(a) = (b-a)F'(z)$, hence $|F(b) - F(a)| = |(b-a)F'(z)| < M(b-a)$.

21. The height of a rectangle of length $b - a$ which has the same area as the region under the graph of $y = F(x)$ between a and b.

REVIEW, PART II.

1. a. Let $O(F) = F_1$, $O(G) = G_1$. Then, $|F_1| \le k_1F$, $|G_1| \le k_2G$ and $|F_1 + G_1| \le |F_1| + |G_1| \le (k_1 + k_2)(F + G)$. Thus $O(F) + O(G) = O(F + G)$.

b. $|FG| = |F|\,|G| \le k_1k_2F_1F_2$. Thus, $O(F)\cdot O(G) = O(FG)$.

c. Let $o(G) = G_2$. Then since $\left|\frac{F_1G_2}{FG}\right| \le k_1\left|\frac{G_2}{G}\right|$,

$$\text{limit}\left|\frac{F_1G_2}{FG}\right| \le k_1 \text{ limit}\left|\frac{G_2}{G}\right| = 0. \quad \text{Thus} \quad o(FG) = F_1G_2 = O(F)\cdot o(G).$$

d. Since limit $\frac{F + o(G)}{G} = \text{limit } \frac{F}{G}$, $F + o(G) \sim G$.

3. Using Maclaurin's formula:

a. $\sin x = x - \frac{x^3}{6}\cos z$ and $\left|\frac{x^3}{6}\cos z\right| \le \frac{x^3}{6}$ if $x \ge 0$.

b. $\cos x = 1 - \frac{x^2}{2} + \frac{x^4}{24}\cos z$ and $\left|\frac{x^4}{24}\cos z\right| \le \frac{x^4}{24}$.

c. $e^x = 1 + x + \frac{x^2}{2}e^z$ and $\left|\frac{x^2}{2}e^z\right| \le \frac{x^2e}{2}$ for $x < 1$.

d. $\ln(1 + x) = x - \frac{x^2}{2}(1+z)^{-2}$ and $\left|\frac{x^2}{2}(1+z)^{-2}\right| \le \frac{x^2}{2}$.

e. $\left(1+\frac{a}{x}\right)^x = \exp\left[x \ln\left(1+\frac{a}{x}\right)\right] = \exp\left\{x\left[\frac{a}{x} - \frac{a^2}{2x^2} + O\left(\frac{1}{x^3}\right)\right]\right\}$

$= e^a \cdot \exp\left[-\frac{a^2}{2x} + O(x^{-2})\right] = e^a\left[1 - \frac{a^2}{2x} + O(x^{-2})\right].$

5. $\lim_{x\to\infty} xe\left[-\frac{1}{2x} + O(x^{-2})\right] = -e/2.$

7. $\lim_{x\to\infty} \frac{xF'}{F} = \lim_{x\to\infty} \frac{xF'' + F'}{F'} = 1 + \lim_{x\to\infty} \frac{xF''' + F''}{F''} = 3.$

9. If there were more than one root in (a,b), then F' would have to vanish in (a,b) by Rolle's theorem. But this would contradict the hypothesis $F'(x) > 0$.

11. $\lim_{x\to 0} \frac{F(x)}{G(x)} = \lim_{x\to 0} (x \sin 1/x)\left(\frac{x}{\sin x}\right) \cos x = 0.$

$\lim_{x\to 0} \frac{F'(x)}{G'(x)} = \lim_{x\to 0}\left[\frac{2x \sin 1/x - \sin 1/x}{\sec^2 x}\right]$ which does not exist.

CHAPTER 15

Section 1, Part I

1. $\frac{35}{6}$.

3. $\pi\sqrt{2}/(\sqrt{2} - 1)$.

5. $\frac{68}{111}$.

7. $\sum_{k=1}^{\infty} \frac{1}{4k^2 - 1}$; converges to $\frac{1}{2}$.

9. $\sum_{k=1}^{\infty} \frac{k^2 + k - 1}{k(k+1)}$; diverges.

11. $\frac{1}{2} - \frac{1}{2^2} - \frac{1}{2^3} - \cdots - \frac{1}{2^n} - \cdots = 0.$

13. $\sum_{k=1}^{\infty} \frac{2k - 1}{(k^2 + 1)(k^2 - 2k + 2)}$; converges to 1.

15. $\lim_{n\to\infty} \frac{n}{n+1} = 1.$

17. $\frac{1}{1} + \frac{1}{\sqrt{2}} + \cdots + \frac{1}{\sqrt{n}} > 1 + \frac{1}{2} + \cdots + \frac{1}{n}$ and $\sum \frac{1}{\sqrt{n}}$ diverges.

19. $r = \frac{3}{2} > 1.$

21. $|S_m - S_n| < \epsilon$ for all $m, n > M(\epsilon)$. (See p. 452.)
$|a_{n+1} + a_{n+2} + \cdots + a_m| < \epsilon$ for all $m, n > M(\epsilon)$. Now let $m \to \infty$.

23. Since $\ln\left(1 + \frac{1}{k}\right) = \ln(k+1) - \ln k$, $b_k = \ln k \to \infty$.

25. Geometric series with $a = 2x$, $r = (2x)^2$. Thus

$$S = \frac{2x}{1 - 4x^2} \quad \text{for} \quad |x| < \frac{1}{2}.$$

27. Geometric series with $a = 1$, $r = \frac{x^2 - 1}{2}$. Thus

$$S = \frac{1}{1 - \frac{x^2 - 1}{2}} = \frac{2}{3 - x^2} \quad \text{for} \quad \left|\frac{x^2 - 1}{2}\right| < 1 \quad \text{or} \quad |x| < \sqrt{3}.$$

SECTION 1, PART II

1. $\dfrac{n}{(n+1)!} = \dfrac{1}{n!} - \dfrac{1}{(n+1)!}$, $S = 1$.

3. $\dfrac{1}{(2n-1)(2n+1)} = \dfrac{1}{2}\left\{\dfrac{1}{2n-1} - \dfrac{1}{2n+1}\right\}$, $S = \dfrac{1}{2}$.

5. $\dfrac{1}{n(n+1)\cdots(n+p)} = \dfrac{1}{p}\left\{\dfrac{1}{n(n+1)\cdots(n+p-1)} - \dfrac{1}{(n+1)(n+2)\cdots(n+p)}\right\}$

$$S = \frac{1}{p(p!)}$$

7. $S_n(1-a) = a + a^2 + \cdots + a^n - na^{n+1}$

$$S = \lim_{n\to\infty} S_n = \lim_{n\to\infty}\left\{\frac{a(1-a^n)}{(1-a)^2} - \frac{na^{n+1}}{1-a}\right\} = \frac{a}{(1-a)^2}.$$

9. $S_n(1-r-r^2) = r - (a_n + a_{n-1})r^{n+1} - a_n r^{n+2}$

$$S = \lim_{n\to\infty} S_n = \frac{r}{1-r-r^2}.$$

SECTION 2, PART I

1. Convergent.
3. Convergent.
5. Divergent.
7. Divergent.
9. Convergent.
11. Convergent.
13. Convergent.

SECTION 2, PART II

1. If
$$O\left(\frac{P(n)}{Q(n)}\right) = n^{-1-\epsilon}, \quad \text{as} \quad n\to\infty, \quad \text{that is}$$
$$\left|\frac{P(n)}{Q(n)}\right| \le kn^{-1-\epsilon} \quad \text{as} \quad n\to\infty,$$
then
$$\left|\int_{n_0}^{\infty}\frac{P(n)}{Q(n)}\,dn\right| \le \int_{n_0}^{\infty}\left|\frac{P(n)}{Q(n)}\right| dn \le \int_{n_0}^{\infty}\frac{k}{x^{1+\epsilon}}\,dx.$$
Converges if $\epsilon > 0$, diverges if $\epsilon \le 0$.

Note that in the integral test, we can ignore any finite number of terms.

3. $\displaystyle\int_2^{\infty}\frac{1}{n(\ln n)^r}\,dn = \int_{\ln 2}^{\infty}\frac{1}{t^r}\,dt\cdot$ Converges if $r > 1$, diverges if $r \le 1$.

5. If $S_n = \sum_{r=1}^{n} 1/\sqrt{r}$, then by the method of the integral test,

$$S_{n-1} = S_n - \frac{1}{\sqrt{n}} \ge \int_1^n \frac{dn}{\sqrt{n}} \ge S_n - 1$$

or

$$\frac{1}{\sqrt{n}}\left\{\int_1^n \frac{1}{\sqrt{n}}\,dn + 1\right\} \ge \frac{S_n}{\sqrt{n}} \ge \frac{1}{\sqrt{n}}\left\{\int_1^n \frac{1}{\sqrt{n}}\,dn + \frac{1}{\sqrt{n}}\right\}.$$

$$\lim_{n\to\infty}\frac{S_n}{\sqrt{n}} = \lim_{n\to\infty}\frac{1}{\sqrt{n}}\int_1^n \frac{1}{\sqrt{n}}\,dn = 2.$$

7. As in the preceding exercise, if $S_n = \sum_{k=1}^{n} \frac{1}{k^p}$, then

$$S_\infty - S_n > \int_{n+1}^{\infty} \frac{1}{k^p}\,dk > S_\infty - S_{n+1} = S_\infty - S_n - \frac{1}{(n+1)^p}$$

or

$$\frac{1}{(n+1)^p} + \int_{n+1}^{\infty} \frac{1}{k^p}\,dk > S_\infty - S_n > \int_{n+1}^{\infty} \frac{1}{k^p}\,dk$$

or

$$\frac{1}{(p-1)n^{p-1}} > \frac{1}{(n+1)^p} + \frac{1}{(p-1)(n+1)^{p-1}} > S_\infty - S_n > \frac{1}{(p-1)(n+1)^{p-1}}.$$

a. $p = 2$, $n = 10$. $\quad \frac{1}{10} > S_\infty - S_{10} > \frac{1}{11}.$

$p = 2$, $n = 1000$. $\quad \frac{1}{1000} > S_\infty - S_{1000} > \frac{1}{1001}.$

This indicates very slow convergence.

b. $p = 3$, $n = 10$. $\quad \frac{1}{200} > S_\infty - S_{10} > \frac{1}{242}.$

$p = 3$, $n = 1000$. $\quad \frac{1}{2{,}000{,}000} > S_\infty - S_{1000} > \frac{1}{2{,}004{,}002}.$

Section 3, Part I

1. Convergent, $\frac{k+1}{(k+2)2^k} < \frac{1}{2^k}.$

3. Divergent, $\frac{k+1}{\ln(k+2)} > \frac{1}{k}.$

5. Convergent, $ke^{-k^2} < \frac{k}{1 + k^2 + \frac{k^4}{2}} < \frac{2}{k^3}.$

7. Convergent, $\frac{1}{\sqrt{k(k+1)(k+2)}} < \frac{1}{\sqrt[2]{k^3}}.$

9. Convergent, $\frac{\sqrt{k}}{k^2 - \sin^2 100k} \le \frac{\sqrt{k}}{k^2 - 1} < \frac{2}{k^{3/2}}.$

Section 3, Part II

1. Since $\lim_{n\to\infty} n^{1/n} = 1$, it follows by **15.13** that the series diverges. See Exercise II-4, Section 2.

3. Converges, $\frac{1}{(\ln n)^{\ln n}} = \frac{1}{n^{\ln \ln n}} < \frac{1}{n^2}$ for $n > e^{e^2}$.

5. Converges, $\lim_{n\to\infty} \left[e\left(1 - \frac{1}{n}\right)^n\right]^n = 1$ (see **15.13**).

7. $\left(a_n - \frac{1}{n}\right)^2 \ge 0$ or $a_n^2 + \frac{1}{n^2} \ge \frac{2a_n}{n}$. Thus

$$\sum_{n=1}^{\infty} \frac{2a_n}{n} < \sum_{n=1}^{\infty} \left(a_n^2 + \frac{1}{n^2}\right).$$

Result is also valid if a_n is not ≥ 0. This will follow from subsequent theorem **15.16.**

9. If $\sum_{n=1}^{\infty} a_n$ and $\sum_{n=1}^{\infty} b_n$ are two convergent series, then so also is $\sum_{1}^{\infty} (a_n - b_n)$. Since

$$(1 - \tfrac{1}{2}) + (\tfrac{1}{3} - \tfrac{1}{4}) + (\tfrac{1}{5} - \tfrac{1}{6}) + \cdots$$

cannot equal zero, we obtain a contradiction.

SECTION 4, PART I.

1. Converges.

3. Converges.

5. Converges.

7. Diverges.

9. Converges.

11. The first few terms of the series are

$$1 - 1 + \frac{1}{2} - \frac{1}{4} + \frac{1}{3} - \frac{1}{9} + \cdots + \frac{1}{k} - \frac{1}{k^2} + \cdots$$

which is *not* an alternating decreasing one. Here, $\sum_{k=1}^{\infty} a_{2k}$ converges while $\sum_{k=1}^{\infty} a_{2k-1}$ diverges. Thus, $\sum_{k=1}^{\infty} a_k$ diverges.

13. .800. (Series can be summed exactly to this number.)

15. .969.

SECTION 4, PART II

1. Converges.

$$D\frac{\ln^2 r}{r} = \frac{(\ln r)(2 - \ln r)}{r^2} < 0 \quad \text{for} \quad r > e^2.$$

$$\operatorname*{limit}_{r\to\infty} \frac{\ln^2 r}{r} = 0.$$

3. Converges. $\operatorname{arccot} n = \arctan \frac{1}{n}$, which is decreasing and approaching 0.

5. Converges. Alternately decreasing and

$$\operatorname*{limit}_{n\to\infty} \frac{1\cdot 3\cdot 5 \cdots (2n-1)}{2\cdot 4\cdot 6 \cdots (2n)} = \operatorname*{limit}_{n\to\infty} \frac{2n!}{(2^n\cdot n!)^2} = \operatorname*{limit}_{n\to\infty} \frac{\left(\frac{2n}{e}\right)^n \sqrt{4\pi n}}{\left(2^n\left(\frac{n}{e}\right)\sqrt{2\pi n}\right)^2} = 0.$$

7. Let $S_n = 1 + \frac{1}{2} + \cdots + \frac{1}{n}$. Since $\frac{1}{n}$ is strictly decreasing,

$$S_n - \frac{1}{n} > \int_1^n \frac{1}{n}\,dn > S_n - 1$$

or

$$1 > S_n - \ln n > \frac{1}{n} > 0 \qquad (S_n - \ln n \text{ is bounded.})$$

To show $S_n - \ln n$ is strictly decreasing, we must show that $S_n - \ln n > S_{n+1} - \ln(n+1)$ or $\ln\left(1 + \frac{1}{n}\right) > \frac{1}{n+1}$. By the mean value theorem,

$$\ln(1+x) = \ln 1 + \frac{x}{1+z}, \qquad 0 < z < x \geq 1$$

and $\ln(1+x) > \dfrac{x}{1+x}$. Now let $x = \dfrac{1}{n}$.

9. Let T_{3n} denote the sum of the given series up to the term $-\dfrac{1}{4n}$ and let

$$S_n = 1 + \frac{1}{2} + \cdots + \frac{1}{n}.$$

Then

$$T_{3n} = \left(1 + \frac{1}{3} + \cdots + \frac{1}{2n-1}\right) - \left(\frac{1}{2} + \frac{1}{4} + \cdots + \frac{1}{4n}\right)$$

or

$$T_{3n} = (S_{2n} - \tfrac{1}{2}S_n) - (\tfrac{1}{2}S_{2n}) = \tfrac{1}{2}(S_{2n} - S_n).$$

$$\operatorname*{limit}_{n\to\infty} T_{3n} = \tfrac{1}{2} \operatorname*{limit}_{n\to\infty} \{(S_{2n} - \ln 2n) - (S_n - \ln n) + \ln 2\} = \tfrac{1}{2}\ln 2$$

(by Exercise 7). Also,

$$\operatorname*{limit}_{n\to\infty} T_{3n+1} = \operatorname*{limit}_{n\to\infty} T_{3n+2} = \tfrac{1}{2}\ln$$

11. Let $T_{rn} = 1 - \dfrac{1}{2} + \dfrac{1}{3} - \cdots - \dfrac{(-1)^{rn}}{rn}$.

Striking out every r^{th} term we obtain a series S whose partial sum of $(r-1)n$ terms is

$$S_{(r-1)n} = T_{rn} + \frac{(-1)^r}{r} + \frac{(-1)^{2r}}{2r} + \cdots + \frac{(-1)^{nr}}{rn}.$$

If r is even,

$$S_{(r-1)n} = T_{rn} + \frac{1}{r}\left(1 + \frac{1}{2} + \frac{1}{3} + \cdots + \frac{1}{n}\right).$$

Since T converges, S diverges. If r is odd,

$$S_{(r-1)n} = T_{rn} - \frac{1}{r}\left(1 - \frac{1}{2} + \frac{1}{3} + \cdots + \frac{(-1)^{n+1}}{n}\right).$$

Thus

$$S = T\left(1 - \frac{1}{r}\right) = \left(1 - \frac{1}{r}\right)\ln 2.$$

Note that $\ln 2 = 1 - \frac{1}{2} + \frac{1}{3} - \frac{1}{4} + \cdots$, which can be derived from Exercise 7 as in Exercise 9.

Section 5, Part I

1. Converges absolutely.
3. Diverges.
5. Converges, but not absolutely.
7. Converges absolutely.
9. Converges, but not absolutely.
11. Converges, but not absolutely.
13. Converges absolutely.
15. Converges absolutely.

Section 5, Part II

1. Converges absolutely; $\left|\dfrac{1}{n}\sin\dfrac{1}{n}\right| \leq \dfrac{1}{n^2}$.

3. Converges, but not absolutely; alternating decreasing series with $\tan \frac{1}{n} \to 0$.

$$\sum \tan \frac{1}{n} > \sum \frac{1}{n}.$$

5. Converges absolutely for $p > 1$; $\left|\frac{\sin \pi n/3}{n^p}\right| \leq \frac{1}{n^p}$. Converges, but not absolutely for $0 < p \leq 1$. Let

$$\frac{2}{\sqrt{3}} S_{6n} = \sum_{r=1}^{n} \left\{\frac{1}{(6r-5)^p} + \frac{1}{(6r-4)^p} - \frac{1}{(6r-2)^p} - \frac{1}{(6r-1)^p}\right\}$$

For large r, the quantity in the parenthesis behaves as $\frac{k}{r^{1+p}}$.

$$\lim_{n\to\infty} S_{6n} = \lim_{n\to\infty} S_{6n+1} = \cdots = \lim_{n\to\infty} S_{6n+5}.$$

7. Series converges since it is alternating decreasing with nth term $\to 0$. For absolute convergence, note that

$$\frac{1\cdot 3\cdot 5 \cdots (2n-1)}{2\cdot 4\cdot 6 \cdots (2n)} = \frac{2n!}{(2^n n!)^2} \sim \frac{\left(\frac{2n}{e}\right)^{2n}\sqrt{4\pi n}}{\left(2^n\left(\frac{n}{e}\right)^n\sqrt{2\pi n}\right)^2} = \frac{1}{\sqrt{\pi n}}.$$

Thus series converges absolutely for $p > 2$.

9. **a.** yes; $\sum_{n=1}^{m} (a_n + a_{n+1}) = 2\sum_{n=1}^{m} a_n + a_{m+1} - a_1$.

b. No; consider $a_n = (-1)^n$.

c. Yes; by comparison test.

SECTION 6, PART I

1. $(-\infty,\infty)$.
3. $[-1,1)$.
5. $(-\infty,\infty)$.
7. $(-\frac{2}{3},\frac{2}{3})$.
9. $(-1,1)$.
11. $(-2,4)$.
13. $[-\sqrt{5}-1,\sqrt{5}-1]$.
15. $[0,0]$.
17. $[-1,1]$.
19. $[0,4)$.

SECTION 6, PART II

1. $\frac{1}{e}$; $\lim_{n\to\infty}\left|\frac{(n+1)^{n+1}x^{n+1}}{(n+1)!} \div \frac{n^n x^n}{n!}\right| = \lim_{n\to\infty}\left|x\left(1+\frac{1}{n}\right)^n\right| = |xe|$.

3. 1; $\lim_{n\to\infty}\frac{(1+\epsilon)^{2^n}}{2^n} = \begin{cases}\infty & \text{if } \epsilon > 0,\\ 0 & \text{if } -1 \leq \epsilon < 0.\end{cases}$

5. e^{-a}; $\left(1+\frac{a}{n}+\frac{b}{n^2}\right)^n = e^{n\ln\left(1+\frac{a}{n}+\frac{b}{n^2}\right)} \sim e^{n\left(\frac{a}{n}+\frac{b}{n^2}\right)} \sim e^a$.

7. 1; $\lim_{n\to\infty}\frac{n!}{a^{2^n}} = 0$ for $a > 1$. $n! \leq n^n$ and

$$\frac{n^n}{a^{2^n}} = \frac{e^{n\ln n}}{e^{2^n \ln a}}.$$

9. $\sum |a_k x^k| \leq \sum |Mx^k|$; radius of latter series is 1. $\sum |nx^k| \leq \sum |a_k x^k| \leq \sum |Mx^k|$; radii of both bounding series are 1. (*Note:* $|a_k| \leq M$ need only be true for all $k > k_0$, and similarly for $|a_k| \geq M$.

SECTION 7, PART I

1. $\ln 2 = .182.$

3. $\ln 3 = 1.099.$

5. $\sum_{n=1}^{\infty} (-1)^{n+1}\frac{x^n}{n^2}$; using Exercise 1, integrate the expansion of $\frac{\ln(1+t)}{t}$ termwise.

7. $S'(x) = \frac{x}{1} + \frac{x^2}{2} + \frac{x^3}{3} + \cdots + \frac{x^{n-1}}{n-1} + \cdots = -\ln(1-x).$

$S(x) = -\int_0^x \ln(1-t)\,dt = (1-x)\ln(1-x) + x.$

9. If $S(x) = \sum_{n=2}^{\infty} \frac{x^{3n}}{2n}$, then $2S(\sqrt[3]{x}) + x = \sum_{n=1}^{\infty} \frac{x^n}{n} = -\ln(1-x)$ (by Exercise 2). Thus

$$S(x) = -\tfrac{1}{2}\{x^3 + \ln(1-x^3)\}.$$

SECTION 7, PART II

1. $\ln(1+x+x^2) = \ln(1-x^3) - \ln(1-x)$. Now use Exercise II-2. $r = 1$.

3. $\ln(1-x-2x^2) = \ln(1-2x) + \ln(1+x)$. Now use Exercise II-2. $r = 1/2$.

5. If $F(x) = \arctan\frac{2x^3}{1+3x^2}$,

$$F'(x) = \frac{6x^2(1+x^2)}{1+6x^2+9x^4+4x^6}$$

or

$$F'(x) = \frac{6x^2}{(1+x^2)(1+4x^2)} = \frac{2}{1+x^2} - \frac{2}{1+4x^2}.$$

Thus also,

$$F(x) = 2\arctan x - \arctan 2x.$$

Now use Example 1. $r = 1$.

7. If $S(x)$ denotes the sum, then $D(x^2S) = 2\sum x^{4n+1} = \frac{2x}{1-x^4} = \frac{x}{1-x^2} + \frac{x}{1+x^2}$.

$2x^2S = \ln\frac{1+x^2}{1-x^2}.$

SECTION 8, PART I

1. $1 - \sum_{n=1}^{\infty} \frac{x^n}{(2n-1)2^{2n}}\binom{2n}{n}.$ $\quad r = 1.$

3. $\sum_{n=0}^{\infty} (-1)^n(n+1)x^n.$ $\quad r = 1.$

5. $\sum_{n=0}^{\infty} \binom{2n}{n}\left(\frac{x}{2}\right)^{2n}.$ $\quad r = 1.$

7. $8x - 3x^2 + \frac{3}{16}x^3 + \cdots + \frac{3\cdot 1\cdot 3\cdot 5\cdots(2n-5)}{2^{3(n-1)}n!}x^{2n} + \cdots.$ $\quad r = 4$

9. $2\sum_{n=0}^{\infty} \binom{2n}{n}\frac{(x/2)^{2n+1}}{2n+1}.$ $\quad r = 1.$

11. $\sec^{-1}\frac{1}{x} = \cos^{-1}x = \frac{\pi}{2} - \sin^{-1}x$. Now use Exercise 9.

SECTION 8, PART II

1. $$\frac{1}{1+x+x^2} = \frac{1-x}{1-x^3} = (1-x)(1+x^3+x^6+x^9+\cdots)$$
$$= 1 - x + x^3 - x^4 + x^6 - x^7 + \cdots \qquad (r = 1).$$

3. If
$$\frac{\sin^{-1} x}{\sqrt{1-x^2}} = \sum_{n=0}^{\infty} a_n x^n,$$
then by differentiating,
$$\frac{1}{1-x^2} - \frac{x}{1-x^2}\frac{\sin^{-1} x}{\sqrt{1-x^2}} = \sum_{n=0}^{\infty} n a_n x^{n-1}$$
or
$$1 - x\sum_{n=0}^{\infty} a_n x^n = (1-x^2)\sum_{n=0}^{\infty} n a_n x^{n-1} = \sum_{n=0}^{\infty} n a_n x^{n-1} - \sum_{n=0}^{\infty} n a_n x^{n+1}.$$
Equating coefficients of like powers:
$$-a_n = (n+2)a_{n+2} - n a_n.$$
This is satisfied by $a_{2n} = 0$, and
$$a_{2n+1} = \frac{2^{2n}(n!)^2}{(2n+1)!}.$$

SECTION 9, PART I

1. $\frac{\sqrt{2}}{2}\left[1 - \frac{(x-\pi/4)}{1!} - \frac{(x-\pi/4)^2}{2!} + \frac{(x-\pi/4)^3}{3!} + \frac{(x-\pi/4)^4}{4!} - \cdots\right],\ r = \infty.$

3. $-\sum_{n=1}^{\infty} (x+1)^n/n,\ r = 1.$

5. $\sum_{n=1}^{\infty} \frac{x^{2n-1}}{(2n-1)!},\ r = \infty.$

7. $\sum_{n=1}^{\infty} \frac{(-1)^{n+1}x^{2n-1}}{(2n)!},\ r = \infty.$

9. $\sum_{n=1}^{\infty} \frac{(-1)^{n+1}2^{2n-1}x^{2n}}{(2n)!},\ r = \infty.$

11. 1.3956.

13. .021372.

SECTION 9, PART II

1. $e^{x^2-1} = e^{-1}\cdot e^{x^2} = e^{-1}\left[1 + \frac{x^2}{1!} + \frac{x^4}{2!} + \cdots + \frac{x^{2n}}{n!} + \cdots\right];\ r = \infty.$

3. $\cos^3 x = \frac{1}{4}(3\cos x + \cos 3x);\ r = \infty.$
$$\cos ax = \cos a\left(x - \frac{\pi}{3} + \frac{\pi}{3}\right) = \cos a\frac{\pi}{3}\cos a\left(x - \frac{\pi}{3}\right) - \sin a\frac{\pi}{3}\sin a\left(x - \frac{\pi}{3}\right).$$
Now use the power series for both $\cos y$ and $\sin y$ and then replace y by $a\left(x - \frac{\pi}{3}\right)$.

5. $\ln(x^2+4x+4) = 2\ln(x+2) = 2\ln[1+(x+1)]$
$$= 2\left\{\frac{x+1}{1} - \frac{(x+1)^2}{2} + \cdots + (-1)^{n+1}\frac{(x+1)^n}{n} + \cdots\right\}$$

7.

$$f'(x) = \frac{2}{x^3} e^{-1/x^2} \quad \text{if } x \neq 0.$$

$$f'(0) = \lim_{x \to 0} \frac{e^{-1/x^2}}{x} = 0.$$

$$f''(x) = \left(\frac{4}{x^6} - \frac{6}{x^4}\right) e^{-1/x^2} \quad \text{if } x \neq 0$$

$$f''(0) = \lim_{x \to 0} \frac{f'(x)}{x} = 0.$$

Similarly, $f^{[n]}(0) = 0$. Here the Maclaurin series $= 0$. Also,

$$\lim_{n \to \infty} R_n(x) \neq 0.$$

Review, Part I

1. Diverges.

3. Converges, but not absolutely.

5. Converges, but not absolutely.

7. Converges absolutely.

9. Converges absolutely.

$$\frac{\sqrt{n+1} - \sqrt{n}}{n} = \frac{1}{n(\sqrt{n+1} + \sqrt{n})} < \frac{1}{2n^{3/2}}.$$

11. $\left|\frac{n+1}{n} a_n\right| \leq 2|a_n|$ (comparison test).

13. $[0,0]$.

15. $[-1,1)$.

17. $[1,3)$.

19. $\ln x = \ln [1 + (x-1)] = (x-1) - \frac{(x-1)^2}{2} + \cdots + \frac{(-1)^{n+1}(x-1)^n}{n} + \cdots.$

21. $\frac{1}{x} = \frac{1/2}{1 + \left(\frac{x-2}{2}\right)} = \frac{1}{2} \sum_{1}^{\infty} \left(\frac{2-x}{2}\right)^n.$

23. $x^2 e^x = x^2 \sum_{0}^{\infty} \frac{x^n}{n!}.$

25. $\lim_{x \to 0} \frac{\frac{-x^5}{5!} + \frac{x^7}{7!} - \cdots}{x^5} = -\frac{1}{5!}.$

27. From Example 2,

$$\lim_{x \to 0} \frac{-\frac{x^3}{2 \cdot 3} + \frac{1 \cdot 3}{2^2 \cdot 5 \cdot 2!} x^5 + \cdots}{x^3} = -\frac{1}{6}.$$

29. $S'(x) = 1 + x^4 + \cdots + x^{4n-4} + \cdots = \frac{1}{1 - x^4}$

$$= \frac{1}{2}\left[\frac{1}{1-x^2} + \frac{1}{1+x^2}\right] = \frac{1/2}{1+x^2} + \frac{1}{4}\left[\frac{1}{1-x} + \frac{1}{1+x}\right]$$

$$S(x) = \tfrac{1}{2} \tan^{-1} x + \tfrac{1}{4} \ln (1+x)/(1-x).$$

REVIEW, PART II

1. $(-1,1)$. **3.** $\left(-\frac{1}{e}, \frac{1}{e}\right)$; let $y = \ln x$.

5. $[-\frac{1}{2},\frac{1}{2})$; See Exercise II-7, Section 5.

7. $D^{10}\left[ex^6\left(1 + \frac{x}{1!} + \frac{x^2}{2!} + \frac{x^3}{3!} + \cdots\right)\right]_{x=0} = D^{10}\frac{ex^{10}}{4!} = \frac{e\cdot 10!}{4!}$.

9. $D^{12}[(x - x^3 + x^5 - x^7 + \cdots]_{x=0} = 0$.

11. For all $|x| \neq 1$.

$$\left|\sum \frac{x^n}{1 + x^{2n}}\right| \leq \sum |x|^n \quad \text{if} \quad |x| < 1.$$

$$= \left|\sum \frac{x^{-n}}{1 + x^{-2n}}\right| \leq \sum |x|^{-n} \quad \text{if } |x| > 1.$$

13. Since

$$\frac{a_n + 1 - 1}{(1 + a_1)(1 + a_2)\cdots(1 + a_n)} = \frac{1}{(1 + a_1)\cdots(1 + a_{n-1})} - \frac{1}{(1 + a_1)\cdots(1 + a_n)},$$

$$S_n = 1 - \frac{1}{(1 + a_1)\cdots(1 + a_n)}.$$

Since

$$(1 + a_1)(1 + a_2)\cdots(1 + a_n) > 1 + a_1 + a_2 + \cdots + a_n, \ \lim_{n\to\infty} S_n = 1.$$

As an example, let $a_n = n$, then

$$1 = \frac{1}{2} + \frac{2}{2\cdot 3} + \frac{3}{2\cdot 3\cdot 4} + \cdots$$

15. a.

$$|a_{n+1}| \leq \frac{b_{n+1}}{b_n}|a_n|,$$

$$|a_{n+2}| \leq \frac{b_{n+2}}{b_{n+1}}|a_{n+1}| \leq \frac{b_{n+2}}{b_n}|a_n|,$$

$$|a_{n+3}| \leq \frac{b_{n+3}}{b_{n+2}}|a_{n+2}| \leq \frac{b_{n+3}}{b_n}|a_n|.$$

$$\left|\sum_{n=N}^{\infty} a_n\right| \leq \frac{|a_N|}{b_N}\cdot\sum_{n=N}^{\infty} b_n.$$

Thus $\sum_{1}^{\infty} a_n$ converges absolutely by the first comparison test **15.12.** Similarly for part **b.**

17. Since $\sum_{n=1}^{\infty} |a_n|$ converges,

$$|a_{n+1}| + |a_{n+2}| + \cdots |a_n| < \epsilon \qquad \text{for all } n, m > n_0.$$

By monotonicity, $(m - n)|a_m| < \epsilon$. Now let $m \to \infty$, to give

$$\lim_{m\to\infty} ma_m = 0. \qquad (\text{since } \lim_{m\to\infty} n|a_m| = 0$$

by convergence of the given series.)

19. Follows directly from Abel's test (Exercise 18). Just let $b_n = \frac{1}{n}$.

21. Convergence follows directly from Dirichlet's test (Exercise 20). Here $\frac{1}{n} \to 0$, monotonically and

$$\left|\sum_{n=1}^{N} \sin n\theta\right| \leq \frac{1}{|\sin \theta/2|}$$

which is bounded, provided $\theta \neq 2n\pi$, $n = 0, \pm 1, \pm 2, \ldots$. For $\theta = 2n\pi$, each term of the series is zero. Thus the series converges for all θ.

23. If both $a, b > 1$ the series converges absolutely. For both $a, b \leq 1$ the series will only converge if, additionally, $a = b$. (See Exercise II-6, Section 4.)

25. Let $S_n = \frac{n}{n+1}$, then by Exercise 24, the desired limit $= \lim_{n\to\infty} S_n = 1$.

Here, $a_n = S_n - S_{n-1} = \frac{n}{n+1} - \frac{n-1}{n} = \frac{1}{n(n+1)}$, but it is not necessary to calculate it.

CHAPTER 16

Section 1, Part I

1. Straight line. **3.** Circle. **5.** Semiellipse.
7. Ellipse. **9.** Hyperbola.
21. $x = h + r \cos \theta$, $y = k + r \sin \theta$.

Section 1, Part II

1. $x = \csc t$, $y = -\cot^2 t$, domain $[0, 2\pi]$.

3. S denotes the initial center, S' denotes the center after the circle has rolled without

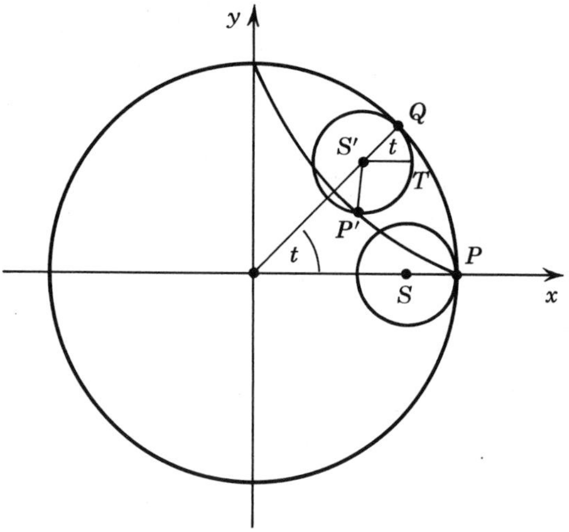

slipping. Thus arc PQ = arc $P'Q$, or $Rt = r(\angle P'S'Q)$. If P' denotes the position of the moving point after it has rolled from its initial position P, then

$$x = OS' \cos t + P'S' \cos(\angle P'S'T) = (R - r)\cos t + r \cos \frac{R-r}{r} t,$$

$$y = OS' \sin t - P'S' \sin(\angle P'S'T) = (R - r)\sin t - r \sin \frac{R-r}{r} t.$$

5. A diameter.

7. In order for the curve to close, the point P must return to $(R, 0)$ for $t = 2n\pi$ (n-integer) or $\sin 2n\pi\,(R - r)/r = 0$. Thus, R/r must be rational.

Section 3, Part I

1. $\langle 0,0\rangle$, $\langle 8,7\rangle$, 119, $\langle 0,0\rangle$, 71.

3. $\langle 4/5,-3/5\rangle$, $\langle 3/5,-4/5\rangle$, $\langle 1/\sqrt{2},-1/\sqrt{2}\rangle$, $\langle \sin\theta,-\cos\theta\rangle$, $\langle b/\sqrt{a^2+b^2},-a/\sqrt{a^2+b^2}\rangle$.

7. $x = 2 + 3t$, $y = 3 + 4t$; $x = 1 + t$, $y = 2$; $x = 2t$, $y = 3 - 2t$.

9. (x,y) satisfies $P(x,y) = 0$ where P is a cubic polynomial.

11. The diagonals are $\mathbf{u} + \mathbf{v}$ and $\mathbf{u} - \mathbf{v}$ where $\mathbf{u}\cdot\mathbf{u} = \mathbf{v}\cdot\mathbf{v}$. Then $(\mathbf{u} + \mathbf{v})\cdot(\mathbf{u} - \mathbf{v}) = \mathbf{u}\cdot\mathbf{u} - \mathbf{v}\cdot\mathbf{v} = 0$.

13. 60° East of North; $4\sqrt{3}$ hr.

Section 3, Part II

1. $(a_1^2 + a_2^2)(b_1^2 + b_2^2) - (a_1b_1 + a_2b_2)^2 = (a_1b_2 - a_2b_1)^2 \geq 0$; with equality if and only if the two vectors are parallel.

3. $|r\mathbf{u} + (1 - r)\mathbf{v}| \leq r|\mathbf{u}| + (1 - r)|\mathbf{v}| \leq \max\{|\mathbf{u}|, |\mathbf{v}|\}$.

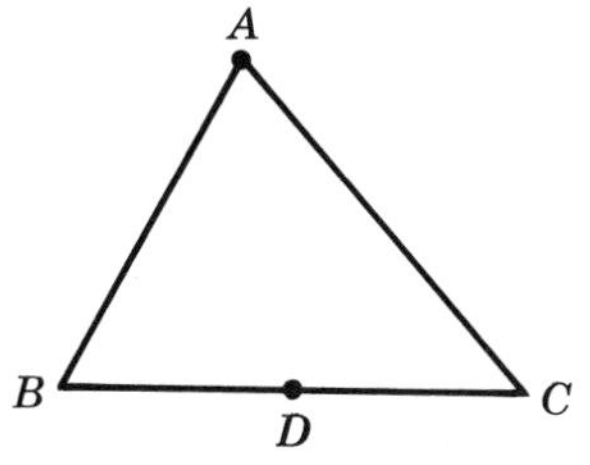

If D is between B and C, then $|AD| < \max\{|AB|, |AC|\}$.

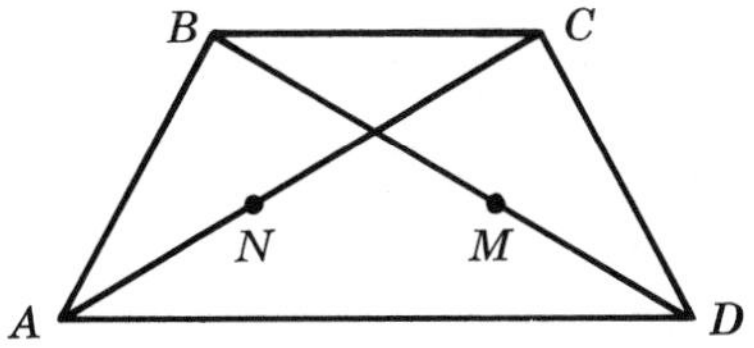

5. Let M denote midpoint of BD, let N denote midpoint of AC, and let $\mathbf{AB} = \mathbf{u}$, $\mathbf{AC} = \mathbf{v}$, and $\mathbf{AD} = \mathbf{w}$. Then

$$\overrightarrow{BC} = \mathbf{v} - \mathbf{u},\ \overrightarrow{CD} = \mathbf{w} - \mathbf{v},\ \overrightarrow{BD} = \mathbf{w} - \mathbf{u},\ \overrightarrow{AN} = \mathbf{v}/2,$$

$$\overrightarrow{AM} = (\mathbf{u} + \mathbf{w})/2,\ \overrightarrow{NM} = (\mathbf{u} + \mathbf{w} - \mathbf{v})/2.$$

$$\overrightarrow{AB}^2 + \overrightarrow{BC}^2 + \overrightarrow{CD}^2 + \overrightarrow{DA}^2 = 2(\mathbf{u}\cdot\mathbf{u} + \mathbf{v}\cdot\mathbf{v} + \mathbf{w}\cdot\mathbf{w} - \mathbf{v}\cdot\mathbf{u} - \mathbf{v}\cdot\mathbf{w})$$

$$\overrightarrow{BD}^2 + \overrightarrow{AC}^2 + 4\overrightarrow{MN}^2 = 2(\mathbf{u}\cdot\mathbf{u} + \mathbf{v}\cdot\mathbf{v} + \mathbf{w}\cdot\mathbf{w} - \mathbf{v}\cdot\mathbf{u} - \mathbf{v}\cdot\mathbf{w})$$

7. Reorder the vectors in increasing order of length, $\mathbf{a}_1, \mathbf{a}_2, \cdots, \mathbf{a}_n, \mathbf{a}_{n+1}$ and note that the sum of the $n+1$ vectors is still zero. We use an indirect proof by assuming $|\mathbf{a}_{r+1}|/|\mathbf{a}_r| > 2$ for all r and obtain a contradiction. By our assumption,

$$|\mathbf{a}_{n+1}| > 2|\mathbf{a}_n| > |\mathbf{a}_n| + 2|\mathbf{a}_{n-1}| > \cdots > |\mathbf{a}_n| + |\mathbf{a}_{n-1}| + \cdots + |\mathbf{a}_2| + 2|\mathbf{a}_1|.$$

However, since $-\mathbf{a}_{n+1} = \mathbf{a}_1 + \mathbf{a}_2 + \cdots + \mathbf{a}_n$,

$$|\mathbf{a}_{n+1}| = |\mathbf{a}_1 + \mathbf{a}_2 + \cdots + \mathbf{a}_n| \leq |\mathbf{a}_1| + |\mathbf{a}_2| + \cdots + |\mathbf{a}_n|$$

which contradicts the previous inequality.

In any closed polygonal figure there must be a pair of sides whose ratio of length of sides ≤ 2. If this was not the case, the polygonal figure could not close. As a simple example consider a triangle.

SECTION 4, PART I

1. $\langle 4,12\rangle$.
3. $\langle 2,-2\rangle$.
5. $t = \pi/2$.
7. $r = 0, \pi/2, \pi, 3\pi/2$.

SECTION 4, PART II

1. Follows immediately from the definition of tangent line.
3. The parametric equations of the tangent line are (see Exercise II-1).

$$X = a\cos^4 t_0 - 4at\cos^3 t_0 \sin t_0,$$
$$Y = a\sin^4 t_0 + 4at\cos t_0 \sin^3 t_0.$$

For $X = 0$, $t = \dfrac{\cos t_0}{4\sin t_0}$ and $Y = a\sin^4 t_0 + a\cos^2 t_0 \sin^2 t_0$.

For $Y = 0$, $t = -\dfrac{\sin t_0}{4\cos t_0}$ and $X = a\cos^4 t_0 + a\cos^2 t_0\sin^2 t_0$.

Thus sum of intercepts $= a[\cos^2 t_0 + \sin^2 t_0]^2 = a$.

5. The tangent line at $t = a$ is given by

$$X = r(a - \sin a) + rt(1 - \cos a),$$
$$Y = r(1 - \cos a) + rt\sin a.$$

The highest point of the rolling circle at $t = a$ is given by $X = ra$, $Y = 2r$. It is easily verified that the latter point is on the tangent line. Similarly for the normal line. Here, the lowest point of the rolling circle at $t = a$ is $X = ra$, $Y = 0$.

SECTION 5, PART I

1. $\langle 2t,2\rangle, \langle 2,0\rangle, 2\sqrt{5}$.
3. $\langle 2\cos t, -2\sin t\rangle, \langle -2\sin t, -2\cos t\rangle, 2$.
5. $\langle -\sin t, -2\sin 2t\rangle, \langle -\cos t, -4\cos 2t\rangle, 1$.
7. $\langle e^t, -e^{-t}\rangle, \langle e^t, e^{-t}\rangle, \sqrt{2}$.
9. $\langle 2\cos t, 2\sin t\rangle, \langle -2\sin t, 2\cos t\rangle, 2$.
11. $\langle -ab\sin bt, ab\cos bt\rangle, \langle -ab^2\cos bt, -ab^2\sin bt\rangle, ab$.
13. The particle must be moving on a circle.

SECTION 5, PART II

1.

$$Y = v_0 t \sin\alpha - 16t^2 \quad X = v_0 t \cos\alpha$$
$$Y = 0 \text{ for } t = 0 \quad\text{and}\quad t = (v_0 \sin\alpha)/16.$$
$$\text{Range} = V_0 \cos\alpha \cdot \frac{v_0 \sin\alpha}{16} = (v_0^2 \sin 2\alpha)/32.$$

At maximum height, $\dfrac{dY}{dt} = 0 = v_0 \sin\alpha - 32t$

or

$$t = \frac{v_0 \sin\alpha}{32}.$$

Maximum height =

$$v_0 \sin\alpha \left(\frac{v_0 \sin\alpha}{32}\right) - 16\left(\frac{v_0 \sin\alpha}{32}\right)^2 = \frac{v_0^2 \sin^2\alpha}{64}$$

Total time of flight = $(v_0 \sin\alpha)/16$.

Trajectory; $Y = v_0 \sin\alpha \left(\dfrac{X}{v_0 \cos\alpha}\right) - 16\left(\dfrac{X}{v_0 \cos\alpha}\right)^2.$

or

$$Y = X \tan\alpha - \frac{16X^2}{v_0^2} \sec^2\alpha.$$

For maximum range, $\sin 2\alpha = 1$ or $\alpha = \pi/4$ and range (max) $= v_0^2/32$.

$\sin 2\alpha = \sin 2\left(\dfrac{\pi}{2} - \alpha\right).$

3. Point is moving on a circle.

SECTION 6, PART I

21. $r = 3$.
23. $r^2 = 2 \csc 2\theta$.
25. $r = -4 \cos\theta$.
27. $x^2 + y^2 = 2y$.
29. $(x^2 + y^2 + y)^2 = x^2 + y^2$.
31. $y = 2$.

SECTION 6, PART II

1. $(-r,\theta)$, $(r,\theta + \pi)$; $(r,-\theta)$, $(r,2\pi - \theta)$; $(r,\pi - \theta)$, $(-r,-\theta)$; $(r,2\alpha - \theta)$, $(-r,2\alpha - \theta + \pi)$.
11. $(0,0)$, $(\sqrt{3},\pi/3)$, $(\sqrt{3},2\pi/3)$.
13. $r = 0$, $(\pm 2,\pi/2)$, $(.4384,\pm 141°20')$.
15. $(6,\pi/6)$, $(6,5\pi/6)$, $(2,-\pi/6)$, $(2,-5\pi/6)$.

SECTION, 7 PART II

1. Note that $r = \dfrac{2}{1 - \sqrt{2}\cos(\theta - 45°)}$.
3. The asymptotes correspond to the denominator being zero.
5. Let $x = r\cos\theta$, $y = r\sin\theta$ in $\dfrac{x^2}{a^2} - \dfrac{y^2}{b^2} = 1$.

SECTION 8, PART I

3. At the origin, 0°; at two other points, $\arctan 3\sqrt{3}$.
5. The curves do not intersect.

SECTION 8, PART II

1.
$$\tan \psi = \frac{r d\theta}{dr}.$$

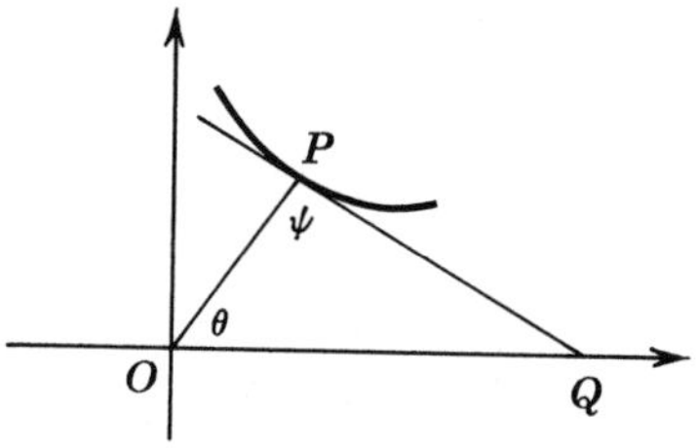

Since $r^2 \sin 2\theta = a^2$,

$$2r \sin 2\theta + 2r^2 \cos 2\theta \frac{d\theta}{dr} = 0 \quad \text{or} \quad r\frac{d\theta}{dr} = -\tan 2\theta.$$

Thus

$$\psi = 180^\circ - \theta \text{ and } \quad \angle \quad PQO = \theta.$$

3. Since $\tan \psi + \tan (\pi - \psi) = 0$,

$$\left. r\frac{d\theta}{dr}\right]_\theta + \left. r\frac{d\theta}{dr}\right]_{\pi+\theta} = 0.$$

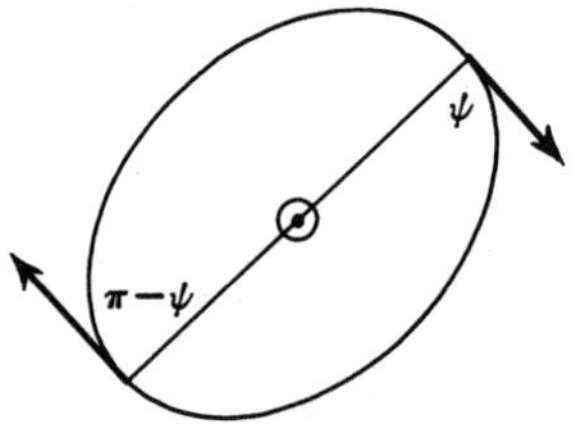

Choose $r\dfrac{d\theta}{dr} = \dfrac{1}{a \sin \theta}$. Then $a \sin \theta d\theta = \dfrac{dr}{r}$

or

$$r = be^{-a \cos \theta}.$$

SECTION 9, PART I

1. $\pi^3/48$.
3. 1.
5. $(e^{2\pi} - 1)/4$.
7. $(\pi + 4)/4$.
9. 25π.
11. $3\pi/2$.
13. $\pi/2$.
15. $\frac{1}{2}$.
17. $\pi a^2/4n$.
19. $(\pi - 2)/8$.
21. $8\pi - 16$.

SECTION 9, PART II

1. At intersection, $\cos 2\theta = \frac{1}{2}$.

$$\frac{A}{4} = \frac{1}{2}\int_0^{\pi/6} [2a^2 \cos 2\theta - a^2]\, d\theta,$$

$$A = a^2[3\sqrt{3} - \pi]/3.$$

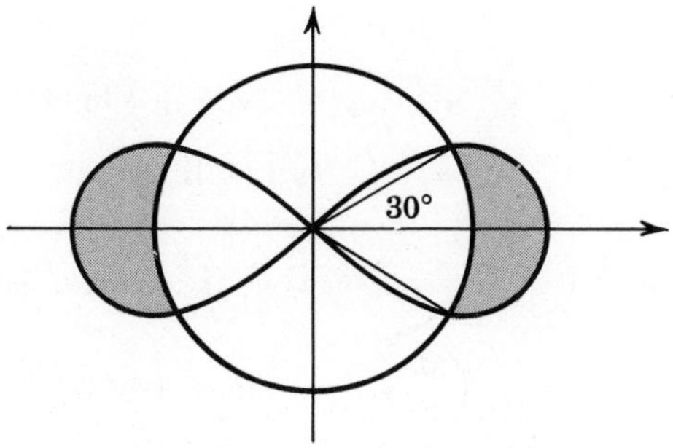

3. $A = a^2\int_0^{\pi/4} \frac{\cos^2 2\theta}{\cos^2\theta}\,d\theta = a^2\int_0^{\pi/4} [\sec^2\theta + 2\cos 2\theta - 2]\,d\theta = a^2(4-\pi)/2.$

5. In rectangular coordinates, the equation is $X^3 + Y^3 = 6XY$. It now follows that $X + Y = -2$ is the asymptote. (Consider $X + Y = \frac{6XY}{X^2 - XY + Y^2}$ and let $Y \to a - X$ in the right hand side).

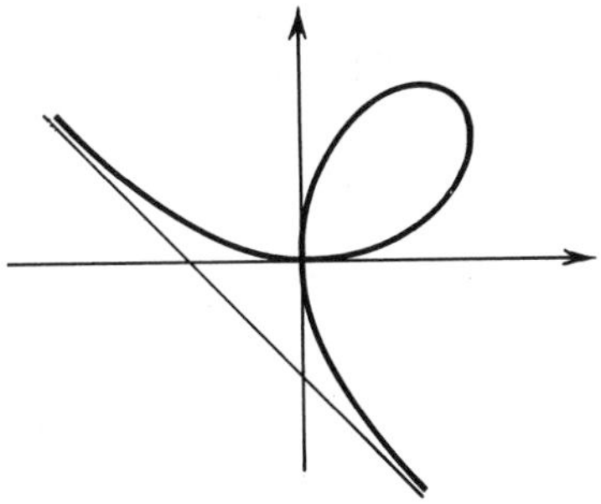

$$A = \int_{3\pi/4}^{\pi} \left\{\frac{36\sin^2\theta\cos^2\theta}{(\sin^3\theta + \cos^3\theta)^2} - \frac{4}{(\sin\theta + \cos\theta)^2}\right\} d\theta + 2.$$

Let $X = \tan\theta$, then

$$A - 2 = \int_{-1}^{0}\left\{\frac{4}{X^2 - X + 1} - \frac{6}{(X^2 - X + 1)^2} - \frac{12X - 6}{(X^2 - X + 1)^2}\right\} dx.$$

To integrate the first two terms in the integrand, let $X - \frac{1}{2} = \frac{\sqrt{3}}{2}\tan\theta$. This will lead to a zero contribution. Then

$$A = 2 + \left.\frac{6}{X^2 - X + 1}\right]_{-1}^{0} = 6.$$

Section 10, Part I

1. $2 - \sqrt{3}$.
3. $\ln(2 - \sqrt{3})$.
5. $\sqrt{5} + \frac{1}{2}\ln(2 + \sqrt{5})$.
7. $2\sqrt{5} + \ln(2 + \sqrt{5})$.
9. $\sqrt{2}(e^2 - 1)$.
11. $3\sqrt{2}$.
13. 2.
15. $3\pi/2$.

SECTION 10, PART II

1. $L = \int_{-2}^{2} \sqrt{1 + 4t^2}\, dt = \int_0^4 \sqrt{1 + m^2}\, dm = 2\sqrt{17} + \frac{1}{2} \ln (4 + \sqrt{17}).$

$$\bar{x} = \frac{1}{L}\int_{-2}^{2} t\sqrt{1 + 4t^2}\, dt = 0$$

$$\bar{y} = \frac{1}{L}\int_{-2}^{2} t^2\sqrt{1 + 4t^2}\, dt = \frac{1}{4L}\int_0^4 m^2\sqrt{1 + m^2}\, dm$$

$$= \frac{1}{4L}\left(\frac{33}{2}\sqrt{17} - \frac{1}{8}\ln (4 + \sqrt{17})\right).$$

3. $L = \int_{-1}^{1} \sqrt{1 + \sinh^2 t}\, dt = 2 \sinh 1.$

$$\bar{x} = \frac{1}{L}\int_{-1}^{1} t\sqrt{1 + \sinh^2 t}\, dt = 0,\ \bar{y} = \frac{1}{L}\int_{-1}^{1} \cosh^2 t\, dt = \frac{2 + \sinh 2}{4 \sinh 1}.$$

5. If the centroid of the semicircular arc is $(0,a)$, then the centroid of the quarter-circular arc from $\theta = 0$ to $\theta = \pi/2$ is (a,a) by symmetry.

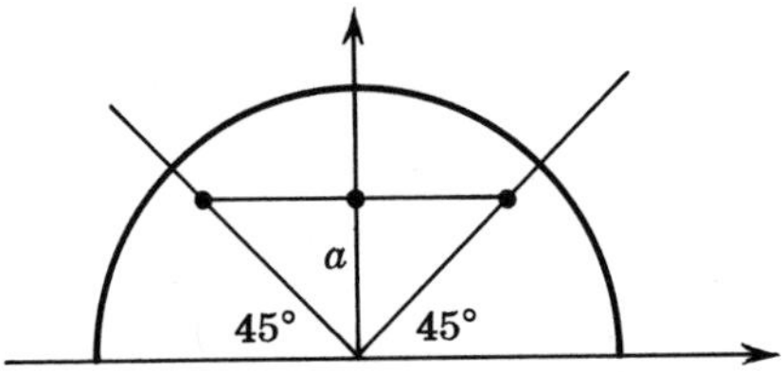

7. $$L = 12 \int_0^{\pi/2} \sqrt{a^2 \cos^4 t \sin^2 t + b^2 \sin^4 t \cos^2 t}\, dt.$$

If $a = b$, $L = 12a \int_0^{\pi/2} \sin t \cos t\, dt = 6a.$

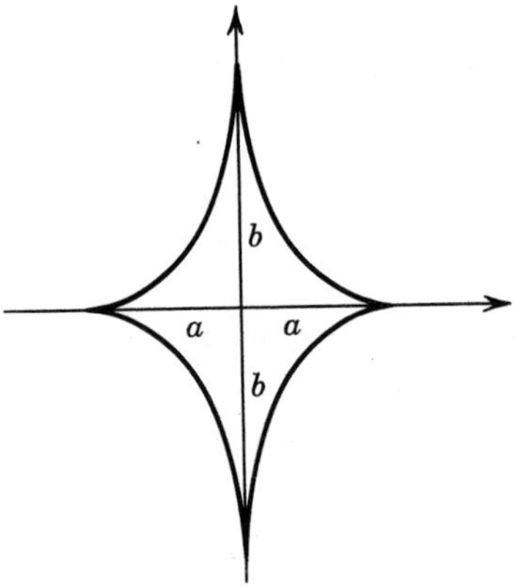

For $a \neq b$, let $\sin^2 t = x$, then

$$L = 6 \int_0^1 \sqrt{a^2 + (b^2 - a^2)\, x}\, dx = 4\frac{b^3 - a^3}{b^2 - a^2} = \frac{4(b^2 + ab + a^2)}{b + a}.$$

SECTION 12, PART I

1. $4\pi(5\sqrt{10} - \sqrt{2})/3$. **3.** π. **5.** $\pi(145\sqrt{145} - 1)/27$.

7. $\pi\left[\frac{e^6 - 1}{e^4}\sqrt{e^4 + 1} + 2 + \ln\frac{e^2 + \sqrt{e^4 + 1}}{1 + \sqrt{e^4 + 1}}\right]$. **9.** $4\pi r^2$.

11. $2\pi a^2$.

SECTION 12, PART II

1. By **16.25**, $S = 2\pi\int_a^b Y(t)|\boldsymbol{\lambda}'(t)|\,dt$ for the curve $\lambda(t) = (X(t),\ Y(t))$, domain $[a,b]$. By Exercise II, Section 10 (top), $2\pi L\overline{Y} = S$.

3.

$$S = 2\pi\sqrt{r^2 + h^2}\cdot\frac{h}{2}$$

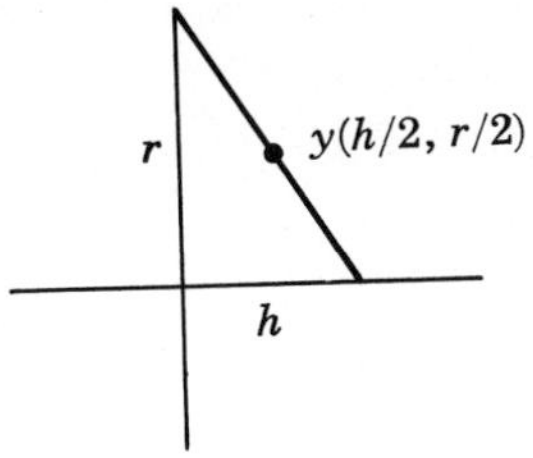

5.

$$S = 2\pi\int_{t_1}^{t_2} a^2\sin t\,dt\ (\mathbf{16.25})$$

$$S = 2\pi a^2(\cos t_1 - \cos t_2).$$

Since

$$h = a\cos t_1 - a\cos t_2,\ S = 2\pi\,ah.$$

$\lambda(t) = (a\cos t,\ b\sin t)$.

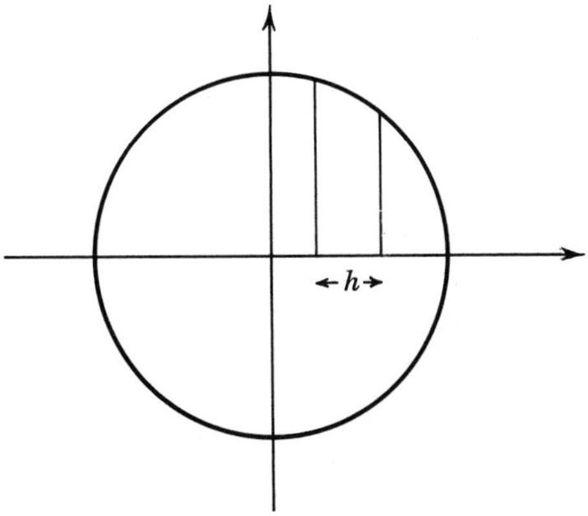

REVIEW, PART I

5. The speed is not constant.

15. 6π; 16. **17.** $3\pi/8$; 4. **23.** $\pi k^2(10\sqrt{10} - 1)/27$.

REVIEW, PART II

1. $x = \frac{3at}{1+t^3}$, $y = \frac{3at^2}{1+t^3}$. Graph is symmetric about the line $x = y$ and has the line $x + y = -a$ as an asymptote.

3. arc $RT = r\theta = RP$. $x = OQ + SP = r\cos\theta + r\theta\sin\theta$, $y = RQ - RS = r\sin\theta - r\theta\cos\theta$.

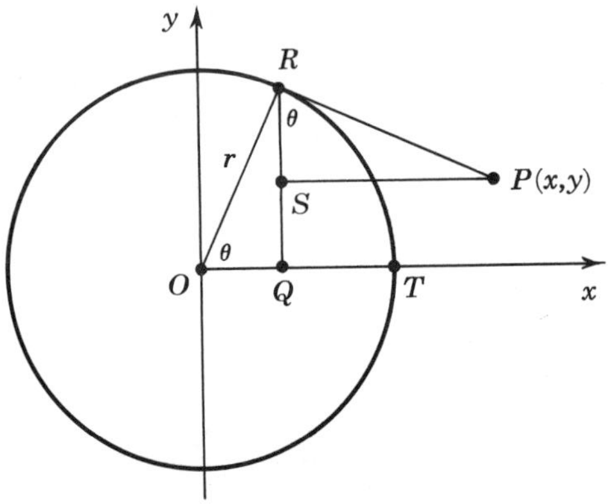

5. All three, since

$$a + b\sin\theta = -(-a + b\sin -\theta),$$
$$a\sin 2(\theta + \pi/4) = a\cos 2\theta,$$
$$a\sin 3(\theta + \pi/6) = a\cos 3\theta.$$

7. The two graphs are mirror images with respect to the Y axis. The points of intersection are on the Y axis, $r = 0$, $\theta = \pi/2$, $r = \sqrt{2}$, $\theta = -\pi/2$, $r = \sqrt{2}$.

9. When furthest from the sun, $\theta = 0$, $\dot{r} = 0$, speed $= |r\dot{\theta}|$. Since

$$r = \frac{2ep}{1 - e\cos\theta}, \quad r(o) = \frac{2ep}{1-e}, \quad \left(\frac{2ep}{1-e}\right)^2\dot{\theta} = 2k.$$

Eliminating $\dot{\theta}$,

$$\text{Speed} = \frac{2k}{r(0)} = (2k) \div \left(\frac{2ep}{1-e^2}\right)(1+e) = \frac{2k}{a(1+e)}.$$

11. Since the force is central there is no acceleration in the θ direction, i.e.,

$$a_\theta = r\ddot{\theta} + 2\dot{r}\dot{\theta} = 0 = \frac{d}{dt}(r^2\dot{\theta}).$$

Integrating,

$$r^2\dot{\theta} = \text{const.}$$

13. a. Starting from $\frac{d^2y}{dx^2} = \frac{\dot{x}\ddot{y} - \ddot{x}\dot{y}}{\dot{x}^3}$, (See notation of Exercise II-8 and result of Exercise I-25,

$$\frac{d^3y}{dx^3} = \frac{d}{dt}\left(\frac{d^2y}{dx^2}\right) \div \frac{dx}{dt}.$$

Now perform the indicated differentiation of $\frac{d^2y}{dx^2}$.

b. $\dfrac{dy}{dx} = 1\Big/\dfrac{dx}{dy}$

$$\frac{d}{dx}\left(\frac{dy}{dx}\right) = \frac{d}{dx}\left(\frac{dx}{dy}\right)^{-1} = \frac{d}{dy}\left(\frac{dx}{dy}\right)^{-1}\cdot\frac{dy}{dx} = -\frac{d^2x}{dy^2}\cdot\left(\frac{dx}{dy}\right)^{-3}.$$

$$\frac{d^3y}{dx^3} = -\frac{d}{dy}\frac{\left\{\dfrac{d^2x}{dy^2}\right\}}{\left(\dfrac{dx}{dy}\right)^3}\frac{dy}{dx} = \frac{3\left(\dfrac{d^2x}{dy^2}\right)^2 - \dfrac{dx}{dy}\cdot\dfrac{d^3x}{dy^3}}{\left(\dfrac{dx}{dy}\right)^5}.$$

CHAPTER 17

Section 1, Part I

1. (0,0,3), (7,0,3), (0,2,3), (0,2,0), (7,0,0), (7,2,0).
3. (−1,1,5), (2,1,5), (−1,3,5), (2,1,2), (2,3,2), (−1,3,2).
5. (0,−2,0), (3,−2,0), (0,1,0), (3,−2,−1), (3,1,−1), (0,1,−1).
7. $x^2 + y^2 + z^2 - x - 9y - 6z + 13 = 0$.
9. $x^2 + y^2 + z^2 + 5x - y + z = 24$.
11. Sphere: center (1,0,0), radius 5.
13. Sphere: center $(0,\frac{3}{2},-\frac{1}{2})$, radius $\frac{3}{2}$.
15. No graph.
19. $x = 2y + z$; a plane.

Section 1, Part II

1. Plane || to xy plane.
3. z axis.
5. Square cylinder with generators || to x axis.
7. $F(x,y,z) = F(x,y,-z)$; $F(x,y,z) = F(-x,y,z)$; $F(x,y,z) = F(x,-y,z)$.
9. If for each point (x,y,z) on the graph there is a point $(\bar{x},\bar{y},\bar{z})$ symmetric to it with respect to (h,k,l), then (h,k,l) must be the midpoint of the segment joining (x,y,z) to $(\bar{x},\bar{y},\bar{z})$ or $\bar{x} = 2h - x$, $\bar{y} = 2k - y$, $\bar{z} = 2l - z$. Thus $F(2h - x, 2k - y, 2l - z)$ must also vanish.
11. **a.** 3 axes — joining centroids of pairs of opposite faces.
4 axes — body diagonals.
6 axes — joining midpoints of pairs of opposite edges.
b. 3 planes — joining midpoints of the 3 sets of parallel edges.
6 planes — joining pairs of opposite edges.

Section 2, Part I

3. We have to show that $|\mathbf{u}| + |\mathbf{v}| \geq |\mathbf{u} + \mathbf{v}|$. Squaring, we obtain $\mathbf{u}^2 + \mathbf{v}^2 + 2|\mathbf{u}||\mathbf{v}| \geq \mathbf{u}^2 + \mathbf{v}^2 + 2\mathbf{u}\cdot\mathbf{v}$. This is obviously valid since $\mathbf{u}\cdot\mathbf{v} = |\mathbf{u}||\mathbf{v}|\cos\theta \leq |\mathbf{u}||\mathbf{v}|$ (Cauchy inequality — see previous exercise.)
5. $|\mathbf{u} - \mathbf{v}|^2 = \mathbf{u}^2 + \mathbf{v}^2 - 2\mathbf{u}\cdot\mathbf{v} = 2(1 - \cos\alpha) = 4\sin^2\dfrac{\alpha}{2}$, $|\mathbf{u} - \mathbf{v}| = 2\left|\sin\dfrac{\alpha}{2}\right|$.
7. Square out each side and compare terms.

Section 3, Part I

1. $x = 2 + 3t$, $y = 3 - 7t$, $z = 1 + 4t$.
3. $\frac{1}{4}, \frac{1}{4}, \frac{1}{2}$; $\cos^{-1}\frac{1}{4}$, $\cos^{-1}\frac{1}{4}$, $\pi/3$.
5. $-\frac{1}{2}, -\frac{1}{4}, -\frac{1}{4}$; $2\pi/3$, $\pi - \cos^{-1}\frac{1}{4}$, $\pi - \cos^{-1}\frac{1}{4}$.
7. $lmn = 0$.
11. $P = (0,0,1)$, $\mathbf{v} = \langle 2,-2,-3\rangle$.
13. Intersects.

SECTION 3, PART II

1. The direction numbers of the line $\perp$ to L_1 and L_2 are given by

$$\begin{vmatrix} 0 & 1 \\ 1 & 2 \end{vmatrix}, \begin{vmatrix} 1 & 1 \\ 2 & -1 \end{vmatrix}, \begin{vmatrix} 1 & 0 \\ -1 & 1 \end{vmatrix} \quad \text{or} \quad -1, -3, 1.$$

Equation of line is then

$$x = 2 - t, y = 3 - 3t, z = t.$$

3. If the parametric equations of the skew lines are

$$L_1\colon x = a + ht, \quad y = b + kt, \quad z = c + lt,$$
$$L_2\colon x = a' + h't', y = b' + k't', z = c' + l't',$$

then t and t' must satisfy

$$(a + ht - a' - h't')h + (b + kt - b' - k't')k + (c + lt - c' - l't')l = 0$$
$$(a + ht - a' - h't')h' + (b + kt - b' - k't')k' + (c + lt - c' - l't')l' = 0,$$

in order to have a mutually perpendicular segment. The determinant of the coefficients of t and t' is

$$\begin{vmatrix} \mathbf{H}^2 & -\mathbf{H}\cdot\mathbf{H}' \\ \mathbf{H}\cdot\mathbf{H}' & -\mathbf{H}'^2 \end{vmatrix}$$

which is zero (by the Cauchy Inequality) if and only if the two given lines lie in one plane (here $\mathbf{H} = \langle h,k,l\rangle$, $\mathbf{H}' = \langle h',k',l'\rangle$). Whence, there is a unique solution.

SECTION 4, PART I

1. $x + y - z = 3.$

3. $x + y = a + b.$

5. $2x + y = 4; y + z = 4, 2x + z = 4.$

7. $4x + y = 6; 2x = 3; y = 6.$

9. $x + y = 2z.$

11. $6x + 10y - z = 23.$

13. $x - y = 1.$

15. $x = 5, y = 1 + t, z = 2t.$

17. $3x + 4y - 9z = 2.$

SECTION 4, PART II

1. The equation must have the form $r(x - h) + s(y - k) + t(z - l) = 0$ where

$$ra + sb + tc = 0,$$
$$r(h - x_0) + s(k - y_0) + t(l - z_0) = 0.$$

Thus

$$r = \begin{vmatrix} b & c \\ k - y_0 & l - z_0 \end{vmatrix}, s = \begin{vmatrix} c & a \\ l - z_0 & h - x_0 \end{vmatrix}, t = \begin{vmatrix} a & b \\ h - x_0 & k - y_0 \end{vmatrix}.$$

3. Express the line of intersection in parametric form and then use Exercise II-1 above.

5. The direction numbers of the lines of intersection are

$$\begin{vmatrix} b_1 & c_1 \\ b_2 & c_2 \end{vmatrix}, \begin{vmatrix} c_1 & a_1 \\ c_2 & a_2 \end{vmatrix}, \begin{vmatrix} a_1 & b_1 \\ a_2 & b_2 \end{vmatrix}$$

and the same but with primed letters. Now use the dot product between two vectors $\mathbf{V}$ and $\mathbf{V}'$ with the above numbers as components, i.e., $\mathbf{V}\cdot\mathbf{V}' = |\mathbf{V}||\mathbf{V}'| \cos\theta$.

7. A vector **V** normal to the plane is given by $\langle a,b,c\rangle$. Then

$$D = \left|\frac{\mathbf{V}}{|\mathbf{V}|}\cdot\overrightarrow{(P - P_0)}\right|$$

or

$$D = \frac{|a(h - x_0) + b(k - y_0) + c(l - z_0)|}{\sqrt{a^2 + b^2 + c^2}} = \frac{|ah + bk + cl + d|}{\sqrt{a^2 + b^2 + c^2}}.$$

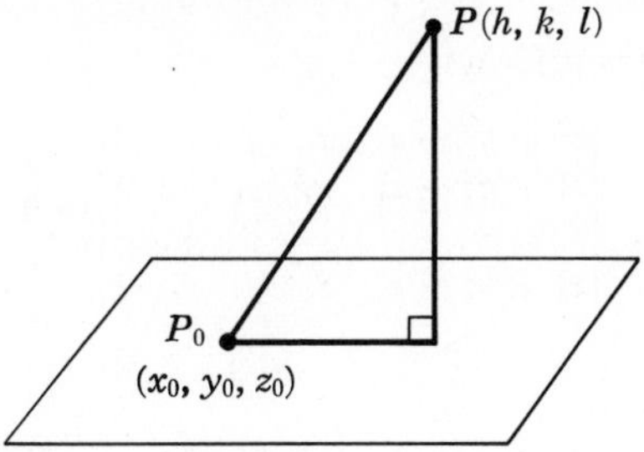

9. The volume of the tetrahedron is the sum of the volumes of the 4 tetrahedrons determined by the point and the four faces. Whence

$$V = \frac{A}{6}(P_1 + P_2 + P_3 + P_4).$$

Here P_i are the perpendiculars, V and A are the volume and area of a face of the tetrahedron, respectively.

SECTION 5, PART I

1. 16, −9.
3. 0.
5. $\langle -25,-18,-5\rangle$, $\langle 6,-6,3\rangle$.

SECTION 6, PART I

17. $x^2/a^2 + y^2/b^2 + z^2/b^2 = 1$; $x^2/a^2 + y^2/b^2 + z^2/a^2 = 1$.
19. $y^2 + z^2 = 4px$.

SECTION 6, PART II

1. $(x^2 + y^2 + z^2 + h^2 - r^2)^2 = 4h^2(x^2 + y^2)$; torus (a doughnut shaped figure).

3. Assume that the given plane is the xy plane and that the given point is $(0,0,a)$. Then

$$\sqrt{x^2 + y^2 + (z - a)^2} = |z| \text{ or } x^2 + y^2 = 2za - a^2$$

a paraboloid of revolution.

5. Since the centroid C must lie on each axis, the axes must intersect (this need not be true for unbounded surfaces). Now consider any point P of the surface. The circle formed by rotating the point about one of the axes must be part of the surface and each point of it is equidistant from C. The same for the rotation of the circle about the other axis, and so on.

SECTION 7, PART I

1. Ellipsoid.
3. Hyperboloid of one sheet.
5. Hyperbolic paraboloid.
7. Elliptic paraboloid.
9. Hyperboloid of two sheets.
11. Elliptic cone.
13. Elliptic paraboloid.
15. Right circular cylinder.

Section 7, Part II

1. The equation must have the form $\frac{x^2}{a^2} + \frac{y^2}{b^2} = (mz + n)^2$. Also $mz + n = 0$ for $z = l$ and $mz + n = 1$ for $z = 0$. Thus

$$\frac{x^2}{a^2} + \frac{y^2}{b^2} = (1 - z/l)^2.$$

3. The equation in determinant form is

$$\begin{vmatrix} x^2 + y^2 + z^2 & x & y & z & 1 \\ x_1^2 + y_1^2 + z_1^2 & x_1 & y_1 & z_1 & 1 \\ \vdots & \vdots & \vdots & \vdots & \vdots \\ x_4^2 + y_4^2 + z_4^2 & x_4 & y_4 & z_4 & 1 \end{vmatrix} = 0.$$

Section 8, Part I

1. $x = t$, $y = 10 + 6t$, $z = 9 + 6t$; $x + 6y + 6z = 114$.

3. $x = a \sin kt_0 + tak \cos kt_0$, $y = b \cos kt_0 - tbk \sin kt_0$, $z = ct_0^2 + 2tct_0$;

$$xa \cos kt_0 - yb \sin kt_0 + 2zct_0 = (a^2 - b^2) \sin kt_0 \cos kt_0 + 2c^2t_0^3/k.$$

7. $L = \sqrt{8} \int_1^3 \sqrt{t^2 + 8}\, dt = \sqrt{8}\, \{\frac{3}{2}(\sqrt{17} - 1) + 4 \ln (3 + \sqrt{17})/4\}$.

Section 8, Part II

1. We have to show equivalently that

$$\begin{vmatrix} x' & y' & z' \\ x'' & y'' & z'' \\ x''' & y''' & z''' \end{vmatrix} = 0$$

if $ax + by + cz = d$. This follows immediately by substituting for any one of the variables x, y, z.

3. Denote the curve by $\lambda(t) = (alt), b(t), c(t))$ and let the fixed point be (0,0,0). The equation of the tangent line corresponding to any value t is

$$\frac{x - a(t)}{a'(t)} = \frac{y - b(t)}{b'(t)} = \frac{z - c(t)}{c'(t)}.$$

Thus

$$\frac{a'(t)}{a(t)} = \frac{b'(t)}{b(t)} = \frac{c'(t)}{c(t)} \text{ for all } t.$$

Integrating,

$$c(t) = k_1 a(t),\ b(t) = k_2 a(t)$$

and $\lambda(t)$ is a straight line.

5.

$$PQ = \sqrt{(at)^2 + h^2}$$

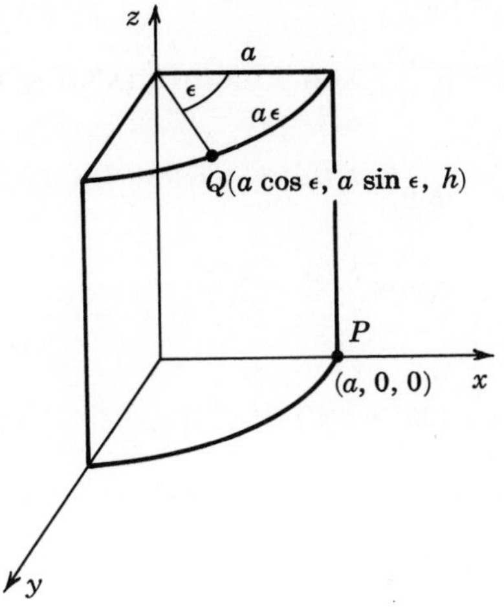

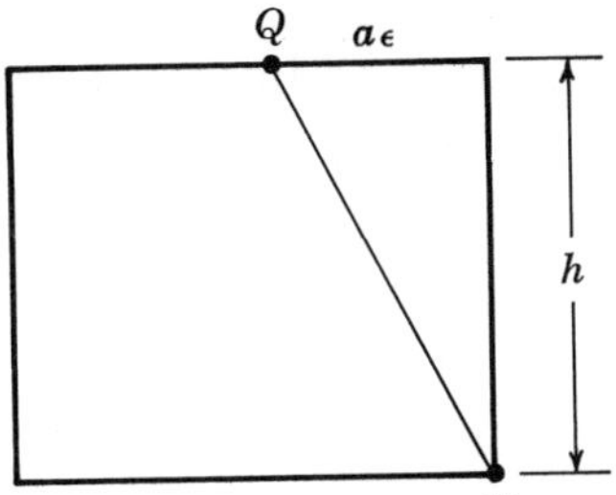

SECTION 9, PART I

1. $\delta(s) = ([\sqrt{2s+1} - 1] \sin [\sqrt{2s+1} - 1], [\sqrt{2s+1} - 1] \cos [\sqrt{2s+1} - 1], 2\sqrt{2}[\sqrt{2s+1} - 1]^{3/2}/3)$.

3. $|y''|/(1 + y'^2)^{3/2}$.

5. $4/5^{3/2}$.

9. $e^{-b\theta_0}/a\sqrt{1+b^2}$.

11. 0.

13. $b^2/a,\ a^2/b$.

SECTION 9, PART II

1. From Exercise I-2, the curvature of $\lambda(t) = (x(t), y(t))$ is given by

$$k = |x'(t)\, y''(t) - x''(t)\, y'(t)| \div [x'(t)^2 + y'(t)^2]^{3/2}.$$

If we now replace t by $h(\lambda)$, we obtain

$$|(x'h')(y'h'' - y''h'^2) - (x'h'' - x''h'^2)(y'h')| \div [x'^2h'^2 + y'^2h'^2]^{3/2} = k.$$

3. The curvature is given by $\dfrac{1}{|\boldsymbol{\lambda}'(t)|}\left|\dfrac{d}{dt}\dfrac{\boldsymbol{\lambda}'(t)}{|\boldsymbol{\lambda}'(t)|}\right| = \dfrac{1}{\rho}$ or $\dfrac{1}{\rho} = \dfrac{1}{|\boldsymbol{\lambda}'|}\left|\dfrac{\boldsymbol{\lambda}''}{|\boldsymbol{\lambda}'|} - \dfrac{\boldsymbol{\lambda}'(\boldsymbol{\lambda}'\cdot\boldsymbol{\lambda}'')}{|\boldsymbol{\lambda}'|^3}\right|$

$$= \frac{\sqrt{[\boldsymbol{\lambda}''(\boldsymbol{\lambda}'\cdot\boldsymbol{\lambda}') - \boldsymbol{\lambda}'(\boldsymbol{\lambda}'\cdot\boldsymbol{\lambda}'')]^2}}{(\boldsymbol{\lambda}'\cdot\boldsymbol{\lambda}')^2} = \frac{\sqrt{(\boldsymbol{\lambda}''\cdot\boldsymbol{\lambda}'')(\boldsymbol{\lambda}'\cdot\boldsymbol{\lambda}') - (\boldsymbol{\lambda}'\cdot\boldsymbol{\lambda}'')^2}}{(\boldsymbol{\lambda}'\cdot\boldsymbol{\lambda}')^{3/2}} = \frac{\sqrt{(\boldsymbol{\lambda}'\times\boldsymbol{\lambda}'')^2}}{(\boldsymbol{\lambda}'\cdot\boldsymbol{\lambda}')^{3/2}}$$

5. $\boldsymbol{\beta}(t) = \boldsymbol{\lambda}'(s) \times \boldsymbol{\nu}(t) = \dfrac{\boldsymbol{\lambda}'(t)}{|\boldsymbol{\lambda}'(t)|} \times \boldsymbol{\nu}(t)$. Now using the previous exercise (4.)

$$\begin{aligned}\boldsymbol{\beta}(t) &= \frac{\rho(t)}{|\boldsymbol{\lambda}'(t)|^5}\boldsymbol{\lambda}'(t) \times \{\boldsymbol{\lambda}'(t) \times [\boldsymbol{\lambda}''(t) \times \boldsymbol{\lambda}'(t)]\} \\ &= \frac{\rho(t)}{|\boldsymbol{\lambda}'(t)|^5}\boldsymbol{\lambda}'(t) \times \{\boldsymbol{\lambda}''(t)(\boldsymbol{\lambda}'(t)\cdot\boldsymbol{\lambda}'(t)) - \boldsymbol{\lambda}'(t)(\boldsymbol{\lambda}'(t)\cdot\boldsymbol{\lambda}''(t)) \\ &= \frac{\rho(t)}{|\boldsymbol{\lambda}'(t)|^3}\boldsymbol{\lambda}'(t) \times \boldsymbol{\lambda}''(t).\end{aligned}$$

Section 10, Part I

1. $(6, 26°34', 131°49')$; $(2\sqrt{5}, 120°, 26°34')$.
3. $(6/5, 8/5, 6)$; $(0, -10, 4)$.
5. $r^2(1 + \sin 2\theta) = z - 5$; $r^2z^2 = 25$; $r^2(b^2 \cos^2\theta + a^2 \sin^2\theta) = a^2b^2$; $r^2 + z^2 - cz = r(a \cos\theta + b \sin\theta)$.

Section 10, Part II

1. Since $x = r \cos\bar{\theta}$, $y = r \sin\bar{\theta}$. $z = z$(cylindrical);
$$x = \rho \sin\phi \cos\theta,\ y = \rho \sin\phi \sin\theta,\ z = \rho \cos\phi \text{ (spherical)};$$
we have,
$$z = \rho\cos\phi,\ r\sin\bar{\theta} = \rho\sin\phi\sin\theta,\ r\cos\bar{\theta} = \rho\sin\phi\cos\phi. \text{ Thus,}$$
$$\bar{\theta} = \theta,\ r = \rho\sin\phi,\ r^2 + z^2 = \rho^2.$$

Review, Part I

1. a. 5, $4\sqrt{5}$, $\sqrt{73}$; now use the law of cosines to obtain the three angles, i.e., $a^2 = b^2 + c^2 - 2bc \cos A$.
b. $3\sqrt{14}$, $\sqrt{21}$, $\sqrt{185}$.
3. It is a degenerate tetrahedron, i.e., a rhombus.
5. Common point is $(1, -2, 0)$; direction numbers of the lines are $1, -1, 2$, and $0, 2, 1$.
7. $x - 1 = 2t$, $y - 3 = 3t$, $z + 5 = -4t$.
9. (a).
11. The equation of the sphere has the form $x^2 + y^2 + (z - a)^2 = r^2$. Thus,
$$4 + (2 - a)^2 = r^2,\ 16 + a^2 = r^2 \text{ and } a = -2,\ r = 2\sqrt{5}.$$
13. $(2x - x_1 - x_2)^2 + (2y - y_1 - y_2)^2 + (2z - z_1 - z_2)^2 = (x_1 - x_2)^2 + (y_1 - y_2)^2 + (z_1 - z_2)^2$.
15. a. The planes $x = 0$, $y = 0$; **b.** Hyperbolic cylinder;
c. Hyperboloid of one sheet; **d.** Hyperboloid of two sheets.
17. a. $2, 2, 2, 6$. **b.** $1, 1, 1, 0$.
c. $\mathbf{i} - \mathbf{j} + \mathbf{k}$, $\mathbf{i} + \mathbf{j} - \mathbf{k}$, $-\mathbf{i} + \mathbf{j} + \mathbf{k}$, $2\mathbf{i} - 2\mathbf{j} - 2\mathbf{k}$.
d. 2. **e.** $\mathbf{u}(\mathbf{w}\cdot\mathbf{v}) - \mathbf{w}(\mathbf{u}\cdot\mathbf{v}) = \mathbf{u} - \mathbf{w} = \mathbf{j} - \mathbf{k}$.
19. $\overrightarrow{AB} = \mathbf{R} + \mathbf{X}$,
$\overrightarrow{BC} = \mathbf{R} - \mathbf{X}$,
$\overrightarrow{AB}\cdot\overrightarrow{BC} = |\overrightarrow{AB}|\,|\overrightarrow{BC}| \cos\theta = \mathbf{R}^2 - \mathbf{X}^2 = r^2 - r^2 = 0$.

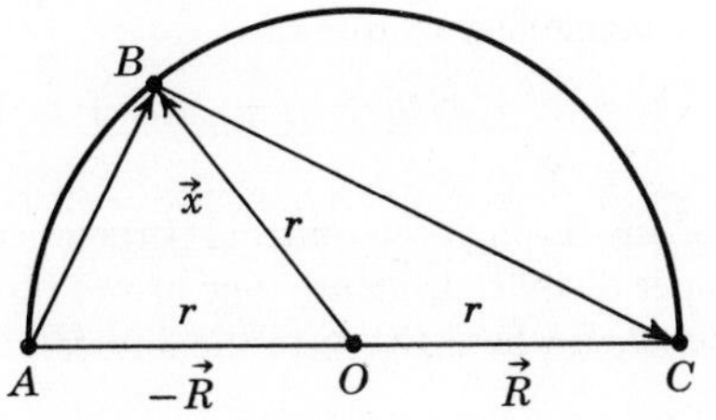

21. a.

$$D(\mathbf{u} \times \mathbf{v}) = \operatorname*{limit}_{t \to 0} \frac{(\mathbf{u} + \Delta\mathbf{u}) \times (\mathbf{v} + \Delta\mathbf{v}) - \mathbf{u} \times \mathbf{v}}{\Delta t}$$
$$= \operatorname*{limit}_{t \to 0} \frac{\Delta\mathbf{u}}{\Delta t} \times \mathbf{v} + \mathbf{u} \times \frac{\Delta\mathbf{v}}{\Delta t} + \left(\frac{\Delta\mathbf{u}}{\Delta t} \times \frac{\Delta\mathbf{v}}{\Delta t}\right) \Delta t$$
$$= (D\mathbf{u}) \times \mathbf{v} + \mathbf{u} \times (D\mathbf{v})$$

b. Similar to **a.**

23. The parallelipiped of Exercise 22 can be decomposed into 6 tetrahedra of equal volume, one of them is formed by any three conterminal edges.

25. a. $\dfrac{x-2}{2} = \dfrac{y}{2} = \dfrac{z-1}{1}$; $\quad 2(x-2) + 2y + (z-1) = 0$;

b. $\dfrac{x-2}{0} = \dfrac{y}{-3} = \dfrac{z - \pi^3/8}{3\pi^2/4}$; $\quad -3y + \dfrac{3\pi^2}{4}\left(z - \dfrac{\pi^3}{8}\right) = 0.$

27. $L = \displaystyle\int_1^3 \sqrt{4t^2 + 4 + 1/t^2}\, dt = \int_1^3 \frac{2t^2+1}{t}\, dt = 8 + \ln 3.$

Review, Part II

1. The general equation of a plane containing the line of intersection is

$$a_1x + b_1y + c_1z - d_1 + \lambda(a_2x + b_2y + c_2z - d_2) = 0$$

where λ is an arbitrary parameter. Since the plane must contain (n,k,l),

$$\lambda = -\frac{a_1h + b_1k + c_1l - d}{a_2h + b_2k + c_2l - d}.$$

3. We determine λ in the above solution such that the two planes are perpendicular, i.e.,

$$\langle a_1 + \lambda a_2, b_1 + \lambda b_2, c_1 + \lambda c_2\rangle \cdot \langle a,b,c\rangle = 0$$

or

$$\lambda = -\frac{aa_1 + bb_1 + cc_1}{aa_2 + bb_2 + cc_2}.$$

5. The planes need not intersect if the graph is unbounded. For example, consider the graph which is all the lattice points, i.e., those points (h,k,l) where h, k, l are integers. Any plane of the form $x =$ integer is a plane of symmetry and all these planes are parallel.

If the graph is bounded, the planes of symmetry will have to intersect since the centroid of the graph, which is unique, must lie in each of the planes. In the previous example, every lattice point is a centroid.

7. a. Solve the simultaneous equations:

$$(x - x_r)^2 + (y - y_r)^2 + (z - z_r)^2 = (x_1 - x_2)^2 + (y_1 - y_2)^2 + (z_1 - z_2)^2,$$

where $r = 1, 2, 3$, for two solutions. By subtracting pairs of equations, we obtain linear equations (planes).

b. The centroid of the triangle has coordinates

$$\frac{x_1 + x_2 + x_3}{3}, \frac{y_1 + y_2 + y_3}{3}, \frac{z_1 + z_2 + z_3}{3}.$$

Now find a point on the line through the centroid perpendicular to the plane of the three given points at the proper distance from any one of the three given points.

9. Coordinates of P are (at,bt,ct) where $PQ \perp$ to the line, ie.,

$$(x - at)a + (y - bt)b + (z - ct)C = 0$$

or

$$t = ax + by + cz.$$

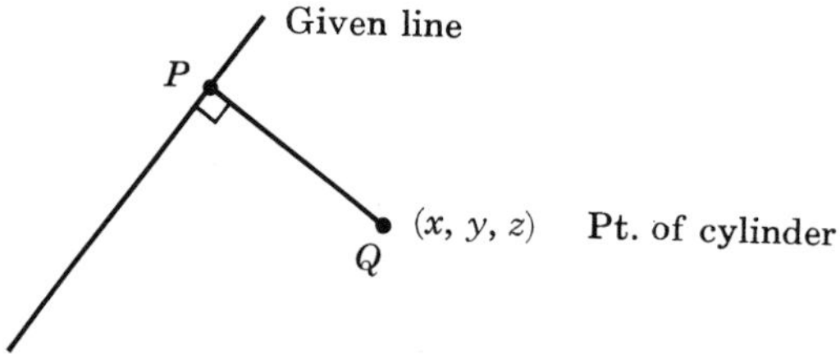

Equation of cylinder is $PQ = r$

or

$$(x - at)^2 + (y - bt)^2 + (z - ct)^2 = r^2$$
$$x^2 + y^2 + z^2 - 2t(ax + by + cz) + t^2 = r^2$$
$$x^2 + y^2 + z^2 - (ax + by + cz)^2 = r^2$$

11. Consider the cylinder formed by lines parallel to the vector $\langle a,b,c\rangle$ and passing through points of the plane curve $x = G(y)$, $z = 0$. The parametric equations of these lines are given by

$$x = x_0 + at,\ y = y_0 + bt,\ z = ct \qquad \text{where } x_0 = G(y_0).$$

Eliminating t,

$$x = x_0 + \frac{az}{c},\ y = y_0 + \frac{bz}{c}.$$

Eliminating x_0, y_0,

$$x - \frac{az}{c} = G\left(y - \frac{bz}{c}\right) \quad \text{or} \quad \frac{x}{a} - \frac{z}{c} = f\left(\frac{y}{b} - \frac{z}{c}\right).$$

13.

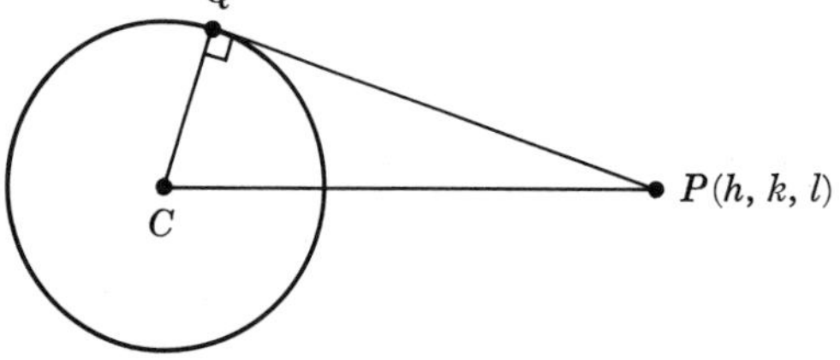

$$PQ = \sqrt{PC^2 - r^2}$$

coordinates of C are $(-a, -b, -c)$, and $r^2 = a^2 + b^2 + c^2 + d$. Thus

$$\begin{aligned} PQ^2 &= (h+a)^2 + (k+b)^2 + (l+c)^2 - a^2 - b^2 - c^2 - d \\ &= h^2 + k^2 + l^2 + 2ha + 2kb + 2lc - d \end{aligned}$$

15. Consider the equation

$$\frac{x^2}{a^2} + \frac{y^2}{b^2} + \frac{z^2}{c^2} = (lx + my + nz)^2.$$

Since it is homogeneous of 2nd degree, it represents a cone whose vertex is at the origin. The intersection of this cone with the plane $lx + my + nz = 1$ must also be on the ellipsoid $\frac{x^2}{a^2} + \frac{y^2}{b^2} + \frac{z^2}{c^2} = 1$. Thus it is the equation of the desired cone.

17. Since

$$\mathbf{e} \times (\mathbf{c} \times \mathbf{d}) = \mathbf{c}(\mathbf{e}\cdot\mathbf{d}) - \mathbf{d}(\mathbf{e}\cdot\mathbf{c}),$$

then

$$(\mathbf{a} \times \mathbf{b}) \times (\mathbf{c} \times \mathbf{d}) = \mathbf{c}(\mathbf{a} \times \mathbf{b}\cdot\mathbf{d}) - \mathbf{d}(\mathbf{a} \times \mathbf{b}\cdot\mathbf{c}).$$

19. Denote the curve by $\lambda(t) = (x(t), y(t), z(t))$ and let the fixed line be the z axis. Then the normal plane to the curve corresponding to $t = m$ is given by

$$x'(m)(x - x(m)) + y'(m)(y - y(m)) + z'(m)(z - z(m)) = 0.$$

The latter equation must contain every point of the form $(0,0,a)$. Whence

$$-x'(m)x(m) - y'(m)y(m) + z'(m)(a - z(m) = 0$$

or

$$z'(m) = 0,\ x'(m)x(m) + y'(m)y(m) = 0.$$

Integrating,

$$z(m) = \text{const.},\ x(m)^2 + y(m)^2 = \text{const.},$$

i.e., λ is a circle.

CHAPTER 18

Section 1, Part I

1. Continuous.

3. Continuous.

5. Discontinuous; H is unbounded in any neighborhood of $x = -1$.

7. Continuous; consider points (x,y) in the open disc $B(0,\delta)$ and assume without loss of generality that $y \leq x$. Then

$$|G| = \left|\frac{x(1 + y^3/x^3)}{1 + y^2/x^2}\right| \leq 2|x| \leq 2\delta.$$

Section 1, Part II

1. No; g takes on all values between -1 and $+1$ in any neighborhood of $y = 0$.

3. Yes; define $F(0,0) = 0$. Now proceed as in the solution of Exercise I-7 above.

5. The continuity of a function of 3 variables is analogously defined as 18.1. F is continuous. Consider points (x,y,z) in the open ball $B(0,\delta)$ and assume without loss of generality that $z \leq y \leq x$.

$$|F| = \left| \frac{x \cdot \dfrac{y}{x} \cdot \dfrac{z}{x}}{1 + \dfrac{y^2}{x^2} + \dfrac{z^2}{x^2}} \right| \leq |x| \leq \delta.$$

7. $f(O + t\langle h,k\rangle) = f(th,tk) = \dfrac{thk^2}{h^2 + t^2k^4}$ if $\langle h,k\rangle \neq \mathbf{0}$. Hence, $\lim_{t\to 0} f(O + t\langle h,k\rangle) = 0 = f(0,0)$ for every vector $\langle h,k\rangle \neq \mathbf{0}$. On the other hand, $f(y^2,y) = 1/2$ for all $y \neq 0$. Hence, f is not continuous at O.

SECTION 2, PART I

1. $(8a + 2b - 6c)/5$.

3. $11/3$.

5. For directions perpendicular to $\langle a,b\rangle$.

SECTION 2, PART II

1. $D_{\mathbf{V}}f = 2(a\cos\alpha + b\cos\beta + c\cos\gamma)$; $\mathbf{V} = \langle\cos\alpha, \cos\beta, \cos\gamma\rangle$. By the Cauchy inquality,

$$D_{\mathbf{V}}f \leq 2\sqrt{(a^2 + b^2 + c^2)(\cos^2\alpha + \cos^2\beta + \cos^2\gamma)} = 2\sqrt{a^2 + b^2 + c^2}.$$

$$\text{Max } D_{\mathbf{V}}f = 2\sqrt{a^2 + b^2 + c^2} \quad \text{when} \quad \frac{\cos\alpha}{a} = \frac{\cos\beta}{b} = \frac{\cos\gamma}{c}.$$

SECTION 3, PART I

1. $-(x + y)^{-2}$, $-(x + y)^{-2}$.

3. 0, 0.

SECTION 3, PART II

1. a. $F_x = \dfrac{x}{x^2 + y^2}$, $F_{xx} = \dfrac{y^2 - x^2}{(x^2 + y^2)^2}$. By symmetry,

$$F_{yy} = \frac{x^2 - y^2}{(x^2 + y^2)^2}.$$

$$F_{xx} + F_{yy} = 0.$$

(Also follows from result of Exercise I-4.)

b. $\dfrac{1}{F^2} = x^2 + y^2 + z^2$; $-\dfrac{F_x}{F^3} = x$; $-\dfrac{F_{xx}}{F^3} + \dfrac{3F_x^2}{F^4} = 1$.

$$\frac{F_{xx}}{F^3} = 3x^2F^2 - 1. \text{ By symmetry,}$$

$$\frac{F_{xx} + F_{yy} + F_{zz}}{F^3} = 3F^2(x^2 + y^2 + z^2) - 3 = 0.$$

SECTION 4, PART I

1. $(a + b + c)/3$.

3. $a + b + c$.

5. Let $w = \sqrt{x^2 + y^2 + z^2}$, $P = (100,200,200)$, $\mathbf{v} = \langle 0,-1,1\rangle$; $P + \mathbf{v} = (100,199,201)$.

$$w(P + \mathbf{v}) - w(P) \doteq \nabla w(P)\cdot\langle 0,-1,1\rangle.$$

$$\nabla w(P) = \left\langle \frac{x}{w}, \frac{y}{w}, \frac{z}{w} \right\rangle_P = \left\langle \frac{1}{3}, \frac{2}{3}, \frac{2}{3} \right\rangle.$$

$$w(P + \mathbf{v}) - 300 \doteq \langle \tfrac{1}{3},\tfrac{2}{3},\tfrac{2}{3}\rangle\cdot\langle 0,-1,1\rangle = 0$$

7. Let $z = \sin x \cos y$, $P = \left(\frac{\pi}{4}, \frac{\pi}{6}\right)$, $\mathbf{v} = \left\langle -\frac{\pi}{180}, \frac{\pi}{180}\right\rangle$, $P + \mathbf{v} = \left(\frac{44\pi}{180}, \frac{31\pi}{180}\right)$.

$$z(P + \mathbf{v}) - z(P) \doteq \nabla z(P) \cdot \left\langle -\frac{\pi}{180}, \frac{\pi}{180}\right\rangle.$$

$$\nabla z(P) = \langle \cos x \cos y, -\sin x \sin y\rangle_P = \left\langle \frac{\sqrt{3}}{2\sqrt{2}}, -\frac{1}{2\sqrt{2}}\right\rangle$$

$$z(P + \mathbf{v}) - \frac{\sqrt{3}}{2\sqrt{2}} \doteq -\frac{\pi}{180}\,\frac{1 + \sqrt{3}}{2\sqrt{2}}.$$

9. In general, if $V = F(x,y,z)$, $P = (l,w,h)$, $Q = (l + \Delta l, w + \Delta w, h + \Delta h)$,

$$V(Q) - V(P) = \Delta V \doteq \nabla V(P)\cdot\langle \Delta l, \Delta w, \Delta h\rangle$$
$$\doteq F_1\Delta l + F_2\Delta w + F_3\Delta h\}_{(x,y,z) = (l,w,h)}$$

Here, $V = xyz$. Thus

$$\frac{\Delta V}{V} = \frac{\Delta l}{l} + \frac{\Delta w}{w} + \frac{\Delta h}{h}$$

where $l = 10.2$, $w = 20.4$, $h = 9.9$, $V = 2059.992$, $\Delta l = \pm.05$, $\Delta w = \pm.05$, $\Delta h = \pm.05$.

$$\frac{\Delta V}{2060} \doteq \pm.05\left(\frac{1}{10.2} + \frac{1}{20.4} + \frac{1}{9.9}\right)$$

or

$$\Delta V \mathrel{\dot{\leq}} (.0125)(2060) \doteq 25$$

Since writing the volume as 2060.0 means the error is within $\pm.05$, we are not justified in the way we rounded off the number.

11. $\nabla f = \langle 2x + 1, 2y - 1\rangle_{(x,y) = (1,-1)} = \langle 3,3\rangle$

$$\text{Max } D_{\mathbf{v}}f = |\nabla f| = 3\sqrt{2}.$$

Similarly,

$$\text{Min } D_{\mathbf{v}}f = -3\sqrt{2}.$$

SECTION 4, PART II

1. It follows from **18.9** that in order for f to be differentiable at the origin, we must have

$$f(h,k) - f(0,0) = Ah + Bk + \epsilon\delta \qquad (1)$$

where $\delta = \sqrt{h^2 + k^2}$ and $\epsilon \to 0$ as $\delta \to 0$.
If we let $h = \delta \cos\theta$, $k = \delta \sin\theta$, then $\delta \to 0$ implies nothing about θ and may thus be arbitrary. By substituting for h and k in (1), we will show that (1) cannot hold. On substituting, (1) becomes $\sin^3\theta - \cos^3\theta = A\cos\theta + B\sin\theta + \epsilon$. Now let $\delta \to 0$, giving

$$\sin^3\theta - \cos^3\theta = A\cos\theta + \beta\sin\theta.$$

This is impossible since θ is arbitrary and thus f is not differentiable at (0,0). However, the two partial derivatives exist. For

$$f_x(0,0) = \lim_{h\to 0}\frac{f(h,0) - f(0,0)}{h} = \lim_{h\to 0}\frac{0 - h^3}{h^3} = -1,$$

$$f_y(0,0) = \lim_{k\to 0}\frac{f(0,k) - f(0,0)}{k} = \lim_{k\to 0}\frac{k^3 - 0}{k^3} = 1.$$

3. The proof is essentially the same as for Exercise II-2, Section 2. If $\mathbf{V} = \langle \cos\theta, \sin\theta\rangle$, then

$$D_{\mathbf{V}}f(P) = 2A\cos\theta + 2B\sin\theta, \qquad \text{where} \quad 2A = f_1(P), \qquad 2B = f_2(P).$$

If we consider a polar coordinate system centered at (a,b), then the endpoints are given by $r = 2A\cos\theta + 2B\sin\theta$ or $r^2 = 2Ar\cos\theta + 2Br\sin\theta$ or $x^2 + y^2 = 2Ax + 2By$. This is a circle whose center is (A,B), radius $\sqrt{A^2 + B^2}$. Since a tangent to the circle at point $P(a,b)$ is $\perp$ to $\nabla f(P)$, the circle is tangent to the graph of $f(x,y) = f(a,b)$ at $P(a,b)$. (Note that the slope of $f(x,y) = f(a,b)$ is given by $-f_1/f_2$).

5. See Exercise I-9 above.

SECTION 5, PART I

1. $8x - 4y + z + 8 = 0$.
3. $x + 2y + 2z = 9$.
5. $4x = 8y + z$.
7. $x + 4y + 13 = 18z$.
9. $x - y - 2z = 2$.
11. Follows from 17.7 and 18.15.

SECTION 5, PART II

1. In order for a tangent plane to exist at the origin, the function must be differentiable there. For a similar example, see Exercise II-2, Section 4. The first derivatives with respect to x and y exist everywhere in the neighborhood of $(0,0)$ and have the value zero there. For

$$F_1(0,0) = \lim_{h\to 0} \frac{F(h,0) - F(0,0)}{h} = 0,$$

and, similarly, $F_2(0,0) = 0$. The derivatives, however, are not continuous at the origin, for

$$F_1 = \frac{y^3}{\sqrt{(x^2 + y^2)^3}}.$$

If we approach the origin along the x axis, $F_1 \to 0$, while if we approach the origin along the y axis, $F_1 \to 1$. If there was a tangent plane, it would have to be the plane $z = 0$ (since $F_1(0,0) = F_2(0,0) = 0$). In cylindrical coordinates, the surface is given by $z = r\sin 2\theta$ and for points corresponding to $\theta = \pi/4$, $z = r$. Thus the distance z of the point of the surface from the point of the plane does not vanish to a higher order than r as must be the case with a tangent plane.

3. If we take the equation of the surface to be $z = F(x^2 + y^2)$ (the axis of revolution is the z axis), then the normal line at $x = a$, $y = b$ is given by

$$x - a = 2atF'(a^2 + b^2), \qquad y - b = 2btF'(a^2 + b^2), \qquad z - F(a^2 + b^2) = -t.$$

Letting $1 + 2tF'(a^2 + b^2) = 0$, we get $x = 0$, $y = 0$, which corresponds to a point on the z axis.

SECTION 6, PART I

1. $\dfrac{dw}{dt} = \dfrac{2(t-1)}{t^3} + \dfrac{2t}{(t+1)^3}$.

3. $\dfrac{dw}{dt} = t^3(1 + 3\ln t)\cos t^3 \ln t + \sin t^3 \ln t$.

5. $\dfrac{\partial z}{\partial u} = 2u$, $\dfrac{\partial z}{\partial v} = 0$.

7. $\dfrac{\partial z}{\partial u} = \dfrac{2u}{\sqrt{1-(u^2-v^2)^2}}, \dfrac{\partial z}{\partial v} = \dfrac{-2v}{\sqrt{1-(u^2-v^2)^2}}.$

9. $\dfrac{\partial z}{\partial u} = \dfrac{5v}{(u+2v)^2} e^{(2u-v)/(u+2v)}.$

11. $\dfrac{\partial w}{\partial r} = \dfrac{3(r^2+s^2+t^2) - 2r(3r-s-2t)}{(r^2+s^2+t^2)^2}.$

13. $\dfrac{\partial w}{\partial u} = \sqrt{1+v^2}, \dfrac{\partial w}{\partial v} = uv/\sqrt{1+v^2}.$

15. By the chain rule,

$$z_u = z_x x_u + z_y y_u \tag{1}$$

$$z_{uu} = z_x x_{uu} + z_y y_{uu} + x_u \frac{\partial z_x}{\partial u} + y_u \frac{\partial z_y}{\partial u}.$$

To obtain $\dfrac{\partial z_x}{\partial u}$, just replace z by z_x in (1), i.e.,

$$\frac{\partial z_x}{\partial u} = z_{xx} x_u + z_{yx} y_u.$$

Similarly for $\dfrac{\partial z_y}{\partial u}$.

17.
$$z_x = 1 + f'(u)u_x, \quad u_x = y,$$
$$z_y = f'(u)u_y, \quad u_y = x.$$
$$\frac{z_x - 1}{z_y} = \frac{u_x}{u_y} = \frac{y}{x}.$$

19.
$$z = f(x), \quad x = u^2 + v^2$$
$$z_u = f'(x)x_u, \quad x_u = 2u,$$
$$z_v = f'(x)x_v, \quad x_v = 2v,$$
$$\frac{z_u}{z_v} = \frac{x_u}{x_v} = \frac{u}{v}.$$

21.
$$F(x,y) = f(u) + g(v), \quad u = y + ax, \quad v = y - ax,$$
$$F_x = f'(u)a + g'(v)(-a), \quad F_{xx} = f''(u)a^2 + g''(v)a^2.$$
$$F_y = f'(u) + g'(v), \quad F_{yy} = f''(u) + g''(v).$$
$$F_{xx} = a^2 F_{yy}.$$

23.
$$\left(\frac{\partial H}{\partial V}\right)_P = \left(\frac{\partial E}{\partial V}\right)_P + P = \frac{\partial g}{\partial V} + P.$$

Section 6, Part II

1. Differentiating twice with respect to t,

$$x f_1(tx,ty) + y f_2(tx,ty) = nt^{n-1} f(x,y)$$
$$x^2 f_{11}(tx,ty) + 2xy f_{12}(tx,ty) + y^2 f_{22}(tx,ty) = n(n-1)t^{n-2} f(x,y).$$

Now set $t = 1$.

3. Either verify directly by differentiating or use Exercise 1**b** above with $n = 1$.

5.
$$F_x = \frac{-y}{x^2+y^2}, \quad F_y = \frac{x}{x^2+y^2},$$
$$F_{xx} = \frac{2xy}{(x^2+y^2)^3}, \quad F_{yy} = \frac{-2xy}{(x^2+y^2)^2}.$$
$$F_{xx} + F_{yy} = 0.$$

7. Let $G(x,y) = F(u,v)$ where $u = \dfrac{ax}{x^2+y^2}$, $v = \dfrac{ay}{x^2+y^2}$. $G_x = F_u u_x + F_v v_x$,
$$G_{xx} = F_u u_{xx} + F_v v_{xx} + u_x(F_{uu}u_x + F_{uv}v_x) + v_x(F_{vu}u_x + F_{vv}v_x).$$
G_{yy} is gotten from the last equation by replacing x by y. Then
$$G_{xx} + G_{yy} = F_u(u_{xx} + u_{yy}) + F_v(v_{xx} + v_{yy}) + F_{uu}(u_x^2 + u_y^2) + 2F_{uv}(u_x v_x + u_y v_y) + F_{vv}(v_x^2 + v_y^2).$$
Also,
$$u_x = \frac{a}{x^2+y^2} - \frac{2ax^2}{(x^2+y^2)^2} = \frac{a(y^2-x^2)}{(x^2+y^2)^2} = -v_y,$$
$$u_y = -\frac{2axy}{(x^2+y^2)^2} = v_x.$$
Thus
$$u_x v_x + u_y v_y = 0$$
$$u_{xx} = -v_{yx}, \quad u_{yy} = v_{xy}, \quad u_{xx} + u_{yy} = 0$$
and, similarly, $v_{xx} + v_{yy} = 0$.
$$u_x^2 + u_y^2 = v_x^2 + v_y^2.$$
Substituting back,
$$G_{xx} + G_{yy} = (u_x^2 + u_y^2)(F_{uu} + F_{vv}) = 0$$
since F is harmonic.

Section 7, Part I

1. $\dfrac{dy}{dx} = -\dfrac{1 + y\cos xy}{2y + x\cos xy}$.

3. $\dfrac{dy}{dx} = \dfrac{4}{x - 3y^2(x^2+y^2)}$.

5. $\dfrac{dy}{dx} = \dfrac{3x^2 - 4xy^2 - 3y}{4x^2y - 3y^2 + 3x}$.

7. $\dfrac{\partial z}{\partial x} = -\dfrac{2xz + y^2}{x^2 + 2yz - 3z^2}$.

9. $\dfrac{\partial z}{\partial y} = \dfrac{3y^2z + z^3}{3(x^3+y^3) + (x+y)z^2}$.

11. Differentiating both equations with respect to u:
$$x + ux_u + vy_u + 2x^2u^2 + 2xx_uu^2 + 2yy_uv^2 = 0,$$
$$2xu + u^2x_u + x^2 + 2xx_uu - y_uv^2 - 2yy_uv = 0.$$
Now solve these simultaneous linear equations for x_u and y_u. To obtain x_v and y_v, differentiate the original pair of equations with respect to v and solve.

Section 7, Part II

1.
$$F(x,y) = 0 \quad \text{where} \quad y = f(x).$$
$$F_1 + F_2y' = 0,$$
$$F_{11} + F_{12}y' + F_{21}y' + F_{22}y'^2 + F_2y'' = 0.$$
$$y'' = -\frac{1}{F_2}\{F_{11} + 2F_{12}y' + F_{22}y'^2\} = (F_{11}F_2^2 - 2F_{12}F_1F_2 + F_{22}F_1^2)/F_2^3.$$

3. $F(x,y,u,v) = 0, \quad G(x,y,u,v) = 0$ where $u = f(x,y)$ $v = g(x,y)$.

Differentiate with respect to x:

$$F_1 + F_3u_x + F_4v_x = 0, \qquad G_1 + G_3u_x + G_4v_x = 0.$$

Now solve for u_x and v_x.
To find u_y and v_y, differentiate the original equations with respect to y.

SECTION 8, PART I

1. $f(0,0) = 0$, min.
3. $F(2,0) = -16$, min.
5. No extremum.
7. $f(-\frac{1}{2},4) = -6$, max.
9. $F(2^{-1/5},\pm 2^{3/10}) = 5\cdot 2^{-2/5}$, min.
11. $(\frac{3}{7})\sqrt{14}$.
13. Let the coordinates of one vertex of the parallelopiped be (x,y,z). Then

$$V = 8xyz, \qquad \text{or}$$

$$\frac{V^2}{8a^2b^2c^2} = \frac{x^2}{a^2}\cdot\frac{y^2}{b^2}\cdot\frac{z^2}{c^2}.$$

Let

$$r = \frac{x^2}{a^2}, \qquad s = \frac{y^2}{b^2}, \qquad t = \frac{3^2}{c^2}.$$

We now have to maximize

$$\overline{V} = rst \quad \text{subject to} \quad r + s + t = 1.$$
$$\overline{V} = rs(1 - r - s).$$
$$\overline{V}_r = s(1 - r - s) - rs = 0 = \overline{V}_s = r(1 - r - s) - rs.$$

Thus, $r = s = t = \frac{1}{3}$ and $V = 8abc/3\sqrt{3}$.

15. We are to maximize $V = xyz$ subject to $xy + 2xz + 2yz = s$. Then

$$V_x = yz + xy\frac{\partial z}{\partial x} = 0 \quad \text{where} \quad y + 2z + 2(x+y)\frac{\partial z}{\partial x} = 0,$$

$$V_y = xz + xy\frac{\partial z}{\partial y} = 0 \quad \text{where} \quad x + 2z + 2(x+y)\frac{\partial z}{\partial y} = 0.$$

Thus

$$z = \frac{x(y+2z)}{2(x+y)} = \frac{y(x+2z)}{2(x+y)} \quad \text{and} \quad x = y = 2z.$$

These are the same subsidiary equations as in Example 4. Now substitute back in the surface equation.

SECTION 8, PART II

1. We wish to minimize (or maximize) $D^2 = (x-a)^2 + (y-b)^2 + (z-c)^2$ where $\phi(x,y,z) = 0$ is an equation of the surface. Thus

$$\frac{\partial D^2}{\partial x} = 2(x-a) + 2(z-c)\frac{\partial z}{\partial x} = 0,$$

$$\frac{\partial D^2}{\partial y} = 2(y-b) + 2(z-c)\frac{\partial z}{\partial y} = 0,$$

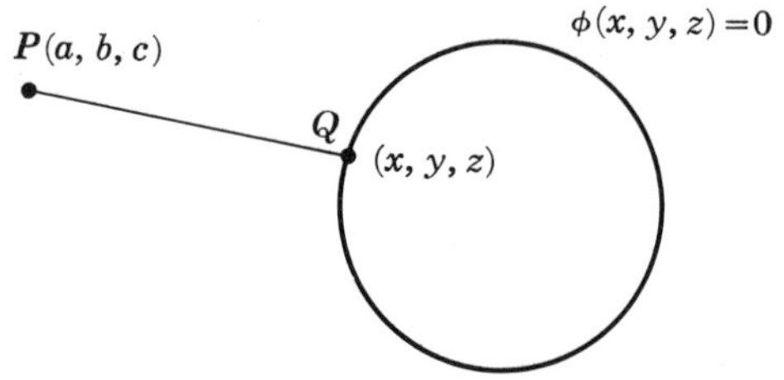

where

$$\phi_x + \phi_z \frac{\partial z}{\partial x} = 0 = \phi_y + \phi_z \frac{\partial z}{\partial x}.$$

Whence

$$\frac{\phi_x}{x - a} = \frac{\phi_y}{y - b} = \frac{\phi_z}{z - c}.$$

Since $\nabla\phi = \langle\phi_x,\phi_y,\phi_z\rangle$, **QP** must be along the gradient at Q and is thus perpendicular to the surface.

Alternatively, consider the level lines, i.e., the family of spheres centered at P. The minimum distance corresponds to the radius of the smallest sphere which is tangent to $\phi = 0$. And since this minimum radius is perpendicular to the sphere, it is also perpendicular to the surface. (Also see solution of Exercise II-2, Section 3, Chapter 13.)

3. $$V = x^n + y^n + z^n \quad \text{where} \quad x + y + z = S \text{ (given)}.$$

$$V_x = nx^{n-1} + nz^{n-1}\frac{\partial z}{\partial x} = 0, \quad 1 + \frac{\partial z}{\partial x} = 0,$$

$$V_y = ny^{n-1} + nz^{n-1}\frac{\partial z}{\partial y} = 0, \quad 1 + \frac{\partial z}{\partial y} = 0.$$

Whence $x = y = z = s/3$. This point can be shown to correspond to the minimum point by the 2nd derivative test. If there are any other extrema, they will be endpoint extrema. On checking the endpoints $(x,y) = (0,0), (s,0), (0,s)$, we obtain a maximum at each endpoint. Here, $V_{\max} = S^n$. See solution of next exercise (4) for an elementary derivation of this.

5. We are to minimize $s = xy + 2xz + 2yz$ subject to $xyz = V$(given). By the A.M.–G.M.,

$$\frac{xy + 2xz + 2yz}{3} \geq \sqrt[3]{(xy)(2xz)(2yz)} = \sqrt[3]{4V^2}$$

with equality, if and only if, $xy = 2xz = 2yz$. Since the right-hand side is a fixed number, the left-hand side is a minimum if $x = y = 2z$ which leads to the same solution as before.

7. The ellipse must be tangent to the circle. Eliminating y between the two equations:

$$\frac{x^2}{a^2} + \frac{2x - x^2}{b^2} = 1.$$

This quadratic must have equal roots. Setting the discriminant $= 0$, we get $a^2 = \dfrac{b^4}{b^2 - 1}$.

$$\text{Area}^2 = \pi^2a^2b^2 = \frac{\pi^2b^6}{b^2 - 1}.$$

Setting $\dfrac{dA^2}{db} = 0$, we obtain $b = \sqrt{3/2}$, $a = 3\sqrt{2}/2$, $A_{\min} = \dfrac{3\pi\sqrt{3}}{2}$.

SECTION 9, PART I

1. $(0,0,c\pi)$.

3. $I_x = \sqrt{a^2 + c^2} \int_0^{\pi/2} (k \sin 2t)(b^2 \sin^2 t + c^2t^2)\, dt,$

$I_y = \sqrt{a^2 + c^2} \int_0^{\pi/2} (k \sin 2t)(a^2 \cos^2 t + c^2t^2)\, dt,$

$I_z = \sqrt{a^2 + c^2} \int_0^{\pi/2} (k \sin 2t)(a^2 \cos^2 t + b^2 \sin^2 t)\, dt.$

5. $k(x(0)^2 + y(0)^2 + z(0)^2)^{-1/2} - k(x(t_0)^2 + y(t_0)^2 + z(t_0)^2)^{-1/2}$.

7. $0, 2\pi$.

9. $2\pi^2 + 4\pi b - \pi ab, a^2/2 + ab/3 + ac/4 + ab^2c/4 + a^2b^2c^3/5$.

SECTION 9, PART II

1.
$$\mathbf{F} = \int_\lambda k\mathbf{n}\, ds$$

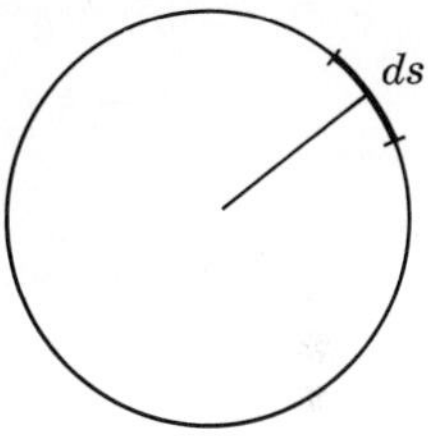

where $\mathbf{n}$ denotes a unit normal vector to the curve. The unit tangent vector is $\left\langle \frac{dx}{ds}, \frac{dy}{ds} \right\rangle$. Consequently, the unit normal vector is given by

$$\mathbf{n} = \left\langle -\frac{dy}{ds}, \frac{dx}{ds} \right\rangle.$$

Then,

$$\mathbf{F} = k\left\langle -\int_\lambda dy, \int_\lambda dx \right\rangle = \mathbf{0}$$

REVIEW, PART I

1. $x + y \geq 0, x - y \geq 0$.

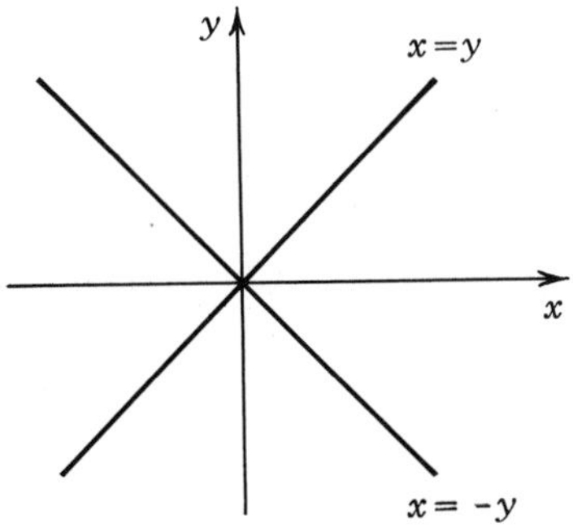

3. $x^2 + y^2 \neq a^2$.

5. $|\nabla f(5,5)| = 10\sqrt{5}$.

11. $4(x-2) + 4(y-2) + 9(z-1) = 0$.

13. 0.

15. $\dfrac{g(t) - (2+t)g'(t)}{(2+t+g(t))^2}$.

17. Minimum (0) for each point on the line $x = 0$.

19. A ridge (crest) above the curve $2x = \ln y$; saddle point $(1,e^2,-1)$.

21. 1.08.

23.
$$\frac{h}{a^2}(x-h) + \frac{k}{b^2}(y-k) + \frac{l}{c^2}(z-l) = 0,$$
or
$$\frac{hx}{a^2} + \frac{ky}{b^2} + \frac{lz}{c^2} = 1.$$
$$\frac{x-h}{h/a^2} = \frac{y-k}{k/b^2} = \frac{z-l}{l/c^2} = t.$$

25. Minimize $S = 2z(x+y)$ subject to $V = xyz$. Thus $S = 2V\left(\frac{1}{x} + \frac{1}{y}\right)$, and there is no minimum since x and y could be taken arbitrarily large.

27.
$$\int_\lambda xy\,ds = \int_{-a}^{a} ay\,dy + \int_{a}^{-a} ax\,dx + \int_{a}^{-a} -ay\,dy + \int_{-a}^{a} -ax\,dx$$
$$= 0.$$
(Also, by symmetry, the integral = 0.)

29. $-\int_0^1 [t^2 + (t+1)^2 + (t-1)^2(2t)]\,dt = -\frac{17}{6}$.

Review, Part II

1.
$$\frac{\partial F}{\partial x} = y\left\{\frac{x^2-y^2}{x^2+y^2} + \frac{4x^2y^2}{(x^2+y^2)^2}\right\}, \qquad \frac{\partial F}{\partial y} = x\left\{\frac{x^2-y^2}{x^2+y^2} - \frac{4x^2y^2}{(x^2+y^2)^2}\right\}$$
for $(x,y) \neq (0,0)$. Now
$$F_1(0,0) = \lim_{h\to 0} \frac{F(h,0) - F(0,0)}{h} = 0,$$
and similarly
$$F_2(0,0) = 0.$$
Also, from above,
$$F_x(0,y) = -y\ (y \neq 0), \qquad F_y(x,0) = x\ (x \neq 0).$$
Then
$$F_{xy}(0,0) = \lim_{k\to 0} \frac{F_x(0,k) - F_x(0,0)}{k} = \lim_{k\to 0} -\frac{k}{k} = -1$$
$$F_{yx}(0,0) = \lim_{h\to 0} \frac{F_y(h,0) - F_y(0,0)}{h} = \lim_{h\to 0} \frac{h}{h} = 1.$$

In general,

$$F_{xy}(a,b) = \underset{k\to 0}{\text{limit}}\ \underset{h\to 0}{\text{limit}}\ \frac{\Delta^2 F}{hk}$$

$$F_{yx}(a,b) = \underset{h\to 0}{\text{limit}}\ \underset{k\to 0}{\text{limit}}\ \frac{\Delta^2 F}{hk},$$

where $\Delta^2 F = F(a+h,b+k) - F(a,b+k) - F(a+h,b) + F(a,b)$. And since the value of the double limits may depend upon the order in which the limiting operations are made, there is therefore no a priori reason why $F_{xy} = F_{yx}$ (always) even if in most practical cases it is.

3. Differentiating $F(x,y,z) = 0$ with respect to y keeping z fixed, we get

$$F_1\left(\frac{\partial x}{\partial y}\right)_z + F_2 = 0.$$

Similarly,

$$F_2\left(\frac{\partial y}{\partial z}\right)_x + F_3 = 0, \qquad F_1 + F_3\left(\frac{\partial z}{\partial x}\right)_y = 0.$$

Then

$$\left(\frac{\partial x}{\partial y}\right)_z\left(\frac{\partial y}{\partial z}\right)_x\left(\frac{\partial z}{\partial x}\right)_y = \left(-\frac{F_2}{F_1}\right)\left(-\frac{F_3}{F_2}\right)\left(-\frac{F_1}{F_3}\right) = -1.$$

5. Recall that in the one dimensional case, we showed that if $F'(x) = 0$ for all x in an open interval I, then $F(x)$ is a constant in S. In the proof, we used the mean value theorem, i.e.,

$$F(x) - F(a) = (x-a)F'(a + s(x-a))$$

where $a \in I$ and $0 < s < 1$. Thus $F(x) = F(a)$ in I. We do the same for the right-hand side of

$$F(x,y) - F(a,b) = \{F(x,y) - F(a,y)\} + \{F(a,y) - F(a,b)\}$$

for (a,b) in S.

$$F(x,y) - F(a,b) = (x-a)F_1(a + s(x-a),y) + (y-b)F_2(a,b + (y-b)t),$$

where $0 < s,\ t < 1$. Thus

$$F(x,y) = F(a,b) \quad \text{in} \quad S.$$

7. a. $D_x^2 FG = F_{xx}G + 2F_xG_x + FG_{xx}$. Thus

$$\nabla^2(FG) = G\nabla^2 F + F\nabla^2 G + 2(F_xG_x + F_yG_y + F_zG_z)$$
$$= 2\nabla F\cdot\nabla G.$$

b.

$$\nabla^2\nabla^2 F = 0, \quad \nabla^2(x^2+y^2+z^2)G = \nabla(x^2+y^2+z^2)\cdot\nabla G + 6G$$
$$= 2(xG_x + yG_y + zG_z) + 6G.$$

$\nabla^2(2xG_x) = 2\nabla x\cdot\nabla G_x = 2G_{xx}$ (*Note:* $\nabla^2 G_x = 0$). Thus

$$\nabla^2\nabla^2(x^2+y^2+z^2)G = 2(G_{xx} + G_{yy} + G_{zz}) = 0.$$

9. Since the angle inscribed in a segment of a circle is constant, the family of surfaces $\phi(x,y,z) =$ constant are ones of revolution formed by rotating the circular arc (APB) about $\overline{AB}$ as an axis. Since $\nabla\phi$ is orthogonal to the surface $\phi = c$ which is one of revolution, it is also orthogonal to each cross section containing the axis.

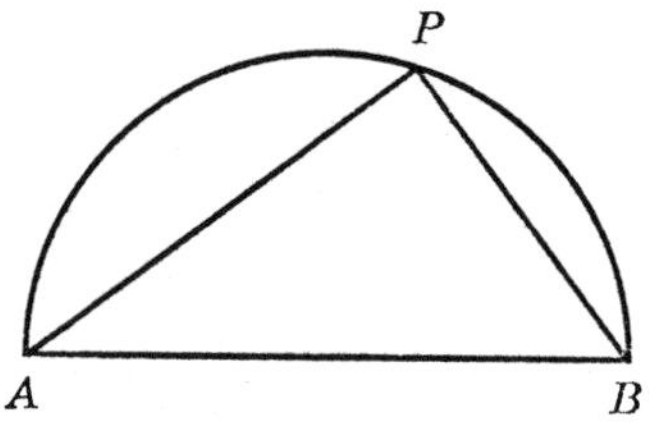

11. The equations of planes containing the z axis is given by $y = mx$. Consequently, along a cross section, we must have

$$z = (mx - x^2)(mx - 2x^2) = x^2(m - x)(m - 2x)$$

which has a minimum when $x = 0$ for all m. However $f(x,y) = (y - x^2)(y - 2x^2)$ does not have a minimum at (0,0). For points (x,y) in the neighborhood of (0,0) we could have

$$y > x^2, \quad y > 2x^2 \quad \text{and} \quad f(x,y) > 0$$

and also

$$y > x^2, \quad y < 2x^2 \quad \text{and} \quad f(x,y) < 0.$$

13. We wish to minimize; $S = x^2 + y^2 + z^2$ subject to

$$ax + by + cz = 2A, \quad \text{where } A = \text{area of triangle.}$$

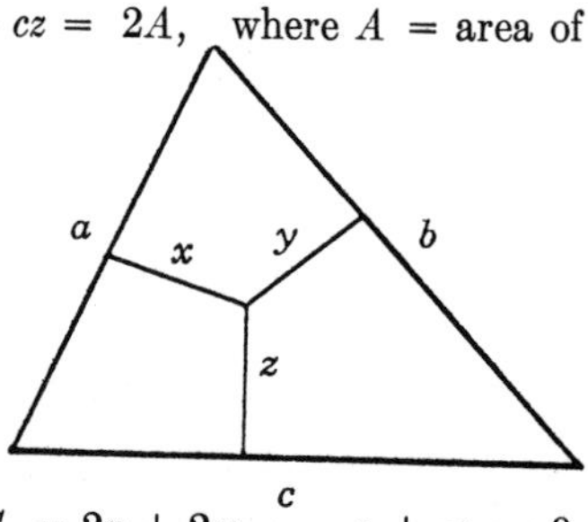

$$S_x = 2x + 2zz_x, \qquad a + cz_x = 0,$$
$$S_y = 2y + 2zz_y, \qquad b + cz_y = 0.$$

Thus

$$\frac{x}{a} = \frac{y}{b} = \frac{z}{c} = \lambda$$

and

$$\lambda(a^2 + b^2 + c^2) = 2A.$$

Alternately, the problem is to find the closest point of the plane $ax + by + cz = 2A$ to the origin. Consequently, we just take the foot of the perpendicular from the origin to the plane.

15. Let $w = (x)^{y^z}$; then $\ln w = y^z \ln x$, $\ln \ln w = z \ln y + \ln \ln x$. Then

$$\frac{\Delta w}{w \ln w} \doteq \frac{z}{y}\Delta y + \Delta z \ln y + \frac{\Delta x}{x \ln x}$$

where $x = 2$, $y = 2$, $z = 3$, $\Delta x = .01$, $\Delta y = -.01$, $\Delta z = -.01$ and $\Delta w = (2.01)^{1.99^{2.99}} - (2)^{2^3}$, $w = (2)^{2^3}$.

$$\frac{\Delta w}{2^{11} \ln 2} \doteq \left(\frac{3}{2}\right)(-.01) + (\ln 2)(-.01) + \frac{.01}{2 \ln 2}.$$

17. Tangent plane at point (a,b,c) of surface is

$$\frac{1}{2\sqrt{a}}(x - a) + \frac{1}{2\sqrt{b}}(y - b) + \frac{1}{2\sqrt{c}}(z - c) = 0.$$

$$\begin{aligned} x \text{ intercept} &= (\sqrt{b} + \sqrt{c})\sqrt{a} + a \\ y \text{ intercept} &= (\sqrt{c} + \sqrt{a})\sqrt{b} + b \\ z \text{ intercept} &= (\sqrt{a} + \sqrt{b})\sqrt{c} + c \\ \text{Sum of intercepts} &= (\sqrt{a} + \sqrt{b} + \sqrt{c})^2 = k. \end{aligned}$$

19.
$$f_1(x + y) = g'(x), \qquad f_2(x + y) = h'(y).$$

But since $f_1 = f_2$, $g'(x) = h'(y)$. The only way the latter equation of two independent variables can be satisfied is that $g'(x) = h'(y) = a$ (constant). Thus

$$g(x) = ax + k_1 \qquad h(y) = ay + k_2.$$

21. Differentiating with respect to x,

$$2xG'(x^2 + y^2) = M'(x)N(y).$$

Similarly,

$$2yG'(x^2 + y^2) = M(x)N'(y).$$

Dividing:

$$\frac{M'(x)}{xM(x)} = \frac{N'(y)}{yN(y)}.$$

Each must be a constant.

$$\frac{M'(x)}{xM(x)} = 2a = \frac{N'(y)}{yN(y)}.$$

Integrating:

$$\ln M(x) = ax^2 + k_1, \qquad \ln N(y) = ay^2 + k_2,$$

$$M(x) = A_1e^{ax^2}, \qquad N(y) = A_2e^{ay^2},$$

$$F(x,y) = G(x^2 + y^2) = Ae^{a(x^2+y^2)}.$$

CHAPTER 19

Section 1, Part I

5. Differentiating $\int e^{ax} \sin bx \, dx = e^{ax}[A \sin bx + B \cos bx] + k$ yields:

$$e^{ax} \sin bx = e^{ax}[(aA - bB) \sin bx + (aB + bA) \cos bx].$$

Whence,

$$aA - bB = 1, \qquad aB + bA = 0,$$

on

$$A = \frac{a}{a^2 + b^2}, \qquad B = \frac{-b}{a^2 + b^2}.$$

7. a. $\displaystyle\int \frac{1}{(t^2+x^2)^2}\,dt = \frac{1}{2x^3}\tan^{-1}\frac{t}{x} + \frac{t}{2x^2(t^2+x^2)} + C.$

b. $\displaystyle\int \frac{1}{(x^2-t^2)^{3/2}}\,dt = \frac{t}{x^2\sqrt{x^2-t^2}} + C.$

c. $\displaystyle\int \frac{1}{t(t^2-x^2)^{3/2}}\,dt = -\frac{[\sec^{-1} t/x + x(t^2-x^2)^{-1/2}]}{x^3} + C.$

d. $\displaystyle\int t^x \ln t\,dt = \frac{t^{x+1}}{(x+1)^2}\{(x+1)\ln t - 1\} + C.$

Section 1, Part II

1.
$$\int_0^1 \frac{x-y}{(x+y)^3}\,dy = \frac{1}{2}\int_0^1 (y-x)\,d(x+y)^{-2}$$
$$= \frac{1}{2}[(y-x)(x+y)^{-2}]_0^1 - \frac{1}{2}\int_0^1 (x+y)^{-2}\,dy$$
$$= (1+x)^{-2}.$$
$$\int_0^1 (1+x)^{-2}\,dx = \frac{1}{2}.$$

By odd symmetry, the other repeated integral $= -\frac{1}{2}$. The integrand is discontinuous at the origin.

Section 2, Part I

1. $l_2 = 20$, $u_2 = 60$, $l_4 = 30$, $u_4 = 50$, $l_n = 40 - 40/n$, 40.
3. $l_4 = 34$, $u_4 = 76$, $l_n = 8(19n^2 - 27n + 8)/n^2$, 152/3.

Section 2, Part II

1. No. The two corresponding repeated integrals have different values due to the discontinuity at (0,0). See Exercise I-1, Section 1.

Section 4, Part I

1. 153/2.
3. $\pi^2(1-e^2)/8e$.
5. 11/2.
7. $-5/24$.
9. $40\tan^{-1} 2 - 80/3$.
11. 9/2.
13. $(\pi + 12)/6\pi$.
15. $\frac{1}{12}$.
17. 5.
19. 22.
21. $\frac{32}{5}$.
23. 16π.
25. 9.
27. 6.
29. $r^3/3$.
31. 5π.

Section 4, Part II

1. $\displaystyle 8\int_0^a dx \int_0^{b\sqrt{1-x^2/a^2}} c\sqrt{1-x^2/a^2-y^2/b^2}\,dy.$

3. $\displaystyle V = \int_0^a dx \int_0^{(a^{2/3}-x^{2/3})^{3/2}} (a^{2/3}-x^{2/3}-y^{2/3})^{3/2}\,dy$ (in first octant).

Now let $y = (a^{2/3}-x^{2/3})^{3/2}\sin^3\theta$, and then let $x = a\sin^3\phi$, to obtain $V = \pi a^3/70$.

5. If we consider the volume in the first octant, it will consist of a cube and three caps.

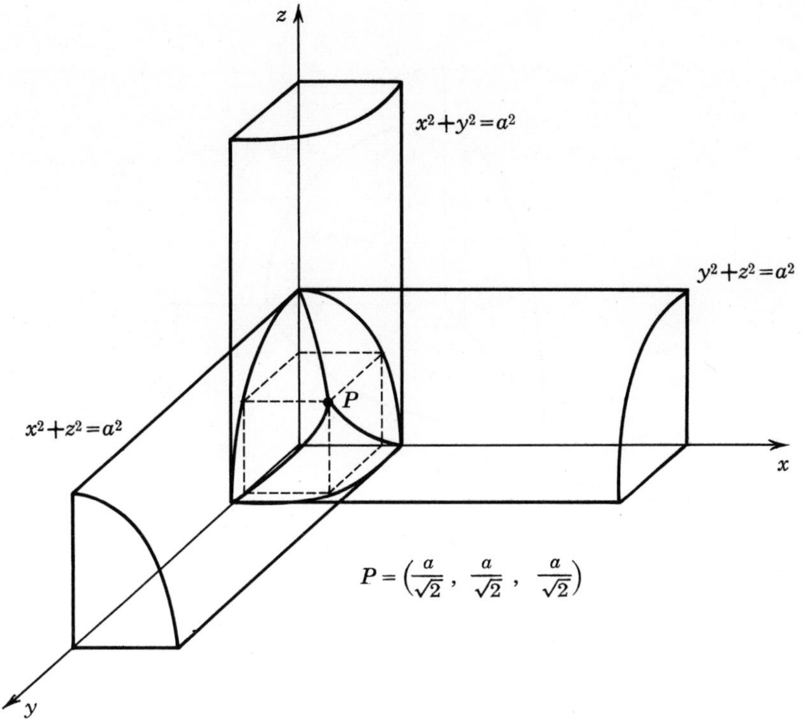

Each of the caps depending on two cylinders only. Now determine the volume of the three congruent caps (as in the previous exercise) to give

$$V = 16a^3(1 - \sqrt{2}/2).$$

7. $$\int_0^a dx \int_0^x G(y)\,dy = \int_0^a dy \int_y^a G(y)\,dx = \int_0^a (a - y)G(y)\,dy$$

Proof is by mathematical induction. Assume

$$\int_0^{x_0} dx_1 \int_0^{x_1} dx_2 \cdots \int_0^{x_{n-1}} dx_n \int_0^{x_n} G(y)\,dy = \frac{1}{n!}\int_0^{x_0} (x_0 - y)^n G(y)\,dy.$$

Now operate on both sides by $\int_0^a dx_0$ to give

$$\int_0^a dx_0 \int_0^{x_1} dx_1 \cdots \int_0^{x_{n-1}} dx_n \int_0^{x_n} G(y)\,dy = \frac{1}{n!}\int_0^a dx_0 \int_0^{x_0} (x_0 - y)^n G(y)\,dy$$

$$= \frac{1}{n!}\int_0^a dy \int_y^a (x_0 - y)^n G(y)\,dx_0 = \frac{1}{(n+1)!}\int_0^a (a - y)^{n+1} G(y)\,dy.$$

Since the inductive statement is valid for $n = 1$, it is also valid for $n = 2, 3, 4, \cdots$.

Section 5, Part I

1. $4\pi(27 - 5\sqrt{5})/3$.
3. $8\pi/3$.
5. $10\pi/3$.

SECTION 5, PART II

1.

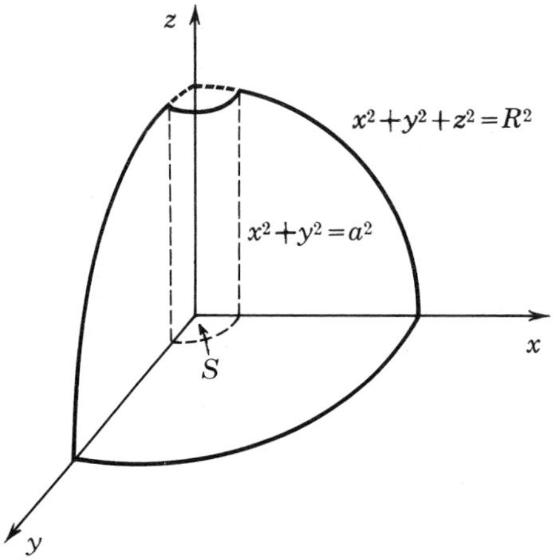

$$V = 8\int_S \sqrt{R^2 - x^2 - y^2}$$

or

$$V = 2\int_{x^2+v^2\le a^2} \sqrt{R^2 - x^2 - y^2}.$$

In polar coordinates,

$$V = 2\int_0^{2\pi} d\theta \int_0^a r\sqrt{R^2 - r^2}\, dr = \frac{4\pi}{3}\,[R^3 - (R^2 - a^2)^{3/2}].$$

3. In $\int_0^\infty e^{-m^2}\, dm = \frac{\sqrt{\pi}}{2}$, let $m = at$ to give $\int_0^\infty e^{-a^2t^2}\, dt = \frac{\sqrt{\pi}}{2a}$. If

$$J = \int_0^x t^2 e^{-a^2t^2},$$

then

$$J^2 = \int_0^x \int_0^x s^2t^2 e^{-a^2(s^2+t^2)}\, ds\, dt.$$

In polar coordinates,

$$\int_0^{2\pi} \sin^2\theta\, d\theta \int_0^x r^5 e^{-a^2r^2}\, dr \le 16J^2 \le \int_0^{2\pi} \sin^2\theta\, d\theta \int_0^{2x} r^5 e^{-a^2r^2}\, dr.$$

Now use $\sin^2 2\theta = \frac{1 - \cos 4\theta}{2}$ and let $r^2 = P$ and integrate by parts. Then let $x \to \infty$.

SECTION 6, PART I

1. $(\frac{12}{5}, \frac{3}{4})$.
3. $(2b/3, h/2)$.
5. $(8a(\pi - 2)/3\pi^2, 16a/3\pi^2)$.
7. $([612 - 3\sqrt{2}\ln(3 + 2\sqrt{2})]/256, 0)$.
9. $(16\sqrt{2}/35, 0)$.
11. $h/2$.
13. $(0, 8a/5\pi)$.

SECTION 6, PART II

1. $$M = \int_0^a dx \int_0^{(\sqrt{a}-\sqrt{x})^2} xy\,dy,$$

$$M_x = \int_0^a dx \int_0^{(\sqrt{a}-\sqrt{x})^2} x^2y\,dy,$$

$$\bar{x} = \frac{M_x}{M} = \frac{2a}{9}.$$

By symmetry, $\bar{x} = \bar{y}$.

3. Lamina bounded by

$$c \le r \le (a^4 \cos^4\theta + b^4 \sin^4\theta)^{-1/4}, \quad \alpha \le \theta \le B,$$

and with density $\rho = \dfrac{\cos\theta}{2r^2}$.

SECTION 7, PART I

1. $|BC|/\sqrt{3}$.
3. $|BD|/\sqrt{3}$.
5. $\sqrt{|AB|^2 + |BC|^2}/\sqrt{12}$.
7. $a/2$.
9. $a\sqrt{5}/2$.
11. $a\sqrt{15}/5$.
13. $ch^3/12$ (h the altitude on side c).
15. $\sqrt{\pi}/4$.

SECTION 7, PART II

1.

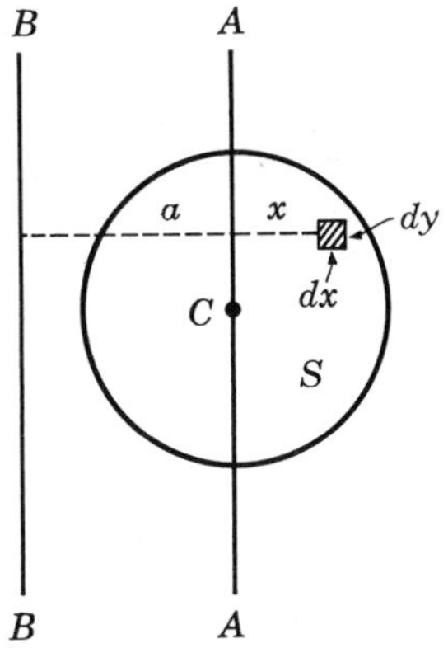

$$I_A = \int_S x^2\rho, \quad I_B = \int_S (x+a)^2\rho,$$

where ρ = density and c = center of mass.

$$I_B = \int_S x^2\rho + 2a\int_S x\rho + a^2\int_S \rho$$

or

$$I_B = I_A + 0 + Ma^2.$$

$\left(\int_S x\rho = 0 \text{ since } c \text{ lies on axis } AA.\right)$

3. a.

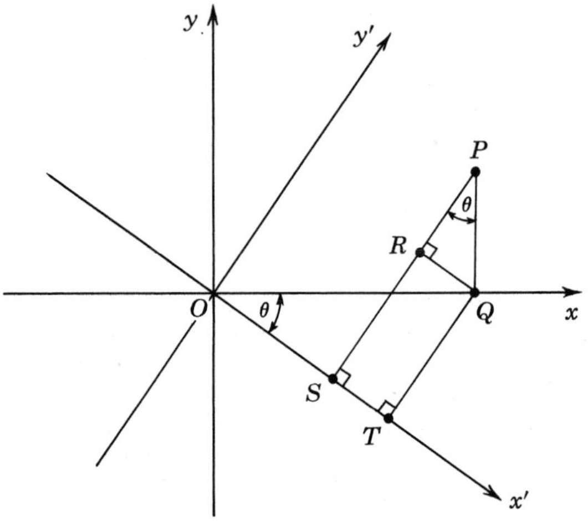

$$OQ = x, \qquad PQ = y$$
$$OT = x', \qquad QT = y'$$

$$x' = OT - ST = x \cos\theta - y \sin\theta,$$
$$y' = PR + RS = y \cos\theta + x \sin\theta$$

$$I_{x'y'} = \int_S x'y' = \int_S (x\cos\theta - y\sin\theta)(x\sin\theta + y\cos\theta)$$

$$I_{x'y'} = \tfrac{1}{2}\sin 2\theta \int_S (x^2 - y^2) + \cos 2\theta \int_S xy$$

or

$$I_{x'y'} = \frac{I_x - I_y}{2}\sin 2\theta + I_{xy}\cos 2\theta.$$

If $I_x = I_y$, choose $\theta = 45°$ to give $I_{x'y'} = 0$, otherwise choose θ such that

$$\tan 2\theta = \frac{2I_{xy}}{I_y - I_x}.$$

b. Use Exercise 2; in order for I_θ to be a maximum or a minimum

$$\frac{d}{d\theta} I_\theta = 0 = (I_x - I_y)\sin 2\theta + 2I_{xy}\cos 2\theta = 2I_{x'y'}.$$

SECTION 8, PART I

1. 27, 0.

3. 48π, 0.

5. $16\sqrt{2}/3$, $-288\sqrt{2}/35$.

7. $(1 - \ln 2)/2$, $\frac{1}{12}$.

9. $2a^3/3$, $a^6/24$.

SECTION 8, PART II

1.
$$V = \int_0^a dx \int_0^{b(1-\sqrt{x/a})^2} dy \int_0^{c(1-\sqrt{x/a}-\sqrt{x/b})^2} dz = \frac{8abc}{120},$$

$$I = \int_0^a dx \int_0^{b(1-\sqrt{x/a})^2} dy \int_0^{c(1-\sqrt{x/a}-\sqrt{x/b})^2} xyz\, dz = \frac{(abc)^2}{27{,}720}.$$

$\left(\text{To simplify the integrations let } \frac{y}{b} = s^2 \text{ and } \frac{x}{a} = t^2.\right)$

SECTION 9, PART I

1. $(a/4,b/4,c/4)$. **3.** $(0,0,\frac{1}{3})$. **5.** $(\frac{15}{8},0,-\frac{3}{4})$.

7. $([2\sqrt{3} + \ln(2+\sqrt{3})]/[4\sqrt{3} - 4\ln(2+\sqrt{3})],$
$0, [14\sqrt{3} - 17\ln(2+\sqrt{3})]/[16\sqrt{3} - 16\ln(2+\sqrt{3})])$.

9. $(9\pi a/64, 3a/8, 9\pi a/64)$.

11. $\int_{-a}^{a} dx \int_{-\sqrt{a^2-x^2}}^{\sqrt{a^2-x^2}} dy \int_0^{\sqrt{a^2-x^2-y^2}} \rho(x^2+y^2)\, dz.$

13. $\int_{-\sqrt{h}}^{\sqrt{h}} dx \int_{-\sqrt{h-x^2}}^{\sqrt{h-x^2}} dy \int_{x^2+y^2}^{h} \rho(x^2+y^2)\, dz.$

15. $\int_2^4 dx \int_{-\sqrt{x^2-4}}^{\sqrt{x^2-4}} dx \int_0^{2-x/2} \rho(x^2+y^2)\, dz.$

17. $\int_0^a dx \int_0^b dy \int_0^c \rho(x^2+y^2)\, dz = \rho abc(a^2+b^2)/3.$

SECTION 9, PART II

1. If I denotes the moment of inertia of a solid S about any axis and I_c denotes the moment of inertia about a parallel axis through the centroid, then $I = I_c + Md^2$ where M is the mass of the body and d is the distance between the two axes.

Let the axis through the centroid be taken as the z axis and let the other axis then be $x = a$, $y = b$. Then

$$I = \int_S \rho\{(x-a)^2 + (y-b)^2\}$$
$$= \int_S \rho(x^2+y^2) + (a^2+b^2)\int_S \rho - 2a\int_S \rho x - 2b\int_S \rho y.$$

Since the z axis passes through the centroid, the last two integrals are zero. Thus

$$I = I_c + M(a^2+b^2) = I_c + Md^2.$$

3. Using Exercise 2, we have $I_L = a^2I_x + b^2I_y + c^2I_z$, where $a^2+b^2+c^2 = 1$. Assume without loss of generality, that $I_x \geq I_y \geq I_z$. By choosing $a = 1$, $b = 0$, $c = 0$, we have Max $I_L \geq I_x$. Also, $I_L \leq (a^2+b^2+c^2)I_x = I_x$ and Max $I_L \leq I_x$. Thus Max $I_L = I_x$. Similarly, Min $I_L = I_z$.

5. a. If we choose a set of rectangular axes with origin at the center of the cube and directions parallel to the edges, we have by symmetry that $I_x = I_y = I_z$, $P_x = P_y = P_z = 0$. Then by Exercise 2, $I_L = I_x$ (for all directions) $= \rho e^5/6$.

b. The moment of inertia about an axis parallel to a face diagonal and passing through the center is $\rho e^5/6$ (from part a). Now by using the parallel axis theorem of Exercise 1, the moment of inertia is $\rho e^5/6 + (\rho e^3)(e/2)^2 = \frac{5}{12}\rho e^5$.

SECTION 10, PART I

1. Cone has equation $\phi = \tan^{-1} a/h$; **a.** $(3h/4,0,0)$; **b.** $\pi a^4h/10$; **c.** $\pi a^2h(3a^2+2h^2)/60$.

3. a. $([3(b^4 - a^4)]/[8(b^3 - a^3)],0,0)$; **b.** $4\pi(b^5 - a^5)/15$; **c.** $4\pi(b^5 - a^5)/15$.
5. a. $3\pi a^4 b/32$; **b.** $(2a/3,0,5a^2b/18)$.

SECTION 10, PART II

1. $$\int_S x^2 = \int_S y^2 = \int_S z^2 = \frac{1}{3}\int_S (x^2 + y^2 + z^2) = \frac{1}{3}\int_S r^2 = \frac{1}{3}\int_0^a r^2(4\pi r^2\, dr) = \frac{4\pi a^5}{15}.$$

3. $\int_S x^m y^n = 0$ if either m or n is odd by centrosymmetry. (For every contribution about the point (x,y) there is the negative contribution about the point $(-x,-y)$.)

REVIEW, PART I

1. 3. **3.** 1. **5.** $\frac{16}{3}$.

7. a. Frustrum of a right cylinder erected on the rectangle (0,0), (0,2), (1,2), (1,0) in the xy plane and cut by the plane $z = x + y$; **b.** same as **a.**, the rectangle being (0,0), (0,1), (2,1), (2,0); **c.** frustrum of a right cylinder erected on the triangle (0,0), (2,0), (2,2) in the xy plane, and cut by the paraboloid $z = x^2 + y^2$; **d.** frustum of a right cylinder erected on the rectangle (0,0), (0,2), ($\sqrt{2}$,2), ($\sqrt{2}$,0) in the xy plane and cut by the plane $z = x + 2y$ and by the right cylinder $x = y^2$.

9. $\frac{1}{4}$. **11.** 0.

13. $$\int_a^b dx \int_c^d dy \int_e^f f(x)g(y)h(z)\, dz = \left\{\int_a^b f(x)\, dx\right\} \cdot \left\{\int_c^d g(y)\, dy\right\} \cdot \left\{\int_e^f h(z)\, dz\right\}$$

15. $V = 4\int_0^1 dx \int_0^{\sqrt{1-x^2}} (dy)/(x^2 + y^2)$; $\bar{x} = \bar{y} = 0$,

$$\bar{z} = \frac{4}{V}\int_0^1 dx \int_0^{\sqrt{1-x^2}} dy \int_0^{1/(x^2+y^2)} z\, dz.$$

17. $V = 4\int_{\sqrt{3\pi/2}}^{\sqrt{5\pi/2}} dx \int_{\sqrt{3\pi/2-x^2}}^{\sqrt{5\pi/2-x^2}} \cos(x^2 + y^2)\, dy$; $\bar{x} = \bar{y} = 0$,

$$\bar{z} = \frac{4}{V}\int_{\sqrt{3\pi/2}}^{\sqrt{5\pi/2}} dx \int_{\sqrt{3\pi/2-x^2}}^{\sqrt{5\pi/2-x^2}} dy \int_0^{\cos(x^2+y^2)} z\, dz.$$

19. $$I_z = 8\int_0^a dx \int_0^{b\sqrt{1-(x/a)^2}} dy \int_0^{c\sqrt{1-(x/a)^2-(y/b)^2}} \rho(x^2 + y^2)\, dz$$

REVIEW, PART II

1. By symmetry, if the left hand repeated integral $= I$, the right hand integral $= -I$. Thus it suffices to show $I \neq 0$.

$$\int_0^1 \frac{(x^2 - y^2)}{(x^2 + y^2)^2}\, dy = 2x^2\int_0^1 \frac{1}{(x^2 + y^2)^2}\, dy - \int_0^1 \frac{1}{x^2 + y^2}\, dy = \frac{1}{x^2 + 1},$$

since

$$\int \frac{dy}{x^2 + y^2} = \frac{1}{x}\arctan\frac{y}{x}, \qquad \int \frac{dy}{(x^2 + y^2)^2} = \frac{1}{2x^3}\arctan\frac{y}{x} + \frac{y}{2x^2(x^2 + y^2)}.$$

Then

$$I = \int_0^1 \frac{1}{x^2+1}\,dx = \frac{\pi}{4}.$$

3. a. $$A = 2\int_0^a y\,dx = \int_0^a 8ax^2\,dx = \frac{8a^4}{3}. \qquad \frac{dA}{da} = \frac{32a^3}{3}.$$

b. $$\frac{dA}{da} = 8a\cdot a^2 + \int_0^a 8x^2\,dx = 8a^5 + \frac{8a^3}{3} = \frac{32a^3}{3}.$$

5. Let $x + t = m$. Then

$$\int_{-t}^{t} f(x+t)\,dx = \int_0^{2t} f(m)\,dm.$$

$$\frac{d}{dt}\int_0^{2t} f(m)\,dm = 2f(2t)$$

and

$$\frac{d^n}{dt^n}\int_0^{2t} f(m)\,dm = 2^n f^{[n-1]}(2t).$$

7. a. $$I = 4\int_0^a dx \int_0^b dy \int_0^c \rho(x^2+y^2)\,dz = \frac{4\rho abc}{3}(a^2+b^2) = M\,\frac{a^2+b^2}{3}.$$

b. $$I = 4\int_0^a dx \int_0^{b\sqrt{1-(x/a)^2}} dy \int_0^c \rho(x^2+y^2)\,dz.$$

Let $\dfrac{x}{a} = m,\ \dfrac{y}{b} = n$ to give

$$I = 4\rho abc\int_0^1 dm \int_0^{\sqrt{1-n^2}} (a^2m^2 + b^2n^2)\,dn = \frac{M(a^2+b^2)}{\pi}\int_{r\le 1} \frac{r^2}{2}\cdot r\,dr\,d\theta$$

or

$$I = \frac{M(a^2+b^2)}{4}. \quad \textit{Note: } \int_{m^2+n^2\le 1} m^2 = \int_{m^2+n^2\le 1} n^2 \quad \text{by symmetry.}$$

c. $$I = 8\int_0^a dx \int_0^{b\sqrt{1-(x/a)^2}} dy \int_0^{c\sqrt{1-(x/a)^2-(y/b)^2}} \rho(x^2+y^2)\,dz.$$

Now let

$$\frac{x}{a} = r, \qquad \frac{y}{b} = s, \qquad \frac{z}{c} = t, \text{ to give}$$

$$I = \int \rho(a^2r^2 + b^2s^2)abc\,dr\,ds\,dt. \qquad \text{By symmetry,}$$

$$\int_B r^2 = \int_B s^2, \qquad r^2 + s^2 + t^2 \le 1.$$

Thus

$$I = \rho(a^2+b^2)abc\int_{r^2+s^2+t^2\le 1} r^2\,dr\,ds\,dt = \frac{4\pi\rho abc}{15}(a^2+b^2) = \frac{M(a^2+b^2)}{5}.$$

(See Section 10, Exercise II-1.)

9. $$I_2 = \int_0^a dx \int_0^{b(1-(x/a)^r)^{1/s}} x^{m-1}y^{n-1}\,dy.$$

Let $\left(\frac{y}{b}\right)^s = v,\ \left(\frac{x}{a}\right)^r = u$ to give

$$I_2 = \frac{a^m b^n}{rs}\int_0^1 du \int_0^{1-u} u^{\frac{m}{r}-1} v^{\frac{n}{s}-1}\,dv = \frac{a^m b^n}{rn}\int_0^1 u^{\frac{m}{r}-1}(1-u)^{\frac{n}{s}}\,du$$

$$I_2 = \frac{a^m b^n}{rn} B\left(\frac{m}{r}, \frac{n}{s}+1\right) = \frac{a^m b^n}{rs}\,\frac{\Gamma(m/r)\Gamma(n/s)}{\Gamma\left(\frac{m}{r}+\frac{n}{s}+1\right)}.$$

$$I_3 = \int_0^a dx \int_0^{b(1-(x/a)^r)^{1/s}} dy \int_0^{c(1-(x/a)^r-(y/b)^s)^{1/t}} x^{m-1}y^{n-1}z^{p-1}\,dz.$$

Let $\left(\frac{x}{a}\right)^r = u,\ \left(\frac{y}{b}\right)^s = v,\ \left(\frac{z}{c}\right)^t = w$ to give

$$I_3 = \frac{a^m b^n c^p}{rst}\int_0^1 du \int_0^{1-u} dv \int_0^{1-u-v} u^{\frac{m}{r}-1} v^{\frac{n}{s}-1} w^{\frac{p}{t}-1}\,dw \quad \text{or}$$

$$I_3 = \frac{a^m b^n c^p}{rsp}\int_0^1 u^{\frac{m}{r}-1}\,du \int_0^{1-u} v^{\frac{n}{s}-1}(1-u-v)^{\frac{p}{t}}\,dv$$

Now let $v = (1-u)\lambda$ to give

$$I_3 = \frac{a^m b^n c^p}{rsp}\int_0^1 u^{\frac{m}{r}-1}(1-u)^{\frac{n}{s}+\frac{p}{t}}\,du \int_0^1 \lambda^{\frac{n}{s}-1}(1-x)^{\frac{p}{t}}\,d\lambda$$

or

$$I_3 = \frac{a^m b^n c^p}{rsp}\,\frac{\Gamma\left(\frac{m}{r}\right)\Gamma\left(\frac{n}{s}+\frac{p}{t}+1\right)}{\Gamma\left(\frac{m}{r}+\frac{n}{s}+\frac{p}{t}+1\right)}\cdot\frac{\Gamma\left(\frac{n}{s}\right)\Gamma\left(\frac{p}{t}+1\right)}{\Gamma\left(\frac{n}{s}+\frac{p}{t}+1\right)},$$

$$I_3 = \frac{a^m b^n c^p}{rst}\,\frac{\Gamma\left(\frac{m}{r}\right)\Gamma\left(\frac{n}{s}\right)\Gamma\left(\frac{p}{t}\right)}{\Gamma\left(\frac{m}{r}+\frac{n}{s}+\frac{p}{t}+1\right)}.$$

11. $$V = \int_{\substack{x^{2/3}+y^{2/3}+z^{2/3}\le a^{2/3}\\ x,y,z\ge 0}} dx\,dy\,dz \text{ in first octant.}$$

In Exercise 9, let $m = n = p = 1$, $r = s = t = \frac{2}{3}$, $b = c = a$. Then

$$I_3 = V = \frac{a^3}{(2/3)^3}\,\frac{\Gamma(\frac{3}{2})^3}{\Gamma(\frac{9}{2}+1)}.$$

Since $\Gamma\left(\frac{3}{2}\right) = \frac{1}{2}\Gamma\left(\frac{1}{2}\right) = \frac{\sqrt{\pi}}{2}$,

$$\Gamma\left(\frac{9}{2}+1\right) = \frac{9}{2}\cdot\frac{7}{2}\cdot\frac{5}{2}\cdot\frac{3}{2}\cdot\frac{1}{2}\Gamma\left(\frac{1}{2}\right), \qquad V = \frac{\pi a^3}{70}.$$

13. a. $V = \int_S dx\,dy\,dz$, S is the region $\left(\frac{x}{a}\right)^{2/3} + \left(\frac{y}{b}\right)^{2/3} + \left(\frac{z}{c}\right)^{2/3} \le 1$. In Exercise 9, let $m = n = p = 1$, $r = s = t = 2/3$. Then

$$\frac{V}{8} = \frac{abc}{(2/3)^3}\,\frac{\Gamma(\frac{3}{2})^3}{\Gamma(\frac{9}{2}+1)} = \frac{\pi abc}{70}.$$

b.
$$I = \int_S (x^2 + y^2 + z^2)\, dx\, dy\, dz.$$

For $\int_S x^2\, dx\, dy\, dz$, $m = 3$, $n = p = 1$, $r = s = t = 2/3$.

$$\int_S x^2 = \frac{a^3bc}{(2/3)^3}\frac{\Gamma(\frac{9}{2})\Gamma(\frac{3}{2})^2}{\Gamma(\frac{15}{2}+1)} = \frac{\pi a^3bc}{2860}.$$

By symmetry, $\dfrac{I}{8} = \dfrac{\pi abc}{2860}(a^2 + b^2 + c^2)$.

15.
$$I_x = 8\int_0^c dz \int_0^{b\sqrt{1-(z/c)^2}} dy \int_0^{a\sqrt{1-(z/c)^2-(y/b)^2}} (y^2 + z^2)\, dx$$

Letting $x' = \dfrac{x}{a}$, $y' = \dfrac{y}{b}$, $z' = \dfrac{z}{c}$,

$$I_x = abc\int_{x'^2+y'^2+z'^2\le 1} (b^2y'^2 + c^2z'^2) = abc(b^2 + c^2)\int_{x'^2+y'^2+z'^2\le 1} y'^2 \text{ (by symmetry)}.$$

$$I_x = \frac{abc}{3}(b^2 + c^2)\int_0^1 r^2(4\pi r^2\, dr) = \frac{4\pi abc(b^2 + c^2)}{15} = \frac{V(b^2 + c^2)}{5}$$

CHAPTER 20

Section 1, Part I

5. basis. **7.** not a basis. **9.** not a basis.

Section 2, Part I

1. 2. **3.** 2. **5.** 2. **7.** 3.

Section 3, Part I

1. $x = 2, y = -3$. **3.** $x = 3, y = -3, z = 2$.

5. $x = 2 - 3z, y = -3 + z$. **7.** $x = -1 + w, y = 2 - w, z = -w$.

9. no solution.

Section 4, Part I

1. 7. **3.** −41. **5.** 30. **7.** −1. **9.** 0.

Section 5

1. $\begin{bmatrix} 1 & -1 \\ -1 & 2 \end{bmatrix}$. **3.** $\dfrac{1}{4}\begin{bmatrix} 2 & 3 \\ 2 & 5 \end{bmatrix}$.

5. $\begin{bmatrix} 1 & 0 & 0 \\ 0 & 0 & 1 \\ 0 & 1 & 0 \end{bmatrix}$.   7. doesn't exist.   9. $\frac{1}{3}\begin{bmatrix} 5 & 7 & -3 \\ 1 & 2 & 0 \\ -3 & -6 & 3 \end{bmatrix}$.

SECTION 7

3. $\{\langle 1/3, -2/3, 2/3\rangle, \langle -2/3, 1/3, 2/3\rangle, \langle 2/3, 2/3, 1/3\rangle\}$

5. $\{\langle 1/\sqrt{3}, -1/\sqrt{3}, 1/\sqrt{3}\rangle, \langle 1/\sqrt{6}, 2/\sqrt{6}, 1/\sqrt{6}\rangle, \langle 1/\sqrt{2}, 0, -1/\sqrt{2}\rangle\}$

7. Yes.   9. no; $if \cdot jf \neq 0$ in violation of 20.22.

SECTION 8

1. ch. value 1, ch. vector $\langle 4,1\rangle$; ch. value -2, ch. vector $\langle 1,1\rangle$.

3. ch. value 6, ch. vector $\langle 8,1\rangle$; ch. value -3, ch. vector $\langle 1,-1\rangle$.

5. ch. value 0, ch. vector $\langle -2,0,1\rangle$; ch. value 2, ch. vector. $\langle 2,2,1\rangle$; ch. value -2, ch. vector $\langle 2,-2,1\rangle$.

7. ch. value 1, ch. vector $\langle 1,1,0\rangle$.

SECTION 9

1. ch. values 2, 4; ch. vectors $\langle 1/\sqrt{2}, 1/\sqrt{2}\rangle$, $\langle 1/\sqrt{2}, -1/\sqrt{2}\rangle$.

3. ch. values 0, 5; ch. vectors $\langle 1/\sqrt{5}, 2/\sqrt{5}\rangle$, $\langle 2/\sqrt{5}, -1/\sqrt{5}\rangle$.

5. ch. values 0, $\sqrt{3}$, $-\sqrt{3}$; ch. vectors $\langle 1/\sqrt{3}, 1/\sqrt{3}, -1/\sqrt{3}\rangle$, $\langle 1/\sqrt{3}, (\sqrt{3}-1)/2\sqrt{3}, (\sqrt{3}+1)/2\sqrt{3}\rangle$, $\langle -1/\sqrt{3}, (\sqrt{3}+1)/2\sqrt{3}, (\sqrt{3}-1)/2\sqrt{3}\rangle$.

7. ch. values -1, 2; ch. vectors $\langle 5/3\sqrt{5}, 2/3\sqrt{5}, 4/3\sqrt{5}\rangle$, $\langle 0, 2/\sqrt{5}, -1/\sqrt{5}\rangle$, $\langle 2/3, -1/3, -2/3\rangle$.

SECTION 10

1. Ellipse, $11x'^2 + y'^2 = 11$.   3. hyperbola, $9x'^2 - y'^2 = 1$.

5. Ellipse, $20x'^2 + 45y'^2, + 80x' + 90y' = 55$.

REVIEW I

1. Yes.   3. No.   5. 2.   7. 3.

9. $x = 2, y = 1, z = -3$.   11. $x = -2 + z + w, y = 3 - z + 2w$.

13. $\begin{bmatrix} 3 & 4 \\ 4 & 5 \end{bmatrix}$.   15. $-\frac{1}{5}\begin{bmatrix} 8 & -4 & 3 \\ 3 & -4 & 3 \\ -2 & 1 & -2 \end{bmatrix}$.   17. Yes.   19. No.

21. Hyperbola, $3x'^2 - y'^2 = 1$.   23. Hyperbola, $4x'^2 - y'^2 = 4$.

CHAPTER 21

SECTION 1, PART I

9. $y^2 = x^2 + c$.

11. $y = cx$.

13. $y = cx^2$.

15. $y = x\ln|x| + c_1x + c_2$.

SECTION 1, PART II

1. (a) Multiply 2nd column by C_1, 3rd column by C_2, and subtract from the first column. The new first column consists only of zeros.

   (b) For *I*–3, $F = 1$, $G = x$,
   For *I*–4, $F = \sin x$, $G = \cos x$,
   For *I*–7, $F = x^2$, $G = 1$.

   (c) Expanding out the determinant:

$$y'' \begin{vmatrix} F & G \\ F' & G' \end{vmatrix} + y' \begin{vmatrix} F & G'' \\ F & G \end{vmatrix} + y \begin{vmatrix} F' & G' \\ F'' & G'' \end{vmatrix} = 0.$$

   Whence

$$\begin{vmatrix} F & G \\ F' & G' \end{vmatrix} = 0 \quad \text{or} \quad F = kG.$$

   For this case the equation vanishes identically. The D.E. for $y = CF$ is then

$$\begin{vmatrix} y & F \\ y' & F' \end{vmatrix} = 0 = Fy' - F'y.$$

3. $z_x = F'(x + G(y))$, $z_y = F'(x + G(y))G'(y)$
   $z_{xx} = F''(x + G(y))$, $z_{yx} = F''(x + G(y))G'(y)$
   $z_xz_{yx} = F'F''G' = z_yz_{xx}$.

SECTION 3, PART I

1. $xy' = y$.

3. $y' = 2x$.

5. $yy' = x$.

7. $(xy' - yy')^2 + (y - x)^2 = (x + yy')^2$

9. $y = x^2 + c$.

11. $xy = c$.

13. $(x - 2)^2 + y^2 = c$.

15. $r^3 + 3\cos\theta = 1 + 3/\sqrt{2}$.

17. $y^2 = (x + 1)^2 + 8$.

23. $x^3 + 3y = c'$.

25. $2x^2 + y^2 = c'$.

27. $y = 0$ and $y = 2$ are the envelopes of the given family of circles.

SECTION 3, PART II

1. $(y + 1)^2 + (x - c)^2 = 1$, $2(y \pm 1)y' + 2(x - c) = 0$. Eliminating $x - c$,
   $(y \pm 1)^2\,(1 + y'^2) = 1$.

3.
$$\begin{aligned} x^2 + y^2 &+ ax + by + c = 0,\\ D(x^2 + y^2) + a &+ by' = 0,\\ D^2(x^2 + y^2) &+ by'' = 0,\\ D^3(x^2 + y^2) &+ by''' = 0. \end{aligned}$$

Eliminating a,b,c,

$$\begin{vmatrix} x^2 + y^2 & x & y & 1\\ D(x^2 + y^2) & 1 & y' & 0\\ D^2(x^2 + y^2) & 0 & y'' & 0\\ D^3(x^2 + y^2) & 0 & y''' & 0 \end{vmatrix} = 0$$

or

$$y'''D^2(x^2 + y^2) = y''D^3(x^2 + y^2)$$

or

$$y'''(1 + y'^2) = 3y'y''^2.$$

Equivalently, since the curvature $\dfrac{y''}{(1 + y'^2)^{3/2}}$ is constant,

$$D\frac{y''}{(1 + y'^2)^{3/2}} = 0.$$

5. $ax^2 + 2bxy + cy^2 = 1$. Differentiate three times, and eliminate a,b,c as in Exercise 3 above.

7. Differentiate twice to give three linear equations in a^2, ab, b^2. Solve. Then eliminate by using $a^2 \cdot b^2 = (ab)^2$.

9. $y' = \dfrac{du - dv}{du + dv} = \dfrac{(u - v)^2 + (u + v)^2}{2(u - v)(u + v)}$

or

$$\frac{u' - 1}{u' + 1} = \frac{u^2 + v^2}{u^2 - v^2}.$$

Thus

$$u' = -\frac{u^2}{v^2} \quad \text{and} \quad \frac{1}{u} + \frac{1}{v} = c.$$

Substituting back,

$$y^2 - x^2 = cx.$$

11. If $y = x$ intersects $F(x,y) = c$ at a 45° angle, then $y = x$ will also intersect $F(y,x) = c$ at a 45° angle by symmetry. Thus $F(x,y) = c$ will be orthogonal to $F(y,x) = c$. $y = x$ intersects $x^2 + (y + 1)^2 = 1$ at a 45° angle, and thus also the family $(x - c)^2 + (y + 1 - c)^2 = 1$. Now solve for c.

SECTION 5, PART I

1. $x^2 + 2xy + 2y^2 = c.$

3. $2y(1 + e^x) - x^2 = c.$

5. $y^2 + 2x \cos y = c.$

7. $x^2y + e^{xy} = c.$

9. $y \tan x = c.$

11. $y^2 - 2e^x \cos y = c.$

13. $x^2 + y^4 = 2xy + 1.$

15. (a) Differentiating with respect to x:

$$M(x,y) + \int_{x_0}^{x} \frac{\partial M(s,y)}{\partial y}\frac{dy}{dx}\,ds + N(x_0,y)\frac{dy}{dx} = 0.$$

Since $\dfrac{\partial M(s,y)}{\partial y} = \dfrac{\partial N(s,y)}{\partial s}$ (exactness condition), we get

$$M(x,y) + \frac{dy}{dx}\int_{x_0}^{x} \frac{\partial N(s,y)}{\partial s}\,ds + N(x_0,y)\frac{dy}{dx} = 0$$

or

$$M(x,y) + \frac{dy}{dx}\{N(x,y) - N(x_0,y)\} + N(x_0,y)\frac{dy}{dx} = 0 = M(x,y) + N(x,y)\frac{dy}{dx}.$$

The boundary-condition is obviously satisfied (just let $x = x_0$, $y = y_0$ to give $0 = 0$).

17. $y = cx$.

19. $e^x(x + y - 1) = c$.

21. $\ln(x^2 + y^2) + 2\tan^{-1}x/y = c$.

SECTION 5, PART II

1. If $I(x,y)$ is an integrating factor then, $I(M\,dx + N\,dy) = du(x,y)$. Consequently, $F(u)\,I(x,y)$ is an integrating factor for arbitrary F.

3. (a) $\dfrac{x\,dy - y\,dx}{x^2 - y^2} = dx$ or $\dfrac{1}{2}d\ln\dfrac{x+y}{x-y} = dx$;

$$x + y = c(x - y)e^{2x}.$$

(b) $\dfrac{x\,dy - y\,dx}{x^2 + y^2} = x\,dx$ or $2\tan^{-1}y/x = x^2 + c$.

SECTION 6, PART I

1. $x^2 = c(x - y)$.

3. $x^2e^{-y/x} + y^2 = c$.

5. $x^3 + 3xy^2 = c$.

7. $\ln|y + 2x - 1| + (x - 2)/(y + 2x - 1) = c$.

9. $\ln|x^2 + 3xy + y^2 + x - y - 1| - \dfrac{1}{\sqrt{5}}\ln\left|\dfrac{2y + 2 + (3 - \sqrt{5})(x - 1)}{2y + 2 + (3 + \sqrt{5})(x - 1)}\right| = c.$

11. $y = c_1e^x + c_2$.

13. $y + \sin x = c_1x + c_2$.

15. $y = c_1e^x + e^{-x}/4c_1 + c_2$.

SECTION 6, PART II

1. Case (a). Assume $a_1x + b_1y + c_1 = 0$, $a_2x + b_2y + c_2 = 0$, has a solution (h,k). Then let $X = x - h$, $Y = y - k$ to obtain a homogeneous equation.
Case (b). Assume the two lines are parallel. Then $a_1x + b_1y = k(a_2x + b_2y)$. Now let

$z = a_2x + b_2y$ to give $\dfrac{1}{b_2}\left(\dfrac{dz}{dx} - a_2\right) = \dfrac{kz + c_1}{z + c_2}$, which is separable assuming $b_2 \neq 0$.

If $b_2 = 0$, so does $b_1 = 0$ and the initial equation is separable.

3. (a) $2p\dfrac{dp}{dy} = e^y, p^2 = e^y + c$ or $\dfrac{dy}{dx} = \sqrt{e^y + c^2}$. Now let $z^2 = e^y + c^2$.

(b)
$$p\frac{dp}{dy} = (1 + p^2)^{3/2} \quad \text{or} \quad \frac{-1}{\sqrt{1 + p^2}} = y + c.$$

Then
$$\frac{(y + c)\,dy}{\sqrt{1 - (y + c)^2}} = dx; \quad -\sqrt{1 - (y + c)^2} = x + k.$$

Finally, $(x + k)^2 + (y + c)^2 = 1$. This also follows immediately from the initial D.E. which states that the radius of curvature $= 1$ and thus is the D.E. for the family of all unit circles in the plane. See also Exercise II-3, Section 3.

5. (a) $p\dfrac{dp}{dy} = F(y)p^3$. Thus $p = 0$ or $\dfrac{dp}{p^2} = F(y)\,dy$. One solution is $y = c$. Integrating:

$$-\frac{1}{p} = \int F(y)\,dy = -\frac{dx}{dy}$$

or

$$-x = \iint F(y)\,dydy.$$

(b) $y'' = -\dfrac{x''}{(x')^3}, \quad y' = \dfrac{1}{x'}.$

Thus
$$-\frac{x''}{(x')^3} = \frac{F(y)}{(x')^3} \quad \text{and} \quad x = \iint F(y)\,dydy.$$

Section 7, Part I

1. $y = 1 + ce^{-x^2/2}$.

3. $y = c/b + ke^{-bx}, (b \neq 0)$.

5. $y = \sin x + c \cos x$.

7. $-y = e^{-2x} + ce^{3x}$.

9. $y = (x^2 + 1)(x^2 + c)$.

11. $y(1 + ce^{x^2/2}) = 1$.

13. $3y^2 + 2e^x = ce^{4x}$.

Section 7, Part II

1. Consider a solution passing through (k,l). The slope of the tangent line at this point is $Q(k) - P(k)l$. The equation of the tangent line is

$$y - l = [Q(k) - lP(k)][x - k].$$

Similarly, the tangent line to a solution passing through $(k,\bar{l})$ is

$$y - \bar{l} = [Q(k) - \bar{l}P(k)][x - k].$$

Solving simultaneously:

$$x = k + \frac{1}{P(k)}, \quad y = Q(k)/P(k),$$

both of which are independent of l and $\bar{l}$.

3. $y'' + (P' - P^2)y = Q' - PQ$ can be rewritten as $D[y' + Py - Q] = P[y' + Py - Q]$.

Thus

$y' + Py - Q = Ae^{\int P\,dx}$ which is a linear equation and can be solved.

SECTION 8, PART I

1. $r^2x = g \ln \cosh rt$.

3. $y = 4P(x + P)$, Solution 2.

5. $I(t) = (1 - ce^{-4t})/20$.

7. $LI(t) = e^{-Rt/L}\left\{\int E(t)e^{Rt/L}\,dt + c\right\}$.

9. $x(t) = 100kt/(10kt + 1)$.

11. $x(t) = a^2kt/(akt + 1)$.

SECTION 8, PART II

1. Tangent line at (h,k) is $y - k = F'(h)(x - h)$ (to curve $y = F(x)$). x-intercept:

$$h - \frac{k}{F'(h)}, \quad y - \text{intercept: } k - hF'(h).$$

Thus

$$2h = h - \frac{k}{F'(h)} \quad \text{and} \quad 2k = k - hF'(h).$$

Since both equations are the same, we solve

$$h = -\frac{k}{F'(h)} = -\frac{F(h)}{F'(h)}.$$

Thus $F(h) = \dfrac{1}{h}$ and curve is the hyperbola $y = \dfrac{1}{x}$.

3. $\dfrac{dI}{dt} + \dfrac{RI}{L} = \dfrac{E_0}{L}\sin ct$. Since $e^{Rt/L}$ is an integrating factor,

$$DIe^{Rt/L} = \frac{E_0}{L}e^{Rt/L}\sin ct.$$

Thus,

$$(R^2 + L^2c^2)I(t) = E_0R\sin ct + E_0Lc(c^{-Rt/L} - c\cos ct).$$

5. Consider a small mass m of liquid at the surface at A. The two forces acting on it are the weight mg downward and the normal force N (due to the pressure forces exerted by the remaining liquid).

Since the mass m is moving in a circle of radius x at constant angular speed w, the resultant of the two forces must be a single force acting towards the center B and equal to $m\dfrac{V^2}{r} = mw^2x$. Resolving N into vertical and horizontal components gives $N\cos\theta = mg$, and horizontal force $= N\sin\theta$ where $\tan\theta = \dfrac{dy}{dx}$. Thus $N\sin\theta = mg\tan\theta = mw^2x$. Thus the D.E. of the surface is $\dfrac{dy}{dx} = \dfrac{w^2x}{g}$ and then $y = \dfrac{w^2x^2}{2g}$, a parabola.

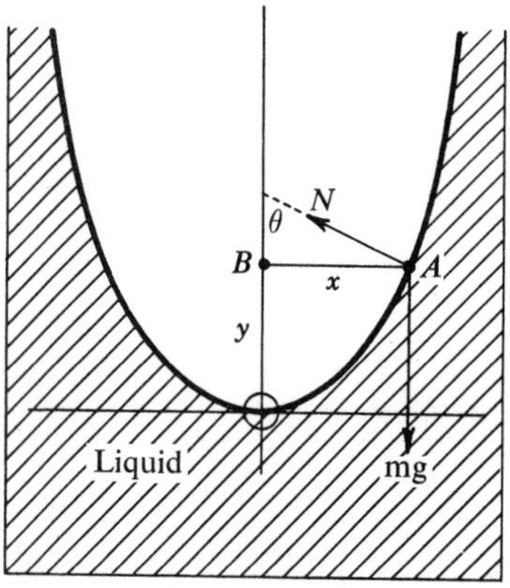

Axial Cross-Section

SECTION 9, PART I

3. $y = c_1e^{3x} + c_2e^{-3x}$.

5. $y = e^{-x}[c_1e^{x\sqrt{2}} + c_2e^{-x\sqrt{2}}]$.

7. $y = c_1e^{5x} + c_2e^{-2x}$.

9. $y = e^{-x/2}[c_1\cos x\sqrt{11}/2 + c_2\sin x\sqrt{11}/2]$.

11. $y = e^{x}[c_1\cos x\sqrt{2} + c_2\sin x\sqrt{2}]$.

13. $y = e^{x/\sqrt{2}}[c_1\cos x\sqrt{26}/2 + c_2\sin x\sqrt{26}/2]$.

15. $y = e^{x/3}[c_1\cos x\sqrt{14}/3 + c_2\sin x\sqrt{14}/3]$.

17. $y = e^{x\sqrt{3}}[c_1\cos \pi x + c_2\sin \pi x]$.

19. $y = 0$.

21. $y = 2e^{2(x-1)} - e^{3(x-1)}$.

23. Simple harmonic motion: $S = S_0\cos wt$.

SECTION 9, PART II

1. If $y = \dfrac{u'}{u}$, then $y' = \dfrac{u''}{u} - \left(\dfrac{u'}{u}\right)^2 = \dfrac{u''}{u} - y^2$.

Now substitute in $\dfrac{u''}{u} + P(x)\dfrac{u'}{u} + Q(x) = 0$.

3. Follows from $P_0y'' + P_1y' + P_2 \equiv D[P_0y' + (P_1 - P'_0)y] + y(P_2 - P'_1 + P_0'')$.

5. (a) Since the equation is exact, we have using the above result (Exercise 3) that $(x - x^2)y' + (4 + 2x - 1)y = \text{const.}$ Integrating again,

$$x^3y = c_1(1 - 5x + 10x^2) + c_2(10x^3 - 5x^4 + x^5).$$

(b) Since the l.h.s. is exact,

$$D((x + x^2)y' + (3x + 2 - 2x - 1)y) = 4x.$$

Thus

$$(x + x^2)y' + (x + 1)y - 2x^2 = \text{const.}$$

Integrating again,

$$xy = x^2 - 2x + c_1 \ln |x + 1| + c_2.$$

SECTION 10, PART I

1. $L(\sin x) = -\sin x - 3 \cos x,\ L(e^{3x}) = 0.$

3. $2y = e^x[c_1 \cos x + c_2 \sin x] + (x + 1)^2.$

5. $13y = e^{-x}[c_1e^{\sqrt{2x}} + c_2e^{-\sqrt{2x}}] - 8 \sin x - \cos x.$

7. $y = c_1 \sin x + \{c_2 - \ln |\sec x + \tan x|\} \cos x.$

9. $5y = c_1e^x + c_2e^{-x} - e^x[2 \cos x + \sin x].$

11. $4y = c_1 - [x^2 + x + c_2]e^{-2x}.$

13. $y = c_1 \cos 2x + c_2 \sin 2x + (x/4) \sin 2x.$

15. $2y = c_1e^{x\sqrt{2}} + c_2e^{-x\sqrt{2}} - 5x.$

17. $2y = c_1 + c_2e^{-x} + e^x.$

19. $3y = c_1 \sinh x(3 + \sqrt{13})/2 + c_2 \cosh x(3 + \sqrt{13})/2 - e^x.$

21. $I = A \sinh t(\sqrt{23} + 5)/10 + B \cosh t(\sqrt{23} - 5)/10 + (50 \sin t - 49 \cos t)/905.$

23. $y = Ae^x + Be^{2x} + Ce^{3x}.$

25. $y = Ae^{3x} + B \cos x + C \sin x.$

SECTION 10, PART II

1. Let $y = v(x)z$. Then as in Exercise II-2, Section 9,

$$(vz)'' + P(vz)' + Qvz = R \qquad \text{or} \qquad z'' + \left(P + \frac{2v'}{v}\right)z' = \frac{R}{v}$$

which is a linear equation in z'. Solving,

$$z = \int \frac{e^{-\int P\,dx}}{v^2}\,dx \int Rve^{\int P\,dx}\,dx.$$

Then $y = v(x)z$. Note that the complimentary solution will appear from the constants of integration.

3. It will suffice due to linearity, to just prove

$$e^{\int P\,dx}D^n = (D - P)^n e^{\int P\,dx}.$$

Proof is by induction. For $n = 1$,

$$(D - P)e^{\int P\,dx} = De^{\int P\,dx} - Pe^{\int P\,dx} = (e^{\int P\,dx}D + Pe^{\int P\,dx}) - Pe^{\int P\,dx}$$
$$= e^{\int P\,dx}D.$$

Assume the result holds for n and then operate on this result with the operator $D - P$ giving

$$(D - P)^{n+1}e^{\int P\,dx} = (D - P)e^{\int P\,dx}D^n = De^{\int P\,dx}D^n - Pe^{\int P\,dx}D^n$$
$$= (e^{\int P\,dx}D^{n+1} + Pe^{\int P\,dx}D^n) - Pe^{\int P\,dx}D^n$$
$$= e^{\int P\,dx}D^{n+1}.$$

Thus the result holds for $n = 2, 3, 4, \cdots$.

5. Since e^x is part of the complimentary solution, we never can get a particular solution of the form ce^x.

Multiplying both sides of the equation by e^{-x} and using Exercise 3 above, we obtain

$$e^{-x}(D - 1)^2y = 1 = D^2ye^{-x}.$$

Integrating twice,

$$ye^{-x} = \frac{x^2}{2} + ax + b.$$

Thus a particular solution is $y_p = \left(\frac{x^2}{2}\right)e^x$ and the complementary solution is $y_c = (ax + b)e^x$.

7. We have

$$L(D)y_c = 0,$$
$$L(D)y_1 = F_1,$$
$$L(D)y_2 = F_2.$$

Adding, using the linearity of $L(D)$, gives

$$L(D)(y_c + y_1 + y_2) = L(D)y = F_1 + F_2.$$

9. The sequence $F, F', F'', F''', \cdots$ must only contain a finite number of linearly independent terms. For example, $F = x^2e^x$. The independent terms are x^2e^x, xe^x, e^x. Thus we assume $y = e^x(ax^2 + bx + c)$ and determine a, b, c by the method of undetermined coefficients. If some of these terms are also part of the complimentary solution, we would then have to multiply them by an appropriate power of x. See Exercises 5 and 6 above.

The method would not work for $F = e^{x^2}$ since each differentiation brings in a new term of the form $x^ne^{x^2}$.

Section 11, Part I

1. Use the same approach as in the proof of Th. 21.22 or else note that

$$(D - a)(D^2 + aD + a^2)y = 0$$

where $a = \sqrt[3]{k}$. Thus,

$$y = c_1e^{ax} + e^{-ax/2}\left(c_2 \cos\frac{ax\sqrt{3}}{2} + c_3 \sin\frac{ax\sqrt{3}}{2}\right)$$

which is analytic.

3. $y = c_0 \sum_{k=1}^{\infty} \frac{x^{2k}}{2^k k!} = c_0 e^{x^2/2}$. Infinite radius of convergence.

5. $$y = c_0\left[1 - \frac{x^3}{3!} + \frac{4^2x^6}{6!} - \frac{4^2\cdot 7^2 x^9}{9!} + \cdots (-1)^r \frac{4^2\cdot 7^2\cdot 10^2\cdots(3r-2)^2x^{3r}}{(3r)!} + \cdots\right]$$
$$+ c_1\left[x - \frac{2^2x^4}{4!} + \frac{2^2\cdot 5^2x^7}{7!} - \cdots(-1)^r \frac{2^2\cdot 5^2\cdot 8^2\cdots(3r-1)^2x^{3r+1} + \cdots}{(3r+1)!}\right].$$

Infinite radius of convergence.

SECTION 11, PART II

1. Let $y = c_0 + c_1x + c_2x^2 + \cdots$ in the D.E. to give
$$x + (c_0 + c_1x + c_2x^2 + \cdots)^2 = c_1 + 2c_2x + 3(3x^2 + \cdots).$$

Equating coefficients of like powers of x (after squaring out):

$$\begin{aligned} c_1 &= c_0^2, && \\ 2c_2 &= 2c_0c_1 + 1 &\text{or}\quad & c_2 = \tfrac{1}{2} + c_0^3, \\ 3c_3 &= 2c_0c_2 + c_1^2 &\text{or}\quad & c_3 = \tfrac{1}{3}c_0 + c_0^4, \\ 4c_4 &= 2c_0c_3 + 2c_1c_2 &\text{or}\quad & c_4 = \tfrac{5}{12}c_0^2 + c_0^5, \\ &\vdots && \vdots \end{aligned}$$

$$\begin{aligned} 2rc_{2r} &= 2c_0c_{2r-1} + 2c_1c_{2r-2} + \cdots + 2c_{r-1}c_r, \\ (2r+1)c_{2r+1} &= 2c_0c_{2r} + 2c_1c_{2r-1} + \cdots + 2c_{r-1}c_{r+1} + c_r^2. \end{aligned}$$

Thus
$$y = a + a^2x + (\tfrac{1}{2} + a^3)x^2 + \cdots$$
where $a = c_0$.
$$\text{If}\quad |c_0| \le \tfrac{1}{2} \quad\text{then}\quad |c_r| < 1, \quad r = 1, 2, \cdots.$$

Thus
$$y < 1 + x + x^2 + \cdots + x^n + \cdots$$
and series converges in $(-1,1)$.

3. The series solution terminates, giving
$$y = c_0(1 - 3x^2) + c_1(3x - x^3).$$

REVIEW, I

1. $y = c\sqrt{1 + x^2}$.

3. $x^2 - xy + 2kx + k^2 = 0$.

5. $(x + 5y + a)^4 = c(x + 2y + 3)$.

7. $x^2 + 4xy - 3y^2 = c$.

9. $\dfrac{dy}{dx} = \dfrac{d}{dx}\left(\dfrac{z - cx}{e}\right) = \dfrac{1}{e}\left(\dfrac{dz}{dx} - c\right) = g(z)$.

11. $dx + xy\,dy = xy\,dx + x^2\,dy$ or $\dfrac{dx}{x} + y\,dy = y\,dx + x\,dy$; $2 \ln x + y^2 = 2xy + c$.

13. $\dfrac{d}{dx}(xy) = 0$; $xy = c$.

15. Separable; $y = ae^{x^3}$, $y = a\left(1 + \dfrac{x^3}{1!} + \dfrac{x^6}{2!} + \dfrac{x^9}{3!} + \cdots\right)$

17. $(D + 2x)y' = 2x$, linear in y'.

$$y' = 1 + c_1e^{-x^2}, \qquad y = x + c_2 + c_1 \int e^{-x^2}\,dx,$$

$$y = x + c_2 + c_1\left(1 - \frac{x^2}{1!} + \frac{x^4}{2!} - \frac{x^6}{3!} + \cdots\right)$$

19. $y = Ae^{6x} + Be^{-x}$

21. $y = Ae^{6x} + Be^{-x} + C$.

23. $y = A \sin 2x + B \cos 2x + (2x^2 - 1)/8$.

25. $y = (A \sin x\sqrt{15}/2 + B \cos x\,\sqrt{15}/2)e^{x/2} + (\sin x - \cos x)/10$.

27. $y = Ae^{x} + Be^{2x} + Ce^{-3x} + e^{-x}/12$.

29. $a = \dfrac{dv}{dt} = g \sin \theta$. $v = gt \sin \theta = \dfrac{ds}{dt}$.

$s = \dfrac{gt^2}{2} \sin \theta$.

31. $(D^2 + k^2)s = 0$.

$$s = A \sin kt + B \cos kt.$$

$$v = \frac{ds}{dt} = k\,(A \cos kt - B \sin kt).$$

at $t = 0$,

$$s = s_0 = B, \quad v = v_0 = kA.$$

Thus

$$s = s_0 \cos kt + \frac{v_0}{k} \sin kt = \sqrt{s_0^2 + (v_0/k)^2}\,[\sin \alpha \cos kt + \cos \alpha \sin kt]$$

or

$$s = \sqrt{s_0^2 + (v_0/k)^2}\,\sin(\alpha + kt)$$

where

$$\sin \alpha = \frac{s_0}{\sqrt{s_0^2 + (v_0/k)^2}}.$$

Thus

$$\text{Amplitude} = \sqrt{s_0^2 + (v_0/k)^2}$$

$$\text{Period} = 2\pi/k.$$

REVIEW, II

1. If the conic has no asymptote parallel to the y-axis, its equation can be rewritten in the form

$$y = \sqrt{Ax^2 + Bx + c} + Dx + E.$$

Thus

$$y'' = \frac{AC - B^2}{(Ax^2 + 2Bx + C)^{3/2}}.$$

Since $D^3(Ax^2 + 2Bx + C) = 0$, the D.E. of all conics in the plane is

$$D^3(y'')^{-2/3} = 0.$$

If the conic is a parabola, $A = 0$. Thus,

$$D^2(y'')^{-2/3} = 0.$$

3. To obtain the orthogonal trajectories of a given D.E., we replace y' by $-1/y'$. This transformation doesn't change the given D.E.

5. Operating on the first equation by $D - a_2$ and the second by a_1 and adding, we obtain

$$(D - a_2)(D - b_1)y - a_1b_2y = (D - a_2)c_1 + a_1c_2 = a_1c_2 - a_2c_1.$$

This is a second-order linear D.E. in y which can be solved in the usual manner. The solution will contain two arbitrary constants. We can arbitrarily assume $y = y_0$ at $t = 0$. To find y' at $t = 0$, substitute $t = 0$ in the first equation giving $\left(\frac{dy}{dt}\right)_{t=0} = a_1x_0 + b_1y_0 + c_1$. Thus we have two conditions to determine the two constants.

7. $D^2y = a\,Dx = -a^2y.$

$$y = A \sin at + B \cos at$$

$$ax = Dy = a(A \cos at - B \sin at).$$

Set $x = 0, y = 1$ at $t = 0$.

$$1 = B, \quad 0 = A.$$

Thus $y = \cos at$, $x = -\sin at$.

9. By the previous exercise, one solution of $y'' = a^2x^{-4}y$ is also one solution of $y'' = a^2y$ (here $n = 2$). Since the solution of the latter equation is $y = A \sin ax + B \cos ax$, the solution of the former equation is

$$y = x(A \sin a/x + B \cos a/x).$$

11. In the first equation, let $z = ue^{-\int P\,dx}$ where $2P = \dfrac{1 - 3x}{1 - x^2}$. This transforms the equation into

$$\left(D^2 + \frac{k+1}{1 - x^2} + \frac{1}{4(1 - x)^2}\right)u = 0.$$

In the second equation, let $w = ve^{-\int P\,dx}$ where here $2P = -\dfrac{(1+x)}{1-x^2}$. This transforms the 2nd equation into

$$\left(D^2 + \frac{k+1}{1-x^2} + \frac{1}{4}\frac{1}{(1-x)^2}\right)v = 0.$$

Thus

$$ze^{\frac{1}{2}\int\frac{1-3x}{1-x^2}dx} = we^{-\frac{1}{2}\int\frac{1+x}{1-x^2}dx}$$

or

$$w = z(1+x).$$

13. The equation will also be the same linear one satisfied by u^2. This follows since u can be $ay_1 + by_2$ where a and b are arbitrary constants and y_1 and y_2 are independent solutions of the given D.E. Letting $z = u^2$, we have by differentiating:

$$\begin{aligned} z' &= 2uu' \\ z'' &= 2u'^2 + 2uu'' = 2u'^2 + 2u(-Pu' - Qu) = 2u'^2 - Pz' - 2Qz \\ z''' &= 4u'u'' - Pz'' - P'z' - 2Qz' - 2Q'z. \end{aligned}$$

But

$$\begin{aligned} 4u'u'' &= 4u'(-Pu' - Qu) = -4Pu'^2 - 2Qz' \\ &= -2Qz' - 2P(z'' + Pz' + 2Qz). \end{aligned}$$

Finally,

$$[D^3 + 3PD^2 + (2P^2 + P' + 4Q)D + 4PQ + 2Q']z = 0$$

15. Consider the v versus t curve.
It must pass through the points (0,0) and (1,0). Also, the area under the curve is s and thus equals 1 or the area under the triangle. Somewhere the slope (a) of the v versus t curve must numerically exceed that of the sides OA and AB of the triangle.

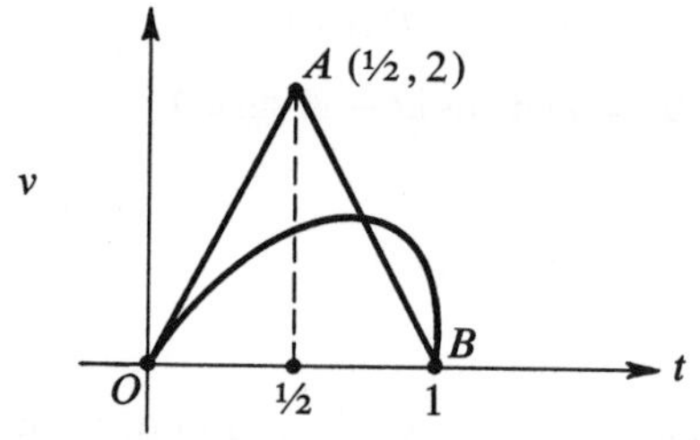

17.
$$\frac{He}{c}Dx + mD^2y = Ee,$$

$$mD^2x + \frac{He}{c}Dy = 0 \qquad \text{at } t = 0,\ x = \dot{x} = y = \dot{y} = 0.$$

Integrating both equations,

$$\begin{aligned} \frac{Hex}{c} + m\,Dy &= Eet, \\ m\,Dx + \frac{He}{c}y &= 0. \end{aligned}$$

Then

$$\frac{Hex}{c} - \frac{m^2c}{He} D^2x = Eet$$

or

$$(D^2 - w^2)x = -\frac{Eewt}{m}$$

where

$$w = \frac{He}{me}.$$

Thus $x = \dfrac{Ee}{mw} t + A \sin wt + B \cos wt$. Using the initial conditions,

$$x = \frac{Ec}{Hw}(wt - \sin wt).$$

Then

$$y = -\frac{1}{w} Dx = \frac{Ec}{wH}(1 - \cos wt).$$

x and y are parametric coordinates for a cycloid. If $s > y_{\max}$, the electron will fail to reach the upper plate. Since

$$y = \frac{2Ec}{wH}\sin^2\frac{wt}{2}, \quad y_{\max} = \frac{2Ec}{wH} = \frac{2Emc^2}{H^2e}.$$

INDEX

Abscissa, 22
Absolute value, 10
Acceleration, 169
  of gravity, 178
  vector, 526
Adjoint matrix, 733
Alternating series, 465
Analytic function, 798
Angle between lines, 35
Antiderivative, 174
Approximations
  by differentials, 130, 630
  by Newton's method, 134
  by Simpson's rule, 271
  by Taylor's polynomial, 440
  by trapezoidal rule, 269
Arc length, 266, 548
Arcsecant, 324
Arcsine, 323
Arctangent, 324
Area, 189, 247
  in polar coordinates, 542
  of a surface of revolution, 557
Arithmetic-geometric mean inequality, 166
Arithmetic mean, 278
Asymptote, 94
  vertical, 94
  horizontal, 96
Augmented matrix, 723

Basis of a vector space, 714
Bernoulli equation, 778
Beta function, 711
Big O, 446
Biharmonic function, 661
Binomial series, 485
Binormal, 605
Boundary conditions, 764
Bounded function, 198

Catenary, 781
Cauchy's formula, 416
Cauchy's inequality, 515, 570
Cavalieri's theorem, 259
Center of curvature, 605
  of mass, 394, 685, 699
Central conics, 384
Centroid
  of a curve, 551

Centroid (*cont.*)
of a plane region, 402
of a solid of revolution, 407
Centrosymmetric, 57
Chain rule, 121
for functions of several variables, 640
Change of variable formula, 217
Characteristic value, 741
vector, 741
Circle, 30
Closed ball, 566
Closed curve, 503
Closed disc, 507
Closed rectangle, 663
Cofactor, 732
Column space, 719
rank, 719
Comparison test for series, 462, 463
Completeness property, 186
Components of a vector, 510
Composite of functions, 68
Concavity, 151
Cone, 596
Continuity, 85
of a curve, 508
of a function of two variables, 618
Convergence, 449
absolute, 470
conditional, 471
Convex figure, 393
Covering of an interval, 225
Critical number, 138
Cross product, 584
Cross section, 590
Curvature, 604
Cycloid, 504
Cylinder, 256, 587
Cylindrical coordinates, 608

Decreasing function, 142
Definite integral, 214
Delta notation, 198
Derivative, 107, 127
Determinant, 727
Diagonal matrix, 728
Differentiable function, 107
Differentiable curve, 522, 599
Differential, 130, 630
Differential equation, 757
exact, 767
homogeneous, 773, 786
linear, 777
nonhomogeneous, 791
partial, 758
second-order linear, 786
separable, 758, 366
Dimension of a vector space, 716
Direction angles, 574
Direction cosines, 574
Directional derivative, 623
Directrix
of a cylinder, 587
of a parabola, 50
Distance formula, 29, 565
Divergent series, 449
Domain of a function, 58
Dominating series, 462
Double integral, 670

Eccentricity, 536
Echelon form, 720
Eigenvalue, 741
Eigenvector, 741
Elementary row operations, 719
Ellipse, 374
Ellipsoid, 594
Elliptic paraboloid, 595
Empty set, 5
Endpoint extremum, 155
Euclidean space, 737
Euler's constant, 469
Exponential function, 289, 300
Exponential laws of growth and decay, 302
Extremum, 137
relative, 146
of a function of several variables, 648
Field, 2
Force field, 656
Force on a dam, 408

Force vector, 527
Function, 58
  algebraic, 61, 340
  composite, 68
  constant, 61
  decreasing, 142
  even, 69
  homogeneous, 645
  increasing, 142
  linear, 61
  monotonic, 142
  odd, 69
  of several variables, 617
  polynomial, 61, 619
  power, 115, 301
  quadratic, 61
  rational, 61, 619
  smooth, 265
  transcendental, 62, 341
Fundamental theorem of the calculus, 211

Gamma function, 711
Geometric mean, 9
Geometric series, 449
Gradient, 629
Graph, 16, 25
  of a function, 63, 618
Greatest integer function, 90
Greatest lower bound, 186

Half line, 518
Harmonic function, 661
Harmonic series, 452
Helix, 600
Hooke's law, 262
Hyperbola, 374
Hyperbolic functions, 296
Hyperbolic paraboloid, 595
Hyperboloid, 596

Implicit differentiation, 126, 645
Improper integrals, 430, 431
Inclination, 35
Increasing function, 142
Indefinite integral, 214
Indeterminate form, 420
Inequality, 3
Infinite limits, 92, 95
Infinite series, 448
Inflection point, 153
Inner product, 514
Instantaneous rate of change, 168
Integrable function, 206
Integral, 206
  line, 655
  lower, 200
  upper, 200
Integral test for series, 457
Integrating factor, 772
Integration
  by change of variable, 217
  by parts, 347
  by trigonometric substitution, 354
  of rational functions, 359
Intercept, 44
Intermediate value theorem, 187
  for integrals, 220
Intersection of sets, 5
Interval of convergence, 476
Inverse function, 281, 332
Inverse matrix, 733
Inverse hyperbolic functions, 336
Inverse trigonometric functions, 322
Isometry, 739

Kinetic energy, 691

Lamina, 396
Latus rectum, 52
Laws of exponents, 289
  of logarithms, 287
Least upper bound, 186
Left-hand limit, 89
Length of a curve, 266
  in space, 601
L'Hospital's rule, 420, 425

Limit, 78
  infinite, 92, 95
  of a sequence, 231
  one-sided, 89
  theorems, 98
Line (s)
  equation of, 42
  in space, 572
  normal, 110, 638
  parallel, 38
  parametric equations of, 572
  perpendicular, 38
  tangent, 110
Line integral, 655
Linear combination, 712
Linear transformation, 735
Linearly dependent vectors, 712
Linearly independent vectors, 712
Little o, 446
Logarithm, 283, 300
Logarithmic differentiation, 296
Lower bound, 185
  of a function, 198
Lower integral, 200
Lower sum, 198

Maclaurin's formula, 439
  series, 489
Major axis of an ellipse, 376
Matrix, 718
Maximum value of a function, 136, 648
Mean value theorem, 140, 639
Midpoint, 16, 23, 566
Minimum value of a function, 136, 648
Minor axis of an ellipse, 377
Moment of force, 394
  of inertia, 689
Monotonic function, 142
Multiple integral, 663

Natural logarithm, 283
Negative half of a line, 573
Neighborhood, 6
  deleted, 6
  symmetric, 6
Newton's approximation method, 134
  second law, 170
Norm of a partition, 236
Normal line, 110
  to a surface, 638
Normal plane to a curve, 600
Normal vector, 578
n-smooth curve, 599
n-smooth function, 640
nth derivative test for extrema, 444

Octant, 564
1-form, 655
One-to-one function, 281
Open ball, 566
Open disc, 507
Open rectangle, 663
Open set, 508
Order, 2
Ordinate, 22
Origin, 14, 23
Orthogonal matrix, 744
Orthogonal projection, 380
Orthogonal trajectories, 766
Orthogonal vectors, 738
Orthonormal basis, 738
Osculating circle, 606
Oval, 393

Pappus, first theorem of, 408
  second theorem of, 558
Parabola, 49
Paraboloid, 595
Parametric equations
  of a line, 517, 572
  of a plane curve, 502
Partial derivatives, 626
Partial fractions, 360
Partial sum of an infinite series, 448
Partition, 190, 669
Periodic function, 313
Plane, 578
  normal, 600
  tangent, 636

Plane curve, 501
Point of inflection, 153
Polar coordinates, 529
Polygonal curve, 545
Polynomial, 61
Position function, 166
Positive half of a line, 573
Positive term series, 456
Power series, 475
Principal normal, 604
Prismatoid, 259
p series, 458

Quadrant, 22
Quadratic equations, 748
Quadric surfaces, 594

Radian measure, 311
Radius of convergence, 475
  of curvature, 604
  of gyration, 691
Range of a function, 59
Rank of a matrix, 720
Ratio test for series, 471
Rectangular coordinate system, 21
  in space, 564
Rectangular polygon, 191
Reduction formula, 351
Regular partition, 190
Remainder term, 438
Repeated integrals, 665
Riemann sum, 236, 671
Right-hand limit, 89
Rolle's theorem, 138
Row rank, 719
Row space, 719

Scalar multiplication, 513
Scalars, 711
Schwarz-Buniakowsky inequality, 224
Second derivative test, 152
Sequence, 229
  bounded, 233
Sequence (*cont.*)
  decreasing, 233
  increasing, 233
  monotonic, 233
Sigma notation, 195
Simple closed curve, 503
Simple harmonic motion, 322, 339
Simpson's rule, 271
Slope, 35
Smooth curve, 522, 599
Smooth function, 265, 640
Solution set, 6, 25
Space curve, 598
Span, 712
Sphere, 566
Spherical coordinates, 609
Strictly decreasing function, 142
Strictly increasing function, 142
Squeeze theorem, 88
Stirling's formula, 461
Subspace, 711
Surface of revolution, 590
Symmetric linear transformation, 745
Symmetric matrix, 745
Symmetry, 51
System of linear equations, 722

Tangent line, 110
  in polar coordinates, 540
  to a curve, 523, 599
Tangent plane, 636
Tangent vector, 521, 599
Taylor's formula, 437
Taylor's polynomial, 435
Taylor's series, 489
Trace, 501
  of a space curve, 598
Translation of axes, 387
  vector, 517, 572
Transpose of a matrix, 743
Transverse axis of a hyperbola, 382
Trapezoidal rule, 269
Triangle inequality, 515, 570
Trigonometric functions, 310
Triple integral, 695

Uniform continuity, 241, 664
Union of sets, 5
Unit normal vector, 605
Unit tangent vector, 604
Unit vector, 516, 570
Upper bound, 185
  of a function, 198
Upper integral, 200
Upper sum, 198

Variation of parameters, 792
Vectors, 509, 569
Vector space, 710
Vector-valued function, 520
Velocity, 167
Velocity vector, 526
Vertex of a parabola, 50
Vertices of an ellipse, 376
  of a hyperbola, 382
Volume, 253, 672

Work, 261

Zero vector, 512